The Will to Live

VAN LOON'S GEOGRAPHY

THE STORY OF THE WORLD
WE LIVE IN

WRITTEN AND ILLUSTRATED BY

Hendrik Willem van Loon., 1882–

MCMXXXVI
SIMON AND SCHUSTER
NEW YORK

Thirteenth Printing

*Ten years ago you sent me a letter and today you get your answer.
What you wrote (I am quoting from the original) was this:*

". . . Yes, but how about geography? No, I don't merely want a new
geography. I want a geography of my own, a geography that shall tell me
what I want to know and omit everything else and I want you to write it
for me. I went to a school where they took the subject very seriously.
I learned all about the different countries and how they were bounded
and about the cities and how many inhabitants they had and I learned
the names of all the mountains and how high they were and how much
coal was exported every year, and I forgot all these things just as fast as
I had learned them. They failed to connect. They resolved themselves
into a jumble of badly digested recollections, like a museum too full of
pictures or a concert that has lasted too long. And they were of no earthly
value to me, for every time I needed some concrete fact, I had to look it
up on maps and in atlases and encyclopedias and blue books. I suppose
that many others have suffered in the same way. On behalf of all these
poor victims, will you please give us a new geography that will be of
some use? Put all the mountains and the cities and the oceans on your
maps and then tell us only about the people who live in those places and
why they are there and where they came from and what they are doing—
a sort of human interest story applied to geography. And please stress the
countries that are really interesting and don't pay quite so much attention
to the others that are merely names, for then we will be able to remember all about them, but otherwise . . ."

*And I, eager as always to oblige when I receive a command from your
hands, turn around and say, "My dear, here it is!"*

HENDRIK WILLEM VAN LOON.

TABLE OF CONTENTS

TABLE OF CONTENTS xiii

LIST OF ILLUSTRATIONS

LIST OF COLORED AND WASH ILLUSTRATIONS

VAN LOON'S GEOGRAPHY

"History is the Fourth Dimension of Geography.
It gives it both time and meaning."

I

AND THESE ARE THE PEOPLE WHO LIVE IN THE WORLD WE LIVE IN

It sounds incredible, but nevertheless it is true. If everybody in this world of ours were six feet tall and a foot and a half wide and a foot thick (and that is making people a little bigger than they usually are), then the whole of the human race (and according to the latest available statistics there are now nearly 2,000,000,000 descendants of the original Homo Sapiens and his wife) could be packed into a box measuring half a mile in each direction. That, as I just said, sounds incredible, but if you don't believe me, figure it out for yourself and you will find it to be correct.

If we transported that box to the Grand Canyon of Arizona and balanced it neatly on the low stone wall that keeps people from breaking their necks when stunned by the incredible beauty of that silent witness of the forces of Eternity, and then called little Noodle, the dachshund, and told him (the tiny beast is very intelligent and loves to oblige) to give the unwieldy contraption a slight push with his soft brown nose, there would be a moment of crunching and ripping as the wooden planks loosened stones and shrubs and trees on their downward path, and then a low and even softer bumpity-bumpity-bump and a sudden splash when the outer edges struck the banks of the Colorado River.

Then silence and oblivion!

The human sardines in their mortuary chest would soon be forgotten.

The Canyon would go on battling wind and air and sun and rain as it has done since it was created.

3

The world would continue to run its even course through the uncharted heavens.

The astronomers on distant and nearby planets would have noticed nothing out of the ordinary.

A century from now, a little mound, densely covered with vegetable matter, would perhaps indicate where humanity lay buried.

And that would be all.

I can well imagine that some of my readers will not quite like this story and will feel rather uncomfortable when they see their own proud race reduced to such proportions of sublime insignificance.

There is however a different angle to the problem—an angle which makes the very smallness of our numbers and the helplessness of our puny little bodies a matter of profound and sincere pride.

Here we are, a mere handful of weak and defenceless mammals. Ever since the dawn of the first day we have been surrounded on all sides by hordes and swarms of creatures infinitely better prepared for the struggle of existence than we are ourselves. Some of them were a hundred feet long and weighed as much as a small locomotive while others had teeth as sharp as the blade of a circular saw. Many varieties went about their daily affairs clad in the armor of a medieval knight. Others were invisible to the human eye but they multiplied at such a terrific rate that they would have owned the entire earth in less than a year's time if it had not been for certain enemies who were able to destroy them almost as fast as they were born. Whereas man could only exist under the most favorable circumstances and was forced to look for a habitat among the few small pieces of dry land situated between the high mountains and the deep sea, these fellow-passengers of ours considered no summit too high and found no sea too deep for their ambitions. They were apparently made of the stuff that could survive regardless of its natural surroundings.

When we learn on eminent authority that certain varieties of insects are able to disport themselves merrily in petroleum (a substance we would hardly fancy as the main part of our daily diet) and that others manage to live through such changes in temperature as would kill all of us within a very few minutes; when we discover to our gruesome dismay that those little brown beetles, who seem so fond of literature that they are forever racing around in our bookcases, continue the even tenor of their restless days minus two or three or four legs, while we ourselves are disabled by a mere pin-prick on one of our toes, then we sometimes begin to realize against what sort of competitors we have been forced to hold our own, ever since we made our first appearance upon this whirling bit of rock, lost somewhere in the darkest outskirts of an indifferent universe.

What a side-splitting joke we must have been to our pachydermous contemporaries who stood by and watched this pinkish sport of nature indulge in its first clumsy efforts to walk on its hind legs without the help of a convenient tree-trunk or cane!

But what has become of those proud and exclusive owners of almost 200,000,000 square miles of land and water (not to mention the unfathomable oceans of air) who ruled so sublime by that right of eminent domain which was based upon brute force and sly cunning?

The greater part of them has disappeared from view except where as "Exhibit A" or "B" we have kindly given them a little parking space in one of our museums devoted to natural history. Others, in order to remain among those present, were forced to go into domestic service and today in exchange for a mere livelihood they favor us with their hides and their eggs and their milk and the beef that grows upon their flanks, or drag such loads as we consider a little too heavy for our own lazy efforts. Many more have betaken themselves to out-of-the-way places where we permit them to browse and graze and perpetuate their species because, thus far, we have not thought it worth our while to remove them from the scene and claim their territory for ourselves.

In short, during only a couple of thousands of centuries (a mere second from the point of view of eternity), the human race has made itself the undisputed ruler of every bit of land and at present it bids fair to add both air and sea as part of its domains. And all that, if you please, has been accomplished by a few hundred million creatures who enjoyed not one single advantage over their enemies except the divine gift of Reason.

Even there I am exaggerating. The gift of Reason in its more sublime form and the ability to think for one's self is restricted to a mere handful of men and women. They therefore become the masters who lead. The others, no matter how much they may resent the fact, can only follow. The result is a strange and halting procession, for no matter how hard people may try, there are ten thousand stragglers for every true pioneer.

Whither the route of march will eventually lead us, that we do not know. But in the light of what has been achieved during the last four thousand years, there is no limit to the sum total of our potential achievements—unless we are tempted away from the path of normal development by our strange inherent cruelty which makes us treat other members of our own species as we would never have dared to treat a cow or a dog or even a tree.

The earth and the fullness thereof has been placed at the disposal of Man. Where it has not been placed at his disposal, he has taken possession by right of his superior brain and by the strength of his foresight and his shot-guns.

This home of ours is a good home. It grows food enough for all of us. It has abundant quarries and clay beds and forests from which all of us can be provided with more than ample shelter. The patient sheep of our pastures and the waving flax fields with their myriads of blue flowers, not to forget the industrious little silk-worm of China's mulberry trees—they all contribute to shelter our bodies against the cold of winter and protect them against the scorching heat of summer. This home of ours is a good home. It produces all these benefits in so abundant measure that every man, woman and child could have his or her share with a little extra supply thrown in for the inevitable days of rest.

But Nature has her own code of laws. They are just, these laws, but they are inexorable and there is no court of appeal.

Nature will give unto us and she will give without stint, but in return she demands that we study her precepts and abide by her dictates.

A hundred cows in a meadow meant for only fifty spells disaster—a bit of wisdom with which every farmer is thoroughly familiar. A million people gathered in one spot where there should be only a hundred thousand causes congestion, poverty and unnecessary suffering, a fact which apparently has been overlooked by those who are supposed to guide our destinies.

That, however, is not the most serious of our manifold errors. There is another way in which we offend our generous foster-mother. Man in the only living organism that is hostile to its own kind. Dog does not eat dog—tiger does not eat tiger —yea, even the loathsome hyena lives at peace with the members of his own species. But Man hates Man, Man kills Man, and in the world of today the prime concern of every nation is to prepare itself for the coming slaughter of some more of its neighbors.

This open violation of Article I of the great Code of Creation which insists upon peace and good will among the members of the same species has carried us to a point where soon the human race may be faced with the possibility of complete annihilation. For our enemies are ever on the alert. If Homo Sapiens (the all-too-flattering name given to our race by a cynical scientist, to denote our intellectual superiority over the rest of the animal world)—if Homo Sapiens is unable or unwilling to assert himself as the master of all he surveys, there are thousands of other candidates for the job and it ofttimes seems as if a world dominated by cats or dogs or elephants or some of the more highly organized insects (and how they watch their opportunity!) might offer very decided advantages over a planet top-heavy with battle-ships and siege-guns.

What is the answer and what is the way out of this hideous and shameful state of affairs?

In a humble way this little book hopes to point to the one and only way out of that lugubrious and disastrous blind-alley into which we have strayed through the clumsy ignorance of our ancestors.

It will take time, it will take hundreds of years of slow and painful education to make us find the true road of salvation. But that road leads towards the consciousness that we are all of us fellow-passengers on one and the same planet. Once we have got hold of this absolute verity—once we have realized and grasped the fact that for better or for worse this is our common home—that we have never known another place of abode—that we shall never be able to move from the spot in space upon which we happened to be born—that it therefore behooves us to behave as we would if we found ourselves on board a train or a steamer bound for an unknown destination—we shall have taken the first but most important step towards the solution of that terrible problem which is at the root of all our difficulties.

We are all of us fellow-passengers on the same planet and the weal and woe of everybody else means the weal and woe of ourselves!

Call me a dreamer and call me a fool—call me a visionary or call for the police or the ambulance to remove me to a spot where I can no longer proclaim such unwelcome heresies. But mark my words and remember them on that fatal day when the human race shall be requested to pack up its little toys and surrender the keys of happiness to a more worthy successor.

The only hope for survival lies in that one sentence:

WE ARE ALL OF US FELLOW-PASSENGERS ON THE SAME PLANET AND WE ARE ALL OF US EQUALLY RESPONSIBLE FOR THE HAPPINESS AND WELL-BEING OF THE WORLD IN WHICH WE HAPPEN TO LIVE.

II

A DEFINITION OF THE WORD GEOGRAPHY AND HOW I SHALL APPLY IT IN THE PRESENT VOLUME

BEFORE we start out upon a voyage, we usually try to find out more or less definitely whither we are bound and how we are supposed to get there. The reader who opens a book is entitled to a little information of the same sort and a short definition of the word "Geography" will therefore not be out of order.

I happen to have the "Concise Oxford Dictionary" on my desk and that will do as well as any other. The word I am looking for appears at the bottom of page 344, edition of 1912.

> "Geography: the science of the earth's surface, form, physical features, natural and political divisions, climate, productions and population."

I could not possibly hope to do better, but I shall stress some of the aspects of the case at the expense of others, because I intend to place man in the center of the stage. This book of mine will not merely discuss the surface of the earth and its physical features, together with its political and natural boundaries. I would rather call it a study of man in search of food and shelter and leisure for himself and for his family and an attempt to find out the way in which man has either adapted himself to his background or has reshaped his physical surroundings in order to be as comfortable and well nourished and happy as seemed compatible with his own limited strength.

It has been truly said that the Lord hath some very strange customers among those who love Him, and indeed we shall find our planet inhabited by a weird and extraordinary variety of

9

fellow-boarders. Many of them, upon first acquaintance, will appear to be possessed of very objectionable personal habits and of general characteristics which we would rather not encounter in our own children. But two billion human beings, even if they do not cut much of a figure when packed in a small wooden box, are still a very respectable number of people and among so many there is of course the widest possible scope for all sorts of experiments of an economic and social and cultural nature. It seems to me that those experiments deserve our attention before anything else. For a mountain is after all merely a mountain until

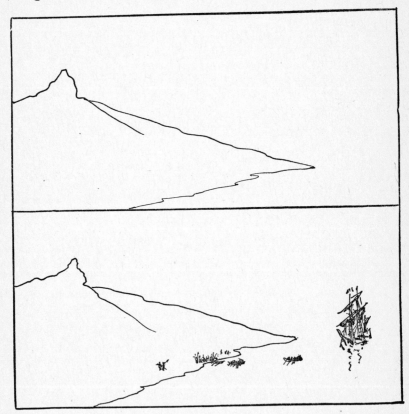

The Human Touch

it has been seen by human eyes and has been trod by human feet and until its slopes and valleys have been occupied and fought over and cultivated by a dozen generations of hungry settlers.

The Atlantic Ocean was just as wide and deep and as wet and salty before the beginning of the thirteenth century as after, but it took the human touch to make it what it is today—a bridge between the New World and the Old, the highway for the commerce between East and West.

For thousands of years the endless Russian plains lay ready to offer their abundant harvests to whomsoever should take the trouble to sow the first grain. But the aspect of that country today would be a very different one if the hand of a German or a Frank, rather than that of a Slav, had guided the iron-pointed stick that plowed the first furrows.

The islands of Nippon would shake and quake just as incessantly, whether they happened to be inhabited by aboriginal Japanese or by the remnants of the now defunct Tasmanian race, but in the latter case they would hardly be able to feed 60,000,000 people. While the British Isles, if they had been overrun by Neapolitans or Berbers instead of having been conquered by the restless fighters from northern Europe, would never have become the center of an empire one hundred and fifty times as large as the mother country and containing one-sixth of all the human beings now assembled on our planet.

Generally speaking, I have paid more attention to the purely "human" side of geography than to the commercial problems which are held to be of such great importance in a day and age devoted to mass production.

But experience has taught me that no matter how eloquent you wax upon the subject of importing and exporting, and the output of coal mines and oil reservoirs and bank deposits, you will never be able to tell your reader something which he can remember from one page to the next. Whenever he has need of such figures he will be obliged to look them up once more and verify them with the help of a dozen contradictory (and

often self-contradictory) handbooks on commercial statistics.
Man comes first in this geography.
His physical environment and background come next.
The rest is given whatever space remains.

III

OUR PLANET: ITS HABITS, CUSTOMS AND MANNERS

LET us begin with an old and trusted definition. "The world is a small, dark object, entirely surrounded by space."

It is not a "sphere" or a ball but a "spheroid", which means first cousin to a sphere and consists of a ball slightly flattened at the poles. The so-called "poles" you can find for yourself by sticking a knitting needle through the center of an apple or an orange and holding the object straight in front of you. Where the knitting needle sticks out of the apple or the orange, there the poles are located, one in the middle of a deep sea (the North Pole) and the other on top of a high mountain plateau.

As for the "flatness" of the polar regions, which goes with the definition of a spheroid, it need not disturb you in the least. For the axis of the earth from pole to pole is only $\frac{1}{300}$ shorter than the diameter taken at the equator. In other words, if you were the proud possessor of a globe of three feet in diameter (and few globes that you can buy in our stores are as large as that —you would have to go to a museum to find one), the axis would be only $\frac{1}{8}$ of an inch shorter than the equatorial diameter, and it would hardly show unless the workmanship had been of exceptional fineness.

Nevertheless the fact is of considerable interest to explorers who are trying to find their way through the polar regions and to those who make a study of the higher forms of geography. But for the purposes of the present book it is sufficient that I have mentioned it. Your physics professor has probably one of those little contraptions in his laboratory that will show you how the poles could not help becoming flat as soon as our speck

of dust began to revolve around its own axis. Ask him to let you
see it. That will save you a trip to the home of all the meridians.

The earth, as we all know, is a planet. We have inherited the
word from the Greeks who had observed (or thought they had
observed) that certain stars were forever moving across the skies
while others apparently stood still. They therefore called the
former "planets" or "wanderers" and the latter "fixed stars"
because, having no telescopes, they could not follow them on
their peregrinations. As for the word "star", we do not know
its origin but it probably has something to do with a Sanskrit
root which was in turn connected with the verb "to strew". If
that be true the stars would then be the little flames "strewn"
all over the heavens, a description which is quite pretty and fits
the case admirably.

The earth turns around the sun and depends upon the sun
for its light and heat. As the sun is more than seven hundred
times as large as all the planets put together, and as the temperature of the sun near the surface is about 6000° Fahrenheit, the
earth need not feel apologetic about borrowing her humble little
portion of comfort from a neighbor who can so easily spare these
few charitable rays and will never know the difference.

In the olden days the people believed that the earth was
situated in the center of the universe, a small, flat disc of dry
land entirely surrounded by the waters of the ocean and suspended in the air like the coffin of Mohammed or a toy balloon
that has escaped the hand of a child. A few of the more enlightened Greek astronomers and mathematicians (the first people
who dared to think for themselves without asking the permission of their priests) seem to have had a very definite suspicion
that this theory must be wrong. After several centuries of very
hard and very straight thinking, they came to the conclusion
that the earth was not flat, but round, and that it did not hang
quietly suspended in the air and in the exact center of the
universe, but that it floated through space and was flying at a

Space

considerable rate of speed round a much larger object which was called the sun.

At the same time they suggested that those other shining little orbs which seemed to revolve around us against a common background of so-called "fixed stars" were merely our fellow-planets, children of the same mother-sun and subject to the identical laws of behavior which regulated our own daily conduct—such as getting up and going to bed at certain regular hours, and being obliged to follow a track which had been laid out for us at the day of our birth and from which we could not stray without running the risk of instant doom.

During the last two hundred years of the Roman Empire the thinking part of the population had accepted this hypothesis as something so self-evident that it could no longer be considered a subject for debate. But when the Church became all-powerful, shortly after the beginning of the fourth century, it was no longer safe to harbor such ideas, least of all that one which proclaimed the earth to be round. We should not judge them too harshly. In the first place the earliest converts to Christianity generally belonged to those classes of society that had been the least exposed to the current learning of the times. And furthermore they were firmly convinced that the end of the world was near at hand when Christ would return to the former scene of His sufferings to separate the good from the evil. He would return in the midst of all His glory and for every one to behold. But, so they reasoned, and quite correctly from their own point of view, if this were to be the case (and they had no doubt upon the subject) then the world must be flat. For otherwise Christ would have to make His re-appearance twice—once for the benefit of the people on the western hemisphere and once for the benefit of those on the other side of the world. Such a procedure, of course, would be absurd and undignified and therefore entirely out of the question.

The Church, therefore, for almost a thousand years insisted upon teaching once again that the earth was a flat disc and that it was the center of the universe. In learned circles, among the scientists of a few of the monasteries and among the astronomers of some of the rapidly growing cities, the old Greek conception of a round world, revolving around the sun together with a number of other planets, was never quite discarded. Only the men who held this to be true did not openly dare to talk about the subject, but kept their ideas strictly to themselves. For they knew that a public discussion would merely upset the peace and quiet of millions of their less intelligent fellow-citizens while it would do absolutely nothing to bring the solution of the problem any nearer.

Since then, the Church people too, with very few exceptions, have been forced to accept the notion that the planet on which we live must be a ball. By the end of the fifteenth century the evidence in favor of this ancient Greek theory had become too overwhelming to be refuted any longer. And it was and is based upon the following observations:

In the first place, there was the fact that when we approach a mountain or a ship at sea, we first of all notice the summit or the top of the mast and only very gradually, as we come nearer, are we able to see the rest of the object under observation.

In the second place, no matter where we are, the scene all around us appears to be a circle. Our eyes therefore must be equally removed from every part of the land or sea under observation and the further we get away from the surface of the earth in a balloon or on top of a tower, the larger that circle gets. If the earth happened to be egg-shaped, we would find ourselves in the middle of a large oval. If it were a square or a triangle, the horizon would be a square or a triangle too.

In the third place, when a partial eclipse of the moon takes place, the shadow of the earth on the moon is a circle and only a ball will cause a circular shadow.

In the fourth place, the other planets and stars too are spheres and why should we alone among so many billions be an exception?

In the fifth place, when the ships of Magellan had sailed long enough in a westerly direction, they finally returned to the

Only round objects give round shadows

place from which they had left and when Captain Cook did the same thing, going from west to east, the survivors of his expedition also came back to the port from which they had sailed.

Eclipse

And finally, when we travel northward towards the poles, the familiar constellations of the stars (the signs of the Zodiac of the ancients) disappear lower and lower below the horizon, but they arise again and come higher and higher, the nearer we return to the equator.

I hope that I have brought forward enough undisputable facts to prove that the planet on which we happen to live must be round. But should the evidence be insufficient to satisfy you, go to any reliable professor of physics. He will take one of those stones that are forever falling from high towers and he will let it do tricks with the law of gravity which prove beyond the shadow of a doubt that the earth must be a sphere. If he uses very simple words and does not talk too fast, you may be able to understand him, but only if you know a great deal more about mathematics and physics than I do.

Here I could indulge in a great many very learned statistics, none of which however would be of the slightest use to you. The average mind (the author's mind included) is simply not fit to

Our speed through space is much faster than that of the fastest cannon-ball

follow such calculations with any degree of comfort. Take light for example. Light travels at the rate of speed of 186,000 miles per second. It goes seven times around the earth while you snap your fingers once. And yet the light from the nearest of the fixed stars (Alpha Centauri, if you want the correct address) must travel four and one-third years at the rate of 186,000 miles per second ere it strikes our eyes. The sun can reach us in eight minutes and Jupiter in three minutes, but the Polar Star, which plays such an important role in the science of navigation, would need forty years to send us a single ray of light.

Alas, most of us get slightly dizzy when we are asked to "imagine" such a distance, and the very idea of a light-year, or the distance covered by a ray of light in a single year, or $365 \times 24 \times 60 \times 60 \times 186,000$ miles becomes something so enormous that as a rule we say "Oh, yes", and then go out and play with the cat or turn on the radio.

But all of us are familiar with railroad trains. Let us try it that way:

An ordinary passenger train, going day and night without stops, would need five-sevenths of a year to reach the moon. But if it started today it would not get to the sun until A. D. 2232. It would need 8,300 years to get to the suburbs where the planet Neptune lives. All that however would be mere child's play compared to a trip to the nearest of the fixed stars, for that would mean a voyage of 75,000,000 years. As for the Polar Star, that train would need 700,000,000 years to get there and 700,000,-000 years is a long time, a very long time. If we put the duration of life for the average human being at about seventy years (which is a very flattering estimate), 10,000,000 generations of human beings would have been born and would have died ere that train got to its final destination.

And now we are only talking about the visible part of the universe. Our telescopes are a great deal better than the funny little contraptions with which the contemporaries of Galileo searched the sky and incidentally made some of the most remarkable discoveries. Even so, they are still very imperfect and until we improve our lenses a thousand-fold we shall not make much headway. Therefore, when we talk about the universe, what we really mean is "that small part of the universe which is visible and which has come under our own personal observation or under the observation of those sensitive photographic plates which are substituted nowadays for the human eye". As

Those few specks—and that is all we know of our
universe

for the rest of the universe, the still invisible part, alas, we know nothing about it. And what is worse, we dare not even guess.

Among all these millions of stars, fixed and otherwise, which are our more immediate neighbors, there are only two which influence our own existence in a very direct and noticeable fashion, and those two are the sun and the moon. The sun, because once every twenty-four hours she provides one-half of our planet with heat and light. And the moon, because she is near enough to us to influence the behavior of the ocean and to cause that strange aquatic phenomenon which we know as the "tides".

The moon is really quite near to us. Therefore, although it is much smaller than the sun (if we represent the sun by our familiar out-sized globe of three feet diameter, the earth would be a green pea and the moon the mere point of a pin) the moon has a much stronger "pull" on the surface of the earth than the sun.

If the earth consisted entirely of solid matter, that pull of the moon would hardly make itself felt. But three-fourths of the surface of the earth consists of water and that water follows the moon on its peregrination across the earth, just as iron filings spread out across a piece of paper will follow the toy magnet you pass across the table.

All day and all night long a broad strip of water, several

The Tides

hundred miles wide, is following in the wake of the moonlight. When it enters bays and harbors and the mouths of rivers and becomes greatly condensed, it causes the tides of twenty or thirty or forty feet difference which make navigation in those waters such a very difficult feat. When the sun and the moon happen to be on the same side of the earth, the pull is of course much stronger than when the moon is there alone, and then we get a so-called "spring-tide"; and a spring-tide in many parts of the world is something very much akin to a small inundation.

The earth is entirely surrounded by a layer of nitrogen and oxygen which we call the atmosphere or the "air". This layer is supposed to be about 300 miles thick and it turns around together with the earth just as the skin of an orange turns around with the inside of the orange which it protects.

The layers of atmosphere

Only a year or so ago a Swiss professor in a specially designed balloon went ten miles up in the air, into that part of the atmosphere which had never been visited before. That was quite a feat, but 290 miles still remain to be explored.

Earthquakes

They keep us warm like so many blankets

The atmosphere, together with the surface of the earth and the sea, is the laboratory in which all our different sorts of weather, our winds and our rainstorms and blizzards and our dry periods, are manufactured. As these influence our happiness and well-being every hour of our lives, we ought to discuss them here in considerable detail.

The three factors which make our climate what it is (but rarely, alas, what it should be) are the temperature of the soil, the prevailing wind and the amount of moisture which is present in the air. Originally "climate" meant the "slope of the earth". For the Greeks had noticed that as the surface of the earth "sloped" further and further towards the poles, both the temperature and the humidity of the spots they visited also changed, and in that way "climate" came to mean the atmospheric condition of any given region rather than its exact geographic position.

Today when we speak of the "climate" of a country, we mean the average weather conditions which prevail there during the different parts of the year and it is in that sense that I shall use the word.

First of all let me say something about those mysterious winds which have played such a great role in the civilization of mankind. For without the regular "trade-winds" of the equatorial ocean, the discovery of America might have been deferred until the age of the steamboat. Without the dew-laden breezes, California and the countries of the Mediterranean would never have reached that degree of prosperity which sets them apart from their neighbors in the north and in the east. Not to mention the particles of rock and sand which, swept forward by the wind, will act as gigantic, invisible sheets of sand-paper, and which after millions of years will grind even the most powerful mountain ranges from the face of the earth.

This word "wind" means literally something that "winds its way". A wind, therefore, is a current of air "winding its way" from one place to another. But why does a current of air wind its way from one place to another? Because some of the air is usually warmer than the rest and therefore lighter and has a tendency to rise as high as it can go. When that happens, there is a vacuum. The cold air, being heavier, rushes into that vacuum, because, as the Greeks had already discovered two thousand years ago, "Nature abhors a vacuum", and air is just as much of a vacuum-hater as water or the human race.

We know of course how we can produce hot air in any given room—by the simple expedient of lighting a fire. Among the planets the sun is the stove and the planets are the rooms which are to be heated. The greatest amount of heat will of course be nearest to the stove (along the equator) and the smallest amount of heat will be found furthest removed from the stove (near the North and South Poles).

Now a stove causes a considerable commotion in the air—a circular commotion. The hot air will rise towards the ceiling. As soon as it gets there, it will be further removed from the original source of heat than it was before, and as a result it will begin to cool off. The cooling process will cause it to lose its lightness and to fall back towards the earth. But as soon as it gets a little lower, it will once more get in touch with the stove. Once more it will grow warmer and lighter and once more it will begin to rise. And so on and so forth, until the stove goes out. But then the walls of the room, which have absorbed considerable heat while

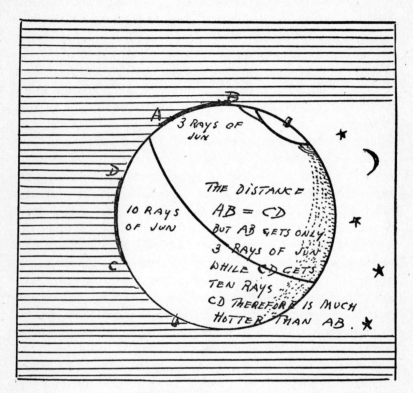

The sun heating the earth

the stove was burning, will keep the room warm for a shorter or longer time, depending upon the material of which they are made.

These walls may be compared to the soil on which we happen to live. Sand and rocks absorb heat quicker than a rain-soaked marsh, but by the same token they let go of it with much greater ease. As a result, the desert is uncomfortably cold a short time after the setting of the sun, while a forest remains warm and comfortable for hours after the entrance of darkness.

Water is a veritable reservoir for the storing up of heat. As a result all countries situated on or near the ocean enjoy a much more even temperature than those located in the heart of a continent.

Since our stove, the sun, burns much longer and more fiercely in summer than in winter, it follows that the summer must be warmer than the winter. But there is something else that influences the action of the sun. If you have ever tried to make the bathroom a little less shivery on an extra cold day with a small electric heater, you will know that much depends upon the angle at which that little stove is placed. The same holds true for the sun. In the tropics, the rays of the sun hit the surface of the earth much more directly than near the poles. A ray of sunlight, therefore, a hundred miles wide, landing fairly and squarely upon a hundred miles of African forest or South American wilderness, will be able to devote its entire strength to these hundred miles of territory and to nothing else. But near the poles, a ray of sunlight a hundred miles wide will cover a stretch of land or ice that is twice as wide (as the picture will show you much more easily than a thousand words could hope to do), and the heating power of those hundred miles of sunlight near the poles will therefore be cut exactly in half, just as an oil-burner which is supposed to keep a six-room apartment at a comfortable temperature will prove a failure when called upon to perform a similar service for a twelve-room flat.

What makes the job of our celestial stove even more complicated is the fact that the sun must also keep the atmosphere

Rain

which surrounds us at an even temperature. But she cannot do this directly. She must do it indirectly, via the earth.

On their way to our planet the sun rays pass through the atmosphere, but they pass through so easily and quickly that they hardly influence the temperature of that faithful terrestrial blanket. Then they hit the earth and the earth stores up the heat and slowly surrenders part of it into the atmosphere. That fact, incidentally, explains why it is so cold on the top of a mountain. For the higher we get, the less the heat of the earth has been able to make itself felt. If (as used to be supposed) the sun heated the atmosphere directly and the atmosphere in its turn heated the earth, it would be just the other way around and our mountain tops would not be covered with snow.

And now we come to the most difficult part of the problem. Air is not just "air" in our sense of the word. It has both substance and weight. The lower layers of air therefore are under a much higher pressure than the higher ones. When you want to flatten out a leaf or a flower you put it between the pages of a book and then put twenty other volumes on top of it because you know that the pressure will be greatest in the book that is at the bottom of the pile. The pressure under which we human beings live is considerably more than most of us suspect. It is fifteen pounds per square inch. That means that we would be crushed flat except for the fortunate circumstance that we are filled with the same air as that which surrounds us. Even so, 30,000 pounds (the pressure upon a body of average size) is a respectable amount. If you have any doubts upon the subject, try to lift a small freight-car.

Within the realm however of the atmosphere itself that pressure is constantly changing. We know this through the invention of Evangelista Torricelli, a pupil of Galileo, who early during the seventeenth century gave us the barometer, that well-known instrument by which we are able to measure the pressure of the air at any time of day or night.

As soon as the first of these Torricellian tubes had been placed upon the market, people began to experiment with them. They noticed that the pressure fell by about an inch for every 900 feet one ascended above sea-level. Then followed another discovery which did so much to make meteorology, the study of atmospheric phenomena, such a reliable science in forecasting the weather.

Certain physicists and geographers began to suspect that there was a definite connection between the pressure of the air and the direction of the prevailing winds or vice versa. But in order to establish some irrefutable law regulating the behavior of all air-currents, it was first of all necessary to spend several centuries collecting the data from which to draw a few definite conclu-

Rainstorms after all are only local affairs

sions. When this had been done, it was shown that certain parts
of the world enjoyed an air pressure well above that of the
mean sea-level, while others had pressures far below the mean
sea-level. The first of these were then called high-pressure areas
and the second low-pressure areas. Next it was definitely established that winds would always tend to blow from high-pressure
areas to low-pressure areas and that the velocity and strength of
the wind would depend upon the highness of the high-pressure
area and the lowness of the low-pressure area. And when the
high-pressure was very high and the low-pressure was very
low, then we would have a very violent wind—a storm, a cyclone or a hurricane.

The winds not only keep our living quarters, the earth, decently ventilated, but they also play a great role in the distribution of that rain without which a normal development of
plant life and animal life would be completely impossible.

Rain is merely evaporated water from the oceans and from
the inland seas and from the inland snow-fields, which is carried along by the air in the form of vapor. As hot air can hold
much more vapor than cold air, the water-vapor will be carried
along without much difficulty until the air grows colder. Then
part of it gets condensed and falls back again upon the surface of
the earth in the form of rain or hail or snow.

The rainfall of any given region therefore will depend almost entirely upon the winds to which it is exposed. If we
have a sea-coast separated from the mainland by mountains (a
very common occurrence) the coastal region will be wet and
damp. For the wind, being forced to rise into higher regions
(where the pressure is lower), will cool off as it gets further and
further away from the sea-level and it will shed its vapor in
the form of rain and snow and will reappear on the other side
of the mountain range as a dry wind without a drop of moisture.

The rainfall of the tropics is both regular and abundant because the enormous heat of the land makes the air rise to a great
height, where it gets cooled off and is obliged to let go of most
of its vapor, which thereupon returns to earth in the form of

heavy sheets of rain. But as the sun does not always stand right over the equator, but moves slightly from north to south, most of the equatorial regions enjoy four seasons, two seasons during which there are terrific rainstorms and two seasons during which the weather is dry.

But those regions which are exposed to steady air-currents running from colder to warmer regions are by far the worst off. For as the winds pass from the cold area to the hot one, their capacity for absorption becomes steadily greater and they are unable to release the vapor they carry, causing many parts of this earth to be turned into deserts where it may not rain more than once or twice every ten years.

So much for the general subject of wind and rain. A detailed discussion will follow when we describe each individual country.

And now a few words about the earth itself, and about that thin crust of hardened rock on which we live.

There are a great many theories about the true inner nature of our planet, but our definite knowledge upon the subject is still exceedingly vague.

Let us be honest. How high have we ever been up in the air or how low down into the bowels of the earth?

On a globe of three feet in diameter, the highest mountain in the world, Mt. Everest, would show about as thick as a thin piece of tissue paper and the deepest hole in the ocean, just east of the Philippine Islands, would be represented by a dent of the size and shape of a postage stamp. Well, we have never yet descended to the bottom of the ocean and we have never yet climbed Mt. Everest. We have been a little higher than the top of this Himalayan giant in balloons and flying machines, but when all is said and done, even after the recent successful flight of the Swiss Professor Piccard, $\frac{29}{30}$ of the atmosphere still remain to be explored. As for the water, we have never yet descended below $\frac{1}{40}$ of the total depth of the Pacific Ocean, and incidentally, the depth of the deepest sea is greater than the height of the highest mountain. Why this should be we do

The crust of the earth is as full of holes as a sponge

not know, but if we dumped the highest mountains of the different continents into the deepest part of the ocean, the tops of Mt. Everest and Aconcagua would still be several thousand feet below the surface of the sea.

In the light of our present-day knowledge however these puzzling facts prove nothing at all about the origin and the subsequent development of the crust of the earth. Neither (as our grandfathers so fondly hoped) need we turn to our volcanoes for an answer about the true inner nature of our planet, for we have come to realize that those are not outlets for the hot substance that is supposed to fill the interior of the earth. If the comparison were not quite so unsavory, I would like to compare them to boils on the skin of the earth, nasty afflictions but purely local affairs which never penetrate very deep into the body of the patient.

In round numbers there are still some 320 active volcanoes left. There used to be 400 others on the active list, but these have since been retired and pensioned off with the rank of ordinary or common mountains.

The great majority of all these volcanoes are situated near the sea-coast. Indeed, the most restless part of the world's crust, Japan (where the seismograph shows a slight volcanic disturbance four times every day or 1,447 times a year) is an island, and so were Martinique and Krakatoa, the most tragic victims of recent volcanic outbursts.

In view of the close proximity of sea to volcano, it was quite

Why not make your own earthquakes?

natural that people should have tried to explain all volcanic eruptions as the result of water seeping into the inner part of the earth, thereby causing a sort of gigantic boiler explosion with the well-known disastrous results of an overflow of lava and steam and what have you. But since then we have discovered several very busy volcanoes hundreds of miles away from the sea, and that theory too has therefore come to naught. Ask me again about all this two centuries hence for at the present moment we can only shake our heads and repeat, "We do not know."

Meanwhile, what about the surface of the earth itself? We used to talk so glibly about the rock of ages that would forever defy the changes of time. Modern science is less confident and regards this rock and all other rocks as something living and therefore subject to constant change. The rain raineth upon it and the wind bloweth upon it and together they cause the mountains to wither away at the rate of three inches every ten centuries. If there were no counter-moves to offset these erosive attacks, all our mountains would have disappeared long ago and even the Himalayas would have been turned into a vast plain in about 116,000,000 years. But there are counter-activities and plenty of them.

In order to get at least a vague idea of what is really happening all around us, take half a dozen clean handkerchiefs and spread them out flat on the table, one on top of the other. Then push all six together by moving your hands very slowly towards each other. You will get a pile of curiously wrinkled linen with mountains and valleys and folds and counter-folds all over it and that pile of curiously wrinkled linen will bear a very close resemblance to the crust of the earth. That crust is part of an enormous structure racing through space and constantly losing some of its heat. Like all things that are cooling off, it is slowly contracting. As you probably know, when an object contracts, the outer surface will get curiously rumpled and creased like a couple of handkerchiefs being pushed together.

The best guess at the present moment (but remember that it

The Rise and Fall of All Mountains

is only a guess) tells us that the diameter of the earth has shrunk
some thirty miles since the beginning of our independent existence as a planet. That does not seem very much when you think
of it as a straight line. But remember the tremendous scope of
the curved planes with which we are dealing. The surface of
the world is 196,950,000 square miles. A sudden change of only
a few yards in diameter would be enough to cause a catastrophe
which none of us would survive.

Nature therefore works very slowly her wonders to perform.
She insists upon maintaining a proper balance in everything she
does. When she allows one sea to run dry (our own Salt Lake
is rapidly dwindling away, the Lake of Constance in Switzerland will be gone in another 100,000 years) she starts another
one in some other part of the world; and when she permits certain mountain-ranges to disappear (the Alps in central Europe
will be as flat as our prairies in another 60,000,000 years) then
another part of the crust in a totally different corner of the globe
is slowly being reshaped and wrinkled into a fresh mountain-
range. That, at least, we believe to be the case, although as a
rule the process is by far too slow and gradual to allow us to
make any concrete observations of the changes that are taking
place.

There is however an exception to this general rule. When
left to herself, Nature is in no particular hurry. But when aided
and abetted by man, she sometimes proves herself an uncomfortably fast worker. And ever since man became truly civilized and
invented his little steam-engines and his little sticks of dynamite,
the surface of the earth has been transformed so rapidly that
our great-grandparents would hardly recognize their own pastures and gardens, were they to come back to us for a little holiday. Our greed for timber and the ruthlessness with which we
have denuded whole mountain-ranges of their blanket of forests
and shrubs have turned vast regions into primeval wildernesses.
For as soon as the forests were gone, that fertile soil which for
so many years had faithfully clung to the rocky surface of the
hill-sides was brutally washed away and the barren slopes be-

came a menace to the surrounding country-side. The rain was then no longer held captive by the turf and by the roots of the trees, but was able to rush down towards the plains in torrents and cataracts, destroying everything it met on its way towards the valleys and plains.

The Glaciers in America

And this unfortunately is not said in a flight of high rhetorical exaggeration. We don't have to go back to the glacial periods when, for reasons as yet unexplained, the whole of northern Europe and northern America lay buried beneath a heavy blanket of ice and snow which dug such dangerous grooves through entire mountain-ranges. We need only go as far back as the era of the Romans, who were first-rate exploiters (weren't they the

"practical men" of antiquity?) and who in less than five generations completely changed the climate of their own peninsula by
the senseless destruction of everything that had thus far helped
to make Italy a country of well-balanced and even temperature.
And what the Spaniards did to the mountains of South America,
when they allowed the fertile terraces, built by countless gen-

The Glaciers in Europe

erations of patient little Indians, to go to ruin, is a fact of such
recent occurrence as to need no further elucidation.

Of course that was the easiest way to deprive the natives of
their livelihood and reduce them to obedience by way of starva-

50,000,000 B. C. and A. D. 1932

tion—just as the extinction of the buffaloes by our own government was the most practical method of turning fierce warriors into dirty, slovenly reservation-parishioners. But these cruel and senseless measures carried their own punishment with them, as any one familiar with our plains or the Andes will tell you.

Fortunately this is one of the few problems of practical geographical importance which has at last penetrated to the consciousness of those who sit in the seats of the mighty. No government today would any longer tolerate such scandalous interference with the soil upon which all of us depend for our well-being. We have no control over the cosmic changes which take place in the crust of our planet. But to a certain extent we can control a vast number of details which make for a greater or smaller rainfall in any given territory and which will prevent fertile regions from being turned into howling deserts. We may not know anything about the inside of this earth, but we have at least learned a great many things about the outside. And every day we add to the sum total of this useful bit of information and use it wisely for the benefit of all.

But I regret to say that we have no such control over the greater part of the earth's surface—that part which we call the oceans and the seas. Almost three-quarters of our globe are uninhabitable because they are covered by a layer of water, differing in depth from a couple of feet (near the shore) to almost 35,000 feet in the famous "deep hole" just east of the Philippines.

This layer of water can be roughly divided into three main parts. The most important of these is the Pacific Ocean which covers 68,500,000 square miles. The Atlantic Ocean covers 41,000,000 square miles and the Indian Ocean 29,000,000. Inland seas account for another 2,000,000 square miles, while lakes and rivers take up about 1,000,000 square miles of their own. All this submerged territory was and is and always will remain lost to us as a place of residence, unless we are able to redevelop those gills which our ancestors of a few million years ago pos-

If we dumped the highest mountains of the world into the deepest part of the ocean (34,210 feet) situated between the Philippines and Japan, even Mount Everest would be more than 5,000 feet under water and the others in proportion. They are: 1–Everest (29,141). 2–Kinchinjinga, also in Asia near Nepal (28,225). 3–Aconcagua in the Argentine (22,834). 4–Chimborazo in Ecuador (20,702). 5–McKinley in Alaska (20,300), the highest mountain in North America. 6–Kilimanjaro in Africa (19,710). 7–Logan in Canada (19,850). 8–Elbruz in the Caucasus (18,465), the highest mountain in Europe. 9–Popocatepetl in Mexico (17,543). 10–Ararat in Armenia (17,090), the mountain on which Noah's ark stranded. 11–Mont Blanc in the French Alps (15,781). 12–Fujiyama in Japan (12,395). (Incidentally, there are twelve more mountains in the Himalayas which are higher than Aconcagua, but I do not mention them here because no one has ever heard of them.)

The highest spot on which human beings live all the year is the village of Gartok (13) in Tibet (14,518). The highest lake is Titicaca (14) in Peru (12,545). The highest cities are (15) Quito (9,343) and (16) Bogota (8,563) in South America. The cloister of the Saint Bernard Pass (17) in Switzerland is the highest spot where people live all the year around in Europe (8,111) while Mexico City (18) is the highest town in North America (7,415). Finally there is the Dead Sea (19) in Palestine, which is 1,290 feet below sea-level.

If the highest mountains should get dumped into the
deepest part of the ocean!

sessed and of which we still show the traces on the day of our birth.

This abundant supply of water may at first seem a complete waste of perfectly good territory and it may make us regret that our planet is as wet as it happens to be. For when we remember that 5,000,000 square miles of the land that is at our disposal are desert and that 19,000,000 square miles are steppes or plains of the semi-useless Siberian variety, while a considerable number of other millions of square miles are uninhabitable because they are either too high for us to live in (like the Himalayas and the Alps) or too cold (like the territory around the North and South Poles) or too wet (like the swamps of South America) or too densely covered with forests (like the forests of central Africa) and must therefore be deducted from the 57,-510,000 square miles that are listed as "land", we feel that we could make excellent use of a few more miles of added territory.

But it is extremely doubtful whether we could exist at all if it were not for this vast reservoir of heat, which we call the sea. The geological remnants of prehistoric times show us conclusively that there have been times when there was more land and less water than today, but invariably these were periods of intense cold. The present balance of $1:4$ between water and land is an ideal one if our present climate is to continue indefinitely, and we shall all of us be much better off if it does not get disturbed.

This vast ocean which encircles the entire globe (in this respect the ancients had guessed right) is, like the solid crust of the earth, in constant motion. The moon and the sun, through their power of gravity, attract it and cause it to rise to a considerable height. Then there is the heat of the day which takes part of it away in the form of vapor. The cold of the polar regions covers it with ice. But from a practical point of view as something directly affecting our own well-being, the air-currents or winds must be accorded first rank for their influence upon the surface of the ocean.

When you blow long enough on your plate of soup, you will notice that the soup begins to move in the direction away from

The Gulf Stream

your mouth. When certain air-currents hit the surface of the ocean for years and years in succession, they will cause "drifts" which will move in a direction away from that particular current. Whenever there are a number of air-currents blowing from different directions, these different "drifts" will neutralize each other. But when the winds are steady, as they are for example on both sides of the equator, the drifts become veritable currents and these currents have played a very important role in the history of the human race and in making certain parts of the world inhabitable which otherwise would be as cold as Greenland's icy shores.

A map of these ocean rivers (for that is what many of those

Hundreds of millions of years ago the continents seem
to have been very different from today

currents really are) will show you where they are located. The
Pacific Ocean has a number of such currents. The most important of these, as important in its way as the Gulf Stream of
the Atlantic, is the Japan current or Kuro Siwo (which means
the Blue Salt Current) which is caused by the north-east trade-
winds. After having done its duty by Japan, it crosses the northern Pacific and bestows its blessings upon Alaska, which it keeps
from being too cold for human habitation, and then, turning
sharply towards the south, gives California its agreeable climate.

But when we speak of ocean currents, we think first of all
of the Gulf Stream, that mysterious river, some fifty miles wide
and 2000 feet deep, which for untold centuries has kept the
northern part of Europe well supplied with the tropical heat of
the Gulf of Mexico and which accounts for the fertility of England, Ireland and all the North Sea countries.

The Gulf Stream has an interesting career of its own. It begins with the famous North Atlantic Eddy, a drift rather than
a current, which like a gigantic maelstrom turns around and
around in the central part of the Atlantic and enfolds within
itself that pool of semi-stagnant water which has become the
home of billions of little fishes and floating plants and which,
as the Sargasso or "Sea-Weed Sea", played a most important
part in the history of early navigation. For once the trade-winds
(the eastern winds that blew just north of the tropics) had
blown your ship into the Sargasso Sea, you were lost. At least,
that is what the sailors of the Middle Ages firmly believed.
Your vessel would find itself caught by miles and miles of solid
sea-weed and every one on board would slowly perish through
hunger and thirst, while the ghastly wreck would remain forever
bobbing up and down beneath the cloudless sky as a silent warning to others who might be tempted to defy the Gods.

When finally Columbus sailed placidly through the heart
of this dullish stretch of water, it was shown that the fairy story
about miles and miles of solid sea-weed had been grossly exaggerated. But even today there is something mysterious and uncanny to most people in that name, Sargasso Sea. It sounds me-

dieval. It smacks of one of Dante's infernal circles. Actually, however, it is no more exciting than the swan-pond in Central Park.

But to return to the Gulf Stream. Part of the North Atlantic Eddy finally finds its way into the Caribbean Sea. There it is joined by a current that moves westward from the coast of Africa. These two currents, in addition to its own water, are too much for the Caribbean Sea. Like a cup that has been poured too full, it flows over into the Gulf of Mexico.

The gulf stream in your kitchen

The Gulf of Mexico has not got room for all this additional humidity and, using the straits between Florida and Cuba as a spigot, it pours forth a broad stream of hot water (80° Fahrenheit) which thereupon is called the Gulf Stream. When the Gulf Stream leaves the spigot, it flows at the rate of five miles an hour, which is one of the reasons why the old sailing vessels gave it a wide berth whenever they could and preferred to make a lengthy detour rather than try to navigate against a current which so severely delayed their own progress.

From the Gulf of Mexico the Gulf Stream moves up northward, following the American coast until finally it is deflected by the shape of the eastern shore, when it begins its voyage across the north Atlantic. Just off the Grand Banks of Newfoundland it meets its own offspring, the so-called Labrador Current, which, coming fresh from the glacial regions of Greenland, is as cold and uninviting as the Gulf Stream is warm and hospitable. Out of the meeting of these two mighty currents arises that terrible fog which has given that part of the Atlantic such a dreadful reputation. It also accounts for the presence of that large number of ice-bergs which have played such a hideous role in the nautical history of the last fifty years. For, cut off by the summer's sun from their solid Greenland moorings (those glaciers that still cover ninety percent of that vast island) these bergs drift slowly southward until they are caught by the eddy caused by the meeting of the Gulf Stream and the Labrador Current.

There they mill around while they slowly melt. But this melting process is what makes them so dangerous, for only the tops remain visible while the ragged edges stay under water, just deep enough to cut through the hull of a ship as a knife cuts through butter. That whole region today is forbidden territory for all ocean liners and it is constantly watched by United States patrol vessels (a special ice patrol, paid for by all nations) who blow up the smaller bergs and warn vessels of the presence of the bigger ones. Fishing boats, however, love this territory, for fishes who were born in the Arctic and were therefore accustomed to the cold temperature of the Labrador Current feel very unhappy in the tepid water of the Gulf Stream. While they are slowly making up their minds whether to go back to the Pole or try to swim across the warm Gulf Stream, they are caught by the nets of those French fishermen whose ancestors patronized the legendary Grand Banks of America hundreds of years before any one else. The two little islands of St. Pierre

Neighbors

and Miquelon, off the Canadian coast, are not only the last remaining remnants of that vast French empire which two centuries ago covered the greater part of the North American
continent. They also bear silent witness to the courage of the Normandy fishermen who had visited our shores at least a hundred
and fifty years before Columbus was born.

As for the Gulf Stream, after leaving the so-called Cold Wall
(produced by the difference in temperature between the Gulf
Stream and the Labrador Current) well to the north, it then
leisurely moves across the Atlantic Ocean and spreads fan-wise
over the coast of western Europe. It touches Spain and Portugal and France and England and Ireland and Holland and
Belgium and Denmark and the Scandinavian peninsula, and bestows upon all these countries a much milder temperature than
they would otherwise enjoy. Having thus done its duty by humanity, this strange current, carrying more water than all the
rivers of the world combined, withdraws discreetly into the
Arctic Sea. This sea thereupon finds itself so full of aquatic substance that it must find relief by sending out a current of its
own, that Greenland Current which in turn is responsible for
that Labrador Current I have just described.

It is a fascinating story.

It is such a fascinating story that I am sorely tempted to give
by far too much space to this chapter alone. But that I must
not do.

This chapter can only be a background—a general background of meteorology and oceanography and astronomy against
which the actors in our play shall shortly act their part.

Now let us drop the curtain for a second.

When it rises, the stage is set for a new act.

That act will show you how men learned to find their way
across those mountains and seas and deserts that had to be conquered ere we could truly call this world our home.

The curtain rises again.

Act II: Maps and methods of navigation.

MAPS. A VERY BRIEF CHAPTER UPON A VERY BIG AND FASCI-
NATING SUBJECT. TOGETHER WITH A FEW OBSERVA-
TIONS ON THE WAY PEOPLE SLOWLY LEARNED
HOW TO FIND THEIR WAY ON THIS
PLANET OF OURS

WE ARE so accustomed to maps that it is almost impossible for us to imagine a time when there were no maps, when the notion of travelling according to a map was as foreign to man's conception of ultimate possibilities as the idea of traversing space in the form of a mathematical formula would be to us today.

The ancient Babylonians, who were such excellent geometrists that they could make a cadastral survey of their entire kingdom (that survey was made in 3800 B. C., or 2400 years before Moses was born), have left us a few clay tablets containing what must have been an outline of their domains, but these were hardly maps in our sense of the word. The Egyptians, in order to get every penny of taxes they could sweat out of their hard-working subjects, also made a survey of their kingdom, which showed that they knew enough about practical mathematics to perform this difficult task. But no maps in the modern sense of the word have so far been found in any of the royal sepulchres.

The Greeks, the most curious-minded and nosey people of the ancient world, wrote endless treatises upon the subject of geography, but we know next to nothing about their maps. Here and there in some great commercial center there seem to have been engraved bronze tablets showing the best route to be followed if a merchant wanted to get from one part of the eastern Mediterranean to another. But none of these tablets has ever been

How Maps became Maps

dug up and we have no idea what they looked like. Alexander the Great, who covered greater distances than any other human being before him and very many after him, must have been possessed of a certain "geographical sense", for he maintained a special body of professional "pacers"—men who went ahead of the army and kept an accurate account of the distances the indefatigable Macedonians wandered on their search for the gold of India. But of regular maps, which would have been understandable to ourselves, not a vestige, not a scrap, not a line.

The Romans, who in quest of plunder (the most marvellously organized "systematic plunderers" of which the world has any account until the beginning of the great colonial epoch in Europe) went everywhere, lived everywhere, built roads everywhere, gathered taxes everywhere, hanged and crucified people everywhere, left the ruins of their temples and swimming-pools everywhere, seem to have been able to administer a world-empire without a single map worthy of the name. It is true their writers and orators quite frequently make mention of their maps and assure us that these were of remarkable accuracy and entirely dependable. But the only Roman map that has come down to us (if we except a small and insignificant piece of an ancient plan of Rome in the second century of our era) is something so primitive and clumsy that it is of no earthly value to modern man except as a historical curiosity.

It is known to historians as the Peutinger map because it was a man by the name of Conrad Peutinger, the town clerk to the city of Augsburg, who first conceived the idea of having it broadcasted by means of the recently invented printing-presses of Johann Gutenberg of Strassburg. Unfortunately Peutinger did not have the original to work from. The manuscript map he used was a thirteenth-century copy of a third-century original and during those thousand years, rats and mice had made away with a great many important details.

Even so, the general outline was undoubtedly that of the Roman original and if that was the best the Romans could do, they still had a great deal to learn. I will draw a copy of it here and let you judge for yourself. After a long and patient study of the document you will slowly begin to recognize what was in the mind of the Roman geographers. But you will also recognize that we have made enormous progress since the days when this spaghetti-shaped "world" was the last word in travel literature for a Roman general bound for England or the Black Sea.

A Roman Map

As for the maps of the Middle Ages, we can pass them by without any special comment. The Church frowned upon all "useless scientific pursuits". The road to Heaven was more important than the shortest route from the mouth of the Rhine to the mouth of the Danube, and maps became mere funny pictures, full of headless monsters (the poor Eskimos, huddled in their furs until their heads were no longer visible, were the originals for this fanciful notion) and snorting unicorns and spouting whales and hippogrifs and krakens and mermaids and griffons and all the other denizens of a world bewildered by fear and superstition. Jerusalem was of course shown as the center of the world, and India and Spain were the ultimate limits, beyond which no man could hope to travel, and Scotland was a separate island, and the Tower of Babel was ten times as big as the entire city of Paris.

Polynesian Woven Map

Compared to these products of the medieval cartographers, the woven maps of the Polynesians (they look for all the world like something done by the children in a kindergarten, but they are exceedingly handy and very accurate) are veritable master-pieces of the navigator's ingenuity. Not to mention the work of the contemporary Arabs and Chinese, who however were ruled out as contemptible heathen. Nor was there any real improve-ment until the end of the fifteenth century when navigation was at last elevated to the rank of a science.

For then the Turks conquered the bridge-head connecting Europe with Asia, land traffic into the Orient was permanently interrupted, and it suddenly became necessary to find a new way to the Indies by way of the open sea. That meant an end to the old familiar system of sailing by the church-towers of the nearest mainland or sailing by the sound of the dogs barking along the water-front. And it was this necessity of finding one's way across the ocean without seeing anything at all for weeks at a time except sky and water which brought about the great improvement in the navigating methods of that day.

The Egyptians seem to have ventured as far as Crete but no further, and even then the visits to the big island seem to have been more a matter of having been blown out of one's course than the result of a well-planned voyage of discovery. The

Medieval Map

Phoenicians and the Greeks were "church-tower sailors" at heart, although a few times they did quite remarkable things and even ventured forth as far as the Congo River and the Scilly Islands. Even then they undoubtedly hugged the shore as much as possible and at night pulled their boats up on dry land to escape being blown towards the open sea. As for the medieval merchants, they stuck to the Mediterranean, to the North Sea and to the Baltic, and were never for more than a few days without a glimpse of some distant mountain-range.

If they found themselves lost in the open, they had only one way in which to discover where the nearest land might be. For that purpose they always carried a few pigeons. They knew that pigeons would take the shortest route to the nearest bit of dry land. When they no longer knew what course to follow, they set one of their pigeons loose and observed the way it flew. Then they steered in that general direction taken by the bird until they saw the mountain tops and could make for the nearest harbor to ask where they might happen to be.

Of course during the Middle Ages even the average person was more familiar with the stars than we are today. He had to be because he lacked all sorts of information which nowadays comes to us in the printed form of almanacs and calendars. The more intelligent skippers therefore could find their way by studying the stars and by setting their course according to the Polar Star and the constellations. But in northern climes, where the sky was usually overcast, the stars were no great help. And navigation would have continued to be a painful and costly business of sailing by God and by guess (mostly the latter) if it had not been for a foreign invention which reached Europe shortly after the first half of the thirteenth century. But the origin and the history of the compass are still shrouded in deep mystery and what I tell you here is a matter of speculation rather than formal knowledge.

Genghis Khan, a little, slant-eyed Mongolian who during the first half of the thirteenth century ruled an empire slightly larger than any other that ever existed (it reached from the Yellow Sea to the Baltic and maintained itself in Russia until 1480) seems to have carried some sort of compass with him when he crossed the vast central Asiatic deserts, bound for the fleshpots of Europe. But it is impossible to say when the sailors of the Mediterranean had their first glimpse of this "blasphemous invention of the Devil", as the Church people called it, which soon afterwards was to carry their vessels to the ends of the earth.

Inventions of that sort, which are of world-wide importance, all seem to start in the same vague way. Some one returning from Jaffa or Famagusta probably brought a compass with him which he had bought from a merchant in Persia, who had told him that he had got it from some one who had just returned from India. The rumor spread through the ale-houses of the water-

Ice

fronts. Others wanted to see the funny little needle that had
been bewitched by Satan and that would tell you where the
north was, no matter where you happened to be. Of course,
they did not believe such a thing could be true. Nevertheless,
they asked their friend to bring them one too the next time he
came back from the East. They even gave him the money, and
six months later they had a little compass of their own. The
darned thing worked! Then everybody must have a compass.
Merchants in Damascus and Smyrna received hurry calls for
more compasses. Instrument-makers in Venice and Genoa began
to fabricate compasses on their own account. Suddenly we hear
of compasses in every part of Europe. And within a few years
the little glass-covered metal box had become such a commonplace sight that no one ever thought it worth while to write a
book about an instrument that everybody had long since taken
for granted.

So much for its career which must forever remain shrouded
in mystery. But as for the compass itself, our knowledge about
it has made great progress since the first sensitive needle guided
the first Venetians from their lagoons to the delta of the Nile.
For example, we have discovered that the needle of the compass
does not point to the true north except on a few spots on the
globe, while at all other places it points either a little to the east
or a little to the west—a difference which is technically known
as the "variation of the compass". This is due to the fact that
the magnetic north and south poles do not coincide with the
north and south poles of our planet but are several hundred
miles toward the south and the north of the geographic poles.
The northern magnetic pole is located in the island of Boothia
Felix, an island to the north of Canada, where Sir James Ross
first located it in 1831, and the southern magnetic pole is situated at 73° S. Lat. and 156° E. Long.

It follows therefore that it is not enough for a captain to
have merely a compass on board. He must also have charts
which show him the variations of his compass in different parts
of the world. That however has to do with the science of navi-

gation and the present volume is no handbook on navigation. Navigation is an exceedingly difficult and complicated branch of learning which refuses very positively to let itself be reduced to simple little words of one syllable. For our present purpose it is enough if you will kindly remember that the compass made its entry into Europe during the thirteenth and fourteenth centuries and that it was of tremendous help in making navigation a reliable science, and not merely a matter of fortunate guessing and hopelessly complicated calculations, which were far beyond the mental reach of most people.

But that was only a beginning.

One could now tell whether one were sailing north or north-by-east or north-north-east or north-east-by-north or north-east or north-east-by-east or in any of the other thirty-two "general directions" indicated by the compass. But for the rest, the medieval skipper had only two other instruments to help him find out in what part of the ocean he might happen to find himself.

In the first place, there was the lead-line. The lead-line was almost as old as the ships themselves. It would show the depth of the sea at any given point and if one had a chart indicating the different depths of the sea through which one was slowly wending one's way, the lead-line would give some indication of the approximate neighborhood in which one found one's self.

And then there was the log. The log originally was a small log of wood which was thrown overboard from the bow and which was then closely watched to see how long it would take before it passed the stern. As the length of the ship from stern to bow was of course known, one could then figure out how much time the vessel needed to pass a given point and that would show (more or less) how many miles the ship was making per hour.

The log of wood was gradually given up for the log-line, a long and thin but very strong piece of rope with a triangular piece of wood at the end. This rope had been beforehand divided into so many pieces by means of "knots" made at regular intervals and it was heaved overboard at the same time that another sailor started a sand-glass running. When all the sand had run through the glass (one knew of course beforehand how long that would take, two or three minutes) one pulled in the line and counted the knots that had run through one's hands while the sand-glass was emptying its contents from one bulb into the other. After that, a very simple calculation would show how fast the vessel was going, or as sailors used to say, "how many knots".

But even if the captain knew the speed of his ship and the general direction it was following, there were the currents and the tides and the winds to upset even the most careful of his calculations. As a result an ordinary ocean voyage, even long after the introduction of the compass, remained a most hazardous undertaking. The people who worked on the theoretical end of the problem realized that in order to make it something else, they would have to find a substitute for the old church-tower.

I am not trying to be funny when I say this. The church-tower or the tree on top of the high dune or the windmill on the dike or the barking of a watch-dog had been of such tremendous importance in the realm of navigation because it was a *fixed point,* something that would not change its position, no matter what happened. And given one such "fixed point", the sailor could then make his own deductions. "I must go further towards the east," he would say to himself, remembering the last time he had been in that part of the world, or "further towards the west or south or north to arrive where I want to be". And the mathematicians of that day (brilliant men, by the way, who, considering the scanty information and the faulty instruments at their disposal, did as good work as was ever done in their particular field) knew perfectly well where the crux of the situation lay. They must find a "fixed point" in nature to act as a substitute for the "fixed point" established by man.

They began their search about two centuries before Columbus (I am mentioning his name because 1492 is the one date every man, woman and child seems to know) and they have not finished it even in this day of wireless time-signals and under-water signals and mechanical steering-gears, when the "Iron Mike" has about driven the old helmsman out of his job.

Suppose you find yourself standing on a round ball at the foot of a tower on top of which there waves a flag. That flag will then be right straight over your head and as long as you remain at the foot of your tower it will be right straight over your head. But if you move away from it and try to look at it, you must lift your eyes at an angle, and that angle will depend upon the distance you are away from the tower, as you will see by studying this picture.

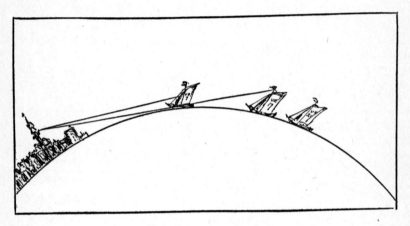

Church-tower navigation

And once this "fixed spot" had been discovered, the rest would be comparatively easy, for it would all be a matter of angles, and even the Greeks had known how to measure angles, for they had laid the foundation for the science of trigonometry which deals with the relationship between the sides and the angles of the triangle.

This brings us to the most difficult part of this chapter, indeed, I might say of the entire book—the search for what we now call latitude and longitude. The true method to establish one's latitude was discovered hundreds of years before longitude. Longitude (now that we know how to find it) looks much

The old conception of the World when the Earth
was the center of the Universe

simpler than latitude. But it offered certain almost insurmountable difficulties to our clockless ancestors. Whereas latitude, being merely a matter of careful observation and even more careful figuring, was something they were able to solve at a comparatively early date. But enough of generalities. Here the problem is, stated as simply as I know how.

You will notice a number of planes and angles. At D you find yourself right beneath the top of the tower, just as you will be standing almost right beneath the sun at 12 o'clock noon if you happen to be on the equator. When you have moved to E

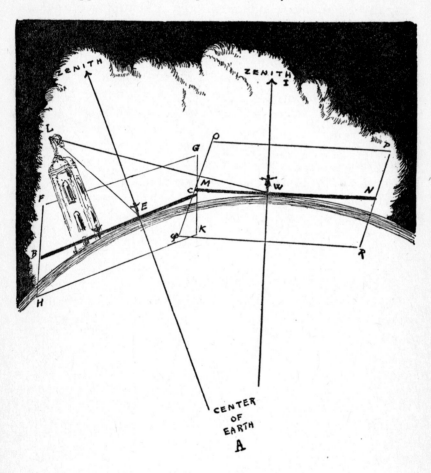

the matter becomes a little more complicated. The world on which you stand is round and you need a flat plane if you are to indulge in any figuring of angles. Therefore you draw a line from the imaginary center of the earth, called A, which runs through your own body and loses itself right above you in a spot called Zenith, the official astronomical name for the point of the heavens directly above the observer and which is the opposite of the Nadir, which is the point of the heavens directly under the observer.

Let us try to do this problem so that you can actually see it, for it is rather complicated. Stick a knitting-needle clean through the heart of an apple and imagine yourself on one side of that apple, sitting with your back leaning against the knitting-needle. The top of the knitting-needle is Zenith and the bottom is Nadir. Then imagine a plane that is at right angles with the place you are sitting or standing and the knitting-needle. When you are standing at E that plane will be the plane called FGKH and BC will be the line on that plane from which you are making your observation. Furthermore, for the sake of convenience and in order to make the problem a little easier, kindly imagine that your eyes are in your toes, on the exact spot where your feet touch the line BC. Then look up at the top of the flag-pole on your tower and measure the angle top-of-flag-pole (or L), the spot where you stand (or E), and the end of your imaginary line BC, which is part of the imaginary plane FGKH, which runs at right angles with the imaginary line Zenith-A, which connects the center of the earth with the point of the heavens directly above you, the observer. That angle, if you know anything about trigonometry, will tell you how far you are away from the tower. Move to W and repeat the process. W will become the point where you touch the imaginary line MN, which is part of the imaginary plane OPRQ, which runs at right angles with the line connecting the center of the earth A with the new Zenith (the Zenith of course changes every time you move an inch) which I shall call Zenith I. Meas-

ure the angle LWM and you know how much further you are
away from the tower.

You see, even in the simplest form it is still quite complicated, and that is why I shall only give you a general outline of
the basic principles upon which modern navigation is based. If
you intend to become a sailor, you will have to go to a special
school for a number of years to learn how to make the necessary
calculations; and then after you have handled your instruments
and your tables and charts for twenty or thirty years, your directors may even make you a captain and trust that you will be
able to take a ship from one port to the next. If you have no
such ambition, you will never understand all this anyway and
so you will pardon me if I make this chapter short and stick to
the general idea.

Since navigation was entirely an affair of angles, no possible
advance could be made in that science until trigonometry had
once more been rediscovered by the people of Europe. The
Greeks had laid the foundations for this science a thousand years
before, but after the death of Ptolemy (the famous geographer
from Alexandria in Egypt) trigonometry had been forgotten or
discarded as a superfluous luxury—something a little too clever
to be quite safe. But the people of India and after them the
Arabs of northern Africa and Spain had no such scruples and
they had nobly carried on where the Greeks had left off. These
words Zenith and Nadir (both of them pure Arabic) bear witness to the fact that when trigonometry was once more admitted
to the curriculum of the European schools (which happened
sometime during the thirteenth century) it was a Mohammedan
and not a Christian branch of learning. But during the next three
hundred years, the Europeans made up for lost time. For although they were once more able to work with angles and triangles, they still found themselves faced by the problem of discovering some definitely fixed point away from the earth to act
as a substitute for their church-tower.

The most reliable candidate for this sublime honor was the

North Star. The North Star was so far away from us that it never seemed to change its position and besides, it was so easy to locate that even the dumbest shrimp-fisherman could find it, once he had lost sight of land. All he had to do was to draw a straight line through the two stars that were furthest to the right in the Big Dipper, and he couldn't miss it. And, of course, there was always the sun, but its course had never been scientifically mapped out and only the most intelligent mariners could avail themselves of its assistance.

As long as people were forced to believe that the earth was flat, all calculations were bound to be hopelessly at odds with the true state of affairs. Early during the sixteenth century there came an end to these make-shift methods. The "disc" theory was discarded for the "sphere" theory and the geographers at last came into their own.

The first thing they did was to cut the earth into two equal halves which were divided by a plane running at right angles with the line connecting the North and the South Poles. The dividing line was called the equator. The equator therefore was everywhere equally far removed from both the North and the South Pole. Next the distance between the poles and the equator was divided into ninety equal parts. Next ninety parallel lines (circles, of course, for remember the earth was round at last) were drawn between the poles and the equator, each one about sixty-nine miles away from the next, since sixty-nine miles represented one-ninetieth of the supposed distance between the pole and the equator.

Geographers gave these circles numbers, beginning from the equator and going up (or down) to the poles. The equator itself became 0° and the poles 90°. Those lines were called degrees of Latitude (the L's of the picture will make you remember how they run) and a little ° placed at the right of the number was used as a convenient symbol for the word "degree" which was too long to be used in mathematical calculations.

All this meant an enormous step forward. But even so, the business of going to sea remained a very dangerous experience.

A dozen generations of mathematicians and sailors had to devote themselves to compiling data about the sun, giving its exact position for every day of every year and every clime before the average skipper was able to handle the latitude problem.

Then at last any reasonably intelligent sailor, provided he could read and write, was able to determine within a couple of miles how far away he was from the North Pole and from the equator, or in technical terms, in what N. Lat. (degree of latitude north of the equator) or S. Lat. he might find himself. It was not quite so easy once he had crossed the equator, for then he was no longer able to fall back upon the Polar Star which is not visible on the southern hemisphere. But that problem too was eventually solved by science, and after the end of the sixteenth century latitude ceased to be a matter of concern to those who went down to the sea in ships.

There remained however the difficulty of determining one's longitude (longitude to make it easy for you to remember that the longitudinal degrees run in a vertical direction) and it took two whole centuries more before that puzzle had been successfully solved. In trying to establish the different latitudes, the mathematicians had been able to start out with two fixed points —the North Pole and the South Pole. "Here," so they could say, "stands my church-tower, the North Pole (or the South Pole) and it will remain there until the end of time."

But there was no East Pole and no West Pole either, because the axis of the earth did not happen to run that way. Of course one could draw an endless number of meridians, circles going around the earth and crossing both poles. But which one of these millions of meridians was the one to choose as "The Meridian" that was to divide the world into halves, so that thereafter the sailor could say, "I am a hundred miles east or west of 'The Meridian' "? The old notion of Jerusalem as the center of the earth was still strong enough to make many people demand that the meridian running through Jerusalem be recognized as Long.° or our vertical equator. But national pride prevented this plan. Every country wanted to have Long.° run through its own capital and even today, when we are supposed to be a little more liberal-minded in this respect, there still are German, French and American maps which show Long.° running through Berlin, Paris and Washington. And in the end, as England was the country which happened to do most for the advancement of nautical knowledge during the seventeenth century (when the problem of longitude was finally solved) and as all nautical affairs were then under the supervision of the Royal Observatory, built in Greenwich near London in the year 1675, the meridian of Greenwich was finally adopted as the particular meridian which was to divide the world into longitudinal halves.

Then at last the sailor had his longitudinal church-tower, but he was still faced with another difficulty. How was he to discover how many miles he was either east or west of that Greenwich meridian, once he was out on the high seas? To settle this matter for good and all, the English government in the year 1713 appointed a special "Commission for the Discovery of Longitude at Sea" which was to solve the problem by the practical expedient of offering large rewards for the best method of "determining longitude on the high seas". A hundred thousand dollars was a lot of money, two centuries ago, and everybody set to work with a will. When the commission was finally disbanded during the first half of the nineteenth century it had spent more than $500,000 in the form of rewards for deserving inventions.

Most of their labors have long since been forgotten and the work they did has been dropped as obsolete. But two inventions, following in the wake of these generous monetary rewards, have proved to be of lasting benefit. The first of these was the sextant.

The sextant is a complicated instrument (a sort of miniature nautical observatory which one can carry under one's arm) which allows the sailor to measure all sorts of angular distances. It was direct heir to the clumsy medieval astrolabe and cross-staff and the quadrant of the sixteenth century, and, as so often happens when the whole world is looking for the same thing at the same moment, three men claimed to be the original inventors and fought bitterly for the honor.

But the excitement caused in nautical circles by the appearance of the first sextants was mild compared to the interest shown in the chronometer when that faithful and reliable time-piece made its appearance four years later, in 1735. The chronometer, invented by John Harrison, an horological genius (he was a carpenter until he became a watch-maker), was a clock which worked so accurately that it made it possible to carry Greenwich time to any part of the world in any clime and in any form, sort or mode of conveyance. This John Harrison had been able to do by providing his clock with something he called a "compensation curve". It altered the length of the balance-spring in proportion to the expansion or contraction caused by changes in temperature in such a way that his chronometer was practically weather-proof.

After endless and unseemly quarrels about the reward, Harrison received his hundred thousand dollars (in 1773, three years before his death). And today, no matter where a ship happens to be, provided it carries a chronometer, it will always know what time it is in Greenwich. And since the sun revolves around the earth in twenty-four hours (it is the other way around, but I am using the expression for the sake of convenience) and passes through fifteen degrees of longitude in one hour, all we need to do in order to determine just how far we have travelled east or west of The Meridian is to first determine what time it is on the spot where we ourselves happen to be and then compare our local time with Greenwich time and note the difference.

For example, if we find (after careful calculations which every ship's officer can make) that it is twelve o'clock where we are, but two o'clock by our chronometer (which gives us the exact Greenwich time), then we know that since the sun travels through fifteen degrees in one hour (which means four minutes for every single degree) and since there is a difference of two hours between our time and that of Greenwich, that we must have travelled exactly $2 \times 15° = 30°$. And we write down in the log-book (a little book so-called because before the general introduction of paper it used to be a piece of wood on which all such figures were written down with chalk) that on such and such a day at noon our ship found itself at Long. 30° West.

Today that startling invention of the year 1735 has lost a great deal of its importance. Every day at noon the Greenwich Observatory broadcasts the correct time all over the world. Chronometers are rapidly becoming superfluous luxuries. Indeed, if we are to believe our navigators, wireless telegraphy will eventually do away with all our complicated tables and our diligent calculations and computations. Then that lengthy chapter of finding one's way across those uncharted seas, where one wave looked so hopelessly much like the next that even the best of sailors could lose himself in less time than it takes to write down this sentence—then that marvellous chapter of courage and endurance and high intelligence will also have come to an end. The imposing man with the sextant will disappear from the bridge. He will sit in his cabin with a telephone clasped to his ear and he will ask, "Hello, Nantucket! (or Hello Cherbourg!)

The new conception of the World in space

Where am I?" And Nantucket or Cherbourg will tell him. And that will be that.

But these twenty centuries of effort to make man's progress across the face of the earth safe and pleasant and profitable will not have been in vain. For they were one of the first successful experiments in international coöperation. Chinese, Arabs, Indians, Phoenicians, Greeks, Englishmen, Frenchmen, Dutchmen, Spaniards, Portuguese, Italians, Norwegians, Swedes, Danes, Germans, they all of them did their share to help the good work along.

That particular chapter in the history of coöperation has now been closed. But there remain enough others to keep us busy for quite a long time.

V

THE SEASONS AND HOW THEY HAPPEN

OUR word season is of Latin origin and it comes from the verb "serere" which means "to sow". "Season" should therefore be used only to indicate the spring—the "sowing time". But very early in the Middle Ages "season" lost that exclusive connotation. Three other seasons were added to divide the year into four equal parts: the winter, or wet season; the autumn, the period of increase (the same root as in "augmentation" or "august" which is not only the "month of the increase" but also a "person of augmented importance"); and the summer, which was the old Sanskrit name for the entire year.

Aside from their practical and their romantic interest to the human race, the four seasons have a most prosaic astronomical background, for they are the direct result of the earth's behavior on its yearly peregrination around the sun, as I shall tell you as briefly and as dully as the subject allows.

The earth turns around its own axis in 24 hours. The earth turns around the sun in about 365¼ days. To get rid of that ¼ day and keep the calendar more or less pure (no, it is not correct, but it is extremely doubtful whether the nations just now would find time in which to agree upon a decent revision) we have a year of 366 days, or leap-year, every four years except in the years which end with two zeros, such as 900, 1100, 1300 or 1900. But the years which can be divided by 400 are an exception to this exception. The last exception was Anno Domini 1600. The next one will be the year of grace 2000.

The earth does not describe a perfect circle on its way around the sun, but an ellipse. It is not much of an ellipse, but enough to make the study of the earth on its course through space a great

The Zones

deal more complicated than if we had to deal with a perfect circle.

The axis of the earth does not stand at right angles to the plane which we could draw through the sun and our own planet, but at an angle of 66½°.

But on its course around the sun the axis of the earth always remains at the same angle which is directly responsible for the variations in the seasons in different parts of the world.

On March 21st, the position of the earth in relation to the sun is such that the light of the sun illuminates exactly one-half of the surface of our planet. As a result, on that particular day, day and night are of equal length in every part of the world. Three months later, when the earth has finished one-fourth of her voyage around the sun, the North Pole is turned towards the sun and the South Pole is turned away from the sun. As a result, the North Pole is celebrating its yearly day of six months, while the South Pole is enjoying its yearly night of six months; and the northern hemisphere is partaking of the long, shining days of the summer, while the southern hemisphere is spending the long winter evenings reading a good book by the fireside. Remember that when we go skating at Christmas, the people in the Argentine and Chile are dying of sun-stroke, and while we suffer from our annual heat-wave, it is time for them to get their skates sharpened.

The next day of seasonal importance is the 23d of September, because then once more the days and nights are of equal length all over the world. Then we reach the 21st of December when the South Pole has turned its face towards the sun and the North Pole has turned its back upon our source of heat. Then the northern hemisphere is cold and the southern hemisphere is warm.

But the peculiar slant of the axis of the earth, together with the earth's rotation, is not alone responsible for the change in seasons. That 66½° angle also gives us our five zones. On both sides of the equator we have the tropical zone, where the rays of the sun hit the surface of the earth either vertically or almost vertically. The northern and southern temperate zones are those regions between the tropics and the polar regions where the sun's rays hit the earth a little less vertically and therefore have to warm a greater surface of soil or water than they do in the tropics. Until finally the two polar regions receive the rays of the sun at such an angle that even in summer each sixty-nine miles of sunlight is obliged to heat almost double that amount of land.

It is not easy to make these things clear on paper. There are planetariums where you can see all this and understand it too in much less time than you need to read this. But only very few of our cities have thought it necessary to establish such a plane-tarium. Go to the Board of Aldermen and tell them that you want one for a Christmas present. While they are looking this difficult word up in the dictionary (it may take them twenty or

Wind

thirty years) you had better try your luck with oranges or apples and a candle and a little black ink to mark off the zones. A
match will do for the North Pole and South Pole. And don't
indulge in comparisons when a fly descends upon your little
home-made planet. Don't say to yourself, "Suppose—just suppose—that we too should be only some sort of fly, crawling aimlessly across the surface of a gigantic orange, a gigantic orange
illuminated by a gigantic candle—both of them little playthings
in the hands of some colossus who wanted an afternoon's entertainment!"

Imagination is a good thing.

But not in the realm of astronomy.

VI

CONCERNING THE LITTLE SPOTS OF DRY LAND ON THIS
PLANET AND WHY SOME OF THEM ARE CALLED
CONTINENTS WHILE OTHERS ARE NOT

ALL of us, without exception, live on islands. But some of
these islands on our planet are so much larger than the others
that we have decided to let them belong to a class of their own
and have called them "continents". A continent therefore is an
island which "contains" or "holds together" more territory than
just an ordinary island like England or Madagascar or Manhattan.

But there are no hard and fast rules. America and Asia and
Africa, being the biggest continuous pieces of land, are continents
by right of their enormous size. Europe, which to the astronomers of the planet Mars undoubtedly looks like a peninsula of
Asia (a little larger perhaps than India, but not very much) has
always insisted on being a continent by itself. The Australians
would undoubtedly go to war if any one dared to suggest that
their beloved island was not really big enough and did not have
enough inhabitants to be ranked among the continents. The
Greenlanders on the other hand seem quite contented to remain
plain, ordinary Eskimos, although the country of their birth is
twice as large as the combined area of New Guinea and Borneo,
the two biggest islands on our planet. While the penguins of
the South Pole, if they were not such humble and amiable creatures, might easily claim to be living on a continent, for the
Antarctic region is surely as vast as all the land between the
Arctic Sea and the Mediterranean.

I don't know how all this confusion arose. But the science of
geography passed through many centuries of absolute neglect.

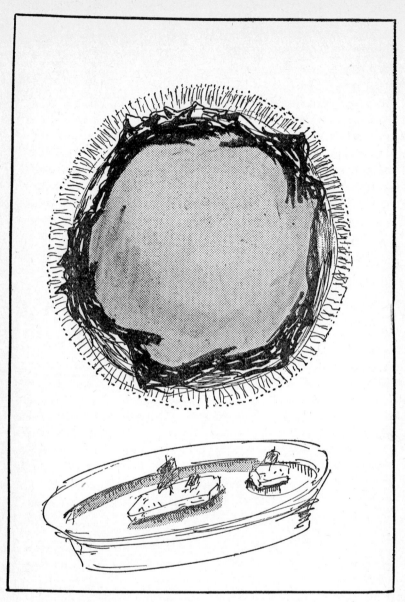

Are our proud continents perhaps islands of some lighter
material which float on the heavier substance of
the earth's interior as pieces of cork will
float on the water in a basin?

During that period, erroneous notions attached themselves to
the body of our geographical information as barnacles attach
themselves to the keel of a ship that lies neglected in port. In the
course of time (and the dark ages of our ignorance lasted about
1400 years) some of those barnacles assumed such gigantic proportions that they were finally mistaken for parts of the ship.

But rather than add to the existing confusion, I will stick to
the generally accepted divisions and I will say that there are five
continents: Asia, America, Africa, Europe and Australia, and
that Asia is four and a half times as large as Europe, America
four times as large, Africa three times, while Australia is a few
hundred thousand square miles smaller. Asia and America and
Africa therefore ought to come ahead of Europe in a handbook
on geography; but if we do not merely pay attention to size but
also consider the role any given part of the world has played
in the historical development of the entire planet, we must begin
with Europe.

Let us first of all look at the map. As a matter of fact, let us

Rockall—the top of a submerged continent in the
Northern Atlantic

look at our maps oftener than we look at the printed page. For you might as well attempt to learn music without an instrument or swimming without water as to try to learn geography without a map. And as soon as you look at a map, or better still, if you can get hold of a globe, you will notice that the European peninsula, bounded by the Arctic Ocean and the Atlantic Ocean and the Mediterranean Sea, is situated right in the heart of that part of the world which contains the greatest amount of land. Just as poor, neglected Australia happens to be situated in the exact center of that other half of our planet which contains the greatest percentage of water. That was advantage number one which Europe enjoyed, but there were others. Asia might be about five times as large as Europe but while one-quarter of all its land was too hot for comfort, another quarter was situated in such close proximity to the North Pole that no one but a reindeer or a polar bear would choose it as a permanent place of residence.

There again Europe scored, for it enjoyed certain advantages which none of the other continents did. The toe of Italy, the southernmost point, although fairly warm, is still some 800 miles removed from the tropical zone. Northern Sweden and Norway run quite a distance beyond the polar circle, but it happens that the Gulf Stream visits their shores and keeps them warm, while Labrador, in an equal latitude, is a frozen wilderness.

Furthermore, Europe has a greater proportion of peninsulas and seas that run way inland than any other continent. Just think of Spain, Italy, Greece, Denmark, Scandinavia, the Baltic, the North Sea, the Mediterranean, the Aegean Sea, the Sea of Marmora, the Gulf of Biscay, the Black Sea, and compare that situation with Africa or with South America, which has the lowest record for that sort of thing. The result of such a large body of water touching almost every part of the mainland is a very moderate climate. That means that the winters are not too cold and the summers are not too hot. Life is neither too easy nor too difficult, so that man becomes neither a loafer (as he does in Africa) nor a beast of burden (as he does in Asia) but is able to mix work

and leisure in a more agreeable and useful proportion than anywhere else.

But it was not only the climate that helped the Europeans to
make themselves the masters of the greater part of our planet
and to maintain themselves as such until they committed suicide
during the four years of their unfortunate civil war of 1914–
1918. Their geological background was another point in their
favor. This, of course, was a mere accident for which they deserve no personal credit. But just the same they plucked the fruit
of all those colossal volcanic eruptions and those gigantic glacial
invasions and those catastrophic floods which had made their
continent what it was, which had placed their mountains where
they could most easily be turned into national frontiers and
which made their rivers flow in such a way that practically every
part of the interior enjoyed direct communication with the sea,
a most important point for the development of trade and commerce before the invention of the railroad and the automobile.

The Pyrenees cut the Iberian peninsula off from the rest of
Europe and became the natural frontier of Spain and Portugal.
The Alps performed a similar service for Italy. The great plain
of western France lay hidden behind the Cévennes, the Jura and
the Vosges Mountains. The Carpathians acted as a bulwark
which separated Hungary from the vast plains of Russia. The
Austrian Empire, which played such an important part in the
history of the last eight hundred years, consisted, roughly speaking, of a circular plain, surrounded by difficult mountain-ranges
which protected it against its neighbors. Without those barriers,
Austria would never have existed as long as it did. Germany too
was no mere political accident. It consisted of a large square of
territory which sloped gently from the Alps and the mountains
of Bohemia towards the Baltic Sea. And then there were islands,
like England and those of the old Greek Aegean Sea, and
swamps like Holland and Venice, all of them natural fortresses
which Providence herself seemed to have placed there for the
development of independent political units.

Even Russia, which we so often hear described as the result

Mountains and seas make excellent natural boundaries

of one man's terrific desire for power (the late Peter the Great of the house of Romanov) was really much more the product of certain natural and inevitable causes than we are sometimes willing to believe. The great Russian plain, situated between the Arctic Ocean, the Ural Mountains, the Caspian Sea, the Black Sea, the Carpathians and the Baltic, was ideally situated for the foundation of a highly centralized empire. The ease with which the United Soviet Republics survived after the downfall of the Romanov dynasty seems to be conclusive proof of this.

But the rivers, too, in Europe, as I have already remarked, ran in such a way that they could play a most important and practical part in the economic development of that continent. Draw a line from Madrid to Moscow and you will notice that all the rivers, without any exception, run either north or south, giving every part of the interior direct access to the sea. Since civilization has always been a product of water rather than land, this fortunate aquatic arrangement was of tremendous help in making Europe the richest and therefore the dominant center of our planet until the disastrous and suicidal war of 1914–1918 made her lose that enviable position. But let the maps bear me out.

Compare Europe with North America. On our own continent two high mountain-ranges run almost parallel with the sea; and the entire middle part, the great central plain of the Middle West, has but one direct outlet to the sea, the Mississippi River and its tributaries, which run into the Gulf of Mexico, a sort of inland sea far removed from both the Atlantic and the Pacific Oceans. Or compare Europe with Asia, where a helter-skelter wrinkling process of the earth's surface and the irregular slopes of all the mountain-ranges make the rivers run in any old direction, while the most important of those water-ways, traversing the vast Siberian steppes, lose themselves in the Arctic Ocean and are of no earthly use to any one except a few local fishermen. Or with Australia, which has no rivers at all. Or with Africa, a vast central plateau which forces the rivers to break through the high fringe of mountains near the coast and prevents sea traffic from using the natural waterways to reach the interior. Then you will begin to understand why Europe, with its convenient mountain-ranges and its even more convenient river systems, with nine times as much coast-line as it would have if it were rounded off as neatly as Africa or Australia, with its moderate climate and its convenient location right in the heart of the land masses of this earth, was predestined to play the role of the leading continent.

But those natural advantages alone would not have been enough to allow this tiny corner of the world to lord it over all its neighbors. Man's ingenuity had to lend a hand. That was easy. For the climate of northern Europe was an ideal climate to stimulate men's brains into activity. It was neither too cold for absolute comfort nor too hot for a regular daily task, but just right to make one feel like doing something. As a result, the inhabitants of northern Europe, as soon as their respective coun-

We can only live on the land between the high
mountains and the submerged valleys called oceans
and seas

tries had duly settled down and were able to guarantee their citizens that indispensable minimum of law and order without which no mental life is possible, began to devote themselves to those scientific pursuits which in the end were to make them the owners and exploiters of the four other continents.

Their mathematics and their astronomy and trigonometry taught them how to sail the Seven Seas with a reasonable assurance of being able to return whence they had come. Their interest in chemistry provided them with an internal combustion machine (that queer motor called a "gun") by means of which they could kill other human beings and animals faster and more accurately than any other nation or tribe had ever been able to do. Their pursuit of medicine taught them how to make themselves comparatively immune against a variety of diseases which hitherto had kept whole regions of the earth in a state of chronic depopulation. And finally the comparative poverty of their own soil (poor when compared to the plains of the Ganges or the mountain-ranges of Java) and the everlasting necessity of living rather "carefully" had gradually developed such deep-seated habits of thrift and greed that Europeans would go to any extreme in order to acquire the wealth without which their neighbors regarded and scorned them as regrettable failures.

As soon as the introduction of that mysterious Indian instrument known as the compass had made them independent of the church-tower and the familiar coast-line and allowed them to roam at will, and as soon as the rudder of the ship had been moved from the side to the stern (an improvement which seems to have occurred during the first half of the fourteenth century and which was one of the most important inventions of all time, since it gave man such command over the course of his vessel as he had never enjoyed before) the people of Europe were able to leave their little inland seas, the Mediterranean and the North Sea and the Baltic, and to make the gigantic Atlantic the high-road for their further exploits of a commercial and military character. Then at last they were able to make the fullest possible use of the fortunate incident which had placed their continent right in the heart of the greatest amount of land on our planet.

They maintained this advantage for more than five hundred years. The steamer succeeded the sailing vessel, but since trade has always been a matter of cheap modes of communication, Europe was able to continue at the head of the procession. And those military authors have been right who maintained that the nation with the biggest navy was also the nation that could dictate its will to the rest of the world. In obedience to this law, the Norsemen had been succeeded by Venice and Genoa, and Venice and Genoa had been succeeded by Portugal, and Portugal as a world-power had been succeeded by Spain, and Spain by Holland, and Holland by England, because each country in turn had had the largest number of battle-ships. Today, however, the sea is rapidly losing its former importance. The ocean as a highroad for commerce is being succeeded by the air. And perhaps it is not so much the Great War which has reduced Europe to the rank of a second-rate continent as the invention of the heavier-than-air flying-machine.

The son of a Genoese wool-merchant changed the course of history by discovering the unlimited possibilities of the ocean.

The owners of a simple bicycle-repair-shop in the outskirts of Dayton, Ohio, did the same for the air. As a result, the children of a thousand years hence may never have heard the name of Christopher Columbus, but they will be familiar with Wilbur and Orville Wright.

For it was a product of their patient and ingenious brains more than anything else which is gradually moving the center of civilization from the Old World to the New.

VII

OF THE DISCOVERY OF EUROPE AND THE SORT OF PEOPLE WHO LIVE IN THAT PART OF THE WORLD

THERE are twice as many people in Europe as there are in North and South America together. There are more people within the confines of that small continent than in America, Africa and Australia together. Only Asia has a greater number of inhabitants than Europe, 950,000,000 against Europe's 550,-000,000. These figures are more or less accurate for they were gathered by the International Statistical Institution connected with the League of Nations, a gathering of learned men who are able to consider such matters with a cool and detached eye and who are under no obligation to doctor the returns to please the local pride of any particular country.

According to that same erudite body, the average net increase in population on this planet is 30,000,000 per year. And that is a very serious matter. For at that rate of speed, the population of the world will double itself in about six decades. And as we still have millions and millions of years to go, I hate to think what conditions will be later on, in the year 19320 or 193200 or 1932000. "Standing room only" in the subway is bad enough. "Standing room only" on our planet would be absolutely unbearable.

And yet that is the prospect before us unless we are willing to face facts and take certain measures before it is too late.

All that however belongs in a handbook on political economy. The question that faces us here is the following: Where did these early settlers of the European continent, who were to play such a great role in history, come from, and were they the first

to arrive upon the scene? The answer, I regret to say, must be
exceedingly vague. Those people probably came from Asia and
they probably entered Europe through the gap between the
Ural Mountains and the Caspian Sea and they probably found
that earlier races of immigrants and older forms of civilization
had preceded them. But until the anthropologists shall have
gathered many more data than are now at their disposal, the
story of those pre-pre-historic invaders is still too vague to be
incorporated in a popular handbook of geography and we must
stick to the later arrivals.

Why did they come? For the same reason that made over a
hundred million people move from the Old to the New World
during the last hundred years—because they were hungry and
the lands toward the west offered them a better chance to survive.

These immigrants scrambled all over Europe, as the immigrants of a later day were to scatter all over the great American
plains. And in the mad rush for land and for lakes (in those
early days, a lake was even more valuable than a piece of land)
all traces of "pure racial stock" were speedily lost. Here and
there along the more inaccessible parts of the Atlantic sea-shore
or in the hidden depths of some obscure mountain valley, a few
of the weaker tribes continued to vegetate, proud of their purity
of race, but having little else to console them for the loss of touch
with the outside world. And therefore when we speak of "race"
today, we have given up all idea of absolute ethnological purity.

We use the expression for the sake of convenience to describe
certain large groups of people who happen to speak the same language (more or less); who have a common historical origin
(more or less); and who during the last two thousand years of
written history have developed certain traits of character and
certain modes of thought and social behavior which have made
them conscious of belonging to what, for lack of a better word,
we continue to call a "racial group".

According to this notion of race (the x of the algebraic equation, invented solely for the sake of cutting through a thousand

From Animal to Man

difficulties) there are three great racial groups in the Europe of today and half a dozen smaller ones.

There are, first of all, the Germanic races, such as the English, the Swedes, the Norwegians, the Danes, the Dutch, the Flemish and part of the Swiss. Then the Latin race, including the French, Italians, Spaniards, Portuguese and Roumanians. Finally the Slavic races, consisting mainly of the Russians and the Poles, the Czechs, the Serbians and Bulgarians. Together they account for about 93% of the total population.

The rest are a couple of million Magyars or Hungarians, a slightly smaller number of Finns, about a million people of Turkish descent (in the little remnant of the old Turkish Empire around Constantinople) and some three million Jews. Then there are the Greeks, who have been so hopelessly mixed with other "races" that we can only guess at their origin but who are more closely akin to the Germanic group than to any other. Finally the Albanians, also probably of Germanic origin, who now seem a thousand years behind the times but who had been comfortably settled on their present day farms five or six centuries ere the first of the Romans and Greeks made their appearance on European territory. And finally the Celts of Ireland, and the Letts and Lithuanians of the Baltic Sea, and the Gypsies, of indefinite number and hazy origin, who are chiefly interesting as an historical warning of what will happen to those who come too late and who arrive just when the last piece of empty land has been occupied by some one else.

So much for the people who populated both mountains and plains of the old continent. Now we must see what they made of their geographical background and what that background in turn made of them. For out of that struggle grew our modern world. Without it, we would still be like the beasts of the fields.

JUST A MOMENT BEFORE WE GO ANY FURTHER WHILE I TELL YOU HOW TO USE THIS BOOK

This book should be read with an atlas. There are a large number of excellent atlases and almost any one will do. For atlases are like dictionaries. Even a bad one is better than none at all.

As you will soon discover, there are quite a number of maps in this volume but these are not meant as a substitute for a regular atlas. I drew them merely to show you the many ways of approach to the subject under discussion and (if I must tell the truth) to get you personally interested in drawing maps according to your own notion of the geographical right and wrong. You see, flat maps, however ingeniously conceived, must be somewhat out of gear. The only approximately correct maps are those pasted on globes but even our globes are not entirely above suspicion for they should really be spheroids. We make them spheres merely for the sake of convenience. The earth, of course, is slightly flattened near the poles but it would take a gigantic globe to show the difference, and so we need not worry about that minor irregularity. Get yourself a globe (I wrote this book with the help of a ten-cent-store globe which was really a pencil-sharpener) and use it to your heart's content, but remember that it is an "approximation" and not an "established fact". The "established facts" will only enter into your life if you should try to qualify for a master mariner's certificate. But in that case, you would have to spend many years mastering an exceedingly difficult branch of science; and this book was not writ for specialists but for the average reader who wants to get some general ideas about the planet upon which he happens to live.

Now let me tell you one thing. The best and most convenient way to learn geography is to revaluate everything into pictures.

Compare the proportions of Greenland and South America on
a globe and on a flat map and notice what a difference that makes!

Don't copy me or anybody else. Look at my pictures if you care
to do so, but regard them merely as a sort of geographical appe-
tizer, as polite suggestions for the meal you intend to prepare
yourself by and by.

I have tried to give you quite a number of samples according
to the geographical notions of the author himself. I have drawn
you two-dimensional maps and three-dimensional maps. It will
take you some time to get accustomed to these three-dimensional
contraptions but, once you see them, you will no longer like the
two-dimensional variety. I have given you maps as seen from
mountain tops and according to the different angles from which
you are able to contemplate a landscape. And I have given you
maps as seen from aeroplanes and Zeppelins and the sort of maps
we might expect to see if the oceans should run dry. I have given
you a few maps which are merely pretty and ornamental and
others which resemble geometrical patterns. Take your choice,

and then *draw your own maps according to your own notions of how the thing should be done.*

Draw maps. . . . Get yourself a small globe or a large globe and an atlas. Buy yourself a pencil and a pad of paper, and then draw your own pictures.

For there is only one way in which you can learn geography so that you will never forget it—*draw pictures.*

VIII

GREECE, THE ROCKY PROMONTORY OF THE EASTERN MEDI-
TERRANEAN WHICH ACTED AS THE CONNECTING
LINK BETWEEN THE OLD ASIA AND THE
NEW EUROPE

THE Greek peninsula is the southernmost point of the much larger Balkan peninsula. This is bounded on the north by the Danube, on the west by the Adriatic, which separates it from Italy, on the east by the Black Sea, the Sea of Marmora, the Bosporus and the Aegean Sea, which separate it from Asia, and on the south by the Mediterranean, which separates it from Africa.

I have never seen the Balkan peninsula from the air but it seems to me that from a high distance it must look like a hand, reaching out from Europe to Asia and Africa. Greece is the thumb. Thrace the little finger. Constantinople the nail on the little finger. The other fingers are the mountain-ranges that run from Macedonia and Thessaly to Asia Minor. Only the tops of these mountain-ranges are visible. The lower parts are covered by the waves of the Aegean, but from a great height one would undoubtedly be able to follow them as closely as the fingers of a hand partly submerged by the water in a wash-bowl.

The skin of this hand is stretched across a skeleton of sturdy mountain-ranges. In the main, these run from north-west to south-east, I might almost say, diagonal-wise. They have Bulgarian, Montenegrin, Serbian, Turkish, Albanian and Greek names but there are only a few important enough for you to remember.

These are the Dinaric Alps, stretching from the Alps of Switzerland to the Gulf of Corinth, the wide bay which separates the northern half of Greece from the southern half, the triangle which the early Greeks mistook for an island (small wonder, since the isthmus of Corinth which connects it with the mainland is only about three and a half miles wide) and which they called the Peloponnesus or the Island of Pelops, who, according to Greek tradition, was the son of Tantalus and a grandson of Zeus, and who at Olympia was honored as the father of all good sportsmen.

The Venetians who conquered Greece during the Middle Ages were prosaic merchants with no interest in a young man who once upon a time in his career had been served up as a roast at his father's dinner table. They found that a map of the Peloponnesus looked very much like the leaf of a mulberry-tree. And so they called it the Morea, and that is the name you will find on all modern atlases.

There are two mountain-ranges in this part of the world which have a separate existence of their own. In the north there are the Balkans which have given their name to the entire peninsula. The Balkans are merely the southern end of a half circle of hills of which the northern part is known as the Carpathians. They are cut off from the rest of the Carpathians by the so-called "Iron Gate"—the narrow ravine through which the Danube has dug itself a path on its way to the sea; and they act as a barrier which forces the Danube to run straight from west to east and to lose itself finally in the Black Sea instead of the Aegean Sea, towards which that river seems bound when it leaves the plains of Hungary.

Unfortunately, this wall separating the peninsula from Roumania is not as high as the Alps and so does not succeed in protecting the Balkan region from the chilly blasts that come blowing down from the great Russian plain. The northern part of the peninsula therefore is quite familiar with snow and ice, but ere the clouds can reach Greece they are stopped by a second wall, the Rhodope Mountains which, by their very name of the "rose-covered hills" (the same word as you will find in rhododendron, the rose-tree, and in Rhodes, the "rose-covered island" of the Aegean), indicate a milder climate.

The Rhodope Mountains reach a height of almost 9000 feet. The highest top in the Balkans, situated near the famous Shipka pass which the Russian armies forced in September of 1877 amidst a great deal of discomfort, is only 8000 feet. The Rhodope Mountains therefore play a very important part in deciding the climate of the rest of the peninsula, and for good measure there is snow-covered Olympus, 10,000 feet high,

Greece

which stands sentinel over the plains of Thessaly, where the real Greece begins.

This fertile plain of Thessaly was once upon a time an inland sea. But the river Peneus (the Salambria of the modern map) cut itself a road-bed through the famous valley of Tempe, and the vast Thessalian lake emptied itself into the Gulf of Saloniki and became dry land. As for Thessaly, the granary of ancient Greece, the Turks neglected it, as they neglected everything, not so much through wickedness of heart as that hopeless Mohammedan inertia which answers all questions of immediate practical importance with a shrug of the shoulder and a brief "What is the use?" And as soon as the Turks had been driven out, the Greek money-lenders got hold of the peasants and continued where the others had left off. Today Thessaly is raising tobacco. It has one harbor, Volo, from which the Argonauts set forth on their quest of the Golden Fleece, a story that was already hoary with age long before the heroes of Troy were born. It also has one industrial town and railroad center, Larissa.

As a matter of curiosity and in order to show how strangely people got scrambled in the olden days, I might mention that this city in the heart of the Greek land of Thessaly has a negro quarter of its own. The Turks, who did not care who got killed fighting their battles for them, had imported several regiments of Sudanese natives from their Egyptian possessions to help them suppress the great Greek uprising of 1821–1829. Larissa was their headquarters during that war and after the war the poor Sudanese were forgotten. They remained stranded and they are still there.

But you will meet with stranger things than that ere we get through. You will hear of Red Indians in northern Africa and Jews in eastern China and horses on an uninhabited island in the Atlantic Ocean. This much for the benefit of the "pure race" enthusiasts.

From Thessaly we cross the Pindus Mountains into the Epirus. This mountain-range, as high as the Balkans, has always been a barrier between the Epirus and the rest of Greece.

Why Aristotle should have identified this part of the world with the original home of the human race will ever remain a mystery, for it is a poverty-stricken country of high hills and wandering herds of cattle, without harbors or decent roads. Of its early population little remained when the Romans on one of their campaigns sold 150,000 Epirotes into slavery (the famous Roman way of establishing law and order). But two parts of the Epirus, separated from the mainland by narrow stretches of water from the Ionian Sea, are interesting. One is Ithaca, the legendary home of long-suffering Odysseus, and the other is Corfu, the early home of the Phaeacians, whose king, Alcinous, was the father of Nausicaa, loveliest of all women in ancient literature and an example of gracious hospitality until the end of time. Today the island (one of the Ionian islands, occupied first by Venice, later by the French, then by the English until ceded by them to Greece in 1869) is chiefly famous as the place of retreat for the defeated Serbian armies in the year 1916 and as a target for some very loose and useless shooting on the part of the Fascist navy only a few years ago. It has however a great future as a winter resort, but is undoubtedly situated on one of the great European earthquake belts.

The Dinaric Alps have a bad record as earthquake producers, while the neighboring island of Zante suffered most severely from an earthquake as recently as 1893. But earthquakes have never yet prevented people from going where it was pleasant to be and we can discount the element of danger. We shall meet with a great many volcanoes on our trip around the world and still find their gentle slopes more densely populated than the less energetic parts of the world's brittle surface. Explain this who may. I proceed from the Epirus further towards the south, and behold, Boeotia!

I mention this region, which lies like a vast, empty soup-plate between the hills of Attica towards the south and Thessaly and the mountains of the Epirus towards the north, most particularly because it is a classical example of that influence of Nature upon Man which I mentioned in the beginning of this book.

To the average Greek of the good classical days, a Boeotian, although he came from the land of Mount Parnassus, the home of the Muses, on the slopes of which the Delphic Oracle had established its shrine, was a clod-hopper, a heavy-witted rustic, a clown, an oaf, a lout, a gawk, a thick-skulled dunderpate, pre-destined for all the cheap slap-stick humor of the early stage.

And yet, the Boeotians by nature were no less intelligent than the rest of the Greeks. Epaminondas, the strategian, and Plu-tarch, the biographer, were Boeotians but they had left their na-tive haunts at an early age. Those who remained behind suffered

The Mediterranean

from the poisonous vapors that arose from the swamp-ridden borders of Lake Copais. In plain, modern medical terms, they probably were victims of malaria, a disease which does not tend to make people brilliant-minded.

The French Crusaders, who set up as rulers of Athens during the entire thirteenth century, began to drain these quagmires, and conditions among the Boeotians improved. The Turks, of course, allowed the mosquitoes to breed to their hearts' content and the Boeotians grew worse. Finally under the new kingdom, a French and afterwards an English company let the muddy waters of Lake Copais flow into the Euboic Sea and turned the bottom of this inland sea into fertile pasture-land.

Today the Boeotian is no more Boeotian than an Athenian or Brooklyn bootblack and, Heaven knows, they are quick-witted enough to get an extra nickel out of a Scotchman or Armenian. The marshes are gone, the vapors are gone, the malaria mosquitoes are gone. And an entire country-side that had been derided for centuries as Exhibit A of rustic numskullery and ignoble imbecility was restored to normal behavior by the draining of a few miasmic swamps.

And then we come to Attica, most interesting of the Greek lands. Nowadays we take the train that goes from Larissa to Athens and that connects with the trunk-lines to Europe. But in the olden days, those who wanted to get from Thessaly in the north to Attica in the south had only one route at their disposal, the route of the famous pass of Thermopylae. It was not really a pass in the modern sense of the word—a narrow gap between two high mountains. It was a narrow track, about 45 feet wide, between the rocks of Mount Oeta and the Gulf of Halae, which was part of the Euboic Sea. It was here that Leonidas and three hundred Spartans sacrificed themselves to the last man to save Europe from Asia, when they tried to halt the advancing hordes of Xerxes in the year 480 B. C. Two hundred years later it was here that the barbarous Gauls were prevented from invading Greece. Even as late as the years 1821 and 1822 the pass played an important military role in the war between Turks and Greeks. Today the pass is no longer visible. The sea has retreated almost three miles from the mainland and all that remains is a fifth-rate bathing establishment where people afflicted with rheumatism and sciatica try to find relief in those hot springs ("thermos" is Greek for "hot", as you will know from "thermometer" and "thermos bottle") which gave their name to a battle-field which shall be remembered as long as mankind continues to honor those who died in defending a lost cause.

As for Attica itself, it is a small triangle—a rocky promontory bordered by the blue waters of the Aegean Sea. Between its many hills lie numerous small valleys, all of them having direct access to the sea and kept fresh and pure by the breezes that come in from the water-front. The ancient Athenians declared that their sharpness of wit and clearness of vision were due to the delightful air they breathed. They may have been right. There were no stagnant Boeotian pools to encourage the thrifty malaria mosquito. As a result, the Athenians were healthy and kept healthy. They were the first people to recognize that man is not divided into two equal parts, body and soul, but that body and soul are one, that a healthy body is necessary to encourage a healthy soul, that a healthy soul is an indispensable part of a healthy body.

In that air it was possible to look all the way from the Acropolis to the Pentelian Mountains that dominated the plain of Marathon and provided the city with marble. But it was not only the climate that made the Athenians what they were, and for that matter are to this very day.

There was the sea that gave the people of Attica direct access to every part of the inhabited and uninhabited world. And there was that geological freak of Nature which had dumped a steep but flat-topped miniature mountain, a sort of mesa more than 500 feet high, 870 feet long and 435 feet wide, right in the heart of the plain surrounded by Mt. Hymettus (home of the best Athenian honey), by Mt. Pentelicus and by that Aegaleus from the slopes of which the unhappy fugitives from Athens watched the annihilation of the Persian fleet in the straits of Salamis a few days after the troops of Xerxes had set their city on fire. This flat-topped, steeply sloped hill had first of all attracted the immigrants from the north, for there they found what we all need—food and safety.

It is a curious fact that both Athens and Rome (or modern London or Amsterdam), the most important settlements of ancient Europe, were situated not immediately on the sea but several miles away from it. The example of Cnossos, the Cretan center of the Mediterranean world hundreds of years before either of them had been founded, may have acted as a warning of that dreadful thing that may happen when one is forever exposed to a surprise attack by pirates. Athens, however, was more conveniently near to the sea than Rome. A short time after he had landed in the Piraeus, then as now the harbor of Athens, the Greek sailor could be with his family. The Roman merchant needed three days for the trip. That was a little too long. He lost the habit of going back to his home city, settled down in the port at the mouth of the Tiber, and Rome gradually lost that intimate touch with the high seas which is of such tremendous benefit to all nations aspiring to world domination.

But gradually these mesa people, these inhabitants of the "top city" (for that is what *acro-polis* meant) moved into the plain, built houses around the foot of their hill, surrounded them with walls, finally connected these fortifications and those of the Piraeus and settled down to a glorious life of trade and robbery which ere long made their impregnable fortress the richest metropolis of the entire Mediterranean Sea. Then their Acropolis was given up as a place of abode and became a shrine—a shrine which lifted its white marble temples proudly against the violet-tinted sky of Attica—a shrine which even today, when an explosion in a Turkish powder-magazine has destroyed some of its more important buildings (during the siege of Athens in 1645), remains unique and sublime among those show-places where the genius of man is revealed in its highest forms of perfection.

When Greece regained her liberty in 1829, Athens had dwindled down to a mere village of 2000 inhabitants. In 1870 it had a population of 45,000. Today it has 700,000, a growth that is only paralleled by some of our own western cities. If the Greeks had not gambled with fate immediately after the Great War and had not foolishly thrown away all those immensely valuable possessions they had acquired in Asia Minor, Athens today would be the center of a mighty Aegean power. But all that may still happen in the near future. The mills of the Gods grind slowly but they continue day and night. And the city called after the shrewdest and wisest daughter of Zeus, born out of her father's brain, has shown itself to have a tremendous power of recuperation.

This brings us to the last and most distant part of the great

Greek peninsula and there, alas, our confident and prophetic words of hope are of no further avail. The curse that rested upon Pelops on account of his father's great wickedness has never been lifted from the land upon which that unfortunate prince bestowed his name. Here, hidden from the sea by mighty mountain-ranges, lay the idyllic land of Arcadia, praised by all poets as the home of simple but honest and lovable shepherds and shepherdesses. Poets are apt to wax most enthusiastic about that of which they know least. For the Arcadians were not more honest than the rest of the Greeks. If they did not practice the shabby tricks of their more sophisticated fellow-Hellenes, it was not because they disapproved of them. It was simply because they had never heard of them. It is true they did not steal, but there was nothing worth the taking in a country of dates and goats. They did not lie, but their hamlets were so small that everybody knew everything about everybody anyway. And if they kept away from the refined and decadent luxuries of those Gods worshipped in Eleusis and other Athenian centers of mysteries, they had a deity of their own, the great God Pan, who could give cards and spades to all the other Olympians when it came to coarse jokes and the low wit of barn-yard yokels.

It is true, then as now the Arcadians could fight, but it did them little good, for like most peasants they loathed discipline and could never agree who would be their commander-in-chief.

Southward of mountainous Arcadia stretched the plain of Laconia, a fertile plain, infinitely more fertile than the valleys of Attica, but sterile as to independence of thought and barren of all ideas that stretched beyond the mere necessities of life. In this plain the most curious city of antiquity was situated. Its name was Sparta and it stood for everything the northern Greeks held in abhorrence. Athens said "yea" unto life and Sparta said "nay". Athens believed in inspired brilliancy, while Sparta worked towards efficiency and service. Athens proudly preached the divine right of her exceptional individuals. Sparta reduced all men to the dreary monotony of the mediocre. Athens opened its doors wide to foreigners. Sparta kept them out of the country or murdered them. The Athenians were born traders, but no Spartan was allowed to soil his hands with business. If we are to judge by the final success of these two policies, the town of Sparta did not do so well. The spirit of Athens has penetrated the whole world. The spirit of Sparta has gone the way of the city that gave it birth—it has disappeared.

You will find a place called Sparta on the modern maps of Greece. It is a village composed of small scale farmers and humble keepers of silk-worms. It was built in 1839 on the spot where ancient Sparta was supposed to have stood. English enthusiasm provided the money, a German architect drew the plans. But no one wanted to go and live there. Today after almost a century of effort, it has 4000 inhabitants. The old curse of Pelops! A curse that makes itself felt even more distinctly in another part of the peninsula—a curse that comes to full fruition in the prehistoric fortress of Mycenae.

The ruins of Mycenae are not far away from Nauplia, the best-known harbor of the Peloponnesus, situated on the gulf of that name. The town was destroyed five centuries before the birth of Christ. But to us people of the modern world it is of more direct importance than even Athens or Rome. For it was here that long before the beginning of written history, civilization for the first time touched the shores of savage Europe.

In order to understand how this came about, look at the three half-submerged ridges of the great Balkan hand that reaches from Europe to Asia. These fingers are composed of islands. Those islands nowadays belong to Greece except for a few in the eastern part of the Aegean which Italy has occupied and continues to occupy for the reason that no other nation wants to go to war on account of a few worthless rocks in a distant sea. For convenience' sake we divide those islands into two groups, the Cyclades near the Grecian coast and the Sporades near the coast of Asia Minor. Those islands, as St. Paul already knew, are within short sailing distance of each other. And they formed the bridge across which the civilization of Egypt and Babylonia and Assyria moved westward until it reached the shores of Europe. Meanwhile that civilization, under the influence of those early immigrants of Asiatic origin who had settled down on the Aegean islands, had already been very distinctly "easternized" and it was in that form that finally it reached Mycenae which should have become what Athens afterwards became, the center of the classical Greek world.

Why didn't this happen? We do not know. No more than we know why Marseilles, the logical successor to Athens as the dominating power of the Mediterranean, should have been forced to surrender that honor to a very modern and very up-start village called Rome. The short-lived glory of Mycenae and its abrupt decline will ever remain a mystery.

But, you will object, all that is history and this is supposed to be a book on geography. But in Greece, as in many ancient lands, history and geography have become so interwoven that the two cannot be discussed separately. And from a modern point of view there are only a few geographical items really worth mentioning.

The isthmus of Corinth has been pierced by a canal about three miles long but too shallow and too narrow for large vessels. Greece, as a result of a series of wars with Turkey (alone and together with Bulgaria, Serbia and Montenegro), almost doubled its territory, then lost one-half of all those new acquisitions because in her dreams of grandeur she underestimated the fighting qualities of the Turks. The Greeks today, as in ancient times, take readily to the sea, and the blue and white flag of the republic (the ancient Bavarian colors imported by the first king of the country after it had regained its independence in 1829) is to be seen in every part of the Mediterranean. Also occasionally in the North Sea and the Baltic, where such Grecian vessels, unlike the Grecian urn of Keats, are famous for their slovenliness and dirt. And for the rest, there are the figs and the olives and currants that are exported to all countries that care for such delicacies.

Will Greece ever return to her ancient glories as so many of her people hope and fervently expect? Perhaps.

But a nation overrun in turn by Macedonians, by Romans, by Goths and Vandals and Herulians and Slavs, conquered and turned into a colony by Normans, Byzantines, Venetians and the unspeakable riff-raff of the Crusades, then almost completely depopulated and repopulated by Albanians, forced to live under Turkish domination for almost four entire centuries and used as a base of supply and a battlefield by the forces of the Allies in the Great War—such a nation has suffered certain hardships from which it will find it extremely difficult to recuperate. As long as there is life, there is hope. But it is a mighty slender one.

IX

ITALY, THE COUNTRY WHICH DUE TO ITS GEOGRAPHICAL SITUATION COULD PLAY THE ROLE OF A SEA-POWER OR A LAND-POWER, AS THE OCCASION DEMANDED

GEOLOGICALLY speaking, Italy is a ruin—all that is left of a vast mountain complex which formed a square like modern Spain but which withered away (as even the hardest rock will do in the course of a few million years) and finally disappeared beneath the waters of the Mediterranean. Only the easternmost part of that ancient mountain-range is visible today, the Apennines, which reach from the valley of the Po to Calabria in the toe of the boot.

Corsica, Elba and Sardinia are visible remnants of that high prehistoric plateau. Sicily was of course another part of it. Here and there in the Tyrrhenian Sea small islands betray the presence of ancient pinnacles. It must have been a terrific tragedy when all that land was captured by the sea. But as it happened some 20,000,000 years ago, when the earth suffered from the last of its great volcanic epidemics, there was no one present to tell the tale. And in the end it proved to be of enormous benefit to those who afterwards were to occupy the Apennine peninsula, for it gave them a country enjoying such sublime natural advantages of climate, soil and geographical location that it seemed almost predestined to become the dominating power of antiquity and one of the most important factors of the development and dissemination of art and knowledge.

Greece was the hand that reached out to Asia, caught hold of the ancient civilization of the valleys of the Nile and the Euphrates, and re-exported this article to the rest of Europe. But all that time the Greeks themselves remained something apart

Italy

from the continent upon which they bestowed their manifold blessings. Their country might just as well have been an island. The fact that it was a peninsula did not do it any good, for rows and rows of mountains, indeed, the whole of the Balkan range, cut it off from the rest of European humanity.

Italy, on the other hand, enjoyed the advantages of being both a sort of island, surrounded on three sides by the sea, while at the same time being very distinctly a part of the land-mass of northern Europe. We often overlook that fact and talk of Spain and Greece and Italy as if they more or less resembled each other. Spain and Greece had much in common. The Pyrenees and the Balkan mountain-ranges were impassable barriers between north and south. But the great plain of the Po was a salient that reached well up into the heart of Europe. The northernmost cities of Italy enjoy a higher latitude than Geneva or Lyons. Even Milan and Venice are of a higher latitude than Bordeaux and Grenoble, while Florence, which we unconsciously associate with the very heart of Italy, is almost on a line with Marseilles.

And furthermore, the Alps, although much higher than the Pyrenees and the mountains of the Balkans, had been formed in such a way as to offer comparatively easy access from south to north. The Rhine and the Rhône, running parallel with the northern frontier of Italy, divided the Alps into two halves; and therefore the valleys of the little brooks and streams running into the Rhine and Rhône, making an angle of ninety degrees with the mother river, offered convenient short-cuts into the plain of the Po—as Hannibal, with a whole circus of elephants, was the first to prove, to the great detriment of the unsuspecting Romans.

Italy therefore was able to play a dual role, that of a maritime nation, dominating the Mediterranean, and that of a continental power, conquering and exploiting the rest of Europe.

When the Mediterranean ceased to be a world sea and the discovery of America made the Atlantic Ocean the center of commerce and civilization, Italy lost its former advantages. Without coal and iron she could not hope to compete with the industrial countries of the west. But for almost twelve hundred years, from the founding of Rome in 753 B. C. till the fourth century of our era, Italy dominated and administered every part of Europe south of the Elbe and the Danube.

Unto the wild Germanic tribes that had just arrived from Asia and were now quarreling violently for the possession of this desirable "far west" Italy gave their first conception of law and order and the superior advantages of a semi-civilized life over the uncertainties and filth of a merely nomadic existence. Of course she enriched herself incredibly at the expense of every one else. But while taking a heavy toll of taxes, she delivered certain "goods" that were to shape the destinies of all those different regions for all times to come. And even today, the more than casual observer, visiting Paris or Bucharest, Madrid or Treves, will at once be struck by a certain similarity of look and outlook on the part of the inhabitants. He will be surprised that he can read the signs on the shops, no matter whether they are in French or Spanish or Roumanian or Portuguese. And then he will realize: "I am in an old Roman colony here. All this land once upon a time belonged to Italy just as the Philippines today belong to us. The first houses were built by Italian architects, the first streets were laid out by Italian generals, the first traffic and commercial regulations were written in the tongue of central Italy", and he will begin to appreciate what tremendous natural advantages were enjoyed by this country that was at once an island and part of the mainland.

At the same time the fortunate geological accident which had enabled Italy to conquer the whole of the known world carried with it certain very decided drawbacks. A country born out of volcanic upheavals was forever threatened to be killed by the very mother that had given it birth. For Italy is not only the classical land of moonlit ruins, orange trees, mandolin concerts and picturesque peasants. It is also the classical land of volcanic eruptions.

Every Italian who reaches the normal threescore and ten (easy in a country where laughter and gracious manners seem to come as natural as grouchy grins and boorishness do in other less favored parts of the world) is sure to have been an active participant in at least one major earthquake and a couple of minor ones before he is reverently carried to the family lot in the Campo Santo. The seismograph (most reliable of instruments I wish all our instruments were as painstakingly true) reported 300 quakes for the period of 1905–1907 alone. The next year, 1908, Messina was completely destroyed. If you want a few vital statistics (and mere figures are often infinitely more eloquent than pages of print) here is the record for the island of Ischia, situated just opposite Capri.

That island alone suffered from earthquakes in 1228, 1302, 1762, 1796, 1805, 1812, 1827, 1828, 1834, 1841, 1851, 1852, 1863, 1864, 1867, 1874, 1875, 1880, 1881, 1883, etc., etc.

As a result of these millions of years of volcanic eruptions, enormous tracts of Italian land got gradually covered with thick layers of tufa or tuff, a soft sort of rock composed of volcanic ash, thrown up by craters when in a state of violent eruption. These layers of tufa are very porous and they have a very decided influence upon the landscape of the entire peninsula. Some of those tufa fields cover areas of not less than 4000 square miles and the classical seven hills of Rome were really nothing but heaps of hardened volcanic ash.

But there are other geological developments, also the result of prehistoric upheavals, which make the soil of Italy so treacherous. The Apennines, which run the entire length of the peninsula, dividing it nearly into halves, are for a great part composed of limestone, a softish substance which lies on top of the older and harder rock formations. This limestone is apt to slide. The ancient Italians were so thoroughly familiar with this fact that even in the absence of volcanic upheavals they used to inspect the boundary lines of every large country estate once in twenty years to see whether the stone marks, indicating where one man's property ended and another man's began, were still in their correct position. And the modern Italians are made to realize this "sliding process" of their soil (and in a very costly and painful way) every time a railroad is pushed out of shape or a road is squashed to pieces or another village is rolled down the embankment of a lovely green mountain.

When you visit Italy you will be surprised at the large number of towns perched on the tops of high hills. The usual explanation is that the original inhabitants fled to those eagles' nests for safety's sake. That, however, was only a secondary consideration. When they moved to those uncomfortable pinnacles, so far removed from the wells of the valley and the main routes of communication, they did so primarily to avoid the dangers of sliding to death. Near the top of the mountains the base rocks of the ancient geological structure usually came to the surface and offered future residents a permanent place of abode. The sides of the hills, covered with soapy limestone, were as dependable as quicksand. Hence those picturesque villages that look so marvellous from a distance and are so incredibly uncomfortable once one is inside.

And this brings us to a consideration of modern Italy. For Italy, unlike Greece, does not merely have its future behind it. It works intelligently and courageously towards a new goal, and if it keeps long hours, it does so to undo the damage of a thousand years of neglect and once more regain its ancient and honorable status among the ranking nations of the earth.

In the year 1870 Italy once more became a united nation and as soon as the struggle for independence was over and the foreign rulers had been driven back across the Alps (where they belonged) the Italians started upon the gigantic and well nigh hopeless task of putting their long-neglected house in order.

First of all they turned their attention to the valley of the Po—the larder from which the whole peninsula could be conveniently fed. The Po is not a very long river as rivers go. As a matter of fact, if you will look at the picture of the comparative length of rivers, you will notice that the Volga is the only European river that is a fit candidate for such honors. The Po, which keeps close to 45° N. Lat., is only 420 miles long but its basin area, the territory from which it draws its tributaries and which therefore comes under its direct influence, is 27,000 square miles. That is not as much as several other rivers have, but the Po has some other qualities which make it unique.

It is navigable for fully five-sixths of its entire length and it is one of the fastest delta-builders of the world. Every year it adds almost three-quarters of a square mile to its delta and pushes it 200 feet further outward. If it continues to do this for another ten centuries, it will have reached the opposite coast of the Istrian peninsula and Venice will be situated on a lake, separated from the rest of the Adriatic by a dam seven miles wide.

Part of this vast amount of sediment which the Po carries to the sea has of course sunk to the bottom of the river and has filled it up with a layer of solid substance several feet thick. In order to keep the ever-rising river from flooding the surrounding landscape, the people living along its banks had to build dikes. They began to do this in Roman times. They are still doing it. As a result, the surface of the Po is much higher than the plain through which it flows. In several villages the dikes are thirty feet high and the river runs at the same height as the roofs of the houses.

But the Po region is famous for something else. Once upon a time, and not so very long ago, geologically speaking, the entire northern plain of Italy was part of the Adriatic Sea. Those lovely Alpine gorges which are now so popular with the summer tourists were narrow bays, like the fjords, the submerged valleys of the modern Norwegian mountains. These valleys were the outlet for the water that descended from the glaciers which then covered the greater part of Europe and of course a great deal more of the Alps than they do today. Glaciers get thickly covered with stones that roll down on them from the mountain slopes between which they pass on their way downwards. Such fringes of rocks are called moraines. When two glaciers meet, two moraines are bound to combine into a moraine double as high as the original ones, which is then called a "median moraine", and when the glacier finally melts, it drops this rocky ballast, which is called the "terminal moraine".

Erosion

These terminal moraines are a sort of geological beaver-dam, for they close the uppermost part of the valley off from the lower. As long as the glacier period lasts, there will be enough water to make the terminal moraines a negligible hindrance for the water on its downward course. But gradually, as the glaciers disappear and there is less and less water, the terminal moraine rises higher than the water and we get a lake.

All the north Italian lakes, the Lago Maggiore, the Lago di Como and the Lago di Garda, are moraine lakes. When man appeared upon the scene and began his works of irrigation, those moraine lakes acted as handy reservoirs. For in the spring, when the snow began to melt, they caught the surplus water which, if it had descended upon the valley in one solid body, would have caused the most destructive inundations. The Lago di Garda can rise twelve feet and the Lago Maggiore as much as fifteen feet and still take care of the extra water. A simple system of locks will then do the rest and tap those lakes according to the necessities of the day.

At a very early date the inhabitants of the great Po plain began to make use of this fortunate circumstance. They connected with canals the hundreds of little streams that feed the Po. They built dams and dikes and today thousands of cubic feet of water pass through these canals every few minutes.

It was an ideal region for the growing of rice. In the year 1468 the first rice plants were introduced by a Pisa merchant and to-day the rice-terraces are a common sight of the central plain of the Po. Other crops, corn and hemp and beet-root, were added and the vast plain, although it has less rainfall than the rest of the Italian peninsula, is the most fertile region of the entire country.

But not only did it provide man with food. It also looked after his wife's garments. Early during the ninth century, the mulberry tree, which is the basic necessity for the cultivation of the silk-worm, made its entrance, brought hither from China by way of Byzantium, the eastern half of the Roman Empire, which survived until 1453 when the Turks took its chief city, Constantinople, and turned it into the capital of their own empire.

The mulberry tree needs a great deal of heat. It found ideal living conditions in Lombardy, the plain of the Po, so-called after the Lombards or Long Beards, a Teutonic tribe from the mouth of the Elbe who lived here for a long time. Today almost half a million people are engaged in the silk industry and their product ranks much higher than that of China and Japan, the original home of Bombyx Mori, that inconspicuous little insect who provides us with the most luxurious of our wearing apparel.

No wonder that the whole of the plain is densely populated. The original town builders, however, kept at a safe distance from the river. Their engineering technique had not yet far enough advanced to provide them with reliable dikes and furthermore they feared the marshes which were an annual occurrence after the spring floods. Turin, the old residence of the house of Savoy, which now rules over the whole of Italy, and the connecting point for the passes that lead into France and Switzerland (the pass of the Mont Cenis going to France and the St. Bernard pass, famous for its dogs and monastery, giving access to the valley of the Rhône) is the only city of any importance directly situated on the Po. But it is so high that it needed have no fear of drowning. As for the other cities, Milan, the capital of that region, meeting-point for five important trade-routes (the St. Gothard road, the Simplon, the small St. Bernard, the Maloja and the Splügen pass), lies half way between the river and the Alps. Verona, the end station of the Brenner pass, one of the oldest connections between Germany and Italy, lies at the foot of the Alps themselves. Cremona, famous as the home of Stradivarius, Guarnerius and the Amati family, the fiddle-making dynasties, lies on the Po, but Padua and Modena, Ferrara and Bologna (the home of one of the oldest universities of Europe) are all at a safe distance from that main artery upon which they depend for their prosperity.

The same is true of two of the most romantic cities of the ancient world, Venice and Ravenna. Venice, the town in which 157 canals, 28 miles in length, serve the purpose of streets, was originally a place of shelter for those who no longer considered them-

Northern and Southern exposure

selves safe on the mainland and who preferred the discomforts of the mud banks thrown up by the Po and several smaller rivers to the dangers that followed in the wake of the Great Migrations. Once there, these fugitives discovered that they had a gold mine in the salt which lay there, so to speak, for the picking. Their salt monopoly started them on the road to riches. Their straw-covered huts became marble palaces. Their fishing boats assumed the size of warships. For almost three entire centuries they were the leading colonial power of the entire civilized world and high-hatted Pope, Emperor and Sultan with a most haughty and at the same time a most elegant air. When news of the safe return of Columbus and the discovery (the supposed discovery, of course) of the road to India reached the Rialto, their business quarter, there was a panic. All stocks and bonds dropped fifty points. For once the brokers were prophets, for Venice never recovered from this blow. Her well-protected trade-routes became a useless investment. Lisbon and Seville succeeded her as the international store-house towards which all of Europe turned for its spices and other Asiatic and American products. Venice, gorged with gold, became the Paris of the eighteenth century. All the rich young men who cared for a genteel education and some rather less genteel entertainment went to Venice. When the carnival began to last the greater part of the year, the end had come. Napoleon conquered the city with a corporal's squad. The canals are still there for you to admire. Another twenty years and the motor-boat will have destroyed them.

The other city, also a product of Po mud, was Ravenna. To-day it is an inland city removed from the Adriatic by six miles of mud. A dull hole, a city that must have driven such famous guests as Dante and Byron to drink and distraction. During the fifth century of our era it was more important than the New York of today, for it was the capital of the Roman Empire—it harbored an enormous garrison and was the main naval base of that time, with the largest wharves and timber supplies.

In the year 404 the Emperor decided that Rome was no longer safe. The barbarians were getting too powerful. And so he moved to the "city in the sea" where he had a much better chance to protect himself against surprise attacks. Here he and his descendants lived and ruled and loved, as you may see to this very day when you stand speechless before those incredible mosaics of that dark-eyed woman who started life as a dancing girl in the circus of Constantinople and died in an odor of sanctity as Theodora, the beloved wife of the famous Emperor Justinian.

Then the town was conquered by the Goths and turned into the capital of their newly founded empire. Then the lagoons began to fill up. Then Venice and the Pope fought for it. Then for a while it became the home of that pathetic exile, whose services to his native city of Florence had been rewarded by a threat of being burned at the stake. He spent silent hours among those famous pine forests that surrounded the city. Then he descended into his grave. And soon afterwards the famous old imperial residence followed his example.

One more word about northern Italy. The kingdom has no coal but it has an almost unlimited supply of water-power. This water-power was just being harnessed when the war broke out. The next twenty years will see a tremendous development of this cheap form of electricity. The lack of raw materials will always remain a difficult problem. But with the proverbial industry of the average Italian citizen, his very sober mode of living and his moderate needs, Italy will be a dangerous rival for other countries which are rich in raw material but poor in man-power.

On the western side, the great plain of the Po is cut off from the Mediterranean by the Ligurian Alps, the connecting link between the Alps proper and the Apennines. The southern slopes of the Ligurian Alps, completely protected against the cold breezes from the north, form part of the famous Riviera, the winter playground of all Europe, or rather of that part of Europe which can afford a lengthy railroad trip and fairly expensive hotels. Its chief city is Genoa, the chief port of the modern kingdom and a city of the most imposing marble palaces,

relics of the day when Genoa was the most dangerous rival of
Venice for the colonial spoils of the Near East.

Toward the south of Genoa lies another small plain, that of
the river Arno. The Arno takes its origin among the mountains
about twenty-five miles north-east of Florence. It flows through
the heart of that city which during the Middle Ages lay on the
highroad that connected Rome, the center of Christianity, with
the rest of Europe and which was able to use this favored commercial position so cleverly that ere long it became the most important banking center of the world. One family especially, that
of the Medici (they started life as doctors, hence the three pills
in their coat of arms, which became the three golden balls of our
own pawnshops) showed such brilliant gifts for that sort of work
that they finally became hereditary rulers of the whole of Tuscany and were able to make their home town the most marvellous artistic center of the fifteenth and sixteenth centuries.

From 1865 to 1871 Florence was the capital of the new
Italian kingdom. Then it dropped slightly back in importance,
but it still is one of those places that one ought to have seen to
appreciate how beautiful life can be if money and good taste
happen to be present in a well-balanced ratio.

The two cities near the mouth of the Arno, which flows
through one of the loveliest garden spots to be found anywhere
outside of the island of Java, are merely of some slight historical
interest. Pisa has a leaning tower which leans because the architects were not very careful in laying their foundations, but which
proved very handy when Galileo wanted to study the habits of
falling objects. The other town is Livorno, which the English,
for some curious reason, call Leghorn, and which is chiefly remembered as the town near which Shelley was drowned in the
year 1822.

From Livorno southward the old stage-coach road as well as
the modern railroad keep close to the seashore. They give the
traveller a quick but hazy glimpse of the island of Elba (Napoleon's place of exile until he unexpectedly descended upon
France to rush towards the final doom of Waterloo), and then

enter the plain of Tiber. This famous river, called the Tevere in Italian, is a sluggish and tawny current, vaguely reminiscent of the Chicago River but not quite so wide, and of the Spree in Berlin, but infinitely less clear. It takes its origin among those Sabine Mountains where the earliest Romans went to steal their wives. In prehistoric times its mouth was only twelve miles west of Rome. Since then it has added two miles to its length, for like the Po, the Tiber is a first-rate mud-carrier. The plain of the Tiber is different from that of the Arno. It is much wider and while the Arno region is healthy and highly fertile, that of the Tiber is barren and a breeder of disease. The very word "malaria" was coined here by those medieval pilgrims who were firmly convinced that the "mal aria"—the "bad air"—was responsible for those dreadful attacks of fever which burned up the body while one was still alive. In consequence of this fear, all the houses in this neighborhood were hermetically sealed as soon as the sun had set. This system of preventive hygiene had one great disadvantage. It kept all the little mosquitoes carefully indoors, but as we only learned about the relationship between malaria and mosquitoes some thirty years ago, we can hardly blame our ancestors for that particular bit of ignorance.

In Roman times this flat territory, the famous Campagna, was decently drained and fairly well populated. But because it lay open and unprotected along the shores of the Tyrrhenian Sea it was an ideal spot for the pirates who infested the whole of the Mediterranean as soon as the Roman policeman had disappeared. The towns were destroyed, the farms deserted, the drainage ditches neglected. Stagnant pools bred malaria mosquitoes and all during the Middle Ages and even as late as thirty years ago, this entire region from the mouth of the Tiber to the Pontine marshes near Monte Circeo was either avoided or passed through as fast as the unfortunate horse could drag the rattling coach.

Arises the question, Why should the most important city of the ancient world have been founded in a plague-spot? Why indeed? Why was St. Petersburg built in a marsh which took hundreds of thousands of lives to drain? Why was Madrid built on a bleak and treeless plateau hundreds of miles removed from everywhere? Why is Paris situated at the bottom of a large saucer, forever dripping with rain? I don't know. Chance mixed with greed—or that famous political foresight which covers such a multitude of blunders! Or chance alone—or greed alone. I don't know. And I am not writing a handbook of philosophy.

Rome was built where it was built, regardless of an unhealthy climate, scorching summers, chilly winters, and an absence of all decent communications. And yet it grew to be the center of a world-wide empire, the holy shrine of a world-wide religion. Under such circumstances, don't look for a single explanation. Look for a thousand different and inter-locking explanations. But don't look for them here, for it would take three volumes like the present one to get to the bottom of the secret.

Nor shall I go into details about the city itself. For I am the last person in the world to do justice to the Eternal City of the eastern hemisphere. It may have been due to those rebellious ancestors of mine who from the year 50 before the birth of Christ until 1650 of our own era felt themselves in the most cordial discord with everything that emanated from Rome. I ought to have wept, standing on the Forum, and I could only see the gangsters and racketeers who under the name of generals and party leaders despoiled all of Europe and a greater part of Africa and Asia, in exchange for those roads which seem to have been their eternal excuse for much that was unspeakably cruel. I ought to have felt a sense of trembling awe before the church devoted to St. Peter's memory and martyrdom, and I could only deplore the waste of so much money upon a building that had not a single claim to either beauty or charm except that it was "bigger" than any other edifice constructed for a similar purpose. And I longed for the harmony of Florence and Venice—for the well-balanced proportions of Genoa. I know of course that I am particularly alone in these feelings. Petrarch, Goethe, everybody that ever amounted to something, has wept tears upon catching his or her first glimpse of Bramante's dome. We will let it go at that, but rather than spoil your taste for a city you will sometime see yourself, I duly note that Rome since the year 1871 is the capital of the kingdom of Italy and that it harbors a city within a city—the so-called Vatican City—which was surrendered to the Pope in the year 1930 and now gives the Pontiff that freedom of action which he had not enjoyed since that fateful day in September of 1870 when the troops of the Italian Kingdom entered the city and proclaimed a constitution instead of that absolute sovereignty which had been the form of Roman government until then.

The modern city of Rome has few industries. It has some terrible-looking monuments, a main street which reminds one of Philadelphia and many people in uniforms. The uniforms are good.

And that brings us to another city, until recently the most populous of the entire peninsula, which is a strange mixture of geography and history and which brings us once more face to face with that irritating puzzle, "Why didn't this city, enjoying every possible natural advantage, take the predominant place occupied by Rome, situated in a dead alley on a mean little river?"

For Naples was right on the sea front at the head of a magnificent bay. It was older than Rome and the territory around it was originally among the most fertile spots along the western Italian coast. Originally the Greeks, who founded Naples, had done their trading with the dangerous Apennine tribes from the safe distance of the island of Ischia. But Ischia proved too uncertain a proposition. It was forever trembling with volcanic emotions and the Greeks had moved to the mainland. The usual and apparently unavoidable quarrels between the colonists (bored because far away from home and badly administered by grasping governors) had caused civil strife and three or four little settlements had been destroyed (it sounds like the beginning of our own country) when a fresh batch of immigrants had decided to begin from the very beginning and had built themselves a town which they called "New City" or "Neapolis," which eventually became Napoli, or in plain English, Naples.

It was already a prosperous commercial center when Rome was still a village inhabited by shepherds, and yet those shepherds must have had a veritable genius for administration, for already in the fourth century before our era Naples was an "ally" of Rome, an agreeable-sounding term, much less harsh than the word "subject" but describing the same sort of relationship. And from that moment on, Naples played the second role, was afterwards overrun by whole hordes of barbarians and finally fell into the hands of one of the Spanish branches of the Bourbon family, whose rule became a byword for scandalous mismanagement and suppression of every form of independent thought and action.

Nevertheless, such were the town's natural advantages that it became the most over-crowded city of the European continent. How all those people lived, nobody knew and nobody cared until the cholera epidemic of 1884 forced the modern kingdom to clean house, which it has done with admirable intelligence and severity.

The background of this marvellous spot is most appropriately occupied by the ornamental Vesuvius. Vesuvius is the neatest and most systematic of all the known volcanoes in the way it spreads its ashes. It rises up to a height of about 4000 feet and is entirely surrounded by lovely little villages which grow a particularly fiery wine, the famous Lacrimae Christi. The ancestors of those villages already existed in Roman days. And why not? Vesuvius was extinct. Since the memory of man, almost a thousand years, there had not been an eruption. There had been vague rumblings in the bowels of the earth in the year 63, but that meant nothing in a country like Italy.

The great surprise was sprung sixteen years later. In less than two days time Herculaneum and Pompeii and a third smaller city were so deeply buried beneath deep layers of lava and ashes that they completely disappeared from the face of the earth. Thereafter, at least once every hundred years, Vesuvius gave signs of being far from extinct. The new crater, rising 1500 feet above the ruins of the original one, is forever belching heavy clouds of smoke. And the statistics for the last 300 years—1631, 1712, 1737, 1754, 1779, 1794, 1806, 1831, 1855, 1872, 1906, etc.—show that Naples is by no means sure of not being turned into another Pompeii.

South of Naples we enter the province called Calabria. It suffers from the fact that it is so far away from the center of the country. It has railroad connections with the north but the coastal regions suffer from malaria, the central part is composed of granite, and agriculture is practiced as it was in the days of the first Roman Republic.

A narrow strait, the strait of Messina, separates Calabria from the island of Sicily. The strait, which is only a little over a mile wide, was famous in antiquity for the presence of two whirlpools, called Scylla and Charybdis, which were said to swallow up whole ships if they ventured so much as half a yard out of their course. The fear those whirlpools aroused gives us an adequate idea of the helplessness of such ancient vessels, for a modern motor-boat putt-putts quietly right through the heart of these eddies without noticing that there is any commotion in the water.

As for Sicily, its geographic position had made it the natural center of the ancient world. Furthermore it enjoyed a delightful climate, was densely populated and highly fertile. But like Naples, life here was perhaps a little too good, a little too easy, a little too comfortable, for the Sicilians during more than two thousand long years submitted peacefully to every form of misgovernment that foreign potentates wished to bestow upon them. When they were not being plundered or tortured by Phoenicians or Greeks or Carthaginians (they were only about a hundred miles away from the northern coast of Africa) or Vandals or Goths or Arabs or Normans or French or by any of the 120 princes, 82 dukes, 129 marquises, 28 counts and 356 barons who derived their titles from this happy island, they were repairing their houses from the damage done by the local volcano, Mt. Etna. The eruption of the year 1908, which completely destroyed the most important city, Messina, is still in everybody's memory. It killed more than 75,000 people.

The island of Malta is really a sort of aquatic suburb of Sicily and therefore ought to be mentioned here, although politically speaking it does not form part of Italy. It is a very fertile island and lies midway between Sicily and the coast of Africa. It dominates the trade-route from Europe to Asia by way of the Suez Canal. After the failure of the Crusades, it was presented to the knights of St. John who thereupon called themselves the Maltese Order, Knights of Malta. In the year 1798 Napoleon took the island on his way to drive the English out of India via Egypt and Arabia (a most ingenious plan which however failed because the desert was so much larger than he had expected). This was an excuse for the English to occupy it two years later and they have been there ever since, much to the chagrin of the Italians but not of the Maltese, who on the whole are better off than they would be under a government of their own people.

I have paid little attention to the east coast of Italy, but it is not very important. In the first place, the Apennines used to reach almost as far as the water-front, making large settlements very difficult. As the other side of the Adriatic was practically uninhabitable on account of the steepness of its hills, the development of trade was not encouraged. From Rimini in the north to Brindisi in the south (from where the mail leaves for Africa and India) there are no harbors of any importance.

The heel of the boot is called Apulia. Like Calabria it suffers from the fact that it is so far removed from civilization, and like Calabria its agricultural methods are those practiced in the days when Hannibal honored this region with his presence, waiting twelve long years for the help from Carthage that was never to come.

There is a city in Apulia which enjoys one of the finest natural harbors in the world but which, alas, has no customers. It is called Taranto and it gave its name to a particularly venomous sort of spider and to a dance by which the people who had been bitten by that spider were prevented from falling asleep and entering into a deadly coma.

The Great War has made geography very complicated, for no account of modern Italy is perfect without mention of the Istrian peninsula which was given to the Italians in recognition of the fact that they had turned against their own allies and joined with the enemy. The city of Trieste was the principal export harbor of the old Austro-Hungarian Empire. Having lost its natural hinterland, it is not doing so well. And finally, tucked away at the further end of the bay of Guarnero, is Fiume, another former possession of the Habsburgs. It was the natural outlet for the German people who had no other good port along the whole of the Adriatic coast. But fear that it might eventually be a rival of Trieste made the Italians clamor for Fiume. When the statesmen who concluded the treaty of Versailles refused to give it to them, they simply took it, or rather, their poet d'Annunzio, an excellent writer and a great scoundrel, took it for them. Then the Allies turned it into a "free state", but finally, after prolonged negotiations between Italy and Yugo-slavia, it was ceded to Italy.

That ends the present chapter, except for the island of Sardinia. This is really a very big island but it is so far away and so few people have ever been there that we sometimes forget that it exists. But it does exist, the sixth biggest island of Europe, covering an area of almost 10,000 square miles. Being the other extreme of that prehistoric mountain-range of which the Apennines were part, it turns its back upon the mother country. The western coast has excellent harbors. The east coast is steep and dangerous and has not a single convenient landing place. During the last two centuries it has played a curious role in the history of Italy. Until the year 1708 it belonged to Spain. Then it went over into Austrian hands. In 1720 the Austrians swapped Sardinia against Sicily, which then belonged to the Dukes of Savoy, whose capital was the city of Turin, situated on the Po. Thereafter the Dukes of Savoy proudly called themselves Kings of Sardinia (from duke to king is a decided step upward) and that is how the modern kingdom of Italy happened to grow out of a kingdom called after an island which not one Italian in a hundred thousand has ever seen.

X

SPAIN, WHERE AFRICA AND EUROPE CLASHED

THE people of the Iberian peninsula are famous for their very pronounced "racial" characteristics. The Spaniard is supposed to be so "racially" different from any other group of people, that one will recognize him anywhere and under all circumstances by his racial haughtiness, his formal courtesy, his pride, his sobriety and his ability to play the guitar and the castanets. For even music has been dragged in to bolster up the "racial theory".

Perhaps so. Perhaps it is as easy to recognize the Spaniard by his haughtiness and pride as by his ability to play the guitar and the castanets. But I have very serious doubts upon the subject. The Spaniards merely took to playing the guitar and the castanets because in their dry and warm climate they were able to use out-of-door instruments. When it comes however to playing them really well, both Americans and Germans are greatly superior to the native talent. If they play them less frequently than the Spaniards do, that is the result of the climate under which they live. You can't very well play the castanets in the pouring rain of a cold Berlin evening nor the guitar when your fingers tremble with frostbite. And as for those qualities of pride and haughtiness and formal courtesy, weren't they all of them the result of centuries of hard military training, and wasn't this military life the direct outcome of the fact that Spain was geologically speaking quite as much a part of Africa as of Europe? Therefore wasn't it bound to be a battlefield for Europeans and Africans until either one side or the other should have won? In the end, the Spaniard was victorious, but the land for which he had been obliged to fight for such a long

The Iberian Peninsula

time had left its imprint upon him. What would he have developed into if his cradle had stood in Copenhagen or Berne? Into a perfectly ordinary little Dane or Swiss. Instead of playing the castanets, he would have yodeled, because the steep walls of a mountain valley with their marvellous echoes invite one to yodel. And instead of living on a little dry bread and sour wine, raised with infinite care and patience on his own neglected soil (neglected again on account of that clash between Africa and Europe), he would have eaten a lot of butter, necessary to protect his body against the eternal dampness of the climate, and he would have drunk aquavit, because the abundant presence of cheap grain would have made gin the almost inevitable national beverage.

And now look at the map. You remember the mountain-ranges of Greece and Italy. In Greece they ran diagonally across the country. In Italy they ran in an almost straight line from north to south, dividing the country into halves but allowing enough space on both sides for the construction of roads that coasted the country from one end to the other, while the salient of the Po plain made the Apennine peninsula an integral part of the European continent.

In Spain the mountains make horizontal ridges which one might almost describe as visible degrees of latitude. After a single glance at the map you will understand how these mountain-ranges must have acted as barriers to any sort of orderly progress. They begin with the Pyrenees.

The Pyrenees, 240 miles long, run in a straight and uninterrupted line from the Atlantic to the Mediterranean. They are not as high as the Alps and therefore it ought to be easier to cross them by means of mountain passes. But that is not so. The Alps, although very high, are also very wide and the roads that run across them, although quite long, rise only very slowly and offer no special difficulties to either man or pack-horse. The Pyrenees on the other hand are only 60 miles wide, and as a result their mountain passes were much too steep for anybody except a goat or a mule. According to well-seasoned travellers, even the mules experienced difficulties. Trained mountaineers (mostly professional smugglers) were able to get through, but only during a few months of summer. The engineers who built the railroads connecting Spain with the rest of the world real-

A Spanish Canyon

ized this, for they built the two trunk lines from Paris to Madrid and from Paris to Barcelona along the shores of the Atlantic and the Mediterranean. Whereas the Alps have half a dozen railroad lines passing over them or under them, the Pyrenees, between Irun in the west and Figueras in the east, are not pierced by a single tunnel. After all, one can't very well dig a tunnel sixty miles long. Neither can one send trains across a track with an inclination of forty degrees.

There is one fairly easy pass in the west, the famous pass of Roncesvalles, where Roland, Charlemagne's famous Paladin, died loyally serving his master's interests until the moment he succumbed under the last of the Saracens' attacks. Seven hundred years later, another army composed of Frenchmen used this pass as an entrance gate into Spain. They got across the pass itself but were stopped before Pamplona, the city that dominates the road on the southern side. During the siege, one of the Spanish soldiers, a certain Ignatius de Loyola, was desperately wounded through a shot in the leg. While recovering, he had those visions which inspired him to found the Company of Jesus, the famous Society of the Jesuits.

The Jesuits afterwards did more to influence the geographic development of a vast number of countries than any other religious organization, more even than those indefatigable travellers, the Franciscans. It was here that they began, defending the only passage across the center of the Pyrenees.

It was undoubtedly this inaccessibility of the Pyrenees which gave the famous Basque people their chance to maintain themselves from prehistoric times until today and which accounts for the independent Republic of Andorra, very high up in the eastern part of the mountains. The Basques, about 700,000 in number, inhabit a triangle that is bounded by the Gulf of Biscay in the north, by the Spanish province of Navarre in the east, while the western frontier follows a line from the city of Santander to the city of Logroño on the Ebro River. The name Basque means the same as our word Gascon, but it has nothing to do with the cronies of the famous Captain d'Artagnan. The Roman conquerors called them Iberians and called the whole of Spain the Iberian peninsula. As for the Basques themselves, they proudly say that they are Eskualdunak, which sounds very un-European and quite like Eskimo.

Just for good measure, and because your guess is apt to be as sound as mine, here are a few of the current theories about the origin of the Basques. Some of the professors who distil racial theories out of skulls and gutturals, believe them to be connected with those Berbers whom I mentioned several chapters ago as the possible descendants of one of the earliest tribes of prehistoric Europeans, the so-called Cromagnon race. Others claim that they are the survivors who saved themselves on the European continent when the romantic island of Atlantis disappeared beneath the waves of the ocean. Still others hold that they have always been where they are now and don't bother to ask where they came from. Whatever the truth, the Basques have shown remarkable ability in keeping themselves aloof from the rest of the world. They are very industrious. More than a hundred thousand of them have migrated to South America. They are excellent fishermen and sailors and iron workers and they mind their own business and keep off the front page of the newspapers.

The most important city of their country is Vitoria, founded in the sixth century by a Gothic king and scene of that famous battle in which an Irishman by the name of Arthur Wellesley, but better known by his English title of the Duke of Wellington, defeated the armies of a Corsican general by the name of Buonaparte, but better known by his French title of the Emperor Napoleon, and forced the latter to leave Spain for good and all.

As for Andorra, this strange commonwealth numbering fully 5000 inhabitants, connected with the outside world by a bridle-path, is the only surviving specimen of those queer little medieval principalities which retained their independence because, as frontier posts, they might render valuable service to some distant monarch and because afterwards they were too far removed from the busy outside world to attract anybody's attention.

The capital has 600 inhabitants, but the Andorrans, like the Icelanders and the people of San Marino in Italy, were ruling themselves according to their own desires at least eight hundred years before we started our experiment in applied democracy. As a sister republic of great antiquity, Andorra should at least enjoy our sympathetic respect. Eight hundred years is a long time. Where shall we be in the year 2732?

In one other respect, the Pyrenees are quite different from

Gibraltar

the Alps. They have practically no glaciers. Once upon a time they may have been covered more thickly with snow and ice than the Swiss mountains, but a few square miles of glacier are all that remain. The same holds true of practically all Spanish ridges. They are steep and difficult to cross. But even the Sierra Nevada, the range of southern Andalusia, only shows a few snow caps from October till March, if that long.

The direction of the mountains was of course of immediate influence upon the Spanish rivers. They all of them start on or near the barren high plateau in the center—the remnant of a terrific prehistoric mountain-range which has worn away in the course of millions of years, and they hasten to the sea, but at such terrific speed and with so many waterfalls that none of them possesses the slightest value as a trade-route. Furthermore, the long dry summers deprive them of most of their water, as you may see in Madrid where the sandy bottom of the Manzanares provides the children of the capital with a nice imitation sea-shore for at least five months of the year.

That is why I won't even bother to tell you the names of most of them. The Tagus on which Lisbon, the Portuguese capital, is situated is an exception. It is navigable almost as far as the Spanish-Portuguese frontier. The Ebro too in northern Spain, which runs through Navarre and Catalonia, can be used by smaller vessels, but larger ones have to pass most of the way through a canal which runs parallel with the river itself. The Guadalquivir (Wadi-el-Kebir or Big River of the Moors) which connects Seville with the Atlantic Ocean can only be used by vessels that draw less than fifteen feet. Between Seville and Cordova, the famous Moorish capital that used to boast of no less than nine hundred public baths before the Christians captured it and reduced the population from 200,000 to 50,000 and the public baths from 900 to 0, the Guadalquivir is only available for small vessels. After that it becomes what most Spanish rivers are, canyon rivers (like our own Colorado) which are a great hindrance to overland trade while contributing practically nothing to commerce along the water routes.

Generally speaking, therefore, Nature was not particularly kind to the Spaniards. The great central part of the country consisted of a high plateau, divided into halves by a low mountain ridge. Old Castile is the name of the northern half and New Castile that of the other. The dividing ridge is called the Sierra de Guadarrama.

The name Castile, which merely means "castle", is a very pretty name. But it resembles those boxes of Spanish cigars of which the label is so much more imposing than the quality of the contents. For Castile is as harsh and ill-favored a land as may be found anywhere. When General Sherman, after his march through Georgia, remarked that henceforth a crow wishing to cross the Shenandoah Valley would have to pack his own rations, he was consciously or unconsciously quoting a remark which the Romans made 2000 years before when they said that a nightingale trying to cross Castile would have to take its food and drink with it or it would die of hunger and thirst. For the mountains which surround this plateau are sufficiently high to prevent the clouds that arise from the Atlantic and the Mediterranean from reaching this unfortunate table-land.

As a result, Castile suffers from nine months of inferno and during the other three months of the year it is exposed to the cold and dry winds which sweep across this treeless tract with such a merciless fury that sheep are the only animals that can live here with any degree of comfort, while the only plant that prospers is a variety of grass, the esparto or halfa grass, which is very tough and can therefore be used for basket-work.

But most of this table-land, called the meseta by the Spaniards (a word which you meet again in our own "mesas", familiar to all those who know New Mexico or follow the adventures of Krazy Kat), is something that closely resembles a plain, ordinary desert, and that makes you understand why Spain and Portugal, although much larger than England, have only half the population of the British Isles.

For further particulars about the shabby poverty of these regions, I refer you to the works of a certain Don Miguel de

Cervantes Saavedra. You may remember that the "ingenious hidalgo" who was his hero bore the proud name of Don Quixote de la Mancha. Well, Mancha was one of those inland deserts with which the plateau of Castile was dotted then as it is now, a bleak, inhospitable stretch of waste land near Toledo, the ancient Spanish capital. The name itself was ominous to Spanish ears, for in the original Arabic, *al mansha,* it meant "wilderness" and the poor Don was really the "Lord of the Wilderness".

In a country like that, where Nature is both stingy and obstinate, Man must either settle down to hard labor and force her to yield him the necessities of life, or he can choose to live as the average Spaniard lives, who as a rule can load all the family possessions on the back of one very small donkey. And that brings us to one of the greatest tragedies that ever occurred as a result of a country's unfortunate geographic position.

Eight hundred years ago, the country belonged to the Moors. It was not the first time the Iberian peninsula had been invaded. For the country possessed valuable mineral deposits. Two thousand years ago copper, zinc and silver were what petroleum is today. Wherever copper, zinc and silver were to be found, rival armies would fight for their possession. When the Mediterranean was divided into two great armed camps and when the Semites (of Carthage, a colony of the Phoenicians and ruthless in its exploitation of subject nations) and the Romans (not of Semitic origin but quite as ruthless in their exploitation of subject nations) were throwing loaded dice (one of the chief early uses made of lead was for the purpose of loading dice) for the treasures of the world, Spain could not long escape her fate. Like many a modern land, unfortunately blessed with natural riches, Spain was turned into a battleground for the mercenaries of two large groups of organized brigands.

As soon as they were gone, the country was used as a convenient land bridge for wild tribes from northern Europe, trying to break into Africa.

And then, early during the seventh century, a camel driver in Arabia had a vision and started a number of desert tribes of whom no one had ever heard, on the war-path, bound for world-domination. A century later, they had conquered all of northern Africa and were ready to tackle Europe. In the year 711 Tarik sailed for the famous Monkey Rock (the only spot in Europe where monkeys continued to live in a wild state) and without meeting any opposition landed his troops near Gibraltar, the famous rock (which incidentally does not look like the well-known advertisement because it turns its back upon the land and not upon the sea) which during the last two hundred years has belonged to England.

Thereafter the old Pillars of Hercules, the straits which Hercules had dug by the simple process of pushing the mountains of Europe and Africa aside, belonged to the Mohammedans.

Could the Spaniards have defended themselves successfully against this invasion? They tried to. But the geography of their country prevented any concerted action, for the mountain-ranges which ran a parallel course and the rivers with their deep canyons divided the country into a number of independent little squares. Remember that even today some five thousand Spanish villages have no direct communication with each other or any other part of the world, except by a narrow track which pedestrians, free from dizziness, may use during certain parts of the year.

And then remember one of the few definite facts which history and geography teach us, that such countries are breeding places for clannishness. Now clannishness has undoubtedly certain good qualities. It makes the members of the same clan loyal to each other and loyal to the common or clan interests. But Scotland and the Scandinavian peninsula are there to show us that clannishness is the deadly enemy of all forms of economic coöperation and national organization. Island dwellers are supposed to be "insular" and to care for nothing except the affairs of their own little islet. But they at least can sit themselves down in a boat once in a while and spend an afternoon with their neighbors, or rescue the crew of a ship-wrecked vessel and hear what the big world is doing. The man of the valley, shut off from the rest of humanity by an almost unsurpassable mountain ridge, has no one but himself and his neighbors and they in turn have no one but themselves and their neighbors.

The conquest of Spain by the Mohammedans was possible because the Moors, although a desert people and therefore great worshippers of the restricted "tribal" idea, were for once united under strong leaders who had given them a common national purpose which made them forget their own petty ambitions. While the Spanish clans fought each one for itself and hated their rival clans as cordially (and often more so) than they hated the common enemy who was driving them out of house and home, the Mohammedans obeyed a single head.

The seven centuries during which the great Spanish war of liberation lasted are an endless recital of treachery and rivalry between the little Christian states of the north that survived because the Pyrenees formed a barrier across which they could not hope to retreat without getting into trouble with the French, who, after a few vague gestures on the part of Charlemagne, had left them completely to their own fate.

Meanwhile the Moors had turned southern Spain into a veritable garden. These desert people appreciated the value of water, and they loved the flowers and trees which were so sadly lacking in their own part of the world. They constructed vast irrigation works and imported the orange, the date, the almond tree, sugar-cane and cotton. They set the Guadalquivir to work to turn the valley between Cordova and Seville into one vast "huerta" or garden where the farmer was able to reap as many as four harvests every year. They tapped the Jucar River which flows into the Mediterranean near Valencia and added another 1200 square miles of fertile land to their possessions. They imported engineers, built universities where agriculture was scientifically studied, and constructed about the only roads the country possesses to this very day. What they did for the progress of astronomy and mathematics we have already seen in the first part of this book. And they were the only people in the Europe of that day who paid the slightest attention to medicine and hygiene, carrying their tolerance in such matters so far that they reintroduced the works of the ancient Greeks into the west by means of their own Arabic translations. And they set another force to work which was to be of tremendous value to them. Instead of shutting the Jews up in ghettos or worse, they gave them free rein to develop their great commercial and organizing power for the benefit of the country at large.

And then the inevitable happened. Almost the whole of the country had been conquered, and there was little danger from the side of the Christians. Other Arab and Berber tribes, thirsting in their miserable deserts, heard news of this terrestrial Paradise. And since Mohammedan rule was autocratic, the success or failure of that rule depended upon the ability of a single person. Amidst these luxurious surroundings, dynasties founded by strong-armed plow-boys degenerated and became weak. Other strong-armed plow-boys, still sweating behind their oxen, cast envious eyes upon the joys of the Alhambra of Granada and the Alcazar of Seville. There were civil wars. There was murder. Whole families were wiped out. Others pushed to the front. Meanwhile in the north, the strong man had made his appearance. Clans were being combined into tiny principalities. Tiny principalities were being combined into small states. Men began to hear the names of Castile and Leon and Aragon and Navarre. Finally they forgot their ancient rivalries long enough to marry Ferdinand of Aragon with Isabel of Castile, the land of the castles.

During this great war of liberation over three thousand pitched battles were fought. The Church turned the "racial" struggle into a conflict of religious aspirations. The Spaniard became the soldier of the Cross—a most noble ambition which was to bring ruin to the country for which he so valiantly fought. For in the same year that the last of the Moorish strongholds, Granada, was taken from the Moors, Columbus discovered the road to America. Six years later, Vasco da Gama sailed around the Cape and found the direct route to the Indies. Therefore, just at the moment when the Spaniard should have taken possession of his own home and should have continued to develop those latent natural forces of his country which had been set into motion by the Moors, he came into easy money. His religious feeling of exaltation made it easy for him to imagine himself a holy missionary when in reality he was nothing but an uncommon (because uncommonly brutal and greedy) brigand. In 1519 he conquered Mexico. In 1532 he conquered Peru. After that, he was lost. All further ambitions were drowned in the steady flow of gold which the cumbersome galleons dumped into the storehouses of Seville and Cadiz. No man would disgrace himself working with his hands when he could belong to the "gold collar class" by demanding his share of the Aztec and Inca plunder.

All the painful work of the Moors became undone. The Moors themselves were forced to leave the country. Next the Jews went, thrown wholesale into filthy vessels to carry them, naked and deprived of all their possessions, wherever it pleased the captain of the ship to put them on land. Their hearts filled with revenge but their minds sharpened by their sufferings, they struck back at their tormentors, had a hand in every heretical enterprise that was directed against the hated name of Spain. But even Providence must take a hand and give these unfortunate sufferers of the Golden Illusion a monarch whose view of life did not extend beyond the cloistered cell he erected for himself in the palace of the Escurial, situated on the outskirts of the bleak Castilian plain, to which he had transferred his new capital city of Madrid.

Henceforth the riches of three continents and the man-power of an entire nation were to be used to curb the aggressions of the unbelievers, the Protestants of the north, the Mohammedans of the south. The Spanish people, changed by seven centuries of religious warfare into a race in whose eyes the supernatural had become the natural, willingly obeyed their royal master. And they bled to death in the attempt just as they impoverished themselves by growing too rich.

The Iberian peninsula made the Spanish people what they

are today. Can the Spanish people now turn around and after centuries of neglect change the Iberian peninsula into what they want it to be, regardless of the past and with only an eye to the future?

They are trying and in some cities, like Barcelona, they are trying very hard.

But what a job! What a job!

XI

FRANCE, THE COUNTRY THAT HAS EVERYTHING
IT WANTS

WE OFTEN hear it said that France does not consider herself a part of the rest of the world, that the French people, who live on a continent, are infinitely more "insular" than their English neighbors who dwell in rainy solitude on an island, in short, that the French, by their persistent and systematic refusal to take any interest, however slight, in the affairs of this planet, are the most selfish and self-centered of all nations and are at the bottom of most of our present troubles.

Well, in order to understand things thoroughly, we must go down to their roots. The roots of any given people are situated deep down in the soil and in the soul. The soil has influenced the soul and the soul has influenced the soil. We cannot understand the one without understanding the other. But when we have grasped the true inner meaning of both, we have a key to the character of almost any nation.

Most of the accusations we hear so often uttered against the French are based upon the truth. But so was that unbounded and unquestioning praise heaped upon them during the days of the Great War, for both their virtues and their defects grew directly out of the geographic position of their country. It had made them self-centered and self-contented, because the land they occupied between the Atlantic Ocean and the Mediterranean was absolutely self-sufficient for their needs. Why go abroad for changes of climate or changes in scenery when you can find all of those in your own backyard? Why travel all over the globe to study differences of language and habits and customs when a few hours in a train will carry you from the twentieth to the twelfth century or from a smiling, verdant country of castles to the magnificent mysteries of a land of sand-dunes and solemn pine trees? Why bother about passports or letters of credit and bad food and sour wine and the dull, stodgy faces of frozen northern peasants when your own food and drink and beds and conversation are about as good as any this vale of tears can provide, when you live in a land where (believe it or not!) they can make spinach a dish fit for human consumption?

Of course a poor Swiss, who has never seen anything except a mountain, or a poor Dutchman, who has never seen anything except a flat piece of green meadow with a few black and white cows, must go abroad once in a while or he would die of bore-dom. A German will sooner or later tire of his exclusive diet of excellent music interspersed with indifferent sausage-sandwiches. An Italian cannot live on spaghetti all his life long. And a Rus-sian must crave an occasional meal without standing six hours in line for half a pound of oleomargarine.

But the Frenchman, lucky devil, lives in an earthly paradise where all things are to be had by all men without a change of cars and therefore he will ask you, "Why should I ever stir from my own country?"

You may answer that this is a hopelessly one-sided point of view and that my Frenchman is all wrong. I wish that I could agree with you but I am forced to admit that France in many respects is a country singularly blessed by Nature and its gen-eral geographical background.

In the first place, France has every sort of a climate. It has a temperate climate. It has a hot climate. It has a medium climate. France is the proud possessor of the highest mountain in Europe. At the same time the French have been able to connect all the industrial centers of their land with canals that run through absolutely flat country. If a Frenchman likes to spend his winter sliding down the slopes of a hill, he moves to a village in the Savoy in the western branch of the Alps. Does he prefer swim-ming to skiing, all he need do is take a ticket for Biarritz on the Atlantic or to Cannes on the Mediterranean. And should he be

France

of a particular curiosity about men and women, should he interest himself in the outward aspect of monarchs in exile and exiles about to turn monarchs, of actors with a future before them and actresses with a future behind them, of fiddle virtuosos or paragons of the piano, of dancers who have lightly upset a couple of thrones and all the other great little people who are in the limelight, he need merely take a chair in the Café de la Paix, and order himself a glass of coffee and cream, and wait. Sooner or later, every man, woman or child who ever made the front page of the world's news-sheets will pass that corner. And what is more, they will pass that corner without attracting any particular attention, for this procession has been going on for almost fifteen centuries and a king or an emperor or even the highest dignitary of the Church causes about as much commotion as a freshman on a college campus.

Right here we come upon one of the unanswerable mysteries of political geography. Two thousand years ago most of the territory that flies the Republican tricolor (and flies it day and night, for the French, once they have hoisted a flag, never pull it down until time and the weather have reduced it to unrecognizable shreds) was part of the great western European plain and there was no earthly (that is to say, geographic) reason why some day all the land between the Atlantic and the Mediterranean should become one of the most highly centralized nations of the world.

There is a school of geography which holds that climate and geographical background play the decisive part in shaping human destinies. Undoubtedly they do—sometimes. Quite as often it is the other way around. The Moors and the Spaniards lived on the same soil and the sun shone with equal violence upon the valley of the Guadalquivir in the year 1200 as it did in the year 1600. But in the year 1200 it bestowed its blessings upon a paradise of fruit and flowers and in the year 1600 it forced its accursed rays upon a parched wilderness of neglected irrigation ditches and weeds.

The Swiss speak four languages, yet feel themselves to be members of one single nation. The Belgians speak only two and hate each other to the point where the desecration of each other's soldiers' graves has become a regular Sunday afternoon pastime. The Icelanders on their little island maintained their independence and self-government for over a thousand years against all comers, and the Irish on their island hardly ever know a moment of independence. And so it goes. Human nature, regardless of the advance of the machine and of science and of standardization of every sort, will always remain an extremely unstable and undependable factor in the general scheme of things. It has been responsible for the many strange and unexpected developments of which the map of the world is the living evidence; and France is merely one of the object lessons which bears me out on this point.

Politically speaking, France seems to be one country. But if you will kindly look at the map you will notice that France is really composed of two separate parts which actually turn their backs upon each other—the valley of the Rhône in the southeast which looks out upon the Mediterranean and the great inclined plain of the north and the west which faces towards the Atlantic.

Let us begin with the oldest of these two halves. The Rhône takes its origin in Switzerland but it really does not become a river of any importance until it has left the Lake of Geneva and has reached the city of Lyons, the center of the French silk industry, where it combines with the Saône, a river which comes down from the north and which has its source only a few miles from that of the Meuse, a river which is as intimately connected with the history of northern Europe as the Saône (combined with the Rhône) is with that of the south. The Rhône is not a very navigable river. Before it reaches the Gulf of the Lion (no, the name Gulf of Lyons which appears on many maps is an error) it has come down some 6000 feet, which accounts for its rapid currents which have not yet been entirely overcome by the modern steamer.

Nevertheless it offered the ancient Phoenicians and Greeks a convenient entrance way into the heart of Europe, for man-power—slave-power—was cheap. The ships could be dragged upstream by these prehistoric Volga boatmen (their fate cannot have been much happier than that of their Russian colleagues) and downstream was a matter of a few days. And so it happened that the old civilization of the Mediterranean made its first attack upon the European hinterland by way of the Rhône valley. Strangely enough Marseilles, the earliest commercial settlement in that region (and still the most important French port on the Mediterranean) was not situated directly at the mouth of the river but several miles towards the east. (It is now connected with the Rhône by means of a canal.) Nevertheless it proved a very good choice, for Marseilles became such an important center of trade that as early as the third century before Christ Marseillian coins had found their way as far as the Austrian Tyrol and the region around Paris. And soon the whole region immediately to the north of it recognized Marseilles as its capital.

Then, during an ill-fated moment in its history, the citizens of the town, hard pressed by wild tribes from the Alps, asked the Romans to come and help them. The Romans came and, as was their habit, stayed. All the land along the mouth of the Rhône became a Roman "provincia" and the name "Provence", which has played such a great role in history, bears silent testimony to the fact that it was the Romans, rather than the Phoenicians and Greeks, who recognized the importance of this fertile triangle.

But here we find ourselves face to face with one of the most perplexing problems both of geography and history. The Provence with its mixture of Greek and Roman civilization, its ideal climate, its great fertility, its front door opening upon the Mediterranean and its back door leading conveniently to the plain of central and northern Europe, seemed predestined to become the logical successor to Rome. It was given every possible natural advantage and then, with all the trump cards in its hands, it failed to play them. During the quarrels between Caesar and Pompey, the Provence took the side of Pompey and the rival gang destroyed the city of Marseilles. But that was a minor incident, for soon afterwards its citizens were doing business once more at the same old stand, while literature and courtly manners and the arts and sciences, no longer safe in Rome, fled across the Ligurian Sea and turned the Provence into an island of civilization entirely surrounded by barbarians.

When the Popes with all their wealth and power were no longer able to maintain themselves in the city of the Tiber (the Roman mob of the Middle Ages was little better than a pack of wolves and as relentless as our own gangsters) they too moved their court to Avignon, the town famous for the first attempt at bridge-building on a large scale (most of the bridge now lies on the bottom of the river, but in the twelfth century it was one of the world's wonders) and where they owned a castle that could withstand a hundred sieges. Thereupon, for almost an entire century the Provence was the home of the head of Christendom, its knights took a very prominent part in the Crusades and one noble Provençal family became the hereditary ruler of Constantinople.

But somehow or other the Provence was never able to play the role for which Nature seemed to have predestined her when she created these delightful and fertile and romantic valleys. The Provence gave us the Troubadours, but even they, although recognized as the founders of that form of literature which has maintained itself ever since in our novels and our plays and our poetry, were never able to make their soft Provençal dialect, the *langue d'oc*, the general tongue of all France. It was the north with its *langue d'oil* (*oil* and *oc* were merely different forms for *oui* or *yes*)—it was the north, which enjoyed none of the natural advantages of the south, which was to found the French state, create the French nation and bestow upon the world in general the manifold blessings of French culture. But sixteen centuries ago, no one could have foreseen this development. For then the entire plain which reaches from the Pyrenees in the south to the Baltic in the north seemed predestined to become part of a vast Teutonic empire. That would have been the natural development. But man not being very much interested in natural developments, everything came differently.

To the Romans of Caesar's time, all this part of Europe had been the Far West. They had called it Gallia because it was inhabited by Gauls, by people belonging to the mysterious race of fair-haired men and women to whom the Greeks had given the general name of Keltoi or Celts. And in those days, there were two kinds of Gaul. One was the region of the Po River, between

the Alps and the Apennines, where the fair-haired savages had
made their appearance at a very early date and which was known
as Gallia Cisalpina or Gaul-this-side-of-the-mountains. That
was the Gaul which Caesar left when he threw his famous dice
and boldly crossed the Rubicon. Then there was the Gallia
Transalpina, the Gaul-across-the-mountains, and that accounted
vaguely for all the rest of Europe. But after Caesar's famous
expedition of the years 58–51 B. C., it came to be associated more
particularly with the France of today. It was a fertile land which
could be made to pay taxes without too much objection on the
part of the natives, hence an ideal domain for intensive Roman
colonization.

The passes between the Vosges Mountains in the north and
the Jura in the south offered no great difficulties to the progress
of an army consisting mostly of infantry. Soon the great plain of
France was dotted with Roman fortresses and Roman villages,
markets, temples, jails, theaters and factories. A small island
in the river Seine, where the Celts still lived on houses built on
poles, and called Lutetia (or Lutetia Parisiorum after the Parisii
who had first taken possession of this natural fortress) became
an ideal spot on which to build a temple dedicated to Jupiter.
That temple stood where Notre Dame arises today.

As the island had direct water communication with Great
Britain (a most profitable Roman colony during the first 400
years of our era) and was an excellent strategic center from
which to watch the turbulent regions between the Rhine and the
Meuse, it quite naturally developed into the chief center of the
vast Roman organization that administered the Far West.

As I told you in the chapter on maps, we sometimes wonder
how the Romans were able to find their way across the whole
island and mainland world of that day, but there can be no question about it—they had an unerring instinct for the right spot,
whether they were building a harbor, a fortress or a trading-
post. A casual observer, after passing six dreary weeks amidst
the rains and fogs of the Parisian valley, may ask himself, "Why
in the name of Mars did the Romans ever select this forlorn

The geology of the Île de France

spot to be their administration headquarters for all their western and northern possessions?" But a geologist with a map of northern France before him could show us.

Millions of years ago, when all this territory was being tortured by incessant earthquakes, and when mountains and valleys were thrown hither and yon as casually as the chips on a gaming table, four heavy layers of rock of different ages were tossed about in such a way that they came to lie on top of each other, like the saucers of one of those Chinese tea-sets which used to delight the hearts of our grandmothers. The lowest and biggest of these saucers stretches from the Vosges Mountains to Brittany, where its western brim lies buried beneath the waters of

The Île de France expressed in the form of saucers

the British Channel. The second one reaches from Lorraine to the coast of Normandy. The third one, the famous Champagne region, encircles the fourth one, appropriately called the Île de France, or the Island of France. This "island" is a vague circle bounded by the Seine, the Marne, the Thève and the Oise; and Paris is situated right in the heart of it. That meant safety— almost complete safety—because it offered the greatest amount of protection from foreign invasion. For the enemy was obliged to storm the steep outer edges of those saucers while the home troops were not only in an excellent position for defence but in case of defeat could leisurely withdraw to the protection of the next saucer-rim and could repeat that performance four times ere they had reached their little island in the Seine, which, by the burning of the few connecting bridges, could be turned into an impregnable fortress.

It was of course possible for a very determined and well-equipped hostile force to take Paris. But it was exceedingly difficult, as the Great War has shown us only recently. It was not only the valor of the French and English that kept the Germans out of the French capital. It also was that geographical accident of millions of years ago which had put every possible natural barrier in the way of the invaders from the east.

France has been obliged to fight almost ten centuries for her national independence. But whereas most countries have been under the necessity of guarding four separate frontiers, France was able to devote all her energies to the protection of her western boundaries; and this probably accounted for the fact that France could develop into a highly centralized modern state long before any of the other nations of Europe.

The whole of the western part of France, situated between the Cevennes and the Vosges and the Atlantic falls quite naturally into a number of peninsulas and valleys which are separated from each other by low mountain ridges. The most western of these valleys is that of the Seine and Oise which is connected with the plains of Belgium through a natural gateway defended since time immemorial by the city of St. Quentin. In modern times it has become a very important railroad center and as such it was one of the main German objectives during the march on Paris in 1914.

The valley of the Seine and that of the Loire are in easy communication with each other by way of the gap of Orleans. As a result thereof that region was bound to play a very important role in the history of France. The national heroine of the French is known as the Maid of Orleans, and the biggest railroad station in Paris is called the Gare d'Orléans, and it was the geographical position of that city on that pass between the north and the south which was responsible for both names. In the Middle Ages, knights in armor fought for such key positions. Today railroad companies fight for such key positions. The world changes. But often enough, the more it seems to change, the more it really remains the same.

As for the connection between the Loire valley and the valley of the Garonne, it followed the present railroad line via Poitiers, and it was near Poitiers that Charles Martel in the year 732 prevented the Moors from pushing any further into Europe, and it was near Poitiers that the Black Prince in the year 1356 so completely annihilated the French forces that France remained under English domination for almost another hundred years.

As for that wide valley of the Garonne, the southern part of which is that famous land of Gascony whence came the dashing d'Artagnan and the noble King Henry IV, that part of France is in direct communication with the Provence and the Rhône valley by way of a valley that runs from Toulouse on the Garonne River to Narbonne, which used to be on the Mediterranean and which incidentally was the oldest of all Roman settlements in Gaul.

Like all such prehistoric highways (for that route was used thousands of years before the beginning of written history) it has always been a source of revenue to some one. Racketeering and profiteering are as old as the human race. If you doubt this statement, go to any mountain pass in any part of the world and remain in that neighborhood until you have definitely located

The Rhine, the Meuse and their Delta

the spot where the road was at its narrowest a thousand years ago. On that exact spot you will find the ruins of from half a dozen to two dozen castles and if you know anything about ancient civilizations, the different layers of stone will tell you: "Here in the year 50 B. C. and in the year 600 and in 800 and in 1100 and in 1250 and in 1350 and in 1500 some robber baron built himself a fortress which allowed him to demand tribute from all passing caravans."

Sometimes you will be surprised to find a flourishing city instead of a mere ruin. But the towers and ravelins and counterscarps and bastions of Carcassonne will tell you how terribly strong such a mountain pass fortress had to be to survive the attacks of all its hungry enemies.

So much for the general landscape of France. Now let me add a few very general characteristics about the people who live in this land between the Mediterranean and the Atlantic. There is one thing they seem to have in common, a certain sense of balance and proportion. I would almost feel inclined to say that the French tried hard to be "logical", if that unfortunate word were not so closely connected with the idea of something dry and dull and pedantic.

It is true that France is the home of one of the highest mountains in Europe. The top of Mont Blanc is now French territory, but that is merely an accident. The average Frenchman is as little concerned about that waste of snow and ice as the average American is about the Painted Desert. What he likes best is the harmonious roll of the hills of the Meuse region and Guyenne and Normandy and Picardy, the pleasant little rivers with their high poplars and their leisurely barges, the haze that hangs over the valleys at night and then turns them into paintings by Watteau. What he knows best are those little villages where nothing ever changes (the greatest strength of any country), those small towns in which the people live or at least try to live as their ancestors did fifty or five hundred years ago, and Paris, where the best living and the best thinking have gone hand in hand for more than ten centuries.

For the Frenchman, contrary to the absurd fables foisted upon us during the Great War, is not a sentimental dreamer, but a most intelligent and eager realist. He stands with both feet flatly on this earth. He realizes that he will live but once and that threescore and ten is all he can expect. And so he endeavors to make himself as comfortable as possible while on this planet and wastes no time imagining the world better than it is. *C'est la vie*—such is life—and suppose we make the best of it! Since food is agreeable to civilized man, let us provide even the poorest with the knowledge of good cooking. Since wine, ever since the days of our Savior, has been regarded as a fit drink for true Christians, let us cultivate the best of wines. Since the Lord in

Paris

his wisdom has seen fit to fill this earth with many things agreeable to the eye and the ear and the nose, let us not indulge in a haughty denial of these divine bounties but partake of them as an all-wise Providence has evidently meant us to do. And since Man is stronger when fighting in a group than when acting alone, let us stick closely to the family as the elementary social unit which is responsible for the weal and woe of all its members just as all the individual members are responsible for the weal and woe of the family.

This is the ideal side of French life. There is another side, much less agreeable, which however grows directly out of the very qualities which I have just enumerated. The family quite frequently ceases to be a pleasant dream and becomes a nightmare. The endless grandmothers and grandfathers who rule the clan act as a brake which prevents all progress. The excellent habit of saving for sons and grandsons and great-grandsons degenerates into a hideous habit of scraping and filching and rooking and pinching and economizing on every necessity of life, including that charity towards one's neighbor without which civilized existence becomes a very drab experience indeed.

But by and large the average Frenchman, of however humble rank or station, seems to carry with him a certain practical philosophy of life which provides him with a maximum of content at a minimum of expenditure. For one thing, he is not ambitious in our sense of the word. He knows that all men are born unequal. They tell him that in America every boy may some day hope to become president of the bank for which he works as a clerk. What of it? He does not want to assume all that responsibility! What would become of his three hours for luncheon? It would of course be nice to have all the money that goes with the job, but the sacrifice of comfort and happiness would be too great. And so the Frenchman works and works industriously and his wife works and his daughters and his sons work too, yes, the whole country works and saves and lives the sort of lives it likes to live and does not try to lead the sort of lives other people think they ought to like to live; and that is a bit of wisdom which does not make for great riches, but which is a better guarantee for ultimate happiness than the doctrine of success preached all over the rest of the world.

Whenever we come to the sea in this geography of ours I shall not tell you that the people of the coast indulge in fishing. Of course they do. What else would you expect them to do? Milk cows or dig for coal?

But when we reach the subject connected with agriculture, we shall make a very curious discovery. Whereas in most countries the population during the last hundred years has been attracted to the cities, fully sixty percent of all Frenchmen continue to live in the country; and France today is the only country in Europe which could withstand a prolonged siege without importing grain from abroad. The ancestral methods of working the fields are gradually making way before the improved methods of modern science and when the French peasant shall have ceased to till his soil as his great-great-grandfather did in the days of Charlemagne and Clovis, France will be entirely self-supporting.

What helps to keep the peasant on the land is the fact that as a rule he is his own proprietor. His farm may not be much of a farm but it is his own. In England and in east Prussia, two parts of the Old World where there is a great deal of agriculture, the farms belong to some vague and distant landlord. But the French Revolution did away with the landlord, whether noble or cleric, and divided his property among the small peasantry. That was often very hard on the former proprietors. But their ancestors had acquired those possessions by right of eminent plunder, so what was the difference? And it has proved of tremendous advantage to the country at large. For it gives more than half of the people a direct interest in the welfare of the whole nation. Like everything else, that state of affairs probably has its disadvantages. It may account for the exaggerated feeling of nationalism among the French. It may explain the provincialism which makes every Frenchman stick to the people of his own village even when he moves to Paris, so that Paris is full of little hotels catering to certain groups of regional travellers, a situation which we could only duplicate if New York had hostelries patronized exclusively by Chicagoans or Kalamazooians or Fresnonians or people from Horseheads, New York. It also explains his utter unwillingness to migrate to other parts of the world, but then again, why should any one move to another country when he is perfectly happy at home?

Next to agriculture, the cultivation of the wine-grape keeps vast numbers of Frenchmen attached to the soil. The entire valley of the Garonne is devoted to vine culture. The city of Bordeaux near the mouth of the Garonne and just north of those vast silty plains called the Landes, where the shepherds walk on stilts and the sheep can remain out of doors all the year long, is the center for the export of this wine, as Cette, on the Mediterranean, is the harbor for the famous wines of the piping hot valley of the Rhône. The wines from Burgundy—the so-called Côte d'Or—are gathered together in Dijon, while those of the Champagne are assembled (and multiplied and divided) in the ancient French coronation city of Rheims.

When grain and wine fail to support the population, industry helps out. The ancient French monarchs were something more than haughty imbeciles who oppressed their subjects and wasted useless millions on the pretty ladies of Versailles. They made their courts the center of fashion and civilized living towards which all the world flocked to learn agreeable manners and to be taught the difference between eating and dining. As a result, even today, a century and a half after the last of the ancient rulers was thrown into the quick-lime of a Paris potter's-field, with his head between his feet, Paris dictates unto the rest of the world what to wear and how to wear it. The industries which provide Europe and America with those indispensable luxuries which most people prefer to the sheer necessities, are centered in and around the Île de France and they provide employment to millions of women and girls. The endless flower fields of the Riviera are the original source whence flows most of our perfumery at six and ten dollars a bottle (a very small bottle, too, but that is the result of our wise decision to tax all those things which we ourselves can't make).

Then came the discovery of coal and iron in the soil of France, and Picardy and Artois grew drab and ugly with those vast dump-heaps of cinders and slag which played such a great part during the battle of Mons, where the English tried to stop the Germans in their march upon Paris. Lorraine became the center for the iron industry. The central plateau fabricated steel. When the war was over, the French hastened to annex the Alsace which provided them with more steel and which, during the last fifty years of German domination, had gone in heavily for textiles. As a result of this recent development, one-quarter of the French people are today engaged in industries, and they can proudly boast that their industrial cities are fully as hideous, as unattractive and as inhuman in their outer aspect as those of England or of our own country.

BELGIUM, A COUNTRY CREATED BY SCRAPS OF PAPER AND
RICH IN EVERYTHING EXCEPT INTERNAL HARMONY

THE modern kingdom of the Belgians consists of three parts:
the plain of Flanders along the shores of the North Sea, the
low plateau between Flanders and the mountains of the east,
rich in iron and coal, and the Ardennes Mountains of the east,
through which the Meuse flows in pleasant curves, bound for
the marshes of the Low Countries a short distance further
towards the north.

The iron and coal deposits centering around the cities of
Liége, Charleroi and Mons (the great war for Democracy had
a strange habit of bringing the names of coal and iron cities to
the front pages of our newspapers) are so plentiful that Belgium
will probably be able to provide the world with those two necessities of modern life long after the coal fields and iron beds of
Germany, France and England shall have been exhausted.

But this country, blessed with what the Germans so often call
the "heavy industry", has curiously enough no good modern
harbors of its own. The coast along the Channel, shallow and
protected by a most complicated arrangement of sand banks
and shallow places, has no ports worthy of the name. The Belgians have dug artificial harbors in Ostende and Zeebrugge and
Nieuwport, but Antwerp, her most important harbor, lies forty
miles distant from the North Sea, and the river Scheldt for the
last thirty miles of its course runs through Dutch territory, a
slightly absurd arrangement and one which might be called
"unnatural" from a geographic point of view but unavoidable in
a world ruled by scraps of paper signed by the delegates to solemn
international conferences. As however Belgium is a country that

was the direct outcome of a number of such conferences, we ought to know something about the historical antecedents that faced their Excellencies whenever they settled comfortably around their green tables to decide the fate of the world.

The Gallica Belgica of the Romans had been inhabited by Celts (the same people as the original settlers of Britain and France) and a number of small Germanic tribes. All of these were forced to recognize the suzerainty of the Romans who pushed forward in a northern direction across the plains of Flanders and over the hills of the Ardennes until they reached the almost impassable marshes which were to give birth to the modern kingdom of the Netherlands. Next it was a minor province of the empire of Charlemagne. Next, by the disastrous treaty of Verdun of 843 it was made part of the central kingdom of Lothair. Next it was divided into a large number of semi-independent duchies and counties and bishoprics. Next, the Habsburgs, the most competent real estate manipulators of the Middle Ages, got hold of it. But the Habsburgs were not looking for coal and iron. They were looking for safe returns on farm land and for quick returns on trade. Hence the eastern part of the country (and by far the most important) was regarded as a semi-wilderness. But Flanders was given every opportunity to develop its latent forces and did so, until during the fourteenth and fifteenth centuries of our era it was by far the richest part of northern Europe.

This was due to a fortunate geographic position which allowed medieval ships of moderate size to penetrate far inland and to the fact that the early rulers of Flanders were men and women of quite exceptional ability who encouraged the development of industrialism while all other feudal chieftains stuck closely to agriculture and despised capitalism as heartily as the Church despised the idea of taking interest on loans.

In consequence of this very wise policy, Bruges and Ghent and Ypres and Cambrai waved fat and rich and opulent, doing the work that other countries should have performed for themselves if their sovereigns had allowed them to grasp their op-

portunities. The subsequent downfall of these early centers of
capitalistic industries was brought about by a combination of
geography and human—all too human—characteristics.

Geography did its share by changing certain currents in the
North Sea which filled the harbors of Bruges and Ghent with
such vast and unexpected masses of sand that those cities became
completely landlocked. While the labor unions (the guilds)
which in the beginning had been a source of tremendous strength,
rapidly degenerated into tyrannical and short-sighted organizations, founded for no other purpose than to slow up and impede
every known form of industrial activity.

From Man to Mole

As the old native dynasties had died out and Flanders had been temporarily annexed by the French, there was no one to intervene and the tides and the walking-delegates between them reduced Flanders to a somnolent region of pleasant little white-washed farms and beautiful ruins which inspire old English ladies to some of their most atrocious water-colors but where the grass has never ceased to grow between the well polished cobble-stones of the ancient tenement quarters.

The Reformation did the rest. For Flanders after a short and very sharp upheaval in favor of the Lutheran doctrines remained faithful to the Mother Church. And when their northern neighbors gained their independence, Holland hastened to close the last remaining port of their old rival, and with Antwerp cut off from the rest of Europe, the whole of Belgium went into a prolonged period of hibernation, out of which it did not arise until the needs of James Watt's hungry machines drew the world's attention to her immense riches in natural materials.

Then foreign capital hastened to the valley of the Meuse and in less than twenty years Belgium had become one of the leading industrial nations of Europe. It was then that the Walloon or French speaking part of the country (everything west of Brussels) came fully into its own, for although it contained only 42% of the total population it soon became by far the richest part of the whole country and the Flemings were reduced to a race of semi-conquered peasants whose language might be tolerated in the kitchen and in the stable but which should never be spoken in the parlor of a civilized household.

To make matters still a little more complicated, the Congress of Vienna of 1815 which was supposed to settle the peace of the world for all time (a sort of Versailles of a century ago) had seen fit to make Belgium and Holland into a single kingdom, so as to have a powerful northern balance against the French.

The end of this strange political marriage came in the year 1830 when the Belgians arose against the Dutch, and the French (as was to be expected) rushed to their assistance. The Great Nations (a little late as usual) interfered. A prince of the house of Coburg, uncle of Queen Victoria (Uncle Leopold was a very serious gentleman who exercised a very *profound influence* upon his dear little niece) was made King of the Belgians. He had just refused a similar offer from the side of the Greeks and never had any reason to regret his choice. For the new kingdom proved to be a success. The mouth of the Scheldt remained in Dutch hands, but Antwerp became once more one of the most important harbors of western Europe.

The Great European Powers had officially proclaimed Belgium a "neutral power". But King Leopold (the son of the founder of the dynasty) was much too shrewd to have any confidence in such paper keep-off-the-grass signs. He worked hard to make his country something more than a third-rate little nation, existing merely by the grace of its richer neighbors. When a certain gentleman by the name of Henry Stanley returned from the heart of Africa, Leopold prevailed upon him to come to Brussels and out of this interview grew the International Association of the Congo, which in due course of time was to make Belgium one of the largest colonial powers of the modern world.

Today the main problem before Belgium, with its magnificent geographic situation right in the heart of the most prosperous part of northern Europe, is no longer an economic one. It is a racial one. The Flemish majority is rapidly catching up with the French minority in the matter of general education and scientific and cultural development. It is clamoring for a share in the administration of the country from which it has been kept separated ever since the founding of the independent kingdom. It insists upon absolute equality for both languages, for Flemish as well as for French.

But I had better leave this subject alone. It puzzles me and I fail to see why it should be that way. The Flemings and the Walloons have a common racial origin and share almost twenty centuries of common history. Yet they live like cats and dogs. In the next chapter we shall meet the Swiss who speak four different languages, German, French, Italian and Romonsch (a

Coal in the making

strange Roman tongue surviving among the mountains of the Engadine) and they get along with each other without any real basic friction. There must be a reason for this but I for one am willing to confess that it surpasses my own understanding.

Heat

XIII

LUXEMBURG, THE HISTORICAL CURIOSITY

But ere I talk of Switzerland I ought to mention a curious little independent principality, the name of which would hardly be known if it had not played quite an important role during the first days of the World War. Luxemburg (the "lützel" or "little" burg) counts only one quarter of a million inhabitants, whose ancestors lived in this neighborhood when it was still part of the Roman province of Belgium. It was however of considerable importance during the Middle Ages on account of the strength of the capital, which was supposed to be one of the "impregnable" fortresses of the world.

That same fact and the jealousy between France and Prussia as to who should own it made the Congress of Vienna of 1815 give the tiny country an independent status as a duchy of which the kings of the Netherlands should be the personal rulers to compensate them for the loss of their ancestral territories in Germany.

Twice during the nineteenth century the small duchy almost caused a war between Germany and France. In order to prevent further difficulties of that sort, the fortifications were finally dismantled and Luxemburg was officially declared to be "neutral territory"—like Belgium.

When the war broke out, the Germans violated this act of neutrality, basing their decision to do so upon the geographical necessity of invading France by way of the flat plains of the north and east without trying the hopeless expedient of forcing the steep tea-cup barriers of the west. (See France.) Luxemburg remained in German hands until 1918. Even now the small duchy is not actually out of danger, for the soil contains a considerable amount of iron ore.

XIV

SWITZERLAND, THE COUNTRY OF HIGH MOUNTAINS, EX-CELLENT SCHOOLS AND A UNIFIED PEOPLE WHO SPEAK FOUR DIFFERENT LANGUAGES

THE Swiss are apt to call their country the Helvetian Confederation, and a rather dowdy lady, called Helvetia, is apt to appear upon the coins and stamps of the twenty-two independent little republics whose representatives gather together at the capital city of Berne to discuss the affairs of the common fatherland.

Since the war, when the greater part of the country (70% of the people speak German, 20% speak French, 6% speak Italian and 2% speak Romonsch) was more or less on the side of the Germans (although maintaining a most scrupulous neutrality), the image of a slightly idealized young hero by the name of William Tell has somewhat tended to replace the Helvetian goddess who, I am sorry to say, was beginning to look more and more like Britannia as she was depicted by the eminent artists of the mid-Victorian period in England. This conflict of coin and stamp deities (they are not restricted to Switzerland; almost any country has one of these queer problems) clearly shows the dual nature of the Swiss Republic. To the outside world, all this is of very little importance. Switzerland, to those of us who are not of Swiss origin, is merely the country of the picturesque mountain-ranges and it is of these that I shall speak in the present chapter.

The Alps, which stretch from the Mediterranean to the Adriatic, are almost twice as long as Great Britain and contain about the same amount of territory. Sixteen thousand square miles of this land belong to Switzerland (Denmark is just about as large) and of these 16,000 square miles, 12,000 are productive in some way because they are covered with forests or vineyards or small bits of pasture. Four thousand square miles are of no use to anybody because they are either covered by the water of the big lakes or form part of some picturesque precipice; and 700 square miles are covered by glaciers. As a result, Switzerland has only 250 inhabitants per square mile, while Belgium has 655, and Germany 347. But Norway has only 22 per square mile, and Sweden has 35, and the idea therefore that Switzerland is merely a sort of gigantic mountain resort, inhabited exclusively by hotel-keepers and their guests is slightly erroneous. For Switzerland, aside from its dairy products, has turned the wide northern plateau between the Alps and the Tura into one of the most prosperous industrial countries of Europe, and it has been able to do so without the help of any raw materials. It has of course a superabundance of waterpower, and furthermore it enjoys a very favorable position right in the heart of Europe, which makes it possible for the finished products of the Helvetian Republic to slide quietly but continuously into at least a dozen surrounding countries.

In a previous chapter I tried to give you an idea of the origin of all such complicated masses of mountain-ridges as are represented by the Alps and the Pyrenees. I told you to take half a dozen clean handkerchiefs, unfold them and put them on top of each other and push them together and then watch the wrinkles and the creases and double-jointed circles and crumples that are the result of such a forcible concentration. The table on which you performed this geological operation was the original base or core of granite (countless millions of years old) across which the younger layers folded themselves during subsequent millions of years, to become those queerly shaped pinnacles which were given their present form and aspect by still other millions of years of incessant wind and rain and snow and ice.

These enormous folds, from ten to twelve thousand feet above the plains, have gradually crumbled into a series of parallel ranges. But in the center of the country (the village of Andermatt on the Gothard pass is the geographical center of the coun-

try) they meet in a vast complex of mountains (the so-called St.
Gothard range) which send the Rhine on its course towards the
North Sea, the Rhône on its way to the Mediterranean, and
which also give birth to those mountain rivers which feed the
lakes of Thun, of Lucerne and Zürich in the north, and the famous Italian lakes in the south. And it is precisely in this neighborhood of glaciers and precipices and valleys, so deep that they
hardly ever see the rays of the sun, in this region of avalanches
and impassable mountain streams, green with the chilly waters of
a dozen glaciers, that the Swiss Republic took its origin.

As usual it was a combination of practical politics with certain
geographical peculiarities of the land which gave the Swiss their
first chance to make a bid for independence. For almost a thousand years the half-savage peasants of these inaccessible valleys
had been left alone by all their more powerful neighbors. What
was the use of hoisting the proud standard of empire when there

Switzerland

was no plunder? At best one could deprive these wild men of a couple of cow-hides. But they were dangerous barbarians with their aptitude for guerrilla warfare and those uncomfortable boulders that came crashing down from the hillsides and that would squash a suit of armor as if it were a piece of parchment, and so the Swiss were treated as the original settlers of the Atlantic coast treated the Indians that lived behind the Alleghenies —they were ignored.

But with the rising importance of the Papacy and the tremendous upward sweep of Italian commerce during and immediately after the Crusades, northern Europe felt a very sincere need of a more direct and convenient route from Germany to Italy than those provided by the St. Bernard Pass (which necessitated a long detour by way of Lyons and the entire Rhône valley, via the lake of Geneva) or the Brenner Pass, which meant

The Mountain Pass

that one had to cross the Habsburg domains with their almost unbearable tariff rates.

It was then that the peasants of the Cantons (the name for the independent little Swiss republics or districts) of Unterwalden, Uri and Schwyz decided to combine and each spend a little money (Heaven knows, they did not have much) upon the road that led from the valley of the Rhine to the valley of the Ticino River. They cut down certain parts of the rock. Whenever the rocks were too hard to be removed by means of pick-axes (try and make a mountain road without dynamite!) they made narrow wooden contraptions which they hung from the side of the mountain walls to circumnavigate difficult corners; and they built some primitive stone bridges across the Rhine, which hitherto had been impassable except by pedestrians during the height of the summer. Part of the way they followed the road that had been traced by the engineers of Charlemagne, four centuries before, but had never been completed; and by the end of the thirteenth century a merchant with a caravan of pack-mules could travel from Basel to Milan by way of the St. Gothard Pass with a fair assurance that he would not lose more than two or three of his animals on account of broken legs and falling stones.

As early as the year 1331 we hear of the existence of a hospice on top of the pass and although it was not opened to carriages until 1820 it was soon one of the most popular routes for commerce between the south and the north.

Of course the good people of Unterwalden, Uri and Schwyz allowed themselves to be paid a slight remuneration for all the trouble they had taken. This steady revenue, together with the impetus this international traffic gave to such cities as Lucerne and Zürich, gave these small peasant communities a new feeling of independence which no doubt had a great deal to do with their open defiance of the Habsburg family. The latter, curiously enough, was also originally of Swiss peasant stock, although they did not mention this fact in any of the genealogies which were preserved in their home castle of Habichtsburg (or Hawk's

Nest) that stood near the spot where the river Aar flows into the Rhine.

I am sorry to be quite so prosaic but it was the tangible revenue derived from a busily patronized Alpine trade-route rather than the bravery of a non-existent William Tell which was responsible for the foundation of what afterwards developed into the modern Swiss Republic. That modern Swiss Republic is a highly interesting political experiment built firmly upon one of the most efficient public-school systems of the world. The governmental machine runs so smoothly and so effectively that even Swiss citizens have to think for a moment when you ask them suddenly who happens to be their President. For their country is run by a Bundesrat—a sort of Board of Managers—composed of seven members, and every year they appoint a new President (usually the Vice-President of the previous year) and custom, though not law, provides that one year he shall belong to the German-speaking part of the country, the next year to the French-speaking part, and the third year to the Italian-speaking sub-division.

This President, however, bears no resemblance whatsoever to the President of the United States of America. He is merely the temporary chairman of a Federal Executive which expresses its will through the mouths of seven individual members. The President, apart from presiding over the meetings of the federal council, is minister of foreign affairs, but his position is so inconspicuous that he has no official residence. There is no Swiss "White House". When distinguished strangers have to be entertained, the party is given in the rooms of the foreign office, and even those parties bear more resemblance to a simple bierfest in a little mountain village than to the semi-royal receptions of the French presidents or their American colleagues.

The main details of the administration are too complicated to be mentioned here but the visitor to this part of the Alps is constantly being reminded that somewhere or other an intelligent and honest person is constantly on the watch to see that things

The Conquest of the Barriers

are being done and are being done both honestly and intelligently.

Take the matter of railroading, which is of course connected with innumerable difficulties. The two main arteries that connect Italy with northern Europe run straight through the heart of the Swiss Alps. The Mount Cenis tunnel connects Paris with Turin (the ancient capital of the kingdom of Savoy) by way of Dijon and Lyons. And the Brenner line provides a direct communication between southern Germany and Vienna, but although it crosses the Alps it does not pass through any tunnel. The Simplon line and the St. Gothard lines however are not only tunnel-borers but veritable mountain-climbers. The Gothard is the older of the two. It was begun in 1872 and finished ten years later. It took eight years to dig the tunnel which is nine and a half miles long and reaches a height of almost 4000 feet. Even more interesting than the tunnel itself are the spiral tunnels between Wassen and Goeschenen. Since the valleys were so narrow that they offered no room for even a single track, the railroad had to do its climbing through the heart of the mountains themselves. Outside of these special tunnels there are fifty-nine other tunnels (several of them almost a mile long), nine large viaducts and forty-eight bridges.

The second most important transalpine road, that of the Simplon, offers us a direct route between Paris and Milan by way of Dijon, Lausanne and the valley of the Rhône as far as Brieg. It was opened for traffic in the year 1906, exactly a century after Napoleon had finished his famous Simplon Pass road with its 250 big and 350 small bridges and its ten long tunnels, the greatest piece of road-building the world had ever seen. The Simplon road, which was much easier to construct than that of the St. Gothard, follows the slowly ascending valley of the Rhône until it reaches a spot about 2000 feet high where the tunnel begins. This tunnel is twelve and a half miles long and provided with double tracks. So is the Lötschberg tunnel (nine miles long) which connects northern Switzerland with the Simplon road and western Italy.

Although one of the narrowest of all mountain-ranges, the so-called Pennine Alps, through which the Simplon road runs, have a climate all their own. There are no fewer than twenty-one peaks of 12,000 feet or more within this small quadrangle and 140 glaciers feed the turbulent streams, which have a most annoying habit of washing away railroad bridges just a few minutes before the arrival of one of the big international express trains. That there never have been any wrecks on account of these aquatic surprise parties speaks highly for the efficiency of the Swiss railroad men. But as I have said before, in this somewhat stiff and rather bureaucratic republic, nothing much is left to chance. Life is too difficult and too dangerous to encourage the amiable philosophy of "muddling through". Somewhere, somehow, some one is forever watching, observing, paying attention.

That such a general tendency towards a rather schoolmasterish punctuality and efficiency does not make for artistic success is a well-known fact. In the line of literature and the arts—painting, sculpture or music—the Swiss have never produced anything that has travelled far beyond their own narrow confines. But then, the world is full of "artistic" nations while only a few can boast of centuries of uninterrupted political and economic growth and development. And the system suits the average Swiss and his wife. What more can we ask?

XV

GERMANY, THE NATION THAT WAS FOUNDED TOO LATE

MERELY for the sake of convenience I have divided the different countries of Europe into racial or cultural groups, and I have started my general discussion with those nations which still showed unmistakable evidences of having been Roman colonies ere they began an independent political existence of their own.

It is true that Rome had also conquered the Balkans and that in one country at least (Roumania) the Latin language has survived as the national tongue. But the great Mongolian, Slavic and Turkish invasions of the Middle Ages have so completely destroyed all evidence of Roman civilization in that part of the world that it would be decidedly erroneous to include the Balkan monarchies in the present discussion, wherefore I shall now bid farewell to the Mediterranean range-of-influence and proceed to that other form of civilization which was of Teutonic origin and which came to be centered around the North Sea and the Atlantic Ocean.

There is (I have already told you that when I spoke of France) a vast semicircular plain which stretches all the way from the eastern Russian hills, where the Dnieper and the Dvina and the Neva and the Volga take their origin, to the Pyrenees. The southern part of that semi-circle was brought under Roman control a very short time after the Germanic tribes began their mysterious migrations towards the west. The eastern part, even then, seems to have been occupied by those nomadic Slavic masses which replenished themselves just as rapidly as they were killed off and which therefore, like the rabbits of Australia, were invincible. Thus the only part that was still available when the hungry Teutonic invaders appeared upon the scene was that big square which stretched from the Vistula on the east to the Rhine delta on the west. The Baltic was its northern limit and in the south a long line of Roman block-houses reminded all newcomers that they were entering upon a "forbidden territory".

The western part of this region was mountainous. First there were the Ardennes and the Vosges, on the western bank of the river Rhine. Then, running due east and west, came the Black Forest, the Tyrolean Mountains, the Erz (or Iron Ore) Mountains (present day Bohemia), the Riesengebirge, and finally the Carpathians which stretched almost as far as the Black Sea.

The rivers in this territory were forced to flow due north. In order of their appearance from west to east there was first of all the Rhine, the most literary of rivers, over which people have fought and wept more copiously than over any other little mountain stream. For the Rhine is really a very modest little rivulet. The Amazon is over five times as long. The Mississippi and Missouri are six times its length, and even the Ohio, which we do not consider much of a river as rivers go in our part of the world, is five hundred miles longer. Then comes the Weser river, with the modern city of Bremen near its mouth. Then the Elbe, which has made Hamburg what it is today. Then the Oder, which gave rise to the city of Stettin, the export harbor for the products of the town of Berlin and its industrial hinterland. Finally there is the Weichsel or Vistula, with the city of Danzig which is now a free state, ruled by a commissioner appointed by the League of Nations.

Millions of years ago all this territory was covered with glaciers. When they retreated they left behind them a large, sandy waste which towards the North Sea and the Baltic degenerated into a trackless morass. Gradually these northern marshes developed a fringe of sand dunes, and these dunes reach almost all the way from the Flemish coast to Königsberg, the old Prussian capital near the Russian frontier. As soon as these dunes had developed, the marshes began to enjoy a certain protection from the tides of the ocean. That meant the beginning of vegetation and as soon as the soil had been prepared for timber, the forests appeared, those same forests which, converted into peat fields, provided our ancestors with an unlimited supply of fairly good fuel.

Both the North Sea and the Baltic, which are the northern and western frontiers of this plain, bear the name of "sea" as a courtesy title. They are really shallow ponds. The average depth of the North Sea is only sixty fathoms (a fathom is six feet) and its greatest depth is not more than 400 fathoms. The average depth of the Baltic is about thirty-six fathoms. The average depth of the Atlantic, on the other hand, is 2170 fathoms while that of the Pacific is 2240 fathoms. These figures show you that you had better think of the North Sea and the Baltic as submerged valleys. A slight elevation of the surface of the earth would once more turn them into dry land.

And now let us look at a map of the dry land of Germany. I mean the map as it is today and as it must have been more or less when human beings followed the retreating glaciers and settled down permanently in this part of the old continent.

These early immigrants were savages. They lived by catching wild animals and by raising a little grain. But they were savages with a very decided sense of beauty, and as their own territory was poor in those metals which could be used for ornaments, they had to send abroad for their gold and silver.

The following statement may come as a mild shock to many of my readers but all original trade-routes are luxury routes. All early contests between the races that inhabited different parts of the world were luxury contests. The Romans learned the main outlines of the geography of northern Europe from traders who had penetrated as far as the mysterious Baltic in search of amber —a sort of petrified resin which Roman matrons used to color their hair. The desire for that hard, concrete lump of limestone, which is sometimes found inside the body of an oyster and with which women delight to attract attention to the pretty curves of their ears or the slenderness of their fingers, has been responsible for more voyages of discovery in the Pacific and in the Indian Ocean than any other cause, including the desire of many honest people to carry the Gospel unto the heathen.

The quest for ambergris, a substance found in the intestinal canals of sperm whales, and the result of what in plain English we would call a bilious attack on the part of the unfortunate whale, has driven more ships to the coasts of Brazil and Madagascar and the Moluccas than the search for herring or sardines or other forms of useful food. For ambergris could be used as a base for many perfumes that smelled deliciously of flowers and distant lands, whereas food was merely food and not half as interesting.

A change in fashions which made the women of the seventeenth century wear their corsets underneath their gowns and out of sight (twelve-course dinners were bad for the figure) was directly responsible for most of our knowledge of the Arctic. As soon as Paris had decided that hats should be adorned with aigrets, those hunters who went after the white herons to deprive them of their head plumes (regardless of the fact that this meant the extinction of one of the loveliest and noblest birds of all creation) penetrated further into the lagoons of our southern states than they had ever done before when they were merely in quest of their daily bread and butter.

I might continue the list for almost a dozen more pages. Whatever was rare and therefore expensive has always been an object of veneration to those who, by a wasteful demonstration of their riches, hoped to impress their less fortunate neighbors. Ever since the beginning of history, luxury rather than necessity has been the real pioneer of progress along the lines of exploration. And when we study the map of prehistoric Germany carefully we can still trace the old luxury routes, for in the main they are the same as those of medieval and modern times.

Take the conditions some three thousand years ago. The mountain-ridges of the south, the Harz, the Erz Mountains and the Riesengebirge were situated hundreds of miles away from the sea. The plain that stretched northwards towards the North Sea and the Baltic had long since changed from marshland into dry land and was now thickly covered with forests. And Man, following in the wake of the glaciers, which had now retreated in the general direction of Scandinavia and Finland, had claimed this entire wilderness as his own. Among the hills of the south, the tribes which inhabited the valleys had found that it paid them to cut down their trees and sell them to the Romans who had occupied strategic positions along the Rhine and the Danube. For the rest, few of these early Teuton nomads and farmers had ever seen a Roman. One Roman expedition had tried to penetrate to the heart of their country, had been ambushed in a dark and water-logged valley and slaughtered off so completely that the experiment had never been tried again. That did not mean however that northern Germany was completely cut off from all contact with the rest of the world.

The great prehistoric trade-route from west to east, from the Iberian peninsula to the plains of Russia, followed the line from the Pyrenees to Paris, through the gaps of Poitiers and Tours, which I described in the chapter on France. It then skirted the Ardennes and from there followed the outskirts of the central European highlands until it reached the northern lowlands now occupied by the United Soviet Republics of Russia. On its course eastward this road was of course obliged to cross a great many rivers and it did this wherever it could find a convenient shallow place. Just as the city of Rome grew out of a ford across the Tiber, so a number of the earliest cities of northern Germany were but the continuation of prehistoric and early historic settlements which were located on the exact spot where today we would find a filling station and a general store. Hanover and Berlin and Magdeburg and Breslau had all of them got their start that way. Leipzig, although originally it was a village in the heart of Slavic lands, was also of commercial origin, for it was there that the mineral products from the Saxon mountains, such as silver and lead and copper and iron, were assembled before they were sent down the rivers and sold to the merchants patronizing the great European highway from east to west.

Of course, once this road reached the Rhine, water traffic began

Germany

to compete seriously with the caravans used for the long overland haul. Water traffic has always been much cheaper and much
more convenient than land traffic, and long before Caesar caught
his first glimpse of the Rhine there must have been rafts used to
carry merchandise from Strassburg (where the Rhine connected
with the hinterland of Franconia, Bavaria and Württemberg)
to Cologne and thence to the marshes of the Low Countries and
eventually to Britain.

It is a far cry from Berlin to Jerusalem, but both cities obeyed
the same geographical rule which insists that cities must arise
wherever important trade-routes cross each other. Jerusalem was
situated on the caravan route from Babylonia to Phoenicia and
from Damascus to Egypt and was an important trade center long
before the Jews had heard of its existence. Berlin, situated on a
river where the routes from west to east and from north-west to
south-east (from Paris to Petrograd and from Hamburg to Constantinople in modern terms) happened to meet, was bound to
become a second Jerusalem.

All during the Middle Ages Germany consisted of a large
number of semi-independent states but until 300 years ago there
was nothing to indicate that some day this western part of the
great European plain would develop into the leading nation of
the world. Curiously enough the modern Germany grew almost
directly out of the failure of the Crusading Movement. When
it became certain that no new territory was to be conquered in
western Asia (the Mohammedans had proved more than a match
for the Christians) the disinherited classes of Europe began to
look for other sources of agricultural wealth. Quite naturally
they thought at once of the opportunities offered by the Slavic
lands situated just across the Oder and the Vistula, which were
inhabited by the wild and heathenish Prussians. One of the old
crusading orders moved, lock, stock and barrel, from Palestine
to east Prussia and transferred its business center from Acre in
Galilea to Marienburg, thirty miles south of Danzig. For two
hundred years these knights fought the Slavs and settled the

farms of their victims with imported nobles and peasants from
the west. In the year 1410 they suffered a terrific defeat at the
hands of the Poles in the battle of Tannenberg, the same place
where in 1914 Hindenburg annihilated the Russian armies. But
somehow or other the order survived even this blow and when
the Reformation occurred, they were still a body of considerable
importance.

It so happened that at that time the order was ruled by a
member of the Hohenzollern family. This particular Grand
Master not only joined the Protestant cause but on the advice of
Martin Luther he declared himself hereditary Duke of Prussia
with Königsberg on the Gulf of Danzig as his capital. Early in
the seventeenth century this duchy was acquired by another
branch of the industrious and shrewd Hohenzollern tribe which
ever since the middle of the fifteenth century had been administering the sandy wastes of Brandenburg. A hundred years
afterwards (in 1701, to be precise) these Brandenburg upstarts
felt themselves strong enough to aspire to something better than
the rank of a mere "prince elector" and they began an agitation
to get themselves recognized as kings.

The emperor of the Holy Roman Empire was willing. Dog
as a rule does not eat dog and the Habsburgs were glad to render
some small service to their good friends the Hohenzollerns.
Weren't they both members of the same club? In 1871, the
seventh Hohenzollern King of Prussia became the first Emperor
of a United Germany. Forty-seven years later, the ninth King
of Prussia and the third Emperor of modern Germany was forced
to leave his throne and his country and that was the end of a
vast holding company which began as a bankrupt remnant of
crusading orders and finished as the strongest and most efficient
power of the great age of industrialism and capitalism.

But now that it is all over and the last of the Hohenzollerns
is chopping wood in Holland, we might as well be honest about
it and confess that those ex-Tyrolean mountaineers were an astonishingly capable sort of men, or at least were clever enough
to surround themselves with servants of extraordinary ability.

For remember that their original territories had possessed no
natural wealth of any sort. Prussia had ever been a land of farms
and forests and sand and marshes. It did not produce a single
article that was fit for export, the only means for any country
to get a favorable balance of trade.

There was a slight change for the better when a German discovered a way by which sugar could be extracted from beets.
But since cane sugar was still infinitely cheaper than beet-sugar
and could be imported by the ship-load from the West Indies,
all this meant very little money in the pockets of either Prussians
or Brandenburgians. But when the Emperor Napoleon, after
having lost his navy in the battle of Trafalgar, decided to destroy England by means of an "inverted blockade" there arose a
sudden but very steady demand for the Prussian beet-sugar. At
about the same time, German chemists established the value of
potash and since Prussia had large potash deposits, the country
could at last begin to work a little for the foreign market.

The Hohenzollerns, however, were always lucky. After the
defeat of Napoleon, Prussia acquired the Rhine region. It was of
no particular value until the industrial revolution put a premium
upon the possession of coal and iron. Quite unexpectedly Prussia
found herself possessed of some of the richest ore and coal fields
of the entire world. And then at last the hard school of poverty
of the previous five hundred years began to bear fruit. Poverty
had already taught the Germans to be thorough and thrifty. It
now showed them how to over-manufacture and under-sell all
other nations. And when there was no longer room enough on
land for the rapidly increasing number of little Teutons, they
took to the sea and within less than half a century they were
among the leaders of the countries which derive their revenue
from the carrying trade.

Hamburg and Bremen, which had been of considerable importance when the North Sea was the center of civilization (a
position it held until the discovery of America made the Atlantic
the main road of commerce) were called back to life and seriously
threatened the claim to exclusive eminence of London and the

other British ports. A large ship canal was dug from the Baltic
to the North Sea, the so-called Kiel Canal, which was opened in
the year 1895. Canals also connected the Rhine and the Weser
and the Oder and the Vistula and the Main and the Danube
(only partly finished), providing a direct aquatic route between
the North Sea and the Black Sea, and Berlin was given access
to the Baltic by means of a canal that ran from the capital to
Stettin.

Whatever human ingenuity could do to assure the majority
of the people a fairly decent living wage was done, and before
the Great War, the average German peasant and working man,
while by no means rich, and accustomed to very strict discipline,
was probably better housed and better fed and in a general way
better protected against accidents and old age than any other
group of people belonging to the same class anywhere else.

How all this was sacrificed by the unfortunate outcome of the
Great War is a very sad story but it does not belong in the
present volume. But as a result of her defeat, Germany lost the
rich industrial districts of Alsace and Lorraine. She lost all her
colonies, her commercial navy and part of the province of
Schleswig-Holstein, which she herself had taken away from the
Danes after the war of 1864. Several thousand miles of former
Polish territory (but thoroughly Germanized by then) were
once again separated from Prussia and returned to Poland, while
a broad strip of land, following the course of the Vistula and
running from Thorn to Gdynia and the Baltic, was put under
Polish suzerainty, that this country might enjoy direct access to
the open sea. Part of Silesia, which Frederick the Great had taken
away from Austria in the eighteenth century, remained in German hands. But the more valuable mineral deposits were given
to Poland, although the textile interests stayed under German
control.

For the rest, Germany was stripped of everything it had acquired during the previous fifty years and its colonies in Asia
and Africa were divided among other nations which had already

more than their share and no surplus population with which to settle them.

Politically speaking, the Treaty of Versailles may have been an excellent document. From the point of view of applied geography, it makes one despair of the future of Europe. I am afraid that those sceptical neutrals who wanted to present Lloyd George and the late Monsieur Clemenceau with a handbook on elementary geography were not so very far wrong.

XVI

AUSTRIA, THE COUNTRY THAT NOBODY APPRECIATED
UNTIL IT NO LONGER EXISTED

THE present Republic of Austria has 6,000,000 inhabitants and 2,000,000 of these live in the capital city of Vienna. As a result of this extraordinary arrangement, the country is top-heavy and the marvellous old town on the Danube (which is a muddy gray and not at all as blue as the famous waltz might make you expect) is slowly degenerating into a dead city where disheartened old men and women wander aimlessly among the ruins of their former glory, while the younger generation has fled abroad to start a new existence amidst happier surroundings or has committed suicide because life at home had become intolerable. Within another hundred years the gay city of Vienna (one of the few cities where the people seemed to be really happy, if often in a sort of childish and careless way), that old, important center of science and medicine and the arts, will have become a second Venice. From being a capital of an empire containing more than 50,000,000 people it has become a mere village dependent upon the tourist traffic and what little importance it retains as a port of call for the boats that carry the products of Bohemia and Bavaria to Roumania and to the Black Sea.

At present the geography of the ancient Danube monarchy (this name, by which Austria was formerly known, expressed the true nature of the country about as well as anything could do) is extremely complicated, for it has been hacked to pieces in such an arbitrary fashion as to be almost unrecognizable. But the former dual monarchy of Austria-Hungary was a perfect example of how natural conditions will influence the formation of strong centralized states. Forget all about frontiers for a moment and look at the map of this region, which was situated almost in the very heart of the European continent, as far away from the toe of Italy's foot as from the nose of the Danish peninsula. It was really an immense circle of flat lands and rolling territory, entirely surrounded by high mountain-ranges. On the west there were the Alps of Switzerland and the Tyrol. In the north were the Erz Mountains and the Riesengebirge (the Giant Mountains) of Bohemia, and the Carpathians, which formed a semi-circle sheltering the Hungarian Puszta (or steppes) against invasions from the side of the Slavic plains. The Danube separated the Carpathians and their southern part, the so-called Transylvanian Alps, from the Balkan Mountains, and the Dinaric Alps were the barrier that protected the plains from the raw winds of the Adriatic Sea.

The people who founded this state had very imperfect maps and their theoretical knowledge of geography was quite negligible. But just as our pioneers who conquered the West followed certain definite tracks and routes without ever having consciously studied an outline of the road that carried them to their final destination, so did those medieval conquerors accumulate their vast holdings by merely doing what was "immediately practicable" without bothering themselves about the theoretical side of the problem. Such things took care of themselves. Nature provided them with certain unavoidable "consequences" and Man, whenever he is wise, quietly obeys her commands.

During the first thousand years of our era, the great Hungarian plain was a veritable no-man's-land, invaded by all the tribes who followed the course of the Danube on their way from the Black Sea to the west and were without any settled form of government. Charlemagne, during his life-long warfare upon the Slavic people from the east, founded a small "mark" or frontier post, as we would call it, which being the eastern mark or "Oester Reich" (the same word as our Austria) gave birth to the principality that eventually was to dominate that entire part of the world. Although at times overrun by the Hungarians and the Turks (the last siege of Vienna by the Turks took place long after Harvard University had been founded) the little mark, firmly handled and efficiently administered, first of all by the Babenberg family and afterwards by the Habsburgs, our Swiss friends whom I mentioned a few pages ago, always came out on top. Eventually these rulers of a petty frontier state even managed to get themselves elected as Emperors of that Holy Roman Empire, which was neither Roman nor Holy nor an Empire, but merely a loose federation of all the different German-speaking races. They held this title until the year 1806 when Napoleon threw it on the scrap-heap because he intended to put an imperial crown on his own proletarian brow.

But even thereafter these not over-brilliant but tenacious Habsburgs managed to keep a finger—and a most important finger—in the German pie until finally in 1866 Prussia pushed them back across their own mountains and bade them stay where they belonged.

Today the old Eastern Mark, reduced to the rank of a seventh-rate nation, torn by internal strife and without any hope for a better future, consists, for the greater part, of that mountainous region which is but a continuation of the Swiss Alps and which contains the remnants of those famous Tyrolean mountains which were handed over to Italy by the treaty of Versailles on the ground that once upon a time they had been part of the ancient Roman Empire. This mountainous region contains two towns of some importance, Innsbruck, where the ancient route to Italy via the Brenner Pass crosses the River Inn, and where everything reminds one of the Middle Ages, and Salzburg, the birthplace of Mozart, which is one of the most beautiful cities of Europe and which tries to keep alive today by providing the world with a few musical and theatrical performances.

Neither these mountains nor those of the Bohemian plateau in the north produce anything of any value. The same can be said of the so-called Viennese basin where the Romans founded an armed camp called Vindobona (or Vienna), a small settlement which gained some notoriety when the famous philosopher-emperor, Marcus Aurelius, died there in the year 180 after one of his many campaigns against the barbarians of the northern Germanic plains. The town, however, did not come into its own until ten centuries later, when the great migrations of the Middle Ages, also called the Crusades, made it the point of departure for all those who tried to reach the Promised Land by following the Danube rather than by entrusting themselves to the racketeering ship-owners of Genoa and Venice.

In the year 1276 it became the residence of the Habsburg family and the center of their vast domains, which eventually included all the land between the mountain-ranges enumerated a few pages back. In the year 1485 the Hungarians captured the city. In 1529 and again in 1683 the Turks laid siege to it. But the town survived all these misadventures until the beginning of the eighteenth century, when it began to disintegrate as a result of a mistaken policy which entrusted every position of any importance in the monarchy to noblemen of strictly Germanic origin. Too much power is a hard thing for all people, and the amiable Austrian knights were no exception. They ceased to be merely amiable and became feeble and weak.

In the old dual monarchy, 47% of the people were of Slavic origin and only 25% (or one-quarter) were Germans, while the rest consisted of Hungarians (19%) and Roumanians (7%) with about 600,000 Italians (1.5%) and about 100,000 Gypsies who stuck pretty closely to Hungary where they were treated more or less like respectable citizens.

The German "masters" apparently were never able to learn the lessons which the rest of Europe was slowly beginning to take to heart. Monarchies and an aristocracy can only survive as long as they are willing to assume leadership. The moment they begin to talk about "service" instead of "leadership", they are doomed. After the endless defeats of the Austrian armies during the Napoleonic wars, the people of Vienna got into such a state of irritation in regard to their princely and grand-ducal and baronial rulers that they practically forced them to leave the town and retire to their country estates, where they vegetated and got completely out of touch with the rest of the land.

It was then that geography came to the assistance of the city. With the nobility out of the way, the merchants and the manufacturers could at last come into their own. Vienna, freed from its ancient fortifications (they were so enormous that the sale of the land they covered paid for the different extensions of the town), rapidly developed into the most important commercial, scientific and artistic center of eastern Europe.

The World War made a sudden end to both riches and glory. The country now called Austria bears practically no resemblance to the empire of which it was the head until only a few years ago. Its future is entirely behind it. It is a state in name only. The refusal of the French to let it join the German Republic was the last straw.

It might just as well be put up for public sale. But who would want to buy it?

XVII

DENMARK, AN OBJECT LESSON IN CERTAIN ADVANTAGES
OF SMALL COUNTRIES OVER LARGE ONES

DENMARK is such a tiny country, as modern nations go (it has only about three and a half million inhabitants of which 750,000 live in the capital) that we might well pass it by, if quantity rather than quality were of any real importance in the affairs of men. But as an example of what can be made out of indifferent material by the application of intelligence combined with a sensible ideal of life (that "moderation in all things" which the Greeks had proclaimed as the highest form of wisdom) Denmark, as well as the other Scandinavian countries, deserves special and most honorable mention.

For that country with its 16,000 square miles and its total lack of natural resources, armies, navies, mines or mountains (at no point does the country rise above 600 feet, which is less than half the height of the Empire State Building) is worth a dozen other countries of infinitely greater size and more pretentions and militaristic ambitions which I could mention if I felt so inclined. The Danish people, entirely through their own efforts, have lowered the illiteracy percentage to zero, they have made themselves the second richest country per capita of all Europe and they have practically abolished both riches and poverty as they are known in the rest of the world, establishing instead a balance of average, moderate well-to-do-ness which is without an equal anywhere else.

Denmark, as one glance at the map will show you, is composed of a peninusla and a number of islands separated from each other by wide open sounds across which the railroad trains are carried on ferries. Its climate is exceedingly unpleasant. All win-

ter long a strong eastern wind is apt to blow across her flat
fields, bringing cold showers of rain and forcing the Danes, like
the Dutch with whom they have so much in common, to spend a
great deal of their time indoors, a circumstance which has contributed greatly to making them a heavy book-reading nation.
In consequence thereof they are a singularly well-informed
group of people who own more books per capita than any other
nation.

But the rain and the wind keep the pastures moist, and the
grass grows and makes the cows fat, and as a result of all this
Denmark alone is able to provide the world with 30% of its
butter. But whereas in most other countries the soil would be
owned by rich and absentee landlords, the Danes, who are essentially democratic (in the social and economic rather than the
political sense of the word) have never encouraged the development of those vast holdings which we have encountered in most
other countries.

There are today 150,000 independent farmers in Denmark
who operate small farms, ranging from ten to a hundred acres,
and there are only 20,000 farms larger than one hundred acres.
The dairy products which are sent abroad are raised and prepared according to the most modern and scientific methods, as
taught by the rural agricultural schools which are merely a continuation of the free High School system spread all over the
country. The buttermilk that is left over as a by-product of the
butter manufacturing is used to feed the hogs which in turn
provide the entire British market with its bacon.

As this trade in butter and bacon is much more profitable than
the raising of grain, the Danes are obliged to import their grain.
They can do this however quite easily and cheaply, as Copenhagen is only two days by steamer from Danzig, and Danzig
is the old export-harbor for the vast granaries of Poland and
Lithuania. Part of this grain is used for poultry-raising and
millions of eggs are sent each year to those same British Isles,
which for some mysterious reason have never been able to grow
anything more palatable than Brussels sprouts.

Denmark in relation to Norway and Sweden

In order to maintain what almost amounts to a monopoly in farm products, the Danes submit to a most rigorous state control of everything that leaves their country, thereby establishing for themselves such a reputation of absolute integrity that their trademark has come to be accepted as a guarantee of absolute purity.

Like all races of Teutonic origin, the Danes are incurable gamblers, and during the last few years their ventures in banking and in stock-market speculation have cost them a tidy sum of money. But the children and the cows and the hogs remained when the banks closed their doors and now they are at work once more. The only difficulties they have got to fear have to do with the rapidly increasing state of bankruptcy of most of their neighbors, making such a simple dish as ham and eggs a luxury beyond the reach of the average man.

The towns on the mainland are of no importance. On the west coast of Jutland (the name of the old peninsula from which so many of the original settlers of England came) lies Esbjerg, which is the main export harbor for all these many agricultural products, and on the east coast lies Aarhus (the double A is pronounced OA in Danish) which is one of the oldest centers of Christianity in this part of the world where the people continued to worship their heroic Pagan Gods (their Odins and Thors and Baldurs) until only four centuries before the discovery of America.

The Little Belt (I believe there are plans now to build a bridge across it) separates Jutland from Fyen, the first of the big Baltic islands. In the center of Fyen (cows, hogs and children) lies the city of Odense (the place sacred to Odin) where Hans Christian Andersen was born, the son of a poor and sickly shoe-maker, but one of the greatest benefactors of mankind.

Then we cross the Great Belt and reach the island of Zealand, the heart of the old Danish Empire. Here at a wide bay, protected from the violence of the Baltic by the small island of Amager, the vegetable garden of the capital, lies the charming city of Copenhagen, the "Merchants' Harbor" of the Middle Ages.

During the ninth and tenth centuries, when the Danes ruled an empire which included England and Norway and parts of Sweden, Copenhagen was merely a fishing village, and Roskilde, about fifteen miles inland, was the royal residence from which those distant domains were administered; but today Roskilde is of no importance, while Copenhagen has gone on increasing in size and importance until now it provides entertainment for one-fifth of the entire population of the country.

Copenhagen is a royal residence, and a few guards in very handsome uniforms present arms when the King goes swimming or fishing or strolls forth to buy himself a package of cigarettes. But you will look in vain for any other manifestations of military grandeur. This small country, which has done some of the hardest and bitterest fighting in the days gone by, and which even as recently as the year 1864 was able to hold its own against Prussia for quite a long time, voluntarily abolished its army and navy and has replaced them by a small corps of state police to enforce whatever neutrality will survive the next outbreak of a general European conflict.

That is about all there is to say about Denmark. The country peacefully goes its own way. The royal family keeps off the front page of the more sensational newspapers and while few people have three overcoats, none go without, and while only a small percentage has an automobile, every man, woman and child possesses at least a couple of bicycles, as you will know for yourself if you have ever tried to cross a street in a Danish city just before the luncheon hour.

In a world devoted to the idea of bigness, Denmark hardly plays a role. In a world devoted to the ideal of greatness, it would occupy quite a considerable position. For if the greatest happiness of the greatest number of people is the ultimate goal to which all governments should aspire, Denmark has done more than enough to justify her continued existence as an independent nation.

XVIII

ICELAND, AN INTERESTING POLITICAL LABORATORY IN THE ARCTIC OCEAN

FROM the days of her ancient imperial glory, Denmark has retained a few scraps of land, including that sixth continent, Greenland, which seems to contain valuable mineral treasures (iron, zinc and graphite) but which is so completely covered with glaciers (only about one-thirtieth of the whole of Greenland is free from ice) that it may never be of any value to any one unless the axis of the earth shifts just a tiny little bit and allows Greenland once more to enjoy that tropical climate which must have prevailed there millions of years ago, as we are able to deduce from the presence of several large coal fields.

Her other colonies are the Faroe Islands (literally the Sheep Islands) which lie 200 miles north of the Shetlands and have a population of about 20,000 people and a capital city called Thorshavn, from where Hudson commenced his dash across the ocean which carried him to Manhattan. And then there is Iceland. The latter is a country of particular interest. Not only on account of its volcanic nature, which makes it a veritable store-house for all those queer phenomena we usually connect with the mysterious fires from old Vulcan's furnace, but also on account of its political development. It is the oldest republic of our planet with a record of self-government which began some eight centuries before our own and which with only a few short interruptions has lasted until today.

The first settlers of the island were fugitives from Norway who found their way to this distant spot in the ninth century.

Although 5000 square miles out of the total of Iceland's 40,-000 are perpetually covered with glaciers and snowfields, and

What lies underneath

only one-fourteenth of the island is really fit for purposes of agriculture, living conditions there were so much more favorable than in the mother country that already by the beginning of the ninth century there were over 4000 homesteads inhabited by free and independent farmers. And these, continuing the habits of practically all early Germanic tribes, at once established a loose form of self-government. It consisted of an "Althing"— a gathering of the different local "Things" or "moots" (which is really the same word as our "meeting"). This Althing met once a year during midsummer on a huge volcanic plain, called the Thingvellir and situated about seven miles distant from Reykjavik, the present capital, which is only a hundred years old.

During the first two centuries of their independent existence, the Icelanders developed enormous energy, composed some of the best sagas that have ever been written, discovered Greenland and America (five centuries before Columbus), and made this northern island, where in the winter the days are only four hours long, a more important center of civilization than the mother country itself.

But the curse of all Germanic races—an all-too-pronounced individualism which makes political or economic cooperation almost an impossibility—had accompanied the natives on their flight towards the west. During the thirteenth century, Iceland was conquered by the Norwegians, and when Norway became part of Denmark, Iceland followed suit. The Danes completely neglected the island, which henceforth was at the mercy of French and even Algerian pirates until all the old prosperity had disappeared, while the literature and architecture of the heathenish period lay forgotten and the ancient wooden buildings of nobles and freedmen were being replaced by huts made out of peat.

Since the middle of the last century, however, there has been a return of some of the old prosperity and with it a renewed demand for complete independence. Today Iceland once more rules itself as it did eleven centuries ago, although outwardly still recognizing the King of Denmark as its sovereign. The biggest city on the island, Reykjavik, has still fewer than 10,000 inhabitants but is the seat of a university. The total number of inhabitants does not surpass the hundred thousand but they have an excellent literature of their own. There are no villages but only isolated farms where the children are taught and taught well by itinerant schoolmasters.

Iceland

Altogether this is a most interesting little corner of the world. Like so many other small countries, it shows what can be done when intelligence is pitted against unfavorable outward circumstances. For Iceland surely is no earthly paradise. While the winters are not very cold, due to the presence of a branch of the Gulf Stream, the summers are much too short to allow the raising of grain or fruit. And then, it is forever raining!

The twenty-nine volcanoes of which the most famous, the Hekla, has been responsible for twenty-eight outbreaks during the period of which we have any historical record, have covered the island with vast tracts of lava, some of which are over a thousand square miles large. Earthquakes have upon occasion destroyed hundreds of farms and enormous fissures or clefts, running often for miles across the solid sheet of lava, and sulphur springs and lakes of boiling mud make travel from one part of the island to the next a somewhat complicated affair. The geysers or hot-water gushers for which Iceland is so famous are interesting rather than dangerous, for although one of these, the famous Big Geyser, sometimes spouts its boiling water as high as a hundred feet, their activity is steadily decreasing.

And yet people not only live on Iceland but want to go on living there. During the last sixty years more than 20,000 of them have moved to America, chiefly to Manitoba. But many of them have returned whence they came. It rains. And it is uncomfortable. But it is home.

XIX

THE SCANDINAVIAN PENINSULA, THE TERRITORY OCCU-PIED BY THE KINGDOMS OF SWEDEN AND NORWAY

THE people of the Middle Ages, who lived in a happy world of fairy stories, knew exactly how the Scandinavian peninsula happened to have got its queer shape. After the good Lord had finished the work of creation, the Devil came along to see what He had been doing those seven long days He had been away from Heaven. When the Devil saw our planet in the first flush of its young loveliness, he lost his temper and got so terribly angry that he heaved a large rock at Mankind's new home. That rock landed in the Arctic Sea and became the Scandinavian peninsula. It was so barren and bleak that it seemed entirely unfit for life. But the good Lord remembered that a little bit of rich earth had been left behind when he got through fashioning the other continents. These remnants he then sprinkled across the mountains of Norway and Sweden. But of course there was not enough to go around and that explains why the greater part of these two countries has always remained a home for trolls and gnomes and werewolves, because no human being could ever hope to make a living from such a poor soil.

Modern man has a fairy story of his own, but it is a scientific one based upon certain facts which he has been able to observe with his own eyes. According to the geologists, the Scandinavian peninsula is merely the remnant of a very old and very large continent which long before the era of the coal forests had stretched from Europe all the way across the Arctic Ocean to America.

We know of course that the present arrangement of our continents is of very recent origin—that the continents seem to be constantly on the move, like leaves floating on a pond, and that several continents, now separated from each other by oceans and seas, were once upon a time a solid mass of land. When the continent of which Norway and Sweden had formed a part disappeared from view, only the eastern-most ridge—the mountain-ranges of Scandinavia—remained above water. So did Iceland and the Faroe Islands and the Shetland Islands and Scotland. The rest now lies at the bottom of the Arctic Ocean. Some day the roles may be reversed. Then the Arctic Ocean will become dry land and Sweden and Norway will be turned over to the whales and the little fishes.

The Norwegians do not seem to lose any sleep on account of this threat to their homeland. They have other things to worry them. The problem, for example, of keeping alive, which is by no means a simple one when you remember that in Norway less than four percent of the total area (only 4000 square miles) can be used for purposes of agriculture. Sweden is a little better off with ten percent, but even that is not so very much.

There are of course certain compensations. One-half of Sweden is covered with woods and one-quarter of Norway is covered with pine and fir forests. These forests are slowly being cut down, but lumbering is not the devastating business it is with us. It is done in the most scientific way imaginable, for both the Swedes and the Norwegians know that their country will never be any good for ordinary agricultural pursuits. That is the fault of the glaciers which once upon a time covered the whole of the peninsula, from the North Cape down to Lindesnaes. These glaciers scraped the soil from the rocky hillsides as completely and efficiently as a hound dog licking a plate. Not only did they deprive the mountains of their hard earned soil (it takes millions of years to make enough soil to cover such a vast stretch of land) but they carried it away with them and deposited it all over that great northern plain of Europe of which I told you in the chapter about Germany.

The scouts who went ahead of the great Asiatic invasion of Europe of forty centuries ago must have known this. When at

The barren soil of the mountains

last they crossed the Baltic, they found Scandinavia inhabited by a few nomads of Finnish origin. It was easy enough to drive them back into the fastnesses of northern Lapland. But when that had been done, how could the new settlers hope to make a living?

There were several ways. In the first place, they could go out and fish. The endless bays and fjords, which were really nothing but deep grooves dug into the rocks by the glaciers trying to reach the ocean, gave the country a coast-line almost six times as long as it would have been if the Norwegian coast had formed a straight line, as it does in Holland or Denmark. The Norwegians are still fishing. The Gulf Stream sees to it that all the harbors, even as far north as Hammerfest, remain open the whole year around. The nooks and crannies of the Lofoten Islands, on the brink of those cool, clean Arctic waters which the cod seems to prefer for breeding purposes, provide work for more than a hundred thousand fishermen and to an equal number of people engaged in the business of canning whatever the trawlers bring on shore.

In the second place, if they did not care to fish, they could turn pirates. All along the Norwegian coast there lies a row of islands and islets which account for seven percent of the country's surface and which are separated from each other by such

a complicated system of narrows and sands and bights and straits
that a steamer going from Stavanger to Vardö has got to carry
two pilots who succeed each other every six hours.

During the Middle Ages when there were no beacons and
buoys and lighthouses (Lindesnaes is the oldest lighthouse on
the Norwegian coast and even that is of comparatively recent
date) no outsiders would come within a dozen miles of this

Norway

dangerous coast. Although the story of the famous Maelstrom
between two of the Lofoten Islands has been greatly exaggerated, no inexperienced skipper would venture into this watery
labyrinth without at least half a dozen natives to show him the
way. Those pirates therefore who made their own familiar fjord
their base of operations knew that they had little to fear as soon
as they were within sight of the home range of mountains and
they made very good use of this natural advantage. They im-

proved their ships and their fighting technique until they could
venture forth as far as England and Ireland and Holland. Once
they had discovered the road to these comparatively nearby
places, they gradually lengthened their voyages until the people
of France and of Spain and of Italy and of far off Constantinople
began to feel uncomfortable whenever some returning merchant-
man reported that he had seen the dragon of a Viking ship somewhere in the neighborhood.

During the early part of the ninth century they plundered
Paris not less than three times. They sailed up the river Rhine
and got as far as Cologne and Mayence. As for England, different tribes of Norsemen fought each other for the possession
of that country as the nations of Europe of today will make war
upon each other for a particularly desirable piece of oil land.

About the same time that Iceland was discovered, Norsemen
had founded the first Russian state, of which they themselves
were to be the rulers for almost seven entire centuries. Still later,
a plundering expedition of two hundred boats (small boats which
could be carried overland whenever necessary) had travelled
from the Baltic to the Black Sea and had caused such consterna-
tion in Constantinople that the emperor of the eastern Roman
Empire had hastened to take these wild men into his service, as
a special sort of body-guard.

Entering the Mediterranean from the west, they had established themselves in Sicily and on the coasts of Spain and Italy
and Africa and had repeatedly rendered the most valuable services to the Papacy in its wars upon the rest of the world.

What has become of all this glory of the ancient Norse nation?

All that remains today is a highly respectable little kingdom
which catches and exports a lot of fish and engages in the carrying trade and fights bitter political quarrels about the language
the people should speak—quarrels of which the world at large
would never notice anything if the Norwegian authorities did
not have the fatal habit of changing the names of their most important cities and railroad stations about once every two or three
years.

And the Gulf Stream did it

Alaska has 590,000 sq. miles of territory and a population
of 60,000. Norway, Sweden and Finland with only
430,000 sq. miles have a population of 12,000,000

As for those cities of Norway, most of them are merely over-
grown villages where everybody's dog knows everybody else's
dog. Trondheim (formerly Nidaros and then Trondhjem) was
the capital of the old Norwegian kingdom. It has an excellent
harbor and as soon as the Baltic is covered with ice, Trondheim
becomes the port from which a great deal of Swedish wood is
shipped to the rest of the world.

The present capital, Oslo, is built near the ruins of a very old
Norwegian settlement which had burned down. It was built by
the Danish King Christian IV and therefore called Christiania
until the Norwegians decided to purge their language of all

Danish souvenirs. Oslo is situated in the richest agricultural part of Norway at the head of the Oslofjord, which runs into the Skagerrak, the broad sound which separates Norway from Denmark and which is really a branch of the Atlantic Ocean.

Such cities as Stavanger or Aalesund or Christiansand only come to life when the whistle of the nine o'clock steamer blows. Bergen, the old Hansa settlement which looked after the commercial needs of the entire Norwegian coast, is now connected with Oslo by means of a railroad. So is Trondheim with a branch road that leads to the Baltic coast of Sweden. Further up north, well above the Arctic Circle, lies Narvik, the harbor for the Swedish iron ore from Lapland. Tromsö and Hammerfest smell everlastingly of fish. These names occur here because it rarely happens that one finds human beings living comfortably at latitude 70°.

It is a strange land. It is a hard land—a land that has driven hundreds of thousands of its sons and daughters away from its shores, asking them to shift for themselves as best they could, and that nevertheless has somehow or other managed to keep their love and loyalty. Take a boat sometime if you have a chance and travel northward. Everywhere it is the same. Some Godforsaken little village, clinging to a bit of grass, just enough for a single goat, and five or six houses and a few ramshackle boats and one steamer a week and people weeping because they see it again—because it is home—because it is their home—because it is part of their flesh and blood.

The International Brotherhood of Man is a noble dream.

It takes on queer aspects in Bodö or in Vardö, ten days away by steamer from nowhere.

Sweden, the other side of the mountain-range that remained after the great Arctic plateau had disappeared beneath the waves of the Atlantic, is a very different country from Norway. People often wonder why these two nations do not decide to form a single nation. It would mean a great saving in the cost of administration. On paper such an arrangement looks emi-

nently practicable. But their geographical background makes it
impossible. For whereas Norway on account of the Gulf Stream
enjoys a mild climate with lots of rain and little snow (in Bergen
the horses shy whenever they meet a man without an umbrella
or a raincoat) Sweden has a continental climate, with long, cold
winters and a heavy snowfall. Whereas Norway has deep
fjords that penetrate for miles into the interior, Sweden has a
low coast with few natural harbors none of which have achieved
the importance of Gothenburg on the Cattegat. And whereas
Norway has no raw materials of its own, Sweden is possessed of
some of the most valuable ore deposits of the whole world. The

Look at a map of the Arctic and this is all you see

unfortunate absence of coal still forces Sweden to export a great deal of these ores to Germany and France, but during the last twenty years the taming of many important waterfalls has made Sweden increasingly independent of coal while the forests that cover such a great part of the kingdom account for the enormously rich Swedish match trust and the far-famed Swedish paper factories.

The Swedes, like the Norwegians and the Danes (one might say like all nations of Germanic origin except perhaps the English) have unbounded trust in the potentialities of the human intellect. Her scientists are therefore given free scope and as a result her chemists have discovered and developed a large number of by-products which are derived from the wood industry and which otherwise would have gone to waste, such as celluloid and artificial silk. But her agriculture, although much higher developed than that of Norway, suffers from the unfavorable climatic conditions which are the result of being situated on the cold and exposed side of that high mountain-range which divides the Scandinavian peninsula so sharply into two halves. Perhaps that is one of the reasons why the people are so fond of flowers. The winters are so very long and dark. Every Swedish home therefore tries to keep bright with flowers and evergreen shrubs.

In a great many other respects also Sweden is different from Norway. In Norway the feudal system of ancient times died out with the Black Death—that terrible plague of the late Middle Ages which abruptly called a halt to all further Viking ambitions and activities. In Sweden, on the other hand, the continued existence of large land-holding interests has allowed the country nobility to maintain itself up to the present time. And although the country is now being ruled by a socialistic government (like the vast majority of all other European countries) Stockholm is still a city with an aristocratic background, in sharp contrast to Oslo and Copenhagen, where the utmost democratic simplicity is as rigidly maintained as courtly manners are practiced in the Swedish capital.

Perhaps this development too is a direct result of Sweden's

curious geographical position. For whereas Norway faces the Atlantic, Sweden is essentially a country that looks out upon an inland sea and its entire economic well-being, together with its history, is interwoven with that of the Baltic.

As long as Scandinavia was still a half-settled wilderness, there was little to choose between the Norsemen of the western coast and those of the east. To the outside they were all of them "Norsemen" and the famous old prayer, "from the fury of the Norse, good Lord, deliver us," was chanted without specifying what particular sort of Norsemen the humble supplicants had in mind.

But after the tenth century there was a change. Then there arose a great and bitter civil warfare between the Swedes of the north, of Svealand, whose capital was situated on the Mälar lake on which the modern capital of Stockholm is situated, and the Goths of the south or Götaland. They were closely related, these two tribes, and worshipped their Gods near the same shrine, the City of the Gods, which was built on the spot where the town of Upsala rises today, the oldest and most important university town of northern Europe. These quarrels, which lasted more than two centuries, greatly strengthened the position of the nobility while at the same time weakening that of the kings. During this period too Christianity had made its entrance into the Scandinavian peninsula, and the clergy and the monasteries happened to take the side of the nobles (in most countries it was the other way around) until finally the Swedish monarchs became so weak that for a century and a half Sweden had to recognize the sovereignty of Denmark.

Europe had almost forgotten that Sweden existed when in the year 1520 the western world was shocked by the tale of one of the most ghastly and inexcusable murders that has ever disgraced the history of man. In that year King Christian II of Denmark had invited all the heads of the Swedish nobility to a great banquet—a sort of love-feast which once and for all would settle all further difficulties between the King and his beloved Swedish subjects. At the end of the festivities all the guests were

taken prisoner and were either beheaded or drowned. Only one
man of any importance escaped. That was Gustavus, the son of
a certain Erik Vasa, who a few years previously had been beheaded by order of that same King Christian. Gustavus had then
escaped to Germany. When he received news of the massacre
he returned to his native land and by starting a revolution among
the ancient yeomen he finally forced the Danes to return to
their own country, whereupon he himself was crowned King
of Sweden.

That was the beginning of that extraordinary era of national
and international adventure which not only made this small and
poverty-stricken land the champion of the Protestant cause in
Europe but which turned Sweden into the last bulwark against
the ever-increasing threat of a Slavic invasion. For the Russians,
after centuries of oblivion, had at last gone on the war-path and
had commenced that famous march to the sea which has not
yet come to an end today.

Sweden apparently was the only country which recognized the
menace. During two whole centuries all her energies were concentrated upon one single purpose—to keep Russia within
bounds and away from the Baltic. In the end, of course, Sweden
was bound to lose. The struggle completely exhausted her
exchequer and it merely retarded the progress of the Russian
steam-roller by a few decades. When it was all over, Sweden,
which had owned the greater part of the Baltic Sea coast, which
had ruled Finland and Ingermanland (where Leningrad is today), Estonia, Livland and Pomerania, had been reduced to a
kingdom of the second rank, with an area of 173,000 square
miles (something between Arizona and Texas) and a population
slightly smaller than that of New York City. (Sweden has
6,141,671 and New York City has 6,930,446.)

Half of this territory is still covered with forests, which in
turn supply the timber needs of almost one-half of the European
continent. These trees are cut down in the winter and allowed to
lie around until after the beginning of spring. They are then

dragged across the snow to the nearest river and are dumped into the gorge. When summer comes and the ice of the inland mountains begins to thaw, the rivers, turned into torrents, pick up the logs and carry them down into the valleys.

The same river which has thus far played the role of the rail-road now becomes the source of power for the saw-mills, which pick up the logs and turn them into anything desired, from a match-stick to a four inch plank. By this time the Baltic has become free from ice, vessels can once more reach the different parts of the eastern coast, and the finished wood products, which thus far have cost very little, except for the wages of the lumber-jacks and the mill-hands, are now entrusted to the steam-boats, which have continued to provide us with the cheapest form of transportation whenever time is not of primary importance.

These vessels serve a twofold purpose. They would be obliged to go home empty unless they could pick up some sort of return cargo. Of course they cannot charge much for these return cargoes and as a result, Sweden gets most of its imports at a very reasonable rate.

The same system is followed in handling the iron ore which is of such excellent quality that it is in high demand even in countries which have ore deposits of their own. As the country is nowhere wider than 250 miles, it is always comparatively easy to reach the coast. In northern Sweden, in Lapland near Kiruna and Gällivara, there are immense deposits of iron which Nature for some mysterious reason has plunked down there right on the surface of the earth in the form of a couple of low mountains. In the summer the ore is taken to Luleå on the Gulf of Bothnia (the northern part of the Baltic) and in the winter, when Luleå is frozen fast, to Narvik in Norway, which, due to the Gulf Stream, remains open all the year round.

Not far from these iron deposits lies Sweden's highest mountain, Kebnekaise (almost 7000 feet high) and there also stands one of the most important power houses of Europe. It is situated well within the Polar Circle but since electricity seems to be indifferent about geographical latitudes, this station is able to run both the railroads and the machinery of the surface mines at a very small cost.

The southern part of Sweden, which got a little of that soil scraped off by the glaciers of the north, is of course the most fertile part of the entire Scandinavian peninsula and therefore the most densely populated. It has a great many lakes. As a matter of fact, Sweden, next to Finland, is the "lakiest" country in the world; 14,000 square miles of it are covered with water. By connecting these lakes with canals, the Swedes have provided that whole part of their country with cheap means of communication, which greatly benefits not only the industrial centers like Norrköping but also the harbors, of which Gothenburg and Malmö are the most important.

There are countries in which Man has submitted to the dictates of Nature until he has become her abject slave, and there are countries where Man has destroyed Nature so completely that he has lost all touch with that great living mother who forever must remain the beginning and the end of all things. And finally there are those where Man and Nature have learned to understand and appreciate each other and have agreed to compromise for their mutual benefit. If you want an example of the latter, go north, young man, and visit the three Scandinavian nations.

XX

THE NETHERLANDS, THE SWAMP ON THE BANKS OF THE NORTH SEA THAT BECAME AN EMPIRE

THE word "Netherlands", which is only used on very official occasions, means exactly what it implies, a combination of "low" localities situated from two to sixteen feet below the level of the sea. A single good flood of prehistoric dimensions, and Amsterdam and Rotterdam and all the most important cities would disappear from the face of the earth.

But this apparent natural weakness of the country has also been the source of its greatest strength. For among these marshes along the banks of the North Sea it was not sufficient for Man to take hold of the country. Ere he could do that, he was obliged to create it, and in that uneven conquest between human ingenuity and the relentless forces of Nature, the Dutch people were triumphant. It taught them to be hard and watchful. In the sort of world in which we happen to live, those qualities are not without merit.

When the Romans visited this distant and lonely part of Europe (which they did about fifty years before the beginning of our era), the entire region consisted of bogs and marshes protected against the ravages of the North Sea by that slender row of sand dunes which stretched all the way from Belgium to Denmark. These dunes were interrupted at irregular intervals by a large number of rivers and rivulets. Most important among the rivers were the Rhine, the Meuse and the Scheldt. Left entirely to their own devices and not hindered by any dikes, these three rivers did exactly what they pleased, and every spring they altered their course and created islands where no islands

A Polder

had ever been before and swept away vast tracts of land that had seemed as solid as the island of Manhattan. I am not exaggerating. Upon one memorable occasion in the thirteenth century, seventy villages and almost a hundred thousand people disappeared from view in the course of a single night.

Compared to their Flemish neighbors who lived on solid ground, these early Hollanders lived a very miserable existence; but a mysterious change, either in the temperature of the water or the salt percentage of the Baltic, gave them their chance. One day absolutely unexpectedly, the fish known as the herring moved from the Baltic into the North Sea. In an age when all the people of Europe were obliged to eat fish on Fridays and when fish as a staple diet of the human race was of much greater importance than it is today, this meant absolute ruin to a large number of Baltic cities and the sudden rise of a corresponding number of Dutch towns, which now began to supply southern Europe with that dried fish which then took the place of our canned goods of today. Out of the herring fisheries came the grain trade, and out of the grain trade grew the commerce with the spice islands of India. There was nothing extraordinary in this. It was the normal development of a commercial state.

But when fate, regardless of all practical considerations, incorporated the Low Countries into the empire of the Habsburgs and decreed that a nation of lusty peasants and fishermen, without any of the graces of life, but tough-fisted and very practical-minded, should be administered by sour officials trained at the court of an absolute monarch who dwelled somewhere in dignified loneliness among the bleak hills of his windswept Spanish Castle-land, then there was bound to be trouble. That trouble expressed itself in a struggle for liberty which lasted eighty years and which ended with a complete victory for the inhabitants of the Low Countries.

The rulers of the newly-founded state, being practical men of affairs, believed sincerely in the principle of live and let live, especially when it meant a profit to them. They therefore offered their hospitality and their protection to all those who in less fortunate countries were being persecuted for their beliefs, religious or otherwise. Most of these refugees (with the exception of a small group of obscure English dissenters, who however did not stay very long) became loyal subjects of the country that had given them the chance to start upon a new and happier career. As a rule their former masters had deprived them of all their liquid assets and had confiscated their savings. But they carried their old ability with them wherever they went, and they contributed most generously to the commercial and intellectual development of their adopted fatherland. And when the war of independence was over, a million people, living in little cities built on the bottom of some old lake or inland sea, boldly assumed the leadership of Europe and Asia and maintained that position for three generations.

Then they invested their money—bought themselves large country estates, foreign pictures (which are of course always so much better than those painted by the talent at home) and spent their days being respectable. They did their best to make their neighbors forget where the money had come from, and very soon the money forgot to come too. For nothing in this world can afford to stand still, least of all our human energy. And those who won't make an effort to hold what they have got will soon lose all, and that goes for ideas as well as for ducats.

The end came during the beginning of the nineteenth century. Napoleon, who knew only as much geography as he needed to win his battles, claimed that since the Low Countries were merely a delta formed by three French rivers, the Rhine, the Meuse and the Scheldt, the country belonged by right of geological descent to the empire of the French. A large N scrawled at the bottom of a piece of paper undid the work of three entire centuries. Holland disappeared from the map and became a French province.

In 1815 however the country regained its independence and went back to work. The colonial heritage, sixty-two times as large as the mother country, has allowed towns like Amsterdam and Rotterdam to maintain themselves quite successfully as centers for the distribution of Indian products. Holland has never been an industrial country. It has no raw materials except a little coal of very indifferent quality in the extreme south. It is therefore not able to provide its own colonies with more than six percent of all their imports. But the development of the tea and coffee and rubber and quinine plantations in Java and Sumatra and the Moluccas and Borneo and the Celebes demands vast amounts of capital. This fact is responsible for the leading position of the Amsterdam stock-exchange, and the importance of Amsterdam as a place where people and nations go to borrow money, while the necessity of carrying all this merchandise to and from Europe made it possible for the Netherlands to remain fifth on the list of national tonnage.

The tonnage of the vessels used for the trade at home is higher than that of any other country. The country is honey-combed with convenient waterways and the canal-boat is the most dangerous rival of the railroad as it can be operated at a minimum of cost in a country where, until recently, the time element did not play a very important role in the daily affairs of men, women, cows, horses and dogs.

A great many of those canals are really drainage ditches, for one-quarter of the kingdom's territory is no land at all, in the usual sense of the word, but merely a piece of the bottom of the sea reclaimed from the fishes and the seals by endless labor and kept dry by artificial means and perpetual watchfulness. Since the year 1450 thousands of square miles of land have been added to the country by the draining of marshes and by turning lakes into "polders". To make such a polder is really very easy if you know how. First of all, you build a dike around the piece of water you have doomed for destruction and on the outside of that dike you dig a wide and deep canal, which is connected with the near-est river into which it can pour its daily surplus by means of a complicated system of locks. When that has been done, you con-struct a few dozen windmills on the top of that big dike and furnish them with a pumping machine. The wind or a small gasoline engine will then do the rest. When all the water has been pumped out of the lake and has been pumped into the canal, you dig a number of parallel ditches across your new "pol-der" and, provided you keep your pumping-mills and pumping-stations working all of the time, these canals will then take care of the necessary drainage.

Some of these polders are quite large and are inhabited by as many as twenty thousand people. If the Zuyder Zee ever gets dried up (the affair may prove a little too costly, now that every nation is on the verge of bankruptcy) there will be room for at least a hundred thousand more. As fully one-quarter of the country consists of such polders, you will easily understand how it happens that the Dutch Department of Rivers, Canals and Dikes disposes of more money every year than any of the other sub-divisions of the government.

Locks

In strange contrast with the high fertility of this low part of the country, the higher regions of the east, where the central European plain met the sea before the formation of the big, marshy delta of the Rhine and the Meuse and the Scheldt, is of very little use to anybody. For thousands of years it was an unloading station for the boulders and the pebbles of the northern European glaciers. In some ways the soil resembles that of New England, only it is much more sandy and it gives the statistics of the Kingdom of the Netherlands that queer twist which allows a country with a density of population of 625 per square

The dike

mile (France has only 191, Russia 17) to carry a ballast of more than 25% of its total area as "territory which is essentially unproductive". (In France the percentage is less than fifteen and in Germany less than nine.)

And this curiously sharp line of demarcation between east and west and fertile and infertile also accounts for the presence of the more important towns in a single small triangle right in the heart of the polder-land. Amsterdam, Haarlem, Leyden, the Hague, Delft and Rotterdam are so close to each other as to form practically one large city and all of them lie close to the protecting bulwark of those famous sand dunes, at the foot of which the Dutch of three centuries ago began to raise and to perfect the pretty little bulbs of a flower called "Tulipa" which their merchants had brought back from Persia and Armenia.

The city of Athens was only as large as eight New York City blocks. Any wheezy old flivver will carry you from one end of Holland to the other in a few hours. And yet, next to the territory of Attica, this narrow strip of land between the Rhine, the North Sea and the Zuyder Zee has probably contributed more to the sum total of our arts and sciences than any other region of similar diminutive proportions. Athens was a barren rock and Holland was a water-logged swamp. But they had two things in common when they suddenly leaped into fame—an excellent geographic location from the point of view of international commerce, and a superabundance of animal spirits and spiritual curiosity, left over from the days when they had been obliged to fight or perish. And out of these their glory was born.

XXI

GREAT BRITAIN, AN ISLAND OFF THE DUTCH COAST WHICH IS RESPONSIBLE FOR THE HAPPINESS OF FULLY ONE-QUARTER OF THE HUMAN RACE

UNTIL a few years ago this chapter would have been entitled "Great Britain and Ireland". Then Man improved upon the handiwork of Nature and turned a geographical unit into two separate entities. And all the obedient scrivener can do is to follow suit and give each of the two countries a separate chapter. Any other course might lead to far-reaching complications, and I would hate to see the Irish Navy sail up the Hudson River to demand an apology for this "insufferable insult to the national pride of Saorstat Eireann".

Dinosaurs drew no maps, but the rocks remained behind to tell their story. And they are all there—the igneous rocks, volcanic products which got cooled off near the surface of the earth, and the granite, born under pressure, and the sedimentary rocks, slowly settling down along the bottoms of lakes and seas, and the metamorphic rocks, like slate and marble, which were really limestone and clay, changed into more valuable materials by the subtle chemistry of the great depths.

They are all there, lying about in disordered profusion, like the furniture in a house struck by a cyclone. They provide us with a geological laboratory of rare interest. They may account for the fact that England, which usually takes to the shooting of rabbits with greater zeal and interest than to the hunting of scientific facts, has given the world so many first-rate geologists. It may of course be the other way around: because there were a great many excellent geologists, we learned more about the geology of England than of any other country. But that hardly seems likely. Swimming champions are usually found near the water and rarely in the heart of the Kalahari Desert.

And so the geology was there and the geologists were there, and what did they tell each other about the origin of the land of their birth?

Try to forget the map of Europe as you have come to know it today. Imagine a world which has only recently emerged from below the surface of the sea, which is still rocking with the effort

The Atlantic, Ireland, England and Europe

of creation. Picture to yourself vast continents rising high and bleak above the waters, rent asunder by eruptions that crush the rocks as a manhole explosion in New York will split the pavement of the streets. Meanwhile the forces of Nature's laboratory continue their patient labors. Incessantly the winds blow from the ocean carrying billions of tons of moisture on their way from west to east, drenching the land and giving it moisture, covering it with a wide blanket of grass and ferns, arranging for the maintenance of shrubs and trees. Day and night and night and day and year after year after year, the tireless waves beat and pound and grind and file and crunch and rasp until the shores of the land wilt and crumble as the snow melts and crumbles before the rays of the insistent sun. And then suddenly the ice—the slow, merciless wall of death that groaningly hoists itself across the steepest side of the highest mountain-ranges, that rumbles ponderously down the slopes of wide valleys, that fills deep

England, Scotland and Ireland

gorges and narrow ravines with frozen water and pieces of rock from the wasted hilltops.

The sun shines—the rain rains—the ice cracks and creeps—the waves gnaw—the seasons follow each other and when Man at last makes his appearance, this is what he finds. A long narrow strip of land, cut off from the rest of the world by a flooded valley which reaches all the way from the Arctic to the Gulf of Biscay, another high plateau rising well above the waves and separated from the narrow strip by an unruly and choppy sea—a few lonely rocks sticking out well above the surface of the sea, a perching place for gulls rather than a habitat for Man.

That vaguely, very vaguely, was the way England came into being. Now let us look at the modern map and see what that shows us.

From the Shetland Islands to Land's End is the same distance as between the middle of Hudson Bay or southern Alaska and the northern frontier of the United States, or, in terms understandable to the average European, from Oslo in Norway to Prague in Bohemia. That means that England, one of the most densely populated countries in the world, with 45,000,000 people, is situated between the same degree of latitude as the peninsula of Kamchatka (opposite Alaska) which also runs from about 50° lat. to 60° lat., and where less than 7000 people just about manage to keep themselves from starving by living on an exclusive diet of fish.

On the east, England is bounded by the North Sea, which is really nothing but an old depression which has gradually run full of water. Again a single glimpse at the map will tell you more than a thousand words. There on the right (the east) is France. Then we get something that looks like a trench across a road, the British Channel and the North Sea. Then the great central plain of England with London in the deepest hollow. Then the high mountains of Wales. Another depression, the Irish Sea, the great central Irish plain, the hills of Ireland, a few lonely rocks further towards the west, rearing their tops above the shallow sea. Finally the rock of St. Kilda (uninhabited

since a year ago as it was too hard to reach) and then suddenly
down we go, down, down, down, for there the real ocean begins and the last of the vast European and Asiatic continent, both
submerged and semi-submerged, here comes to an end.

As for the different seas and bays and channels that surround
England, I had better mention them in some detail. I have done
my best not to clutter this book with unnecessary names which
you would forget as soon as you had turned to the next page. But
here we are on classical ground, for this strange little island has
influenced the life of every man, woman and child on the whole
of the planet for at least four entire centuries. That, however,
has not been entirely a matter of chance or racial superiority.
That the English have made the best of their opportunities is
undoubtedly true. But Nature had given them a tremendous advantage when she placed their lovely island right in the heart of
the greatest amount of land in the eastern hemisphere. If you
want to realize what that means, think of poor Australia, lost
amidst an endless expanse of water, left entirely to its own devices, with no neighbors, with no chance to get new ideas from
anywhere; and then compare Australia's position with that of
England, which, like a spider in a net, was equally far removed
from all the four corners of the world, yet, unlike the spider,
was safely protected from the rest of humanity by a convenient
moat of salty water.

Of course this peculiar location meant nothing as long as the
Mediterranean was still the center of civilization. Up to the end
of the fifteenth century, England was just another slightly remote island, holding about the same position in men's minds as
Iceland does today. "Have you ever been to Iceland?" "No, but
I have an aunt who went there once. Funny place—interesting
island—but too far away—means five days of seasickness."

That is exactly what England meant to the people of the first
ten centuries of our era—three or four days of seasickness—and
remember, a Roman galleon was even less comfortable than a
seven hundred ton steamer from Leith to Reykjavik.

Gradually, however, the knowledge about these outskirts of

civilization increased. The painted savages who lived in small round huts, sunk well into the ground and surrounded by a low earthen wall, were tamed by the Romans who, listening to their speech, came to the conclusion that they must belong to the same racial stock as the Celts of northern Gaul and who found them on the whole docile and willing to pay tribute without talking too much about their "rights". It was doubtful anyway whether they had any "rights" to the soil they occupied, for it appeared almost certain that they were newcomers and had taken the land away from an older race of invaders of whom the traces could be found here and there among the less accessible regions of the east and west.

The Roman occupation of England lasted, roughly speaking, four centuries, almost as long as the time during which the white man has been the dominating race in America. Suddenly, almost abruptly, it came to an end. For almost five hundred years the Romans had been able to keep the hungry Teutonic tribes out of their European domains. Then the badly defended barriers gave way, the flood of barbarians swept across southern and western Europe. Rome recalled her foreign garrisons. Temporarily, of course, for no empire ever acknowledges itself beaten until years after it has ceased to exist. A few regiments were left behind to guard the high earthen wall which protected the plains of Britain from the invasions of the savages who dwelled among the impassable mountain-ranges of Scotland. Other castles guarded the boundaries of Wales.

But one day the regular supply ships failed to come from across the water. That meant that Gaul had been lost to the enemy. From that moment on the Romans in England were cut off from the mother country and connections were never reestablished. A little later news appeared from the coastal towns that foreign ships had been seen off the mouth of the Humber and the Thames, and that villages in Durham and York and Norfolk and Suffolk and Essex had been attacked and plundered. The Romans had never dreamed of fortifying their eastern frontier because it had not been necessary. But now some mysterious pressure (whether hunger or wanderlust or an enemy in the rear, we shall never know), which had pushed the advance guard of the Teutons across the Danube and through the mountain passes of the Balkans and the Alps, was carrying raiding parties of Saxon pirates all the way from Denmark and Holstein to the shores of Britain.

The Roman governors, the Roman garrisons, the Roman women and children who must have inhabited those charming villas of which we continue to find the remnants, disappeared from view—disappeared as mysteriously and silently as the earliest white settlers along the coast of Virginia and Maine vanished from the face of the earth. They dissolved into space. Some of them were murdered by their own servants. The women were married by kind-hearted natives—a strange fate for a proud race of conquerors, but one that has overtaken more than one group of "colonials" who have neglected to take the last ship home.

Thereafter chaos—and groups of savage ax-men from Scotland and Caledonia, industriously killing off their Celtic neighbors who had grown soft during the centuries when Rome had acted as the national and international policeman. Then the usual mistake made under such distressing circumstances—the bright idea that invariably spells ultimate disaster: "Let us call in a few strong men from somewhere else and hire them to do our fighting for us." The strong men came from the marshes and the plains between the Eider and the Elbe. They belonged to a tribe called the Saxons, which tells us nothing about their origin, for northern Germany was full of Saxons.

Why they should ever have become identified with the Angles is another problem that will probably never be solved. The term Anglo-Saxon was invented centuries after they had made their first appearance upon the English scene. Anglo-Saxon is now a slogan which makes people fight: the Anglo-Saxon blood—the Anglo-Saxon traditions. Well, one fairy story is as good as the next, and therefore if it makes people happy to think themselves superior to all other people, why not? But the historian must regretfully announce that the Angles as a racial unit are the little brothers of the Lost Tribes of Israel—they have often been mentioned in spurious chronicles of the past but no one has ever been able to find a trace of their whereabouts. As for the Saxons, they were about on a par with the hordes of northern European immigrants one might have seen in the steerage of an ocean liner of thirty years ago. But they were strong. They worked and fought and played and plundered with equal zest. They were given five centuries in which to organize the land over which they now ruled as hereditary masters, and during that period they were able to force their own tongue upon the poor Celtic natives, who rapidly lost all recollection of the few Latin words they had picked up while working in the kitchen of some noble Roman lady. Then they in turn were thrown out of house and home by still another wave of Teuton immigrants.

In the year 1066 England became a Norman dependency, and for a third time the British Isles were forced to acknowledge a sovereign from over the seas. Soon, however, the tail was wagging the dog. The British colony proved to be a more profitable investment than the temporary motherland in France and the Normans left the continent and settled down in England for good.

Their final defeat and the loss of their properties in France were a blessing in disguise for the English. They ceased to be forever looking towards the continent and they became conscious of the existence of the Atlantic Ocean. Even so, England would probably not have started upon her maritime career when she did if Henry VIII had not fallen in love with a lady by the name of Anne Boleyn, who informed him that the road to her heart led through a well-lighted church. This had meant a divorce from His Majesty's lawful spouse, the mother of Bloody Mary, and this had caused a definite break between England and Rome upon the subject of the Pope's supremacy over all Christendom. Since Spain took the side of the Pope, England must then learn how to sail ships and defend herself, or else perish as an independent nation and become a Spanish province. In this curious, roundabout way, a divorce quarrel was the real cause which taught the English how to become expert navigators; and having learned their new trade, the marvellous geographic position of their home country did the rest.

The change, however, did not take place without a very severe domestic struggle. No one can reasonably expect one class of society to commit suicide for the benefit of another, and it was no more than natural that the feudal chiefs who had ruled supreme ever since the Norman conquest should have tried to prevent their country from giving up its agricultural habits and going in for commerce on a world-wide scale. Feudalism and capitalism have always been each other's sworn enemies. The medieval knight looked down upon business as something totally unworthy of free men. A merchant in his eyes was something like a bootlegger. You used him but did not allow him to come in by the front door. Trade therefore was mostly left to foreigners, mainly to Germans, to people who came from the North Sea and the Baltic, the famous "Easterlings" who gave

The Factory conquers the Farm

England its first notion of a coin of an absolute and unquestionable value, the "Easterling's pound"—the pound sterling of today. The Jews were expelled and were so rigorously kept out of the country that even Shakespeare can have known his Shylock merely from hearsay. The coastal towns did a little fishing, but the main occupation of the country was and for centuries to come remained the pursuit of agriculture. Nature had greatly favored the land for this purpose, more especially for stock-breeding, for the soil was often too rocky to raise grain, while offering abundant fodder for cows and sheep.

During two-thirds of the year the winds blew (and continue to blow) from the west, which meant rain, as any one will remember who ever was obliged to spend part of a winter in London. Today agriculture, as I told you when we talked of the northern European states, is no longer as absolutely dependent upon Nature as it used to be a thousand or even a hundred years ago. We can't as yet make rain, but the chemical engineer has taught us how to overcome many difficulties which the con-

Great Britain is a country of Lighthouses

temporaries of Chaucer and Queen Bess accepted as acts of God against which there was neither remedy nor redress. There again the geological structure of the island proved a great boon to the landowners of the east. A cross-section of the British Isles shows that they resemble a soup plate, tilted much higher in the west than in the east. It is a result of the fact, mentioned before, that England is part of a very old continent, that the oldest mountains which used to cover the east have been entirely worn away by water and wind, while the younger rock formations of the west are still standing upright and won't be gone before another ten or fifteen million years. These younger mountains which occupy the territory called Wales (one of the last strongholds of some of the original Celtic tongues) act as a fence to break the force of the Atlantic rainstorms ere they reach the lowlands of the east, and they temper their violence so successfully that the great eastern plain enjoys an almost ideal climate for the purpose of raising grain and cattle.

Since the invention of the steam-boat, which allows us to order our grain from the Argentine or Chicago, and since the introduction of cold storage for the purpose of transporting frozen meats from one end of the world to the other, no nation, able to pay the price, is any longer dependent upon its own farms and fields for the purpose of feeding the home population. But until a hundred years ago, the owners of the food supply were also the masters of the world. Whenever they decided to lock the doors of their larder, millions of people died a slow death of starvation. The wide plain formed by the British Channel in the south, the Severn in the west (the river that divides Wales from England and runs into the British Channel), the Humber and Mersey in the north, and the North Sea in the east was therefore the most important part of the old England, for it produced the greatest amount of food.

Of course, when I speak of a plain, I do not mean a plain in the sense of the word to which we ourselves are accustomed. The great central English plain is no flat pancake like Kansas but consists of a rolling landscape. The river Thames (which is

almost as long as our own Hudson, 215 miles against 315) runs
through the heart of it. The Thames takes its origin among the
Cotteswold Hills, famous for their sheep and for the presence
of the city of Bath, where ever since the days of the Romans,
the victims of British cookery have come together to partake of
the hot calcium and sodium baths and fortify their constitutions
by further slabs of underdone beef and half-drowned vegetables.

The Thames then flows between the Chilton Hills and the
White Horse Hills, provides the University of Oxford with
a convenient water supply for its rowing experiments, and finally
enters the lower Thames valley, situated between the low hills
of the East Anglian Ridge and the North Downs, which would
run all the way to France if the strait of Dover had not eaten
its way through this soft chalky substance in its laudable effort
to connect the Atlantic with the North Sea.

It is on this river that the world's biggest town is situated.
Like Rome and most other cities that go back to obscure and
remote dates, the city of London was not an accident or the result of a sovereign's whim. It was located where it stands today
as a result of sheer economic necessity. In order to get from
southern England to northern England without being dependent
upon the proverbially bad good will of the nefarious tribe of
ferrymen, it was necessary to construct a bridge. And London
arises at the exact spot where the river ceased to be navigable
but was not too wide to allow the engineers of twenty centuries
ago to build something that would safely carry people and
merchandise from one shore to the next without getting their
feet wet.

When the Romans left, a great many things were changed
in the British Isles, but London remained behind and today,
with more than 8,000,000 population, it is still more than an entire million ahead of New York. It covers an area five times as
large as ancient Babylon, the biggest city of antiquity, and four
times as large as that of Paris. For London is a city of low buildings. The Englishman, with his insistence upon privacy and his

desire for being allowed to mind his own business, refuses to live in a bee-hive and as a result, London moves horizontally, whereas our American cities have a tendency to move vertically.

The heart of London, the "city", is now merely a workshop. In the year 1800 it still had 130,000 inhabitants. The number has since shrunk to less than 14,000. But every day almost half a million people come down to the city to administer the billions of capital which England, out of her vast surplus wealth, has invested in foreign enterprises, and to supervise the distribution of those almost incredible quantities of colonial products which lie heaped up in the store-houses stretching all the way from the Tower Bridge to a distance of twenty miles below London Bridge.

As the Thames must remain open to traffic all the time, the only way to handle the shipping was by building docks and warehouses along both sides of the river. Those who want to know what international commerce really means should visit these London docks. It will give them the uncomfortable feeling that New York is after all still some sort of a provincial village, a little too far removed from the main highways of trade to be of any special importance. Eventually this may change. The center of commerce seems to be moving westward. But London still is supreme in her knowledge of the technique of foreign trade, while New York is only beginning to learn the rudiments.

But I am running ahead of my subject. I have got to get back for a moment to the English plain of the year 1500. Its entire southern rim consisted of mountains. In the extreme west lay Cornwall, the geological continuation of Brittany from which it was separated by the British Channel. Cornwall is a curious land where the Celtic tongue maintained itself until two centuries ago and where strange stone monuments, in all respects resembling those of Brittany, bear out the theory that once upon a time all these regions must have been inhabited by people of the same race. Cornwall, by the way, was the first part of England to be discovered by the sailors from the Mediterranean. The Phoenicians in their quest of lead and zinc and copper (re-

England enjoys the enormous advantage of being situated in the heart of the land-masses of our planet

member that they flourished at the beginning of the metal age)
used to come as far north as the Scilly Islands. There they
met the savages from the fog-bound mainland and did their
bartering.

The most important city of this whole region is Plymouth, a
military port without much shipping except an occasional Atlantic steamer. On the other side of Cornwall lies the Bristol
Channel, the "Wrong Channel" of the maps of the seventeenth
century because skippers who returned from America were very
apt to mistake it for the British Channel and were then ship-

wrecked among these treacherous waters where the tide may rise as high as forty feet.

North of the Bristol Channel lie the mountains of Wales. They were of no great importance to anybody until the discovery of their coal and iron beds and of the copper deposits of the nearby island of Anglesey which turned that part of the country into one of the richest industrial units of the entire kingdom. Cardiff, an old Roman fort, is now one of the greatest coal centers of the world. It is connected with London by means of a railroad which dives underneath the river Severn. This tunnel has gained almost as much fame in engineering circles as the bridge which connects the mainland of Wales with the island of Anglesey and the island of Holyhead, from where one starts for Kingston, the port of the city of Dublin in Ireland.

This ancient quadrangle of England, where every city and village is so hoary with age and history that I almost fear to mention their names lest I be tempted to make this a geography of England rather than the whole world, has until this day remained the backbone of the land-owning classes. In France, where large estates are not absolutely unknown but rather rare, there are ten times as many land-owners as in this part of Britain. In Denmark the proportional difference is even greater. That this class of county-squires has lost so much of its former importance and now merely survives as a social institution which teaches the rest of the world the correct way to wear golf-breeches and to kill time by killing what are sometimes called "our dumb friends," is not due to any lack of virtue of their own but rather to that sudden change in our economic life brought about by the invention of a practical and workable steam-engine by James Watt. When that mathematically inclined instrument-maker of the University of Glasgow began to play with his grandmother's tea-kettle, steam was still a plaything used to work a few slow and laborious pumps. When he died, steam ruled supreme and land was no longer the source of riches.

It was then, during the first forty years of the last century, that the center of economic gravity, which ever since the begin-

The North Sea

ning of history had lain in the south, moved northward to Lancashire where the vapor of water set the cotton mills of Manchester a-spinning, and to Yorkshire, where steam turned Leeds and Bradford into the woollen centers of the whole world, and to the so-called Black Country where horse-power made Birmingham the breeding-place for all those millions of tons of steel plates and girders which were needed to build the ships that must carry the finished products of the British Isles to the ends of the earth.

The upheaval caused by the substitution of steam for human muscles was the most formidable revolution mankind had ever experienced. The engines, of course, were not able to think for themselves, and they needed a certain number of human attendants to feed them and tend them and tell them when it was time to begin and to stop. In return for such very simple services, the farm hands were promised what to them seemed riches. The country people listened to the lure of the city. The cities grew by leaps and bounds. The contractors for tenement houses grew rich. And within a remarkably short space of time eighty percent of the country population had moved to the towns. It was then that England accumulated that vast surplus wealth which will keep her going long after all her other assets shall have been exhausted.

Many people nowadays are asking themselves whether that point has actually been reached. Time only will tell—time, meaning the next ten or twenty years. But it will be very interesting to see what happens. The British Empire up till now has been the result of a series of accidents. In this it resembled the Roman Empire. The Roman Empire was the center of the Mediterranean civilization and it had to conquer its neighbors in order not to lose its own independence. As soon as England had become the center of the Atlantic civilization, it was obliged to follow a similar policy. Now at last the era of world-wide exploitation seems to have come to an end. Commerce and civilization are beginning to move across the ocean. What only a few years ago was the heart of a vast empire is rapidly becoming an over-populated island, somewhere off the Dutch coast.

It seems too bad. But that is the way things happen on our planet.

SCOTLAND

The Romans knew of the existence of the Scotch as our own ancestors along the Atlantic seaboard knew about the existence of the Five Nations. Somewhere in the north, beyond the last line of imperial block-houses and the last of the Northumbrian hovels, there lay a land of unhospitable mountains inhabited by rough tribes of shepherds and sheep-owners. They dwelled in almost legendary simplicity, counted descent through the mother instead of the father, as all the rest of the world did, had no roads except a few trails almost too steep for a horse, and had resisted all efforts to civilize them with such ferocious violence that the best policy had seemed to be that of leaving them strictly alone. But as they were also formidable cattle-thieves and had a way of suddenly descending from their mountains to steal the sheep of the Cheviot Hills and the cows of Cumberland, it was considered wise to protect these regions by means of a high wall running all the way from the Tyne to the Solway and bid them stay out on pain of death by means of the sword or crucifixion.

This was done, and during the four centuries of Roman domination in England, the Scots, with the exception of a few punitive expeditions, were rarely exposed to the blessings of civilization. They continued their old commercial relations with their Celtic cousins in Ireland, but their needs were few and they rarely came in contact with the rest of the world. The ancient Roman wall is gone but even today the Scots live very much a life of their own, and they have been able to develop a culture of their own.

The fact that Scotland is such a dreadfully poor land may have helped them to retain their individuality. The greater part of their country is mountainous. Long before the appearance of Man these mountains were as high as the Alps. Erosion (wind and rain) wore them gradually away and great geological upheavals did the rest. Then came the ice, the same ice that covered Scandinavia, and the little bit of soil that had accumulated in the valleys was swept away by it. No wonder that only ten percent of the population of Scotland can maintain themselves in the Highlands. The other ninety percent are gathered together in the Lowlands, a narrow strip of land, often not more than fifty miles wide, which runs from the Clyde in the west to the Firth of Forth in the east. In this valley a wide rift between two mountain-ranges of volcanic origin (most of its castles are built on the necks of extinct volcanoes) lie the two big Scottish cities, Edinburgh, the ancient capital, and Glasgow, the modern city of iron and coal and shipbuilding and manufacturing. These two are connected by a canal. Another canal, running from Loch Linnhe to the Moray Firth, allows small vessels to go directly from the Atlantic to the North Sea without being obliged to navigate the difficult waters between John o' Groats and the Orkneys and Shetlands, remnants of the big continent that reached from Ireland to the North Cape of Norway.

But the sort of prosperity found in Glasgow is not the sort of prosperity that makes a country rich, and the average Scotch peasant spends his days getting just a little too much to eat to die of starvation but never quite enough to feel that he is really alive. This has perhaps made him a little too "careful" in spending his few hard-earned pennies but it has also taught him to depend entirely upon his own efforts, upon his own intellectual courage, regardless of what the rest of the human race may say.

The historical accident which made Queen Elizabeth die bestowing the throne of England on her Scotch cousin James of the house of Stuart, made Scotland a part of the English Kingdom. Thereafter the Scotch could enter England at will, and whenever that island proved too narrow for their ambitions they could roam across the length and the breadth of its Empire.

Their thrift and intelligence and their general lack of emotions made them ideally fit for leadership among the provinces in distant climes.

THE FREE STATE OF IRELAND

And now a different story, one of those inexplicable tragedies of human destiny in which a race possessed of unlimited mental possibilities was seen to turn its back deliberately upon the task in hand and to waste its strength in the futile pursuit of some lost cause; while on a nearby island an implacable enemy was ever on the alert, stolidly relentless in its determination to humiliate and enslave those who had failed to learn that an enlightened self-interest is the primary law of existence.

Who was to blame? I don't know. Nobody knows. Geology? Hardly. Ireland, also a remnant of the great Arctic continent of prehistoric days, would have been much better off if during the period of readjustment the center of the land had not sunk so deep below the mountainous ridges of the seaboard, giving the entire country the shape of a soup-plate and making it almost impossible for the few rivers to wend their way towards the sea without developing such a large number of curves as to be practically unnavigable.

The climate? No, for it is not very different from that of England, only perhaps a trifle more moist and a little more foggy.

The geographic situation? Again the answer is no, for after the discovery of America Ireland was the nearest and the most conveniently located of all European countries to engage in commerce with the New World.

Then what? Once more I am afraid it was the incalculable human element which upset all prophecies, turned every natural advantage into a physical disability, victories into defeat and courage into a sullen acceptance of a dreary and not very cheerful fate.

Has the atmosphere anything to do with it? We have all of

If the British Channel should run dry

us heard how dearly the Irish people love their fairy stories. Every Irish play and every Irish peasant tale mentions elves and werewolves and goblins and leprechauns and, truth to tell, in these prosaic days we sometimes get a little tired of their kobolds and pixies and all their whimsical relatives.

Ireland

Wandering again, you will say. What, if you please, has all this got to do with geography? Nothing with the geography that consists of the enumeration of mountains and rivers and cities and vital statistics upon the export of coal and the import of woollens. But man is not merely a tummy in search of food. He has also got a mind and the gift of imagination. And there is something unnatural about this country called Ireland. When you see other countries from a distance, you say to yourself, "There is a piece of land. It seems to be high or flat, brown or black or green. There are people there and they probably eat and drink, are all handsome or ugly, happy or miserable, and they live and die and are buried with or without the benefit of clergy."

But with Ireland it is different. Ireland has an air of other-worldliness or rather un-worldliness. An air of solitude pervades the sky. The loneliness of the atmosphere becomes almost tangible. Whatever was true yesterday is now surrounded by doubt. What seemed so simple only a few hours before has suddenly become complicated. Just towards the west lies the deep abyss of the silent ocean. It is less mysterious than the land at your feet.

The Irish, conscious of their unhappy past, have blamed everybody and everything for that terrible fate which made them a subject race for a longer period than any other nation. But there must have been a quality in their own mental make-up, a subtle defect of perception, which allowed the uninterrupted continuation of conditions that were wellnigh unique in the annals of history. And this weakness, for all I know, may have grown out of that very soil for which they were ever ready to die but rarely prepared to live.

As soon as the Norman conquerors of England had put their recently acquired house more or less in order they cast covetous glances across the Irish Sea which, like the North Sea, is really a submerged valley rather than a bona fide part of the ocean. Circumstances favored their ambitious designs upon this rich island. The native chiefs were forever quarrelling among each other. All efforts to turn the entire island into a single monarchy had failed. To the contemporaries of William the Conqueror, Ireland was "the trembling sod". The country was full of wide-eyed priests eager to bring the blessings of Christianity unto the heathen of all the world, but there were no roads, there were no bridges, there were no means of communication of any sort. All those little elements that are of such tremendous importance in making ordinary daily life more agreeable and more harmonious had been conveniently overlooked. The center of the island, being so much lower than the border regions, was a bog and stayed a bog. For marshes have an unfortunate habit of refusing to drain themselves and when the human soul is filled with poetry, the human hand is apt to neglect washing the dishes.

The rulers of England and France, being mighty sovereigns, were on excellent terms with the powers that ruled the world at that time. Had not Pope Innocent III rushed to the aid of his beloved son John, declaring Magna Charta "null and void" and damning the nobles to perdition who had dared to force their King to sign so outrageous a document? When one of the warring Irish chieftains appealed to Henry II for aid against his more successful rivals (I have forgotten exactly how many there were of them at that moment) certain invisible wires were pulled in Rome and Pope Adrian IV obligingly signed a piece of parchment which granted unto His English Majesty the hereditary lordship over Ireland. A Norman army, composed of 200 knights and less than a thousand other troops, thereupon occupied Ireland and forced the feudal system upon a people who still dwelled amidst the simple virtues and pleasures of a tribal system long since obsolete in the rest of the world. That was the beginning of a quarrel which officially at least did not end until only a few years ago, which even today may break into the front page news with the suddenness and the violence of a volcanic eruption.

For the Irish landscape, like the Irish soul, lent itself ideally to a warfare of murder and ambush, a conflict in which high ideals and low deeds of treachery got themselves so hopelessly intermixed that it looked as if nothing short of the complete extermination of the original natives could settle the problem. Alas, these are no idle words. Upon several occasions the conquerors tried the experiment of wholesale slaughter and deportation, followed by the confiscation of all the worldly goods for the benefit of the King and his henchmen. What Cromwell, for example, did to the Irish after suppressing the rebellion of 1650, when the Irish with their marvellous sense of the unreal and their great intuitive gift for doing the wrong thing at the wrong moment had taken the side of worthless King Charles, is still in the memory of many who were born centuries after that foul crime. As a result of this attempt to settle the Irish question definitely and for all time, the population of the island was reduced to 800,000 and the rate of starvation (the rate of living had never been very high) was raised to such proportions that those who could beg, borrow or steal the money necessary for a short sea voyage moved hastily to foreign shores. The others remained behind, nursing their grievances, tending their cemeteries and living on a diet of potatoes and hope that had to support them until the exigencies of the Great War brought them final relief.

Geographically speaking, Ireland has always been part of northern Europe. Spiritually speaking, Ireland until very recently was located somewhere in the heart of the Mediterranean. And even today, when the island has attained the rank of a dominion and enjoys the same wide degree of self-government as Canada or Australia or South Africa, it continues to be a world apart. Instead of working for a united fatherland, the people have divided themselves into two separate and mutually hostile parts. The southern and Catholic half, containing about 75% of the entire population, enjoys the status of a "free state" and has retained Dublin as its capital. The northern half, usually known as Ulster, and consisting of six counties, inhabited almost exclusively by the descendants of Protestant immigrants, remains a part of England and continues to send its representatives directly to the British Parliament in London.

That is the situation at the moment of sending this volume to the binder. What it will be one year or ten years from now, no one can foretell. But for the first time in over a thousand years, the fate of Ireland is in Irish hands. They now are at liberty to develop their ocean ports and turn Cork and Limerick and Galway into real harbors. They can experiment with those cooperative systems of agriculture which have proved such a success in Denmark. Their dairy products are able to compete on an equal basis with those of the rest of the world. As free and independent citizens, they can at last play their role among the other nations of the world.

But can they forget their past sufficiently well to prepare intelligently for the future?

XXII

RUSSIA, THE COUNTRY WHICH WAS PREVENTED BY ITS GEOGRAPHICAL LOCATION FROM EVER FINDING OUT WHETHER IT WAS PART OF EUROPE OR OF ASIA

As FAR as the American government is concerned, Russia does not exist. Its rulers have been outlawed, its diplomatic representatives are stopped at the frontier, American citizens are warned that if they go to Russia they do so at their own risk and must not count upon Washington to come to their assistance if they should get into difficulties. But, geographically speaking, Russia occupies one-seventh of all the dry land of our planet, it is twice as large as the whole of Europe and three times as large as our own country and it has as many inhabitants as the four biggest countries of Europe combined. Yet we have a minister in Monrovia and in Addis Ababa, but none in Moscow.

For all this there must be a reason. This reason, outwardly seen, is a political one. In reality it is of a decidedly geographic origin, for the Russian state, more than any other country I can think of, is a product of its physical background. It has never been quite able to make up its mind whether it wanted to be a part of Europe or of Asia. These mixed emotions caused a conflict of civilizations, and this conflict of civilizations is responsible for the present condition of affairs. All of which I hope to make clear with the help of a very simple map.

But first of all let us try to answer the question, is Russia a European nation or an Asiatic one? For the sake of argument suppose that you belonged to the tribe of the Chukchi and were living on the shores of the Bering Strait and that you did not

like the life you were leading (for which I would not blame you,
for it is pretty poor pickings in that frozen corner of eastern
Siberia) and suppose that you decided you would follow Horace
Greeley's advice and go west. And suppose that you were not
much of a mountaineer and decided to stick to the flat plains of
your childhood days. Well, you could walk west for a couple of
years without any hindrances except the nuisance of being forced
to swim across a dozen very wide rivers. In the end you would
of course find yourself face to face with the Ural Mountains. But
these Ural Mountains, which on all maps are shown as the
dividing line between Asia and Europe, are not really much of
an obstacle, for the first Russian explorers who moved into
Siberia (fugitives from justice but elevated to the dignity of
"explorers" as soon as they had found something valuable)
carried their boats across the Urals; and you try to carry a boat
across the Rockies or the Alps!

After leaving the Urals, another trek of half a year or so
would bring you to the Baltic. You would therefore have wandered from the Pacific to the Atlantic (for the Baltic after all
is merely a branch of the Atlantic) without ever having left
fairly flat country. And all that country would have been part
of a plain which covers almost one-third of Asia and one-half
of Europe (for it connects with the great German plain which
only stops when it reaches the North Sea) and which suffers
from one tremendous physical disadvantage, in that it looks out
upon the Arctic Sea.

That was the curse of the old Russian Empire, which during
hundreds of years spent most of its blood and treasure upon
costly and useless efforts to reach "warm water"; and it is one
of the greatest handicaps of the U. S. S. R., the Union of Soviet
Socialist Republics (the political successors to the ancient and defunct house of Romanov) which is not unlike a structure consisting of eighty floors and eight thousand rooms, but with no
other means of entrance or exit than two little windows connecting with the fire-escape of the third floor rear.

You are accustomed to think of our own Republic as one of

Europe

enormous proportions, compared to such funny little countries as France or England. But this plain, which flies the Russian flag from one end to the other, is forty times as large as France and one hundred and sixty times as large as England and three times as big as Europe, and it contains one-seventh of all the land of our entire planet. Its main river, the Ob, is as long as the Amazon. Its second biggest river, the Lena, is as long as the Missouri. Of its lakes and inland seas, the Caspian in the west is as large as Lakes Superior, Huron, Michigan and Erie combined. The Aral Sea in the center is four thousand square miles larger than Lake Huron while the Baikal Lake in the east is almost twice as large as Lake Ontario.

The mountain peaks in the south, which cut this plain off from the rest of Asia, rise to a height which compares well with the highest summits of our own continent, for Mt. McKinley in Alaska is 20,300 feet and Mt. Elbruz in the Caucasus is 18,200 feet. The coldest spot on the surface of the earth is found in north-eastern Siberia, and the part of the plain that lies well within the Arctic Circle is as large as France, England, Germany and Spain put together.

In every possible way this region encourages extremes. No wonder therefore that the character of the people who inhabit these steppes and tundras has been so very definitely influenced by their natural surroundings and that they think and act according to a system or pattern which would be considered grotesque in any other part of the world. No wonder that for centuries they were able to practice a most devout form of piety and then suddenly could drop all ideas of God and banish Him and His name from even the curriculum of their schools. No wonder that for hundreds of years they were willing to submit to the rule of a man whom they considered infallible and divinely inspired, to arise one day and destroy him, and thereupon accept the tyranny of an impersonal economic doctrine which may promise to bring them great blessings in the future but which for the moment is quite as cruel and relentless and autocratic as any Czar has ever dared to be.

The Russian landscape

The Romans had apparently never heard of Russia. The Greeks who went to the Black Sea for their grain (remember the story of the Golden Fleece?) just as we do today had there encountered certain tribes of wild men whom they called the "mare-milkers" and who, judging by a few pictures on vases that have come down to us, may well have been the ancestors of the modern Cossacks. But when the Russians made their definite appearance upon the horizon of history, they lived in the square formed by the Carpathian Mountains and the Dniester in the south, the Vistula in the west and the Pripet marshes and the Dnieper in the north and east. To the north, in the Baltic plains, lived their cousins, the Lithuanians and the Letts and the Prussians, for the latter, who have given their name to the leading German power of modern times, were originally a Slavic tribe. To the east of them lived the Finns who are now restricted to the territory that lies between the Arctic, the White Sea and the Baltic, and to the south there were Celts and Germans or a mixture of both.

A little later, when the Germanic tribes began their wanderings through central Europe, they found it convenient whenever they were in need of servants to raid the encampments of their northern neighbors. For they were a docile race and accepted whatever Fate brought them with a shrug of the shoulders and a silent, "Well, such is life!"

These northern neighbors seem to have had a name for themselves which to the Greeks sounded something like "Sclaveni". The dealers in human flesh, who raided the region of the Carpathians to stock up on their living merchandise, used to say that they had caught so many Slavs or slaves, until gradually the word "slave" became a trade-name for all those unfortunate creatures who were the legal property of another. That those same Slavs or slaves should eventually have developed into the largest and most powerful centralized state of the modern world is one of the great jokes of history, but unfortunately, the joke is on us. If our immediate ancestors had only been a little more far-sighted, we would never have found ourselves in our present predicament. As I shall try to explain to you in a very few words.

The Slavs lived peacefully in their little triangle. They bred profusely. Soon they needed more land. The road to the west was blocked by powerful German tribes. Rome and Byzantium closed the gateways that led to the fleshpots of the Mediterranean. There only remained the east and so eastward they flocked in search of further territory. They crossed the Dniester and the Dnieper and did not stop until they reached the Volga, the Big River, the mother of all rivers, as the Russian peasant calls it, because with its superabundant fish-supply it was able to feed hundreds of thousands of people.

This Volga, the biggest of all European rivers, takes its origin way up in the north among the low hills of the central Russian plateau, those same hills which offered such splendid opportunities for the building of fortresses that most of the early Rus-

The old Russian trade-route

sian cities are to be found right there. In order to reach the sea, the Volga is obliged to skirt these mountains and to make a wide circle towards the east. It follows the outline of this ridge so carefully that the right bank is high and steep while the left bank is low and flat. The detour caused by the hills is quite considerable. In a straight line, the distance from Tver, near where the Volga begins, to the Caspian Sea is only 1000 miles. But the road the river actually travels is 2300 miles long. As for the drainage or basin area of this biggest of all European rivers, it beats that of the Missouri by some 40,000 square miles (Volga 563,000 and Missouri 527,000) and it covers a territory as big as Germany, France and England put together. But like everything else in Russia, this river must do something just a little queer. The Volga is an eminently navigable river (before the war it had a fleet of its own of 40,-000 little boats), but when it reaches the city of Saratov it has descended to sea-level. The last hundreds of miles are therefore run below sea-level. This however is not as impossible as it sounds. For the Caspian Sea

Europe: The Continent of coasts, islands and rivers

into which it flows, situated in the midst of its salty desert, has shrunk so considerably that it now lies 85 feet below the level of the Mediterranean. Another million years and it will be a fit rival for the Dead Sea, which holds the record with 1290 feet below sea-level.

Incidentally it is the Volga which is supposed to be the mother of all the caviar we eat. I purposely use the expression "is supposed to be" for very often the Volga is only the caviar's stepmother and the tunny-fish rather than the sturgeon has been responsible for that far-famed Russian delicacy.

Until the general introduction of the railroads, rivers and oceans were the natural routes which people followed in search of trade or plunder. Cut off from the open sea by their Teutonic enemies of the west and their Byzantine competitors from the south, the Russians were forced to depend upon their rivers as soon as they were obliged to look for more free land. And the history of Russia from the year 600 until the present day is forever connected with the two big rivers, one the Volga, which I have just mentioned, and the other the Dnieper. But of the two, the Dnieper was by far the more important, for it was part of the main road that led from the Baltic to the Black Sea, and that was undoubtedly as old as the caravan route that led through the great German plain. Please look at the map and try to follow me there.

Starting in the north we find that the Gulf of Finland is connected with Lake Ladoga (about the size of our Lake Ontario) by means of the Neva, the river on which Leningrad is situated. Then there is a small stream running due south from Lake Ladoga and which is known as the Volkhov, the connecting link between Lake Ladoga and Lake Ilmen. On the south side of Lake Ilmen we find the Lovat River. The distance between the Lovat River and the Duna River is not very great and the country is flat enough to allow people to use it as a portage. Once he had overcome this difficulty, the traveller from the north could then float leisurely down the Dnieper until he finally reached the Black Sea, a few miles west of the Crimean Peninsula.

Trade is no respecter of boundaries and commerce is not very much interested in race. There were profits to be made by those who carried merchandise from the land of the Norsemen to that of the Byzantines and that is why they came to establish themselves definitely in these parts of the world. All during the first five or six hundred years of our era this was a trade-route, pure and simple, and it followed the geological depression between the hills of Galicia and Podolia (the outskirts of the Carpathians) on the one side and the central Russian plateau on the other.

But when this region got gradually filled up with Slavic immigrants, conditions changed. For then the trader became the political overlord and he ceased his endless wanderings and settled down to become the founder of a dynasty. The Russians, with all their brilliant qualities of mind, have never been very good administrators. They lack the more rigid mental precision of their Teutonic neighbors. Their soul is too full of doubt. Their mind is too often upon other things. And they are too fond of talk and speculation to be very good at a game that demands concentration and quick decisions. Hence the comparative ease with which a number of men were able to set themselves up as local potentates. Of course, at first their ambitions did not reach very far. But they needed a place to live. And when they had built themselves a semi-royal residence, they needed homes for their retainers. That is the way most of the old Russian cities came into being.

Cities, however, especially when they are young and vigorous, are apt to attract the attention of the outside world. Missionaries in Constantinople heard of this wonderful new opportunity to save souls. They paddled northward along the river Dnieper as the Norsemen had paddled southward several centuries before. They combined forces with the local rulers. The monastery became the annex of the palace. The stage was set for the Russia of the Romanovs. Kiev in the south and the rich commercial city of Novgorod the Great (no relation to Nizhni-

Novgorod, which is situated on the Volga where the Oka joins it) became so opulent and famous that even western Europe heard of their existence.

Meanwhile the patient peasants continued to increase their numbers as they had done during the last ten thousand years

The Old Russia

and, once more finding themselves in need of more farms, they burst the bonds of their homeland, that fertile valley of the Ukraine, the richest granary of all Europe, and they began to move into the central Russian plateau. As soon as they had reached the highest point, they followed the river that ran eastward. Very slowly (what is "time" to a Russian peasant?) they crept down the valley of the Oka until at last they reached the Volga and founded another New-Town or Novgorod, which was to command the plains that were to be theirs for all eternity.

But "all eternity", in history at least, never seems to last so very long. For early in the thirteenth century the Great Disaster put a temporary check upon all their ambitions. Through the wide gap that lay between the Ural Mountains and the Caspian Sea, the salt-infested wilderness of the Ural River, thousands of little yellow men came trotting westward until at last it seemed as if Asia was to pour its entire population into the heart of Europe. The little Norse-Slavic principalities of the west were caught completely by surprise. In less than three years the whole of the Russian plain, rivers, seas, hills, were all of them in the hands of the Tartars, and it was only a matter of great good luck (an epidemic among the Tartar ponies) which saved Germany and France and the rest of western Europe from a similar fate.

As soon as they had raised a new crop of horses, the Tartars once more tried their luck. But the bulwark of Germany and Bohemia held fast and the invaders, describing a wide circle, hacked and plundered and burned and murdered their way through Hungary and then settled down in eastern and southern Russia to enjoy the spoils of victory. During the next two centuries Christian men and women and children were forced to kneel in the dust whenever they met a descendant of the terrible Genghis Khan and kiss the stirrup of his horse or suffer the penalty of instant death.

Europe heard of this, but Europe did not care. For the Slavs worshipped God according to the Greek rites and western Europe worshipped God according to the rites of the Romans. Therefore, let the heathen rage and let the Russian people become the most abjectly miserable slaves that ever trembled at the crack of a foreign whip, for they were heretics and deserved no better fate. In the end, this indifference was to cost Europe very heavily, for those patient Russian shoulders, which accept whatever burden is put upon them by "those in power", acquired that disastrous habit of unreasoning submission during the two and a half centuries of Tartar domination.

Left to themselves, they would never have been able to throw off that terrible yoke. The rulers of the little principality of Moscow, an old frontier post of the Slavs in the east, were responsible for setting their country free. In the year 1480, John III (the Ivan the Great of Russian history) refused to pay the annual tribute to the master of the Golden Horde. That was the beginning of open resistance. Half a century later, the foreign visitation came to an end. But although the Tartars disappeared, their system survived.

The New Russia

The new rulers had a fine natural feeling for the "realities" of life. Some thirty years before, Constantinople had been captured by the Turks, and the last of the Eastern Roman Emperors had been killed on the steps of the church of the Holy Sofia. But he left a distant relative behind, a woman by the name of Zoe Palaeologa. She happened to be a Catholic. The Pope, seeing a chance of bringing the straying sheep of the Greek church back into his own fold, suggested a marriage between Ivan and Zoe. The wedding took place and Zoe changed her name to

Sophia. But nothing came of the deeply laid plans of the Pope. Instead, Ivan grew more independent than ever. He realized that this was his opportunity to assume the role formerly played by the rulers of Byzantium. He adopted the coat-of-arms of Constantinople, the famous double-headed eagle, representing both the eastern and western Roman Empires. He made himself sacrosanct. He reduced his nobles to the rank of servants. He introduced the old strict etiquette of Byzantium at his own little court of Moscow. He played with the idea that he was now the only "Caesar" left in the world and his grandson, emboldened by the continued success of his house, finally proclaimed himself Emperor or Caesar of all the parts of Russia he was able to conquer.

In the year 1598 the last descendant of the old Norse invaders, the last scion of the Rurik family, died. After fifteen years of civil war, a member of the Romanov family—Moscow nobles of no particular consequence—made himself Czar, and from then on the geography of Russia is merely the reflection of the political ambitions of these Romanovs, who had many positive faults but a corresponding number of such very positive virtues that we may well overlook some of their failings.

For one thing, they were all of them possessed of the fixed idea that no sacrifices were too great when it was a question of giving their subjects direct access to "open water". They tried it in the south and hacked their way through to the Black Sea, to Azov and Sebastopol, only to find that the Turks cut them off from the Mediterranean. But these campaigns assured them the royal allegiance of the ten Cossack tribes, the descendants of the old Kazaki or free-booters, adventurers or runaway serfs who during the previous five centuries had fled into the wilderness to escape from their Polish or Tartar masters. They engaged in a war with the Swedes who had held practically all the territory around the Baltic since their successful participation in the Thirty Years War, and finally, after half a century of fighting, Czar Peter could order hundreds of thousands of his subjects into the marshes of the Neva to build him his new capital of St.

Petersburg. But the Finnish Gulf was frozen over for four months of every year, and "open water" was as far off as ever. They followed the Onega River and the Dwina River right through the heart of the Tundra region—the mossy plains of the Arctic—and they built themselves a new city on the White Sea which they called after the Archangel Michael; but the inhospitable Kanin peninsula was as far removed from Europe as the frozen shores of the Hudson Bay, and the Murman coast was carefully avoided by all Dutch and English skippers. The task seemed hopeless. There remained no other way out than to try the eastern route.

In the year 1581 a band of runaway slaves and adventurers and prisoners of war from half a dozen European nations, all in all some sixteen hundred men, had crossed the Ural Mountains and, driven by necessity, had attacked the first Tartar Khan whom they met on their way east, the ruler of a region called Sibir or Siberia. They had defeated him and had divided his possessions among themselves. But knowing that the arm of Moscow reached far, they had offered this territory to the Czar rather than await the day the troops of the Little Father should follow them to hang them as deserters and rebels, instead of rewarding them as true patriots who had contributed to the glory of their beloved sovereign.

This strange method of colonization was kept up for almost a century and a half. The vast plain that lay stretched out before these "bad men" was sparsely populated. It was fertile. The northern half was prairie but the southern half was covered with woods. Soon they had left the river Ob behind them. Then the Yenisei was reached. As early as 1628 the advance-guard of this unsavory army of invasion reached the Lena and in 1639 they stood on the shores of the Sea of Okhotsk. Further towards the south they built their earliest fortress on Lake Baikal, shortly after the year 1640. They explored the Amur River in 1648. In the same year a Cossack by the name of Dejnev had sailed down the Kolyma River in northern Siberia, had followed the shores of the Arctic Ocean until he reached the strait that separates Asia from America and had returned to tell the tale, which however attracted so little attention that when Vitus Bering, a Danish navigator in Russian employ, rediscovered these straits eighty years later he was permitted to give them his own name.

From 1581 till 1648 is a period of 67 years. When you consider that it took our own ancestors about two centuries to cover the distance between the Alleghenies and the Pacific coast, it becomes evident that the Russians are not always as slow as we are sometimes led to believe. But not content with having added the whole of Siberia to their original holdings, the Russians finally crossed from Asia into America, and long before George Washington was carried to his grave, there was quite a thriving Russian colony around a fort called after the Archangel Gabriel, now known as Sitka, the town in which the formal transfer of Alaska from Russia to America took place in the year 1867.

As far as energy and personal courage and reckless bravery

Eastern Siberia

were concerned, these earliest Russian pioneers compared more than favorably with our own. But the Asiatic conception of Empire that still dominated the minds of those in power in Moscow and Petersburg prevented the normal development of a region where riches of every sort awaited the men who would know how to exploit them. Instead of developing the pastures and the forests and the mines, Russia turned Siberia into a gigantic jail.

The first prisoners arrived during the middle of the seventeenth century, fifty years after Yermak had crossed the Urals, and they consisted of priests who refused to say mass according to the orthodox formula and who were therefore sent to the banks of the Amur to starve and freeze to death. Since then there has never been any interruption of that endless procession of men and women (and ofttimes children) who were being driven into the wilderness because their European sense of individualism had come into conflict with the Asiatic notion of conformity that was the basic law of the old Russian form of government. The peak of these deportations was reached in the year 1863, shortly after the last great Polish revolution when more than 50,000 Polish patriots were moved from the Vistula River to the neighborhood of Tomsk and Irkutsk. No precise statistics have ever been kept of the total number of these involuntary emigrants, but from 1800 to 1900, when the system was slightly modified under heavy pressure from abroad, the mean annual average of exiles was about 20,000. That, however, did not take into account the ordinary criminals, the murderers and petty thieves and pickpockets, who as often as not were shackled to men and women of great spiritual refinement whose only error consisted in loving their fellow-men more than they deserved.

When their actual time of punishment had come to an end, the survivors were given little pieces of land near one of the exile villages and were allowed to become independent farmers. On paper this was a marvellous scheme to get the country inhabited by white men, and it allowed the imperial government to show its European stock-holders that it was really not as bad as it was sometimes painted—that there was some system in all this Siberian madness—the "criminal" was being educated to become a useful and productive member of society. In practice, however, it worked so well that the greater part of these so-called "free settlers" disappeared from the face of the earth without leaving trace of their whereabouts. Perhaps they went to live with one of the native tribes, became Mohammedans or heathen, and bade farewell to Christian civilization. Perhaps they tried to escape and were eaten by the wolves. We don't know. Russian police statistics show that there were always between thirty and fifty thousand ex-convicts on the loose, hiding in the forest or the mountains, preferring any sort of hardship to the prison-yards of the Little White Father. But the imperial flag no longer flies over the Siberian bull-pen. It is now the flag of the Soviets. There has been a new deal. But the cards are the same, and they are of Tartar origin.

What happened to Russia when the old agricultural system of barter and serfdom came to an end and was replaced by capitalism and industrialism is a matter of general knowledge. A few years before Lincoln signed the act of emancipation, the Russian serfs had been set free. In order to keep them alive, they were given a little bit of land, but never quite enough, and the land that was given unto the slave was taken away from the master. As a result, neither the master nor his former servant got enough to be able to pay his way. And all the time, foreign capital was reaching out after the hidden mineral treasures of the vast Russian plain. Railroads were built—steamship lines were organized—and European engineers waded through the mud of semi-Asiatic villages built around a replica of the Paris grand opera and asked themselves whether such things could be.

That primitive barbaric strength that had given the founders of the Russian dynasty the courage to attempt the impossible had spent itself. A weak man, surrounded by priests and women, now sat on the throne of the great Peter. And when he pawned that throne to the money-lenders of London and Paris and accepted their terms which forced him to take part in a war that was abhorrent in the eyes of most of his subjects, he signed his own death-warrant.

A little, bald-headed man, a graduate of the great Siberian school of exile, took hold of the ruin and began the work of reconstruction. He discarded the old European model and he discarded the old Asiatic model. He discarded everything old. He built ever with an eye for the future, but it was still the eye of the Tartar.

What that future will be, we shall know a hundred years hence. Here it is sufficient if we give you a vague outline of the modern Soviet state, but only a very vague one, for the system is in a constant state of flux. The Bolshevists are engaged in an experiment, and they are as ruthless in discarding what proves impracticable as a chemist who suddenly realizes that he has been working according to the wrong formula. Furthermore, the system is so absolutely different from anything to which we ourselves have been accustomed these last five hundred years that it is difficult to reduce it to the usual European or American terminology of statecraft with its continual references to "representative government" and "democracy" and "the sacred rights of the minority". These terms mean nothing to a youngster brought up in a Bolshevist school. He has never even heard of them, except as an example of the folly of his ancestors.

In the first place, the Bolshevist conception of government is not based upon that rule of government of all the people, by all the people, for the benefit of all the people, which we teach our children as the most desirable ideal of statesmanship, whether we quite believe in it or not. Bolshevism recognizes only one class of society, that of the proletarians, the wage-earners, the workers, preferably those who work with their hands. And in order that this class may attain some of the good things of this world from which it has so far been deprived, it has declared a ruthless war upon all those who in any way could remind the

The Great Russian Plain

people of the year 1932 of the old "bourgeois" or middle-class
form of government which was based upon private profit and
private gain.

So far so good. Violent upheavals are nothing new in this
world. Charles of England and Louis of France lost their heads
a long time before Lenin was born. But when they died, a man,
rather than a system, came to an end. When Nicholas II was
murdered, it was not only a man but also the entire system this
man had embodied and represented which was scrapped and
which was forcibly removed from the Russian consciousness.
The old account was closed and two little red lines were drawn
at the bottom of the page. Then a fresh, new page was started
and at the top of it appeared the name, "The Communist Party
of Russia, Inc."

Now Communism as an economic system is nothing new. The
old monastic orders were really communistic institutions and
they in turn were based upon the communism of the early Christian Church, which recognized neither rich nor poor and did not
believe in private property. The Pilgrims, when they came to
America, intended to form a communistic community. But all
these efforts to bring about a more equitable division of this
world's goods had been conducted on a relatively small basis.
They had never touched the lives of the people at large. And
there is where the Bolshevist experiment differs from all others.
It has turned the whole of the Russian plain from the Baltic
to the Pacific into one vast political and economic laboratory
where everybody is supposed to work for just one purpose—
the well-being and happiness of the mass, regardless of the present happiness and well-being of the individuals. But just as in
the older days it was never quite possible for a Russian to rid
himself of that duality of character which had been caused by
the dual nature of his country, half-Asiatic and half-European,
so the new Russian too is suffering from a conflict of enthusiasms
which very frequently defeat their own ends.

The basic structure of the new Soviet Society is undoubtedly
of European origin. The methods employed to put it into action

are entirely Asiatic. Karl Marx and Genghis Khan have joined forces to bring about the Millennium and what will come of this extraordinary experiment I do not know. One prophecy is as good as the next.

But already Bolshevism has accomplished certain results with which the rest of humanity will have to deal very seriously at the risk of seeing its own civilizations go to pieces.

In the older days, Russia was ruled for the sole benefit of a small group of land-owners and supporters of the Czar, just as it had been in the days of the Tartars. It is still being ruled by a small group of people. But now they belong to the inner circle of the Communist party. They are fewer in number than the old-style nobility but even more devoted in their loyalty to the principle of autocracy.

There is however a great difference between the dictatorship of the Czars and that of the Bolshevists. The small group of people who are now governing Russia are not working for their own benefit. They receive such wages as any American plumber or stevedore would sniff at, provided he happened to have work and was receiving any wages at all. And the truly gigantic energy developed by these new tyrants (who are infinitely more ruthless than the Czar's ministers ever dared to be) is directed towards one single object—to make everybody in the world work and to see to it that the workers, in exchange for their labors, are guaranteed enough food, enough living space and every possible opportunity for leisure of the more intelligent sort.

To our western way of thinking, all this is about as topsy-turvy as Einstein's conception of a four or five dimensional universe. But one-seventh of all the land of this planet, a country three times as large as our United States, is now living under this system and it is making itself felt all over the world. It is not being preached by some poor little country like Norway or Switzerland, but by one of the richest nations on earth, possessed of every form of wealth. Pious prayers and angry editorials will hardly upset it because the Russian people are completely cut off from the rest of the world, read very few foreign books, never see any but strictly censored foreign newspapers, and might as well be living on the planet Mars for all they really know about their neighbors. The leaders, of course, are aware of the criticism that is levelled against them, but they don't care. They are too busy doing other things, organizing their White Russian Republics and their Ukrainian Soviet Republic and their Trans-Caucasian Federation of Soviet Republics and their Kirghiz Soviet Republic and their Bashkir Republic and their Tartar Soviet Republics, to spend much time worrying about the approval and disapproval of that western world which they profess to regard as a pathetic historical revival, a nice exhibition for the museum of anti-religion, opened a year ago in the Czar's former palace.

Time will show us what is to become of this strange experiment, this Asiatic mysticism combined with the European sense of actuality. But the Great Russian Plain has come to life and the rest of the world would do well to take notice, for Bolshevism may be only a dream, but Russia is a fact.

XXIII

POLAND, THE COUNTRY THAT HAD ALWAYS SUFFERED FROM BEING A CORRIDOR AND THEREFORE NOW HAS A CORRIDOR OF ITS OWN

POLAND suffers from two great natural disadvantages. Its geographic position is most unfortunate, and its nearest neighbors are its fellow-Slavs of Russia. A real feeling of brotherhood is said to be a wonderful thing, but rarely as practiced between nations of a similar race.

We do not know where the Poles originally came from. Like the Irish, whom they resemble in so many ways, the Poles are intensely patriotic, ever ready to die for their country, but rarely willing to live and work for it. The record of the valorous deeds of their ancestors, as compiled by their own leading historians, makes the earliest Polish heroes stow-aways on Noah's Ark. But when the Poles are first mentioned in any reliable historical document, Charlemagne and his braves had been in their graves for almost two entire centuries. Some fifty years after the battle of Hastings, however, the word Poland began to mean something more than the name of a vague territory that was supposed to lie somewhere in the wilderness of the Far East.

To the best of our present knowledge, the Poles lived originally near the mouth of the Danube, were set upon by invaders from the east, were forced to pull up stakes, and moved westward until they reached the Carpathian Mountains. They thereupon passed through the regions just evacuated by the other great branch of the Slavic race, the Russians, and finally found a safe place of refuge among the primeval forests and the marshes of that part of the great European plain which is situated between the Oder and the Vistula.

They could not possibly have chosen a worse location. A man

The North Pole

sitting on a chair in the middle of the main entrance to the Grand
Central Station enjoys about as much quiet and privacy as a
farmer in this territory, which is in reality the front door of
Europe and the only passageway at the disposal of those who
wanted to go west to conquer the European lands bordering on
the North Sea, or those who wanted to go east to plunder Russia.
The constant necessity of being prepared to fight on two fronts
at the same time, gradually turned every Polish land-owner
into a professional soldier and made every castle into a fortress.
As a result, the military side of life was stressed at the expense
of everything else. And commerce never took hold in a country
where a state of war was the normal condition of life.

There were a few towns but all of them were situated in the
center of the country and along the banks of the Vistula. Krakow,
in the south, has been built where the Carpathian Mountains dissolved themselves into the plains of Galicia. Warsaw, in the
middle of the Polish plain, and Danzig, near the mouth of the
river, depended for their business life on foreign merchants.
Further inland, however, the country was almost empty, for
there were no other rivers until one reached the Dnieper, which
was in Russian territory, and Vilna, the old capital of Lithuania,
never grew beyond the status of a small princely residence.

Such buying and selling as were absolutely necessary were
in the hands of the Jews, who had fled to the outskirts of Europe when the Crusaders in their holy zeal had slaughtered the
inmates of several of the better known ghettos of the Rhine
region. A few hardy Norsemen, such as had founded the Russian
state, might have done the country no end of good. But they
never came to this part of the world. Why should they? There
was no convenient trade-route running north and south or east
and west and there was no city of Constantinople at the other
end of the long trail to reward them for the fatigue and the hardships of their trip.

And so the Polish people were caught between the Germans,
who hated them because, although they were fellow-Roman-
Catholics, they also were Slavs, and the Russians, who despised

them because, although they were fellow-Slavs, they were not Greek Catholics, and the Turks who loathed them because they were both Christians and Slavs.

If the energetic Lithuanian dynasty, which did so much for the country during the days of the Middle Ages, had survived, things might have gone a great deal better, but in the year 1572 the Jagiellans died out and upon the death of the last king the nobles, grown rich during the many years of frontier fighting and enjoying almost despotic rights on their vast but isolated estates, succeeded in turning the country into an elective monarchy. That elective monarchy lasted from 1572 until 1791 and when it was destroyed, it had long since degenerated into a very painful joke.

For the throne of Poland was simply sold to the highest bidder and no questions asked. Frenchmen and Hungarians and Swedes in turn were rulers of a kingdom which meant nothing to them except as a possible source of graft and revenue. When these monarchs omitted to surrender part of their spoils to their henchmen, the Polish nobles did what their Irish friends had done a thousand years before. They called in their neighbors to come and help them "get their rights". Those neighbors, Prussia and Russia and Austria, were only too happy to oblige, and Poland ceased to exist as an independent nation.

In 1795, during the last of the three great divisions, Russia got 180,000 square miles with 6,000,000 people. Austria got 45,000 square miles with 3,700,000 people, and Prussia got 57,000 square miles with 2,500,000 people. This hideous wrong was not undone until one hundred and twenty-five years later. And then the Allies, in their fear of Russia, went to another extreme. They not only made the new Polish Republic much larger than it had any right to be, but furthermore, in order to give Poland a direct outlet to the sea, they established the so-called "Polish Corridor", a strip of land which runs from the old province of Posen to the Baltic Sea and which cuts Prussia into two parts which now have no longer any direct connection with each other.

It takes no profound knowledge of either geography or history to predict what will happen in connection with this unfortunate corridor. It will remain an object of hatred and distrust between Germany and Poland until either country shall have grown strong enough to destroy the other and then poor Poland will become once more what it has always been, a buffer-state between Russia and Europe.

In the first flush of victory it seemed a glorious achievement. But building spite-fences across each other's territory is not going to bring the economic and social problems of our time any nearer to their final solution.

XXIV

CZECHOSLOVAKIA, THE ONLY CHILD OF THE VERSAILLES TREATY THAT HAS MADE GOOD

FIVE years ago I began to write this book. Since then I have had little reason to change my opinion about most of the countries that came up for discussion. If I were rather harsh on them then, what could I say now, when almost all of them are rushing from one mistake and blunder to the next, when revolution and counter-revolution are following each other with increasing rapidity, when dictatorships are destroying the last vestiges of that Democratic Ideal of live and let live that was to be the reward for those four dreadful years of wholesale murder and destruction?

The one country that stands forth as an exception is Czechoslovakia. If ever it was clearly demonstrated that men are infinitely more important than measures, it is in the case of the old land of Bohemia. For the new republic of Czechoslovakia too was an artificial state, a commonwealth created by a stroke of the pen of the Old Men of Versailles. It is true, it was founded upon the ruins of what had once been an independent kingdom. But for so many centuries Bohemia had ceased to function as an independent unit, that most people had forgotten its ancient glory. When several other parts of the former Austro-Hungarian monarchy were added to the Czech nucleus, it seemed that the world was once more to witness the sad spectacle of a man-made community which like all the others would soon become a menace to the peace of Europe.

Today, after it has been thoroughly tried out in the cauldron which the late Georges Clemenceau left us as his sole legacy, it has a much better chance of survival than any of the other nations which made their appearance upon our map when the Congress of Versailles finally rested from its futile labors.

The country started out with one very definite disadvantage. It was entirely landlocked and found itself caught between two powerful rivals, Germany and Poland. And the second menace to its safety was the amalgamation of several Slavonic tribes which had been living separated from each other for almost four centuries and which had gone through entirely different processes of training. For whereas the Austrian monarchy had been either too wise or too happy-go-lucky to destroy all spirit of independence in Bohemia, the Hungarians and the Russians, with their aggressive and narrow minded nationalism, had done everything within their power to retard the cultural progress of those parts of modern Czechoslovakia which had fallen into their hands as the result of the wars of conquest of the previous four centuries.

Hence the highly educated Czechs might very easily have used or rather abused their own superior abilities to turn the Slovaks and the Moravians and the Salicians and the inhabitants of the Carpathian Mountains into a subject race. And, for a while it looked as if Czechoslovakia would also find itself with a "minority problem" upon its hands. But within a short space of time, these difficulties were most successfully overcome. The Slovaks, who were essentially peasant people without ever having enjoyed any of the educational advantages which the Habsburgs had established within the frontiers of old Bohemia, were encouraged to make up for lost time. They were given all the schools they needed. They were also taught the new trade of administration, without which no modern state can possibly hope to survive, and they were readily admitted to the government at Prague, as soon as they had qualified themselves for their new duties. Until today the country offers almost the only example (together with Switzerland) of a European nation in which people with different national backgrounds live in peace and amity with each other, and are also eager to coöperate for a common national ideal. Once their President Thomas Masaryk (himself born in Moravia of a father who was a native of Slovakia) and his able Minister of Foreign Affairs, Edward Beneš, had accomplished this, they had to face a most difficult economic problem.

The old Bohemia had been not only one of the richest agricultural possessions of the ancient Habsburg monarchy but it also had been developed into a highly industrial province with a great deal of iron and coal and a world-famous ability in the difficult art of glass making. Furthermore the industrious Czech peasants had always been exceedingly clever at different forms of home industries (after twelve hours in the fields they must have something to do in their spare hours) and Bohemian rugs and shoes were famous all the world over.

But the old territory into which these products could be imported free of duty—one of the few but very concrete advantages of the ancient Habsburg monarchy—had now been divided into a dozen small and mutually jealous little nations and principalities, each one of which had surrounded itself with heavily spiked tariff walls, not merely in order to protect itself but also in the faint hope of thereby killing as many of its neighbors as possible. And whereas formerly a wagon load of beer from Pilsen (Plzen, if you want to find it on the map) could have been sent to Fiume without being once stopped on the way by customs officers, it must now change cars at three different frontiers (most of these pleasant new nations did not even trust each other with their railroad cars) and it is obliged to pay duty at almost every little frontier station, and when it finally gets to its destination after some four or five weeks (the trip could easily be done in four or five days) the beer has most likely turned sour and is fit to be thrown away.

It is to the everlasting credit of the ruler of Czechoslovakia and of his main advisor that they alone among the statesmen of the new Europe have recognized that such a policy must inevitably lead to suicide, for all the nations concerned, and that they have tried to take the steps necessary to bring about a definite eastern European customs union, which as much as possible shall follow the lines of the old Habsburg monarchy.

Writing this as an American who still believes that a reasonable democracy is the best because also the most human form of government, I sincerely wish that the whole central European muddle could be left to Masaryk and Beneš. A pious hope but a futile one. The only consolation I can possibly find in the present sad state of affairs is the fact that under these two practical leaders Czechoslovakia has now become so well prepared for all eventualities that in case of a conflict it is the only country that is bound to survive. Then, when the final debris is being cleared away, Masaryk and Beneš may be the engineers who can reconstruct that new central European community of interest that is as necessary to our peace and well-being as Austria was to the peace and well-being of the Europe of four centuries ago.

If Masaryk had been born fifty years later, we might even have a chance at a United States of Europe. But in that case there would not now be an independent state called Czechoslovakia. And as it is the only country of eastern Europe that seems to speak the same language as we do on our side of the Ocean, that would deprive us of the one dependable friend in that distant and little known part of the world. Wherefore we had better not indulge in any further useless ifs and should gratefully accept the fact that there is at least one country in central Europe that has come safely through the ordeals and trials of the post-war period and that has not let its national aspirations blind it to the demands of international common sense and decency.

XXV

YUGOSLAVIA, ANOTHER PRODUCT OF THE TREATY OF VERSAILLES

THE official name of this country is the Kingdom of the Serbs, Croats and the Slovenes. Of these three ethnical groups (tribes sounds too much like African natives and might offend them) the Serbs, who are the most important, live in the east along the banks of the Save which joins the Danube at a point where the capital Belgrade has been built. The Croats live in the center between the Drave, also a tributary of the Danube, and the Adriatic, while the Slovenes occupy the little triangle between the Drave, the Istrian peninsula and Croatia. Modern Serbia however is composed of several other racial groups. It has absorbed Montenegro, the picturesque mountain state, famous for its four hundred years of war against the Turks, and affectionately remembered ever since the days we danced to the tune of "The Merry Widow" waltz. And it also has annexed a well-known remnant of the old Austrian Empire, the provinces of Bosnia and Herzegovina, old Serbian territory, but taken away from Turkey by the Austrians, and the source of that ill-feeling between the Serbians and the Austrians which finally ended in the murder of Serajevo in 1914, the immediate (although by no means the real) cause of the Great War.

Serbia (the old habit is too strong—hereafter when I write Serbia I really mean the Kingdom of the Serbs, Croats and Slovenes) is essentially a Balkan state and its history is essentially that of a country subjected to five hundred years of Moslem slavery. Since the war it has a sea-front on the Adriatic, but it remains cut off from its own sea-front by the Dinaric Alps. Even if it could build railroads across the Dinaric Alps (and railroads cost a lot of money) there would be no convenient harbors ex-

Cold

cept perhaps Ragusa (or Dubrovnik, as it is now called), one of the great medieval distributing centers for colonial merchandise. It was the only Mediterranean city which refused to accept defeat after the discovery of the direct ocean routes to America and India and it continued to send its far-famed Argosies (ships from Aragusia) to Calicut and Cuba until a foolish participation in the ill-fated expedition of the Armada deprived it of its last remaining squadrons.

Unfortunately Dubrovnik offers no facilities to modern steamers. As for Fiume and Trieste, the natural outlets for Serbia, the Old Men of Versailles gave one of these cities to Italy and the other one she took for herself, although she really had no need for them as they would only compete with Venice, which aspired to regain its ancient and honorable position as mistress of the Adriatic. As a result, the grass now grows in the dockyards of Trieste and Fiume while Serbia, as of old, must send its agricultural products by one of three routes. It may send them down the Danube to the Black Sea, which is about as practical as if New York should export its merchandise to London by way of Lake Erie and the St. Lawrence River. It may send them up the Danube to Vienna and from there through one of the mountain passes to Bremen, Hamburg or Rotterdam, which is also an exceedingly expensive procedure. Or it may send them by rail to Fiume, where the Italians of course do their best to ruin their Slavic competitors.

In this respect, therefore, nothing has been changed since the days before the war when Serbia was kept a land-locked state at the instigation of the Austrian Empire. It is a bit sad to reflect that pigs were primarily responsible for the outbreak of that terrible disaster. For Serbia had only one great article of export —pigs—and by putting impossible duties on pigs, the Austrians and the Hungarians were able to ruin the only trade from which Serbia derived any profit at all. The dead Austrian Grand Duke was the pretext for the mobilization of all the armed forces of Europe. But the underlying cause of all the ill-feeling in the north-eastern corner of the Balkans was the duty on pigs.

And speaking of pigs, pigs prosper on acorns. That is why they were so plentiful in the triangle between the Adriatic and the Danube and the mountains of Macedonia, for it is densely covered with oak forests. There would be more forests today if the Romans and the Venetians had not denuded these hills in a most irresponsible fashion to get wood for their vessels.

What other resources does the country have to feed and clothe its 12,000,000 inhabitants, outside of pigs? There is some coal and iron but there seems to be already by far too much coal and iron in this world, and it would be very costly to carry it all the way by rail to one of the German ports, and as I have said before, Serbia has no decent harbor of its own.

After the war Serbia got part of the great Hungarian plain, the so-called Voyvodika, which is good agricultural land. The valleys of the Drave and Save will provide it with enough grain and corn for its own people. The Morava valley connecting with that of the Vardar River is a good enough trade-route which connects northern Europe with Saloniki on the Aegean Sea. It is really a branch of the great trunk lines connecting Nish (the birthplace of Constantine the Great and the spot where Frederick Barbarossa, on his ill-fated expedition to the Holy Land, was entertained for a while by the famous Serbian Prince Stephen) with Constantinople and Asia Minor.

But, generally speaking, Serbia cannot look forward to a great future as an industrial state. Like Bulgaria it will have to remain a nation of fairly prosperous Slavic farmers. Who has ever been able to compare a six-foot peasant from Skoplje (or Uskub) or Mitrovitsa to a cockney workman from Manchester or Sheffield will have some doubts whether such a fate is entirely without its compensations. Belgrade may forever remain an amiable little country town like Oslo or Bern, but does it really want to compete in size with Birmingham or Chicago? Perhaps it does. The modern soul is a strange thing and the Serbian peasant would not be the first to have his sound ancestral standard of values upset by the counterfeit cultural ideals of our Hollywood prophets.

XXVI

BULGARIA, THE SOUNDEST OF ALL BALKAN COUNTRIES,
WHOSE BUTTERFLY-COLLECTING KING BET ON THE
WRONG HORSE DURING THE GREAT WAR AND
SUFFERED THE CONSEQUENCES

This is the last of the little principalities that grew out of the
great Slavic invasion of some twenty centuries ago. It would
be more important in size and number of inhabitants if during
the World War it had not taken what ultimately proved to be
the wrong side. But such things will happen even in the best
regulated nations. Better luck next time. On the Balkan peninsula, the "next time", when speaking of war, means a dozen or
half a dozen years hence. We are apt to speak in a slightly contemptuous manner of these half-civilized Balkan people who are
forever fighting among each other. But do we ever realize with
what sort of an inheritance of strife and cruelty and bloodshed
and slavery and plunder and rape and arson the average Serbian
or Bulgarian boy starts out upon his career through life?

Of the earliest inhabitants of Bulgaria we know nothing. We
have found their skeletons, but skulls do not talk. Were they
perhaps related to those mysterious Albanians, the Illyrians of
Greek history, compatriots of the long-suffering Odysseus, that
mysterious race which speaks a tongue unlike that of any other
people on earth, who ever since the beginning of history have
maintained themselves among the Dinaric Alps along the coast
of the Adriatic and who today form an independent state, ruled
over by a native tribal leader who made himself their legitimate
sovereign as soon as a Vienna tailor had provided him with a
nice, new uniform in which to hold court at Tirano, the new
capital of a nation of 98% analphabets? Or is this the home

country of the Romani, who were also known as the Wlachs and who must have spread all over Europe as they also bestowed their name upon Wales and the Welsh and the Walloons of Belgium? We had better leave the solution of that puzzle to the philologists and confess that we do not know.

But when we reach the era of the written chronicles, what endless invasions, wars and calamities! There were, as I have already told you, two main routes leading from the gap between the Urals and the Caspian Sea to the west. One went northward of the Carpathians and led to the impenetrable forests of the northern European plain. The other followed the Danube and by means of the Brenner Pass carried the hungry savages to the heart of Italy. The Romans knew this and they therefore used the Balkans as their first line of defence against that "foreign scum", as they were pleased to call those despised barbarians who eventually were to destroy them. Lack of soldiers gradually forced them to retreat to their own peninsula and leave the Balkan peoples to their fate. When the great migrations had come to an end, not a trace remained of the original Bulgarians. The Slavs had assimilated them so completely that not a single word of the ancient Bulgarian tongue survives in the Slavic dialect spoken by the so-called Bulgarians of today.

The position however of the new conquerors was exceedingly precarious. In the south they had to deal with Byzantium, that eastern remnant of the Roman Empire which was Roman in name only but Greek in purpose and structure. From the north and the west they were forever threatened by raids on the part of the Hungarians and the Albanians. Next the Crusaders passed through their territory, an unholy army of holy men, the disinherited from all nations, ready to plunder Turk or Slav with equal ferocity. Finally the threat of an all-overpowering Turkish invasion and those last desperate appeals to Europe to come and protect the common soil of Christendom against the degrading touch of the infidel. And the sudden hush that spread through the land when fugitives from the Bosporus told how the Moslem Sultan had ridden his horse up the steps of Saint Sofia to desecrate the most holy of all the holy shrines of the Greek church. Followed by the panic when the reddening sky of burning villages told of the steady advance of Turkish troops, marching westward through the blood-soaked valley of the Maritza. And thereafter four entire centuries of Turkish mis-rule. And then, at last, during the beginning of the last century, a first faint stirring of hope. A swineherd in Serbia started a rebellion that was to make him a king. Next that terrible war of extermination between Greek and Ottoman, turned into a major European issue by an English poet who hobbled to his welcome death in the pestiferous village of Missolonghi. And then the beginning of that great struggle for liberty which was to last for another hundred years. Let us be lenient in judging our Balkan friends. They have been the leading actors in the tragedy of man's martyrdom.

Among the modern Balkan states, Bulgaria is one of the most important. It is composed of two very fertile regions, both of them excellently suited to all sorts of agriculture: the plain in the north between the high ridge of the Balkan Mountains and the Danube, and the plain of Philippopolis in the south between the Balkans and the Rhodope Mountains. This valley, protected on both sides, enjoys a mild Mediterranean climate. It exports its products through the harbor of Burgas, just as the sterner products of the northern plain, grain and corn, are sent abroad by way of Varna.

Otherwise there are very few towns, for the Bulgarians are essentially a peasant people. Sofia, the present capital, lies on the old trade-routes from north to south and east to west. For almost four hundred years it was the residence of the Turkish governors who, from their fortified palace on the Struma River, ruled the whole of the Balkan peninsula, with the exception of Bosnia and Greece.

When Europe finally became conscious of the plight of its fellow-Christians, delivered to the mercies of the Moslem invaders, Mr. Gladstone's constituents did a great deal of talking about the Bulgarian atrocities; but the Russians were the first to take action. Twice their armies crossed the Balkan Mountains. The fighting to force the Shipka Pass and to subdue the fortress of Plevna will be remembered as long as people realize that there have been a few wars which were absolutely unavoidable, if the world was ever to progress from slavery to comparative freedom.

As a result of the last of these Slavic relief-expeditions, the great Russo-Turkish conflict of 1877–1878, Bulgaria was made an independent principality under a ruler of German origin. This meant that the patient and intelligent Bulgarian peasants got trained by people with a Teutonic sense of order. That may be responsible for the fact that today Bulgaria has the best schools of all the different Balkan states. The large land-owners have completely disappeared. The peasant owns his own land as he does in Denmark and in France. The illiteracy percentage has been sharply reduced and everybody works. It is a simple country of farmers and lumbermen. It is a veritable reservoir of physical endurance and energy. Like Serbia, it may never be able to compete with the industrialized states of western Europe. But it may still be there when the others are gone.

XXVII

ROUMANIA, A COUNTRY WHICH HAS OIL AND A ROYAL FAMILY

THE list of the Slavic nations of the Balkans has come to an end. But there exists one other Balkan state which none of us, however, is likely to forget, as it has a habit of crashing into the front pages of our newspapers with a frequency that is at times a bit painful. That is not the fault of the Roumanian peasants. They are born and till their fields and die very much as peasants are in the habit of doing all the world over. It is due to the incurable vulgarity and the unspeakable bad taste of that Anglo-German dynasty which thirty years ago succeeded the highly respectable Prince Charles of Hohenzollern on the throne of a kingdom founded by the grace of God, Prince Bismarck and a certain Benjamin Disraeli.

It was in the year 1878 that these two gentlemen came together in Berlin and after paying their duties to the Deity decided to elevate Walachia (the land of the Wlachs) to the rank of an independent principality. If the present reigning family can ever be persuaded to remove itself to Paris, where people do not care how much dirty laundry is washed, as long as it is done with French soap, Roumania may go far, for Nature has been extraordinarily kind to this great plain between the Carpathians, the Transylvanian Alps and the Black Sea. Not only could it be turned into a granary as rich as that of the Russian Ukraine, of which it is the natural continuation, but the richest oil deposits of Europe are to be found near the city of Ploesci, where the Transylvanian Mountains join the plains of Walachia.

Unfortunately, the farms both of Walachia and Bessarabia between the Danube and the Prut are in the hands of large landowners, most of them absentee landlords who spend their rev-

enues in Bucharest, the capital, or in Paris, but never among the
people whose labor makes them rich.

As for the petroleum, the capital invested is usually owned
abroad; and the same is true of the iron deposits of Siebenbergen
or Transylvania, the enormous complex of mountains taken away
from Hungary and given to Roumania in exchange for the more
than highly doubtful services which the latter country had rendered the Allies during the Great War. But as Transylvania had
originally been part of the old Roman province of Dacia, and
had been made part of Hungary as late as the twelfth century,
and as the Hungarians had treated the Roumanians of Transylvania very much as the Roumanians of old Roumania treat the
Hungarian minority of Transylvania today, we might just as
well forget about it. These hopeless and intricate national puzzles can never be solved until every idea of nationalism shall
have disappeared from the face of the earth. At the moment of
going to press there seems to be little chance that such a miracle
will happen.

According to the latest available statistics, the former Kingdom of Roumania counted 5,500,000 Roumanians and 500,000
Gypsies, Jews, Bulgarians, Hungarians, Armenians and Greeks.
The new Roumania, the so-called Greater Roumania, has 17,-
000,000 inhabitants, of which 73% are Roumanians, 11% Hungarians, 4.8% Ukrainians, 4.3% Germans and 3.3% Russians
in Bessarabia and the Dubrudja, the land south of the delta
of the Danube. As all these races dislike each other most cordially,
do not in any way belong to the same ethnographical stock, but
happen to have been thrown together by the artificial decisions
of a peace conference, the material is there for a first-rate civil
war, unless the foreign creditors intervene to save their invest-
ments.

Bismarck once said that the whole of the Balkans was not
worth the bones of a single Pomeranian grenadier. One feels
that in this, as in so many other things, the grouchy old founder
of the last German Empire may have been right.

XXVIII

HUNGARY, OR WHAT REMAINS OF IT

THE Hungarians, or Magyars, as they prefer to call themselves, are very proud of the fact that they are the only people of Mongolian origin who were able to maintain themselves on European soil and to found a kingdom of their own, for their distant cousins, the Finns, were until very recently always a part of somebody else's empire or kingdom. Perhaps the Hungarians in their present misery have stressed their great warlike qualities a little more than was strictly necessary. But no one can deny that as a bulwark against the Turks they have rendered a tremendously important service to the rest of Europe. The Pope recognized the value of this buffer state when he raised the Magyar chieftain, Stephen, to the rank of Apostolic King of Hungary.

For when the Turks overran eastern Europe, it was Hungary which kept them within bounds. They were the first barrier, as Poland was to prove the second when Hungary at last was overrun. Under the leadership of one John Hunyadi, a humble nobleman of Vladic origin, Hungary became in truth one of the few defenders of the faith who was entitled to that name. But those same wide plains on both sides of the Tisia and Danube, which had so greatly attracted the Tartar horsemen that they had decided to settle down for good, were to prove the source of many internal evils.

Wide open spaces make it comparatively easy for a few strong men to dominate their neighbors. For where can the poor peasants go when there is neither sea nor mountains? Hungary therefore became a country of large land-owners. Far removed from the center of government, the land-owners maltreated their peasants so outrageously that soon the latter cared very little whether they were Magyar or Turk.

279

When Sultan Suleiman the Great marched against the West in the year 1526, the last of the Hungarian kings could not collect more than 25,000 men when he tried to stop the Mohammedans. On the plain of Mohács this Hungarian army was completely annihilated. Twenty-four thousand out of a total of 25,000 perished. The King himself was killed, together with all his advisers, and more than 100,000 Hungarians were dragged back to Constantinople to be sold to the slave-dealers of Asia Minor. The greater part of Hungary was annexed to Turkey. The rest was occupied by the Austrian Habsburgs who then began a tug of war with the Mohammedans for the unhappy land until the beginning of the eighteenth century when all of Hungary became part of the Habsburg domains.

Then, however, a new struggle for independence was started, the war against the German masters, and it continued for two entire centuries. The Hungarians fought with reckless bravery, and at last they were able to achieve a semblance of independence by recognizing the Emperor of Austria as Apostolic King of Hungary, and acquiring the status of a dominion.

But no sooner had they obtained what they considered merely to be their own good right than they must start upon a policy of persecution against all those who were not of Magyar blood. This policy was so short-sighted and deprived of common sense that soon they were without a friend in the whole wide world. They noticed this during the Congress of Versailles, when the number of inhabitants of the ancient Apostolic kingdom was reduced from 21,000,000 to 8,000,000 and three-fourths of all its former territory bestowed upon deserving neighbors.

This left Hungary a mere shadow of its old glorious self, a state not unlike Austria, one big city without any hinterland. Hungary was never very much of an industrial country. The large land-owners had had a prejudice against those ungainly chimneys that are an indispensable part of all well-regulated factories and they had not cared for the smell of smoke. As a result the Hungarian plain remained available for the purposes of agriculture, and Hungary today has the highest percentage of agricultural land of any country. Since most of this has always been under cultivation, the people should have been comparatively well off; yet the prevailing poverty has been so great that between 1896 and 1910 the country lost almost a million inhabitants through emigration.

As for the subject races of the old kingdom, the Magyar minority knew so well how to make its subjects uncomfortable that they too moved away by the boatload and the trainful, to help in the development of our own nation. We may as well give you a few figures, for what happened in Hungary happened to a lesser extent in practically all those countries where a small class of hereditary landlords had succeeded in making themselves supreme.

Just before the beginning of the Turkish wars of the sixteenth century, the Hungarian plain was densely populated and had more than 5,000,000 inhabitants. The Turkish domination reduced that number to 3,000,000 in a little less than two centuries. When finally the Austrians had driven the Turks away from the Puszta (the Magyar name for the plains), Hungary was so sparsely populated that immigrants from all over central Europe hastened to occupy the deserted farms. But the Magyar nobles, considering themselves the dominant race, the fighting race *par excellence*, would grant unto those newcomers none of the rights which they themselves enjoyed. The subject races, therefore, who accounted for almost one-half of the total population never were able to feel any real affection towards their adopted country.

Was it any wonder that during the Great War they felt a lack of inner loyalty which in the end caused the dual monarchy to crumble to dust, like an old building shaken by an earthquake?

XXIX

FINLAND, ANOTHER EXAMPLE OF WHAT HARD WORK AND INTELLIGENCE CAN ACHIEVE AMID HOSTILE NATURAL SURROUNDINGS

THERE only remains one more country before we leave Europe. Turkey today retains little of her former European possessions except Constantinople and a small slice of the Thracian plain and we had therefore better save our Turkey for to-morrow. But the Finns are part of Europe, and very much so.

They used to live all over Russia, but the more numerous Slavs pushed them northward until they reached that strip of dry land which connects Russia with Scandinavia. There they settled down, and there they have been ever since. The few Lapps who were living in the forests offered no difficulties, for they moved to Lapland in the Scandinavian peninsula, and were contented to give European civilization a wide berth.

As for Finland, it is unlike any other country in Europe. For tens of thousands of years it had been covered by glaciers. These have scraped the original soil so completely away that today only ten percent of the land is fit for cultivation. The moraines of the glaciers, the stones and the dirt carried down by these slow-running rivers of ice had filled up the ends of a great many valleys. When the great thaw set in, these valleys were filled with water, and that was the origin of those endless mountain lakes with which Finland is dotted. The word "mountain lake", however, should not call forth the image of another Switzerland, for Finland is a low country and rarely rises above a height of 500 feet. The number of these lakes is around 40,000. Together with the marshland that stretches between them, they occupy 30% of the total area of the state. They are entirely surrounded by those valuable forests which cover 62% or two-thirds of the total area and which provide the greater part of the world with the woodpulp necessary for the manufacture of books and magazines. Part of this wood is manufactured into paper on the spot. But Finland has no coal. It has enough fast-running rivers to be able to develop some water-power. But the climate, which is not unlike that of Sweden, turns these rivers into ice for five months of every year, and then the power stations are, of course, unable to function. The wood therefore has to be carried away by ships. Helsinki (Helsingfors until the late war) is not only the political capital but also the chief export-harbor for Finnish lumber.

But ere I finish this chapter, let me draw your attention to an interesting object lesson of what education may do for a people. The granite bridge connecting Scandinavia with Russia was entirely inhabited by people of Mongolian origin. But the western half, the so-called Finnish half, was conquered by the Swedes while the eastern half, inhabited by the Karelians, became Russian territory. After five centuries of Swedish influence and domination, the Finns of the east had become a civilized European nation, superior in many ways to several countries which enjoyed a much better geographical situation. But the Karelians, after an equally long period under the rule of the Russians, who some day hoped to exploit the riches of the Kola peninsula and the Murmansk coast, were exactly where they had been when the Muscovite Czars first insisted upon their submission. Whereas in Finland proper, which did not get in touch with Slavic culture until the year 1809 when Sweden lost this province to Russia, the number of analphabets is one percent, it is 97% in Karelia, which has always been under Muscovite influence. Yet the two people are the same and probably have the same natural ability for spelling c-a-t cat and t-a-i-l tail.

XXX

THE DISCOVERY OF ASIA

Two thousand years ago the Greek geographers were fighting among themselves about the original meaning of the word Asia. So there is no use in trying to solve the problem today. The theory that the word *Ereb* or "darkness" was the name which the sailors from Asia Minor had bestowed upon the land in the west where the sun went down and *Açu* or "glorious" upon the land in the east where the sun arose seems to be as good or as bad as any other.

Then we come to the next point, which is of greater importance. How and when did the people of Europe begin to suspect that they were not the center of the world? That their own home was but the small peninsula of an infinitely larger piece of land inhabited by ever so many more people, many of whom enjoyed a much higher degree of civilization, so that the Trojan heroes were fighting each other with weapons of such prehistoric shape that the intelligent Chinese had long since placed them in their museums of obsolete historical curiosities?

Usually Marco Polo is mentioned as the first European to visit Asia, but there had been others before him, although we know very little definite about them. As has happened so often in the realm of geography, it was war rather than peace which widened our knowledge of the Asiatic map. The chance to do business with the people over seas made the Greeks familiar with Asia Minor. The Trojan war was not without its educational side. The three great Persian expeditions against the west helped matters along very nicely. I doubt whether the Persians knew where they were going. Did the Greeks mean much more to them than the Indians of the west meant to General Braddock when

284

The Great Asiatic-European Plain

he moved into the wilderness to attack Fort Duquesne? I doubt
it. The return visit of Alexander the Great, a couple of centuries
later, was already something more than a mere military campaign, and Europe got its first scientific ideas about the territory
lying between the Mediterranean and the Indian Ocean.

The Romans were by far too much pleased with themselves
to take a really serious interest in "foreign" lands. As a source
of revenue, to allow them to live a more luxurious existence at

Asia

home, all foreign countries were grist to their mill. But the people whom they administered meant nothing to them whatsoever. Provided they paid their taxes and worked on the roads, they could live and die and quarrel among themselves as they pleased. They never even tried to understand what happened around them. In a crisis they called for the guards, did enough shooting to reestablish order, and washed their hands of the whole affair.

Pontius Pilate was neither a weakling nor a scoundrel. He was merely a typical Roman colonial administrator with a good record for "regularity" and highly commended by those at home for his beautiful ignorance about the natives entrusted to his care. Once in a while some queer person like Marcus Aurelius would come to the throne, who derived a positive pleasure from sending a diplomatic mission to the mysterious, slant-eyed people of the Far East. When they returned and told of the strange things they had seen, they were a seven days' wonder. Then the Roman mob tired of them and went back to the exciting daily shows of the Colosseum.

The Crusades taught Europe a few things about Asia Minor, Palestine and Egypt, but the world continued to end on the eastern shores of the Dead Sea.

The story which finally made Europe "Asia-conscious" was not the result of a serious "scientific" expedition, but was due to the labors of a hack-writer who had never set eyes upon the countries of which he wrote, a poor penny-a-liner looking for a subject that might prove popular.

The father and uncle of Marco Polo were Venetian merchants whose business dealings had brought them into contact with Kublai Khan, the grandson of Genghis Khan. Kublai Khan happened to be a man of great intelligence who thought that his people would be benefited by the introduction of a certain amount of western efficiency. He had heard that two Venetians occasionally visited Bokhara, a country in Turkestan between the Amu-Darya and the Syr-Darya at the foot of the Altai Mountains. He invited them to come to Peking. They went and were received with great honors. After several years they decided that their families needed them. The Khan bade them go home for a while and return and bring their bright young son and nephew Marco, about whom they had been talking so much.

In the year 1275, after a trip of three and a half years, the Polo family returned to Peking. Young Marco was all he had been said to be. He became a favorite at the court of Peking, was made governor of a province, received titles and honors, but after two dozen years he got homesick and so returned to Venice by way of India (he did that part of the voyage on ship-board) and Persia and Syria.

His neighbors, not in the least interested in tall stories, nick-named him Marco Millions, for he was forever telling them how rich the Khan was and how many golden statues there were in this temple or that, and how many silken gowns the concubines of such and such a prime-minister owned. Why should they believe such yarns, when it was well-known that even the wife of the Emperor of Constantinople had only a single pair of silk stockings?

And Marco Millions might have died and his story might have died with him if Venice and Genoa had not engaged in one of their little quarrels just then, and if Marco, as commander of a Venetian galley, had not been taken prisoner by the victorious Genoese. He remained in prison for a year, sharing his cell with a citizen from Pisa by the name of Rusticiano. This Rusticiano had had some experience as a writer. He had popularized a number of Arthurian tales and cheap French novels, the Nick Carter stuff of the Middle Ages. He quickly recognized the publicity value of the great Polo story, and during their time in jail he pumped Marco dry for information. Taking down everything Marco told him, he gave the world a book which is read quite as much today as when it was first published in the fourteenth century.

What probably gave the book its success was its constant references to gold and to riches of all sorts. The Romans and the Greeks had vaguely spoken of the opulence of eastern potentates but Polo had been on the spot, had seen all these things with his own eyes. The efforts to find a short-cut to the Indies really date from that time. But the task was difficult.

Finally in 1498 the Portuguese got as far as the Cape of Good Hope. Ten years later they were in India. Forty years later they were in Japan. Meanwhile Magellan, coming from the east, had reached the Philippine Islands, and by that time the exploitation of southern Asia was in full swing.

So much for the general outline. How Siberia was discovered, I have already told. The first visitors to the other countries will be given honorable mention when we get to them.

XXXI

WHAT ASIA HAS MEANT TO THE REST OF THE WORLD

EUROPE gave us our civilization but Asia gave us our religion. What is even more interesting, Asia gave the world the three great monotheistic religions which now dominate mankind. Judaism, Christianity and Mohammedanism are all of Asiatic origin. It is curious to reflect that when the Inquisitioners were burning their Jews, both the executioners and their victims were appealing to deities of Asiatic origin; that when the Crusaders were killing the Mohammedans and vice versa, it was a conflict of two Asiatic creeds which bade them do murder upon each other; and that whenever a Christian missionary gets into a dispute with a follower of Confucius, the two are merely engaged in a purely Asiatic exchange of opinions.

But Asia did not only give us our religious beliefs. It also gave us the fundamentals upon which we have constructed the entire fabric of civilization. In the pride of our recent technical inventions, we may loudly boast of "our great western progress" (we occasionally do), but that much vaunted progress of the west is merely a continuation of the progress that was begun in the east. It is highly doubtful whether the west would have been able to do anything at all if it had not learned the rudiments of everything it knows in the schools of the east.

The knowledge of the Greeks was not the result of cerebral spontaneous combustion. Mathematics and astronomy and architecture and medicine did not, like Pallas Athene, jump forth from the head of Zeus, armed from head to foot, ready for the glorious battle upon human stupidity. They were the result of slow and painful and deliberate growth, and the real pioneering work was done along the banks of the Euphrates and the Tigris.

From Babylon the arts and sciences then travelled to Africa. Here the dark-skinned Egyptians took them in hand until the Greeks had at last reached a sufficiently high degree of civilization to appreciate the beauty of a geometrical problem and the loveliness of a perfectly balanced equation. From that moment on, we can speak of a truly "European" science. But that truly "European" science had had an Asiatic ancestor who had lived and prospered more than 2000 years before.

And Asia bestowed further blessings upon us. The domestic animals, the dog and the cat and the useful quadrupeds, the docile cow and the faithful horse, together with the sheep and the hog, were all of them of Asiatic origin. When we think of the role played by these useful creatures during the era before the invention of the steam-engine, we begin to realize the debt we owe to Asia. To which we must add the greater part of our bill-of-fare, for practically all of our fruits and vegetables, most of our flowers and practically all of our poultry is of Asiatic origin and was brought to Europe by the Greeks, the Romans or the Crusaders.

Asia, however, was not always a Lady Bountiful from the east, carrying rich blessings from the banks of the Ganges and the Yellow River to the poor barbarians of the west. Asia could also be a terrible taskmaster. The Huns, who during the fifth century ravaged central Europe, were of Asiatic origin. The Tartars, who followed them seven centuries later and turned Russia into an Asiatic dependency to the everlasting detriment of all the other European nations, hailed from the desert regions of central Asia. The Turks, who during five long centuries caused so much bloodshed and misery and made eastern Europe into what it is today, were an Asiatic tribe. And another hundred years may see a united Asia once more upon the warpath and eager to repay us for some of the things we have done to her children since Berthold Schwartz invented his gunpowder.

XXXII

THE CENTRAL ASIATIC HIGHLANDS

THE 17,000,000 square miles of Asia are divided into five unequal parts.

First of all, and nearest to the Arctic, lies the great plain which I have already mentioned when I spoke of Russia. Next come the central highlands. Then the high plateaus of the south-west. Next the peninsulas of the south; and finally the peninsulas of the east. As I have already described the great Arctic plain, I can continue at once with the second part of the program.

The central Asiatic highlands begin rather mildly with a series of low mountain chains which form more or less parallel lines running invariably from east to west or from south-east to north-west, but never from north to south. In many places, however, the crust of the earth has been badly broken and twisted and folded and tortured by great volcanic upheavals. Thus we get the irregular contours of the Yablonoi Mountains east of Lake Baikal, the Khangai and Altai Mountains west of Baikal, and the Tien-shan Mountains just east of the Balkash Lake. To the west of these mountains are the plains. To the east lies the high plateau of Mongolia where the Gobi desert is situated, the home of the ancestors of Genghis Khan.

West of the Gobi desert lies the slightly lower plateau of east Turkestan. It is the valley of the Pamir River, which aimlessly loses itself in the nearby lake of Lob-nor, famous through the discoveries of the Swedish traveller, Sven Hedin. On the map the Pamir looks like a small desert brook. Yet it is one and a half times as long as the Rhine. For remember, Asia is the country of the gigantic proportions.

Just north of Turkestan there is a gap between the Altai and

Tien-shan Mountains. It is the land mentioned on our atlases as Jungaria, and it leads up to the Khirgiz steppes. It consists of an enormous valley which was the gateway through which all the desert tribes, the Huns, the Tartars and the Turks, started upon their marauding expeditions against Europe.

South of the Tarim basin, due south-west to be more accurate, the landscape becomes exceedingly complicated. The Tarim basin is cut off from the valley of the Oxus or the Amu-Darya (which loses itself in the Aral Sea) by a high plateau, the Plateau of Pamir, also called the Roof of the World. The Pamir Mountains, already known to the Greeks, were on the direct route from Asia Minor and Mesopotamia to China. They were a good deal of a barrier but could be crossed by a number of mountain passes. These passes average between 15,000 and 16,000 feet in height. Remember that Mount Ranier is only a little over 14,000 feet high, Mont Blanc a little over 15,000 feet. Then you get some idea of a mountainous territory where the passes lie at a higher altitude than the highest mountain tops of America and Europe, where the mountains themselves therefore dwarf anything we ourselves have to offer in the shape of crinkled globe-crust.

But the Pamir plateau is merely a beginning. It is a sort of terminal from which the big mountain-ranges radiate in all directions. There is the Tien-shan range, which I have already mentioned, running northward. There is the Kuen-lun range, which cuts Tibet off from the Tarim basin. There is the Karakoram, which is short but very, very steep; and finally we have the Himalaya range, which in the south cuts Tibet off from India and which breaks all records for "highest above sea-level", with altitudes of more than 29,000 feet or over five and one half miles, reached by both Everest and Kanchanjanga.

As for the plateau of Tibet, with an average height of 15,000 feet, it is indeed the most elevated country in the whole world. The Bolivian plateau in South America is between 11,000 and 13,000 feet high but it is practically uninhabited, whereas Tibet, which covers an area equal to two-fifths of that of Russia, has a population of almost two million people.

This shows to what extremes of air-pressure the human body can accustom itself. Those Americans who have crossed the Rio Grande know the discomforts they experience when they are allowed to spend a few days in the delightful Mexican capital which is only 7400 feet high. They are warned beforehand not to hustle as they do at home, and to take it easy until their heart

The High Plateau of Tibet

ceases to pump like a sledgehammer whenever they walk half a block. The Tibetans not only walk a hundred blocks in a day but they carry everything the country needs on their backs across mountain passes which are quite frequently too steep for mules and horses but which are the only connection they have with the outside world.

Although Tibet is about sixty miles further south than the semi-tropical island of Sicily, the snow remains on the ground for at least six months of every year and the thermometer not infrequently goes down to—30°. Nevertheless, this high plateau with its terrible wind storms, raging across the bleak salt-bogs of the south, its dust and snow and general discomforts of living, has become the home of an exceedingly curious religious experiment.

During the seventh century, Tibet was merely a principality like so many other Asiatic states, ruled over by a king who lived in Lhasa, the City of God. One of these kings was converted to Buddhism by his Chinese wife. Since that day, Buddhism has flourished in Tibet as nowhere else in Asia. Lhasa is to the Buddhists what Rome is to the Catholics, or Mecca to the Mohammedans—the holy of holies.

The Buddhism of Tibet is not the pure original doctrine of the gentle Indian prince who lived and died six centuries before the birth of Christ. It is the usual degenerate form, full of devils and spooks, and it has forgotten a great many of the noble teachings of the founder of that great Asiatic faith. But Tibet has been a bulwark of Buddhism which has been of great help in preserving that religion against the attacks of the Mohammedans from the west and the pagan creeds of southern India. Its uninterrupted success may in part have been the result of a very extraordinary arrangement which that church provides for an almost automatic continuation of the institution of the Buddhistic papacy.

The Buddhists have always believed in the reincarnation of the soul. It follows that the soul of Gotama himself must continue somewhere on this earth. All that was necessary was to find him and make him head of all the faithful. Now it is well to remember that Christianity, which is so much younger than Buddhism, has a great many ideas and institutions in common with its old neighbor and rival. Pious Buddhists were in the habit of eschewing the Devil and the flesh long before John the Baptist retired into the wilderness. Their monks practiced celibacy, poverty and chastity ages before Saint Simeon climbed to the top of his pillar in the valley of the Nile. They also exercised high political functions. During the reign of Kublai Khan, the grandson of Genghis Khan and an ardent convert to Buddhism, the abbots of an important Tibetan monastery were recognized as the political rulers of all Tibet. In return for this favor, the new Dalai Lama, in his quality of spiritual over-lord of the whole Buddhist world, officially crowned the Tartar Khan Emperor of Mongolia, just as Pope Leo III had crowned Charlemagne. In order to keep the dignity of Lama (or superior spiritual ruler) in the same family, the first Lamas broke the rules of celibacy and remained married until they had begotten a son to succeed them. But during the fourteenth century a great reformer arose among the Tibetan monks, a sort of Martin Luther of Buddhism. When he died, the old monastic orders had been reestablished in all their former rigor and their head, the Dalai Lama, "the Lama as big as the ocean", was once more recognized as their spiritual shepherd by one-quarter of all the people on earth. He was to be assisted in his task by the Pantshen Lama or Glorious Teacher, who was to be a sort of vice-pope. The method of succession, which was then introduced, has never been changed.

When either the Dalai Lama or the Pantshen Lama dies, the survivor sends for a list of all the male children born in Tibet immediately after the demise of his colleague, for the spirit of the dead man must now live in one of those babies. After prolonged prayers, three names are chosen, and these names are written on slips of paper. These are then thrown in a golden casket, provided several centuries ago for the occasion by one of the Chinese emperors. Then the abbots of all the great monasteries of Tibet gather together in the immense palace of the Dalai Lama. There are 3000 such monasteries in the country, but only a few are big enough to send delegates to this Buddhistic college of cardinals. After a week of fasting and praying, they draw one name out of the golden casket. The child who bears that name is held to be the reincarnation of the Buddha and is surrendered to the monks to be prepared for his task.

His fate is not a very happy one. It is to the advantage of the powerful abbots to keep him in the background and to make him a weakling, so that he may do their bidding and let them live comfortably at the expense of the other five-sixths of the populace, who are not monks but who are engaged in some productive labor and must therefore support their spiritual mentors. Should the poor youngster prove "difficult", then there are several subtle ways and means to allow him to "return to Paradise". Does he come up to the just expectations of his tutors, then he leads a terribly dull and monotonous existence and dies young anyway from sheer lack of exercise and boredom.

Nevertheless and notwithstanding, the system continues. Systems of that sort always do, whether 12,000 feet up in the air

The Mountain Gap

or at sea-level. As for the mountain-ranges which protect Tibet against the neighbors from the south and which protect it so well that until only a few years ago no foreigner had set foot upon this holy land of the living Buddha for more than seven hundred years, these mountain-ranges are so much in the public prints that they are better known and to a larger number of people than the mountains of Vermont. For our time, which loves records, has cast an envious eye upon the last remaining mountain top of any importance that remains unscaled. Mount Everest was called after the colonel of engineers who brought this part of the Himalayas into maps for the English geodetic survey, some time during the middle of the last century. It is 29,000 feet high, which makes it just twice as high as Mount Ranier. It has defied all attempts of man to reach the summit. The last of the great Everest expeditions in 1924 got to within a few hundred yards of the top. Two men volunteered to make the final climb. Armed with oxygen apparatus, they bade farewell to the rest of the party. They were last observed when they were within 600 feet of the final pinnacle. After that, they were never seen again. Mount Everest remains unconquered.

But for ambitious mountaineers this is an ideal region. Being situated in the heart of Asia, the country of the Gigantic Dimensions, the mountains must of course assume proportions compared to which the Swiss Alps become little sand piles made by boys and girls playing along the sea-shore. In the first place, these mountains of eternal snow, as the Hindus call them, are almost twice as wide as the Alps and cover thirteen times more territory. Some of their glaciers are four times as long as the most important glacier of Switzerland. There are forty individual mountain tops of more than 22,000 feet height and several of the mountain passes are more than twice as high as those of the Alps.

Like all other parts of the Great Fold which runs all the way from Spain to New Zealand, the Himalayas are of comparatively recent date (even younger than the Alps) and count their age in millions of years and not in hundreds of millions. It will take a great deal of sunshine and rain to destroy them and reduce them to flat country, but the forces of Nature, hostile to rock formations, are busily engaged. Already the Himalayas are cut into irregular pieces by the deep ravines of half a hundred brooks and rivers. The Indus, the Ganges and the Brahmaputra, the three most important rivers of India, help this labor of disintegration along at a merry clip.

Politically speaking, too, the Himalayas, with their tremendous length of 1500 miles, offer a more diversified spectacle than any other mountain-range. For they are not merely the natural frontier between two adjoining countries, as are the Alps and the Pyrenees. They happen to be so wide that quite a number of independent states are tucked away in them. Some of these, like Nepal, the home of the famous Gurkhas, who have retained a certain degree of independence, are four times as large as the republic of Switzerland and have almost 6,000,000 inhabitants. Others, like Kashmir (where our grandmothers got their shawls and where the English recruit their famous Sikh regiments), which is now part of the British domains, have an area of some 85,000 square miles with a population of over 3,000,000.

Finally, if you will look once more at the map, you will see a curious thing in regard to two of the big rivers, the Indus and the Brahmaputra. They do not run down from the Himalayas the way the Rhine runs down from the Alps, or the Missouri runs down from the Rockies. Instead they take their rise behind the main chain of the Himalayas. The Indus originates between the Himalayas and the Karakoram ridge. The Brahmaputra flows first from west to east through the plateau of Tibet. Then it makes a sharp turn and starts upon that short voyage from east to west to join the Ganges which runs through the heart of the broad valley between the Himalayas and the plateau of Deccan, in the central part of the Indian peninsula.

Running water, of course, has a terrific erosive power, but it does not seem likely that these two rivers could have dug their way through the Himalayas if they had begun to flow after the mountains had been made. And we are therefore obliged to draw the conclusion that these rivers must be older than the mountains. The Indus and the Brahmaputra were there before the crust of the earth began to heave and groan and very slowly produced those gigantic folds which were to become the highest mountain ranges of the modern world. But their growth was so slow (time is after all only an invention of man, eternity is timeless) that the rivers, by dint of their erosive energies, managed to remain on the ground floor, so to speak.

There are geologists who claim that even now the Himalayas are still gaining. Since the thin concrete shell on which we live contracts and expands like the skin of our body, these geologists may be right. The Swiss Alps, as we know for a fact, are travelling slowly from east to west. The Himalayas, like the Andes of South America, may be moving upward. There is only one law in the laboratory of Nature which holds good for all creation—there must be constant change and the punishment for those who fail to obey is death.

XXXIII

THE GREAT WESTERN PLATEAU OF ASIA

From Pamir in the center a wide mountain-range, which is really nothing but a series of high plateaus, runs due west until at last it is stopped by the waters of the Black Sea and the Aegean.

All of these plateaus have familiar names, for they have played a most important role in the history of human progress. I might go a little further and say *the* most important role. For unless all our present ethnological speculations are wrong, these highlands and valleys between the Indus river and the shores of the eastern Mediterranean were not only the nursery which hatched that branch of the human race to which we ourselves happen to belong, but they also acted as a sort of grammar school in which we learned the rudiments of those sciences and the first principles of those moral tenets which eventually were to set Man apart from the rest of the animal world.

In order of their succession, the first of these highlands is the plateau of Iran. It is a vast salty desert about 3000 feet high, entirely surrounded by high mountain-ranges. Even in the north where it borders upon the Caspian Sea and the Turanian desert and in the south where it borders upon the Persian Gulf and the Arabian Sea, there is not a sufficient amount of rainfall to let this region have a single river worth the name. Baluchistan, separated from India proper by the high Kirthar range, and since 1887 part of the British domains, has a few indifferent streams which lose themselves into the Indus river, but its deserts have been feared ever since a greater part of Alexander's armies perished there from thirst on the way back from India.

Afghanistan, which was so much in the limelight a few years ago when it fell into the hands of a ruler who tried to publicize himself and his country by a very spectacular trip through Europe, has a river, the Helmund. This begins in the Hindu Kush, one of the high mountain-ranges that radiate southward from Pamir and which loses itself in the salty Lake of Seistan on the border between Persia and Afghanistan. Afghanistan, however, enjoys a much better climate than Baluchistan and in many other ways this country is of much greater importance. The original trade-route between India and northern Asia and Europe ran through the heart of this country. It went from Peshawar, the capital of the north-west frontier province, to Kabul, the capital of Afghanistan, by way of the famous Khyber Pass, and then crossed the high Afghan plateau until it reached Herat in the west.

About fifty years ago Russia and England began their fight for the ultimate control of this buffer state. As the Afghans happened to be excellent fighting men, those peaceful penetrations from south and north had to be accomplished with more than the usual care and circumspection. The disaster of the first Afghan war of 1838–1842, when a mere handful of English returned to tell how all the others had been massacred during the attempt to force an unpopular ruler upon the unwilling Afghan people, was never quite forgotten; and thereafter England proceeded across the Khyber Pass with careful tread. But when the Russians in 1873 occupied Khiva and were known to be heading for Tashkend and Samarkand, the English from their side were forced to make some move lest they wake up one morning to hear the armies of the Czar doing a little practice shooting on the other side of the Suliman Mountains. And so, while His Imperial Majesty's representatives in London and Her Royal Majesty's representatives in St. Petersburg were assuring the respective imperial and royal governments that their intentions towards Afghanistan were wholly unselfish and of a most respectable and laudatory nature, the engineers of both governments were working on elaborate plans to bless poor Afghanistan, "cut off by cruel Nature from direct access to the sea", with a railroad system that should henceforth allow the benighted Afghans to partake at first hand of the blessings of western civilization.

The World War unfortunately interfered with these projects.
The Russians got as far as Herat, from where today you may
travel by rail via Merv in the Turkoman Socialist Soviet Republic to the harbor of Krasnovodsk on the Caspian Sea and
thence by boat to Baku and western Europe. Another line runs
from Merv by way of Bokhara to Kokand in the Uzbeg Republic
and is to continue from there to Balkh. Balkh is at present a third-
rate village, situated among the vast ruins of that ancient Bactria
which 3000 years ago was as important as Paris is today. It was
the original center of that highly ethical religious movement
started by Zoroaster (or Zarathustra) which not only conquered
Persia and penetrated as far as the Mediterranean, but which in
a modified form was so popular among the Romans that for a
long time it was one of the most serious rivals of Christianity.

England meanwhile has been pushing her railroad from
Hyderabad to Quetta in Baluchistan, and from there to Kanda-
har, where in the year 1880 the British had avenged themselves
for their defeat of the first Afghan war.

But there is still another part of the Iranian plateau which
deserves some attention. Today it is merely the shadow of its
former greatness but it must have been an extraordinarily interesting land when the name of Persia stood for all that was
most excellent in painting and literature and above all things in
the difficult art of living. The first period of glory came six centuries before Christ, when Persia was the center of an empire
which reached all the way from Macedonia to India. This was
destroyed by Alexander, but five hundred years later, under the
dynasty of the Sassanids, the Persians restored the ancient realm
of Xerxes and Cambyses. They restored the Zoroastrian faith in
all its former purity, collected the sacred writings into one volume, the famous Zend-Avesta, and made the desert flower with
the roses of Ispahan.

Early during the seventh century the Arabs conquered Persia
and Mohammed defeated Zoroaster. But if it is true that one

The total amount of land and water on our planet

The Land Bridge from Asia to Europe

shall know a country by its literature, then the works of Omar, the tent-maker's son from Nishapur, bear witness to the exquisite taste that flourished once upon a time in these desert lands between Kurdistan and Khorasan. A professor of mathematics, dividing his time between algebra and quatrains upon the delights of love and the beauties of old red wine, is a phenomenon of such rare occurrence that only a civilization both wise and mellow would have tolerated his presence in the hallowed halls of pedagogy.

Today's interest however in Persia is of a more prosaic nature. The country has oil, and that is about the worst thing that could possibly happen to a nation too weak to defend its own interests. Theoretically speaking, the natives of any given place are supposed to be the chief beneficiaries of the treasures that lie hidden beneath their ancestral grave-yards. In practice it works out differently. A few of the Sultan's intimate friends in far away Teheran grow rich from granting concessions, and several thousand men and women living near the wells may find occasional employment at pretty meagre wages. But the rest goes to the foreign investor who thinks that Persia is the name of a rug.

Unfortunately, Persia seems to be one of those countries which will always be poor and badly administered. Its geographical location is very little of a blessing and very much of a curse. It is a desert, but when a desert is situated on the main road, which in turn is part of a land bridge connecting two of the most important parts of the world, then that desert will forever be a battle-field and a bone of contention between opposing interests. And what I have just said of Persia holds true of this entire western part of Asia.

The final highlands in the chain of plateaus that run all the way from Pamir to the Mediterranean are Armenia and Asia Minor. Armenia, the westward continuation of the great platform of Iran, is a very old land, old in the formation of its volcanic soil and old in the suffering of its people. It is another bridge country. Whosoever wanted to wander from Europe to India had to pass through the valleys of the high Kurdistan Mountains, and among those travellers have been some of the most notorious cut-throats of all time. Its history goes back to the days of the deluge. It was on the top of Mount Ararat, the highest mountain of this entire region, which rises 17,000 feet above sea-level and almost 10,000 feet above the plain of Erivan, that Noah's ark landed when the waters of the earth had begun to recede. This we know for certain because when Sir John de Mandeville, the Belgian physician, visited these regions in the beginning of the fourteenth century, he still found parts of the old craft lying around near the top. But when the Armenians themselves, who belong to the racial group of the Mediterranean and who therefore are our very near cousins, moved into these hills is still quite uncertain. At the recent rate of extinction, however, there soon won't be any more of them left. In one single year, 1895–1896, the Turks, who were then the masters of the Armenian plateau, murdered several hundred thousand of them; and the Turks are by no means their worst enemies and not half as savage with them as the Kurds.

The Armenians have always been very pious Christians. But although they had adopted Christianity long before Rome, their church had retained several institutions, such as an hereditary priesthood, which made it a most obnoxious organization in the eyes of all good Catholics of the west. Europe therefore sat quietly by while the Mohammedan Kurds slaughtered Armenians and stole their territory.

Then came the Great War, and the Allies, trying to get into Turkey by the back door in order to relieve the English in Mesopotamia, stamped across all this territory. Such names as Lake Van and Lake Urmia, of which the world had never heard before, although they are among the biggest of all mountain lakes, suddenly appeared in the news of the day; and Erzerum, an Asiatic frontier town of the old Byzantine Empire, attracted more attention than it had done since the days of the Crusades.

When the fighting came to an end, it is small cause for surprise that the surviving Armenians wished a plague upon all of their tormentors and joined the Soviet Union. They were allowed to form the republics of Azerbaijan and Armenia, between the Caspian and the Black Sea at the foot of the Caucasian Mountains, which Russia had added to its territory during the first half of the nineteenth century.

Then, turning from the traditional victims of Turkish wrath to the Turks themselves, we wander a little further westward and enter the plateau of Asia Minor.

Asia Minor, once merely a province of the empire of the old Sultan, is today all that remains of that Turkish dream of world dominion. On the north it is bounded by the Black Sea, on the west by the Sea of Marmora, the Bosporus and the Dardanelles, which cut it off from Europe, and in the south by the Mediterranean, from which the interior is separated by the Taurus Mountains. Across this territory, which is considerably lower than Iran, Persia or Armenia, runs a famous railroad, the so-called Bagdad railroad which has played such an important part in the history of the last thirty years. For both England and Germany wanted to have the concessions for the railroad that was to connect Constantinople with Bagdad on the Tigris and Smyrna, the great harbor of the Asiatic west coast, with Damascus in Syria and with Medina, the holy city of the Arabs.

No sooner had these two nations reached a compromise than French capital insisted upon a share in the future revenue. The French were thereupon given the northern part of Asia Minor where Trebizond, the export harbor for Armenia and Persia, was still waiting for suitable communications with the west. Foreign engineers then began to survey their roads through these ancient lands where the Greek philosophers of the Athenian colonies had first speculated upon the true nature of man and the universe, where solemn church councils had given the world the iron-bound faith by which the people of Europe had lived for over a thousand years, where Paul of Tarsus was born and where he had preached, where Turk and Christian had fought for the supremacy of the Mediterranean world, and where in some forsaken desert hamlet an Arab camel-driver had dreamed his first dreams of being Allah's one and only prophet.

This railroad as planned was to keep well away from the coastline, skirting those almost mythical seaports of ancient and medieval history—Adana and Alexandretta and Antioch and Tripoli and Beirut and Tyre and Sidon and Jaffa, the only harbor of the rocky land of Palestine—and devoting itself chiefly to the mountains.

When the war broke out, the railroad played exactly that role which the Germans had expected. The railroad, with its excellent German equipment, together with the presence of two big German battle-ships in Constantinople, were the two highly practical "considerations" which made the Turks join the Central Powers rather than the Allies. And how well that road had been planned from a strategical point of view was shown during the next four years. For the war was finally decided on the ocean and in the west. The eastern front never collapsed until long after the western front had begun to melt away. And the world learned to its surprise that the Turk made as good a soldier in the year 1918 as he had done in 1288 when the Seljuk Turks conquered the whole of Asia and cast their first longing glances across the Bosporus at the impregnable walls of imperial Constantinople.

Up to then that mountainous plateau had been quite well-to-do. For Asia Minor, although part of the land bridge between Asia and Europe, had never quite suffered the fate of Armenia and the Persian plateau of Iran. This had been due to the fact that Asia Minor was not only part of a commercial highroad but also the terminal station for all the routes leading from India and China to Greece and Rome. For when the world was still young, the most active intellectual and commercial life of the Mediterranean was not to be found in Hellas itself. It flourished among the cities of western Asia which the Greek cities of the mainland had converted into Greek colonies. Where the ancient blood of Asia had mingled with the new race until it produced a mixture that for sheer intelligence and sharpness of wit has rarely found its equal. Even in the modern Levantines, of highly unsavory reputation in regard to business integrity and general honesty, we can detect traits of the old stock which for half a thousand years had been able to hold its own against its many enemies.

The final disintegration under the rule of the Seljuks was inevitable. As a degenerative force, the Turks have always been

Jerusalem

without a single rival. But today this small peninsula is practically all that remains of the ancient glories of the Ottoman Empire. The Sultans themselves are gone. Their ancestors, after residing for almost a century in Adrianople, the only other Turkish city left in Europe outside of Constantinople, had moved to the latter city in the year 1453, and from there had ruled a territory which included the whole of the Balkans, all of Hungary and the greater part of southern Russia.

Four centuries of inexpressible mismanagement sufficed to

ruin this empire and make it what it is today. Constantinople,
the oldest and most important example of a commercial monopoly which for thousands of years held the key to the grain trade
of southern Russia, that same Constantinople, so favored by
Nature that its harbor came to be known as the Golden Horn,
the Horn of Plenty, so filled with fish that no one ever need go
hungry, was reduced to the rank of a third-rate provincial city.
For the masters of the New Turkey, who had salvaged what was
left when peace was declared, wisely concluded that the degenerate background of Constantinople, a hodge-podge of Greeks
and Armenians and Levantines and Slavs and the accumulated
riff-raff of all the Crusades, was not the place from which to try
the well nigh impossible task of rejuvenating the Turkish people and turning them into a modern nation. They therefore chose
themselves a new capital, the city of Angora in the heart of the
Anatolian Mountains, more than 200 miles east of Constantinople.

Angora was old, very old. Four hundred years before our
era, a tribe of Gauls had lived here, the same sort of Gauls who
afterwards took possession of the plains of France. It had passed
through all the vicissitudes of all the cities situated on this main
road of trade. The Crusaders had captured the city. The Tartars
had done likewise. Even as late as 1832 an Egyptian army had
destroyed that whole neighborhood. But it was there that Kemal
Pasha founded the capital city of his new fatherland. He purged
it of all the elements that could not be assimilated. He swapped
his Greeks and Armenians for Turks who lived in these other
countries. He built up his army and his credit with equal brilliancy. And he made the New Turkey a going concern, though
Heaven knows, the mountains of Anatolia, after fifteen centuries
of warfare and neglect, yield little enough that is considered of
any value to a Wall Street banker who is looking around for
possible prospects in the loan market.

All the same, Asia Minor is generally recognized as being of
the utmost importance for the future trade between Asia and
Europe. Smyrna is regaining the position it already held when

the Amazons, the female warriors of the ancient world, ruled this part of Asia and founded their curious state in which all male children were put to death and in which no man was allowed to set foot except once a year and then exclusively for the purpose of continuing the race.

Ephesus, where Paul still found the natives worshipping the image of the Chaste Diana, the ideal goddess, by the way, for a race of Amazons, has disappeared from the face of the earth, but the region nearby may become one of the most lucrative fig gardens of the world.

Further towards the north, past the ruins of Pergamum (the great literary center of the ancient world which gave us our word parchment), the railroad skirts the plain of Troy to connect with Panderma on the Sea of Marmora. Panderma is only a day's trip by boat removed from Scutari where the famous Orient   Express   (London–Calais–Paris–Vienna–Belgrade–Sofia–Constantinople) has connections with the trains that run to Angora and Medina and those which via Aleppo–Damascus–Nazareth–Ludd (change cars for Jerusalem and Jaffa)—Gaza–Ismailia–Kantara connect with Suez and from there up the Nile as far as the Sudan.

If it had not been for the Great War, that road could have been made profitable by transporting goods and passengers for India and China and Japan from western Europe by rail as far as Suez and then sending them the rest of the way by ship. But by the time the damage of four years' fighting shall have been repaired, the aeroplane will probably be in general use for the passenger traffic.

The eastern part of Asia Minor is inhabited by the Kurds, the ancient enemies of the Armenians. The Kurds, like the Scotch and most mountain peoples, are divided into clans and have too much individual pride to take kindly to a commercial or an industrial civilization. They are a terribly old race, already mentioned in the cuneiform inscriptions of the Babylonians and by Xenephon in his "Retreat of the Ten Thousand" (what a dull book!) They belong to the same original stock as we do but they have been converted to Mohammedanism. As such they have never trusted their Christian neighbors, but this holds good of all the other Moslem states that were founded in consequence of the Great War, and not without cause as all of us who lived during those days, when "official misstatements" were part of the national strategy, have every reason to remember.

When peace was finally declared, nobody was satisfied and many new feuds and quarrels were added to the old ones, all the more as several European powers now installed themselves as "mandatory rulers" over parts of the old Turkish Empire and proved to be but little less cruel in their dealings with native races than the Turks had been.

The French, who had invested a great deal of money in Syria, took hold of Syria, and a French High Commission, amply supplied with money and troops, undertook to rule the three million odd Syrians who most certainly had not asked to be turned into a European "mandate", which meant a colony but with a slightly less offensive name. Soon different elements that had been part of the old Syria were beginning to forget their dislike for each other in one common hatred for the French. The Kurds made peace with their hereditary enemies, the Roman Catholic Maronites of Lebanon (the old home of the Phoenicians), and the Christians ceased to maltreat the Jews, and the Jews ceased to despise both Christians and Mohammedans, and the French were obliged to erect a great many gallows in order to maintain themselves. But order apparently has been re-established and Syria is rapidly becoming another Algeria. That does not mean that the people like their mandatory rulers any better than before but merely that the leaders have been hanged and the others lack the courage to go on fighting.

As for the valley of the Tigris and the Euphrates, it was elevated to the rank of a monarchy and the ruins of Babylon and Nineveh are now part of the Kingdom of Irak. But the new potentates hardly enjoy the freedom of action of Hammurabi or Assur-Bani-Pal, for they have been forced to recognize England's suzerainty. King Feisal has to await word from London whenever he wants to decide upon something more important than the re-digging of a few ancient Babylonian drainage canals.

As for Palestine (the land of the Philistines), which is also part of this region, it is so strange a country that I shall have to be very short about it for fear of filling the rest of this book with a description of a little state, no larger than some ninth-rate European principality like Schleswig-Holstein, but which somehow or other has played a greater role in human history than many a first-class empire.

The original ancestors of the Jews, after leaving their miserable villages in eastern Mesopotamia, and after wandering through the northern part of the Arabian desert, and crossing the plains between Mount Sinai and the Mediterranean, and spending a few centuries in Egypt, finally retraced their steps. They stopped when they had reached the narrow strip of fertile land between the mountain-ridge of Judea and the Mediterranean and engaged in bitter warfare with the original natives, whom they finally deprived of a sufficient number of villages and cities to found an independent Jewish state of their own.

Their lives cannot have been very comfortable. In the west, the Philistines, non-Semitic settlers from the island of Crete, were in full possession of the coastal region, cutting the Jews completely off from the open sea. In the east, one of the strangest natural phenomena of which we have any record, an enormous rift in the rocks, running a straight course from north to south and going as deep as 1300 feet below sea-level, separated their country from the rest of Asia. This sink, which is very much today as it was when John the Baptist chose it as his place of residence, begins in the north between the Lebanon and the Anti-Lebanon and follows the valley of the Jordan, the Lake of Tiberias or Sea of Galilee, which is 526 feet below sea-level, the Dead Sea, which is 1292 feet below sea-level (the Death Valley in California is only 276 feet, and the deepest spot on the American continent) and from there (for the River Jordan stops dead in the Dead Sea, which contains 25% salt on account of the constant evaporation) through the ancient land of Edom (where

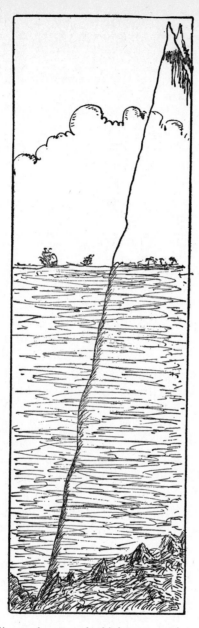

The distance between the highest mountain top and
the lowest ocean depth is 11½ miles or
1/700 of the earth's diameter

the Moabites lived) to the Gulf of Akaba, a branch of the Red Sea.

The southern part of this sink is one of the hottest and most desolate regions of the world, full of asphalt and sulphur and phosphates and other diabolical ingredients which modern chemistry has made highly profitable (just before the war the Germans founded a formidable Dead Sea Asphalt Company) but which must have inspired the people of long ago with horror and fear, and which made them attribute the destruction of Sodom and Gomorrah by an ordinary earthquake to an act of vengeance on the part of their Gods.

The sudden change of climate and scenery when they had crossed the mountain ridge of Judea, which runs parallel with this great rift, must have made a tremendous impression upon the earliest invaders from the east and probably inspired that jubilant cry of a land "overflowing with milk and honey". For the modern visitor to Palestine will find very little milk and the bees apparently have long since died for lack of a sufficient number of flowers. That, however, is not due to a change in the climate, as one hears so often said, for the climate today seems little different from the climate in the days when the disciples of Jesus wandered from Dan to Beersheba without bothering much about the problem of their daily bread and butter, since there were enough dates and there was enough native wine for the simple needs of all travellers. But the Turks and the Crusaders between them played the role of climate. The Crusaders began by destroying whatever remained of the old irrigation works which had been built during the days of independence and during the centuries of Roman domination. The Turks had, as usual, done the rest. A soil which only needed water to bring forth rich harvests was systematically neglected until nine-tenths of the farmer populace had either died or moved away. Jerusalem became a sort of Bedouin village where a dozen Christian sects and their Mohammedan neighbors were forever engaged in far from edifying quarrels. For to the Mohammedans, Jerusalem is also a very Holy City. The Arabs consider themselves the direct descendants of that unfortunate Ishmael who together with his mother Hagar was driven into the wilderness by Abraham at the request of the latter's wedded wife, the redoubtable Sarah.

But Ishmael and Hagar had not perished of thirst, as seems to have been Sarah's little plan, but Ishmael had married an Egyptian girl and had become the founder of the whole of the Arabian nation. Today therefore he and his mother lie buried just outside the Kaaba, the center of the most holy of all places of worship in Mecca which all Mohammedans must visit at least once during their lifetime, no matter how difficult the voyage or how far the distance that separates them from that hallowed spot.

As soon as the Arabs had conquered Jerusalem, they erected a mosque over the rock upon which, according to tradition, their distant cousin Solomon, another direct descendant of Abraham, had built his famous temple. That happened Heaven only knows how many centuries ago. But the fight for the ownership of that rock and the walls around it, part of which is the traditional "wailing wall" of the orthodox Jews, is responsible for the continual quarrels between the two races that now make up the population of the Palestinian mandate.

And what can one hope for the future? When the English captured Jerusalem, they found the people to consist of 80% Moslems (Syrians and Arabs) and 20% Jews and Gentile Christians. The English, as the rulers of the largest Mohammedan empire of the modern world, could not afford to hurt the feelings of so many of their loyal subjects and dared not surrender half a million Palestine Moslems to the mercies of less than a hundred thousand Jews, who had many entirely justifiable axes to grind.

The result was the usual post-Versailles compromise which satisfied nobody. Palestine today is a British mandate and British troops maintain order between the different nationalities. The governors are selected from among the best-known English Jews but the country is nevertheless a colony and does not enjoy that complete political independence of which Mr. Balfour had spoken so eloquently but also so vaguely when at the beginning of the Palestine campaign he referred to those regions as the future home of the Jewish race.

Matters would become a great deal simpler if the Jews themselves knew what they wanted to do with the old mother-country. The orthodox Jews of eastern Europe and especially those of Russia want to keep it as it is now, a vast theological seminary with a little museum of Hebrew antiquities. The younger generation, remembering the wise words of the Prophet that "the dead should bury the dead", and feeling that too much weeping about the past joys and glories of bygone days is apt to interfere quite seriously with the glories and the joys of to-morrow, hope to make Palestine into a normal, modern state, something like Switzerland or Denmark, a going concern of men and women who have rid themselves of the memories of the Ghetto and who are more interested in good roads and good irrigation canals than in squabbling with their Arab neighbors about a few old stones which may or may not have been the well from which Rebecca drew the water but which are now merely a hindrance to progress.

Since most of Palestine consists of rolling territory with a de-cided slope from east to west, it is indeed possible to reclaim the neglected and exhausted soil for purposes of agriculture. The sea winds which blow the greater part of each day spread their heavy dew across the entire landscape and make it ideally fit for the cultivation of olives, and Jericho, the only city of any importance ever built in the terrible Dead Sea region, may once more become a center for the trade in dates.

And as the soil of Palestine contains neither coal nor oil, it will escape the attentions of the foreign promoter and will be allowed to work out its own problems as Yahweh and the Mo-hammedan majority will permit.

XXXIV

ARABIA—OR WHEN IS A PART OF ASIA NOT A PART OF ASIA?

ACCORDING to the maps in our ordinary atlases and according to the handbooks on geography, Arabia is a part of Asia. But the proverbial visitor from Mars, ignorant of the history of our planet, would probably come to a different conclusion and would decide that Nejd, the famous Arabian desert, is really nothing but a continuation of the Sahara from which it is separated by an inconsequential and rather shallow bay of the Indian Ocean known as the Red Sea.

This Red Sea is almost six times as long as it is wide and full of reefs. Its mean depth is about 300 fathoms, but where it connects with the Gulf of Aden, which is really part of the Indian Ocean, the depth varies between only two and sixteen fathoms. It is possible that the Red Sea, which is full of little volcanic islands, was originally an inland lake which did not get elevated to the rank of a sea until the Straits of Persia were formed, just as the North Sea did not really become a sea until after the formation of the British Channel.

As for the Arabs themselves, they seem to have no desire to be either African or Asiatic, for they call their country "the island of the Arabians", which is rather a large order for a piece of territory six times as large as the whole of Germany. The number of inhabitants is not at all in proportion to the size of their country. It does not exceed that of greater London. But the original ancestors of these 7,000,000 modern Arabs must have been possessed of extraordinary physical and mental qualities for they have been able to impress themselves upon the world at large in quite an extraordinary fashion, and that without the slightest assistance from the side of Mother Nature.

In the first place, they lived in a country with a climate that is not fit for human beings. Not only is this continuation of the Sahara Desert completely deprived of rivers, but it is also one of the hottest places on earth, except in the extreme south and east where the coast is so damp and moist as to be practically uninhabitable for Europeans. But in the center of the peninsula and in the south-west where the mountain-ranges reach a height of almost 6000 feet, the life of both Man and beast is made intolerable by those sudden changes in temperature which take place immediately after dark and which cause the thermometer to fall from 80° to 20° in less than half an hour's time.

If it were not for the underground water the interior would be entirely uninhabitable. As for the coastal regions they are not much better off except the territory immediately north of the British settlement of Aden.

From a commercial point of view, however, the whole blessed peninsula is not worth as much as the lower part of the island of Manhattan. But the island of Manhattan will have to do a great deal better than it has done so far if it ever wants to equal Arabia in its general influence upon the cultural development of the world.

Curiously enough the Arab peninsula has never been a country as France or Sweden are countries. As a result of the irresponsible promises made to everybody and everything during the Great War when the Allies were badly in need of a few extra men, a baker's dozen of so-called independent states now stretches all the way from the Persian Gulf to the Gulf of Akaba and even further northward where Transjordania, ruled by an Emir who takes his orders from Jerusalem, separates Palestine from the Syrian desert. But most of them are mere names like El Hasa and Oman, along the Persian Gulf, Hadramut in the south and Yemen and Asir along the Red Sea, just south of El Hejaz which is perhaps the only one of any importance. For the Hejaz not only has a railroad of its own (the final part of the Bagdad road which now runs as far as Medina and which eventually will be continued to Mecca) but it also is in control of the two holy cities of the Moslem world, Mecca, the place where Mohammed was born, the Bethlehem of the Moslems, and Medina where he lies buried.

Neither of these two oasis cities amounted to much early during the seventh century when they became the center of such stirring events. Mohammed, who was responsible for their fame, was born in 567 or 569, several months after the death of his father. Soon afterwards his mother died too and he was thereupon entrusted to the care of an impecunious grandfather. At an early age he became a camel-driver and travelled all over Arabia with the caravans who hired his services. He may even have crossed the Red Sea, and there is a possibility that he visited Abyssinia which was then trying to turn Arabia into an African colony (and having an easy time of it as the different desert tribes hated each other too cordially to be able to put up a concerted fight).

At an uncertain age he married a widow. Her property allowed him to give up his wandering life and open a little store of his own, dealing in grain and camel-feed. Like many other people suffering from epileptic fits, he had strange hallucinations when in a state of semi-consciousness, and, like many other people affected by that unpleasant ailment, he tried to console himself for his unfortunate affliction by telling his neighbors that he had gone into a trance in order to receive a revelation from God. Not being a man of great originality of thought, he did not find it easy to develop some definite and new system of religion of his own. He vaguely talked about restoring the ancient faith of Abraham and Ishmael. For a time he even seems to have played with the idea of adapting the Christian faith to the needs of his wild neighbors who would never have listened to any one talking to them of meekness and asking them to turn the other cheek to their enemies. In the end, and under the pressure of his Meccan neighbors, who laughed rather heartily at the vegetable-vender turned prophet and who threatened his life when he began to take himself a bit too seriously, he fled to Medina and there he started upon his career as a preacher in all seriousness.

I cannot go into details about his doctrines. If you are interested, buy a Koran and try to read it, though you will find it hard sledding. Suffice it here to state that as a result of Mohammed's labors, the different Semite tribes of the great Arabian desert suddenly became conscious of having to fulfil a mission. In less than a century they had conquered all of Asia Minor and Syria and Palestine, together with the whole of the northern coast of Africa and Spain. Until the end of the eighteenth century they were a constant menace to the safety of Europe.

Well, a people who could do all that and in only a few years must have been possessed of extraordinary mental and physical abilities. According to all those who have ever had anything to do with them (including Napoleon, who was a bad judge of women but who knew a good soldier when he saw one) the Arabs are terrific fighters, and their medieval universities were concrete proof of their intellectual gifts and their interest in science. Why in the end they should have lost so much of their former prestige, I could not say. It would be very easy here to indulge in a few high sounding theories about the influence of the geographical background upon the character of men and then prove that desert tribes have always been great world conquerors, but there are just as many desert people who have never amounted to anything. Also there are just as many mountaineers who have done all sorts of wonderful things. And then again there are other mountaineers who have never risen far above the ranks of drunken and careless and lazy loafers. No, I am sorry, but I have never been able to draw a single general moral lesson from success or the lack thereof on the part of any nation.

But what has happened once may happen again. The great reform movement of the middle of the eighteenth century which purged Mohammedanism of all forms of idolatry and which gave rise to the puritannical sect of the Wahhabites with their insistence upon frugal and simple living, may cause the Arabs to go on the warpath once more; and if Europe continues to waste its strength on civil warfare they may become as dangerous to us as they were twelve centuries ago. Their terrible peninsula is a vast reservoir of "hard" people, of people who rarely smile, who rarely play, who take themselves with dignified seriousness and who cannot be corrupted by the pleasant prospects of material wealth because their needs are so simple that they have never felt the lack of anything better.

Such nations are ever a potential source of danger. Especially when they have a just reason to feel themselves aggrieved. And in the case of Arabia, as in that of all Asia, Africa, America and Australia, the White Man's conscience is not quite as clear as we might wish.

XXXV

INDIA, WHERE NATURE AND MAN ARE ENGAGED IN
MASS-PRODUCTION

ALEXANDER THE GREAT discovered India. That happened
three hundred years before the birth of Christ. But Alexander
did not get very far beyond the Indus River, and although he
crossed the Punjab, the home of the Sikhs, he never penetrated
the heart of the country of the true Hindus who lived then as
they do now in the wide valley of the Ganges, situated between
the Himalayas in the north and the plateau of Deccan in the
south. Eighteen centuries had to go by before the people of Europe got their first reliable information about this wonder-land
of Marco Polo. That happened when the Portuguese Vasco da
Gama reached Goa on the coast of Malabar.

Once the sea route from Europe to the land of the spices and
the elephants and the golden temples had been established, information poured in upon the geographers at such a vast rate
that the map-makers of Amsterdam were kept working over-
time. Since then every nook and corner of the teeming peninsula
has been thoroughly explored. This is the lay of the land in as
few words as possible.

In the north-west India is cut off from the rest of the world
by the Khirdar Mountains and the Suliman range which run
from the Arabian Sea as far as the Hindu Kush. In the north the
barrier consists of the Himalayas which run in a semi-circle all
the way from Hindu Kush to the Gulf of Bengal.

Please remember that everything connected with India is on
a scale which dwarfs the geographical proportions of Europe
and makes them look almost ridiculous. In the first place, India
itself is as large as all of Europe outside of Russia. The Hima-

India

layas, if they were a European mountain-range, would run from Calais to the Black Sea. The Himalayas have forty peaks which are higher than the highest mountain of Europe. Their glaciers are on the average four times as long as the glaciers of the Alps.

India is one of the hottest countries on earth and at the same time in several parts it has the records for the world's annual rainfall (1270 cm. per annum). It has a population of over 350,000,000 people who speak 150 different languages and dialects. Nine-tenths of them still depend for their livelihood upon their own crops and when the annual rainfall is insufficient, they die of starvation at a rate of 2,000,000 per year. (I am giving you the figures for the decade between 1890 and 1900.) But now that the English have stamped out the plague, have made an end to inter-racial warfare, have built vast irrigation works and have introduced the first rudiments of hygiene (paid for of course by the Indians themselves) they are increasing at such a rate that soon they will be just as badly off as they were in the days when pestilence and hunger and the death-rate of their babies kept the ghats of Benares working twenty-four hours each day.

The big rivers of India run parallel with the mountain-ranges. In the west it is the Indus which runs first of all through the Punjab and then breaks through the mountains of the north, where it provided the prospective conquerors from northern Asia with a convenient passage-way to the heart of Hindustan. As for the Ganges, the holy river of the Hindus, it follows a course which runs almost due east. Before it reaches the Gulf of Bengal, the Ganges is joined by the Brahmaputra which also takes its origin among the peaks of the Himalayas and which runs due east until it is forced to make a detour by the Khasi Hills, changes its course from east to west and shortly afterwards joins the Ganges.

The valleys of the Ganges and the Brahmaputra are the most densely populated part of all India. Only in China are there a few spots where quite so many millions of people must fight each other for the barest necessities of life. On the western banks of the moist and marshy delta of these two enormous rivers lies the city of Calcutta, the chief manufacturing center of India.

As for the products of the Ganges valley, more commonly known as Hindustan, or the land of the true Hindus, they are numerous and would probably be profitable if that whole part of the world did not suffer so hopelessly from chronic overpopulation. In the first place, there is rice. The people of India and Japan and Java do not eat rice because they happen to be so fond of it, but they eat rice because rice yields more food per square mile (and per square foot and per square inch) than any other plant that has thus far been domesticated.

The cultivation of rice is both difficult and messy. That is not a pleasant word, but it happens to be the only word that will adequately describe a procedure which forces hundreds of millions of men and women to spend the greater part of their time wading through mud and liquid manure. For the rice is originally sown in mud. When the little plants are about nine inches high they are dug out by hand and transplanted into flooded fields which must remain under water until it is time for the harvest, when the disgusting pap is allowed to run away by means of a highly complicated system of drainage ditches until it finally reaches the Ganges. At this point the Ganges provides both bathing and drinking water for the pious who have gathered together in Benares, the Rome of the Hindus and probably the oldest city in the world. By this time that putrid liquid has acquired such a degree of holiness that it can whiten sins which no other form of ablution could possibly hope to cleanse.

Another product of the Ganges valley is jute, a vegetable fibre which was first sent to Europe a century and a half ago to be used as a substitute for cotton and flax. Jute is the inner bark of a plant which needs almost as much moisture as rice. The bark itself has to be soaked in water for weeks before the fibre can be extracted and sent to the Calcutta factories to be changed into ropes and jute bags and a coarse sort of clothing which the natives wear.

Then there is the indigo plant from which we used to get our blue color until the recent discovery that it could be extracted much more economically from coal-tar.

Finally there is opium, which was originally grown to deaden the pain of that rheumatism which was inevitable in a country where the greater part of the population spent so much of its time slushing knee-deep through mud, cultivating its meagre daily portion of rice.

Outside of the valley on the slopes of the hills, tea plantations

Rice

have taken the place of the old forests. For the shrub which produces these tiny but valuable leaves needs a great deal of hot moisture and therefore grows best on mountain slopes where the water does not hurt the tender roots.

Southward of the Ganges valley lies the triangular plateau of Deccan which has three different types of vegetation. The northern mountains and those of the west are the center for the trade in teakwood, a very durable sort of timber which does not warp or shrink and which does not corrode iron. It used to be in great demand for ship-building purposes until the introduction of the iron steamer, but is still used for a number of purposes. The interior of Deccan, which has very little rain and is another dreaded hunger spot, raises cotton and a very little wheat.

As for the coastal regions, Malabar on the west and Coromandel on the east, they enjoy enough rain to support a large population providing them amply with rice and millet, a sort of grain which we import for chicken feed but which the natives of India eat instead of bread.

The Deccan is the only part of India where coal and iron and gold are found, but these deposits have never yet been seriously exploited, for the rivers of Deccan have too many rapids to be of any use, and the construction of railroads would hardly pay in a part of the world where the natives, being totally without worldly goods, never stir beyond their own villages.

The island of Ceylon, east of Cape Comorin, is really a part of the Indian peninsula. The Palk Strait which separates it from Deccan is so filled with reefs that it must be dredged continually in order to be kept navigable. The reefs and sandbanks which form a sort of natural bridge between Ceylon and the mainland are called Adam's Bridge, because Adam and Eve escaped that way from Paradise after they had incurred the wrath of God by their disobedience. For according to the people of this part of the world, Ceylon was the original Paradise. It still is a Paradise compared to the rest of India. Not only on account of the climate and its fertility and the abundance (but not superabundance) of rain and its moderate temperature, but because it has escaped one of the worst evils of India. By remaining faithful to Buddhism, which the Indians rejected as being of such sublime spiritual value as to be entirely beyond the grasp of the average man, it has escaped the rigors of the caste system which until very recently was an inseparable part of the Hindu religion.

Geography and religion are much more closely connected than we usually suppose. In India, where everything is done on a superlative scale, religion has since thousand of years dominated Man's mind so completely and absolutely that it has become an integral part of everything the Hindu says and thinks and does and eats and drinks or carefully avoids to say or do or eat or drink.

In other countries, too, religion has often interfered with the normal development of life. The Chinese, with their veneration for the departed ancestors, bury grandpa and grandma on the southern slopes of their mountains. That leaves them only the cold and wind-swept northern slopes open for the cultivation of their daily bread. As a result of this otherwise highly laudable affection for the departed relatives, their own children starve to death or are sold into slavery. Indeed almost every race (we ourselves included) is handicapped by strange taboos or mysterious ancient laws of divine origin which quite frequently interfere with the progress of the whole nation.

In order to understand how religion has affected the Hindu country, we must go back to almost prehistoric times, to at least thirty centuries before the first of the Greeks had reached the shores of the Aegean Sea.

At that time the Indian peninsula was inhabited by a race of dark-skinned people, the Dravidians, who were probably the original inhabitants of the Deccan. The Aryan stock (the same stock from which we ourselves have sprung) divided itself into two groups and left its ancient home in central Asia in search of more agreeable climes. One part moved westward and settled down in Europe, afterwards crossing the ocean and taking possession of northern America. The other trekked southwards through the mountain passes between the Hindu Kush and the Himalayas and took possession of the valleys of the Indus and the Ganges and the Brahmaputra and from there penetrated into the plateau of Deccan. By following the coastal region between the western Ghats and the Arabian Sea they finally reached southern India and Ceylon.

The newcomers, being infinitely better armed than the natives, treated the latter as the stronger races have always treated the weaker ones. They spoke derisively of them as the Black Men, took their rice fields away from them, stole their women whenever their own supply ran out (the trip across the Khyber

Pass was too difficult to let them bring many women all the way from central Asia), killed them whenever they showed the least signs of rebellion, and forced the survivors to retire to the most undesirable parts of the peninsula where they could live or

India is full of Indians

starve as they wanted. But there were by far more Dravidians than Aryans and as a result there was a constant menace that the lower form of civilization would influence the higher one. The only way by which this could be prevented was by keeping the Black Man strictly in his place.

Now the Aryans, like all the people of our race, have always had a tendency towards dividing society into a number of sharply differentiated social layers or castes. The idea of "caste" is known all over the world and it exists in America even in this year of enlightenment. It runs all the way from our discrimination against the Jews, based upon our unwritten code of social prejudice, to the formal laws of certain southern states which force Negroes to ride in Jim Crow cars. New York is a proverbially broad-minded city but I would not for the life of me know where to take a dark-skinned friend (Negro or Hindu or even Javanese) for dinner, and our trains pay homage to our feeling of caste by providing us with Pullman cars and day-coaches. I don't know much about the caste system of the Negroes in Harlem, but I have seen enough of the mortification of German-Jewish families when their daughters married men of Polish-Jewish descent to realize how wide-spread this feeling of "being something different from the common run of humanity" is in all of us.

But with us the caste system has never developed into a hard and fast rule of social and economic behavior. The doors leading from one class to another are supposed to be kept carefully closed but we all know that those who can push hard enough or who have a little golden key or who are merely able to make enough noise banging the windows outside will sooner or later be admitted. The conquering Aryans of the Indies, on the other hand, had the doors leading from one class to another filled up with masonry; and from that moment on each group of society was locked up in its own little compartment and it has been forced to stay there ever since.

Now a system like that is never an accident. People don't just suddenly invent it to please themselves or to be nasty to their neighbors. In India it was the result of fear. The priests and the warriors and the farmers and the day-laborers, the original classes of the Aryan conquerors, were of course hopelessly outnumbered by the Dravidians whose country they had just taken away. They were bound to take some desperate measure by which to keep the black man in "his proper place". But when they had done this, they went one step further, a step which no other race has ever quite dared to take. They gave their artificial "caste" system a religious twist and decreed that Brahmanism was to be the exclusive possession of the three upper classes, leaving their humbler brethren to shift for themselves outside the true spiritual pale. And thereupon, in order to keep themselves free from the defiling touch of all people of humbler birth, each individual caste surrounded itself by such a complicated barrier of ritual ceremonies and sacred usages that finally no one but a native was able to find his way in that maze of meaningless "verbotens".

If you want to know how such a system would work out in practical every-day life, try to imagine what would have happened to our own civilization if nobody during the last three thousand years had been allowed to proceed beyond the status of his father, grandfather or great-grandfather. What would have become of the personal initiative of the individual?

There are signs all around that India is on the eve of a great social and spiritual awakening, but until very recently such a change was deliberately held back by those who dominated all classes of Indian society, by the Brahmans, the hereditary members of the highest of all castes, that of the priests. The faith of which they were the undisputed leaders was known by the rather vague name of Brahmanism. Brahma, around whose personality this religion was built up, might be called the Zeus or Jupiter of the Hindu Olympus, the divine essence enhancing all creation, the beginning and end of all things. But Brahma, as a mere all-embodying idea, was much too vague, too unsubstantial for the average person, and therefore, while he continued to be worshipped in a general way as a venerable old gentleman who had done his duty when he created this world, the actual management of our planet was thought to have been surrendered to certain of Brahma's deputies, a number of Gods and Devils of not quite such excellent social standing as Brahma himself, but relatives of the All-Highest nevertheless, and as such to be treated with the utmost consideration.

That opened the door wide for the introduction of all sorts of strange, supernatural creatures, like Siva and Vishnu and a whole army of spirits and spooks and ghouls. They introduced the fear element into Brahmanism. People no longer tried to be good because being good was in itself something after which Man should strive but because it was the only way in which he could hope to escape the wrath of all the evil ogres.

Buddha, the great reformer who was born six centuries before Christ and who knew what a noble thing Brahmanism in its purer form could be, tried to make the prevailing creed of his day the spiritual power it had been once upon a time. But although at first he was victorious, his ideas proved too unpractical, too noble, too elevated for the vast majority of his fellow-countrymen. As soon as the first enthusiasm had died down, the old Brahmans returned in full force. It is only during the last fifty years that the leaders of India have come to realize that a religion based (as far as the man in the street is concerned) almost completely upon ritual and empty ceremonial acts of devotion must eventually perish as a hollow tree must perish when it no longer is able to extract its nourishment from the living earth. And Hinduism is no longer that dead and hideous spiritual affliction which it may have been a few generations ago. The doors and windows of the old temples are being opened up wide. The younger men and women of India are conscious of the disaster that might have destroyed them if, divided against themselves, they had been unable to offer a united front against the foreign master. Strange things are happening along the banks of the Ganges. When strange things happen among 350,000,000 people, they are apt to form a new chapter in the history of the world.

India, although it has several large towns, is still essentially a country of villages, for 71% of the people continue to live in the country. The rest are spread among the cities of which you should at least know the names. There is Calcutta, at the mouth of the Ganges and Brahmaputra. It began as an insignificant fishing village, but during the eighteenth century it became the

center for Clive's operations against the French and developed
into the leading harbor of all India. It lost a great deal of its
former importance when the Suez Canal was opened, because
steamers found it more convenient to go directly to Bombay or
to Karachi than to Calcutta when they happened to have a cargo
for the Indus region or the Punjab. Bombay on its little island
is also a creation of the East India Company, which intended to
use it as a naval base and a harbor of export for the Deccan cotton trade. It was so eminently suited for this purpose that it attracted settlers from all over Asia and became the home of the
last remaining group of followers of the Persian prophet,
Zoroaster. These Parsees belong to the richest and most intelligent group of natives. Their worship of fire as something holy
which must not be defiled, makes it impossible for them to burn
their dead. Hence Bombay has attracted a sort of lugubrious attention as the city where the Parsee corpses are thrown to the
vultures, a form of extinction which is so swift that it seems almost preferable to the slower method of being eaten by ordinary worms.

On the eastern shores of the Deccan peninsula lies Madras,
the main port of the coast of Coromandel. The French city of
Pondicherry, a little towards the south, is a reminder of the
days when the French were the most serious rivals of the English and when Dupleix and Clive fought for the possession of
the whole of India, in that war that led up to the ghastly incident
of the Black Hole of Calcutta.

But most of the important cities are naturally situated in the
valley of the Ganges. In the west there is first of all Delhi, the
old residence of the Mogul emperors who had chosen this city
because it commanded the entrance gate from central Asia into
the valley of the Ganges so thoroughly that he who was master
of Delhi was also master of all India. Further down the river
lies Agra, the residence of four members of the Mogul dynasty,
one of whom erected the Taj-Mahal in memory of a woman
whom he had greatly loved. Still further towards the south

is Allahabad, a holy city of the Mohammedans, as the name implies. In this same neighborhood lie Lucknow and Cawnpore, well known for their connection with the great mutiny of 1857.

Then further down the river we reach Benares, the Rome and Mecca of all good Hindus who not only come here to bathe in the holy waters of the river but also to die that they may be burned in one of the ghats on its shores and their ashes strewn upon the river of their desire.

But I had better stop right here. Whenever you touch upon a subject of India, whether you approach it as an historian, a chemist, a geographer, an engineer or a mere traveller, you find yourself right in the heart of profound moral and spiritual problems. And we people of the west should proceed carefully when we enter into this labyrinth in which we are both strangers and newcomers.

Two thousand years before the learned councils of holy men in Nicea and Constantinople tried to formulate the creed which afterwards was to conquer the western world, the ancestors of these people about whom I am writing in so familiar a fashion had already settled obscure points of doctrine and faith which to this very day disturb the minds of my own neighbors and will probably continue to disturb them for another dozen centuries or so. It is easy, far too easy, to condemn things that are strange to us. Most of what I know about India is strange to me and gives me a feeling of discomfort, a bewildered sense of uneasy irritation.

But then I remember that I used to feel the same way towards my grandfather and grandmother.

And now at last I am beginning to realize that they were right. Or at least, that, if they were not always entirely right, neither were they always as absolutely wrong as I used to think them to be. It was a hard lesson. But it tended to teach me a little humility. And Heaven knows, I needed it!

XXXVI

BURMA, SIAM, ANAM AND MALACCA, WHICH OCCUPY THE OTHER GREAT SOUTHERN PENINSULA OF ASIA

THE peninsula which contains these four ancient kingdoms, independent, semi-independent and subject, is four times as large as the Balkan peninsula. The first of the four when we start from the west, Burma, enjoyed complete independence until the year 1885 when the English, to the general approval of the natives and the world at large, sent the last of the local rulers into exile and annexed the country and made it part of their empire. Nobody objected much except the king himself but he was a true representative of a type that has no longer any reason to exist, except in the movies, the proverbial "Oriental potentate" who as a rule was nothing but an undetected lunatic. Needless to say that he was not even a local product but an import from the north. The peninsula as a whole has suffered a good deal from that kind of gentry. The situation of the local mountain-ranges was chiefly responsible. Whereas India was cut off from the north by high mountains which ran from east to west and therefore enjoyed a certain natural protection, the whole of this unfortunate peninsula is taken up by five independent mountain ridges which run from south to north and thereby offer almost ideal means of access to any one wishing to move from the harsh grass-land of central Asia to the rich coast-land of the Bay of Bengal and the Gulf of Siam and the South China Sea. And the sort of men bred by central Asia we have already met wherever our maps were dotted by an abundance of ruined cities and pillaged farms.

Lest you should shed unnecessary tears over the fate of the last of the independent Burmese potentates, know ye that in order to celebrate his accession to the throne he had revived the good old Asiatic custom of killing all his relatives. The Turkish sultans had always done that as a mere matter of precaution, like taking out accident insurance when you are elected president of a South American republic. But in the eighties of the last century the story of these hundred odd brothers and cousins and nephews, slaughtered in cold blood, did not read quite so well, and an English governor took the place of the former monarch. Since then the country, whose population consists of only three percent Hindus but ninety percent Buddhists, has greatly prospered and the Irrawaddy River, which is navigable all the way from Rangoon to Mandalay, has become an artery of trade such as it had never been before. It has seen more rice boats and oil tankers and ships of all sorts than ever before during its long history.

As for Siam, the country just east of Burma and separated from it by the Dawna Range and the Tanen-Tanng-gyi Mountains, it owes its continued independence to a combination of circumstances of which the mutual jealousy between England in the west and France in the east is most certainly not one of the least important. And furthermore, Siam has been singularly fortunate in its rulers. Old King Chulalongkorn, who held the throne for over forty years, was a descendant of a Chinaman who during the latter half of the eighteenth century had delivered Siam from the Burmese. By cleverly playing his western neighbors against those from the east, and by a few trivial concessions and above all things by not surrounding himself with English and French advisers but by choosing his experts from among the much less dangerous smaller nations, this enlightened Siamese reduced the number of analphabets in his domains from 90% to 20%, founded a university, developed railroads, made the Menam River navigable for over 400 miles, installed an excellent postal and telegraphic system and trained his army sufficiently well to make himself not only a desirable ally but also a potentially dangerous enemy.

Bangkok on the Menam delta grew until it finally had almost a million inhabitants, a great many of whom still live on rafts anchored in the river, which gives Bangkok the aspect of a sort of eastern Venice. Instead of closing the country to foreign immigration, the industrious Chinese were liberally encouraged to settle down in the capital and they now form one-ninth of the total population and have greatly contributed towards making Siam one of the most important rice exporting nations. The interior is still densely covered with very valuable forests and teakwood is an important article of export. And good luck or good sense made the Siamese rulers retain at least a part of the Malacca peninsula which contains the richest tin deposits of the world.

On the whole, however, the government of Siam has been opposed to the industrialization of the country. The inhabitants of all tropical lands will have to remain primarily interested in agriculture and other simple pursuits if they wish to survive. Siam seems to be one of the few Asiatic countries where the desirability of such a policy has been understood. Let Europe have its factories and slums, as long as Asia can keep its villages and fields. They may not be the sort of villages the westerling likes, but they suit the eastern temperament, and the factory does not.

By the way, the agricultural riches of Siam are somewhat different from those of most other countries. Outside of a million hogs, raised by the Chinese, the country can boast of no less than 6,000,000 tame buffaloes and 6822 elephants, which are in domestic service and hire out as derricks and trucks.

French Indo-China, the name usually given to all the French possessions in the peninsula, consists of five parts. The first one of these, going from south to north, is Cambodia, which occupies the valley of the big Mekong River as far as the delta. It raises cotton and grows pepper. Nominally it is still a kingdom, but under French supervision. In the interior, in the midst of the dense forests just north of the great lake called Tonlé-Sap, lie some of the most interesting ruins that have ever been uncovered. They were built by a mysterious race, the Khmers, of whom we know remarkably little. During the ninth century of our era, these Khmers built themselves a capital in northern

Cambodia called Angkor. It was no small affair, for the walls formed a square each side of which was not less than two miles long and thirty feet high. At first, under the influence of Hindu missionaries, the Khmers were Brahmans, but in the tenth century Buddhism was accepted as the official religion of the state. The spiritual explosion caused by this change from Brahmanism to Buddhism found an expression in the construction of a vast number of temples and palaces, all of which were built between the twelfth and fifteenth centuries when Angkor, the capital, was destroyed, leaving behind those most stupendous architectural ruins, compared to which the far famed efforts of our own Mayans were the work of simple-minded beginners.

There is a theory that Angkor was originally built on the sea and long before the delta of the Mekong had been formed. But in that case, the sea would have retreated more than 300 miles. That would be a record. For in historical times the sea has never retreated much more than five miles in the case of Ravenna and seven miles in the case of Pisa. The why and how and wherefore of Angkor will probably always remain a secret. But here stood a city that was as important in its time as New York is today. And it is gone. It has become a subject for picture postal cards, sold at a penny a piece to the visitors of the Paris colonial exhibition. And yet, once upon a time, it was a center of civilization while Paris was still a collection of evil-smelling mud hovels. It is all very strange!

As for the delta of the Mekong, today it is part of the French colony of Cochin-China which the French occupied in 1867 when their imperial prestige needed a little boosting after the disastrous failure of the great Mexican expedition. It has one excellent harbor, Saigon, where a few thousand French officials eagerly await the day when they can return to the home country to rest in peace and honor from their difficult labors in administering the four million Cochin-China entrusted to their care.

To the east of Cochin-China lies Anam, which also continues to be a kingdom although since 1886 it has enjoyed the "protection" of the French. The interior produces timber but the coun-

The mountain passes of Asia

try is mountainous and has no roads and has therefore remained almost completely undeveloped.

Tongking in the north is much more important because it not only has an excellent river, the Song-Koi, but also on account of the presence of coal and cement. It really is a part of China and as such raises and exports cotton, silk and sugar. Its capital is Hanoi which since 1902 is the chief seat of government for all the French possessions in Indo-China. These include, beside the four countries just mentioned, a narrow strip of land in the interior, called Laos, annexed in 1893, and which I set down here merely for the sake of vital statistics. The southernmost part of this big peninsula is divided into two parts. The so-called "Federated Malay States" consist of four small semi-independent principalities under British protection, and the rest is a crown colony known administratively as the Straits Settlements. It was exceedingly important for England to get hold of the Malay peninsula, for the mountains, which sometimes rise to a height of 8000 feet, contain some very rich tin deposits and the climate allows a vast variety of tropical products to be grown here at practically no cost. Rubber, coffee, pepper, tapioca and gambier (necessary in the dyers' trade) are exported in large quantities from Penang, on the straits of Malacca, and from Singapore, a city of over half a million inhabitants, situated on a small island which controls all the great sea routes between north and south and east and west.

Singapore, the Lion City, is almost as old as Chicago, having been built by that famous Sir Stamford Raffles who foresaw the strategic importance of this point while administering the Dutch colonial possessions during the time Holland was part of the Napoleonic empire. In 1819 Singapore was a jungle. Today it has more than 500,000 inhabitants, the strangest variety and hodge-podge of races and languages to be found almost anywhere in the Orient. It is as strongly fortified as Gibraltar and is the terminal station of a railroad line which connects it with Bangkok in Siam, but not as yet with Rangoon in Burma. It will play a great role when the inevitable clash between the east and the west finally takes place. In anticipation of that event, it maintains a set of bar-rooms, the splendor of which is famous all over the Orient, and loses almost as much money on the annual races as the city of Dublin.

XXXVII

THE REPUBLIC OF CHINA, THE GREAT PENINSULA OF EASTERN ASIA

CHINA is a very large country. It has a circumference of 8000 miles, a distance about equal to the diameter of the globe, and it is larger than the whole European continent.

The Chinese people form fully one-fifth of the total population of our planet and they knew how to use gunpowder and how to write letters at a time when our ancestors still painted their faces a pale blue and hunted the wild boar with a stone axe. To give an adequate description of such a country in a few pages is out of the question. All I can give you is a sketch, an outline. The details (if you are interested) you can afterwards fill in by yourself, for there is enough literature on China to upholster two or three libraries.

China, like India, is a peninsula, but a semi-circular peninsula, not a triangular one. In another very important way it is different from India. No obliging mountain-range cuts it off from the rest of the world. On the contrary, the mountains of China resemble the fingers of a hand stretching out westward. In consequence thereof, the rich Chinese plains bordering upon the Yellow Sea have at all times been wide open to the hardy pioneers of central Asia.

In order to overcome this handicap, the Chinese emperors of the third century before our era (the period during which Rome and Carthage fought for the mastery of the Mediterranean) constructed a gigantic wall, 1500 miles long and 20 feet wide and more than 30 feet high, which ran all the way from the Gulf of Liao-tung to Kiayu-Kwan, just west of Su-chow on the borders of the Gobi Desert.

This granite barrier has done its duty well and honorably. In the seventeenth century it fell before the onslaughts of the Manchus. All the same, a fortification which has held its own for almost twenty centuries is no mere trifle. Those we build nowadays are useless after ten years and have then got to be renewed at enormous cost.

As for China proper, not counting in Mongolia and Manchuria (which at the time of writing this chapter seems to be rapidly falling into the hands of the Japanese) and Tibet and Turkestan, it is a vast circle neatly divided into three almost equal parts by the Yangtsze-Kiang in the south and the Hwang-Ho in the north. The northern part, in which Peking is situated, has very cold winters and moderately hot summers, as a result of which the people eat millet and no rice. The central part, protected against the winds from the north by the Tsing-ling-shan range, has a much warmer climate and a much denser population which eats rice and does not know the sight or taste of grain. The third part, south China, has warm winters and very hot and moist summers and raises everything that will grow in the tropics.

Northern China is again divided into two parts, the mountain regions of the west and the plains of the east. These mountain regions of the west are the famous loess country. Loess is a very fine sort of loam, looking a yellowish gray, and it is very porous, as a result of which the rain of Heaven disappears as fast as it touches the earth, while rivers and brooks cut themselves deep ravines which makes travel from one part of the country to the other as difficult as it is in Spain.

The plain of the east is situated on the Gulf of Chih-li which is so rapidly being filled up with the deposits carried down by the Hwang-Ho that it is almost unnavigable and has no good harbor. A little further towards the north there is another river, much smaller than the Hwang-Ho but quite as useless from the point of view of navigation. That is the Pei-Ho, which has the distinction of being the Chicago River of Peking, the great drainage canal which looks after the sewage disposal of the Chinese capital. As conditions in China change from hour to

The Big Chinese Rivers

hour I will merely say that Peking has been the capital of the
Celestial Empire for nine centuries, or ever since the days when
William the Bastard conquered England, but that I have no idea
whether at the time this book goes to press it will be the Chinese
capital, a mere Chinese city or the temporary or definite residence of a Japanese general.

It is however a very ancient town and it has seen a great many
ups and downs. In 986 it was conquered by the Tartars who rebaptised it Nanking or the "southern capital". In the twelfth
century the Chinese recaptured it but did not care to retain it as
their capital and made it a second-rate provincial center, called
Yen-shan Fu. Half a century later it was once more taken by
another Tartar tribe who now called it Chung-tu or the "central
capital". Another century later it was occupied by Genghis Khan,
who however refused to come and live there in fatuous ease but
remained faithful to his tent in the heart of the Mongolian Desert. One of his successors, the famous Kublai Khan, felt differently. He rebuilt the ruins of Peking and baptised them Yenking or "the great court", although at that time they were better
known by their Mongolian name of Cambaluc or the "city of
the Khan".

Finally these Tartars were expelled too, and a king of Chinese origin, the first one of the famous Ming dynasty, mounted
the throne. Yenking or the "great court" then became Peking or
the "north court". As Peking it has ever since remained the
center of the Chinese government, but so far removed from the
rest of the world that it was not until the year 1860 that a European ambassador was allowed to visit the capital in his official
capacity and with all the pomp and circumstance befitting a man
whose father had given the British Museum the Elgin marbles.

The city in the hey-day of its power must have been tremendously strong. The walls were sixty feet thick and almost fifty
feet high and defended by square towers and gateways which
were fortresses in themselves. On the inside, the city was like a
Chinese puzzle, containing a number of smaller cities, the one
inside of the other, an imperial city, and a Manchu city and a

Chinese city and, after the middle of the nineteenth century, a foreign city.

Until the Boxer outbreak of 1900 the foreign diplomatic representatives lived in a small square of their own just between the

The Chinese wall is the only structure made by
human hands that would be visible by the
astronomers of the moon

Manchu city and the Chinese city. After the siege, this diplomatic ghetto was strongly fortified and heavily garrisoned with troops of the different countries to prevent a recurrence of this most unfortunate incident. Peking, of course, contains a number of palaces and temples. But here I would like to draw attention to a very interesting difference between the temperaments of the people of China and those of India which explains to a certain degree why these two countries have practically nothing in common except that they are both of them hopelessly overpopulated.

The Hindus have always taken their Gods very seriously and when they built them a temple it must be the biggest, the most expensive and the showiest temple the money of the poor sweating peasants could buy. "Not a cent for public improvements, but millions for the Gods!" was the slogan of the Brahmans. The Chinese are nominally Buddhists but every Chinaman from the humblest laundry-man in Mott Street to the most powerful of the old Mandarins had fallen under the influence of that shrewd old sage, Kung-fu-tsze or Confucius, who during the second half of the sixth century had preached his gospel of common, everyday horse-sense without wasting much time upon vague discussions about the Life Hereafter. And it was completely in keeping with the Confucian notions about the "sensible thing to do" that the Chinese rulers spent the greater part of their revenue upon public improvements, upon canals and irrigation dams and Chinese walls and river improvements, but just enough upon their temples and shrines not to make the Gods feel that they were in any way being slighted.

As the ancient Chinese were a people of tremendous artistic ability, they could achieve much more satisfactory results and at a much smaller cost than the natives of the Ganges valley. It is true that nowhere in China does the traveller find anything at all comparable to the vast structures of India. A few gigantic statues of animals guarding the gardens of the Ming rulers, some sixty miles north of Peking, and here and there a large Buddha. That is all. The rest is of modest dimensions, albeit of excellent proportions. But curiously enough, the art of China appeals to the people of the west much more than does the art of India. Chinese paintings and sculptures and pottery and lacquer-work fit into a European or American home, whereas their Indian counterparts disturb the harmony and are slightly upsetting, even when seen in a museum.

To the modern business world China is important because it has very large coal deposits and the second largest iron deposits

in the world. When the English and German and American
mines get exhausted, we can still go to the province of Shan-si
to keep warm.

To the south-east of the province of Chih-li lies the province
of Shan-tung with the peninsula of that name which separates
the Gulf of Chih-li from the Yellow Sea. This part of China is
very mountainous, except for the valley of the Hwang-Ho,
which formerly ran due south into the Yellow Sea. But it
changed its course suddenly in 1852, and that little affair showed
us that a flood in China really meant a flood. In order to find a
parallel for the Hwang-Ho's behavior we would have to imagine the Rhine suddenly making up its mind to flow into the
Baltic or the Seine deciding to run into the North Sea instead of
the Gulf of Biscay. As the Hwang-Ho has changed its mouth
ten times since the end of the seventeenth century we are by no
means certain that the present channel will be definite. Dikes
and dams which in other parts of the world are apt to keep a river
within bounds are of no avail against such rivers as the
Hwang-Ho and the Yang-tsze, for the dikes through which the
river broke in the year 1852 were fifty feet high and they tore
apart like tissue paper.

And then there is something else that makes these rivers such
a nuisance. You must have heard the Chinese referred to as the
yellow race and you must have seen articles in the newspapers
about the Yellow Peril, etc., etc. As a rule we associate the idea
of yellow and Chinese with the color of a Chinaman's face. But
when the emperors of China called themselves Hwang-ti, which
meant Lord of the Yellow Earth, they were not thinking of their
subjects but of the land inhabited by these subjects. The yellow
loess mud carried down by the Hwang-Ho turns everything in
northern China yellow—the water of the river, the water of the
sea, the roads, the houses, the fields, the clothes of the men and
women. And it is that yellow dust which has given its name to a
race which for the rest is really not much more yellow than the
average city dweller of the west.

In order to permit his subjects to proceed from northern

China to central and southern China without running the risk of a long sea voyage, one of the Chinese emperors who lived during the thirteenth century ordered a canal to be built that should connect the Hwang-Ho with the Yangtsze-Kiang. It was more than a thousand miles long and fulfilled its purpose faithfully until the year 1852 when the Hwang-Ho moved from the Yellow Sea to the Gulf of Chih-li and the canal was destroyed together with the old river bed. But this Grand Canal, the longest in the world, shows that the ancient rulers of the land were men of enlightened views.

But to return to the peninsula of Shan-tung. Its hard granite coast has been responsible for the formation of several very important harbors. One of those, Wei-hai-wei, just east of Chi-fu, was until recently in English hands. The British had "rented" it from China when Russia occupied Port Arthur on the other side of the Gulf of Chih-li to use it as a naval base and a station of their Trans-Siberian railroad. The "renting contract" stipulated that England should withdraw as soon as the Russians had disappeared from the Liao-tung peninsula. But when Japan took Port Arthur in 1905, the English remained. The Germans, not to be outdone, must then occupy the bay of Kiao-Chow, further towards the south, and the city of Tsing-tao, both of them also parts of the Shan-tung peninsula. This meant that the Great War also had its reverberations in the Far East. Germans and Britons fought for the possession of something which belonged to neither of them and, as usually happens in such cases, a third party, the Japanese, got away with the stolen goods.

In order to regain a little of the goodwill of the Chinese, Wei-hai-wei and Kiao-Chow have since been returned to China. But if Japan succeeds in taking Manchuria, the old game will probably begin all over again. Look for the details in the next edition.

In the east central China consists of a wide and fertile plain which is really the continuation of the plain of northern China, but the interior is mountainous. Through these mountains the Yangtsze-Kiang wends its tortuous way until at last it reaches

the East China Sea. It takes its origin in the province of Sze-
chuen, a region almost as large as France, but supporting a much
larger population as the red soil is exceedingly fertile. Several
mountain-ranges running from south to north cut it almost completely off from the rest of the world. As a result it has suffered
but little from the visitation of the White Man and is distinctly
more Chinese than the rest of China.

Continuing its course towards the sea, the Yangtsze next trav-
erses the province of Hu-peh where the famous city of Han-
kow is situated. This was the center of the revolution of 1911
which upset the last emperor of the Manchu dynasty and turned
the oldest monarchy in the world into a republic. Up to Han-
kow the Yangtsze is navigable for sea-going vessels with a displacement of not more than 1000 tons. Below Hankow, the
river is the main artery of commerce for central China until it
reaches Shanghai, the center of China's foreign trade and one
of the first Chinese harbors which was opened to foreign commerce at the conclusion of the so-called "opium war" between
England and China in the year 1840–1842.

To the south of the Yangtsze delta lies Hang-chow, which
Marco Polo knew as Kinsai, and in the east Su-chow, the name
of which suggests tea. The suggestion is correct. The lower part
of the Yangtsze valley is very fertile and it was for this reason
that Nanking, which is situated where the Yangtsze begins its
delta, was for a long time not only the most important city of
central China but also the residence of its emperor.

Partly on account of its historical past and partly on account
of its strategic position, half-way between Canton and Peking,
and partly because it is not directly menaced by the guns of foreign warships, the city of Nanking was chosen as the center of
that government which at the moment of writing (Jan. 2, 1932,
seven minutes past midnight) seems to be the "official government" of China.

As for southern China, it is a mountainous country and, although it raises tea and silk and cotton, it has always been a comparatively poor region. Once upon a time it was covered with

forests, but the forests were cut down and the soil was washed away by the rain, and the bare rocks remained. Hence wholesale emigration to all parts of the world which have not yet passed laws restricting the number of Chinese visitors.

The most important city in southern China is Canton, which is the main harbor of import into China just as Shanghai is the most important center for export to Europe. At the mouth of the Canton River (the city itself is a few miles inland) lie two foreign possessions. On the right bank, Macao, all that remains of the Portuguese possessions in China and now merely a sort of oriental Monte Carlo, and Hong-Kong, a city which the English took during the opium war and have kept ever since.

Of the two islands off the coast of southern China, Hai-nan is still Chinese, but Formosa, an old Dutch colony, has belonged to Japan since the Chinese-Japanese War of 1894–1895.

Ninety percent of the Chinese are, always have been and probably always will be farmers who live on their own products and starve when there is a bad season. But forty-eight harbors have been opened up for the foreign trade and their main exports are silk and tea and cotton. Curiously enough, there is no export of opium. The Chinese emperors have always tried to protect their people against this unfortunate habit-forming drug and gradually the old poppy fields have been changed into cotton fields.

As for railroads, the Chinese fought the idea longer than any other nation because, with their respect for the memory of their parents and ancestors, they feared to upset the peaceful slumbers of these departed worthies when the engines should come thundering down the roads of iron. The few miles built in 1875 between Shanghai and Wu Sung, its harbor, caused such a storm of protest that they were immediately discontinued. And even today the Chinese railroads describe wide circles around all cemeteries. Still, there are now over 10,000 miles of railroad in actual use and the bridge across the Hwang-Ho near Tsi-nan is the biggest railroad bridge in the world.

As for China's foreign trade, almost 60% is still in the hands of England and her colonies and that probably explains why England has been obliged to discontinue her old ruthless policy towards the inhabitants of the Celestial Empire. A boycott of English goods by these industrious Celestials would mean a loss

The Grand Canal in China

of millions of dollars a day. It is good policy to keep on friendly terms with a customer who happens to represent the interests of one-fifth of the entire human race.

When the earliest ancestors of the Chinese dimly emerged from the nebulous realm of the past, they were already living on the Yellow Earth along the banks of the Hwang-Ho, north-west from the heart of the present China. The fertile loess fields must have been very desirable in the eyes of an agricultural people.

Furthermore it also settled the housing problem, for it allowed a man to dig himself a comfortable little home in the side of a convenient hill and not bother about draughty walls or a roof that leaked.

According to reliable accounts of travellers who are familiar with that part of the world, there are spots which are known to be densely populated but where one fails to see a single vestige of human habitation until the first rays of light tell of the coming of another day. Then, like so many rabbits who swarm out of their holes to enjoy the sun, those men, women and children begin their endless tasks of gathering food until eventide, when they disappear once more into the bowels of the earth.

Having occupied the mountains, the Chinese then spread eastward. The turbulent Hwang-Ho carried millions of tons of mountain loess into the plains and thereby fertilized them until they were fit to support further millions of human beings. The Chinese followed in the wake of the river and twenty centuries before the beginning of our era (1500 years before the founding of Rome) the Chinese had wandered as far as the Yangtsze and the center of their empire had been moved from the Hwang-Ho region to the great plain of central China.

During the fifth and fourth centuries before the birth of Christ, three great moral teachers arose among them, Kung-fu-tsze or Confucius, Mang-tsze or Mencius, and Lao-tsze, whose name has not been latinized. What the religious conceptions of the Chinaman were at the time these three prophets made their appearance, we do not know. Nature apparently was worshipped as the forces of Nature will always be worshipped by those who depend upon them for their living, and not Confucius nor Mencius nor Lao-tsze were religious founders in the sense of the word as applied to Christ or Buddha or Mahommed.

They merely taught a moral code based upon the acceptance of man as a pretty inferior and not very brilliant product of creation but capable of great development provided he fell into good hands and was willing to listen to the precepts of his elders and betters. From our own Christian point of view, these three can of course be accused of preaching a very worldly and decidedly materialistic doctrine. None of them said much about humility and meekness or preached that we must return good for evil. They knew that the average man was not capable of such noble and elevated deeds, and furthermore they seem to have doubted whether such a rule of conduct was really for the ultimate good of the community at large. Wherefore they suggested such things as that evil should be answered with justice and that one should pay one's bills and keep contracts and honor the memory of honorable ancestors.

These three Chinese philosophers spread their morality pretty thin but every one got at least a smear of it. I don't say that this was a better system than ours or a worse one. But it was a system not devoid of certain very definite advantages. It gave a people consisting of 400,000,000 different individuals, speaking a couple of dozen different dialects (a Chinaman from the north finds it just as hard to understand a brother Chinaman from the south as a Swede trying to make conversation with an Italian) and living under entirely different circumstances, at least one thing in common—a decidedly Chinese attitude towards the ups and downs of life, a practical philosophy of existence which will pull the humblest of coolies through hardships that would either kill the average European or American or would drive him to commit suicide.

And these ideas were sufficiently simple to be understood by almost every one. As a proof whereof I refer you to the miracles of assimilation performed by the Chinese during the 4000 years of their history. They are preposterous and at the same time fabulous. During the tenth century China became part of the greatest empire that ever existed, that Mongolian commonwealth that reached from the Baltic to the Pacific. But all those Mongolian rulers were like Kublai Khan. They ended by becoming Chinamen. After the Mongolians came the Mings (1368–1644), the last purely Chinese dynasty to rule the country. They were succeeded by a Tartar prince who came from Manchuria and who was the founder of the Manchu dynasty.

But although the Chinese, as a token of submission to their Manchu masters, were forced to grow their hair long and wear a pig-tail and shave the rest of their heads, the Manchus soon became even more Chinese than the Chinamen themselves.

After the last Manchu invasion the Chinese were left completely to themselves and by merely guarding their harbors against all foreign visitors from the west, the civilization of China had a chance to settle down for a little rest. But the moment it did this, it petrified more completely than any other country of which we have ever heard. Its political system became even more rigid than that of the old Russia of pre-revolutionary days. Literature froze, even their incomparable art became as stereotyped as that of the Byzantine mosaic makers of ancient Constantinople. Science no longer made any progress. If by chance some one still happened to invent something new it was at once discarded as foolish and undesirable, just as the medical department of our own army tried to discourage the use of chloroform because it was both new and foolish. Because they were cut off so completely from the rest of the world and never had a chance of finding out what other nations were doing, it was easy for the Chinese to convince themselves that their own methods were best, that their own army was invincible, that their own art was the most sublime art ever wrought by the hands of human beings and that their own customs and habits were so superior to those of all other nations that it was ridiculous to compare the two. Many other countries have in a mild way tried such a policy of exclusion but it has always ended in disaster.

Since the early half of the sixteenth century the Chinese had allowed a few "foreign devils", hailing from Portugal and England and Holland, to settle in two or three of their Pacific ports for the sake of the profits that were to be derived from the trade with Europe. But the social status of those unfortunate foreigners had been most unsatisfactory. They were treated like a respectable colored doctor who by chance is obliged to travel on the same boat with a delegation of the descendants of Virginia's first settlers.

When England in 1816 sent Lord Amherst (nephew of Jeffrey and the man who interviewed Napoleon on St. Helena in 1817) to ask the Son of Heaven to mitigate the hardships from which the English merchants suffered in Canton, he was told that an interview with the Celestial Majesty depended upon his willingness to kow-tow before the imperial throne. The kow-tow, which literally meant "knocking the head three times upon the ground before the sacred throne" was something which a Dutch sea-captain could afford to do, for once he had kow-towed himself out of the reception room he knew that he could take home enough tea or spices to be comfortable for the rest of his life. But the representative of His British Majesty was somewhat differently placed. Lord Amherst curtly refused and as a result was not even allowed to enter the gates of Peking.

Meanwhile Europe, growing rich in consequence of the invention of James Watt and the application of steam for the purpose of exploiting our little planet, was clamoring for new worlds to conquer. China of course was No. 1 on the list. The direct excuse for the outbreak of hostilities was not exactly flattering to the pride of the white race, least of all for that part of it which ever since 1807, when Dr. Morrison had reached Canton as the first European missionary, had been telling the Chinese what a fine thing Christianity really was and why they should give it a chance. Even those pedantic and narrow-minded Mandarins (merely a Chinese title for administrator) who then ruled China were still sufficiently steeped in the teachings of Confucius to refuse to let their people be exposed to the unlimited importation of opium. But the British India Company was making millions of pounds out of the sale of poppy-seed to the people of the Yangtsze and the Hwang-Ho. The British India Company insisted upon importing opium into China and the Chinese authorities refused to let the stuff be landed. Opium and hurt feelings then led to the war of 1840 in which the Chinese, to their dumbfounded surprise, discovered that they were absolutely no match for the despised foreigners and that during the centuries of voluntary seclusion they had dropped so far behind the rest of humanity that it was doubtful whether they would ever be able to catch up.

This fear bids fair to come true. Ever since the disastrous days of the Opium War, China has been completely at the mercy of the westerner. The Chinese people, who are apt to go on plowing and harvesting, no matter who is fighting in the adjacent fields, have at times given evidence of the fact that they are beginning to realize that something is wrong with their country. The first outbreak of discontent occurred about eighty years ago. The Chinese then blamed the disasters of their hapless land upon the "foreign" Manchu dynasty and rose up in rebellion to set themselves free.

While the Manchus were engaged in a war with England and France, southern China started the so-called Tai-ping rebellion. They ceased to shave their heads and they cut off their pig-tails, but the imperial armies, led at first by an American engineer named Ward and afterwards by an Englishman, a certain Charles George Gordon, a sincere Christian and a profound mystic, were much too powerful for the poor misguided revolutionists. The "Emperor" whom they had elected to replace the Manchus burned himself alive with all his wives and concubines in his residence in the city of Nanking. Hundreds of thousands of people were executed and Gordon returned to England to devote himself to acts of charity and piety, performed in his leisure hours when he was not drilling troops, and to prepare for his tragic end of which you shall hear in the chapter on Africa.

Then in 1875 there was a slight difference of opinion between the Manchus and Germany, and Germany sent a squadron to purify the Chinese coast of pirates. During 1884 and 1885 there was a war with France which cost the Chinese Anam and Tong-king, and in 1894 there was a war with Japan, now thoroughly Europeanized, which ended with the cession of the island of Formosa.

Then began the great European rush for armaments and strategic points. The Russians took Port Arthur, the English took Wei-hai-wei, the Germans took Kiao-Chow and the French took Kiang Hung on the left bank of the Mekong River. America, which has thus far always mixed sentiment (and often, alas, sentimentality) with its foreign policies, talked vaguely about "maintaining the open door" and the European nations were turning the territory they had stolen into impregnable fortresses and closed the door whenever their uncle from across the ocean was not looking.

The Chinese people, patient and plodding though they are by nature, began to grasp the fact that they were being cheated right and left. Once more holding the foreign Manchu dynasty responsible for all their humiliations and misery, they started the unfortunate Boxer rebellion of the year 1901. They began their operations by murdering the German ambassador (their plausible excuse was that he had first struck a Chinaman) and then besieged the foreign legations in Peking. As a result an army of Russians, Japanese, Englishmen, Austrians, Germans, Italians, French and Americans marched to the relief of the sorely beset foreign quarter, saved the ministers and their families from an untimely end, and then by way of retribution plundered Peking as that rich city had never been looted before. The Forbidden City, the heart of the imperial residence, was broken into. Nothing was spared, no matter how holy it might be to the Chinese, and the German commander-in-chief, who arrived with an extra 20,000 men (when the shooting was already over but the plundering still in full swing) had been instructed by his imperial master to "follow in the footsteps of the Huns"—an unfortunate expression which came home to roost a little over a dozen years later and which was one of the worst boomerangs old Wilhelm ever sent forth during the days when he indulged in that sport in preference to his present craze for chopping wood.

Condemned to pay enormous indemnities and humiliated in every possible way by their ever more aggressive European neighbors, the Chinese people once more rose in rebellion in the year 1911 and this time they were successful, for the Manchu dynasty was abolished and China was turned into a republic.

But this time, however, the Chinese had learned the lesson that the nations of the west are not primarily interested in chapters from the writings of Confucius, but care much more for coal concessions and iron concessions and oil concessions and that therefore those possessed of these valuable raw materials must either know how to defend their property or sink it to the bottom of the ocean if they want it to be absolutely safe. In short, China began to recognize the necessity of following the example of Japan by taking a short course in "westernization". Foreign teachers were engaged from all over the world, but principally from Japan, which was nearby and handy.

In the meantime, Russia had started upon its ambitious plan to convert one-sixth of the world into an industrial state, administered according to the Gospel of Saint Marx; and Russia, being a very close neighbor of China could whisper strange words into the ears of the long-suffering coolies who had been born to sweat and work, no matter who ruled them or whether they were being exploited by the English or the French or the Japanese.

The result of all these conflicting ideas, plans and emotions is the chaos which has descended upon China since the end of the Great War, during which it was forced to take the side of the Allies in a quarrel in which as usual it had nothing to gain and a great deal to lose.

I am no prophet. I don't know what will happen during the next ten or fifteen years. Conditions probably won't change very much, for poor China tried too late to catch up with the procession. But may the good Lord have mercy upon us if she ever does, for oh, what a bill we shall have to pay then! What a bill!

XXXVIII

KOREA, MONGOLIA AND MANCHURIA, IF THE LATTER
STILL EXISTS WHEN THIS BOOK IS PUBLISHED

LET us begin with a short and elementary lesson in practical economics.

The Japanese, cooped up on their little island, and as prolific as Italians, need more land. All the pretty words in the world and all the treaties in the world and all the well-meant speeches of all the well-meaning old ladies and gentlemen in the world won't change this fact. For it is really a law of Nature which states that when I am strong but hungry and find myself on a raft somewhere in mid-ocean in the company of somebody else who is weak but who has a pocket full of ham sandwiches, I will in the end get my share of those ham sandwiches, or I shall have died in the attempt. Being a decent sort of a person, carefully brought up by God-fearing parents, I may resist the temptation for one day or for two days or even three days. But the hour will come when I will say, "Give me some of those sandwiches or I will throw you overboard—and be quick about it!"

My early training may assert itself sufficiently to let me treat the owner of the sandwiches more or less generously and allow him to keep part of the supplies, but I am going to still that terrible gnawing feeling in my entrails if I have to commit murder to do so. Multiply the case of the man on the raft by a million-fold or ten million-fold and you will begin to appreciate the problem that faces the Japanese people.

They live in a country that is smaller than California (155,-652 square miles for California and 148,756 square miles for Japan) and of these only 16,000,000 acres can be used for agriculture, which is less than 2% of all the arable land of America. If you want the comparison to come a little nearer home, it is a trifle less than the improved farmlands of New York State alone. Even with the help of one of the best staffs of scientific agricultural experts to be found anywhere in the world, you will see at a glance what sort of problem it is that faces these poor island folk. Living so near the sea-shore they would of course fish; but although they have now reached the point where they are raising certain sorts of fish in the muddy water of their rice fields, the difficulty remains unsolved and unsolvable in view of the fact that the population increases by more than 650,000 people a year.

It was inevitable therefore that Japan should look for more territory; and it was only natural that first of all she should think of the badly administered and sadly neglected lands that lay just across the China Sea. America would have suited her better, but it was too far away and besides is much too strong. Australia was also too far away, and nine-tenths of that continent are a desert and of no possible use to anybody. But Manchuria was within easy reach, and the road to Manchuria was indicated by the land bridge of the Korean peninsula from which the mainland of Japan was separated by the narrow Strait of Korea. This strait is only 102 miles wide and is conveniently divided into halves by the Tsushima islands, those islands near which the Japanese fleet destroyed the Russian squadron in the year 1905, and killed Russia as a possible rival in eastern Asia.

As for the Korean peninsula, which is situated in the same latitude as southern Italy and Sicily, although it has a much colder climate, it was in no position to defend itself. The Koreans who called their country Ch'ao Hsien or "the chosen land of the morning quiet", were descendants of Chinese immigrants who had occupied the country in the twelfth century before the birth of Christ. They had easily conquered the natives, a very primitive race who had lived in caves and subterranean holes in the mountains of the interior. These immigrants from the west had then established a kingdom of their own, which however was never able to gain complete independence from the mother

If the Pacific Ocean should run dry

country of China and which was forever being harassed by Japanese pirates.

In the year 1592 Japan made her first attempt to get hold of Korea. Japan never would have dared to start upon so ambitious a campaign unless she had been fully prepared. The preparations consisted of several hundred blunderbusses which Portugal had sold them. Relying upon her superior armament, Japan sent 300,000 men around the Strait of Korea, engaged in a war which lasted five years, and was then defeated only by the superior numbers of the Chinese who came to the assistance of the Koreans.

But it was this invasion, during which Seoul, the capital of Korea, was destroyed, and during which all sorts of horrible atrocities were committed, which accounts for the hereditary hatred of the Korean people for everything Japanese. But what will you? The Koreans were weak and the Japanese were strong; and when, during the last quarter of the nineteenth century, the Koreans were forced to grant all sorts of economic and political concessions to the Russians, the Japanese had an excellent excuse for a fresh campaign.

The immediate causes for a war are rarely interesting. It is the real underlying motives that count. In this case, as in the case of the expedition of 1592, they were to be found directly and absolutely in the necessity of the Japanese government to provide its rapidly increasing population with food.

As soon as Japan had defeated Russia and had driven the Muscovite troops back from the Yalu River, the river that separates Korea from Manchuria, Korea became a Japanese protectorate. In 1910 it became a part of the Japanese Empire quite as much as Formosa, which the Japanese had taken from the Chinese in 1895, or the southern half of the island of Sakhalin, which they had taken from the Russians in the year 1905 in lieu of a war indemnity. Today already half a million Japanese have moved in among the twenty million Koreans. The rest will follow in due course of time.

As for Manchuria, it had long been a bone of contention between the two nations that fought for supremacy in the northern half of the Pacific. After the Peace of Portsmouth, which made an end to the Russo-Japanese war, the fate of the country was sealed. Who was there left to protect Manchuria against Japan? Nominally the country still belonged to China, but China, after the Boxer Rebellion, was much too weak to protect anybody, even herself. Why didn't the Manchus put up a fight? A people energetic enough to conquer all of China and to establish themselves as the rulers of one-fifth of the total population of the earth must surely know how to fight. But the Manchus had long since moved southward into China. The six percent that remained of the original population were mainly little farmers without an interest in the land. The other sixteen million people, spread over a territory four times as large as England and Scotland, lived as they had always lived, which meant that they had just enough to eat not to die, but as for fighting, why should they?

And when Manchuria is gone, it will be the turn of Mongolia. For Mongolia is a very big country, almost 1,400,000 square miles, or eleven times as large as the British Isles and it has a population of less than 2,000,000 people. The southern regions are uninhabitable because they form part of the Gobi Desert but the rest consists of grass-lands, eminently suited for purposes of cattle-breeding. Otherwise the Mongolians, who depended for their success upon their cavalry, would never have been able to raise those tough ponies which carried them triumphantly from the Pacific to the Atlantic.

Many people seem to experience a profound indignation at what they are inclined to denounce as a brutal expression of "Japanese ambition". I would rather call them "Japanese necessities". In matters of international policy, a certain healthy egoism is rather a desirable quality. Japan has got to find an outlet for the extra people at home. It is finding such an outlet in northern Asia, in a part of the world that is very lightly populated, and that has been accustomed to such outrageous forms of government that the inhabitants cannot possibly be worse off now than they were ever before.

If the Atlantic Ocean should run dry

If this northern Asiatic safety-valve did not exist, the Philippines, the Dutch East Indies, Australia, New Zealand and the western coast of America would be forever exposed to a Japanese invasion and we would be obliged to station a battle-ship in front of every Polynesian island lest it be towed away over night by a Japanese cruiser.

On the whole, the present arrangement seems much more practical. Those who feel inclined to shed tears at these callous and selfish utterances, are politely requested to weep on the shoulders of our own Indians.

XXXIX

THE JAPANESE EMPIRE

JAPAN, before it started upon its career of world-conquest at the expense of its neighbors, consisted of more than 500 islands which follow a semi-circle reaching all the way from the peninsula of Kamchatka in the north to the coast of the Chinese province of Kwang-tung in the south, a distance equivalent to that between the North Cape of Europe and the center of the Sahara Desert in Africa.

Of these islands, which vary in size between the whole of England and Scotland and Manhattan, 518 are inhabited by some 60,000,000 people. The total number of Japanese, according to the latest statistics, is over 90,000,000 but that takes in 20,000,000 Koreans and several Polynesian islands which have been Japanese territory since the recent Great War.

For all practical purposes, however, it is sufficient to remember the names of Honshiu, the main island in the center, Hokka-ïdo, the next biggest island in the north, and Shikoku and Kiushiu, the two big islands immediately south of Honshiu. The capital is Tokio, with over 2,000,000 inhabitants, situated in a fertile plain in the center of Honshiu. The harbor of Tokio is Yokohama.

An even larger city is Osaka, in the southern part of the same island, the center of the important Japanese textile industry. North of Osaka lies Kioto (Tokio is merely Kioto turned around), the ancient capital of the Empire. Other cities, whose names you will occasionally encounter in our newspapers, are Kobe, the port of Osaka, and Nagasaki on the southern island of Kiushiu, the most convenient port for all vessels coming from Europe.

As for the word Yedo, which you will often find in your history books, it is merely the ancient name of the city of Tokio during the period when it was the residence of the Shoguns. When the Shoguns lost their power in the year 1866, the emperor moved from Kioto to Yedo, the city was rebaptised Tokio, and it began that extraordinary development which has made it one of the biggest cities of the modern world.

But all these towns live in constant peril of being wiped out. The Japanese islands, which are merely the outer edges of the great Asiatic mountains, (the Japanese Sea, the shallow Yellow Sea and the East China Sea are of very recent date, like the North Sea which turned England into an island), are part of the volcanic ridge that stretches from the island of Sakhalin to Java in the Dutch East Indies, and they are in almost constant motion. The seismographic observation statistics of Japan reported 27,485 earthquakes between 1885 and 1903. That gives an average of 1447 per year or four per day. Of course, most of these are of no particular importance. A slight shiver in a tea-cup, a rattling of a chair against the wall and that would be all. But one gets some idea of the danger to which this island region is exposed when you realize that Kioto, the ancient capital, was shaken 1318 times during the ten centuries of its existence. Of these 1318 shakings, 194 were classified as "strong" and 34 as absolutely "destructive". The earthquake of September, 1923, which destroyed the city of Tokio almost completely and which killed more than 150,000 people and lifted certain small islands a couple of feet in the air, while sinking others below sea-level, was of such recent date as still to be remembered by all of us.

People often associate earthquakes with volcanic disturbances. Some of them are undoubtedly the result of volcanic eruptions. But most earthquakes are caused by a sudden sliding among those layers of rocks which lie beneath the soil on which we live. When such layers move only two or three inches, the result is a commotion which may merely upset a few trees and shrubs but which, if it takes place in exactly the right spot (the wrong spot would be better) may cause a catastrophe like that

of Lisbon in 1755, when 60,000 people were killed, or Canton
in China in 1920 when the number may have been as high as
200,000. According to the conservative estimate of one of the
greatest seismological experts, the earthquakes of the last forty
centuries, the so-called "historical period" of man, have cost
the lives of 13,000,000 people, which, when all is said and
done, is quite a considerable number.

Earthquakes, of course, may happen almost anywhere. Only
a year ago the bottom of the North Sea was severely shaken
by an earthquake, and the mud flats of the islands at the mouth
of the Scheldt and the Rhine trembled sufficiently to give the
clam-diggers a moment of great uneasiness. Yet the North Sea
region is as flat as a pancake. The Japanese islands, on the other
hand, are situated on the top of a high ridge which on the eastern
side descends into one of the deepest holes in the bottom of the
ocean our scientists have so far been able to locate. The famous
Tuscarora Deep descends to over 28,000 feet, which is only
6000 feet less than the record depth between the Philippines
and the Marianas or Ladrones. It surely is no mere accident
that more than half of all the disastrous earthquakes of Japan
have taken place along the eastern shores where the coast makes
a sheer drop of about six miles.

The Japanese, however, like most people who live in earthquake belts, lose little sleep on account of this eternal menace
to their safety. They till their fields and play with their children and eat their meals and laugh at Charlie Chaplin just like
the rest of us. The experience of ages has taught them to build
a kind of cardboard house which is perhaps a little draughty in
winter but which causes the minimum of danger when it comes
tumbling down about its owner's ears. Of course, when they want
to imitate the west and build sky-scrapers as they did in Tokio,
then the damage runs into the hundreds of millions. But, generally speaking, Japan has adapted itself better than any other
country to this inevitable geological handicap. Just as, generally speaking, they seem to have succeeded in making life a
much more harmonious and agreeable adventure than most of

Japan

the nations of the west. I am not thinking of the pretty postal
cards with little geisha girls drinking tea underneath a cherry
tree, or the toy gardens of Madame Butterfly. I am merely repeating what all travellers have told us who visited Japan before
it gave up its ancestral customs and habits and manners (the
manners especially seem to have been exquisite) and tried to
turn its islands into suburbs of Chicago and Wilkes-Barre. As
that incredible change from the old Japan unto the new has had
a very decided influence upon our own safety and happiness and
will continue to do so in an increasing manner, we ought to
know at least a few things about these people who, whether we
like it or not, will be our neighbors as long as the Pacific does
not run dry.

Japanese history is of much more recent date than Chinese.
The Chinese calendar goes back to 2637 B. C. (about the time
Cheops was building his little pyramid) but the oldest Japanese
chronicle dates back only to 400 A. D. At that time the present
so-called Japanese race was already in existence. Strictly speaking, however, there is no "Japanese race", for, like the English,
the Japanese are a mixture. The original inhabitants were the
Ainos who were gradually driven to the more remote northern
islands by three successive waves of invaders from southern
China and the Malayan peninsula, from central China, and from
Manchuria and Korea. As a result, the original civilization of
Japan was really an extension of Chinese civilization, and whatever the Japanese knew they had learned from the Chinese.

Their relations with China grew even more intimate when
Japan followed the Chinese example and allowed herself to be
converted to Buddhism. But when a new creed replaces an older
one, the new creed cannot help being influenced to a certain extent at least by the older one. That is a lesson all missionaries
have been obliged to learn, whether they preached Christianity,
Mohammedanism or Buddhism.

The first Buddhist apostles who reached Japan in the sixth
century of our era found that the Japanese had developed a re-

ligious system of their own which had grown out of the soil, so to speak, and which was very well suited to their needs. It was called Shinto-ism from the word Shinto which seems to be the equivalent of our expression "the divine pathway". It was a much nobler creed than the spook and devil worship so prevalent all over the rest of Asia. It accepted the world as a unit of indestructible force and taught that we are responsible for whatever use we make of that force, because, no matter how insignificant the result may be, it will be a permanent result. The present official creed of Japan is a mixture of Buddhism and Shinto-ism. It lays great stress upon one's duty towards the community at large. Like the Englishman, the Japanese, who is also essentially an island-dweller (without necessarily being an insular person), has a very sincere and deep-seated conviction that he owes his country certain very definite duties. Shinto-ism also lays stress upon the respect due the ancestors. But it does not carry this veneration to the point of absurdity which turns so much of China into a vast cemetery where the dead rule the living and where the grave-yards occupy the space that should be used to raise food for the living.

But the great cleavage between Chinese and Japanese civilization did not take place until much later, not until the latter half of the sixteenth century when, after an endless period of quarrelling and fighting between little independent potentates who paid no more attention to their emperor than a knight of the Holy Roman Empire did to his, the government fell at last into the hands of a man of power.

Eight hundred years before, in far away Europe, the Major Domos or house-stewards of the old Frankish kings had pushed their masters into a monastery and had then taken it upon themselves to rule the country. As they were much better fitted for the job than the men they replaced, nobody had objected. The Japanese people, having endured civil war for almost four centuries, did not care who ruled them as long as they got peace. And so they did not object or rush to the defence of their hereditary rulers when the highest official of the imperial court, the head of the rich and influential Tokugawa family, made himself the dictator of the country. This Japanese Major Domo promoted the Emperor to a sort of deity on earth, the spiritual father of all the Japanese, but of such remote spiritual perfection that, like the Lamas of Tibet, he must forever remain invisible to the mass of his subjects.

This arrangement lasted almost two entire centuries. The Shoguns (for that was the title by which these dictators were known and it meant as much as our "commander-in-chief") ruled in Tokio and the Emperors idled their time away behind their costly screens in the silent palace of Kioto. It was during the Shogun era that Japan adopted that strict feudal system which was to influence the character of her people in so profound a way that even today, after almost eighty years of industrialism, the Japanese are still feudalists at heart, and contemplate the problems of life from an angle that is totally different from that of their European and American competitors. It took some time to perfect the details of this new arrangement, but after the year 1600 Japanese society was divided definitely into three different groups. The highest of these castes consisted of the Daimyos, the members of the feudal nobility, the big landowners. The second one consisted of the Samurai, hereditary warriors corresponding to the knights of medieval Europe. All other people belonged to the third class, that of the Heimin or commoners.

This system was not ideal but history has quite convincingly taught us that the mass of the population is never deeply interested in any theory of government. All the average citizen asks is, "Does it work? Does it guarantee me peace and quiet and give me the assurance that whatever I have gained through my own efforts and in the sweat of my brow will actually belong to me and that no one can take it away from me without due process of law?"

And for more than two centuries the system did work. The Shogun was recognized as the political leader of the state. The Mikado was worshipped as the spiritual head of the nation. The

How Japan was made

Daimyos and the Samurai, forced to adhere to a very strict code
of "noblesse oblige", either did what was expected of them or
were politely requested to disembowel themselves according to
the most solemn rites of hara-kiri. And the subjects labored at
their different trades and professions.

Even then the country was getting to be slightly over-crowded.
Often the people were obliged to subsist on very little. But they
had always been very sober and frugal in their tastes and did not
ask for much. And Nature appeared to be a faithful friend. The
Kuro Siwo (which means the Blue Salt Current, a sort of second
cousin to our own Gulf Stream) which started in the equatorial
region just north of the Dutch East Indies, then flowed past
the Philippines and then crossed the Pacific to bestow its blessings upon the west coast of America, provided the country with
an even climate. A narrow strip of cold water just off the Japanese east coast prevented the country from enjoying quite as
mild a temperature as California, but even so it was much better
off than continental China.

Everything, so it seemed, was in favor of a normal and rational development of those blessed islands when a certain
Mendes Pinto, a Portuguese navigator who had lost his bear-
ings, appeared upon the scene and upset the entire future course
of Japanese history. For the Portuguese not only visited distant countries to trade with them, but also to bring them the
enlightened blessings of their own religious system.

At first, unless all chronicles have agreed to lie upon this
one point, the Christian missionaries, whose headquarters were
in Goa in India and in Macao near Canton in China, were received with great courtesy and were given every opportunity
to explain the advantages of their own creed over that which
for so long had ruled supreme among the Japanese. They
preached their gospel and they made many converts. Then
other missionaries, belonging to a different religious order, arrived from the nearby Philippine Islands which belonged to
Spain. They too were welcomed, but the Shogun began to feel
uneasy about their presence when he discovered (what native

prince has ever failed to make that discovery sooner or later?) that these holy men were invariably accompanied by less holy men, garbed in iron armor and carrying strange iron rods that would send heavy leaden bullets through as many as three common Japanese soldiers at the same time.

It is only during the last fifty years that we have begun to

The Old Japan

understand the Japanese point of view about the very painful incidents which thereupon happened. These incidents have given the Japanese a reputation for cold-blooded cruelty which did not seem in the least in keeping with what we had learned about them from other sources. The decision of the Shogun to close Japan against all further activities on the part of the Christian missionaries was not the result of any sudden dislike on his part for the people from the west. It was caused by fear, by fear lest the whole country be rent asunder by religious strife and its riches be despoiled by the captains of those same merchantmen that carried the messengers of peace and good-will to the shores of Japan and then departed without paying for the goods that had been ordered to provide a return cargo.

The Jesuit influence had been strongest in the island of Kiushiu, nearest to the Portuguese settlements in China. At first the Fathers had humbly spoken of the Prince of Peace. As soon as they had gained the upper hand, they began to destroy Japanese temples, demolish Japanese images and force thousands of peasants and nobles to accept the cross at the point of the gun.

Toyotomi Hideyoshi, then the strong man of Japan, saw all this and realized what the inevitable end must be. "These priests," so he announced, "came here preaching virtue, but their virtue is only a means of concealing their pernicious designs against our Empire."

On July 25th of the year 1587, five years after a first Japanese embassy had paid its respects to the Pope and to the Kings of Spain and Portugal, all Christian priests were banished from Japanese territory. Merchants were given permission to visit Japan as before, but under supervision of the government. The Portuguese Jesuits left. Their place was immediately taken by Spanish Franciscans and Dominicans from the nearby Philippines. They came disguised as special ambassadors to Hideyoshi. Their trick was discovered. Nevertheless, they were treated with courtesy but were told not to preach. They disobeyed this order, built themselves a church in Yedo and began to baptise people all over the land. Next they built a church in Osaka. Next they appropriated a church in Nagasaki which had belonged to the Jesuits. Next they turned openly against their rivals, the Jesuits, and accused them of having been too conciliatory in their methods of bringing the Good Tidings to the Japanese. In short, they committed every error of judgment and taste to be found in the repertory of professional fanatics. When they were finally deported by Hideyoshi's orders, they returned as fast as they were expelled. After years of futile warnings, the Japanese, who thus far had shown the utmost patience and tolerance towards these unwelcome Spanish friars, came to the conclusion that nothing could save them but the most drastic of measures.

Rather than witness a repetition of that civil war which had been so disastrous to their country during the previous four hundred years, they voluntarily closed their country against all

The New Japan

further foreign aggression; and those Christian missionaries who disregarded that edict were put to death.

During wellnigh a century and a half Japan remained in a state of voluntary exile from the rest of the world. Almost, but not completely. One little window remained open through which a great deal of Japanese gold flowed westward and through which at least a few scraps of western science penetrated into the interior of that strange country. The Dutch East India Company had been a rival of the Portuguese for Japan's commercial favors. But the Dutch were traders, pure and simple, and had but little

interest in other peoples' souls. Neither did the English. For a
long time it was a toss-up which of the two nations would win
out. But the English managed rather badly on this occasion,
and lost.

After the execution of the last of a series of Portuguese diplomatic missions sent to Japan, an inexcusable official murder, the
Dutch too were deprived of many of their former privileges.
But as long as their Japanese venture paid an annual dividend of
almost eighty percent, they decided to hang on. They were
forced to reside on the little island of Deshima, a square rock
300 yards long and 80 yards wide, situated in the harbor of
Nagasaki and hardly big enough to exercise the dogs they
brought with them to keep them company. They were not allowed to bring their wives and were never permitted to set
foot on the mainland.

They must for once have exercised the patience of the angels
(not exactly a national characteristic) for the slightest infringement of any of the hundreds of regulations, laid down by the
Japanese authorities, brought immediate reprisals. One day the
East India Company decided to build a new storehouse. The
date, according to the custom of the times, was painted on the
façade with the usual prefix A. D. or "anno Domini". As this
was a direct reference to the Dominus of those Christians whom
the Japanese had come to regard as we ourselves regard Bolshevist agitators fresh from Moscow, the Shogun gave orders not
only to remove the offensive letters but to tear the entire building down and raze it to the ground and to remind the Dutch of
that terrible edict of expulsion of the Portuguese which had
ended with the words:

"As long as the sun warms the earth, let no Christian be so
bold as to come to Japan and let all people know that if King
Philip himself or even the very God of the Christians break
this commandment, they shall pay for it with their heads."

The officials of the Dutch East India Company seem to have
taken the lesson to heart, because Deshima remained in Dutch
hands for 217 years. During those 217 years there was a steady

drain of Japanese gold and silver, for the Dutch were cash traders and whatever the Japanese ordered from abroad had to be paid for on delivery.

In this way, too, Europe got an occasional bit of news from these hermits of the Pacific. These stories are agreed that conditions in the Empire were far from satisfactory. Japan was rapidly becoming an object lesson of the doctrine that no nation can ever hope to be completely sufficient unto itself. Towards the end, too, the youth of Japan were beginning to grow increasingly restive. They had heard vague stories about the wonderful science of western Europe. They began to book-leg scientific and medical works by way of Deshima. They spelled out queer Dutch words and learned that the world at large had been moving at a terrific pace while Japan alone had stood still.

Then in 1847 the King of Holland sent a trunkful of scientific books to the court of Yedo as a present, together with a map of the world, warning the Japanese against the further folly of isolation. All this time commercial relations between China and Europe and America were rapidly on the increase. Vessels bound from San Francisco for Canton sometimes suffered shipwreck on the Japanese coast and the sailors, being without consular or diplomatic protection, fared rather badly. In 1849 the captain of an American man-of-war threatened to bombard Nagasaki unless eighteen American seamen were returned to him at once. Once more the King of Holland warned his Japanese colleague against the dangers of continuing a policy that could only lead to disaster. These letters from the Hague merely expressed what all the world had long since known. Sooner or later, Japan would have to open her doors to western commerce, and if she refused to do so peaceably she would be obliged to do so by force.

Russia, which was pushing further and further down the coast of Alaska, was slowly making plans to increase its hold upon the western Pacific. The only country that could act without being suspected of having territorial ambitions was America. In 1853 Commodore Perry with four warships and 560 men entered

Uraga Bay. This first visit caused such a panic as Japan had never experienced. The Emperor officially invoked the aid of Heaven and as soon as Perry was gone (he remained only ten days to deliver a letter from the President to the Emperor) the Dutch were requested to furnish a warship, forts were manned, old Portuguese guns were mounted and everything was done to prepare for a second visit of these steam-propelled monsters from the east.

All over the country the people took sides. Most of them were in favor of isolation at all costs, but others declared for the policy of the open door. The Shogun, belonging to the latter, lost much of his power and was denounced as a "friend of the foreigners". But in the end it was the Emperor who benefited most from that ever-famous visit of Admiral Perry.

The Shogunate, as the undisputed head of an absolutely feudal system of government, had long since outlived its own usefulness, as had those Daimyos and Samurai who still insisted upon carrying their swords as if they lived in 1653 instead of 1853 and were still actually engaged in the laudable task of suppressing civil war. It was time for a change all along the line.

By mere chance it so happened that the Emperor, who was then the nominal head of the nation, was also a young man of extraordinary ability and great intelligence. He prevailed upon the Shogun to resign and once more took hold of the reins of government. He let himself be persuaded that further isolation meant suicide, and now welcomed all foreigners as cordially as before that he had repelled them. And the Meiji, or era of enlightenment which he inaugurated, changed Japan from a sixteenth century feudal state into a modern, industrialized nation.

To ask whether such a complete reversion of feelings on such a tremendous scale is ever a good and desirable thing for any people is to pose a useless question. Factories and large armies and large navies and coal mines and steel foundries may make for happiness or they may not. I don't know. Some say yes and others say no. It will always depend a great deal upon the individuals in question. The Russians, ten years ago, nursed their souls and loved their saints. Today they burn their saints in the kitchen stove and their souls now dwell with perfect contentment in the exhaust pipe of an engine.

Personally I believe that such developments are absolutely inevitable. In themselves they are neither absolutely good nor absolutely bad because they are necessary and are part of that development by which we hope to set ourselves free from the worries of hunger and the fear of economic uncertainty. That the machine, who is both the father and the mother of such a change, also destroys a great deal that is desirable and beautiful, no one will dare to deny. That the Japan of Hokusai and Utamaro would have been a much more interesting country to visit than the Japan of the Japanese standard oil and the Tokio gasworks, is undoubtedly true. But Hokusai and Utamaro are dead and gone and the Tokio housewives prefer cooking on gas to cooking over a slow charcoal fire; and that is the answer.

Fujiyama, the venerable white-haired volcano which has not spoken a word since 1707, now looks down upon cigarette ads where formerly little children offered flowers to a wayside shrine. The holy deer in the temple park hurt their feet on tin cans thrown away by careless picnic parties.

But Fuji knows—some day, this too will come to an end.

XL

THE PHILIPPINES, AN OLD ADMINISTRATIVE PART OF MEXICO

THE Philippines belong to that row of islands which runs in a semi-circle from Kamchatka to Java. These bits of dry land are remnants of the outer edge of the old continent. They were high enough to remain above sea-level when the waters of the Pacific covered the bottom of those valleys since then known as the Sea of Japan, the East China Sea and the South China Sea.

There are more than 7000 islands in the Philippine group, but only 462 of these are bigger than a square mile. The others are merely large cliffs or little bits of marshland, so insignificant that only one-quarter of them have even been given a name. All of them together are about as large as England and Scotland and they have a population of 11,000,000 natives, with a very large number of Chinese and Japanese and about 100,000 whites. This whole group at one time must have been highly volcanic although today we can only locate twenty-five real volcanoes. Even those, with two or three exceptions, seem to have stopped working at their trade.

For this we ought to be duly grateful, as the Philippines are very dangerously located from a geological point of view. The deepest hole in the ocean which we have so far been able to locate lies just east of the Philippines. That is the spot of which I told you and which is so deep that if we used it as a burial ground for the Himalayas, Mount Everest, the highest mountain of our planet, would still be 5000 feet under water. If things should ever begin to slide in that little corner of the world, there would be few left to tell the tale.

The most important of the Philippine islands is Luzon. It has the shape of a pollywog and in the center rises to a height of 7000 feet. The most important city and the capital of the whole group is situated on the east coast of Luzon, and its name is Manila. The Spaniards founded it in 1571, on the ruins of an old Mohammedan settlement, and it is called after a weed, the nilad, which grew abundantly all over the place. In the year 1590 it was given those walls which were to prove more enduring than the rule of those who built them.

But even under the bad Spanish management, Manila soon developed into the most important commercial center of the whole Far East. The harbor was full of boats from China and Japan and India and even from faraway Arabia. They came to this port to exchange their merchandise for those European products which the Spaniards had brought to the Philippines by way of their Mexican possessions in Central America. For, rather than risk the voyage across the Indian Ocean and by way of the Cape, which would have exposed them to the attacks of the British and the Dutch, the Spaniards sent their vessels directly from Manila to the Gulf of Tehuantepec, then carried the goods across the American isthmus, and on the other side reloaded them into vessels that sailed for home by way of Cuba and Porto Rico.

To the south of Luzon lie a dozen fairly large islands of which Samar and Panay (with the well-known city of Iloilo, the second largest city of the Philippines) and Negros and Cebú are the best known. To the south of these lies Mindanao, only a little smaller than Luzon, and famous for the stubborn resistance with which the natives, the Mohammedan Moros, have fought both Spaniard and American to retain their independence. The biggest city of Mindanao is Zamboanga, which faces the Sulu Sea, for, generally speaking, the Philippines have always turned their back upon the Pacific. Their real interests lay in the west, they traded with the west, and it was from the west that they got their religion and their first concepts of civilization. That they were discovered by people who approached them from the east was pure accident.

Magellan, who landed here in 1521, had merely taken this unusual route to settle a point of law that was threatening difficulties between his employer, the King of Spain, and the Pope. In the year 1494 the Pope, in order to make an end to all further strife between his beloved children of the Iberian peninsula had taken a ruler and had divided the whole world into two equal parts by drawing a line from the north to the south just west of the Azores and the Cape Verde Islands (roughly corresponding to our fiftieth degree of longitude west of Greenwich). He had given the Spaniards everything to the west of that line and the Portuguese everything to the east. That was the famous treaty of Tordesillas upon which the Spaniards based their right to execute all those who dared to pass "beyond the line" and which made the first English and Dutch expeditions to the American mainland such very hazardous enterprises, for whoever was caught "beyond the line" was immediately hanged like a common pirate.

The Pope, however, who had made this venture into applied geography, the notorious Alexander VI, the father of Cesare and Lucrezia Borgia, was himself a Spaniard; and the Portuguese claimed that the treaty had not been quite fair to their interests. Hence a century of wrangling and fighting as to who owned what. In connection with this quarrel, Magellan, although a Portuguese, had been hired by the King of Spain to proceed to the Indian Ocean by way of the eastern route and to decide whether the rich spice islands of the Moluccas lay within that part of the Indies which the Pope had given to the Portuguese or to the Spaniards. The Portuguese proved to be right. They got the Moluccas, which shortly afterwards they lost to the Dutch, but the Spaniards, who had come upon the Philippines in this accidental way, kept them for their own benefit and administered them from Mexico. This meant a wholesale exodus of friars from the New Castile to a territory that promised more profitable results than would ever be obtained among the fast dwindling races of Central America.

The friars, it must be confessed, did a thorough job among

their Filipino charges. Indeed, if they had only been a little
less successful, our own task in the Philippines would have been
a good deal easier. For when we acquired those ancient Spanish
possessions in the year 1898, we were for the first time in our
political existence called upon to deal with a people who were
almost 100% Catholic.

We may not be a Protestant nation in the official sense of the
word, but our general philosophy of life is decidedly Protestant
and very decidedly un-Catholic. We may be inspired by the best
of intentions towards the Philippines, give them endless good
roads, thousands of schools, three universities, hospitals, doctors,
nurses, incubators, meat and fish inspection, hygiene and a thousand and one benefits of progress of which the Spaniards had
never even heard. But all these generous expressions of good-
will mean comparatively little to people who from their earliest
childhood have been taught to regard such worldly comforts
and advantages as something very nice and very pleasant but
not to be compared to the chance of gaining salvation in another
world, where hygiene and hospitals and good roads and schools
shall no longer be of any interest to anybody.

XLI

THE DUTCH EAST INDIES, THE TAIL THAT WAGS
THE DOG

I HAVE already told you how Japan and Formosa and the Philippines are merely the outer mountainous edges of the old Asiatic continent which in the course of millions of years got separated from the mainland by the waters of the Pacific Ocean.

The Malay Islands on the other hand (Malaysia, Insulinde, Indian Archipelago, the Dutch East Indies—they are known by so many different names) are not merely part of the old outer edge of Asia. They are the remnants of an enormous peninsula as large as that of China, which reached from Burma and Siam and Cochin-China eastward to Australia. During the earliest ages of our geographical history this peninsula may have been directly connected with the Asiatic continent (then infinitely larger than today) and afterwards, during a period about which we are a little better informed, it was separated from Australia only by a narrow strip of water, not much wider than the present Torres Strait between Queensland and New Guinea.

The reason for the cataclysmic changes which have turned so vast a piece of dry land into a group of oddly shaped islands, running all the way from Borneo, which is as large as the whole of the Scandinavian peninsula, down to thousands of tiny bits of rock located wherever they happen to be most inconvenient to navigation, is not hard to discover. This part of the world was among the most volcanic regions of the earth. Even today Java retains the blue ribbon for volcanic activities. During the last three centuries, however, the hundred and twenty odd volcanoes of Java have on the whole been very well-behaved, as have those of Sumatra, a little towards the west.

When Brahmanism, the old religion of India, was prevalent among the Javanese, the priests used to placate the spirits that dwelled in the bowels of the earth by an occasional offering of human beings, who were pitched bodily into the boiling cauldron of the craters—apparently with success, for although the volcanoes continue to puff and roar and occasionally go on a rampage, there has been no major catastrophe for several centuries.

But the remnants of Krakatoa lie there as a dreadful warning of something that may happen again at any moment. On the morning of the 26th of August of the year 1883 the island of Krakatoa, situated in the Sunda Strait between Sumatra and Java, was very much as it had always been since a prehistoric eruption had blown away the top of its crater and had cut the island up into several small pieces. Two days later, the whole northern part of the island was gone. Where there had been hills 1500 feet high there now was a deep hollow, lying more than a thousand feet below the surface of the Indian Ocean. The noise of that explosion was heard 3000 miles away. Ashes were blown 17 miles up in the air. The volcanic dust spread all over Africa, Europe, Asia and America and even as far north as the North Cape. The sky for six weeks afterwards was strangely colored as if there had been a forest fire somewhere in the neighborhood.

But the disturbance caused on the ocean was much more disastrous than that caused on land, for Krakatoa was uninhabited. A tidal wave more than 50 feet high swept along the coast of Java and killed 36,000 people. It wiped out harbors and villages and destroyed large vessels as if they had been kindling wood. Ceylon and Mauritius were affected by these waves. They made themselves noticeable near Cape Horn, which is almost 8000 miles away, and they were faintly observed in the British Channel which is 11,000 miles distant from the Strait of Sunda.

A year ago the remnant of the Krakatoa volcano was once more beginning to show signs of activity. And no one can foretell when or where the subterranean lightning will strike next. As for the people who live here, they are like all the others who live under similar circumstances. They pay no more attention than a small boy in one of our tenement districts pays to the trucks that are driven right across his baseball game in one of the most crowded streets of the Italian quarter.

The Dutch East Indies compared to Europe

This fatalistic attitude may be due to the Mohammedan faith. It may also be the result of just plain ordinary contentment with life and the conviction that volcanic eruptions, like foreign dominations or floods or fires, are all of them negligible incidents in life and of small importance to the man who tills his fields, whose ancestors ever since the beginning of the world have tilled these same fields, whose children will till these same fields, and who none of them ever want or expect to go without sufficient nourishment.

This sounds as if I were trying to describe Java as a sort of earthly Paradise. It is hardly that, but it has been so supremely favored by Nature as to deserve a page of its own.

There is the soil, 28% of which is of volcanic origin. That soil, if treated at all kindly and understandingly, will yield three complete harvests every twelve months.

There is the climate, which although hot enough to favor the cultivation of every known tropical plant, is not excessive and which in the mountainous regions is much more agreeable than that of New York or Washington during the summer. For Java and the other islands of Insulinde, although so near the equator that the days and nights are almost equally long, is on all sides surrounded by the sea. It therefore has moisture enough for all purposes and the temperature never goes higher than 96° Fahrenheit, nor lower than 66°, with a mean annual temperature of 79°. The seasons follow each other with sharp regularity. The rainy season of the western monsoon (an Arabic word meaning "season" and the name of those seasonal winds that blow regularly in this part of the world) lasts from November to March. Then it rains every day at a certain hour. This season is followed by the so-called dry monsoon, when it does not rain at all. The short intermediary period is known as the "canting season".

As a result of these favorable climatic conditions, Java, which is only 622 miles long and 121 miles wide (a sort of rectangular breakwater, protecting the islands of the inner archipelago against the violence of the southern Indian Ocean) is able to support 42,000,000 people, while Sumatra and Borneo, although much larger, have only one-tenth of that population. And because of its great fertility, the island has from the very beginning attracted the attention of the white man.

The Portuguese were the first to appear upon the scene. Then came the English and the Dutch, but the English gradually concentrated all their forces upon the exploitation of British

India and left Java and the other Malaysian islands to the Dutch. Having committed every possible mistake of which the European was capable, in dealing with a native populace during the first three centuries of their rule, the Dutch seem at last to have learned a few primary lessons of colonial management. They interfere just as little as possible with the native and are gradually drawing him more and more into the administration of his own country, knowing that the time will come when for good or evil these people will insist upon being given their liberty. With an army of 30,000 men, of which only one-fifth are white, one will never be able to rule a territory fifty times as large as the mother country if the inhabitants have really made up their minds that the foreigner must go. The old days, therefore, of "forced labor" and "government plantations" are gone forever. Schools and railroads and hospitals are taking the place of the old punitive expeditions. If eventually one will have to give up these regions as the sovereign master, one may hope to remain behind as an indispensable part of the economic fabric. The old guard, which was firmly convinced that "a native was all right as long as he knew his place", is slowly giving ground to a younger generation, which knows that facts are mightier than slogans and that this universe of ours was created on the principle of eternal change.

As for the other islands that belong to the Dutch group, none of them is as highly cultivated as Java. Celebes, that queerly shaped, spidery island just west of the Moluccas, the original spice-islands for which the English and the Portuguese and the Spaniards and the Dutch fought each other so bitterly all during the seventeenth century, is being slowly groomed by the Dutch to become a second Java. Today Macassar, the town where the oil came from with which our Victorian grandfathers adorned their locks and which made our Victorian grandmothers knit their endless "antimacassars", is one of the most important cities of the Java Sea, doing a regular business with Surabaya and Semarang, the main ports on the northern coast of Java, and being in regular communication with Tandjong Priok, which is the harbor of Batavia, the capital, just as Weltevreden is the residential quarter and Buitenzorg the seat of government.

The Molucca Islands themselves are not as rich as they used to be, but their inhabitants, the Amboinese, are still renowned for their ability as sailors. Four hundred years ago these same

Java

Amboinese were dreaded far and wide as the most voracious cannibals of the Pacific Ocean. Today they are exemplary Christians although, curiously enough, they have given the Dutch East Indian army its best fighting regiments.

Borneo, the main remnant of the old submerged Asiatic peninsula, suffers from under-population due to the strange native belief that head-hunting makes for holiness. The Dutch have been trying to kill this popular pastime by the most drastic forms of punishment. But in the interior no young man, even today, is allowed to marry until he has at least one head to his credit. This prolonged process of mutual extermination (the Borneo people will exhibit their gruesome conquests as proudly and as unconcernedly as an expert golf player will show you his cups) has kept the number of the inhabitants way below par. But now at last the rivers are being opened up, and oil and coal and diamond companies are constructing roads, and the savages are gradually being persuaded to turn to the more peaceful pursuits of agriculture. Thus the island, in due course of time, may be able to support twenty times its present population without noticing the difference.

The northern part of Borneo belongs to the English. The north-western corner is an independent state, called Sarawak, and ruled by the descendants of an Englishman, the famous Rajah Brooks, who arrived in the island as Sir James Brooks to suppress a local rebellion and who remained to become its independent sovereign.

Another island of tremendous importance is Sumatra in the east, which runs parallel with the Malay peninsula. It is highly volcanic and will grow almost anything, but unfortunately it is cut into two distinct halves by a high mountain-range which has greatly retarded its development until the introduction of railroads. The automobile and the flying machine will do more to open up this territory to western commerce than any other mechanical agency would ever have been able to do.

Between Sumatra and Borneo lie the islands of Banka and Billiton which, being a continuation of the Malay peninsula, are also exceedingly rich in tin. East of Java lies the famous island of Bali, where the ancient native form of life has been best preserved, and then come Flores and Timor, just north of Australia, and finally New Guinea, which is really part of the Australian mainland and of which only the western half is in Dutch hands. The island, which would cover the greater part of central Europe, from Paris to Odessa, has hardly been touched. There are no rivers leading to the interior and the population is very small, due in part to cannibalism and in part to the backwardness of the natives, forever decimated by disease and man-hunting. Here and there in the interior there are remnants of pygmy tribes, indicating that the island must have been settled at a very early age.

But then, this whole part of the world is very old and according to one theory at least, it is in this region that Man first of all bade farewell to his anthropoid cousins, the apes. Hence the skull of that earliest man-like creature, the famous Pithecanthropus Erectus, which was found in the island of Java, and the presence in Borneo and Sumatra of those big, man-like apes which are known as the orang-utan.

This is indeed a curious world, this world of ours. One branch of the family progressed until it was able to build zoos provided with tropical heat. And the other half went to live in them.

XLII

AUSTRALIA, THE STEP-CHILD OF NATURE

SPEAKING of the wasteful methods of Nature and the lack of an apparent purpose in creation, the late Hermann Ludwig von Helmholtz, the famous German scientist, a specialist in the field of physiological optics, is said to have made the remark that if any instrument-maker should ever have dared to favor him with a contraption quite as clumsy as the human eye, he would have denounced the man as an incompetent bungler who did not know his business.

I am glad Helmholtz did not extend his investigations beyond the realm of physiology and electricity for I would hate to repeat what he would have said about the way the deity handled the geographical arrangement of our planet.

Take a country like Greenland. There it lies, almost buried beneath thousands of feet of snow and ice. If those 827,000 square miles could be moved to the middle of the ocean, they might support a population of millions of people. Now they offer a scant living to a few thousand ice-bears and a handful of half-starved Eskimos. But as a sublime example of bad executive management, I offer you Australia. For Australia, although officially registered as a continent, is just about exactly everything a well-regulated continent should not be.

In the first place, its location is so unfortunate that although the Portuguese, the Spaniards and the Dutch had suspected its existence for over a hundred years and had done their best to discover it, the whole of that enormous territory of almost 3,000,-000 square miles (as large, therefore, as the United States) was not actually seen by the eyes of a white man until the year 1642, when Abel Tasman, flying the flag of the Dutch East India

Company, circumnavigated the country and took posssession of it in the name of the United Netherlands.

But this visit of state was perfectly useless from a practical point of view. The Dutch were not interested in this wilderness and allowed their title to lapse. When James Cook was sent to the Pacific to observe the transit of the planet Venus in the year 1769 (a century and a quarter therefore after Tasman's voyage) the map-makers of Amsterdam and London were still quite uncertain where exactly they must place this Terra Australis Incognita in the midst of the vast expanse of water that went by the name of the Great Peaceful Ocean.

Not only did Australia suffer from a bad location, but in the second place it had a very unfortunate climate. The climate is fairly good along the east coast and along the eastern part of the southern coast where Adelaide, Melbourne, Sydney and Brisbane, the four big cities, are located. But the northern coast is uncomfortably wet and the western coast is uncomfortably dry, which means that the most inhabitable part is also the furthest removed from the great trade-routes which connect Asia with Africa and Europe.

In the third place, the whole of the interior is a desert without any rain and its subterranean water supply is so badly located that systematic irrigation will always be extremely difficult.

In the fourth place, the highest parts are practically everywhere along the outer edges of the continent. The interior therefore resembles a hollow bowl, and, since water does not flow uphill, it has no rivers worthy of that name. The Darling River, the largest of all Australian rivers (1160 miles long) takes its origin among the mountains of Queensland, not so many miles away from the Coral Sea, a part of the Pacific Ocean. But instead of running eastward into the Pacific, it flows westward to lose itself in Encounter Bay, and for the greater part of the year (remember that it is winter in the southern hemisphere when it is summer in the northern, and vice versa) it consists mainly of a series of pools and is of no earthly use to anybody.

In the fifth place, there were no natives who could be trained

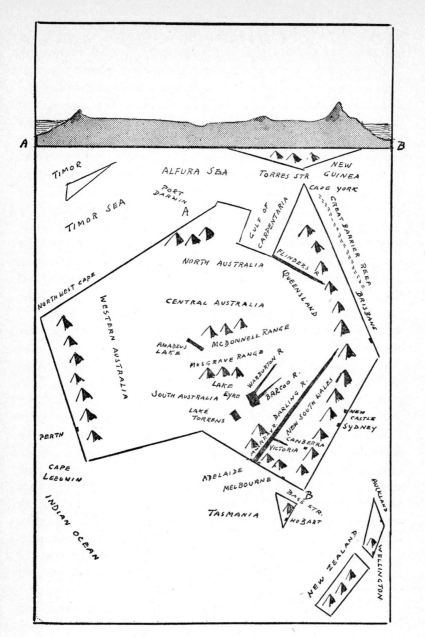

Australia

to do the white man's chores. The unfortunate Australians, about whose origin we are still very much in the dark, might just as well have lived on another planet, as far as their relations with the rest of mankind were concerned. Left entirely to their own devices, they never rose very high beyond the status of some of our more primitive animals. For example, they never learned how to build houses nor how to raise grain nor how to use a spear or an arrow or an axe. They knew how to handle the boomerang, as indeed a great many other people all over the world had done at one time or another. But whereas the others had eventually graduated from that very clumsy weapon to the sword and the spear and the bow, the Australians had remained exactly where they had been shortly after their ancestors had learned to walk on their hind legs without the support of their arms. The most generous way of classifying them would probably be to say that they resembled "the hunting type" of the earliest period of the Stone Age. And even then we are rather hard on the typical stone-age man who was as a rule a much better artist than any aboriginal Australian has ever been.

And finally, this poor continent had apparently been told to shift for itself long before the earth had been covered by those plants and shrubs which have contributed so much to our own comfort and happiness. It had developed a specific dry-climate flora of its own which is undoubtedly of profound interest to our professional botanists but which offers the white settler, intent upon raising a profitable crop of something or other (anything at all as long as it pays him for his trouble), only very slight prospects for a profitable future. Kangaroo grass and salt bush make fairly good food for sheep, but the common prickly spinifex is too much even for the hard-palated camel. And one cannot very well grow rich raising eucalyptus trees, although some of them will grow as high as 400 feet, the only rivals of our own sequoias in California.

As for the farmers who hastened to this new promised land in 1868 when it definitely ceased to be a penal colony, they found themselves faced by a collection of living fossils which

The Atlantic

The Pacific

absolutely refused to let themselves be domesticated. Once more
it was the isolated position of Australia which had allowed all
these curious prehistoric creatures to continue their existence
long after they had been exterminated in every other part of the
world. The complete absence of all the larger and more intel-

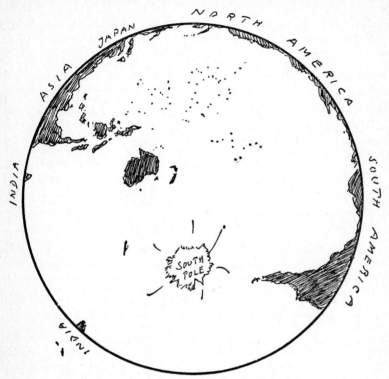

Australia's isolation

ligent mammals of Asia and Africa and Europe had not forced
these Australian quadrupeds to improve their intellectual capacities or die out. From sheer lack of competition they had always remained as they had been on the day they were born.

We are all of us familiar with the strange animal called the
kangaroo. The kangaroo belongs to the family of the marsupials.
Marsupials are animals which have a pouch in which they carry

their young who are born imperfect and who then grow to perfection inside this pouch. During the tertiary period, the whole earth was inhabited by marsupials. Today there remains only one variety of marsupial in America, the opossum, but Australia has quite a large number of them.

Another prehistoric remnant are the so-called Monotremata, the lowest sub-class of the mammals, creatures which have but a single outlet for all the excretory channels of the body. The best-known among these is the grotesque ornithorhynchus paradoxus or water-mole, a brownish creature some twenty inches long, with short fur and the bill of a duck (which in the young has even got teeth) and web-feet with long nails and a poisonous horny spur on the heels of the males—a walking museum of everything that Nature has ever invented or discarded during the millions of years of her evolutions forward and backward.

As for the rest of the Australian fauna, it contains a most formidable museum of animal curiosities: birds with feathers that are formed like hair; birds that can only walk and are unable to fly; birds that laugh like jackals; cuckoo birds which look like pheasants and pigeons as large as chickens; rats with web-feet and rats with tails that allow them to climb trees; lizards able to walk on two legs; fishes with gills and lungs which date back to the days of the ichthyosaurus and which are really a mixture of fish and amphibian; wild dogs that resemble both a jackal and a wolf and that may be the descendants of pariah dogs imported into Australia by some of the earliest immigrants from the Asiatic mainland; and a whole menagerie of other monstrosities.

But that is not all. Australia also has an assortment of insects of its own and they are more to be feared than tigers and snakes. There are the jumping ants, for Australia is El Dorado of the jumpers. Mammals, birds, insects, they all of them jump in preference to flying or running. There are ants that live in skyscrapers of their own making. There are ants that will eat their way through anything short of a cast-iron door, for they are able to cover ordinary tin and lead boxes with a particular

acid which causes the metal to oxidize and allows the ants to dig
a tunnel through which they can enter into the interior and then
destroy the contents at their own leisure.

There are the flies which hatch their eggs in the skins of sheep
and cows, and mosquitoes which make the swampy regions of
southern Australia absolutely uninhabitable, and the grasshop-
pers, able to destroy the labor of years in as many minutes, and
the ticks which attach themselves to the flocks and live on their
blood, and the cockatoos who look so pretty and so harmless but
are able to do terrific damage when operating en masse, as they
are apt to do in that part of the world.

But the worst of all these manifold local plagues is not of
Australian origin at all but an import from Europe. I refer to
Brer Rabbit, a harmless enough creature in his usual haunts,
but a terrific nuisance among the sandy wastes of a continent
where the creatures can breed *ad libitum*. The first rabbits were
introduced from England in the year 1862 for the purpose of a
little sport. The colonists were bored. Hunting rabbits would be
a pleasant diversion to break the monotony of life in the bush.
A few of these rabbits escaped and they set up house-keeping in
the well-known rabbit fashion. Astronomers, accustomed to deal
with large figures, have tried to compute the number of rabbits
that must be at large at the present moment in Australia. They
have come to the conclusion that there must be almost 4,000,-
000,000 of them. As forty rabbits eat as much as one single sheep,
that represents a herd of 100,000,000 sheep. Draw your own
conclusions. Entire regions have been devastated by these ro-
dents. Western Australia was so badly eaten by the hungry
conies that an effort was made to protect it from further invasions by means of a gigantic fence of chicken-wire, a sort of
Chinese rabbit-wall, over three feet high and three feet below
the ground, to prevent the vermin from digging holes underneath. But, driven by necessity, they soon learned to climb these
fences and the plague continued unabated. Poison was then
tried, but also in vain. Wild animals which regulate the rabbit
supply in the rest of the world were not to be found in Australia,

or refused to adapt themselves to this strange land and died as soon as they were imported. And in spite of all the white man has done, the rabbits continue to multiply as merrily as the sparrow, another European importation which is now the dread of all Australian garden lovers, and as rapidly as the prickly-pear which has taken to the arid Australian soil as a seal takes to water.

Nevertheless, and in spite of these terrific handicaps, the immigrants have succeeded in making Australia the most important

Australia is found

wool-growing country of the world. Today Australia, with almost 80,000,000 sheep, looks after one-quarter of all the wool we wear, and wool accounts for fully two-fifths of the country's exports.

As the Australian mainland is much older than Europe, it is self-evident that it must contain a great variety of minerals. The gold rush of the early fifties drew attention to the Australian gold fields. Since then, lead, copper, tin, iron and coal have also been located, but oil has not yet been found. Diamonds occur, but they are rare. Semi-precious stones, on the other hand, such as opals and sapphires, occur in large quantities. Lack of capital and bad means of transportation have prevented a thorough exploitation of these treasures but that will come in time when Australia shall at last have recovered from years of financial

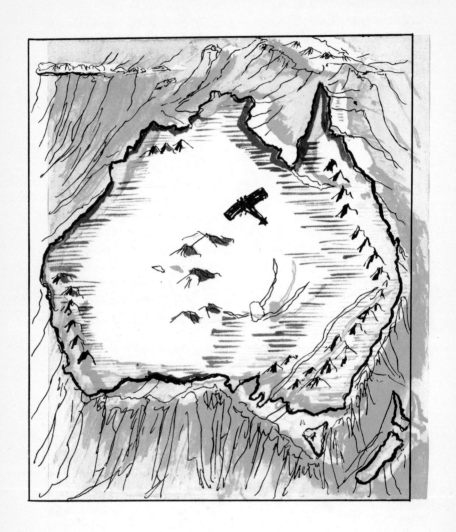

Australia

mismanagement and shall once more be counted among the solvent nations.

Meanwhile Australia enjoys the distinction of having been, next to Africa, the most difficult continent to explore. By the beginning of the nineteenth century her three main divisions were fairly well understood. There was the table-land of the west,

The Pearl Diver

which had an average altitude of 2000 feet, although in some spots it went as high as 3000 feet. This table-land was also the gold land, but it had no harbors and only one city of any importance, called Perth. Then there were the eastern highlands, very ancient mountain-ranges which rain and wind had gradually worn away until the highest top, Mount Kosciusco, was only 7000 feet above sea-level. This was the part of the continent with good harbors, which therefore attracted the first colonists.

Between these two elevated plateaus lay a wide plain which

never rose above 600 feet and which in the region of Lake Eyre actually sank below sea-level. This plain was cut into halves by two mountain-ranges, the Flinders range in the west and the Grey range in the east which connected in the north with the mountains of Queensland.

As for the political development of the country, it has been peaceful but only fairly successful. The first immigrants were people, who according to the laws of England of the latter half of the eighteenth century, were considered "criminals", but who usually were guilty of no worse crime than that poverty or misery which had driven them to commit some petty offence like the theft of a loaf of bread or a few apples. The first penal settlement was in Botany Bay, so called because Captain Cook, who discovered it, arrived there just when all the little flowers were in bloom. The colony itself was called New South Wales and Sydney was the capital. The island of Tasmania, then part of New South Wales, was converted into a penal station in 1803, and the convicts were gathered together in the neighborhood of the present city of Hobart. In 1825 the city of Brisbane, the capital of Queensland, was founded. During the thirties a settlement at the head of the bay, called Port Phillip, was named after Lord Melbourne and it became the capital of the province of Victoria. Adelaide, the capital of South Australia, dates back to the same period, but Perth, the capital of West Australia, remained an insignificant village until the days of the great gold rush of the early fifties. As for the northern territory, administered by the Commonwealth very much as our own territories used to be administered by Washington, although it has an area of half a million square miles, it has only 5000 inhabitants of whom less than 2000 live in Port Darwin on the Timor Sea, one of the finest natural harbors in the world but without a vestige of trade.

In the year 1901 these six states, with 6,000,000 inhabitants of which three-quarters lived in the east, formed the Commonwealth of Australia and seven years later they decided to build themselves a new capital called Canberra, situated 150 miles south-west of Sydney and not far away from Mount Kosciusco, the highest mountain of all Australia.

In the year 1927 the Dominion took possession of its new headquarters. But the parliament of the new Commonwealth will have to do some very deep thinking ere it can pull the nation out of its present difficulties. In the first place, the Labor Union Government, which had been in control ever since the Great War, has been so needlessly costly that the Commonwealth is no longer able to get any credit from the money-lenders of Europe. It is doubtful whether the new government that has recently succeeded the Labor Party will be able to overcome this financial handicap without making some very serious concessions. In the second place, Australia suffers from a most dreadful under-population. Tasmania and New South Wales have eight people to the square mile. Victoria has twenty. But Queensland and South Australia have only one and West Australia only one half per square mile. And even these have been so thoroughly steeped in labor union lore that they are among the world's most incompetent and indifferent workmen and cannot live without a great many public holidays, devoted to sport and horse-racing.

Well then, who is to do the work that is necessary to keep a nation going?

Italians are not wanted, although they would be perfectly willing to come. But the English middle-class element which is predominant in the political life of the Commonwealth has coined the phrase, "Australia for the Australians", which means the exclusion of everything that is not strictly white and of English middle-class origin. The hardworking Italian is neither, and he is therefore discouraged from crossing the Torres Strait. The Japanese and the Chinese, being yellow of color, are out of the question. The Polynesians and the Malays and the Javanese are of a chocolaty hue and therefore anathema. I repeat the question—who is to do the work? And I add that I do not know the answer. But 3,000,000 square miles of land lie practically uninhabited, and other parts of the world are hopelessly over-populated. This will provide the usual solution.

XLIII

NEW ZEALAND

NEW ZEALAND, together with her newly acquired possessions among the Samoan Islands, is one and a quarter times as large as England and Scotland together. The population is 1,500,000, of whom 143,000 live in Wellington, the capital, which is situated on the North Island.

It was first seen by Abel Tasman in the year 1642 and was called by him after that southern island province of his native land in which the first part of this geography was written. Some three centuries before it had been discovered by the Polynesian canoemen, those marvellous mariners of the Pacific, whose queerly shaped straw maps were so dependable that they could sail thousands of miles from home and always be sure of finding their way back.

These Polynesian conquerors became the ancestors of the warlike and handsome race of the Maoris, of whom there were some 50,000 left in the year 1906, and who since then seem to be again on the increase. The Maoris are evidently one of the few examples of a native stock which has been able to maintain itself against the white man and to adopt some of the more agreeable virtues of western civilization without at the same time drinking itself to death. They have given up several of their ancient habits and customs, such as eating their enemies and tattooing their faces, and they send representatives to the New Zealand parliament and build churches which are in every way as unattractive as the chapels constructed by their white masters, all of which bids well for the future, as far as the racial problem is concerned.

During the first quarter of the nineteenth century both the

French and the English tried to get hold of these islands by means of their respective missionaries. But in the year 1833 the Maoris put themselves under the protection of the English and in the year 1839 the English formally took possession of all New Zealand territory.

If the French squadron had been three days earlier, New Zealand would today be a French colony like New Caledonia and the Marquesas and so many other islands of the Pacific. In 1840 the islands became a dependency of the Australian colony of New South Wales and in 1847 an English Crown Colony. In the year 1901, New Zealand was given a chance to join the Australian commonwealth but, proud of the fact that it had never been a penal establishment, it declined the honor. Since 1907 it has been an independent dominion with an English governor-general but a representative government of its own.

As for the geological aspect of these two big islands, they have probably never been part of the Australian mainland, for the Tasman Sea which separates them is more than 15,000 feet deep and 1200 miles wide. They are probably the remnants of a high mountain-range which once upon a time formed the western shores of the Pacific. But the changes have been so numerous that it is difficult to state precisely how the present islands came into being. What makes their case even more difficult is the fact that they have so little in common with each other. Whereas North Island is a tremendously volcanic region (a sort of Yellowstone Park of the Pacific), South Island, separated from North Island by the Cook Strait, which is only 90 miles wide, is a replica of Switzerland with a few Norwegian fjords thrown in for good measure.

New Zealand is not in any way tropical. It is as far removed from the equator as Italy and enjoys the same sort of climate. This means that it is much more likely to become a permanent European establishment than Australia. All sorts of European fruits, such as peaches and apricots and apples and grapes and oranges, can be cultivated in the valleys, while the mountain sides provide excellent grazing fields for cattle. Flax grows as

well here as in the moist climate of the old Zeeland and the slow
growing trees of the North Island, exported chiefly from Auck-
land, make excellent timber.

In the year 1901 New Zealand annexed a number of islands
of the Pacific. Among them were the Cook Islands and the Island
of Rarotonga from where, according to the Maori belief, New

New Zealand looks very much like Norway

Zealand got its first Polynesian settlers. The Cook Islands are
still of volcanic origin but thereupon we leave the volcanic belt
and get into the midst of the coral islands.

These are formed by little marine organisms, the Anthozoa or
"flower-animals", which die but whose assembled skeletons are
responsible for the thousands of reefs and islets which dot this
part of the Pacific Ocean. These polyps are fussy creatures. They
can only live in fresh salt water of a certain temperature. A single

frost will kill them. They cannot descend lower than about 120 feet. Whenever we find coral deposits lower than that, we know that the bottom of the ocean must have sunk from its original level. But they have been building their little islands for millions of years and their work is more enduring than that of the best masons. As they depend upon a constant supply of water-in-motion, the polyps who live in the center of the edifice are apt to die off first. The edges then continue to grow and finally they form a so-called atoll, an island consisting of a narrow ring of solid material with a circular lagoon in the center. There is usually a single entrance to such a lagoon and it is always away from the prevailing winds as the waves on the other side provide the polyps with a more abundant food supply and therefore make them grow faster.

A number of such atolls which grow cocoanuts and produce copra now belong to New Zealand and the German share of Samoa was given to the dominion as a mandate in recognition of the excellent services of the New Zealand troops during the Great War. What they are going to do with it, I do not know.

XLIV

THE ISLANDS OF THE PACIFIC WHERE PEOPLE NEITHER
TOILED NOR SPUN BUT LIVED JUST THE SAME

THE Atlantic has hardly any islands at all. The Pacific has
by far too many. The Caroline Islands, the Marshall Islands
and the Hawaiian Islands lie north of the equator. All the others
lie south of the equator. They usually make their appearance in
groups. Easter Island, the place where we have found those
mysterious gigantic stone statues, is an exception. It lies by itself,
but it is much nearer to South America than to Australia.

The Pacific Islands can be divided into three distinct groups.
There are the islands which are undoubtedly the remnants of
the vast Australian continent of prehistoric geological times. New
Caledonia, the French penal settlement, is an example of this
sort of island. Then there are others like the Fiji Islands, Samoa,
the Hawaiian or Sandwich Islands and the Marquesas, which
are of distinct volcanic origin. Finally there are the coral islands
like the New Hebrides.

Of all these thousands of islands (many of the coral islands
are only a few feet above water) the most important ones are
the Hawaiian Islands, where Captain Cook was murdered by
the natives on his way home in the year 1779. In the year 1810
they became the center of a large South Sea Empire which continued to exist until 1893, when they were annexed by the United
States. Outside of their great fertility they are of tremendous
importance as half-way stations between America and Asia.

They are a bit shaky. Kilauea, a volcano with the unusual
height of 4400 feet, continues to be active. The volcano on Maui,
another island of the group, has the biggest crater of the world.
But the marvellous climate easily makes up for an occasional

worried glance at the smoke plumes of these old but none too trustworthy friends. Honolulu on the island of Oahu is the capital.

The most important city of the Fiji Islands is Suva, a port of call for all steamers from America to Australia and New Zealand.

The capital of Samoa is Apia.

Another island of which you sometimes hear is Guam in the Ladrones, half-way between Japan and New Guinea and an important American cable station.

Then there is Tahiti, a French possession among the Society

The Coral Island

Islands, where the South Sea movie stories are supposed to come from.

Finally there are dozens and dozens of other islands belonging to the three general groups of Melanesia and Micronesia and Polynesia. They seem to form regular barriers across the Pacific, running in three parallel lines from north-west to south-east, and making navigation in the Pacific something very different from that in the Atlantic where Rockall is the only danger spot between Ireland and the American coast.

It is said that these islands offer a most agreeable home to all those who find our modern machine-made civilization too complicated for their simple tastes and who prefer peace and quiet and agreeable companions to noise and hurry and the angry looks of jealous competitors. I suppose they are more restful than, let us say, the corner of Broadway and Forty-Second Street. But they are so dreadfully far away—and do they really grow an herb that will allow the average man to escape from himself?

XLV

AFRICA, THE CONTINENT OF CONTRADICTIONS AND CONTRASTS

AFRICA, like Australia, is the remnant of a much older continent, the greater part of which disappeared beneath the waves of the sea a great many million years ago. Until comparatively recent times it was still connected with Europe. Arabia, geographically speaking a continuation of the Sahara, and Madagascar, which has the fauna and flora of Africa, Asia and Australia, seem to indicate that there may have been a land connection between these three continents as recently ago as the era during which life first appeared upon our planet.

It is all very complicated and we shall have to discover a great many more data before we shall be able to say, "It was thus and thus and not otherwise". In the meanwhile it is not a bad idea to mention these theories. They show us that the surface of our planet is constantly changing—that nothing is today quite as it was yesterday and that our descendants a million years hence will look at our maps (if they are still interested in our funny little globe, having long since learned to fly to other and bigger planets) with ill-concealed surprise, just as we contemplate a hypothetical map of the Tertiary or Silurian age and ask ourselves, "Can such things ever have been?"

What finally remained of all this ancient territory and what has not changed since the beginning of our so-called "historical times" consists of two parts, a large square of land north of the equator and a smaller triangle south of the equator. But both the square and the triangle suffer from the same geographical disadvantage. Their outer rims are higher than the interior and as a result the interior resembles a gigantic saucer. Such a condition, as we have already seen in the case of Australia, is very bad for the country at large. The high edges of the saucer prevent the sea winds from penetrating into the interior, which is therefore apt to turn into a desert, and furthermore they deprive that interior of its natural outlets towards the sea. For when the African rivers finally reach the ocean, after having wandered all over the landscape, they must break their way through a series of mountain-ranges. That means that they suffer from water-falls and cataracts where they are least wanted. It means that ships cannot use these rivers to reach the interior of the country. It means that trade must wait until artificial harbors have been constructed and until railroads have been built that circumnavigate the water-falls. In short, it means isolation.

To most of us Africa is merely the "black continent" and we usually associate it with tropical forests and Negroes. As a matter of fact, one-third of the 11,300,000 square miles which the continent occupies (it is therefore three times as large as Europe) are desert and of absolutely no value. The population of 140,-000,000 is divided into three groups of which one, that of the Negroes, is black, while the other two, the Hamites and the Semites, vary all the way from a dark chocolate to the whiteness of polished ivory.

It is natural, however, that the Negro should have forced himself more upon our attention than his lighter-colored neighbors. Not only does he impress us as something queer when we first see him, but the mistaken economic conceptions of our ancestors have dragged him all over the globe as a cheap and docile form of labor, and it is not always pleasant to be reminded of this disgraceful error of judgment. For Negro slavery has been one of the worst misfortunes that could possibly have overtaken both races, that of the white man as well as that of the black. We shall return to it a little later but we must first talk of Africa as it was before the invention of Negro slavery.

The Greeks were familiar with Egypt and with the Hamitic race which inhabited the valley of the Nile. The Hamitic races

Africa

had occupied northern Africa at a very early date and had pushed
the original, darker-skinned inhabitants southward in the general direction of the Sudan while keeping the northern border
of the Mediterranean for their own exclusive use. The term
Hamitic is a very vague one. There are no typical Hamites as
there are typical Swedes or Chinamen. The Hamites are a mixture of Aryans and Semites with a heavy sprinkling of Negro
and a number of older races that were already on the premises
when these invaders from the east made their first entry.

When they reached Africa they were probably still in the
nomadic stage of development, and as a result they spread all
over the valley of the Nile and went further southward into
Abyssinia and westward as far as the Atlantic seaboard. The
Berbers of the Atlas Mountains are pure Hamites—or as pure
as any Hamite can possibly be—and several of the wandering
tribes of the Sahara are of Hamitic origin. The Abyssinians, on
the other hand, are now so hopelessly mixed with Semites as to
have lost a great many of their Hamitic traits. While the Fellahs,
the small-boned farmers of the Nile valley, are also of Hamitic
stock although mixed beyond recognition by thousands of years
of intermarriage with other races.

As a rule, when we try to classify different races, language
comes to our rescue. But in northern Africa the spoken tongue is
of very little help. There are Semitic tribes which speak only
Hamitic and Hamitic tribes which speak only Arabic, while the
Copts, the ancient Christians of Egypt, are the only people who
have retained a knowledge of the ancient Hamitic tongue. The
Greeks and Romans were apparently just as much puzzled as
we are. They solved the difficulty by calling all the people who
came from this neck of the woods "Ethiopians" or "black faces".
They wondered at their pyramids and at the negroid lips of their
Sphynx (or are the lips Hamitic? Ask the professors!) and ad-
mired the patience of their long-suffering peasants and the wisdom of their mathematicians and the learning of their physicians,
but they never seemed to have bothered to ask where these people might have come from. They spoke of them as Ethiopians.

One word of warning! If you should ever go to north Africa, be careful not to call all these people "Niggers" just because they are often rather dark-skinned. They might resent it and some of them are among the best fighters in the world. They have got the blood in them of those Egyptian warriors who conquered the whole of western Asia. They may even be the descendants of those Semitic Carthaginians who almost deprived Rome of the mastery of the Mediterranean. They may be the great-grandchildren of those Arab conquerors who not so very long ago overran the whole of southern Europe, or the children of those Algerian chieftains who put up such a terrific struggle when France tried to conquer Algeria and when Italy tried to get a foothold in Tunisia. Even if their hair be a little kinky, be careful and remember the fatal day in 1896 when the fuzzy-haired Ethiopians pushed the white-skinned Italians into the Red Sea.

So much for the Hamites, the first people the Europeans saw after they had sailed successfully across the Mediterranean. And little need be added about the Semites, with whom the Europeans came in very painful contact when Hannibal introduced the do-mesticated elephant to the plains of the Po. But once Carthage had been destroyed, the road to Africa lay open; and it is a curious fact that so few Europeans availed themselves of the opportunity to find out what lay beyond that vast sandy region to which the Romans had given the name of Numidia.

Nero, of all emperors, was the first to take a serious interest in African exploration. His expeditions apparently got as far as that village of Fashoda which some thirty years ago was al-most the cause of a war between France and England. But the Nero-Nile expedition does not seem to have been the white man's furthest-south even in those long ago days. It now seems likely that the Carthaginians several centuries before had already crossed the Sahara and had visited the Gulf of Guinea. But Carthage had been destroyed and all knowledge about that central part of Africa was definitely lost. For the Sahara was a barrier which frightened even the hardiest explorers. They might, of course, have followed the coast regions. But these were so completely lacking in harbors that the problem of getting a fresh water supply became an almost insurmountable obstacle. Africa has a coast line of only 16,000 miles, while Europe, one-third its size, has a coast line of 20,000 miles. As a result, navigators who wanted to land anywhere on the African coast were obliged to drop anchor several miles away from land and must then cross the surf in an open row-boat, a procedure so uncomfortable and so dangerous that few of them ever tried it.

And so we had to wait until the beginning of the nineteenth century before we learned a few definite facts about the geography of Africa. Even then these sources of information were merely incidental, for the Portuguese, the first explorers of the African west coast, were on their way to the Indies and had very little interest in the land of the naked blackamoors. Since they could not reach India and China without circumnavigating that big barrier of the south, they felt their way along the African coast as carefully as a blind man trying to get out of a dark room. Without in any way looking for them they stumbled upon several islands, the Azores and the Canary Islands and the Cape Verde Islands. Finally in 1471 they reached the equator. Then in 1488 Bartholomew Diaz spotted the Storm Cape, now the Cape of Good Hope or briefly, the Cape. In 1498 Vasco da Gama rounded that cape and definitely located the shortest route from Europe to the Indies.

When that had been done, Africa once more dropped out of sight. It was a hindrance to navigation. It was too hot and too dry or too hot and too damp. The people were savages. The skippers of the sixteenth and seventeenth centuries, on their way to the Orient, called at the different islands, the Azores, Ascension, St. Helena, whenever scurvy and a high death rate among their sailors forced them to buy a few fresh vegetables. But African land to them was bad land. Give it a wide berth. And the poor heathen of that vast continent might have continued to dwell in peace if it had not been for the kindheartedness of the first man who was ever ordained a priest in the New World.

Bartolomé de las Casas was the son of a man who had accompanied Columbus on his original voyage to America. The son, appointed Bishop of Chiapa in Mexico, received as compensation for his services a piece of land with the Indian occupants attached to it. In other words, he became a plain, ordinary slave-holder. Every Spaniard then living in the New World had a certain number of Indians who worked for him. It was a bad system but, like so many bad systems, it was tolerated because,

On the way to the Slavery Coast

being everybody's business, it was nobody's business. It just happened that las Casas one day clearly realized just how bad the system was and how unfair it happened to be to the original owners of the land, who were now forced to work in the mines and perform all sorts of menial tasks which they never would have touched while they were still free.

He went to Spain to do something about it. The all-powerful Cardinal Jimenes, confessor of Queen Isabella, thought that he was right, appointed him "Protector of the Indians" and sent him back to America to write a report. Las Casas returned to Mexico but found his superiors completely cold on the subject. The Indians had been given unto the Christians to do their bidding, just like the animals of the field and the birds of the air and the fishes of the sea. (See Genesis 1: 28.) Why start something that would upset the entire economic fabric of the New World and furthermore would very seriously interfere with profits?

Then las Casas, who took his God-given task very seriously, had a bright idea. The Indian preferred death to captivity, as had been proved in Haiti where the number of natives had dropped from 1,000,000 to 60,000 in less than fifteen years. But the Negro of Africa did not seem to mind being a slave. In the year 1516 (direful date in the history of the New World) las Casas published the details of his famous humanitarian scheme for the complete liberation of his Indian charges. Each Spaniard living in the New Spain was to be granted the right to import twelve African Negroes and the Indians were to be allowed to return to what remained of their own farms after the immigrants had deprived them of all the better parts.

Poor las Casas lived long enough to come to a true realization of what he had done. His shame (for he was an honest man) was such that he retired to a monastery in Haiti. Afterwards he returned to public life and tried once more to fight the battles of the unfortunate heathen. But nobody listened to him, and when he died in 1556 new plans were under way to bind the Indians even more fully to the soil, and the African slave trade too was in full swing.

What this trade meant to Africa during the 300 years of its existence we can only guess from the few reliable figures that have come down to us. The actual slave-hunting was not done by white men. The Arabs, who could wander at will over the entire northern part which had gradually been converted to Mohammedanism, held a monopoly of that racket. They had sold an occasional shipload of blackamoors to the Portuguese ever since the year 1434, but their business did not assume the gigantic proportions of the later days until the year 1517. There was big money in it. The Emperor Charles V (he of the famous Habsburg chin) bestowed upon one of his Flemish friends a grant which allowed him to carry 4000 African slaves each year

The Delta of the Nile

to Haiti, Cuba and Porto Rico. The Fleming at once sold his imperial patent to a Genoese speculator who paid him 25,000 ducats for it. The Genoese in turn sold it to a combination of Portuguese and these Portuguese went to Africa and got in touch with the Arab dealers and the Arab dealers raided a number of Sudanese villages until they had about 10,000 slaves together (one must count on a heavy percentage of loss during the voyage) who were then packed into the hold of some evil-smelling carack and dispatched across the ocean.

Rumors of this new and easy way to get rich spread far and wide. The Papal Bull which had divided the whole world into two halves, one of which belonged to Spain and one to Portugal, made it impossible for the Spaniards to visit the "slave coast" themselves. The actual business of buying and transporting this black merchandise was therefore left to the Portuguese. But as soon as the power of the Portuguese had been broken by the English and the Dutch, slave-running became a monopoly of these two Christian nations. They continued to provide all the world with their "black ivory" (as the Bristol and London merchants playfully called it) until the year 1811 when Parliament finally passed a bill making the traffic in slaves a felony punishable with a fine and deportation. But it was a long time from 1517 until 1811 and until even afterwards, for slave-smuggling continued for fully another thirty years in spite of all the English warships. It did not fully come to an end until the early sixties of the nineteenth century when practically all European and American nations had abolished slavery definitely. (The Argentine abolished it in 1813, Mexico in 1829, U.S.A. in 1863, Brazil in 1888.)

How important the trade was in the eyes of Europe's rulers and statesmen is proved by the efforts they made to gain a monopoly of the slave traffic for the sole benefit of their own country. The refusal of Spain to continue a slave contract, thus far held by a few English merchants, even led to a war between England and Spain; and one of the stipulations of the famous peace treaty of Utrecht definitely transferred the West India slave monopoly from the Dutch to the English. Not to be out-done, the Dutch, who in 1620 had landed the first African slaves on Virginian soil, hastened to avail themselves of a law passed during the reign of William and Mary which had opened up the slave trade with the colonies to all the nations of the world. Indeed the Dutch West India Company, which through its scandalous neglect was responsible for the loss of Nieuw Amsterdam, only escaped bankruptcy because it made so much money out of its traffic in slaves.

We have very few statistics upon the subject, for the slavers were usually not the sort of men who took a scientific interest in their business; but those we have are appalling. The French Cardinal Lavigerie, archbishop of Carthage and founder of the famous Pères Blancs (the missionaries who have done so much good in northern Africa) and a man therefore thoroughly conversant with African affairs, estimated that at least 2,000,000 people per year had been lost to Africa on account of the slave trade, including those who were killed by the hardships of the march to the coast, the children who died because they were too young to be of any value and were therefore left to the mercies of the wild animals, and those who were actually shipped away to foreign shores.

Dr. Livingstone, another highly competent judge, put the actual number of slaves taken away from their homes every twelve months (regardless of those who died because they were left behind without any protection) at 350,000, of whom only 70,000 ever reached the other side of the ocean.

Between 1700 and 1786 not less than 600,000 slaves were brought to Jamaica alive, and during the same period more than 2,000,000 slaves were carried from Africa to the West Indies by two of the smaller English slave companies. By the end of the eighteenth century, Liverpool, London and Bristol maintained a fleet of 200 vessels with a total capacity of 47,000 Negroes, which plied regularly between the Gulf of Guinea and the New World. In 1791 when the Quakers and the enemies of slavery in general began their agitation against this outrage, a survey of the slave stations along the Bight of Benin showed 14 English, 15 Dutch, 4 Portuguese, 4 Danish and 3 French. But the British were better equipped and handled one-half of the

The water-hole

whole trade, the rest being divided among the other four nations.

Of the horrible things that happened on the mainland we learned very little until much later, when the British, in order to stamp this business out by the roots, went on shore in search of further violaters. It then appeared that native chieftains had been among the chief offenders, selling their own subjects as unceremoniously as those German rulers of the eighteenth century sold their regiments of recruits to the English for the purpose of squelching that little rebellion in Virginia and Massachusetts. But the general organization of the business had always been in the hands of the Arabs. This is rather curious. The Koran highly disapproves of such pursuits and Mohammedan law in general is much more lenient towards the slaves than the Christian edicts used to be. According to the laws of the white man, the child of a slave by her master was in turn held to be a slave, whereas according to the Koran, such a child must follow the status of the father and must therefore be considered as free.

The opening up of the Congo by the unspeakable Leopold of Belgium and the demand for cheap labor to work His Majesty's concessions started a temporary revival of the slave trade between the Portuguese colony of Angola and the interior of the Congo basin. But fortunately when that miserable old man (a medieval scoundrel on a constitutional throne in a modern democratic country—as strange a contradiction in terms as had been seen for a long time) died, the Congo Free State had already been taken over by the Belgian state and that meant the end of the last attempts to make money out of buying and selling human beings.

The beginning of the relation between the white man and the black one was therefore as unfortunate as it possibly could be. But what followed was just as bad. The reasons for this unfortunate state of affairs I must now describe in as few words as possible.

In Asia the white man came face to face with races that were either as civilized as he was himself or more so. Which meant that they were able to fight back and that the white man must mind his p's and q's or suffer the consequences.

The great Sepoy rebellion in India of the fifties of the last century, the terrible insurrection of Diepo Negoro, which twenty years before had almost deprived Holland of Java, the expulsion of all foreigners from Japan, the Boxer Rebellion of only a few years ago in China, the present unrest in India and the open defiance of Europe's and America's notes in regard to Manchuria by Japan are lessons which the white man could not afford to ignore.

In Australia the white man came in contact with the poor, savage remnants of the early Stone Age whom he could kill at will and with as few pangs of conscience as he destroyed the wild dingos that ate up his sheep.

The greater part of America was practically uninhabited when the white man arrived. The high and healthy plateaus of Central America and the north-western part of the Andes (Mexico and Peru) had a dense population, but the rest was almost empty. The few wandering nomads could be easily pushed aside and disease and degeneration then did the rest.

But in Africa conditions were different, for in Africa, regardless of slavery, regardless of sickness, regardless of bad gin, regardless of bad treatment, the population refused to die out. What the white man destroyed in the morning was replaced over night. Yet the white man insisted upon taking the black man's property. The result has been a holocaust of blood, the like of which the world has rarely seen; and the end is not yet. It is a struggle between the white man's gunpowder and the black man's tropical fertility.

Let us look at the map and give you a general outline of where things stand at the present moment.

Roughly speaking, Africa can be divided into seven parts and these I shall now take up, one by one. We begin in the left upper corner, in the north-west, the infamous coast of Barbary which made our ancestors tremble with fear whenever they had to sail past it on their way from northern Europe to the ports of Italy and the Levant. For it was the land of the terrible Barbary pirates and capture by them meant years of slavery until the family at home had borrowed enough money to set their poor cousin free.

This whole territory consists of mountains, and quite high mountains, too. And these mountains explain why that country had to develop as it did and why even today it has not yet actually been conquered by the white man. They are very treacherous mountains, full of ambushes and deep ravines, allowing a marauding party to make their attack and disappear without any one being the wiser.

Aeroplanes and long distance guns are of comparatively little value here. It was only a few years ago that the Spaniards met with a number of terrible defeats at the hands of the Riff people. Our ancestors knew this, and they preferred to pay an annual tribute to the different Sultans ruling this part of the African coast, rather than risk their navies and their reputations on dangerous expeditions against harbors which no white man had ever been allowed to visit. They maintained special consuls in Algiers and Tunis whose business it was to arrange for the ransom of their captured subjects and they supported religious organizations which had no other purpose than to look after the fate of the sailors who had been unfortunate enough to fall into the hands of the Moors.

Politically speaking, this north-western corner of the African continent is now divided into four separate parts, all of which however take their orders from Paris. The process of infiltration and occupation began in the year 1830. A common, ordinary fly-swatter was the immediate cause of the outbreak of hostilities but the real reason was that old public scandal of the north-western Mediterranean, piracy.

At the Congress of Vienna the European powers had decided that "something must be done" to suppress piracy in the Mediterranean. But of course the different powers could not decide who was to undertake the job, for the hero might keep some territory for himself and that would be unfair to the others—the usual story of all diplomatic conferences.

Now there were two Algerian Jews (all business in northern Africa had been in the hands of Jews for centuries) who had a claim against the French government for grain delivered to the French government in the days before Napoleon—one of those old claims that are forever cropping up in the chancellories of the Old and New World and that have been the cause of so many misunderstandings during the last two centuries. If nations, like individuals, would only pay their bills as they go along, we surely would all of us be much happier and certainly much safer.

In the course of the negotiations about this little grain bill, the Dey of Algiers one day lost his temper and hit the French consul with his fly-swatter. Then there was a blockade and a shot was fired (probably by accident, but such things are always happening where there are war-ships around) and an expeditionary force sailed across the Mediterranean and on the fifth of July of the year 1830 the French marched into Algiers and the Dey was taken prisoner and sent into exile and the war was on in all seriousness.

The mountain people found a leader, a certain Abd-el-Kader, a pious Mohammedan and a man of great intelligence and courage, who held out against the invaders for fifteen years and who did not surrender until the year 1847. He had previously received the promise that he would be allowed to remain in his own country, but this promise was broken and he was taken to France. Napoleon III however set him free on condition that he would never again disturb the peace of his fatherland and Abd-el-Kader retired to Damascus, where he spent the rest of his days in philosophic meditations and pious deeds and where he died in 1883.

Long before his demise the last revolt in Algeria had been suppressed. Today Algeria is merely another department of France. Its people have the right to choose their own representatives and protect their interests in the French parliament in Paris. Its young men have the honor to serve as conscripts in the French army, but that is not entirely a matter of choice. But from an economic point of view, the French have done a great deal of excellent work to improve the living conditions of their new subjects.

The plain between the Atlas Mountains and the sea, called the Tell, raises grain. The Shat plateau, so called after many small salt lakes, is a grazing country, and the mountain slopes are more and more being used for wine-growing, while large irrigation works are under construction to allow the raising of tropical fruit

The Nile

for the European market. Iron and copper deposits have been located and railroad lines connect them with Algiers (the capital) and with Oran and Bizerta, the three main harbors on the Mediterranean.

Tunis, immediately to the east of the department of Algiers, is still nominally an independent state with a king of its own, but since 1881 it has been practically a French protectorate. But as France has no surplus population, most of the immigrants are Italians. The latter have a hard time competing with the Jews who moved to this part of the world centuries ago when it was still a Turkish possession, where they had a better chance to survive than under Christian rule.

Next to Tunis, the capital, the city of Sfax is the most important town. Two thousand years ago the land of Tunis was of more importance than it is today for then it formed part of the territory of Kart-hadshat, which the Romans called Carthage. The harbor, which had room for 220 vessels, may still be seen. Otherwise very little remains, for when the Romans really wanted to do a job, they did it thoroughly and their hatred of Carthage (inspired of course by fear and jealousy) was such that they did not leave a single house standing when they finally took the city in 146 B. C. They burned it down to the ground. The charred ruins, lying sixteen feet below the level of the present soil, are all that remains of a city that once upon a time had almost a million inhabitants.

The north-western corner of Africa is officially known as the independent sultanate of Morocco. There still is a sultan but since 1912 he too is merely a puppet of France. Not that he ever amounted to much. The Kabyles, the mountain folk of the Anti-Atlas, were too strongly entrenched to bother much about this distant majesty who for safety's sake varied constantly between his two capitals, Morocco in the south and the holy city of Fez in the north. These handy mountains were such a menace that the valley people never even undertook to cultivate their fields. Their harvests would be stolen anyway.

One can say a great deal against French rule in these parts of

Africa

Africa, but when it comes to the safety of the public highroads, they have performed wonders. They moved the center of government to Rabat, a city on the Atlantic, where the French navy can lend a helping hand in case of need. Rabat is several hundred miles north of Agadir, another Atlantic port which unexpectedly got into the lime-light four years before the outbreak of the Great War when the Germans sent a gun-boat there to remind France that Morocco must not become another Algiers, an incident which helped a great deal to bring about the final disastrous conflict of the year 1914.

A small corner of Morocco just opposite Gibraltar is a Spanish colony. It was given to Spain as a peace-offering when France took possession of Morocco. The two cities of Ceuta and Melilla are best known from the newspaper stories of recent date mentioning the defeats which the unwilling Spanish troops suffered at the hands of the natives, the so-called Riff-Kabyles.

To the west of the Riff Mountains lies Tangier, the internationalist city where during the eighteenth and nineteenth centuries the European ambassadors accredited to the court of the Sultan of Morocco used to reside. The Sultan did not want them too near his own court and Tangier was therefore chosen as their place of residence.

The future of this entire mountainous triangle is no longer a matter of doubt. In another fifty years, that whole region will be French, together with the second natural division of Africa which we shall discuss now—that of the great brown desert, the As-Sahra of the Arabs, the Sahara of our modern maps.

The Sahara, which is almost as large as the continent of Europe, runs all the way from the Atlantic to the Red Sea and on the other side of the Red Sea it continues under the guise of the Arabian peninsula. In the north, except for the Atlas triangle of Morocco, Algiers and Tunis, the Sahara is bordered by the Mediterranean and in the south by the Sudan. The Sahara is a plateau, but not a very high one, for most of it lies at an altitude of only 1200 feet. Here and there are the remnants of old mountain ridges, worn away by wind and sand. There are a fair num-

ber of oases where the subterranean water allows a few thrifty
Arabs to lead a not over-abundant existence. The density of
population is 0.04 per square mile which means that the Sahara
is practically uninhabited. The best known among the wandering
desert tribes are the Tuaregs, excellent fighters. The other Sa-
harians are a mixture of Semite (or Arab) and Hamite (or
Egyptian) and Sudanese Negro.

The French Foreign Legion looks after the safety of travellers
and does this exceedingly well. These French Legionnaires
(who, by the way, are never allowed on French soil) may be a bit
rough at times, but they have a tough problem on their hands.
To police a region as large as Europe with a mere handful of
men is no job for saints. Therefore, if we can believe common
rumor, very few saints have been encouraged to enlist. The old
caravan roads are beginning to lose their importance. The tractor-
wheeled automobile has taken the place of the smelly camel. It
is much less costly and infinitely more dependable for very long
distances. The days when tens of thousands of camels would
foregather in Timbuktu to bring salt to the people of the western
Sahara are gone forever.

Until the year 1911 that part of the Sahara which borders on
the Mediterranean was ruled by a Pasha of its own who recognized the Sultan of Turkey as his over-lord. In that year the
Italians, knowing that the French were going to take Morocco
as soon as they could do so without provoking a war with Germany, suddenly remembered that Libya (the Latin name for
Tripoli) had once upon a time been a very prosperous Roman
colony. They crossed the Mediterranean and took 400,000 square
miles of African territory and hoisted the Italian flag over it
and asked the world politely what it was going to do about it.
As nobody was particularly interested in Tripoli (sand without
iron or oil) the descendants of Caesar were allowed to keep their
new colony and they are now busy building roads and trying to
raise a little cotton for the textile factories of Lombardy.

On the east, this Italian experiment in the difficult art of
colonizing is bordered by Egypt. This country owed most of its

prosperity to the fact that it was really a sort of island cut off from the west by the Libyan desert and protected against the south by the Nubian desert, while the Red Sea and the Mediterranean took care of the boundaries in the north and in the east. The actual Egypt, the Egypt of history, the ancient land of the Pharaohs, which was the great store-house of art and learning and science of the ancient world, consisted of a very narrow strip situated along the shore of a river almost as long as the Mississippi. The real Egypt, not counting the desert, is smaller than the kingdom of the Netherlands. But whereas Holland can feed only 7,000,000 people, the Nile valley is so fertile that it is able to support double that number. When the great irrigation works, begun by the English, shall have been finished, there will be room for many more. But the Fellahs (the tillers of the soil who are almost without exception Mohammedans) will have to stick to their farms, for industry is not easy in a country which has neither coal nor water-power.

Ever since the great Mohammedan conquest of the eighth century, Egypt had belonged to Turkey, under a khedive or king of its own. In 1882 England occupied the country under the pretext that its financial conditions were so hopelessly bad as to warrant interference on the part of a competent European power. But the demand of Egypt for the Egyptians became so strong after the Great War that the English were forced to renounce their claims and Egypt was once more recognized as an independent kingdom which had a right to conclude all sorts of treaties with other foreign powers except commercial treaties, which must first of all be submitted to England. The British troops were to be withdrawn from all Egyptian cities except Port Saïd. Finally Alexandria, which had become the main commercial port on the Mediterranean since Damietta and Rosetta on the delta had lost their importance, must be allowed to remain an English naval base.

It was a generous agreement and a perfectly safe one, for meanwhile England had definitely occupied that eastern part of the Sudan through which the Nile happens to flow. By getting

Africa

control over the water of this river upon which 12,000,000 little brown Egyptians depend for their living, England is certain that it can always make its wants more or less understood in distant Cairo.

Any one however at all familiar with political conditions in the Near East will hardly blame England for trying to maintain

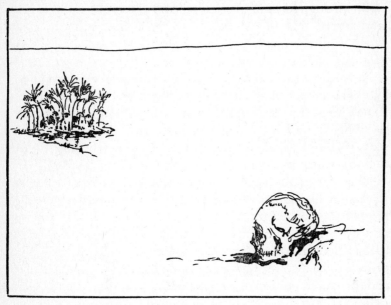

Oasis

a strong hold upon this part of the world. The Suez Canal, the short cut to India, runs entirely through Egyptian territory and it would be suicidal for England to let some one else get hold of that salty artery of trade.

The canal, of course, is not of England's making. As a matter of fact, the British government tried as hard as it could to prevent de Lesseps from beginning to dig any canal at all. There were two reasons why England should have opposed this plan. In the first place, England did not have the slightest confidence in the oft-repeated assertions of Napoleon III that the canal, built by

French engineers and with French money, was merely a commercial venture. Queen Victoria might love her dear brother in the Tuileries, who once upon a time had done service as a special London constable when her beloved subjects were on the verge of rioting for bread, but the average Englishman did not care to hear that name which reminded him too much of a certain nightmare of half a century before. And in the second place, England feared that this short cut to the Indies and China and Japan would seriously interfere with the prosperity of her own good city on the Cape of Good Hope.

Nevertheless, the canal was built and Signor Verdi composed his noble opera, "Aïda", in honor of the occasion and the Khedive ruined himself providing free board and lodging and free tickets to "Aïda" to all his foreign visitors, who filled not less than sixty-nine vessels when they went a-picnicking from Port Saïd to Suez, which was the terminus of the canal on the Red Sea.

Then England changed her tactics and her prime-minister, Benjamin Disraeli, who belonged to a race that has never yet been accused of lacking in business ability, managed to get hold of a majority of the canal stock which until then had belonged to the Khedive. And as Napoleon no longer counted and the route proved to be a god-send for the trade between Asia and Europe and produced almost $40,000,000 a year in revenue alone (28,000,000 tons passed through it in 1930, which is almost one-third of the total number of tons that passed through our own Sault Ste. Marie Canal), there have been no further complaints from the side of the British government.

By the way, the famous antiquities of Egypt are situated all over the land. The pyramids you will find in the neighborhood of Cairo where Memphis was once upon a time located. But Thebes, the old capital of upper Egypt, was situated several hundred miles further up the river. Unfortunately the tremendous irrigation works of Assuan have turned the temple of Philae into little islands which are now entirely surrounded by the muddy waters of the Nile and which are therefore doomed to ultimate destruction. The grave of King Tut-ank-Amen, who

died fourteen centuries before the beginning of our era, is also
to be found in that part of Egypt, as are the graves of many other
kings whose former household possessions and whose mummies
are gathered together in the museum of Cairo which is fast becoming a cemetery as well as one of the world's most interesting
collections of antiquities.

The third part of Africa, geographically different from all
other sections, is the Sudan. The Sudan runs almost parallel
with the Sahara but it does not continue quite so far eastward because it is brought to a sudden halt by the high plateaus of Abyssinia which separate it from the Red Sea.

Now in the great international bridge game played with
Africa as a stake, when one nation announces "three spades" the
others at once answer "four diamonds". England had taken the
Cape from the Dutch during the beginning of the nineteenth
century. The original settlers, being Dutch and therefore obstinate, had packed their belongings in their covered wagons,
had inspanned their oxen and had trekked northward (these are
now perfectly good English words. Since the late Boer War you
will find them in any good dictionary.) The English were playing the game the Russians had played in the sixteenth century
during the conquest of Siberia. You will remember how it was
played. As soon as enough Russian fugitives had settled a new
region of Siberia, the Czar's troops went after them and informed
them that since they were originally Russian subjects, the land
they had just occupied was therefore of course Russian property
and the government in Moscow would let them know when to
expect the tax-collector.

The English were forever following the Boers further northward, trying to annex their territory. It had come to several very
disagreeable conflicts, for the Boer farmers, having spent most
of their lives out in the open, were better shots than the Cockney
regiments turned loose against them. After the battle of Majuba
in 1881 (Gladstone, who was eminently fair in this matter, on
that occasion gave a lesson in forbearance which all statesmen
might well copy: "Just because we were defeated last night and

our pride is hurt is no reason why we should insist on the shedding of more blood!"), the Boers gained a temporary respite and regained their independence.

But all the world knew what the end would be of this struggle between the British Empire and a handful of farmers. English land companies, acquiring enormous tracts of land from native chiefs, were creeping up further and further northward. Meanwhile British troops, in order to establish order all over Egypt, were slowly but steadily working their way southward along both banks of the Nile. A famous English missionary was exploring the central region of Africa with the most brilliant results. Plainly the English were digging themselves a tunnel right through the heart of the Dark Continent. They had started building operations simultaneously in Cairo and in the Cape (the usual way for tunnels to be constructed). Sooner or later the two ends would meet in the region of the great lakes where both the Nile and the Congo came from, and then England could run her trains from Alexandria to Table Bay (so-called after the Table Mountain, that curiously shaped mesa that forms a natural background for Capetown) without a change of cars.

What England was so evidently trying to do along a line running from north to south, France now planned to do along a line running from west to east, from the Atlantic to the Red Sea, let us say from Dakar in the Senegal to Djibouti in French Somaliland which was also the port of entry for the whole of Abyssinia and which even then was connected by railroad with the Abyssinian capital of Addis Ababa.

Such gigantic projects take time but not quite as much time as we sometimes feel inclined to believe when we look at the map and contemplate the terrific difficulties that were to be overcome ere that line should ever have reached such a hard-to-get-at spot as Lake Chad, just north of Nigeria—and from there the hardest part of the route would begin, for the eastern Sudan (now the Anglo-Egyptian Sudan) was as inhospitable a region as the Sahara.

Capital, however, in the hands of an energetic modern power,

The Suez Canal

especially if it sees a chance of making one hundred cents on the dollar, will dynamite its way through time and space as lightly and easily and usually as ruthlessly as a war tank going through a flock of geese. The Third French Republic, trying to regain the prestige the Second Empire had lost, was energetic enough, and the stockings and the hidden old cigar boxes of the French peasants produced the necessary capital. The struggle for the right of way from west to east in competition with the right of way from north to south was on in all seriousness and the French, who ever since the beginning of the seventeenth century had been fighting with the English and the Dutch for the possession of the land situated between the Senegal and Gambia Rivers, now used that territory as a political can opener with which to get at the contents of the unlimited area of the whole of the Sudan.

I can't go into the details of all the operations and machinations and the diplomatic steps and the commercial steps and the lying and cheating and horse-dealing and cajoling that had to take place before France could claim the greater part of the western Sudan as part of their African Empire. Even today they keep up the pretense of being merely the temporary administrators of a number of protectorates and mandates, but everybody has gradually learned what that means. The gangsters who have acquired exclusive control over the New York milk racket will probably call their band of cutthroats "The Milk Dealers' Protective Association". European nations, quick to learn even from our humble highwaymen, have coined the word "mandates". But the results are about the same.

Geographically speaking, the French have made a wise choice. Most of the Sudan is very fertile, which of course explains the fact that the natives are by far the most intelligent and industrious of all the different Negro tribes that inhabit Africa. Part of the soil is the same sort of loess as that found in northern China, and as Senegambia (merely another name for Senegal) is not cut off from the sea by a mountain ridge, the interior has sufficient rainfall to allow the people to raise cattle and corn. The African Negro, by the way, is no rice-eater, but a mealie-eater, "mealie" being a sort of second-cousin to our own corn-mush but a little less delicately prepared. They are also very remarkable artists whose curious bits of sculpture and pottery when exposed in our museums never fail to attract the attention of the multitudes

Kilimandjaro

because they look for all the world exactly like the most recent masterpieces of our own futurist painters.

The Sudanese, however, have one great disadvantage from the white man's point of view. They are ardent followers of the Prophet whose missionaries overran and converted the whole of northern Africa. In the Sudan, one race especially, the Fula or Fellatah, a mixture of Negroes and Berbers, who are to be found everywhere south and east of the Senegal River as the dominating class of society, have long been a menace to French authority. But railroads and roads and airplanes and tanks and caterpillar tractors are more powerful than all the Sudras or verses of the Koran. The Fellatahs are learning to drive flivvers. Romance is rapidly making its exit by way of the gas-station.

Before the French and the English and the Germans settled down in the Sudan, the greater part of this territory belonged to those charming native princes who had grown rich stealing each other's subjects and selling them into slavery. Some of these potentates have gained a certain sad fame as among the most picturesque but also the most brutal of by-gone despots. The King of Dahomey with his highly efficient army of Amazons is still fresh in the memory of those who as children saw the last of his troops perform at our country fairs; and that may have been one of the reasons why the natives put up so little resistance when the European war ships appeared. No matter how greedy the new white master might be, he was always a great improvement on the black tyrant who had just been deposed.

The greater part of the southern Sudan is cut off from the ocean by a high mountain ridge which follows the coast line of the Gulf of Guinea. This prevents such rivers as the Niger from playing a really important part in the development of the interior, for like the Congo, the Niger is obliged to take a very roundabout way to avoid the main mass of these hills. Then just before it reaches the coast, it must dig a channel through these rocks with the result that there are a number of cataracts where they are least wanted (that is, near the sea) while the upper part of the river is apt to be navigable enough but there is nobody there to navigate it.

In the case of the Niger even this does not hold true. It is really more of a succession of long lakes and small pools than a regular river, as Mungo Park discovered in 1805 when he gave his life to find the river of which he had dreamed since he was a small boy in Scotland. This may have been responsible for the fact that the Sudanese, deprived of all water-ways, were able to make such a success of their overland trade-routes, and that

Timbuktu, on the left bank of the upper Niger, could become such a very important center of trade, the Nizhni-Novgorod of Africa, where the north and the south and the east and the west came together to do business.

Timbuktu owes a great deal of its popularity to its queer name which sounds like the magic formula of some mysterious African witch-doctor. In the year 1353 it had been visited by the Ibn Batuta, the Marco Polo of the Arab world. Twenty years later it made its first appearance on Spanish maps as a great market for gold and salt, substances which were of almost equal value in medieval days. When the English Major Gordon Laing reached it in the year 1826, after having crossed the Sahara from Tripoli, it was merely the ruins of its former self, having been repeatedly attacked and destroyed by Tuareg and Fellatah marauders. On his way to the coast Major Laing was murdered by the Fellatah of Senegambia, but from that time on, Timbuktu was no longer another mysterious Mecca or Khiva or Tibet, but became a plain, ordinary "objective" of the French forces operating in the western Sudan.

In the year 1893 it was taken by a French "army", consisting of one French naval ensign and six white men, accompanied by twelve Senegalese. The power of the desert tribes had not yet been broken, for soon afterwards they killed off most of the white invaders and almost completely destroyed a relief corps of two hundred men which was coming up from the coast to avenge the defeat of the naval contingent.

But of course it was then merely a matter of time before all of the western Sudan should be in French hands. The same held true of the region around Lake Chad in the central part of the Sudan, which was easier of access because the Benue River, a tributary of the Niger which runs due east and west, is much more navigable than the Niger itself.

Lake Chad, which lies about 700 feet high, is very shallow and rarely deeper than about 20 feet. In contrast to most other inland seas, the water is fresh and not salt. But it is growing smaller and smaller all the time and in another century it will

Congo and Niger

be merely a marsh. One river loses itself in this lake. It is called
the Shari, and the fact that it is merely an inland river which
starts a thousand miles from the sea and ends a thousand miles
from the sea, yet is as long as the Rhine, will give you a better
idea of the proportions of central Africa than almost anything
else I can think of.

The mountainous Wadai region east of Lake Chad acts as the
great divide between the Nile, the Congo and the Chad region.
Politically it belongs to the French and is supposed to be an administrative part of the French Congo. It also marks the end
of the French sphere of influence, for on the east of it begins the
eastern Sudan, now known as the Anglo-Egyptian Sudan, a
country which the ancients knew as the land of the White Nile.

When the English began to survey their road from the Cape
to Cairo and decided that they must occupy this most valuable
strategic point or run the risk of losing it to some other nation,
the eastern Sudan was a desert, plain, simple and fancy. The Nile
was absolutely unnavigable, and there were no roads. The people, at the mercy of all the scum from the nearby deserts, were
poor and wretched beyond belief. Geographically it was without any value, but politically its possibilities were enormous. In
1876 therefore, England induced the Khedive of Egypt to entrust the administration of these hundreds of thousands of square
miles of "nominal Egyptian territory" to that same General
Gordon whom we have already met in the chapter on China,
assisting the Peking government to repress the Tai-Ping rebellion. Gordon remained in the Sudan for two years and with
the help of a very clever Italian assistant, one Romolo Gessi,
he accomplished the one thing most needed: he broke up the
last of the slave rings, shot the leaders and set more than 10,000
men and women free and allowed them to return to their homes.

As soon, however, as this stern Puritan had turned his back
upon the Sudan, the old terrible conditions of misgovernment
and oppression returned. The result was the outbreak of a movement for complete independence, a sort of "Sudan for the Sudanese and all the slave-trading we want". The leader of this

The desert

rebellion was a certain Mahommed Ahmed, who called himself a Mahdi or leader to show the faithful the road of the true Moslem faith. The Mahdi was successful. In 1883 he conquered El Obeid in Kordofan, which is now connected with Cairo by rail, and later in the same year he destroyed an Egyptian army of 10,000 men under Hicks Pasha, an English colonel in the service of the Khedive. Meanwhile, in 1882, England had assumed a protectorate over Egypt and the Mahdi now had to contend with a more dangerous enemy.

But England was too experienced in colonial affairs and knew the difficulties too well to rush into any rash expeditions. For the moment she counselled the Egyptian government to withdraw its troops from the Sudan. General Gordon was once more sent to Khartum to arrange for the withdrawal of the remaining Egyptian garrisons. But no sooner had he reached Khartum than the forces of the Mahdi swept northward and left Gordon and his companions marooned in Khartum. He sent urgent messages for relief. But Gordon was a Puritan mystic. Gladstone, who was then the head of the British government, was an Episcopal mystic. These two mystics, the one in London on the Thames and the other in Khartum on the Nile, did not like each other. And because they did not like each other, it was impossible for them to cooperate intelligently.

Gladstone sent a relief expedition, but much too late, for when it was still several days away from Khartum the town was taken by the forces of the Mahdi, and Gordon was murdered. That happened in January of 1885. In June of the same year the Mahdi died. His successor maintained himself as ruler of the Sudan until the year 1898 when an Anglo-Egyptian army under Kitchener wiped his followers from the face of the desert and recaptured the entire territory as far south as Uganda, which is on the equator.

The English have done an enormous amount of good in improving the condition of the natives by giving them roads, railroads, safety, by stamping out all sorts of hideous and unnecessary forms of disease, the usual things which the white man does for the black man and for which the white man expects the black man to say thank you, if he is that foolish, but for which the black man will shoot the white man in the back just as soon as he can, as the white man will well enough know if he has had a couple of centuries of colonial experience.

The railroad southward from Alexandria and Cairo now runs as far as El Obeid in the west and Port Sudan on the Red Sea in the east. If in the years to come an enemy should suddenly destroy the Suez Canal, England can still transport her troops from east to west via this railroad that runs through the valley of Egypt and then recrosses the Nubian Desert.

But now we have got to go back a few years and see how the Mahdi revolt was to have the most far-reaching influence upon the development of Africa in a way which had nothing at all to do with the Mahdi himself or his ambitions to become the independent ruler of the land of his fathers.

When the Mahdi uprising began, the Egyptian forces furthest towards the south were forced to find a refuge in a part of central Africa which was then practically unknown. Speke had crossed it in 1858 when he discovered Lake Victoria, the mother lake, so to speak, of the river Nile. But most of the land between Lake Albert and Lake Victoria was still terra incognita. This Egyptian force, under command of a German physician, a certain Dr. Eduard Schnitzer, better known by his Turkish title of Emin Pasha, had disappeared from sight after the fall of Khartum, and the world was curious to know what had become of its leader.

The job of finding him was entrusted to an American newspaper man by the name of Stanley. His name was really Rowlands, but he had adopted that of a New Orleans merchant who had been very good to him when he had first landed in America, a poor English boy who had run away from the workhouse. Stanley was already famous as an African explorer for the voyage which he had undertaken in 1871 to find Dr. Livingstone. Since then England had begun to realize the importance of keeping at least a few fingers in the African pie and the London

The Zambesi Falls

Daily Telegraph cooperated with the New York *Herald* in defraying the cost of the voyage. This expedition, which lasted three years and which was undertaken from east to west, proved that the Lualaba which Livingstone had suspected of being part of the Congo was in reality the beginning of that river. It also showed the vastness of the territory traversed by the Congo River on its circuitous route to the sea and it brought home tales of strange native tribes, the presence of which no one so far had suspected.

It was this second voyage of Stanley's which drew the attention of the world to the commercial possibilities of the Congo and which made it possible for Leopold of Belgium to found his Congo Free State.

When at last the fate of Emin Pasha became a subject of world-wide concern, it was only natural that Stanley should be selected as the man best fitted to find him. He began his search in 1887 and the next year he found Emin in Wadelai just north of Lake Albert. Stanley tried to persuade this German, who seems to have exercised a tremendous power over the natives, to enter the service of the King of the Belgians, which would probably have meant that the great lake region of Africa would also have been added to the territory of the Congo colony. But Emin seems to have had plans of his own. As soon as he reached Zanzibar (he really was not anxious at all to be "saved") he got in touch with the German authorities and it was finally decided to send him back, well provided with men and money, to try to establish a German protectorate over the high plateau between the three great lakes of Victoria, Albert and Tanganyika. Along the coast of Zanzibar the German East Africa Company had acquired large interests as early as 1885. If the lake region were added, Germany would be able to frustrate the English plans for dividing all of Africa into two parts by a broad strip of English territory running from Egypt to the Cape. But in 1892 Emin was murdered near Stanley Falls on the Congo by Arab slave-dealers who wanted to avenge some of their colleagues deservedly hung by the stern German in his younger days.

Nothing therefore came of the Emin's dream of the new Germany on the high plateau of Tanganyika. As a result, however, of his disappearance, the greater part of central Africa had now been definitely put upon the map. And that brings us to the fifth natural division of Africa, the high mountainous regions of the east.

These stretch all the way from Abyssinia in the north to the Zambesi River in the south where the territory known as South Africa begins. The northern part of this region is inhabited by Hamites, for the Abyssinians and the Somalis, although they have kinky hair, are not Negroes. The southern part consists of Negroes and a great many Europeans.

The Abyssinians are Christians of a very old vintage, having been converted as early as the fourth century, almost 400 years before we had a single Christian community in central Europe. Their Christian sentiments, however, did not prevent them from making perpetual war upon their neighbors. In the year 525 they even crossed the Red Sea and conquered the southern part of Arabia, the Arabia Felix of the Romans (in contrast to the Arabia Deserta of the interior). It was this expedition which had made the young Mahommed realize the necessity for a strong and united Arab fatherland and which had started him upon his career as the founder of a religion and a world-empire.

One of the first things his followers did was to drive the Ethiopians away from the coast towns of the Red Sea and to destroy their business relations with Ceylon and India and far-away Constantinople. After that defeat, Ethiopia became a sort of Japan which took no further interest in outside affairs until the middle of the last century when the different European powers began to cast longing glances in the general direction of the peninsula of Somaliland, not because Somaliland was of any possible value, but because it was situated on the Red Sea which soon would be merely an extension of the Suez Canal. France was the first to arrive upon the scene and to occupy the harbor of Djibouti. The English, after a punitive expedition against the Emperor Theodore of Abyssinia, during which that extraordinary monarch killed himself rather than fall into the hands of his enemies, took British Somaliland which, situated just opposite Aden, gave them command of the gulf of that name. The Italians took a slice north of the French and British possessions with the intention of using the coastal region as a base of supplies from where to conduct a glorious expedition against Abyssinia.

This glorious expedition took place in the year 1896, and on that occasion the Italians lost 4500 white and 2000 native troops, with a slightly smaller amount of prisoners. Since then the Italians have left their Abyssinian neighbors alone although they are now the owners of another part of Somaliland, south of the British settlement.

In the end, of course, Abyssinia will go the way of Uganda and Zanzibar. But the difficulties of transportation, not overcome by the single railroad line from Djibouti to Addis Ababa, and the broken up nature of the entire Abyssinian plateau which makes it a natural fortress, together with the realization that those black men will under circumstances fight back with great bitterness, have so far saved that ancient kingdom from the usual annexation by one of her European neighbors.

South of Abyssinia and east of the Congo lie the three great African lakes. Of those the Nyasa sends tributaries to the Zambesi River, while Lake Victoria is responsible for the River Nile and the Tanganyika Lake connects with the Congo, suggesting that this region must be the highest part of Africa. The investigations of the last fifty years completely bear this out. Kilimanjaro, southeast of Lake Victoria, is 19,000 feet high and Mount Ruwenzori (the Mountain of the Moon of Ptolemy, which Stanley rediscovered some twenty centuries later) is 16,700 feet, with Kenya (17,000) and Elgon (14,000) close seconds.

This whole region was originally volcanic but the African volcanoes have not been working at their trade for a good many centuries. Politically the entire territory is divided into a number of sub-divisions, all of them however under British rule.

Uganda, a cotton-raising country, became a protectorate in 1899.

The former possessions of the British East Africa Company, now Kenya Colony, were made part of the empire in 1920, while the erstwhile holdings of the German East Africa colony became a British mandate in 1918 and are now part of the Tanganyika territory.

The most important town on the coast is Zanzibar, the capital of an old slave-trading sultanate over which the English established a protectorate in 1890. The town was a great center for Arab merchants from all over the Indian Ocean. They were probably responsible for the spread of the Swahili language, the jargon of Zanzibar, which is now spoken all over the east coast of Africa just as Malayan has become the "lingua franca" of the islands of the Dutch East Indies. At the present time a slight knowledge of Swahili is the most valuable asset for anyone wishing to do business along the three thousand miles of the Indian Ocean front and their millions of square miles of hinterland. If he will also bother to learn a little Bantu, the language of all the South African Negroes, he can, with a few words of Portuguese and a smattering of pidgin-Arabic and a sentence or two in Cape Dutch be sure of all of his meals while travelling from one end of the continent to the other.

That closes the chapter on northern Africa, except for the narrow coastal region that lies between the Atlantic and the mountains of the Sudan and the Cameroon Mountains. This strip of land has been known these last four hundred years as Upper Guinea and Lower Guinea. I have already mentioned the Guineas when I spoke of slavery, for it was there that the "black ivory" was gathered ere it was made ready for shipment to the rest of the world. Today that coast belongs to a number of nations, but none of these settlements is of any interest to anybody except a few stamp-collectors.

Sierra Leone is an old English settlement which, like Liberia just to the west of it, was intended to be a homeland for former slaves. Neither Sierra Leone nor Liberia, with its capital city of Monrovia (so-called after our President Monroe) amounts to anything except sad disappointments in the hearts of a good

many perfectly honest men and women who had hoped for better things when they generously offered their money to return
the black man to the country of his great-grandfather's birth.

The Ivory Coast is French, and Accra will eventually be a
harbor of the French Sudanese Empire. Nigeria is English. The
capital is Lagos. Dahomey was an independent native state until
the French took it in 1893.

Cameroon was German until the war. It is now a French protectorate. So was and is Togo. The rest is part of the French
Congo, making the whole of that part of the world a large
French equatorial empire with little foreign enclosures which
eventually will be acquired by the French in exchange for either
cash or for something some other power may want in another
part of the world.

The Dutch East Indian Company, in order to shorten the
voyage from Batavia to Amsterdam, had maintained an overland route of its own by way of Persia and Syria and Alexandria.
But every time there was a quarrel between two Mesopotamian
potentates the mails and the caravans were so hopelessly delayed
that the bulk of the merchandise continued to be sent by way of
the Cape.

In order that nothing might interfere with the steady flow of
its Indian products, the Dutch thereupon occupied a few harbors
along the coast of Guinea which they could also use as slave
ports, took St. Helena and fortified the Cape.

In 1671 the Dutch, who like all good merchants liked to have
things in writing (think of the absurd comedy of "buying" Manhattan in exchange for $24.00 worth of gadgets!) bought the
land around the fort of Capetown from the Hottentots. That
meant the end of the Hottentots for, deprived of their land,
they were forced to move northward into the region of the
Orange River and the Vaal which was occupied by their hereditary enemies, the Bushmen. It seemed a punishment from
Heaven that those same Dutch farmers, who had been terribly
cruel in their dealings with both Hottentots and Bushmen,

should afterwards have suffered a similar fate. For Capetown
was occupied by the English in 1795 and then it was the turn
of the Boers to move northward. They repeated this maneuver
a number of times until the year 1902, when the last of their
two independent republics, the Transvaal and Orange Free
State were definitely annexed by the English.

Capetown, however, has remained the most important harbor
of the whole triangle. But the coastal region counts for nothing
compared to the tremendously rich interior. This interior consists of a high plateau dotted with low hills, a sort of mesa here
called kopjes. On the west this plateau is cut off from the Atlantic by the Komas highlands. On the east it is separated from the
Indian Ocean by the Matoppo Mountains and in the south it is
cut off from the Capetown region by the Drakensberg Ridge.

None of these mountains has any glaciers. All the rivers
therefore of this entire region depend upon rainfall for their
water supply. As a result they are wild torrents in the winter
and dry, hollow roads in the summer, and as they have got to
break their way through a mountain ridge ere they reach the sea
(with the exception of the rivers in Natal, which therefore is
the richest of the different countries that now make up the
U. S. A. or Union of South Africa) they are of no possible use
as roads of commerce to the interior.

In order therefore that the hinterland might have access to
the sea, a number of railways have been constructed. Before the
war the most important of these roads was the one between Pre-
toria and Lourenço Marques on the Delagoa Bay in Portuguese
East Africa. Since the war the roads to Swakopmund and Lü-
deritzland in the former territory of German South-west Africa
(now a mandate of the Union) have been finished; and northward one can now go by rail as far as Lake Tanganyika and then,
after having crossed the lake by boat, one can take another train
from there for Zanzibar.

In order to get that far north, one is obliged to spend an uncomfortable day crossing the Kalahari desert but once this has
been left behind, one enters into the hilly territory of Rhodesia,

so-called after Cecil Rhodes, the founder of the old British
South African chartered company and one of the earliest prophets of a united South Africa under British domination. That
dream has partially come true. The different chartered companies and the former Boer republics and the Kaffir and Zulu
nations are now all of them part of the Union of South Africa
which was proclaimed in 1910. But as the Boer element which
lives in the country districts seems to be gaining on the English
element which had been chiefly attached to the cities by the discovery of gold around Johannesburg and diamonds near Kim-
berley, there is a violent struggle going on to decide which of
the two rival elements shall be the deciding factor. By way of
compromise, Capetown has been made the place where the parliament of the Union meets, but Praetoria, the old capital of the
Transvaal Republic, has been promoted to act as the seat of the
government.

As for the two unusually large remnants of the ancient Portuguese Empire which continue to separate the U. S. A. from the
Atlantic and the Indian Ocean, Angola in the west and Mozambique in the east, they are so badly administered that sooner or
later they will be taken over by one of their more powerful
neighbors. Just now, with agricultural products at a lower price
than ever before and cattle-raising at a complete standstill, the
South Africans are not in search of fresh pastures and grain
fields. When times return to normal, these Portuguese colonies
will be annexed without the firing of a single gun. For South
Africa is developing a new race, neither Dutch nor English but
purely South African. And it is so rich in mineral wealth, in
copper and coal and iron, and the soil is so fertile that it may
well develop into a sort of United States on a slightly smaller
scale.

At the other side of the Strait of Mozambique lies the island
of Madagascar which measures 230,000 square miles and is
slightly larger than the Republic of France to which it belongs.
The population is about 4,000,000. It is a mountainous island
and the eastern part, exposed to the trade-winds, has excellent

timber which is exported from the harbor of Tamatave, connected by rail with the capital, Tananarivo.

The people look more like Malays than like Negroes. But Madagascar must have been separated from Africa at a very early period in our geological history for none of the usual African animals are to be found on the island.

East of Madagascar lie two little islands which were of great importance when the India trade still followed the route of the Cape. They are Mauritius and Reunion. Mauritius, an old fresh water vegetable station of the Dutch East India Company, is now English, and Reunion is French.

As for the other islands which, geographically speaking, belong to Africa, I have already mentioned St. Helena, while Ascension, further to the north in the Atlantic, is also a coaling and a cable station. The Cape Verde Islands are Portuguese. They lie a few hundred miles west of the coast of Mauretania, now occupied by the insignificant Spanish colony of Rio de Oro. The Canary Islands are Spanish, and Madeira and the Azores are Portuguese, and Teneriffe, with its well known volcano, is Spanish. As for the island of St. Brandon, in which all honest skippers of the seventeenth and eighteenth centuries believed as firmly as we ourselves believe in the tables of multiplication, that was situated here too. But no one could ever quite find out where because it went to the bottom of the ocean as soon as any vessel came near it and only reappeared when the visitor was gone. That seems to me to have been a very sensible thing to do on the part of an African island. It was the only way in which it could escape being occupied by a foreign power.

Most continents can be reduced to a few simple images. We say "Europe" and we see the dome of St. Peter's and ruined castles on the Rhine and the silent fjords of Norway and we hear the troika bells of Russia. Asia calls forth pictures of pagodas and masses of little brown men bathing in a wide river and strange temples, ten thousand feet up in the air, and the placid symmetry of old Fuji. America means sky-scrapers, factory

Discovery of the South Pole

chimneys, an old Indian on a pony going nowhere in particular. Even far off Australia has its symbols, the Southern Cross, the amiable kangaroo with his inquisitive and intelligent eyes.

But Africa, how shall we reduce that land of contrasts and extremes to a single symbol?

It is a land of torrid heat without any rivers! Yet the Nile is almost as long as the Mississippi and the Congo is only a little shorter than the Amazon River and the Niger just as long as the Hwang-Ho. It is a land of torrential rains and insufferable moisture! Yet the Sahara alone, the dryest of all deserts, is larger than all of Australia and the Kalahari is as big as the British Isles.

The people are weak and helpless, the black man does not know how to defend himself! Yet the most perfectly organized military machine the world has ever seen was developed among the Zulus, and the desert Bedouins and other northern tribes have been known to charge successfully against European troops armed with machine guns.

Africa has no convenient inland seas like the Baltic or our own Great Lakes! Granted, but Lake Victoria is as large as Lake Superior, Tanganyika is as big as the Baikal Sea, Nyasa twice as big as Lake Ontario.

Africa has no mountains! But Kilimanjaro is 5000 feet higher than Mount Whitney, the highest peak of the United States, and Ruwenzori, just north of the equator, is higher than Mont Blanc.

Then what is wrong with this continent? I don't know. Everything is there but nothing seems to be where it could possibly be of any use to anyone. The whole arrangement is wrong. With the exception of the Nile, all these rivers and mountains and lakes and deserts serve no purpose. Even the Nile, which at least flows into a sea of great commercial importance, is hampered by too many cataracts. As for the Congo and the Niger, they have no comfortable access to the sea, while the Zambesi starts where the Orange River should end and the Orange River ends where the Zambesi should start.

Modern science may eventually make the desert bear fruit and drain the marshes. Modern science may find ways to cure the dysentery and the sleeping sickness, which have wiped out entire countrysides in the Sudan and the Congo region, as modern science has set us free from yellow fever and malaria. Modern science may turn the high central and southern plateaus into a replica of the French Provence or the Italian Riviera. But the jungle is strong and persistent and the jungle has a handicap of millions of years. Let modern science relax but for a moment and the jungle and all its atrocities will be back at the white man's throat and will throttle him and it will breathe its poisonous breath into his nostrils until he dies and is eaten by the hyenas and the ants.

Perhaps it is the lightless tropical forest which has put its dreadful stamp upon the whole African civilization. The desert may be frightening but the shimmering dark forest is terrifying. It is so full of life that it has become lifeless. The struggle for existence must proceed quietly lest the hunter himself become the hunted. And so day and night and night and day creation devours itself beneath the high roof of the listless leaves. The most harmless-looking insect has the most deadly sting. The most beautiful flower carries its secret burden of poison. Every horn and hoof and beak and tooth is against every other horn and hoof and beak and tooth. The pulse-beat of existence is accompanied by the crunching of bones and the tearing asunder of soft brown skins.

I have tried to talk of these things with Africans. They laughed at me. Such was life. Life was either stark poverty or overwhelming abundance. There was no golden mean. One either froze or one roasted. One either drank coffee from golden cups with an Arab merchant in Mogador or one took a pot-shot at an old Hottentot woman. She was no good anyway. For this land of contrast seems to do dreadful things to people. It warps their vision. It kills their susceptibilities to the finer sides of life. The ceaseless carnage of the veldt and forest gets into their

blood. And a quiet little mousy official, fresh from the stiff respectability of a slumbering Belgian village, turns into a monster who has women flogged to death because they fail to bring
an extra pound of rubber; and then quietly smokes his after-
dinner cigar while the insects devour some poor black devil, mu-
tilated because he was in arrears with his ivory.

I am trying very hard not to be unfair. Other continents, too,
have greatly contributed to the sum total of human cruelty and
malevolence. But gentler forms walk across the countryside.
Jesus preaches, Confucius teaches, Buddha implores, Mahommed sternly points to his harsh virtues. Africa, alone, has
borne us no prophet. Other continents have been greedy and
selfish but at times the spirit has conquered the flesh and they
have gone forth upon some mighty pilgrimage, the purpose of
which lay hidden far beyond the gates of Heaven.

The only sound of marching feet across the African desert
and through the shrubs is that of flint-eyed Arabs in search of
their human prey, of Dahomeyan Amazons, ready to pounce
upon a sleeping village and steal the children of their neighbors
to sell them into foreign slavery. In other parts of the world
women ever since the beginning of time have tried to make
themselves desirable in the eyes of their men that they might
attract them and gain their favor. In Africa alone women have
deliberately made themselves hideous that they might repel
all those who should meet them unaware.

I might continue this bit of special pleading *ad infinitum*. But
this book is getting much too long and so you had better try to
find an answer for yourself.

People have been faced by the same perplexing question ever
since they first gazed upon the useless grandeur of the Pyramids and looked suspiciously at the tracks that lost themselves
in the sands of the distant desert. But none of them returned any
the wiser.

XLVI

AMERICA, THE MOST FORTUNATE OF ALL

THE American continent is the most obliging continent of all. I am speaking, of course, of America as a purely geographical unit, not as an economic factor in the development of industry nor as a political laboratory for experiments in diverse new forms of government. But from a geographical point of view, America is almost everything that possibly could be desired.

It is the only continent on the western hemisphere and therefore has no immediate competitors as Africa, Asia and Europe have. It is situated between the two largest seas of the world and it was settled by white men during a period when the Atlantic had just become the center of civilization.

It reaches from the North Pole to the South Pole and therefore enjoys every sort of climate. That part which lies nearest to the equator is also the highest and therefore enjoys a temperature which makes it fit for human habitation.

It has practically no deserts. It has been blessed with wide plains which are situated in the moderate zone and which are therefore predestined to become the world's granaries.

It has a coast line which is neither too simple nor too complicated and which is therefore eminently fitted for the establishment of deep-sea harbors.

As its chief mountain-ranges run from north to south, its fauna and flora could freely escape the advance of the glaciers of the ice period and had a better chance to survive than those of Europe.

More than almost any other continent it is blessed with coal and iron and oil and copper and those other raw materials which the machine age needs in ever increasing quantities.

North America

It was practically uninhabited when the white man arrived (there were only 10,000,000 Indians on the whole continent) and there was therefore no teeming native population to prevent the invaders from doing whatever they pleased to do or to interfere seriously with the development of the country according to the white man's plans. As a result America has no serious race-problem except the unfortunate ones of its own making.

The tremendous economic opportunities of the new and empty continent attracted the most energetic elements from every other nation and together these were able to develop a mixed race of their own, which has adapted itself to its novel and unusual but very simple geographical background in a remarkably short space of time.

And finally and perhaps most important of all, the people who inhabit that continent today have no history of their own that is forever dragging them back to a past that will never come back. Unencumbered by that unfortunate luggage (which everywhere else has proved itself to be more of a nuisance than a blessing) they can forge ahead much faster than other races which must push the ancestral wheelbarrow ahead of them wherever they go.

As for the actual geographic features of the two American continents, they are not only very simple and much more symmetrical than those of any other continents, but in their main features North and South America resemble each other so closely that we can discuss them at the same time without running any risk of causing any confusion in the reader's mind.

Both North and South America resemble triangles with the sole difference that the South American triangle is situated a little further towards the east than the northern triangle, which undoubtedly accounts for the fact that South America was discovered long before North America and was already fairly well known while most of North America still bore the legend of "terra incognita".

Both the western sides of the triangles of North and South America consist of a mountain ridge which runs sharply from the north to the south and which occupies approximately one-third of the surface while the other two-thirds in the east consist of a wide plain, separated from the ocean (in both cases) by two shorter mountain-ranges, the hills of Labrador and the Appalachians in North America and the mountains of Guiana and the Brazilian highlands in South America.

In the matter of their rivers, too, the two continents behave similarly. A few of the less important ones run northward while the St. Lawrence and the Amazon run almost parallel with each other, and the Parana and the Paraguay imitate the Mississippi and the Missouri by meeting each other halfway and then running the rest of their course at right angles with the St. Lawrence and the Amazon respectively.

As for Central America, the narrow strip of land which runs from east to west, geologically speaking it is really a part of the northern continent. Then suddenly, in Nicaragua, the landscape and the fauna and flora begin to change and it becomes part of the southern continent. The rest of Central America consists of high mountains, which is one of the reasons why Mexico, although as near the equator as the Sahara Desert, is a densely populated country with an excellent climate.

South America, of course, is much nearer to the equator than North America and the Amazon River practically follows the line of the equator in the course of its magnificent career from the Andes to the Atlantic. But speaking in very general terms (as I am now doing) here we have a magnificent case wherewith to study the influence of the geographical surroundings upon Man and of Man upon his geographical surroundings.

Nature built herself two large states and finished them both in practically the same way. A main entrance on the right, a high wall on the left, and a large open space in the middle provided with a richly stored larder. Then she gave the northern stage to a company of Germanic strolling actors, who thus far had played the smaller theaters in the provincial towns, a troupe of humble origin, accustomed to long hours and the plain roles of butchers and bakers and candlestick-makers. But the southern stage she rented out to noble old tragedians of the best Mediterranean school, who were accustomed to perform only in the presence of royalty and each one of whom could handle a sword or a rapier with a grace entirely unknown to their northern colleagues whose arms were stiff from the handling of spade and

The sequoia as historical contemporary

axe, whose backs were prematurely bent by their ceaseless struggle with an unyielding soil.

Then she raised the curtain on both stages at almost exactly the same moment and bade the world come in and watch the entertainment. And behold, ere the first act was half over, neither stage looked quite the same as it had done when the opening lines were spoken. And when the second act began, such a change was noticeable among the ladies and gentlemen and

The Polar Regions

The Equator

the children of the cast that the audience gasped and whispered, "Can such things be?"

The vessels of the old Vikings looked very picturesque but they were exceedingly clumsy vehicles when it came to the actual business of sailing them across a choppy sea. As a result those hardy Norsemen were continually blown out of their normal course, for they had neither compass nor log and their sailing rig was as clumsy as that of those Egyptian feluccas which you may still admire on a roll of papyrus painted in the valley of the Nile, 3000 years ago.

Now if you will kindly look at the map of the Gulf Stream (there are several in this book) you will see that the Gulf Stream, after having crossed the ocean from Africa to America, recrosses the northern part of the Atlantic from the south-west to the north-east in a leisurely fashion, bestows its blessings upon the coast of Norway, visits the Arctic Ocean, and then decides to go home by way of Iceland and Greenland, where it changes its name and its temperature, to travel southward once more, first as the Greenland current and next as the Labrador current, that accursed stream which sprinkles chunks of Greenland's azure glaciers all over the northern part of the Atlantic.

The Norsemen, sailing by God and by guess, as my own ancestors used to call this procedure, had reached Iceland as early as the ninth century. Once, however, regular communications had been established between Iceland and Europe, the discovery of Greenland and America became inevitable. Just as a Chinese or Japanese junk, blown out of its course, must inevitably reach the shores of British Columbia or California, being carried thither by the Kuro Siwo, the Gulf Stream of the Pacific, so a Norseman, bound from Trondheim to Iceland and being prevented by fog from locating his place of destination (and even today with all the instruments in the world, a fog is a terrible thing), would sooner or later find himself on the east coast of Greenland, or, if the fog continued and his luck held out, on the very coasts of the great land-barrier to the east which those

early visitors called Vineland, because it raised a kind of grapes
from which they could make an excellent sort of wine.

Now it is well to remember that there have been a great many
discoveries made of which the world at large never heard at all.
The average skipper has an instinctive fear of making a fool of
himself before his colleagues by telling them a yarn which none
of them will believe anyway, and which afterwards may prove

Greenland

to have been the result of an hallucination, or of low clouds mistaken for a mountain-range, or a strip of sunlight, maybe, interpreted as a flat coast. Australia was undoubtedly seen from the
distance by a number of French and Spanish sailors long before
Abel Tasman set foot on shore and cut himself a new goosequill
to report to the authorities in Batavia about the monstrous size
of the natives. The Azores and Canary Islands were discovered
and forgotten and re-discovered so often that our school books
have a hard time trying to find out just exactly when they should
be first mentioned among the world's great discoveries. French
fishermen had undoubtedly found their way to the Grand Banks

of Newfoundland centuries before the days of Columbus. But
they merely told their neighbors that the fishing was good and
let it go at that. Fish interested them. Another piece of land was
just another piece of land. There was enough land in Brittany
for everybody. Why worry about something that lay so far away
from home?

Newfoundland

As in everything I have ever written I have steadfastly defended the doctrine that humanity comes ahead of nationality,
I shall not lose myself in the usual acrimonious disputes concerning the desirability of celebrating Columbus Day or Leif
Ericsson Day or a day in honor of some French sailor who eventually may be dug out of the archives of Normandy. Suffice it to
say that we have documentary evidence proving that the Norsemen visited these shores during the first ten years of the eleventh
century and that a small group of sailors, preponderantly Spanish but with certain foreign admixtures, and more or less obey-

ing the commands of an Italian captain, visited these shores during the last ten years of the fifteenth century, and that when they arrived here they found out that they could not possibly be the original discoverers because the country was already inhabited by people who were of unmistakable Asiatic origin, wherefore, if the honor of "having been there first" must go to any specific group of people, the Mongolians are the logical candidates for all our future commemorative tablets.

We have a monument to our Unknown Soldier. Another and slightly larger pile of marble erected to our Unknown Discoverer would not be out of place. But as the relatives of that poor man are now forbidden by law to set foot on the soil of our continent, I fear me that nothing will ever come of this plan.

Concerning the descendants of those first intrepid explorers who undoubtedly hailed from the Far East, we know a great deal, but the one thing that would really interest us will probably remain a mystery until the end of time. And that one thing is this—how did the people of Asia actually reach the American continent? Did they sail across the narrow northern part of the Pacific Ocean, or did they walk across the ice of the Bering Strait, or did they come at a time when America and Asia were still connected by a narrow bridge of land? Well, we just don't happen to know. Nor can I see that it matters very much. When the white man reached these distant shores he came in contact with a race which, except in a few isolated spots, had barely passed out of the late stone age and which had not yet reached that stage of development when the wheel was used to relieve the human back of its manifold burdens or when the domesticated animals had set their owners free from the everlasting drudgery of gaining a meagre daily livelihood by means of hunting and fishing. Even with his bows and arrows the copper-colored man was no match for the white man who was able to kill his enemies at a distance by means of a gun.

The red man, reduced from the rank of a host to that of a

The Three Discoveries of America

guest, will continue to exist for a few centuries longer. Then he will be completely absorbed by his former enemies and will only survive as a vague historical memory. That is too bad, for the red man had many very excellent qualities, both of body and mind.

But that is the way things happen and I don't see what we can do about it.

And now let us for the last time look at a map.

From the Bering Strait to the Isthmus of Panama the west coast of America is protected against the Pacific Ocean by a barrier of high mountains. This barrier is not everywhere of the same width and parts of it consist of parallel ridges, all of which, however, run in the same direction, that is to say, from north to south.

In Alaska this mountain-chain is clearly a continuation of the mountains of eastern Asia. It is divided into two sections by the wide basin of the Yukon River, the main river of this northern territory, which was part of the Russian Empire until the year 1867 when the United States acquired these 590,000 square miles of wilderness in consideration of 7,000,000 American dollars.

The reason Russia was satisfied with so little was probably due to her ignorance about the country's potential riches. Seven million dollars for a few fishing villages and a chaos of snow-covered mountains seemed quite a good bargain at that time. But in 1896 gold was discovered in the Klondike, and Alaska got on the map, as the popular saying has it. The trip of a thousand miles from Vancouver to Juneau and then via Skagway and the Chilkoot and Chilkat passes to Dawson, the center of the Klondike territory (carrying one's pack on one's own back, as animals were very expensive and could hardly wade through the dense snow at the elevation of 3500 feet just south of the Polar Circle), was about as inconvenient as any trip ever undertaken by mankind in search of material wealth. But a pot of gold at the end of the trail awaited the early arrivals, and on

North America

such occasions every man is always certain that he will be the first on the spot.

Since then, however, it has been found that Alaska is not merely a gold land (as well as the country most densely covered by glaciers) but that it also has a great deal of copper and silver and coal, besides being an ideal country for fur-trapping and fishing. As a result the revenue derived from it during the first forty years of its existence as an American territory has been twenty times as large as the original cost.

Just south of Alaska, the mountain-range gets split into two parts of which the eastern branch, the Rockies, turn further inland, while the western branch continues to run exactly parallel with the ocean. But while the Rockies never change their name until they lose themselves among the highlands of Mexico, the mountains of the Pacific slope, after they have bade farewell to Mount McKinley, the highest mountain of the Alaska range and the highest peak on the whole North American continent (20,-300 feet) are known by quite a number of different names. In Canada they are called the St. Elias Range and the Coast Range. But after they have passed Vancouver Island (a rocky island cut off from the mainland by Johnston Strait and the Strait of Georgia) they are divided into two parts, of which the western half is still called the Coast Range while the eastern hills are known as the Cascades in Washington and Oregon and the Sierra Nevada in California. The wide open space between the two is the valley of the Sacramento River and the San Joaquin River which meet in the middle just before they run into San Francisco Bay, the widest and deepest and the best sheltered harbor of the world, which connects with the Pacific Ocean by means of the famous Golden Gate.

When the advance guard of the Spanish pioneers reached the valley, it was absolutely uncultivated. Today by means of irrigation it has been turned into the fruit garden of the world where apples and peaches and plums and oranges and apricots grow and prosper in exchange for a very reasonable amount of labor.

This valley proved to be a veritable godsend to California,

for when the great gold rush of the forties of the last century had come to an end, the miners and their followers discovered that they could hope to make quite a comfortable living by merely changing their profession and by becoming fruit farmers instead of prospectors. In Alaska and in Australia, once the veins of gold had been exhausted, there was no possible chance of feeding the multitudes, and they disappeared as fast as they had come, leaving behind them their empty towns and villages and tin cans. But California, instead of being impoverished by its golden treasures, as most gold-providing countries have been, was actually enriched by them, and the fact should be noted down as unique in the history of mankind.

When it was shown that way down deep below the soil there lay vast reservoirs of oil, the future of the state was entirely insured. It is true that this entire region is a bit shaky and that the deep incision of the Gulf of California may cause an occasional shifting of the different layers of rock which are apt to be dangerous (especially when followed by fire) but earthquakes are only temporary inconveniences while sunshine and an agreeable and even climate are permanent blessings. California has only started upon its career as one of the most densely populated spots of the entire northern continent.

Between the Sierra Nevada and the actual range of the Rockies lies an enormous valley consisting of three parts. In the north lies the Columbia plateau which sends the Snake River and the Columbia River to the Pacific and in the south it is bordered by the Wasatch Mountains and the Colorado plateau through which the Colorado River has dug its famous canyon. Between these two plateaus lies the depression known as the Great Basin which the Mormons chose as their permanent place of residence after they had been forced to flee from the eastern part of the United States and which in spite of its lack of moisture (the Great Salt Lake is full of water but it is much saltier than the ocean) they have in less than a single century been able to turn into a most profitable venture.

That this entire region is of a highly volcanic nature and that

How America dawned upon Europe

it must have been shaken about considerably is shown by the fact that from the bottom of the Death Valley, which is 276 feet below the surface of the ocean, one can see the top of that Mount Whitney which is the highest peak of the entire United States (14,496 feet).

To the east of the Rockies lies that tremendous plain which on the north is bounded by the Arctic Ocean, on the south by the Gulf of Mexico and on the east by the Laurentian Highlands of Labrador and the Appalachians of the United States. That part of the world alone could, if brought under the proper cultivation, feed the whole population of our globe. The so-called Great Plains (where the Rockies gradually slope off into the flat country) and the Central Plains through which the Mississippi and the Missouri and the Ohio and the Arkansas and the Red Rivers flow to the Gulf of Mexico, are one vast granary. The northern part is less well favored because here the rivers, the Mackenzie and the Athabasca and the Saskatchewan and the Albany River, all lose themselves either in the Arctic Ocean or in the Hudson Bay and are therefore only of local importance, being frozen up for the greater part of each year. But the Missouri, which rises near the Yellowstone Park in Montana and the Mississippi (together with the Missouri the longest river in the world), which takes its origin on the divide between Lake Winnipeg in Canada and Lake Superior, are navigable almost all the way from their sources to their deltas and pass through a region that in centuries to come will resemble eastern China in its density of population.

The other lakes of this slightly elevated region which is the divide between the Hudson Bay (or the Arctic Ocean), the Atlantic and the Gulf of Mexico, are Lake Michigan, Lake Huron, Lake Erie and Lake Ontario. The latter two are connected by a short river which is unnavigable on account of a water-fall, called Niagara (Niagara is a little wider than the Victoria Falls of the Zambesi River but only half as high, while the Yosemite Falls beat them both with a height of over a thousand feet) and they are therefore connected by a canal, the Welland Canal.

The Huron Lake and Lake Superior are also connected by a canal, the Sault Ste. Marie Canal, which has more tonnage pass through its locks than the Panama Canal and the Suez Canal and the Kiel Canal put together.

The waters of these lakes then pass into the Atlantic Ocean through the St. Lawrence River, emptying into the St. Lawrence

The Caribbean

Bay which is a sort of inland sea, situated between the Canadian mountains in the west, the island of Newfoundland in the east (it was "New" when John Cabot found it in 1497 and in 1500 when it got its first Portuguese governor-general) and Cape Breton Island and Nova Scotia and New Brunswick in the south. The Cabot Strait, separating Newfoundland from Cape Breton Island, bears witness to the fact that this region was first visited by an Italian.

As the northern part of Canada, the so-called Northwestern Territory, is too cold to be entirely suited to the white man's oc-

cupation, we rarely hear of it except in connection with its picturesque local police force. It is a land of lakes and most of it
used to belong to the Hudson Bay Company. This company
was founded in 1670, exactly fifty-nine years after Henry Hudson, the discoverer of the bay that bears his name, had been murdered there by his mutinous sailors. The "adventurers of England" who organized the company lived up to their name but

If the Caribbean should run dry

without much discrimination. Had they been given another half
century they would have killed off all the live stock of the lakes
and forests (even during the breeding season the slaughter of
fur-bearing animals did not cease) and the Indians, most liberally supplied with fire-water, would have exterminated themselves completely by way of the gin bottle. Wherefore the
Queen's Most Gracious Majesty finally intervened, annexed
most of the company's sovereign territory to Her Majesty's
dominions in Canada and left the Hudson Bay Company behind
as an historical curiosity which still (though greatly diminished
in size) continues to do business in the same region (262 con-

The Panama Canal

secutive years under the same management—no mean record, if you please, for any business house!) but no longer on the old, irresponsible scale of former times.

The Labrador peninsula between the Hudson Bay and the St. Lawrence is too near the cold currents that come from Greenland's icy shores to be of any value to anybody. But the Dominion of Canada is only at the threshold of its enormous future and today suffers chiefly from a very serious lack of population.

Politically Canada is one of the most interesting remains of a former dream of empire. We are apt sometimes to forget that when George Washington was born, the North American continent belonged for the greater part to France and to Spain and that the English colonies along the coast of the Atlantic were only a small Anglo-Saxon enclave surrounded entirely by hostile nations. As early as 1608 the French had established themselves at the mouth of the St. Lawrence River. Then they had turned their attention to the interior, first of all travelling due west until Champlain reached Lake Huron. They explored the entire region of the Great Lakes, Marquette and Joliet found the upper part of the Mississippi, and La Salle in 1682 descended the river to the sea and took possession of its entire valley which he called Louisiana after King Louis XIV. By the end of the seventeenth century, the French were laying claim to all the land as far as the Rocky Mountains, beyond which the territories of His Most Catholic Majesty of Spain were supposed to begin. The Alleghenies, which were a real barrier in those days, separated this enormous French colonial empire from the English and the Dutch possessions along the Atlantic seaboard and from Florida which was another colony of Spain.

If Louis XIV and Louis XV had known a little more geography; indeed, if a map had ever meant something more important to these artistic monarchs than a color scheme that could be worked out very nicely in a new Gobelin, the people of New England and Virginia would now probably speak French and the whole of North America would be administered from Paris. But those who decided the destinies of Europe did not realize what the New World meant. As a result of their indifference, Canada became English, Quebec and Montreal ceased to be French cities and a few generations later, New Orleans and the whole of the Far West were sold to the Republic that had been recently founded by a few rebellious little English provinces along the Atlantic seaboard. And even the great Napoleon thought that he had done a clever stroke of business when he looked at the stack of American golden dollars which he had got in exchange for what is now the richest part of the United States.

In 1819 Florida was added to these newly acquired domains, and in 1848 Texas and New Mexico and Arizona and California and Nevada and Utah were taken away from Mexico; and less than a hundred years after it had seemed certain that the northern half of the continent was to be a hinterland of two Latin powers, it had completely changed hands and had become an extension of the great north European plain.

As for the subsequent economic development of those heterogeneous parts which the chances of war, but above all things the indifference and lack of foresight of the original owners, had so suddenly and unexpectedly thrown together, it took on such proportions as the world had never seen. As soon as the first railroads had been constructed and the first steamers had been built, hundreds of thousands of immigrants followed the water routes to the Great Lakes or crossed the Alleghenies to take their share of the Great Plains and make them ready for human habitation and raise that wheat which was to make Chicago the most important grain center of the world.

When the triangle between the Great Lakes, the Alleghenies and the foothills of the Rockies were found to contain coal and oil and iron and copper in unprecedented quantities, this region became the great factory area of the new commonwealth with cities like Pittsburgh and Cincinnati and St. Louis and Cleveland and Detroit and Buffalo attracting laborers from all over the world to assist the earlier arrivals in exploiting these hidden treasures. And as these towns needed harbors from which to export their steel and iron and their oil and their automobiles, the old colonial settlements of the Atlantic seaboard, New York and Boston and Philadelphia and Baltimore achieved positions of eminence which they had never enjoyed before.

Meanwhile the southern states, at last emerging from the dark days of the reconstruction period (infinitely more disas-

The first railroad track

trous than the Civil War itself had been), were scraping together enough money to begin raising their cotton crops without the assistance of slave labor. Galveston and Savannah and New Orleans returned to life. The railroads and telegraph lines and telephone wires turned the whole nation into one enormous farm and factory. 60,000,000 Europeans crossed the ocean in less than half a century and joined the earlier arrivals in planning and building and making and selling and such a workshop as they set up the world had never seen before. But neither had Nature ever given a nation such unlimited opportunities as we enjoyed—

a gigantic plain with an excellent climate and an excellent soil, protected on both sides by convenient mountain-ranges and practically uninhabited—almost inexhaustible resources—handy water-ways to which history had added an almost more important gift, one nation and one language and no past.

What these advantages really mean to a nation we realize as soon as we go a little further down south and reach Mexico and Central America. Mexico, with the exception of the peninsula of Yucatan, where the ancient Mayans lived, is a mountainous region which slowly increases in height from the Rio Grande towards the south until in the plateau of Sierra Madre and that of Anáhuac it reaches peaks of sixteen and seventeen thousand feet. Most of these higher mountains like Popocatepetl (17,543 feet) and Orizaba (18,564) and Ixtaccihuatl (16,960) are of volcanic origin, but Colima (13,092) is the only active volcano at the present moment.

On the Pacific side, the Sierra Madre rises sharply from the coast; but on the Atlantic side the mountains slope down more gradually and since the European invaders came from the east it was easy enough for them to find their way to the interior. The advance guard arrived during the first years of the sixteenth century. That was the time of Spain's great disappointment because the new discoveries of that damnable Genoese had proved to be a flop, a howling failure, no gold, no silver, naked savages who lay down and died when you tried to make them work, and endless mosquitoes.

Then rumor began to spread that beyond the mountains of the nearby mainland there lived an emperor of a people called the Aztecs, who dwelled in golden castles and slept in golden beds and ate from golden plates. Ferdinand Cortez and his three hundred adventurers landed in Mexico in the year 1519. With the help of one dozen cannon and thirteen blunderbusses he conquered the whole realm of poor Montezuma who was strangled to death ere he could witness the complete annihilation of what only a short time before had been a nation not much less effi-

The Mississippi

ciently administered than the realm of the Habsburg monarch
in whose name he was murdered.

After that and for almost 300 years, until 1810 to be exact,
Mexico remained a Spanish colony and was treated as such. Several of her native products were no longer allowed to be cultivated for fear that they might compete with the less acceptable

Yosemite

products of the mother country. And most of the wealth which
the soil produced disappeared into the pockets of a few rich land-
owners or was set apart for the benefit of those religious establishments which even today are fighting to retain their hold upon
the common lands.

Then, during the middle of the last century, shortly after the
grotesque adventure of poor Austrian Maximilian, who had
hoped to become Montezuma's successor with the help of the

French, it was discovered that Mexico was not only a very rich agricultural country but that her soil contained as much or perhaps more iron and oil deposits than the United States. Thereupon the 15,000,000 Mexicans, of whom nearly 40% were still of pure Indian stock, were almost as badly off as they had been when Cortez first visited them. For now the big banking interests took a hand in their internal affairs and arranged for revolutions, which were then answered by counter-revolutions on the part of

The Soil of the Plains

the natives, until the record of a hundred years (it averages twenty revolutions per year) was broken just before the Great War and it seemed that the whole country would dissolve into murder and bloodshed. Fortunately during the Great War, when the big financial interests were otherwise occupied (that war cost a great deal of money), Mexico had a breathing space, and today a few strong men are trying to undo the harm of three centuries of neglect and sickness and analphabetism and apparently with success, for Vera Cruz and Tampico (the two harbors on the Gulf) are reporting larger and larger export figures. For half a dozen years Washington and Mexico City have not merely been on speaking terms, but have actually spoken to each other almost politely and with a smile.

The isthmus of central America which connects the two continents is exceedingly fertile, raises coffee, bananas, sugar and whatever else foreign capital is willing to plant there; but the climate is hard on the white man, and the black man is not particularly interested in working for the white man, and the volcanoes, which abound in this region, are hard on both the blacks and the whites.

To most people Guatemala, Honduras, Nicaragua and Costa Rica are merely romantic names, unless they collect postage stamps, for this one rule holds good all over the world: "the emptier the country's national treasury, the more elaborate its stamps". But the next country, the Republic of Panama, is of importance to us. It is a child of our own, though I suppose we had to take it, as we are the only independent nation which has to guard a Pacific as well as an Atlantic sea-front, and if we had waited for Colombia to sell it to us, we would still be haggling with the Colombian senators about the price they wanted to affix their signature to the deed of surrender.

That this isthmus was only a very narrow strip of land had already been known to the Spaniards after Balboa from his peak in Darien had contemplated both oceans at one and the same moment. And as early as the year 1551 the Spaniards were playing with the idea of digging a canal of their own. Since then every generation was to hear of new plans. Every man of any importance in the realm of science favored the world with at least one set of blue-prints showing how the puzzle could be best solved. But digging a canal through almost thirty miles of hard rock was a serious problem until Alfred Nobel made his unfortunate invention and gave us that dynamite with which he expected to remove tree-stumps and boulders from a farmer's fields but which he never intended to be used for the more common purpose of killing one's neighbors.

Then came the California gold rush when thousands of people hastened to Panama so as not to be obliged to make the long detour via Cape Horn; and for them the trans-isthmus railroad was built in 1855. Fifteen years later the world heard of the unexpected success of the Suez Canal. Ferdinand de Lesseps, its author, now decided to try his hand at connecting the Pacific with the Atlantic. But the company he founded was scandalously mismanaged and his engineers had made so many errors in their calculations and his workmen died so miserably from malaria and yellow fever, that after eight years of struggle against the forces of Nature and the less direct but even more disastrous forces of

The Interior of a Volcano after the outer crust has eroded away remains behind as a solid mountain

the Paris Exchange, the French company went most disreputably out of existence.

Then nothing was done for almost a dozen years and palm trees grew out of the smokestacks of the locomotives left behind by de Lesseps, until finally in the year 1902 the United States government bought the rights of the bankrupt French concern. Thereupon Washington and the Republic of Colombia began to haggle about the price that America would eventually have to pay for a strip of land wide enough for her canal. Until Theodore

Roosevelt, tired of the delay, arranged for a private little rebellion of his own in that somewhat out-of-the-way part of the
world, recognized the new and independent Republic of Panama
in less than twenty-four hours, and began to dig. That happened
in the year 1903 and in 1914 the job was finished.

This changed the Caribbean Sea from an inland sea to part of
the commercial highway between Europe and Asia and it greatly
increased the value of the islands which cut it off from the Atlantic Ocean. The Bahamas, which are English, and Cuba are a
little too far out of the way, as is of course Bermuda, another
English possession half way between New York and Florida.
But Jamaica (English) and Haiti and San Domingo (nominally
independent but ask Washington!) are in a better position to
derive some benefits from the canal. So is Porto Rico and so are
all the Lesser Antilles, the small islands to the east and the
south, which face the Greater Antilles, Cuba, Haiti, Jamaica and
Porto Rico.

These Lesser Antilles were of much greater value to the European nations of the seventeenth century than the American
mainland. For they were hot and sufficiently moist to raise sugar-
cane and the slaves, once on shore, could not disappear in the
jungle. Today they still raise sugar and cocoa and coffee but most
of them would be deeply grateful if they could make a few extra
pennies as halfway stations for ships bound from Europe to the
Panama Canal. In order of their appearance these are first of all
the so-called Leeward Islands, St. Thomas, Santa Cruz, St.
Martin, Saba, St. John, St. Eustatius (a small rock, chief port
for smuggled supplies during the Revolution), Guadalupe,
Dominica, Martinique (very volcanic like most of the others and
almost destroyed by Mt. Pelée in 1902), St. Lucia and St. Vincent and Barbados.

The Windward Islands consist of Blanquilla (which belongs
to Venezuela), Bonaire, Curaçao and Oruba, which are Dutch.
All of these islands once upon a time were part of the outer ridge
of a mountain chain that connected the Guiana Range of Ven-

ezuela with the Sierra Madre of Mexico. That mountain ridge
was destroyed but the high individual tops remained behind.

From an industrial point of view, none of these islands is doing any too well. The abolition of slavery has destroyed the former riches of all of them and today they are best known as winter
resorts or coaling stations or oil-distributing centers. Only Trini-
dad, just off the delta of the Orinoco, retains some of her prosperity because its volcanoes have favored it with large asphalt
deposits, worked by Hindus, who came here to take the place
of the old slaves and who now form one-third of the total population.

During the war when we learned more geography and in a
shorter space of time than we had ever done before (to forget
most of it just as rapidly when we no longer were under any
necessity of knowing where Kut-el-Amara and the Isonzo might
possibly be located) it was quite customary for the younger generation to switch from German (which soon was to be a dead
language anyway) to Spanish, on the ground that there was "a
great future for that language in South America". That future
did not particularly manifest itself while the actual fighting was
going on. Indeed, business transactions with that vast continent
suffered a very serious slump.

Afterwards we discovered the reason. All the technical details
of foreign trade in Peru and Brazil and Ecuador and whatever
these other countries might be called had thus far been entrusted
to patient little German clerks who were supposed to be familiar
with that sort of thing, which was most unfortunately beyond the
mental reach of their employers. When South America joined
the Allies (for most of them had a few German ships in their
harbors and needed loans) these poor Teutonic ink-slingers had
been sent to concentration camps and the foreign correspondence
of those South American commercial establishments had come
to a sudden end, to be resumed as soon as peace had been declared
and the Heinies were back at their ledgers.

Gradually the truth then began to dawn upon us. Although South America was a continent of tremendous natural wealth, it was so hopelessly underpopulated and in many respects so far behind the rest of the world that it would take at least another half century before it would be of the slightest value to any one

APPALACHIANS
230 000 000 YEARS
OLD
6.7000 FEET HIGH

HIMALAYAS
45.000 000 YEARS
OLD
29.000 FEET HIGH

ROCKIES
100.000.000 YEARS
OLD 14.000 FEET HIGH

The oldest mountains are by no means the highest

except the few rich families who had either retained their possessions from the days of Spanish domination or had gained them afterwards in their quality of uncle or nephew to one of the quick-change South American presidents.

Now if in the present volume I devote only a few pages to South America, do not suspect me of anti-Latin feelings. On the contrary, being of northern descent myself, I am able to appreciate the many virtues of the southern races much better than they

South America

are able to do themselves. But at the beginning of this book I told you that I would try to write a "human" geography, being firmly convinced that the importance of any given piece of land depends entirely upon the sum total of the contributions the inhabitants of that particular territory, be it large or small, have made to the sum total of human happiness in the form of science or commerce or religion or one of the arts. From that angle, alas, South America so far has been almost as barren as Australia or Mongolia. Which, I repeat, may be due to the lack of population, which in turn may be due to the fact that a great deal of South America lies just beneath the equator and that in the other parts the white man has never been able to replace the native or is so swamped by half-breeds of different hue (mulattoes, who are the descendants of whites and Negroes, Mestizos, who are the children of Indians and whites or Zambos, who are the offspring of Negroes and Indians) that they are never quite able to assert their political or intellectual powers.

South America has been the scene of some strange political experiments. A Brazilian Empire was something quite new under the sun although it lasted less than a century, and that extraordinary Jesuit free state in Paraguay (which lasted much longer than the empire on its eastern front) will probably always receive honorable mention in learned works devoted to applied Utopias. And South America produced at least one man of more than extraordinary ability, the great Bolivar who not merely set his own country free, as our own George Washington did, but who was directly or indirectly responsible for the successful outcome of most of the revolutionary movements of the entire continent. I do not for a moment doubt that there have been a great many other men who have loomed large in the local histories of Uruguay and Bolivia, but our planet at large has never heard of them and I wonder seriously whether upon close acquaintanceship they would prove to be of the calibre that is necessary to elevate them to the rank of world figures. And so it will be sufficient for the purpose of this book if I present you with a brief catalogue of mountains, rivers and states and promise you faithfully that I will fill in the human details a thousand years hence.

The entire western coast of South America consists of a continuation of our own Rockies and of the Mexican Sierra Madre and it is known as the Cordilleras de los Andes or the Andes for short. The Andes was the Spanish name which the conquerors had given to those irrigation canals which the Indians had built all over the slopes of their native hills. By merely destroying those canals and dams, the Spaniards were afterwards able to let many tribes starve to death and since the Conquistadores had taken the long and dangerous trip across the ocean to get rich quick and not to found a permanent home in a new world, this was as good a way of robbing the natives of their possessions as any other.

When approaching the South Pole, the Andes break off into a number of islands of which Tierra del Fuego is the best known. Between Chile and Tierra del Fuego lies the strait which Magellan navigated with such great difficulty on the white man's first trip around the world and which is still called after him. The southernmost point of the island is Cape Horn, so called after the native town of the man who discovered it (the little town of Hoorn in Holland) and not after a cow, as so many people seem to believe. The Strait of Magellan is of course of great strategic importance. Hence the Falkland Islands which guard it are British territory.

The Andes, like the whole of this enormous mountain-range that runs from the Arctic to the Antartic Circle, are volcanic. The Chimborazo in Ecuador (now extinct) is 20,702 feet high. The Aconcagua in the Argentine beats them all with 22,834 feet. While the Cotopaxi with 19,550 feet (also in Ecuador) holds the record for being the highest active volcano of the entire planet.

The South American Andes resemble their North American sisters in two other respects. The high mountain ridges enclose several wide plateaus which form the natural confines for such states as Bolivia or Ecuador. Furthermore there are very few convenient passes so that the railroad between Argentine and Chile, the only trans-Andean railroad, has to climb to a height

The Railroad across the Andes

which far surpasses that of the Swiss mountain passes like the St. Bernard or the Gothard ere it can bore its tunnels.

As for the mountains of the east, the Appalachians of South America, they consist of the Guiana Ridge in the north and the Brazilian Highlands of the east, each one containing a number of independent Sierras and Serras of its own, and forming the remnants of a much vaster range which was gradually cut in two

South America

by the valley of the Amazon. The Amazon is not the longest river in the world but the river that takes care of more water than any other. It literally has hundreds of branches of which more than fifteen are quite as long as the Rhine, while several others, such as the Madeira and the Tapajos, are a great deal longer.

North of the Guiana Mountains there is another valley, that of the Orinoco River. The Orinoco, which is actually connected with the Amazon by way of the curious Rio Negro (imagine the Ohio being part of the Mississippi and the Potomac at the same time!) is much better suited for navigation than the Amazon. For it does not have to break its way through the mountains just before it reaches the sea, as the Amazon is obliged to do, and its mouth is almost twenty miles wide, while the river itself, a terrific water-carrier, maintains a steady depth of 300 feet for several hundred miles inland, which is of great convenience to sea-going vessels.

As for the Parana, the north–south river of South America, on the way to the sea it picks up the Paraguay and the Uruguay rivers and then becomes the Rio de la Plata on which Monte-video, the capital of the state of Uruguay is situated. Like the Orinoco, the Parana is a good inland water-way.

In one particular respect, South America is much better off than most of the other continents, except Europe. It has practically no deserts. Except for northern Chile, most of her country enjoys a sufficient amount of moisture, while the Amazon region and the whole of the eastern coast of Brazil are drenched by equatorial rains which make the Amazon territory much more densely and evenly wooded than that of the Congo. But as a result of its steady rainfall, the rest of the continent, especially in the southern part, which is not quite so near the equator, is excellently suited for purposes of agriculture, and the Argentine pampas and the Orinoco llanos and the Brazilian campos are close rivals of our own Great Plains.

As for the countries which we find on South America today, few of them grew out of what we might call historical inevitability. They were the unexpected and haphazard results of successful revolutions rather than the products of slow growth and development. The United States of Venezuela with a population of 3,216,000 is a little too near the equator to develop a very energetic race of men. But around the Lagoon of Maracaibo in the north oil has been discovered and that has made Maracaibo the most important harbor of Venezuela, a position thus far held

The Llanos of Venezuela

by La Guaira, the port of Caracas, the capital, which lies rather inconveniently just behind a low mountain ridge that separates it from the sea.

On the west of Venezuela lies Colombia with the capital city of Bogota, which lies so far inland that it was a most inconvenient place to reach until the introduction of a regular airplane service with Barranquilla at the mouth of the Magdalena River. Colombia is fertile and has great natural wealth and furthermore, like the United States, it is situated on two oceans. But it will need lots of immigrants from northern Europe before it can begin to develop any of its natural resources.

Ecuador is also a poor country and, although the port of

Amazon River

Guayaquil, the harbor of Quito, the capital, has done a great
deal better since the opening up of the Panama Canal, there is
nothing to report about this nation except that it used to export
a lot of quinine and nowadays exports more cocoa than anything
else.

Peru, further south along the coast of the Pacific, was the seat
of a very powerful Indian state when the Spaniards first arrived
in the New World. It was ruled by a caste of nobles, the Incas,
or children of the sun, who elected the supreme ruler or the Inca
of the whole country, who thereupon was granted despotic rights.
Nevertheless and in spite of or because of their feudal character,
the Peruvians had developed a much higher and much more
human form of civilization than the Aztecs.

But when Pizarro reached these parts, the Inca empire was
more than 400 years old and that is a long time for any particular
form of government to last. There were many political parties in
the land and there was rivalry between different groups of
nobles. Pizarro played one side against the other and then in
1531 conquered the whole country. He imprisoned the reigning
Inca and turned the Indians into slaves. Whatever could be
stolen or plundered was dragged away and sent to Spain. The
ruins of the old Incas, the remnants of roads and castles around
Lake Titicaca way up in the Andes (3300 square miles of water
12,875 feet above sea-level) and endless old bits of pottery and
other bits of art show us what was lost when a capable and competent race was suddenly transformed into the indolent and miserable natives who now wander aimlessly through the streets of
Cuzco, the old capital, or take part in some revolution.

Lima is the modern capital where the future fate of Peru's
treasures in silver and copper and oil is to be decided, unless the
President of the Republic and his foreign banking friends have
long since removed the contents of these mines and have deposited them in the vaults of the Banque de France. Such things
are possible. They explain why this chapter can be so short.

Bolivia, the poor land-locked state, was not always a land-
locked state and La Paz, the capital, once upon a time had direct

access to the sea. But during the famous saltpetre war of 1879–1882 when Peru and Chile fought for the Arica district, Bolivia was foolish enough to side against Chile. When Chile won the war, Bolivia lost her coastal region. Bolivia is a very rich country. Among other things it is the third tin-producing country of the world, but a density of population of less than five per square mile, a total population of less than 3,000,000 and most of those Indians who remained behind when the Inca Empire was destroyed—no, it will take a great deal of time to do anything with or for that unfortunate land.

The two southernmost states, Chile and the Argentine, are by far the most important of the entire continent but their prosperity is a direct result of their geographical situation. They lie in the temperate zone. Hence they have fewer Indians (the tropics make them breed faster) and they have attracted a better class of immigrants.

Chile is richer in natural wealth than the Argentine. Arica (from where you take the railroad for Bolivia), Antofagasta, Iquique and Valparaiso are the four most important harbors of the west coast of South America, just as Santiago, the capital, is the largest city of that entire region. The southern part of Chile is beginning to raise cattle which is slaughtered and frozen and sent to Europe from Punta Arenas on the Strait of Magellan.

As for the Argentine, it is the great cow-country of South America. The flat territory along the Parana River, almost as large as one-third of Europe, is the richest part of the entire continent. Meat and wool and hides and butter are exported in such quantities that they have been able to affect our own prices for those commodities in a most unpleasant fashion. The steady immigration of Italian laboring men and farmers during the last ten years will make the Argentine one of the greatest grain and flax producers of the western hemisphere, while the sheep culture makes Patagonia one of the most dangerous competitors of Australia.

The capital of the Argentine is Buenos Aires, also on the Rio de la Plata, just opposite the small state of Uruguay which has very much the same soil and climate as the Argentine and which, having rid itself of the last of its Indian population, does in a small way, but very successfully, what the Argentinians are doing on such a very large scale that very often they run the risk of coming to grief through over-speculation and bad financial management.

If the Straits of Magellan should run dry

Paraguay finally, the third of the Rio de la Plata states and in many ways the most favored of them all, would now be prosperous if it had not been for the disastrous war of 1864–1870 when the poor Indians, trained in military service by their former Jesuit masters (who however in 1769 had lost the country to the Spanish crown), had gone on the war-path in behalf of a crazy man who also happened to be their President. This poor man, having quite needlessly declared war on all his three powerful neighbors, continued the fight until five-sixths of the male population of the entire country had been killed. At the end of this period of slaughter, conditions were so bad that the Paraguayans had to revert to polygamy to get their country repopulated. It will take another century however ere this rich little state shall have fully recovered from that catastrophe.

There remains one more country to be discussed—Brazil. As a colony it was badly neglected, first by the Dutch and afterwards by the Portuguese who forbade the natives and the settlers to deal with any one except a few accredited merchants of Lisbon and who kept this entire region in a state of almost complete economic bondage until the year 1807 when the royal family of Portugal was forced to flee before Napoleon and moved over the Rio de Janeiro. Then the tables were turned and for almost a dozen years the despised colony ruled the mother country. And when His Portuguese Majesty sailed for Lisbon in 1821 he left his son, Dom Pedro, behind as his representative. A year later the son proclaimed himself Emperor of an independent Brazil. And since then the Portuguese language is the only tie that binds the colony to the erstwhile mother country, for the house of Braganza, which had probably given Brazil the best government any South American state had ever enjoyed, was forced to abdicate in 1889 as the result of a military upheaval, and the last of the American emperors left for Paris and the cemetery.

Brazil, with 3,285,000 square miles of territory and therefore as large as the United States and covering half of the entire South American continent, is at the same time the richest of all the different countries south of the equator. It is divided into three parts,—the Amazon lowlands or the valley of the Amazon; the coastlands of the Atlantic; and the highlands, where Santos is the town which provides half of the world with its daily coffee. Besides coffee Brazil grows rubber in the Pará or Belem district, just south of the mouth of the Amazon, and in Manaos where the Rio Negro joins the Amazon. Then there are the tobacco and the cocoa of Bahia on the east coast and the grazing fields of the high plateau of Matto Grosso. And finally there are the diamonds and the other precious stones of the darkest interior, gems which are so difficult to reach that they have never been very thoroughly exploited. And the same holds true for the iron ore and the other metals which are all of them awaiting the building of more railroads.

And finally there are three little European colonies in South America, the only remnants of the old colonial possessions of the seventeenth and eighteenth centuries. They are British Guiana or Demerara; Dutch Guiana or Surinam, which the Dutch got in exchange for the New Netherlands and the city of Nieuw Amsterdam; and French Guiana or Cayenne. If the French had not chosen Cayenne as one of their penal colonies and if we did not see an occasional scrap of unpleasant scandal coming from that lost and unhealthy swamp and attaching itself right to the center of our front pages, we would feel tempted to forget that the Guianas existed. Which would probably be just as well for they contribute very little to either the prosperity or the sum total of happiness of the human race, and they are the living reminders of the day when the whole of South America meant but one thing to the visitor from over the seas—a rich store-house to be plundered at will.

Waste: The deserted mine

XLVII

A NEW WORLD

I wanted to find out how high Kilimanjaro was. After a book has been written and rewritten five or six times, rows of figures are apt to do strange things. What with copying and recopying and infinite corrections scribbled all around them, they have a way of playing hide-and-seek with themselves. One moment they are one thing. The next moment they are something else. If you have ever been snow-blind, you will know what I mean.

"But," you will answer, "that really can't be much of a problem. Look it up in some reliable handbook of geography or in an encyclopedia or in an atlas and copy it."

That would be very simple if these blessed geographies, encyclopedias and atlases were ever able to agree upon any given fact. But apparently they are not. I have got most of the standard volumes on geography right here on my desk and they are a subject of constant delight. Not that they are particularly amusing reading. Geography is not supposed to be a very amusing subject. But when it comes to doing tricks with mountain tops and oceans they are sublime. River basins and the drainage areas of inland seas stretch and shrink and shrink and stretch. The mean average temperature of any given part of the world never stays mean or average very long but makes the mercury of the different meteorological stations behave like a stock-market ticker during a panic. And the bottom of the ocean heaves and sighs like Noodle's tummy after a particularly exciting chase after a cat.

I don't want to destroy any further illusions in a world that has already lost its faith in so many things. But I come out of this struggle with "the facts of geography" having a profound

495

doubt about all further vital statistics. I suppose that this unfortunate diversity of opinions is the result of our incurable vice of nationalism. Every little country must have a few figures all its own, so as to be really able to manifest its sovereign independence.

But that was merely a detail. There were other problems, of which I shall enumerate a few. One half of the world measures weight and distance according to the decimal system. The other half sticks to the duodecimal system. To revaluate meters and kilometers into yards and miles accurately, not merely approximately, is no easy matter, as the gun manufacturers of the Great War learned to their intense discomfort. However, with the help of a competent mathematical assistant (I am no genius at that sort of thing) the necessary calculations can be made. But how about the proper names of countries and mountains and rivers? How should these be spelled? The Gulf of Chili—Gulf of Tjili —Gulf of Tschili—Gulf of Tshi-li—take your choice, my friends! Hindu-Kush — Hindoe-koesch — Hindu-Kutch — Hindu-Kusj—which one do you prefer? But that would not be so bad if at least the different big language groups had been able to agree upon the proper way of spelling Russian or Chinese or Japanese or Spanish names. But every major tongue has at least two and sometimes three conflicting systems of transcribing these strange tongues into the native vernacular.

To add to this confusion of tongues, every tiny scrap of land that can boast of a dialect of its own now claims full and equal rights for "the sacred language of the ancestors", and the map of Europe that used to be fairly simple before the war has recently blossomed forth with a multicolored linguistic flora which makes the reading of Mr. Cook's old and reliable "Continental Railroad Guide" a labor only to be compared to the efforts of Champollion while tackling his first half-dozen Egyptian hieroglyphics.

I am not trying to formulate an alibi. What I have writ, I have writ, but please be lenient with some of my heights and depths. When eminent encyclopedias and statistical handbooks

contradict themselves three or four times on three or four different pages, what is the poor amateur going to do?

I suppose in the end he will do what I did. He will call a
plague upon all these learned tomes and buy himself a copy of
the "World Almanac" and he will say: "I am going to stick to
this one book, and if anybody wants to sue me because I have
made Kilimanjaro 19,710 feet high (in the Britannica it is 19,-
321; in Andrews' Geography, 19,000; in Tarr and McMurry,
19,780; in the Oxford Advanced Atlas, 19,320; in the World
Almanac, 19,710) I shall tell him to go and see the publishers
of the *World-Telegram*, Inc., and let him fight it out with
them."

But what I was going to say when I started upon this Kilimanjaro—Kiliman'djaro—Kilimantscharo—Kilimansjaro topic was
this. I was looking for my World Almanac which had inad-
vertently hidden itself behind a dozen atlases, and during that
search I got hold of a pamphlet that had been sent me a short
while before. It was a pamphlet devoted to the life and the work
of Sir Ronald Ross. In very polite terms the author hinted that
Sir Ronald, if not absolutely in want, was so far removed from
affluence that we might do something about making him at least
reasonably comfortable during the rest of his days—and may
they be many. Of course his needs were not exorbitant. Scientists
rarely count their reward in dollars and dimes. But having completely ruined his health in the pursuit of his studies, he could
do nicely with a more convenient sort of invalid's chair.

I put the pamphlet aside and thought of our own Walter
Reed. I have forgotten what our grateful country has done for
his widow. If I remember rightly the good lady was given a
"mailing frank" (such as any twelve-in-a-dozen congressman
enjoys), and of course she receives the pension that is usually
paid to the widows of officers in the Medical Corps, and there is
a hospital somewhere called after him.

Well, being in a meditative sort of mood, I looked for a
volume on the history of epidemics. And then suddenly I was
struck by an idea. These two men, Reed and Ross, of whom no

one ever seems to have heard, have done more for the development of this earth than hundreds of explorers whose names are familiar to every child in the lowest grades of our grammar schools. By discovering the cause of malaria and yellow fever and by showing us the way in which the world can be set free of those pestilential afflictions, they have opened up more new territory than we shall be able to develop during the next hundred years. The million-murdering mosquito has at last been called to a halt. Anopheles has been driven into a corner and has been forced to listen to the reading of his own death sentence.

It would be easy to add several pages to this chapter on the "Influence of Medicine upon the Geography of the World." Small-pox, beri-beri, sleeping sickness and dozens of other ailments have had to be conquered before the greater part of our world could be made fit for man's permanent habitation. But all this is a little outside of my own "field", so to speak. I know too little about that subject. Nevertheless, the names of those two doctors have set me thinking and wondering.

There is a great deal of unrest in this world. When one looks at the map, one finds little bits of red appearing everywhere. Discontent is breaking out like a severe case of the measles. And books by the ton are being written in an effort to diagnose the case and to suggest suitable remedies. I had never thought very much about it (an author leads such a sheltered life) until I came to write this book. Then suddenly the whole problem became so very simple and Ross and Reed were responsible.

Day-dreaming over a map is really a very pleasant and instructive pastime. There lies Rhodesia—a whole world by itself. Cecil Rhodes was a promoter. He made a few people rich. He killed a great many natives. He turned brigand and started a little war of his own and lost. He turned statesman and started a big war and won. There are a great many monuments to murdered women and children which could bear the legend: "C.R. sculpsit", but a grateful country overlooked these trifles and called a vast new province after him.

A little further northward lies the Congo with its Stanley-villes and Leopoldvilles and the unmarked graves of countless natives tortured to death because they were behind on their rubber quota or slow in bringing in elephant tusks.

Hudson gave his name to a bay which in turn bestowed its

We have fertilized by far too many of our fields in
this way

name upon a rich land company. What that land company did to the original inhabitants makes another terrible chapter in the sad volume devoted to the Martyrdom of Man. But we need not go so far abroad. We ourselves have never yet kept a single treaty with our Indians. What my own ancestors did unto the brown men of those far away spice islands which they conquered three hundred years ago is usually not taught in the public schools of Holland and it is perhaps just as well. What happened in the Putomayo region of South America is still in every-body's memory.

The crimes the different native potentates of Africa and the Arab slave-dealers committed in the silent Senegambian forests make us wish that Dante had reserved a special department of his Inferno for monsters of that particular variety.

The man-hunts with horses and dogs, organized to extermi-nate the aborigines of Australia and New Zealand are rarely mentioned in the histories devoted to the early years of these distant territories.

Why go on?

I am merely repeating what everybody already knows.

But what few people seem to realize is that the Great Era of Exploitation has definitely come to an end, that most of the present unrest is due to the unwillingness of the former victims to play that role any longer.

There is very little use in sitting in high judgment upon the Errors of the Past. It is more profitable to collect our thoughts and devise ways and means by which we shall be able to avoid a few of the mistakes of the future. Well, the men and women of the type of Reed and Ross are there to show us the way.

Sentimental meditations upon the glories of a problematic Utopia will get us nowhere. To say that since we have spent dozens of centuries "taking away" we must now spend other dozens of centuries "giving" will hardly solve the problem. Charity is as bad as brigandage. Charity is really just as unfair to the recipient as to the donor. To set the Indian native free from the tyranny of the English Raj and then leave him un-defended to the mercy of the Moslem mountaineers would be merely another blunder.

Nor would it benefit the Chinese or the Javanese or the Burmese if we should suddenly pack up all our little railroads and flivvers and flying machines and remove our telephone booths and our filling stations and bid them go back to the bless-ings of the Gandhi's loin-cloth and the crocodile-gnawed sampan. The machine has come to stay. The natives have adapted their

What is the answer?

lives to fast means of transportation and communication. They have fallen into the habit of calling on the white man's doctor when the child develops diphtheria rather than send grandmother to the voodoo priest. When they want to visit their friends, they prefer a jitney-bus to a ten-hour walk across a painful track.

And a world accustomed to money and to bank-notes is not going back to the pails of honey and the spoonfuls of salt and all the other clumsy trivialities of the ancient system of barter.

For better or worse, this planet of ours has become one large, going concern, and the date over the doorway is 1932, not 932 or 32 B. C.

There is, however, a solution, and the labors of Reed and Ross show us the general direction of the road we shall have to follow. For these two men neither "took" nor "gave"—they "co-operated". They could never have done what they did without the assistance of thousands of others. Neither did they stamp out malaria and yellow fever for the exclusive benefit of the black man or the white man or the yellow man. Without regard to color or creed they bestowed their blessings upon the whole of humanity. When Goethals and Dr. Gorgas dug the Panama Canal (Goethals drew the blue prints and Gorgas gave him the man-power with which to translate his drawings into cubic feet of excavated rock) they were not thinking of either the Pacific or the Atlantic alone, nor of America alone, but of the world as a whole. When Marconi invented his wireless, he did not stipulate, "Only Italian ships must be allowed to use the radio in case of disaster". The Zanzibar tramp was benefited as much as the fastest trans-Atlantic greyhound.

You probably see what I am driving at.

No, I am not going to suggest the formation of a new society. That is not necessary. The problem will take care of itself. If it does not, there won't be any problem in a couple of centuries because there won't be any people left to worry about it.

We no longer live in a world the future of which we can leave to itself. That policy went out when steam and electricity came in and when Patagonia and Lapland, Boston and Han-kow became neighbors, able to confer with each other in less than two minutes. We are no longer manufacturing goods for ourselves alone or raising grain for the home village. Japan can make our matches cheaper than we can ever hope to do and the Argentine can grow enough wheat to keep the whole of Germany from starving and at much smaller cost.

We no longer can offer the Chinese Coolie or the Rand Kaffir one-twentieth of the wages we would pay a white man, because Moscow has a broadcasting station that carries very far and a staff of polyglot announcers who inform the black and the yellow man that he is being cheated out of something that really belongs to him.

We are no longer able to plunder and filch and rob as heartily as our fathers did because—well, if you really want to know—because our conscience won't let us or if we ourselves should have happened to be born without that spiritual compass, because the collective conscience of mankind has at last reached the point where it is beginning to get a first flickering suspicion that honesty and common decency are as inevitable in international affairs as they are in those of private citizens.

No, I am not going to preach a sermon. I am not going to send you home with a "message". But if you have read this far, I would like to ask you to sit quite still for another half hour and draw your own conclusions.

Thus far we have always lived as if we were a sort of accident —as if our stay on this planet was only a matter of years or at best of centuries. We have behaved with the indecent greed of passengers on a passenger-train who know that they will only have ten minutes for the three-course dinner to be served at the next halting-place.

Gradually we are beginning to realize that we not only have been here quite a long time but that we are going to stay here almost indefinitely. Why the hurry and why the rush? When you move to a town where you expect to spend the rest of your days, you plan for the future. So do your neighbors, the butchers and bakers and grocers and the doctors and undertakers. If they didn't, the whole place would be in such hopeless disorder that it would be uninhabitable in less than a week's time.

When you come to think of it, is there really such a very great difference between the world at large and your own native village? If there is any difference, it is one of quantity rather than quality. And that is all!

You will say that I have wandered all over the place, from Kilimanjaro by way of Dr. Reed and Dr. Ross to planetary-planning for the future.

"But What," as Alice might have asked, "is the use of a Geography without a little Travelling?"

Paris, April, 1931
New Orleans, May, 1932

A FEW FACTS

Area of the earth: 196,950,000 sq. m.
" " " land: 57,510,000 "
" " " water: 139,440,000 "

Area of oceans
Pacific 68,634,000 sq. m.
Atlantic 41,321,000 "
Indian 29,340,000 "

Area of continents
Asia 17,000,000 sq. m.
Africa 11,500,000 "
North America 8,000,000 "
South " 6,800,000 "
Europe 3,750,000 "

Equatorial circumference of the earth: 24,902 miles.
Meridianal " " " " 24,860 "
Diameter through equator: 7,926.667 "
" " poles: 7,899.988 "
Highest mountain: Mt. Everest 29,141 feet
Deepest hole: between Philippines and Japan 34,210 "

Population of continents
Asia 950,000,000
Europe 550,000,000
N. & S. America 230,000,000
Africa 150,000,000
Australia 7,000,000

Population of the earth:
in round figures 2,000,000,000.

Highest mountains of each continent
Asia	Everest	29,141	ft.
S. America	Aconcagua	22,834	"
N. America	McKinley	20,300	"
Africa	Kilimanjaro	19,710	"
Europe	Elbrus	18,465	"

Longest rivers
Mississippi-Missouri	4,221	miles
Nile	4,000	"
Amazon	3,900	"
Ob	3,200	"
Yangtsze	3,100	"

Largest cities
London	7,742,212
New York	6,930,446
Berlin	4,297,000
Chicago	3,376,438
Paris	2,871,039
Osaka	2,453,573
Buenos Aires	2,153,200
Tokio	2,070,913
Moscow	2,025,947

(There are only 9 cities in the world with a population of over 2,000,000. Of these, 4 are in Europe, 2 in the U.S.A., 1 in South America and 2 in Japan.)

INDEX

DIASPORA

TRANSLATED FROM THE GERMAN BY
RICHARD AND CLARA WINSTON

WITH A CHAPTER *"A History of the Jews in America"*
BY RONALD SANDERS

DIASPORA

THE POST-BIBLICAL
HISTORY OF THE JEWS

WERNER KELLER

HARCOURT, BRACE & WORLD, INC., NEW YORK

To all who have the truth at heart

FREDERICK THE GREAT:
   Can you give me one single, irrefutable proof of God?

JEAN BAPTISTE DU BOYER, MARQUIS D'ARGENS:
   Yes, Your Majesty, the Jews.

"We now acknowledge that for many, many centuries blindness has covered our eyes, so that we no longer see the beauty of Thy chosen people and no longer recognize in its face the features of our first-born brother. We acknowledge that the mark of Cain is upon our brow. For centuries Abel lay low in blood and tears because we forgot Thy love. Forgive us the curse that we wrongfully pronounced upon the name of the Jews. Forgive us that we crucified Thee in the flesh for the second time. For we knew not what we did. . . ."

> Pope John XXIII:
> A penitential prayer composed
> shortly before his death
> on June 3, 1963

CONTENTS

xi

LIST OF ILLUSTRATIONS

PREFACE

In the year 1843 the French archaeologist Paul-Emile Botta first opened the gate into the world of Old Testament history. Relief statues that he had discovered in Khorsabad were identified as those of Sargon II, the Assyrian King who once upon a time removed the Ten Tribes of Israel, which were thereafter to vanish without a trace. Another century of untiring research and vast excavations that churned up the ancient soils of Egypt and the Near East were to follow. Only then did the documents and monuments brought to light begin to show, in broad outline, the tremendous panorama of two thousand years in the history of the people of Israel.

Almost at the very time that Botta was making his finds in the Land of the Two Rivers, the rediscovery of the history of the Jews was beginning in the heart of Europe. Leopold Zunz launched the first scholarly investigation of the past of the Jews. From 1853 to 1875 the Jewish historian Heinrich Graetz labored over the first comprehensive account, his *History of the Jews from the Oldest Times Down to the Present,* in eleven volumes. It was to be followed by many others.

Nevertheless, the post-Biblical history of the Jews remains to this day unknown to the wider public. There is a great gap in the minds of most persons between the end of the story as told by the Old Testament and the tragic events of the recent past. Two thousand years of Jewish history remained largely a blank to even well-educated non-Jews, and to Jews as well. It was all the easier, therefore, for this void to fill with prejudices and calumny, with hatred, hostility, and sluggishness of the heart.

Knowledge alone can banish ignorance and prejudice, and there are many indications that a turning point has been reached. But the sins of omission and the committed crimes of two thousand years are too deeply rooted to be removed from the world overnight. What has been done can never be undone, but it must soberly and objectively be recognized for what it was. Only a confrontation with the long historical agony of the Jewish people can sanctify the present efforts toward a new course. New understanding is bound to remain fragmentary if it is restricted to the present and the most recent past. Our new perspective must take in the whole wide field of the preceding twenty centuries.

No other people has experienced a history like that of the descendants of the People of the Book in the Diaspora. The whole world has served as backdrop for their destiny, from the Near East, Egypt, and Africa to Europe and America and even India and China. When the Jewish people were expelled from the land of their fathers, they found a whole world a "house of bondage." Only a few happy hours have intervened amidst long periods of suffering. But despite all oppression and misery, without a state or a country of their own, defenseless, powerless, and without rights, this people has survived all storms and disasters. No threats of death have ever swerved them from their faith in God. And they survived. Despised and persecuted, down through the centuries they enriched the nations of the world by great cultural contributions. Neither Islam nor Christianity is conceivable without Israel. Jesus, Spinoza, Marx, Freud, and Einstein all sprang from this remarkable stock.

Surrounded as it is by the nimbus of divine mystery, it constitutes one of the great enigmas of world history. For God revealed himself to this people. The continued existence of the Jews after eras of the most terrible persecutions is the greatest of miracles. The two thousand years of dispersal literally fulfilled the prophecy pronounced three thousand years ago in the fifth book of Moses.

This work is an attempt to trace the major outlines of that astonishing phenomenon. The subject is so vast that I have been able to consider only a small part of it. But what I have presented here may reawaken a long overdue recollection of momentous happenings and provide some notion not only of the sufferings of the Jewish people, but also of its greatness and importance since the days of its being scattered among all nations.

A definition of "Jew" is not easy. The Jews are either the people of God or the people of the Bible or a race (a scientifically untenable notion) or a religion or a human group *sui generis*. Who they are depends on the principles, prejudices, and standards of the observer. For the purpose of this historical study we need not become involved in the dispute. In the interests of a just historical picture, it was essential to include persons from this group who have influenced Western culture, even though these persons might not be adherents of the Jewish religion. Our arbitrary criterion was that the person in question or his forebears belonged to the Jewish community.

I wish to thank my publisher, Willy Droemer, who generously and with great understanding made possible and supported the writing of this book. I am also indebted to Dr. Felix Guggenheim of Beverly Hills for advice, valuable suggestions, and loans of books. I am grateful also to my wife, Helga, for her indispensable assistance all along the way.

WERNER KELLER

Ascona
July 18, 1966

DIASPORA

PROLOGUE

"Now the Lord said unto Abram: 'Get thee out of thy country, and from thy kindred, and from thy father's house, unto the land that I will show thee. And I will make of thee a great nation, and I will bless thee, and make thy name great; and be thou a blessing. And I will bless them that bless thee, and him that curseth thee will I curse; and in thee shall the families of the earth be blessed.' "

GENESIS 12:1–3

PROPHECY AND BIBLICAL TIMES

"And the Lord shall scatter you among the peoples, and ye shall be left few in number among the nations . . ." (Deuteronomy 4:27).

Never in all history, to no other people and to no other religion, has so strange a history been prophesied. No other prophecy has so literally been fulfilled as that made in the fifth book of Moses to the people of Israel.

Toward the middle of the first century before Christ, the time for the fulfillment of those prophetic words approached. That was the dark and fateful hour when the people of Israel would lose the holy city of Jerusalem and their great sanctuary, the Temple; when they would be deprived of their own state and finally of their homeland, to be scattered among the nations. The immense narrative of the Old Testament comes to an end before the disaster. The book of the Maccabees finishes with its tale of the heroic struggle of the Jews for freedom, for the sake of their religion, against the Seleucid rulers, those most powerful successors of the shattered empire of Alexander.

One last time, after achieving liberation, Israel held the reins of government in her own hands. But the young kingdom was scarcely born when a new power appeared on the scene. Rome, on her way to becoming mistress of the world, was beginning her advance into the East. After the conquest of Carthage, Spain, and Greece, she set out to subjugate the lands from the Hellespont to the Nile.

On the eve of these events the people of Eretz Israel were already ancient, compared with other nations. Their earliest childhood and youth lay far back in the past; the nation had already entered maturity. Their memories of national growth and experiences as a people embraced a span of nearly two thousand years.

What a history the children of Israel already had behind them! They had witnessed the rise and collapse of the empires of the ancient East. The scene of their experiences was that part of the inhabited earth which extends in a great arc from the valley of the Nile along the coast of the Mediterranean toward Asia Minor, and on to the river valleys of the Tigris and Euphrates down to the estuaries in the Persian Gulf—that "Fertile Crescent" in which the first high cultures arose.

It has scarcely ever been Israel's fortune to intervene decisively in the march of history as a significant political power. Almost always she had been the victim and bone of contention in the incessant struggles for power among the rival empires. One major reason for this was her geographical situation. From earliest times Canaan had lain in the path of the great conquering armies that marched between Egypt and Mesopotamia.

The tribe from which the people of Israel sprang is encountered soon after the beginning of the second millennium B.C. The patriarch Abraham set out on a great migration in the course of which he touched all the lands of the ancient world whose rulers would later figure in his people's history. With his family and herds, he traveled thousands of miles through the broad area between Mesopotamia and the land of the Nile: from Ur of the Chaldees upstream along the Euphrates as far as Haran in northwestern Mesopotamia, then southward to the land of the Jordan. During a drought came an interlude in Egypt, after which Father Abraham and his son Isaac lived as herdsmen in the Promised Land. A famine compelled Jacob, who was renamed Israel (Warrior of God), to move once more with his clan to the land of the Nile. In the kingdom of the pharaohs the children and grandchildren of Israel multiplied into a numerous people.

After a stay of four hundred years came the exodus. Moses led the people of Israel out of oppression and slavery, escaping the house of bondage that Egypt had become for them. Upon Sinai Moses received the revelation which was the Torah with the Ten Commandments, the God-given law that henceforth was to dominate the consciousness of the Hebrews. There followed the time of trials and preparation, the forty years of wandering in the desert. Toward 1230 B.C., after East Jordania had been taken under the leadership of Moses, there began the conquest of the land west of the Jordan, under Joshua. The land was distributed among the Twelve Tribes, and the children of Israel became a settled people. During the times of the Judges they matured, in the course of long struggles with the Canaanites, into a nation. Menaced by the Philistines, the people chose Saul as their first king. Soon afterward, under David and Solomon, they reached the height of their power as a nation.

Under Saul the tribe of Judah first began to play a significant part in the history of the nation. It soon acquired a dominant position among the tribes. For out of the tribe of Judah came the line of David; within the territory of Judah was Jerusalem, which David conquered in about 1000 B.C. and made the new capital of the country. Here his son Solomon built the magnificent Temple on Mount Moriah. But the era of the first crowned heads in the history of Israel was as brief as it was brilliant. After barely a hundred years of unity, the young state split into two kingdoms: the northern Kingdom of Israel and the southern Kingdom of Judah.

The political, cultural, and religious contentions both within and without the two kingdoms persistently sharpened. Idolatry spread. The prophets thundered their immortal denunciations, called upon Israel to return to God and his law, but the passionate warnings went unheard. The old prophecy of the scattering sounded repeatedly through the centuries as the great prophets invoked visions of woes to come.

With the rise to power of the cruel Assyrians, those visions began to become realities. In a series of bloody conquests the Assyrians won hegemony in the Near East. Tiglatpileser III, the Phul of the Bible, invaded Eretz Israel and carried many inhabitants away into captivity. A decade later, the fierce Sargon II conquered Samaria, capital of the northern Kingdom of Israel, and transported the majority of the remaining inhabitants—above all, the upper classes—to distant provinces of his empire. Colonists were settled in their place. That act sealed the fate of the northern kingdom. Its Ten Tribes were never heard from again.

A century and a half later the knell tolled for the Kingdom of Judah as well. Under King Nebuchadnezzar of Babylon, ruler of that Kingdom of the Chaldeans that had followed the collapse of Assyria, Judah was devastated, Jerusalem conquered and destroyed. Solomon's Temple went up in flames. In two successive wholesale removals the flower of the nation was carried into exile, into the Babylonian Captivity. A smaller portion of the people succeeded in escaping to Egypt. Only a few, tillers of the fields and vineyards, remained in the land. No foreigners were brought in, however, to settle the depopulated areas.

The cycle had been completed. The great-grandsons of Abraham and Moses had returned to the Euphrates and Nile rivers, whence these two leaders had once come. Seven hundred years after the entry into Canaan, the story of the children of Israel seemed to have come to an end. The structure of government was annihilated, the land devastated. The majority of its former inhabitants lived in foreign parts. How many other peoples and tribes of the ancient Orient have been conquered, carried away, and scattered by great rulers? Their traces have been lost forever, for they surrendered their identity. The Ten Tribes of the northern kingdom had met a similar fate—they, too, had vanished, drowned in the Assyrian flood.

But the great turning point came in the "land of exile." In Babylonia there began that profound process of spiritual renewal and purification that saved the people even after the downfall of their state. What Ezekiel (36:26) had hinted at was fulfilled: "A new heart also will I give you, and a new spirit will I put within you. . . ." At that time the cornerstone was laid for the future continuance of the people, for a life as a people even in dispersion among the nations.

Wrenched from their homeland but united by a common religion, by common feelings and thoughts, by common manners and hopes for the future, the captives of Babylon faithfully preserved the qualities of their culture. They did not mingle with the natives. "By the waters of Babylon" the exiles from Judah for the first time grasped the full significance of the words of their prophets. They learned that life was not necessarily dependent on having a state and territory of their own, not even upon the Temple. Instead of offering sacrifices in the central sanctuary, they assembled in small groups in private houses for prayer. For the first time what we now call a congregation took shape. And when they finally set about erecting special houses for prayer meetings and the reading of the Scriptures, they were on their way to creating synagogues.

After the fall of the Babylonian Empire in 538 B.C., King Cyrus of Persia permitted the Jews to return home and authorized the rebuilding of the Temple in Jerusalem. Something altogether new began: When the people slowly, group by group, returned from exile, the Davidian dynasty did not come to power. Jerusalem and the reconstructed Temple formed the core of a restoration founded on the primacy of the spiritual over the secular principle. Henceforth the chief of the priests of Jerusalem, bearing the title of high priest, took the king's place. Judea, as the land of the children of Israel was now called, became a theocratic republic.

Under Ezra, the priest sent from Babylon, the covenant with God was renewed. Ezra was the first to convoke the "Great Council" of elders, which later developed into the Sanhedrin; and Ezra also proclaimed the Torah to be the law of Israel. This religious law, which also covered all aspects of daily life, became mandatory for the entire people. Those who submitted to this law of God thereby professed that they belonged to Eretz Israel and to the congregation of the Temple in Jerusalem—whether they had returned to the homeland or still remained in the Diaspora, in Babylon and Egypt. The Promised Land and Jerusalem itself became the religious center for all Jews, even those in the remotest parts of the known world.

The stringency of the Law, the rule of priests, scribes, and teachers of the Torah, and a now unshakable monotheistic faith formed the character of Judaism. It may be said that the history of Judaism began with Ezra.

In the fourth century B.C. Judea and the Jews of the Diaspora were again caught up in vast historical upheavals. After Alexander the Great had smashed the power of the Persians and built a vast empire, the people of Israel found themselves confronted by something hitherto unknown. In the past they had dealt only with the powers of the ancient Orient. Now, however, they for the first time came into contact with conquerors from the continent that henceforth was to determine the course of world history —Europe. For the first time "Japhet entered the huts of Shem." The world-wide victory of Greek culture took its course; Hellenism cast its spell upon the peoples of the ancient world. And Hellenism provided a great challenge and a dangerous threat to Judaism.

For a century after the death of Alexander, however, the small theocratic republic remained virtually untouched by the new spirit, although the Jews of the Diaspora, especially in Alexandria, came more and more under its spell. There, the Jews began speaking Greek and translated the Torah into Greek. Yet the really important decision was taken in Judea. The bitter confrontation began after Judea was annexed, around 200 B.C., by the largest of the successor states, the kingdom of the Greco-Syrian Seleucids. In 169 B.C. the Syrian despot Antiochus Epiphanes (ruler from 175 to 163 B.C.) began to Hellenize Judea by force. He banned the Jewish religion, ordered the worship of statues of the Greek gods, and installed a statue of Zeus in the Temple in Jerusalem. Popular resistance flared. These absolutistic demands on the part of the pagan state threatened the innermost core of Judaism. Under the leadership of the heroic Maccabees, the religious war was fought with a success that surpassed all expectations. Begun as a defense against the suppression of religion, it ended with political liberation. National independence, lost centuries earlier, was restored.

After domination by five successive Great Powers—Assyrian, Babylonian, Persian, Greco-Egyptian, and, finally, Greco-Syrian—Judea found herself free from foreign rule. The dynasty of the Maccabees, called Hasmonaeans after their ancestor Hashmon, finally renewed the Jewish kingship also. In 104 B.C. Judah Aristobulus—great-grandson of the priest Mattathias, who had initiated the struggle against Antiochus Epiphanes, and grand-nephew of the Judah whose heroism had won him the epithet Maccabee (the Hammer)—assumed the title of King of Judea.

But the dream of a free kingdom of the Jews was to be short-lived. Scarcely eight years had passed after the resurrection of the Jewish state, and scarcely forty after the revival of the kingdom, when free Judea's last hour approached. Torn by partisan struggles and dynastic intrigues, the new state was driven straight into the arms of Rome, then reaching out toward Asia.

THE CURTAIN FALLS
IN THE ORIENT

I IN THE POWER OF ROME

ERETZ ISRAEL BECOMES A ROMAN PROVINCE

A series of mighty wars of conquest, over a period of a mere hundred and fifty years, had so increased the power of Rome toward the end of the second century B.C. that nothing could any longer resist her. In 146 B.C., at the end of the Third Punic War, nothing was left of Carthage in North Africa but a smoking heap of ruins. In taking over the heritage of Hamilcar and Hannibal, Rome became mistress of the western Mediterranean. That same year, 146, once-proud Macedonia became a Roman province. In 133 B.C. Numantia fell and Spain, after protracted resistance, was finally subjugated. And in the same year Rome also acquired her first possession across the Aegean: Attalus III, the last king of Pergamon, bequeathed his kingdom to the Romans. It was to become the nucleus of their Asian province.

The appearance of Rome in Asia prompted Mithridates Eupator, the King of Pontus, who himself wanted to be master of Asia Minor, to organize a coalition against Rome in 88 B.C. Rome at this time was weakened by the first civil war between Marius and Sulla, and Mithridates was a formidable enemy. It took two decades and three wars before Rome defeated this dangerous opponent; she thereupon proceeded to establish her rule in the Near East from Asia Minor to Egypt.

Pompey, former consul and future triumvir, received dictatorial powers for the entire area of the coast of Asia Minor in 67 B.C. A general of remarkable ability who had previously suppressed an uprising in Spain,

Pompey proved on this new assignment that he fully deserved the epithet *Magnus* (the Great).

First of all, he dealt with the plague of piracy. Favored by the downfall of the kingdoms of the Near East and the weakness of the Roman fleet, bands of pirates had sprung up along the coasts of Asia Minor and in the Greek Archipelago. They had succeeded in inflicting great damage on naval commerce in the eastern Mediterranean and were seriously interfering with the grain supply for Italy. Pompey assembled five hundred ships and an army of one hundred and twenty thousand men. Within three months he had annihilated the pirates and established the security of the Inland Sea. Then he began the subjugation of the East.

In 66 B.C. Pompey defeated Mithridates and forced King Tigranes of Armenia, the second great opponent in the East, to bow to the new world power and become a Roman "ally." With Asia Minor and Armenia disposed of, Pompey prepared to administer the deathblow to the already decaying Seleucid monarchy.

At the time of the Passover in the year 65 B.C. the legate Scaurus, sent by Pompey, appeared in Damascus. Here, too, Rome assumed hegemony. As ill luck would have it, at this very time a civil war was raging in neighboring Judea.

Salome, the only queen who ever sat on the throne of Judea, died in 67 B.C., after a happy regency of nine years. Her sons were promptly engaged in a murderous fraternal struggle for succession. The elder brother, Hyrcanus II, who had been high priest under Salome, was proclaimed king in Jerusalem after her death. His brother Aristobulus II forced him to renounce the throne and the office of priest, and himself assumed power. Hyrcanus was feeble in body and will, but there came forward as his protector and manipulator a man from a family whose lust for power, cruelty, and deviousness were to produce dire results in the history of Judea. This man was Antipater, governor of Idumea and father of the subsequent King Herod I. By promising him twelve Judean cities, Antipater persuaded the king of the Nabatean Arabs, Aretas III, to attack Aristobulus. With a strong Arabian force Aretas defeated Aristobulus and besieged him in Jerusalem.

As soon as the Roman Legate Scaurus heard about these events in Damascus, he set out for Judea at once, determined to profit by the situation. The emissaries of the hostile brothers met him after he entered Judea. In order to win over the Roman Legate, each of the two offered the tremendous sum of four hundred talents (about five hundred thousand dollars). Scaurus decided in favor of Aristobulus and ordered Aretas to call off the siege of the Temple Mount, where Aristobulus had barricaded himself, and to withdraw from Jerusalem. This did not, however, end the conflict. A short time later an entirely different decision was made.

Pompey had personally directed operations in Syria, and he had now come to Damascus. In the spring of 63 B.C. both brothers called upon him there and asked him to mediate their dispute. Hyrcanus complained bitterly that Aristobulus had unseated him, although he was the elder and hence entitled to the kingship. His argument was confirmed by several high-ranking Judeans whom Antipater had wisely taken with him as witnesses. Aristobulus appeared before Pompey with a royal retinue. Even before the hearing he had presented Pompey with a precious gift worth five hundred talents. Hyrcanus, he maintained, was totally unfitted to rule. In the interests of orderly government he himself had been forced to assume power.

In addition to the hostile brothers, a delegation from the Jewish people arrived, with entirely different proposals. It argued for restoration of the old theocracy headed by priests, without a king.

Pompey listened to all three parties and reserved his decision. First, he wanted to subdue King Aretas; that seemed to him the pressing problem from Rome's point of view. He therefore enjoined the disputants to remain patient and preserve the peace until he decided among them.

The order was not obeyed. Aristobulus, sensing Pompey's antagonism, accompanied the Roman army into East Jordania and returned immediately to Judea. He made preparations to fight the Romans to preserve the independence of Judea. Pompey, seeing his suspicions confirmed, abandoned his march against the Arabs and with his legions set out in pursuit of Aristobulus. The usurper was arrested outside of Jerusalem. But although the adherents of the other parties, fearing the wrath of the Romans, opened the gates to the Roman army, surrendering Jerusalem to Pompey, the followers of Aristobulus had gathered on the Temple Mount, determined upon bitter resistance. Even for the superior Roman arms, the fortress on the Mount was difficult to take by direct assault. In the course of a three-month siege a great catapult was brought from Tyre to bombard the fortifications with heavy stones. At last, on a Sabbath in the autumn of 63 B.C., the Romans succeeded in breaching the wall.

The priests continued their services in the Temple, ignoring the Roman soldiers who came rushing in with bared swords. They would not fight on the Sabbath and allowed the Romans to cut them down without resistance. At the end of the massacre Pompey, accompanied by his bodyguard, stepped into the Holy of Holies, which no one but the high priest was permitted to enter. So this was the room of which so many mysterious tales were told! Curiously, Pompey regarded the cult implements and vessels; but he left them inviolate. Nor did he touch the treasury of the Temple. In fact, on the following day he ordered the purification of the Temple and the resumption of services.

Against the partisans of Aristobulus Pompey proceeded without mercy. He had all leaders of the liberation movement beheaded. More than twelve thousand persons lost their lives, besides the patriots who had fallen in battle.

The victor made a decision fraught with grave consequences for the future. The entire country was declared subject to tribute and placed under the protection of Rome. It was, however, permitted autonomy in domestic affairs. Hyrcanus II was confirmed in his dignity as high priest but had to renounce the title of king. He would be only the ethnarch, ruling under Roman sovereignty. Thus the free state of the Hasmonaeans had been ended by force after an existence of almost eighty years. Henceforth Rome determined the course of the history of Judea.

In 61 B.C. Pompey, victor in the Asiatic campaign, made his triumphal entry into Rome crowned with the golden laurel. He had brought home vast booty from the East, taken from the treasure houses of Mithridates and many other Asiatic princes. In addition, there were tributes from Syria and Cilicia. Subject rulers and princes walked before the white horses that drew the triumphal chariot—among them, with bowed heads, the members of the royal family of the Hasmonaeans: Aristobulus, his son Antigonus, and two daughters of his eldest son, Alexander. Seventy years earlier, when their ancestor Johanan, a son of Simon the Maccabee, had sent an embassy to this city of Rome, a time of freedom had just dawned after long struggles against an oppressive foreign power. Rome had received the ambassadors of the people of Israel with all honors, had acknowledged them representatives of an independent, friendly nation, and had concluded a treaty of alliance with Judea (I Maccabees 8:23 ff.)—only now to strip the people of Judea of all power.

In addition to the family of Aristobulus, Pompey had brought back with him a host of other Jewish prisoners, whom he sold as slaves. They became the nucleus of a Jewish colony in Rome that was soon to grow to considerable importance. In the course of time many of these slaves were emancipated by their owners, since they proved of little use because of their strict observance of the Sabbath and other customs prescribed by Mosaic law. The freedom of others was bought by relatives in Judea. Most of the freedmen remained in the capital. They settled as a close community in a quarter on the right bank of the Tiber, at the foot of the Vatican hill, and remained faithful to the religion of their fathers. With them, the Dispersion in Italy had begun.

As the result of her conquests in Asia, Rome had become the overlord of many other Jewish communities in Syria, Asia Minor, and the islands of the Ionian Sea. The Jews in the capital intervened where necessary in behalf of their brethren, especially when religious rights were involved.

While Rome celebrated her victory, Zion veiled her head in mourning. The blow that Pompey had delivered to Judea numbed the country for several years. But soon there were new disturbances, struggles and intrigues for the regency, uprisings against the arbitrariness and whims of the Roman officials. Judea also felt the effect of the wars among the mighty triumvirs of Rome, which were soon to shake the entire empire.

The popular uprising against Roman rule began under a protégé of Pompey, Gabinius Aulus, Proconsul of Syria. During the journey back to Rome, Alexander, the eldest son of Aristobulus, contrived to make his escape. Back in Judea, he mustered a sizable army of guerrillas from among the patriots. Gabinius, however, sent against him Mark Antony, who defeated him in the vicinity of Jerusalem. Gabinius himself inflicted heavy losses upon Alexander's army at the fortress of Alexandrium. A third attempt by Alexander to stir the country to rebellion against Rome likewise miscarried. Aristobulus, who escaped from Rome, met with no better fortune. He, too, was defeated, along with the rebels he had gathered around him; he was taken prisoner again and brought back to Rome.

In 54 B.C. Rome relieved Gabinius of his post. He was replaced by the wealthy Crassus, who since the year 60 had been allied with Pompey and Caesar in the First Triumvirate. Crassus was preparing a campaign against the Parthians and needed money for his war chest. He therefore imposed crushing taxes upon Judea and ensured that they were ruthlessly collected. He eyed the treasures of the Jerusalem Temple, and had immense sums and valuable objects carried away. The violation of the sanctuary, deliberately calculated to humiliate the Judeans, promptly led to a new uprising. In 53, while Crassus and his troops were engaged in battle against the Parthians, Galilee rose.

The Parthians inflicted an annihilating defeat upon Crassus, who himself was killed during a retreat. His successor, hastily dispatched from Rome, was none other than that Cassius who nine years later would organize the conspiracy against Julius Caesar. Cassius took brutal measures in Judea; he suppressed the uprising and sold thirty thousand Jews as slaves. On the advice of the devious Antipater, Cassius executed Pitholaus, the Hasmonaean commander who had also participated in the rebellion of Aristobulus.

Meanwhile a grave crisis was shaking the Roman world to its foundations. After the death of Crassus the relationship between the other two members of the Triumvirate, Julius Caesar and Pompey, deteriorated so gravely that armed conflict became inevitable. In 49 B.C. the civil war broke out. On January 11 Caesar crossed the Rubicon. Pompey and his followers withdrew to the eastern half of the empire. Caesar planned to send Aristobulus, then still a captive in Rome, to Syria with two legions to fight Pompey, whom the King of the Jews detested. But before Aristobulus could leave Rome, he was poisoned by followers of Pompey. Shortly afterward his son Alexander was executed in Antioch.

After the deaths of these two Hasmonaeans, who had fought so passionately and bravely for the freedom of their country, only two male members of the dynasty were left: Antigonus, the politically rather ungifted son of Aristobulus, and Hyrcanus II, the irresolute high priest and ethnarch, who more and more became a helpless tool of the ambitious Idumean, Antipater.

When Pompey was defeated at Pharsalus on August 9 in 48 B.C. and was killed seeking refuge in Egypt, the cunning Antipater instantly adapted to the new situation. He went over to the camp of victorious Caesar, swaying Hyrcanus to do likewise. Very soon he had an opportunity to prove his "loyalty." Caesar's campaign in Egypt did not begin prosperously. Antipater provided him with heavy reinforcements, himself took part in the battles, and obtained vigorous support for Caesar's legions from the numerous Jews of Egypt. Caesar showed his gratitude. He confirmed Hyrcanus in the office of ethnarch and high priest and appointed Antipater procurator of Judea, at the same time conferring Roman citizenship upon him. Unwittingly, Caesar was supporting a government that had long ceased to enjoy the respect of the best part of the population.

But at the same time Caesar issued a number of other decrees so generous that his name was to enjoy grateful remembrance among the Jews. Judea henceforth was not required to pay taxes to Rome, nor to supply recruits for the Roman army, nor to quarter Roman troops. The port of Jaffa (Joppa) was returned to the Jews, so that Judea's foreign trade once more had access to the sea. Caesar even permitted the destroyed fortifications of Jerusalem to be reconstructed.

The dictator also showed favor to the Jews of the Diaspora. He expressly permitted the Jews in all communities throughout the empire to hold their divine services, to collect contributions for the Temple in Jerusalem, to conduct their own affairs and run their own judiciary. In short, he granted them internal autonomy. A letter to the authorities on the island of Paros indicates how carefully Caesar insisted on the observance of his orders: "The Jews of Delos have petitioned me that you are hindering them by ordinances from preserving their traditional customs and performing their worship. It has aroused my displeasure that you forbid them to live according to their laws and to contribute money for common feasts and for divine services, especially since these things are not even forbidden them in Rome. . . . It is therefore requisite that you immediately rescind all such ordinances directed against these our friends and allies, for the sake of their services to us and their loyalty."

Antipater had now become the actual ruler in Judea. His word was decisive in all significant matters. Hyrcanus, the high priest and ethnarch, had become little more than a figurehead. Antipater unscrupulously pursued dynastic policies. He skillfully set about securing his own future and that of his sons, appointing the eldest, Phasaelus, strategus (commander) for Judea and his second son, Herod, for Galilee.

The twenty-five-year-old Herod showed what he was capable of as soon as he assumed his first post. In Galilee scattered soldiers from Aristobulus' partisan bands, under the leadership of a Hasmonaean supporter named Ezekiah, were waging guerrilla warfare against everyone they regarded as an enemy. They attacked members of Antipater's retinue, as well as Greeks, Syrians, and Romans. Herod promptly sent troops against these "bandits," as he called these patriots, and had Ezekiah and his captains executed.

Death sentences could by right be imposed only by the Sanhedrin in Jerusalem. Indignation over Herod's act swept the country. Members of the families of the unjustly executed men complained to the Sanhedrin, and they were supported by representatives of Jerusalem's foremost families, who in other respects certainly did not sympathize with the partisans. What was involved here was the sanctity of the law itself, the preservation of a tradition long held inviolable.

Hyrcanus, the high priest by grace of Antipater, hesitantly yielded to the pressure. In his feebleness he feared to incur Antipater's wrath if he took action against the Procurator's son. Nevertheless, Herod was called before the Sanhedrin. He appeared before the assembled elders in a purple mantle and surrounded by a retinue of soldiers. Herod was well aware that the Roman Governor of Syria had emphatically demanded his acquittal of the Sanhedrin. In the face of this support, the members of the high court did not dare to raise their charges. The situation was complicated by disunity: the aristocratic, conservative Sadducees among the priestly nobility, who accepted only the written law of the Torah, were engaged in a permanent struggle with the Pharisees, who emphasized the validity of oral tradition as well as of the Torah. The Pharisees also held the doctrine—originally foreign to Judaism—of the resurrection of the dead, and politically were opposed to the Hasmonaeans. One of these Pharisees, Shemaiah, chief of the Sanhedrin and one of its most learned members, rose and spoke boldly in these words:

"Everyone, whoever he is, who comes to be tried by this Sanhedrin, presents himself in a submissive manner, with hair disheveled and in a black mourning garment, to move us to compassion. But this admirable man Herod, who is accused of murder . . . stands here clothed in purple and with his hair finely trimmed, and with his armed men about him, so that if we condemn him by our law he may slay us, and by overbearing justice may himself escape death. Yet I do not make this complaint against Herod himself, for he is, to be sure, more concerned for himself than for the laws. But my complaint is against yourselves and your king [*i.e.*, Hyrcanus, the ethnarch] who gave him license to do so. But remember that God is great, and that this very man whom you are going to acquit for the sake of Hyrcanus will one day punish you and your king also."

The historian Josephus, who recalls this speech, goes on to say: "Shemaiah was not wrong in any part of this prediction; for when Herod had received the kingdom he slew all the members of this Sanhedrin and Hyrcanus himself. He spared Shemaiah alone."

After these intrepid words of Shemaiah, the Sanhedrin was prepared to pronounce the death sentence upon Herod. But Hyrcanus intervened, for he feared Antipater and the Romans. He postponed the sentencing and advised Herod to flee. Herod secretly departed from Jerusalem and sped to the safety of the Romans in Damascus. Instead of punishment, Herod received the post of commander in Celesyria, the fruitful lowlands between Lebanon and Antilebanon.

In 44 B.C. the terrifying news spread through all the Roman provinces that Julius Caesar was dead, assassinated in the Senate by his adversaries. Jewry, in Judea and in the Diaspora, heard the tale with alarm; and Judea felt the consequences sooner than all the other provinces. The death of Caesar brought an old tormentor to the country. The conspirator Cassius, fleeing from Rome, took command of the Syrian legions. Nine years before, he had suppressed the uprising in Galilee, and subsequently had enslaved thirty thousand of the rebels. Now he was back, haughty as ever and equally inhuman. He needed a great deal of money for the impending struggle with the men of Caesar's party who had taken command. Cassius issued Draconian orders to collect contributions for his war chest from all the provinces under his control, including Judea, which Caesar had explicitly exempted from Roman taxation.

Antipater and Herod, who were now dependent on Caesar's murderer to maintain their position, promptly obeyed the order. By the most ruthless means they collected seven hundred talents, or approximately eight hundred and seventy-five thousand dollars. Those who refused to pay the special tribute were reduced to slavery. Cassius had the inhabitants of four cities which could not raise their levies dragged off to the slave markets. The hatred these measures aroused led to a conspiracy against Antipater. In 43 B.C. he was poisoned at his own court.

The days of Cassius were numbered also. At the Battle of Philippi (42 B.C.) the army of the new Triumvirate (Octavian, Mark Antony, and Lepidus) defeated the troops of Cassius and Brutus. Mark Antony became master of the entire Roman Orient. Herod at once bestirred himself to win the favor of the new master. He had learned the technique from his father, and it was in his blood. Mark Antony soon came to appreciate how valuable this man was to him and to Rome—for Herod was willing to do anything for anyone who controlled the empire. Antony himself had had experience with the unruly inhabitants of Judea fifteen years before, and was glad for the proffered assistance. He appointed Herod and his elder brother Phasaelus tetrarchs; they had the power, but not the title, of kings. Hyrcanus remained ethnarch, but he was now more of a figure-head than ever. The sons of Antipater seemed well on their way to uncontested dominion over Judea.

At this point an unforeseen event obstructed their bold plans. At the beginning of 40 B.C. Syria was overrun by Rome's most dangerous enemies in the Orient, the Parthians. They could not have chosen a better moment. The peoples of the Near East, victims of unending oppression, were only waiting for the opportunity to throw off the yoke of Rome. Their lot had by no means improved under the rule of Mark Antony. Like Cassius before him, the Triumvir extracted enormous sums of money from the groaning populace. He needed it, not to prepare for war, but for his inconceivably extravagant festivals at the court of the Ptolemaic queen for whom he had developed a boundless passion—Cleopatra. Mark Antony had succumbed so completely to Caesar's one-time mistress that he could think of little else.

In the winter of 42–41 the Parthians, hailed by the subjugated peoples as liberators, had occupied Syria and Phoenicia up to the border of Judea. With the Parthians was Antigonus Mattathias, son of the last king of Judea, Aristobulus II. By promising these allies huge sums, he had obtained the support of a large corps of Parthian cavalry for the invasion of Judea. Aided by patriots, hailed by the overwhelming majority of the people, Antigonus took Jerusalem. Herod could only flee.

Antigonus dealt harshly with his uncle, Hyrcanus, who had betrayed the cause of the Hasmonaeans and, therefore, in the eyes of Antigonus, of Israel. Antigonus had his ears cut off—which meant that, by law, Hyrcanus could never again hold the office of high priest—and turned him over to the Parthians as a prisoner. Phasaelus, Herod's brother, who had also been captured, committed suicide.

Like his grandfather, Judah Aristobulus I, and his father, Antigonus called himself both king and high priest. Twenty-three years after Pompey's capture of Jerusalem and Hyrcanus' forced renunciation of the kingship, Judea had a king of the Hasmonaean dynasty once more. But that proved to be only a brief episode. For in the autumn of that same year, 40 B.C., Rome made a decision of fateful import to the future of the country.

HEROD, KING BY THE GRACE OF ROME

Herod had fled to Rome by a roundabout route. There he met Mark Antony, whom he had vainly sought in Egypt, and succeeded in winning the Triumvir over to the plan he had conceived out of ambition and the desire for vengeance upon the Hasmonaeans: that he, Herod, replace Antigonus as King of Judea. Octavian, too, was persuaded to accept this plan. In a solemn session of the Senate Herod was elected King of Judea and recognized as a vassal and ally of Rome. After the meeting of the Senate, Josephus writes, "Antony and Caesar [Octavian] went out of the Senate house, with Herod between them, and with the consuls and other magistrates before them, in order to offer sacrifices and to deposit their decrees in the capitol. Antony also feted Herod on the first day of his reign."

The Idumenean's dream was close to fulfillment. But his title, he knew, existed only on parchment for the present. His enemy Antigonus still held the actual throne in Jerusalem. Herod would have to wrest it from him by force of arms.

Herod returned to Judea in 39 B.C. with an army consisting of mercenaries and non-Jews. Unfortunately for the Hasmonaean dynasty, Antigonus did not know how to rally the power of the whole people, although their hearts were on his side. The war lasted for two years, both sides fighting with the utmost cruelty. Finally, Roman troops, which in the meantime had beaten back the Parthians, were free to come to the aid of Herod. In 37 B.C., after a siege of two and a half months, Jerusalem was compelled to yield to the hated Edomite. Herod's mercenaries waded in blood. King Antigonus was led away in chains. Herod, fearing that Antigonus might plead his cause successfully in Rome if he were allowed to live, bribed Antony with a large sum of money to have Antigonus killed.

The former king was scourged and beheaded in Antioch. "Mark Antony was the first among the Romans," remarks the Greek historian and geographer Strabo, "who executed a king with an ax. He did so because he thought there was no other way to convince the Jews that they must recognize Herod as king in Antigonus' stead. . . . He thought that a shameful execution would weaken the memory of Antigonus and diminish the hatred of the Jews for Herod."

With the violent end of Antigonus, the rule of the Hasmonaeans came to an end, after one hundred and three years. Surrounded by Roman legionaries, stained with the blood of the patriots, Herod began his rule exactly ten years after Caesar had appointed his father Procurator of Judea. The high priest had formerly headed the nation; later the high priest-king had come of a dynasty sprung from the people. Now for the first time a secular king assumed the rule of the land, one who was neither of a priestly family nor even a born Jew, but a foreigner of low birth, appointed by the hated Romans.

By cunning and violence, intrigue and murder, Herod had made his way to the throne. As king, he continued on the same course. His reign began with ruthless persecution of his enemies and possible rivals. Forty-five adherents of Antigonus from the foremost families were executed. His revenge did not stop at the members of the Sanhedrin before whom he had once stood as an accused murderer. The elders and teachers of the Law were banished from Judea. Herod spared only two: Shemaiah, the president of the Sanhedrin, who had opposed him during his trial, and Abtalion, the deputy of Shemaiah. These men had "advised the citizens to receive Herod when Jerusalem was besieged."

A constant prey to fear and suspicion, Herod did not rest during the following years until he had completely exterminated the Hasmonaean family. By flattery and promises he lured old Hyrcanus II, who was living with the Parthians, back to Jerusalem. He then had the eighty-two-year-old ethnarch executed for alleged high treason. He had his own seventeen-year-old brother-in-law, Aristobulus III, secretly drowned while bathing. Accused of the crime by his mother-in-law, Alexandra, who wrote to Cleopatra and begged her intercession, Herod was required to appear before Mark Antony to answer to the charges. But he propitiated the Roman by lavish presents, and was released unpunished. Thereafter his murderous temper knew no bounds. He executed his wife, Mariamne, whom he had loved passionately, and soon afterward her mother. Ultimately he killed his two sons by Mariamne.

Herod's position was once again seriously threatened when Mark Antony broke with Octavian and attempted to realize Cleopatra's dream of a kingdom in the East. On September 2, 31 B.C., Antony and Cleopatra were defeated on land and sea at Actium. Cleopatra fled to Egypt, followed by Mark Antony. A year later both died by their own hands.

Henceforth Octavian was sole ruler of the Roman world. Herod needed to ingratiate himself with the new master. Before Octavian had begun his victorious campaign that was to transform the kingdom of the Ptolemies into a Roman province, Herod appeared before him on the island of Rhodes. Submissively, he removed his royal diadem and delivered a skillful speech of justification. He made no attempt to conceal his loyalty to Antony. "If you judge me by my alacrity in serving Antony," he said, according to Josephus, "I admit that I cannot deny what I have done; but if you will only examine how I behave toward my benefactors in general, and what sort of friend I am, you will find that I will be the same to yourself." Octavian received Herod "very benevolently" and returned his diadem to him.

Octavian was to become the Emperor Caesar Augustus, and republican Rome an empire.

Confirmed as king and ally, certain of the favor of Augustus and thus finally secure in his position, Herod now made it his ambition to transform his country into a model Roman-Hellenistic kingdom. Resplendent palaces and pagan temples, monuments, gigantic arenas, and racecourses sprang up in the cities. Within a few years vast, pompous, extravagantly expensive building projects transformed the appearance of town and countryside. But Herod also built citadels at all strategic points within the kingdom.

Samaria was magnificently rebuilt. A new city, adorned by a temple in honor of Augustus, rose upon the ancient, battle-scarred hill where the capital of Israel's northern kingdom had once stood. Herod named the city Sebaste. Along with Jerusalem, the ancient Holy City of Jahweh and of the Jewish people, the country now had a "Holy City of Augustus."

South of Carmel, on the seacoast, the grandest of these city-building projects was undertaken. A new port with great man-made quays sprang up. A theater, an amphitheater, and a hippodrome completed the Greco-Roman pattern of public buildings. Here, too, a temple to Augustus was built. This new city was named Caesarea in honor of the Emperor.

Even Jerusalem was invaded by foreign architecture and foreign customs. Herod did not want his capital to lag behind other capital cities in magnificence. There was only one act of sacrilege he did not dare to commit; Herod forbore to build a pagan temple in the Holy City.

After the rebuilding of the old royal castle in the Temple square—which had been called Antonia in honor of Mark Antony—a fortified palace with gardens was erected near what is now the Jaffa Gate. Looming over this palace were three menacing towers. At enormous expense a complete revamping of the entire Temple area was undertaken. There had long been a Greek theater in Jerusalem, and a large circus outside the walls. Now Herod transplanted the hated pagan games into the heart of Israel's most sacred place.

Along with all these new buildings, along with the pomp and ceremony at King Herod's court, the noise of secular sports and the turmoil of games and shows had made their entry into the venerable Holy City. Through the narrow streets that for centuries had seen only bands of reverent pilgrims there now poured a colorful lot of athletes and gymnasts, jugglers and gladiators, musicians and acrobats. The clamor of the spectators in the amphitheater and the racecourse filled the air. Romans, Greeks, and hosts of other foreigners sat in the stands. Within sight of the Temple the mob howled at the cruel games of Rome, at the bloody battles of men against men and of men against beasts.

Herod showed not the slightest consideration for the feelings of the people whose king he called himself. He made no attempt to disguise his sympathy for the Greco-Roman way of life, and he reigned like the satrap of a foreign power. His sons, the future regents of Judea, were educated in Rome. He counted cultured Greeks among his friends and advisers. The historian Nicolaus Damascenus lived at his court as one of his intimates. Damascenus instructed Herod in philosophy and rhetoric. The office of treasurer was held by Ptolemaeus. Herod boasted openly of feeling closer to the Hellenes than the Jews.

Hatred seethed amid the populace, which had to bear the vast expenses of the court and the building projects and at the same time look on helplessly while its traditional rights were flouted and its religious feelings offended. The office of high priest had been reduced to an instrument of the King's will. The Sanhedrin had been replaced by a council of Herod's kinsmen and favorites that was blindly submissive to him. The country teemed with spies, and the slightest signs of rebellion were nipped in the bud. The Edomite whom the people wholeheartedly hated was protected by a bodyguard of mercenaries consisting of Thracians, Gauls, and Germans.

HILLEL AND THE LAW

Country and people seemed to have been relegated to their grim fate and to have lost their spiritual and intellectual leaders. The time had been when patriots and prophets had called upon the nation to throw off foreign yokes. But now there seemed to be none to cry out against injustice. The Pharisees lived withdrawn from public view, as though they had closed their eyes and ears to everything that was going on around them. They avoided the court; they did not take part in any government affairs. And since they thus refrained from all political activities, they also remained remote from any revolutionary stirrings. They knew how hopeless, how foolish any uprising would be.

Nevertheless, they were neither cowed nor inactive. Quietly, they had begun the great work of rescuing the spiritual goods of the Jewish nation. With premonitions that an inescapable catastrophe was descending upon Eretz Israel, they devoted all their strength to caring for, consolidating, and developing the Torah, the spiritual and secular Law.

A group of scholars became the nucleus of this project. Its intellectual leader was the head of the Sanhedrin who had long ago defied Herod, Shemaiah. He and his deputy Abtalion had earlier refused to take the oath of allegiance to Herod upon his accession, but they were not punished for this courageous act. Together with other Pharisee scholars they devoted themselves to elucidating problems of the Law on the basis of the Torah and the "oral tradition." After the death of the aged leaders, however, teachers of the Law took their place who were little suited for the duties of their important office. The newly revived Sanhedrin seemed incapable of fresh ideas and creative thinking. It began to seem as if the study of the Law had been extinguished in the Holy City where devotion to it had long been greatest. But at this juncture there appeared a man destined to develop the teachings and the life-style of the Pharisees to high perfection and to usher in a new era in the history of Judaism. This man was Hillel.

"When the Teaching was forgotten, Ezra came from Babylon and restored it," recounts a tradition from much later times, "and the Teaching was again forgotten when Hillel came from Babylonia to establish it anew." Another passage relates: "In the fortieth year of his life [about 35 B.C.] Hillel came from Babylonia to learn from the heads of the schools, Shemaiah and Abtalion. He was destitute and earned his bread as a water carrier. His daily earnings amounted to a tarpeik. Of this he gave half to the doorkeeper of the school and fed himself and his family with the other half. Once he had made no money and the doorkeeper therefore did not admit him. He therefore clambered up on the overhang of the roof and seated himself by the barred window, in order to hear the words of the living God from the mouths of Shemaiah and Abtalion. It was the even of a Sabbath, and snow had fallen. When morning came, Shemaiah said to Abtalion: 'My brother, our schoolhouse is ordinarily bright every day, and today it is dark. Perhaps there is a mist?' When they looked up, they saw a human figure at the window. They climbed up and found the snow three ells high upon the numbed Hillel. They cleared the cold blanket away from him, bathed and anointed him, and warmed him at the wood fire. All said: 'For this man's sake it is worth breaking the Sabbath.' "

Such a man was also worthy of becoming head of the Sanhedrin.

With Hillel, a new spirit entered the religious life. He laid the foundations for a wider, freer interpretation and application of the old laws. Hitherto the authoritarian strictness of the Law had dominated religious thinking. Hillel placed the emphasis upon a system of living interpretation of the Law in keeping with the requirements of the times and the changes in ways of living. In a dark and critical age this great scholar disclosed new ideas to the minds of his people; he led them into a sphere of intellectual activity that helped arm them against all dangers and preserve their great religious and philosophical contributions for the future.

Pre-eminently learned in the Scriptures, Hillel forged a noble and simple doctrine, which elevated love of neighbor above all else. Adapting the ancient Biblical injunction "love thy neighbour as thyself" (Leviticus 19:18), he answered a pagan who wanted to convert to Judaism and had asked for a quick exposition of the doctrine: "What you yourself do not like, do not do to another. That is the whole Law; everything else is only explanation of it. Go hence and learn it."

The Law and the rites were, for Hillel, only means to moral perfection.

At Hillel's side as his deputy in the Sanhedrin was another Pharisee whose memory has remained green: Shammai. In addition to the "House of Hillel" the Talmud speaks of the "House of Shammai." Seldom had two men of such opposing character joined in harmonious common work. Hillel was popular among the people because of his nature; he was regarded as a model of gentleness and modesty. Shammai was gruff and curt with his fellow men. The difference became almost proverbial; it has been memorialized in many anecdotes. Once a pagan came to Shammai and said: "I want to enter Judaism on condition that I can become high priest." He was rudely sent packing. Then he went to Hillel with the same proposal. Hillel gave him instruction and soon dissuaded him from insisting on his absurd condition.

Hillel continued his work until about A.D. 10. Regarded as a Nasi—the word originally meant "prince" but came to have the sense of "spiritual leader"—Hillel was the ancestor of the future dynasty of patriarchs in Eretz Israel. Many great men were to emerge from his school. But for the time being the great change Hillel inaugurated continued to be confined to the schools, limited to a small circle. For the political struggles of the time scarcely permitted the people, whose very existence was threatened, time to reflect. They had to turn their attention upon quite other matters than spiritual goods.

THE PROCURATOR AGAINST THE PATRIOTS

Until his last breath Herod had reigned with unremitting cruelty. Persecutions and oppressions went on without end. Not even the resplendent rebuilding of the Temple in Jerusalem reconciled the people to his rule, though this had been the tyrant's secret aim. Herod had lavished marble and gold upon his new Temple, so much so that no one could refrain from admiring it. An old proverb declares: "He who has not seen the Temple of Herod has never seen anything beautiful." But even upon the holy site Herod had not failed to offend the feelings of believers and to violate the Law. High above the main entrance of the Temple, where all images were strictly forbidden, he had installed a gigantic gilded eagle, symbol of the power of pagan Rome.

In 4 B.C. Herod died at the age of seventy, after a horrible and lingering illness. Only a few weeks before he had had two "most celebrated interpreters of the Jewish laws" burned alive for inciting their pupils to pull down and smash the blasphemous eagle; he had followed up that act by the execution of his own son Antipas. With great pomp his body was carried from Jericho to the fortress of Herodium, south of Jerusalem, and there interred.

On the very day of the funeral Ptolemaeus, the treasurer and keeper of the Great Seal, read the testament of the deceased king. He had appointed three of his younger sons as his successors: Archelaus as heir of the royal dignity for Judea; Herod Antipas as tetrarch for Galilee and Peraea, part of East Jordania; and Philip as tetrarch for the district east and northeast of the Sea of Galilee up to the Syrian frontier. Herod's family recognized Archelaus as king; the mercenary troops paid him homage; but disturbances broke out among the people at the news of the despot's passing. Instead of mourning for Herod, lamentations arose for his many innocent victims. The people demanded atonement. They demanded reforms—above all, reduction of the unbearable burden of taxes.

On the eve of the Passover there were tumultuous demonstrations in Jerusalem, which ended with a massacre. The troops, incited by Archelaus, rushed upon the crowds thronging to the Temple district. Some three thousand persons were slaughtered. On orders from the new king, the pilgrims had to leave Jerusalem; the Passover would not be celebrated this year.

From that moment on, Archelaus was no less hated by the people than his tyrannical father. The blood bath had proved that nothing but betrayal, repression, and killing could be expected from these Idumeans—certainly not respect for the laws of the patriarchs or freedom for Judea. In Jerusalem, and soon afterward throughout the country, all the bitterness and indignation that had been stored up during the lifetime of Herod erupted the moment Archelaus departed for Rome to be confirmed as King of Judea by Augustus.

Publius Quintilius Varus, the Roman legate in Syria who was responsible for the maintenance of peace and public order in neighboring Judea, transferred a legion to Jerusalem. At the same time the Roman knight Sabinus hastened to Jerusalem; Augustus had appointed him procurator to guard the interests of the empire during the absence of Archelaus. Sabinus moved into the palace close by the temple, promptly robbed the royal treasure chamber, and instituted a reign of terror.

At the time of the Feast of Weeks (Pentecost) there were great protest demonstrations by the pilgrims who had poured into Jerusalem. A massacre followed. Legionaries set fire to the halls surrounding the Temple; they next stormed the sanctuary itself and plundered its treasure—no less than four hundred talents passed into the hands of the Procurator. After this act of robbery, however, the Romans had to beat a hasty retreat and barricade themselves in the palace. Sabinus was no longer master of the situation; he was besieged.

Meanwhile in Galilee, long the breeding ground for rebels, Judah the Galilean, son of the patriot Ezekiah whom Herod had executed, gathered bands of insurrectionists around him. His men armed themselves by a sudden assault on a royal armory and began to wage bitter guerrilla warfare. In East Jordania, Simon, a former slave of Herod, gathered a band of freebooters and declared himself king; in Jericho and other places these rebels or bandits stormed the royal palaces and burned them down. A prodigiously strong shepherd named Athrongas—he, too, now adorned by a royal diadem—and his three brothers led their partisans against both Roman and royal troops; at Emmaus they defeated a Roman cohort. But there was no unified planning and no one man to organize and lead all these rebels. The patriotic insurrection in behalf of freedom developed more and more into disorderly banditry from which the peaceful population suffered more than those against whom the uprising had originally been directed.

When news of the sedition reached Varus, he led two legions in forced marches from Antioch. In Galilee he had the city of Sepphoris burned down and the inhabitants, most of them adherents of Judah ben Ezekiah, sold as slaves. Emmaus, too, went up in flames. But it was only after the army of Varus appeared at the gates of Jerusalem that the Jews abandoned the siege of Sabinus' legion, which until then had been shut up in the palace.

Varus ordered his troops to comb through the entire country. Some two thousand freedom fighters fell into the hands of the Romans. The popular insurrection ended with cruel executions: On orders from Varus, all the prisoners were crucified.

Month after month, meanwhile, the heirs of Herod waited impatiently in Rome for Augustus to determine the succession to the throne. Herod Antipas and Philip had soon followed Archelaus to the capital. But Augustus took his time. He waited until the uprising had been repressed and an embassy dispatched by the people had arrived from Jerusalem— joyfully greeted by the Jewish community of Rome, which at this time numbered some eight thousand people. Then the Emperor convoked an assembly in the new temple of Apollo on the Palatine. Everyone was given a chance to speak, and the Emperor listened attentively to all. The representatives of the people expressed their bitter complaints, described the repression of every freedom under the tyrannies of Herod and Archelaus, and pleaded with the Emperor to spare them any such rule in the future. It would be best for Judea, they urged, if it were accorded the rights of an autonomous country with a republican constitution under a Roman procurator.

Several days passed before Augustus pronounced his decision. On the whole, he confirmed Herod's testament. Archelaus received Judea, Samaria, and Idumea, but was recognized only as ethnarch, not as king. No mention was made of the proposals advocated by the representatives of the people.

Archelaus' reign was destined to be only a brief interval, however. For despite the Emperor's strict command that he treat his subjects mildly, he ruled as ruthlessly as his father. Within a few years another embassy of desperate Judeans lodged complaints in Rome once more. Whereupon the Emperor relieved Archelaus of his post and in A.D. 6 banished him to Gaul.

Judea was finally incorporated into the province of Syria and made subject to a largely independent governor, or "procurator." Only Galilee-Peraea and the territories along the upper Jordan remained under the other sons of Herod, Herod Antipas and Philip. Just seven decades after

Pompey had taken Jerusalem, Rome ruled directly in the heart of Eretz Israel.

Caesarea, Herod's new port, became the official seat of the Roman procurator and the headquarters of the Roman army. A permanent Roman garrison moved into the Tower of Antonia on the Temple Mount; from there it could supervise what went on in the sanctuary. Of Judea's one-time autonomy only the office of high priest and the revived Sanhedrin were left. All higher judiciary functions now lay in the procurator's hands. He alone was empowered to impose a death sentence, and all important decisions of the Sanhedrin required the consent of Rome. The procurator was also responsible for the collection of the staggering taxes and tolls. Judea's independent political life had been destroyed. Religious life alone remained untouched.

Under Coponius, Augustus' first procurator, the first popular disturbances began. The immediate cause was the census that had been ordered for purposes of taxation; it included not only a careful count of heads, but also an estimate of wealth. The Jews resolutely opposed this census, which was a symbol of serfdom to them. With considerable difficulty the high priest Joazar and the more moderate elements in the country succeeded in calming the agitation and persuading the people to bow to the measures ordered from Rome. But the peace did not last long. The procurators became more high-handed; anger at the Roman occupation forces spread throughout the country, and a fanatical movement dedicated to active resistance swiftly won the upper hand.

The impulse to rebellion did not arise among the scholars, those "scribes" who dedicated their lives solely to studying and interpreting the Torah. The moderate Pharisees lived in the hope of strengthening their people for the difficult times ahead by enjoining them to adhere strictly to the faith of their fathers and to wait patiently for the dawn of a better future. Neither the school of Hillel, which taught patience and submission, nor the somewhat sterner school of Shammai preached a word that might have provoked active resistance. Passive resistance, however, seemed advisable to the moderate Pharisees.

A group of extreme patriots, the Zealots, began engaging in revolutionary activity. Led by Judah ben Ezekiah of Galilee, who had escaped Varus' police and informers, and by the radical Pharisee Zadok, they conspired to wage war upon the Roman oppressor. They wanted to "save the Law and spare Judaism the shame of renouncing God in order to serve the heathen." Founded as a radical resistance party at the moment Rome was beginning its direct rule over Judea and had ordered the census, the small group grew steadily in strength as the bitterness mounted. Thousands and tens of thousands joined the Zealots. Members of the movement scattered through the country preaching and stirring up unrest, until they had fomented a popular uprising against Rome: for freedom of religion, freedom from oppression, freedom for the nation.

Along with the dark clouds that were gathering above Judea, serious trials, repressions, and persecutions were also looming for the Jews of the Diaspora. They, too, were to share in the fate of the homeland.

"THE DISPERSED FROM JUDAH"

By this time the Jewish communities were scattered widely. "They have found entrance into all states," the geographer Strabo wrote. "It is not easy to find any region in the whole world where this people has not been accepted, and where it has not assumed a leading position." What the last prophet of the Old Testament, Malachi, in the days of Ezra, had foreseen, had long since become a reality: "For from the rising of the sun even unto the going down of the same My name is great among the nations; and in every place offerings are presented unto My name, even pure oblations; for My name is great among the nations, says the Lord of hosts" (Malachi 1:11).

Knowledge of the lives and tribulations of these dispersed Jews has been almost entirely lost. The book of their history has never been written. Only fragments of documents in all the languages of the ancient world retail single incidents, episodes, which reflect the destinies of those who had been separated from the mother country, the "dispersed of Judah," who are so frequently mentioned by the prophets from Isaiah on. Thousands of them were carried away as prisoners of war, thousands upon thousands led into exile by the conquerors and generals of the ancient Orient, or sold as slaves. They lived as strangers, most of them in humble and humiliating circumstances, though some of them rose to prosperity. Always, however, they were small islands in the midst of peoples of different customs and pagan religions.

Many of them were lost forever. But the majority, those who lived in communities, survived the centuries. A close bond held them together. For even thousands of miles from the land of Israel their eyes continued to be directed toward their native soil. In their religion, in their longings and hopes, Jerusalem remained their Holy City. The living tie to the land of their fathers was never broken. From far and near messengers of the Diaspora hastened to the city of David when difficult questions of interpretation of the Law were involved. From Jerusalem the festival calendar, specifying the dates of the High Holy Days, was received every year. And year after year bands of pilgrims traveled over the long caravan routes to Jerusalem; year after year contributions for the Temple arrived from the scattered communities, in uncertain times guarded by heavily armed men. No other people has ever provided such examples of inseparable attachment throughout long eras of its history.

For more than half a millennium numerous Jewish communities lived in the lands of the Nile. Their first traces are lost in the dim past when the pharaohs of the Middle Kingdom were rulers of Egypt. Sporadically, almost casually, the Bible mentions them. Jeroboam, the "warrior of the people," fled to Egypt to Pharaoh Shishak (Shoshenk I), where he remained until the death of King Solomon and then became King of the northern Kingdom of Israel. Pharaoh Necho, after his victory over King Josiah on the plain of Megiddo, took hosts of prisoners back to Egypt with him, and soon afterward removed Josiah's son Jehoahaz to Egypt. And when the prophet Jeremiah, fleeing with hordes of refugees from the Babylonian destruction of Temple and Holy City, set foot on the soil of Egypt, he addressed his words to "all the Jews that dwelt in the land of Egypt, that dwelt at Migdol, and at Tahpanhes, and at Noph, and in the country of Pathros . . ." (Jeremiah 44:1). Some of these "captains of the army" under Johanan ben Koreah founded a Jewish military colony deep in the southern part of the land of the pharaohs, on the island of Elephantine, near present-day Assuan. The Pharaoh entrusted them with the task of guarding the southern boundary of Egypt. With them were men who established rural settlements and built their own temple to the Lord so that they could celebrate the traditional festivals of Israel. As everywhere else in the world of the time, the Jews in Egypt enjoyed the reputation of being brave soldiers, capable farmers, cattle breeders, and artisans, as well as reliable subjects.

Papyri found in Elephantine between 1904 and 1906 testify to lively contacts between the Jews of the Egyptian Diaspora and the authorities in Jerusalem. A copy of a letter to High Priest Johanan has been preserved, as well as a communication indicating that the seven-day Passover festival was celebrated in the Egyptian colony. When the Persians succeeded the Babylonians as rulers of the Near East, and extended their empire all the way to the Nile, an unknown prophet wrote: "In that day there shall be five cities in the land of Egypt that speak the language of Canaan, and swear to the Lord of hosts. . . . In that day shall there be an altar to the Lord in the midst of the land of Egypt, and a pillar at the border thereof to the Lord" (Isaiah 19:18–19).

In the Ptolemaic period the metropolis that Alexander the Great had founded on the Nile became the most important center of Jewish life in Egypt. Two of the five quarters of Alexandria were inhabited by Jews; they formed a gigantic community, which toward the beginning of the Christian era contained nearly one hundred thousand people. Some estimates go as high as three or even five hundred thousand. Alexandria itself at that time was second only to Rome as a great focal point of the civilized world. The Jews of Alexandria enjoyed full civil rights and were employed in all crafts. Like their Greek fellow citizens they engaged in commerce and served in the administration as well as in the army. Tradition has it that Onias, the son of the high priest Onias III, and Dositheus, both of whom had fled to Egypt from Syrian oppression, rose to be commanders of the Egyptian army.

At the head of the Jews of Egypt was an ethnarch who, Strabo relates, "directs their community affairs, pronounces justice, and confirms their contracts as if he were the real ruler of a state." The Jews of Egypt held public worship in the synagogues, of which there were a large number in their densely populated quarters of Alexandria. The main synagogue must have been their pride, however, and one of the main sights of the city. "He who has not seen the synagogue of Alexandria with its double colonnade has not seen the glory of Israel. . . . Seventy-one golden seats stood there, for that many elders. In the middle was a wooden platform on which stood the chasan [prayer leader] of the synagogue, waving with a cloth when the congregation had to cry 'Amen,' and at the signal all would with one voice cry, 'Amen.' And the people sat there not in disorder, but in orderly rows: the goldsmiths sitting by themselves, the silversmiths by themselves, then the blacksmiths, then the miners, then the weavers. . . ."

Alexandria, with its famous library and its academies, had become the meeting place of the best minds of the Greek-speaking world. In this new "Athens of the East" the Jews, too, made significant contributions to intellectual and cultural creativity from the third century B.C. onward. A new Jewish literature, departing entirely from tradition, was born during this period. Its purpose, as Cecil Roth has pointed out, was to familiarize the Hellenistic Jews with their own national culture and to persuade pagan critics of the superiority, or at least of the rationality, of Judaism. Historians composed accounts of the kings of Judea; poets wrote dramas or epics on Biblical subjects; archaeologists studied the antiquities of the Hebrews; apologists defended their people against the anti-Semites of the age; philosophers studied the Mosaic law and attempted to demonstrate that it was not incompatible with "modern" Greek culture, or even that it anticipated that culture.

Fragments of manuscripts and ancient parchments mention the works of Jewish writers who contributed vigorously to Alexandrian literary life. Among them were Aristobulus, the teacher of Ptolemy Philometor, who wrote a commentary on the Pentateuch, which he dedicated to the King; Ezekielus, the first Jewish dramatist; Theodore, the author of a heroic poem on the rape of Diana; and Philo the Elder. But more important, especially for the future, than the works of all these writers was another enterprise that first saw the light in Alexandria.

The Jews living in the foreign environment of Egypt had all too quickly forgotten their mother tongue. At the services in the synagogue they could no longer follow the divine Word. Because of this inevitable consequence of exile, the determination arose in Alexandria to translate the Hebrew Scriptures. About 250 B.C. the Torah was translated into Greek. Thus was created the famous Septuagint—whose existence was to have immeasurable consequences for the entire world. For the first time in history the Holy Book had left the closed circle of the people of Israel; for the first time non-Jews, literate Greeks, and, later, Romans as well could become acquainted with the doctrines of Judaism. More than three centuries before the missionary journeys of Paul, the Septuagint provided the pagan world with a profound insight into the religious life of the people of Israel and the seemingly incomprehensible faith in a single invisible God.

The flourishing Jewish colony of Egypt also spread into the neighboring countries of North Africa. Large independent communities formed in the land of Cyrene (present-day eastern Libya), especially in the cities of Cyrene and Berenice. The latter was regarded as a virtual Jewish city-state. The Jews in Berenice were confirmed in their internal autonomy by Emperor Augustus, who also confirmed their right to send donations to the Temple in Jerusalem.

The Diaspora in Syria was also numerous and important, especially in Asia Minor. Since the time of the Seleucids there had been Jewish communities in the city-states of Miletus and Ephesus; there were others in Sardis and Halicarnassus, and in the Ionian islands off the coasts of Asia Minor. Still more sprang up when independent small states arose in Asia Minor.

What high esteem the Jews of that time enjoyed for their military virtues is apparent from a letter written in about 200 B.C. by the Seleucid King Antiochus III (the Great) to his satrap in Lydia. "I have resolved," he declared, "to bring two thousand Jewish families from Mesopotamia and Babylonia in order to transfer them to the most important sites and garrisons. . . . For my forefathers have well tried their loyalty and their exemplary obedience." Shortly afterward, with the uprising in Judea against Antiochus Epiphanes, prisoners from Israel were taken to Syria and

Asia Minor, as is evidenced by Greek inscriptions of the period bearing the names of Jewish slaves and freedmen. And after Pompey's victory Jews from the Diaspora also moved into Greece, where they swiftly established themselves, for by now Greek was the common language of the entire eastern Mediterranean. Thus by the first century B.C. there were already synagogues in Athens and Corinth, in Thessalonica and Philippi. First settlements of Jews were beginning along the Black Sea, and at the same time Jewish communities were springing up in Italy, formed by freed or ransomed slaves and by merchants who had come from Egypt and Greece, chiefly in connection with the grain trade.

The history of the ancient Jewish communities in Mesopotamia remains dark for centuries. After the time of Ezra, when the empire of the Persian kings extended from the Indus to the Nile, virtually all news from such communities had ceased. They had hailed and faithfully served Cyrus, their liberator, and his successors, and in similar fashion they acknowledged Alexander after he had destroyed the Persian power. They remained obedient subjects who asked nothing but religious freedom. Any interference with their religion, however, inevitably led to opposition. For religion they were prepared to die, as Alexander discovered when he attempted to compel the Jews of Babylon, by severe threats, to take part in the rebuilding of the destroyed temple to Baal.

The communities of Babylonia lived in comparative peace for a very long time, far from the battles raging in the Mediterranean lands, where the wars among the successor states of the Alexandrian empire were followed by Roman wars and civil wars that affected almost all the peoples of the known world. Babylonia never entered the Roman sphere of hegemony; the Euphrates constituted the boundary of Roman influence. Nevertheless, the close ties between the Jews of Babylonia and Jerusalem continued even after the Roman conquest of Judea. As always, pilgrims made their way to Jerusalem to celebrate the great festivals there. They were allowed to pass freely by the border guards of the Parthians and the Romans. From Nehardea and Nisibis, the two chief Jewish communities in the Land of the Two Rivers, contributions for the Temple continued to flow to Jerusalem.

It was not until the lifetime of Herod, however, that Babylonia, the "Mother of the Diaspora," suddenly re-entered the mainstream of Jewish history. The Parthian army that had advanced into Syria and Judea in 40 B.C. had a number of Jewish detachments, and the deposed Hyrcanus II, whom the Parthians carried off to Babylonia, was held in high honor by the Jews there. During the reign of Herod a five-hundred-man band of Jewish cavalrymen from Babylonia arrived suddenly in Judea. King Herod assigned them Bathyra in East Jordania as their place of residence.

At his command they assumed the task of escorting pilgrims, who were often imperiled by robbers on the long caravan trails from the Euphrates. But aside from these episodes, there is little information. Babylonia remained remote, and only after many years was the Diaspora community there to rise to great importance.

FIRST RELIGIOUS PERSECUTION IN ROME

In the days of Emperor Tiberius, whom Augustus had appointed his heir, the first persecution of Jews began in the heart of the empire. Repressive measures, whose aim was actually to extirpate the obscure idolatries that had reached Rome from the Orient, were turned against the many thousands of Jews living by the Tiber, whose freedom to practice their religion was in fact sanctioned by the Roman state.

Soon after the Jewish community had first become established in Rome, innumerable other foreign cults had begun trickling into the city, much to the displeasure of the priests and augurs, who resented infringements upon the official state religion. The notorious cult of Cybele had spread with great rapidity, as had the rites of Egyptian mysteries and the orgiastic religions of Asia Minor. There was even a temple to Isis in the city on the Tiber, a place where, a contemporary complained, "obscenities go on incessantly." Many Roman women began, as Suetonius irritably noted, to profess an attachment to "Egyptian and Jewish rites." But the Jewish community suffered from these developments largely because of an unfortunate chain of circumstances.

Emperor Augustus had always maintained a benevolent attitude toward the Jews, and had explicitly confirmed their rights in an edict which has been preserved: "Caesar Augustus, high priest and tribune of the people, ordains thus: Since the nation of the Jews have been found grateful to the Roman people, not only in this time but in times past also, and chiefly in the time of my father,* Caesar, when Hyrcanus was high priest, it has seemed good to me . . . that the Jews have liberty to make and use their own customs, according to the laws of their forefathers . . . and that their sacred money be not touched, but be sent to Jerusalem." Augustus even ordered sacrifices for the Jews, and his wife, Livia, sent sacred gifts to the Temple.

But Tiberius, the new master of the world, did not like the Jews. He

* Augustus was actually only an adopted son of Julius Caesar.

detested Judaism, which seemed to him, as to most Romans, quite incomprehensible. Moreover, it differed from other religions in claiming, it was said, to be superior to all others. Undoubtedly a personal experience had also contributed decisively to the Emperor's attitude. As chance would have it, one of the most malignant enemies of the Jews had ingratiated himself into Tiberius' favor. This was the writer Apion, a Hellene who had come from Alexandria, where for some time infamous lies and charges against everything Jewish had become the fashion. To be sure, in that vast city on the Nile delta, Greeks and Jews had been colliding, intellectually and economically, since the time of the first Ptolemies. Disputes had raged between Greek philosophers and Jewish thinkers. Along with the Septuagint, Jewish philosophical writers were producing works that aroused astonishment and admiration in the cultivated Greek-speaking world, which meant considerable circles in Rome, as well as in Athens, Corinth, and Antioch. But of course the masses of the people in Alexandria knew nothing of these matters.

The country's native Egyptians and the Greeks who had been settled by Alexander and the subsequent Ptolemaic kings in the brilliant Hellenic city that Alexandria became were actuated by altogether different matters —problems that flowed out of the vigorous economic life of the city. The Nile metropolis had become the greatest transfer port in the empire. And Egyptians and Greeks encountered the "foreigners" of the Jewish quarters in shipping and shipbuilding, in importing and exporting, in freight traffic up and down the Nile, and in the crafts, in government service, and in the army. Many of these Greeks and Egyptians objected to the fact that the Jews had been recognized as citizens of the capital with the same rights as "natives"; and they waxed indignant over the competition of these talented and competent "foreigners." The harsh struggle for existence in daily life inevitably gave rise to anger and envy. Envy turned to hatred of the strangers—among whom were families who had been settled in Alexandria far longer than many Greeks.

It is scarcely surprising that this hostile mood was reflected in writings whose intention was to undermine the prestige of Jewish citizens, to whip up scorn and provoke discrimination against them. The pamphlets soon enjoyed a wide and receptive readership. Apion, a vain and ambitious man, was among the authors of such pamphlets. In speeches and writings, especially in his *Egyptian History,* he fomented popular hatred of the Jews. No matter how preposterous his fables—and some of them were fantastic indeed—they were believed. For Apion tricked out his atrocity stories as "historical traditions," allegedly drawn from ancient sources. One of these "sources" was a piece of hate literature that had been com-

posed by the Egyptian priest Manetho in the first half of the third century
B.C., filled with slander against Jews and their religion.

The ancient Israelites, Apion maintained, had falsified their own history.
In fact, during their stay in Egypt they had actually been a tribe of
lepers, condemned by Pharaoh Amenophes to forced labor in the quarries.
Moses, in reality an apostate Egyptian priest named Osarsis, placed himself at the head of these lepers, found allies in the shepherd tribe of
Hyksos, and defeated the Pharaoh. Thus he had reigned over Egypt for
a time, until at last the Egyptian people drove the lepers out of the land.
From Osarsis, according to Apion, had come those laws of the Jews which
held that the gods of the Egyptians were no longer to be honored and
their sacred animals were to be slaughtered.

The Temple in Jerusalem, Apion reported, contained a gilded ass's
head. This the Jews had worshiped as late as the lifetime of Antiochus
Epiphanes. And when they ate unleavened bread in the spring, they
were commemorating the bread they had originally fashioned out of
stolen loaves.

But the most monstrous of Apion's tales in his *Aigyptiaka*—which was
subsequently echoed by Greek and Roman historians and turns up in
Tacitus, Plutarch, and Juvenal—was the following "revelation":

Every year the Jews seized a Greek, fattened him in their temple, and
carried him off to the woods, where he was put to death, to the accompani-
ment of special rites and wicked curses against the Greeks. Here was the
full-blown story of ritual murder, that most repulsive of all slanders, which
so often in the Middle Ages and well into modern times provided the
wretched pretext for ferocious persecutions of the descendants of the people of Israel.

Such was the literary conscience of the man whose tales found eager
auditors in aristocratic circles of Athens and at the court in Rome, where
his imperial patron, Tiberius, called him *cymbalum mundi*—the bell of
the world. This was the Roman world's reliable "informant" on the Jews.

So much for the background of the persecutions.

Two scandals in Rome, which provided ample material for society gossip,
became the grounds for the Emperor's taking harsh anti-Jewish measures
—the first in the Roman Empire outside of Judea.

The first scandal concerned Paulina, a Roman matron of eminent family
who had secretly become a follower of the cult of Isis. She had rejected
the advances of a young man named Decius Mundus, who was infatuated
with her. The disappointed lover succeeded in bribing the Egyptian priests
to inform Paulina that the god Anubis wished to spend a night with her in
his temple—as the Isis cult prescribed. Flattered by this high honor, the

Roman woman obtained her husband's consent. On the appointed night she went to the temple of Isis and in total darkness stayed with her "god" until the next morning.

Mundus, meeting Paulina three days later, could not forbear from revealing the successful trick to her. Paulina, outraged, informed her husband of the shameful trick that had been played on her, and demanded that he use his influence to obtain redress. Thus the story came to the attention of the Roman authorities.

The other story was of a different cast, no more than a commonplace embezzlement that would scarcely have become a sensation if it had not involved another woman of note. Fulvia, the wife of Senator Saturninus, had become a convert to Judaism and presented valuable gifts to the Temple in Jerusalem. Four Jews to whom these gifts had been entrusted turned out to be thieves; they had simply kept the gold and the precious objects for themselves.

Such scandals were grist to the mills of Sejanus, commander of the Praetorian Guard. As Tiberius' adviser he was utilizing every opportunity to intensify the dislike Tiberius had already formed toward Jews and Orientals in general. He therefore reported both incidents to Tiberius, who was devoting himself to his vices on the island of Capri. Tiberius, infuriated by these "Oriental" deceptions, ordered the guilty priests crucified, the temple of Isis demolished, and the statue of Isis thrown into the Tiber. (The young man who had played the god Anubis was merely banished; Tiberius was himself enough of a lecher to be tolerant toward one who had acted out of passion.) At the same time he proposed to the Roman Senate that all Jews and proselytes be expelled from Rome. Four thousand Jews were deported to Sardinia, where they had to contend with the robber bands that plagued the island. The persecutions threatened to extend throughout Italy. Jews who had been conscripted into the army were forced to assume duties or even to fight on the Sabbath and on their holidays; but the Jewish soldiers refused to obey, preferring to accept harsh punishments instead. As a final penalty, the synagogue in Rome was ordered stripped of the cult utensils, but after the death of the anti-Jewish Sejanus the Emperor rescinded this order.

This was the first persecution of the Jews in Rome, and, in fact, anywhere in the Occident—the first of innumerable others.

PONTIUS PILATE

"Now Pilate was sent as procurator into Judea by Tiberius." Thus Josephus begins his account of the new governor of Judea. The brutal and well-nigh all-powerful Sejanus had made this appointment. "Inflexible in character and ruthlessly harsh," Philo of Alexandria describes Pontius Pilate, a man characterized by "corruptibility, robbery, violence, insults, abuse, constant executions without judgment, and boundless cruelty." Pilate must have gone to Judea with the deliberate intention of provoking the people.

As soon as he had become acquainted with Jewish customs, he found an effective means of doing so. One night he had troops from Caesarea secretly bring ensigns bearing pictures of the Emperor into Jerusalem. Hitherto the Romans had respected the Jews' abhorrence of images, which were regarded by them as a forbidden deification of men. Never before had Roman standards with the imperial portrait been displayed in the city of David. Not even Herod and his sons had dared to infringe upon the Torah's strict prohibition of "idolatry."

Word of this mockery of the Law spread rapidly through the populace. Day had barely dawned when agitated crowds began to form. Bands of Jews also began pouring out of Jerusalem toward Caesarea. For five days and nights they lay prostrate before the Procurator's palace, pleading with him to rescind the order. Pilate remained obdurate. Finally, he had the petitioners surrounded with heavily armed men and threatened to have them cut down, one and all, if they did not cease their disturbance and go quietly home.

The reaction of the people took him by surprise. When they saw the Roman soldiers advancing upon them with naked swords, they threw themselves instantly upon the ground and bared their necks, crying that they would sooner suffer death than see their laws transgressed. Pilate shrank from a massacre; he yielded, and had the imperial ensigns brought back to Caesarea.

Pilate once again outraged the people by taking money from the Temple treasury for the building of an aqueduct. One day, when the Procurator had come to Jerusalem, the angry populace surrounded his judgment seat and protested this theft of the sacred money, even for so good a cause. Pilate was prepared. Warned by informers, he had sent soldiers among the crowd, disguised in ordinary dress. At a signal from him, the Romans produced whips and sticks from under their garments. In the bloody tumult that followed, many Jews were badly injured and some killed.

Pilate's reign of terror continued until after the fall of his patron, Sejanus. Tiberius then recalled the Procurator. Pilate was transferred to Vienna (present-day Vienne in southern France), where, it is said, he committed suicide.

At the time that Pontius Pilate was Governor in Judea there lived and worked in Galilee a pious Jew who, like Hillel, regarded love of neighbor as the supreme commandment: Rabbi Josuah, or Jesus. His teachings, spread by his disciples among the pagans, generated the first of the daughter religions that were to spring from Judaism: Christianity. And the Christians were to influence the future destinies of the Jews as did no other power on earth.

"We are confronted with two facts," writes Dr. Joseph Klausner, Professor at the Hebrew University in Jerusalem. "First, that Jesus was born a Jew, lived and died in the midst of Israel, and was in every respect a Jew; but secondly, that his disciples and even more their disciples turned away from Israel, or, rather, that the overwhelming majority of the Jews did not accept the doctrine of Jesus, opposed him throughout his life, and did not become Christian even when the whole world was drawing closer and closer to Christianity."

No contemporary secular source and none of the Jewish traditions of those days make any reference to the appearance and the preaching of Jesus. His name is only mentioned many decades later by Josephus, Tacitus, and Suetonius, when they speak of the primitive Christian community.* "It might be expected," Professor Klausner observes, "that the earliest reports on Jesus and his teachings would be found in the Talmud. For Jesus lived at the time in which the schools of Hillel and Shammai were flourishing, and in which the cornerstone had already been laid for the magnificent religious and literary structure we call the Talmud. But in fact that is not the case. The number of passages in the Talmud—we are speaking only of the old editions or manuscripts that were not subject to Christian censorship—on Jesus and his doctrine is very small, and even these few passages are without any special historical character since they are rather polemics . . . than objective contributions of historical value. . . . In an age so full of disturbances because of the rule of the House of Herod and the Roman procurators, the appearance of Jesus constituted so unimportant an event that the contemporaries paid no attention to it." By the time Christianity had spread mightily and attained world-wide influence, "the time in which Jesus had lived was too remote for the Talmud sages to

---

* The mention in Josephus is quite possibly a later interpolation.

Model of Herod's reconstruction of the Temple in Jerusalem. The foundations of the massive wall surrounding the forecourts remain to this day in the Wailing Wall.

Detail from the Arch of Titus in Rome, showing the sacred utensils from the Temple in Jerusalem being borne in a Roman triumph. Enslaved Jews in fetters can be seen between laurel-wreathed Romans.

ABOVE: Excavated ruins of the synagogue in Capernaum on the Sea of Galilee, from A.D. 200

LEFT: Catacombs of Bet-Shearim, near Haifa, called the Tomb of the Sanhedrin, burial place of important teachers of the Law of the second century A.D., including Judah ha-Nasi, editor of the Mishnah

A Radanite, one of the Jewish merchants who established regular commerce between France and China and India four hundred years before Marco Polo's travels. A terracotta of the Tang dynasty (618-907).

Model of the Jewish bath in Speyer, built c. 1100. A ritual bath (mikveh) has been a feature of every Jewish community from ancient times. The tub must contain at least 210 gallons and be filled only with "living" water, that is, spring or river water or collected rain water.

Synagogue in Worms, built *c*. 1180, destroyed in 1938, restored 1958-1960

Interior of Worms synagogue

Interior of a former synagogue in Córdoba, where an important Jewish community flourished from the eighth through the fifteenth centuries. In the tenth century the Jewish foreign minister of Caliph Abd er-Rahman III helped create the first Talmudic academy on Spanish soil here.

BELOW, LEFT: Interior of a former synagogue in Toledo, now María la Blanca Church
RIGHT: Wall ornamentation of an old synagogue in Toledo, now called El Tránsito

Portrait, with signature, of
Maimonides, outstanding Jewish
philosopher of the Middle Ages

Jewish hats in Europe, thirteenth
century: (1) England, (2) and
(3) France, (4), (5) and (6)
Germany, (7) Holland, (8) Italy

Jews of Prague wearing Jewish
badges (fifteenth century)

A page from the Pesach Haggada (book of popular tales), from which the head of the household reads aloud at the Passover feast. Manuscript of Israel ben Rabbi Meïr of Heidelberg, early fifteenth century.

The Manesse manuscript of twelve aphoristic poems in Middle High German, showing Süsskind von Trimberg, the only known Jewish minnesinger, c. 1250-1300

"Jews' bodkin" from the trial of
the Passau Jews in 1447 for
alleged desecration of the host

Oaths taken by Jews were often
accompanied by degrading
ceremonies in German law courts
of the Middle Ages. The Jew
(kneeling, with patch on left
arm) being sworn in here puts his
hand on a Hebrew Bible open
to Exodus 20:7 ("Thou shalt not
take the name of the Lord thy
God in vain . . ."). From Ulrich
Tengler's *Laienspiegel*
(Augsburg, 1509).

unravel in their true form the historical events that centered around the Christian Messiah. They contented themselves with recording the popular tales that were circulating about him and his life."

Pilgrims from the distant banks of the Tigris and the Euphrates were, in these early days of the Roman Empire, bringing strange news to Jerusalem—accounts of the founding of a Jewish republic in the heart of Babylonia, now under the rule of the Parthians.

Two young brothers, Asinai and Anilai of Nehardea, one of the chief Jewish cities in Babylonia, had been shamefully punished by the owner of a workshop where they were employed as weavers. The brothers fled, and gathered around themselves a sizable band of other disgruntled young men who under their command began attacking and pillaging the cities and villages of the region inhabited by people of other religions. Their forces grew so strong that they were able to defeat the troops sent against them by the Parthian King's satrap, who attacked on the Sabbath, thinking the Jews would not defend themselves.

Artabanus III, King of the Parthians, heard of these bold soldiers, and because he himself was involved in difficulties with rebellious satraps he decided to use the services of the heroic pair, rather than waste his substance in fighting them. He guaranteed them safe-conduct, received them in audience, and concluded an alliance with them. The brothers were given command over an entire province and henceforth ruled over a Jewish republic as vassals of the Parthian King, who required of them only a regular tribute. They built fortresses and with their Jewish troops defended the inhabitants of the countryside around Nehardea during a period of great unrest.

Their rule lasted fifteen years, until A.D. 42. Then it collapsed—because of a heathen woman. One day Anilai saw the beautiful wife of a Parthian general and fell in love with her. He killed her husband in single combat and married her. So great was his love for her that he could not bring himself to forbid her the idolatrous worship to which she was attached, and so a pagan prayed to her foreign gods in the house of a Jewish princeling. This violation of their laws angered the soldiers; they pressed Asinai to urge his brother to relinquish his wife, or to forbid her her idolatry. Soon after the quarrel, Asinai died; the pagan woman had secretly poisoned her husband's brother.

Anilai did not long survive him. He fell in battle with a Parthian army led by a Parthian general whom he had once taken prisoner and humiliated, forcing him to ride naked on an ass. Anilai's army was defeated and scattered to the four winds.

After the collapse of this Jewish republic the Babylonians unleashed a massacre in many of the cities and villages inhabited by Jews. A remnant fled to the city of Seleucia on the Tigris. But there Syrians and Greeks united against the strangers, and killed thousands of them. Even in Ctesiphon, the capital of the Parthian kingdom, where many had taken refuge, persecutions began, and once more they had to flee. They found peace at last in the cities that had been the centers of their old communities, Nehardea and Nisibis.

AGRIPPA, LAST KING OF JUDEA

Once more the affairs of Judea appeared to be taking a turn for the better. Once again the country was freed of the harsh government of Roman procurators—for a few years.

After the death—or, perhaps, murder—of Tiberius, Judea once more acquired a king of her own: Julius Agrippa, a grandson of Herod and his Hasmonaean wife, Mariamne. Agrippa's appointment was among the first acts of the new Emperor, Gaius Caligula. Agrippa, who had been in prison, was released immediately after Tiberius' death. The new Emperor showered him with evidences of his favor. With his own hands he placed the diadem upon Agrippa's head, and he requested the Senate to confer the office of praetor upon him—a "request" that was promptly obeyed.

Caligula's friendship had come at a critical juncture in the life of the Prince of Judea, when after an adventurous and extravagant youth he was so bedeviled by debts that he considered taking his own life. On top of all this, an incautious remark of his, comparing Tiberius and Caligula to the detriment of the former, had resulted in his being cast into prison.

When the surprising news of the appointment arrived from Rome, great rejoicing broke out in Judea. No one suspected that the Emperor who had thus smiled upon Agrippa would soon bring suffering and horror down upon Eretz Israel, and upon the Jews of the Dispersion as well.

On the Emperor's orders, Agrippa was to travel to Judea by way of Alexandria. But this choice of routes led to a wave of persecution against the Jews in the great community on the Nile. In Alexandria the tensions between the Greek and Jewish populations had increased to the breaking point. The many years of incitement by anti-Semites—chief among them being Apion—had borne evil fruit. Agrippa's coronation and his friendship with Caligula only intensified the ill feeling. It was feared that the favor the new Emperor had shown to the new King of the Jews would also extend to the Jewish community in Egypt. Consequently, the ringleaders of the anti-Semitic groups were only waiting for an opportunity to take action against the Jews.

It came when Agrippa arrived in Alexandria in the summer of the year 38, and was cordially greeted by the Jewish community. Two municipal officials, Isidorus and Lampon—"intriguers, demagogues, slanderers, and brigands with the pen," as the philosopher Philo writes—staged a counter-demonstration in the Gymnasion. Ugly jokes and libelous verses were re-cited, and a scandalous skit directed against Agrippa was put on: Karabas, a harmless idiot well known in the city, appeared on the stage as "King of the Jews," with a crown of sheets of papyrus on his head, a ragged blanket draped around him as a royal robe, and a whip in his hand as a scepter. Boys with sticks played his bodyguard. The howling crowd hailed him as *Marin,* the Syrian word for "Lord." The excited mob then stormed into the Jewish quarter, carrying with them statues of the emperors that stood about in all public places. They broke into the synagogues and placed the statues inside. One mob went so far as to drag a quadriga and a statue of Caligula into the famous principal synagogue.

Horrified representatives of the Jewish community hastened to Avillius Flaccus, the Roman Governor, and asked for protection. The Governor refused. The anti-Jewish party had made thorough preparations; they had persuaded Flaccus, who felt insecure since the death of Tiberius, that the way to win the favor of the new ruler was to show special zeal in promoting the cult of the emperors, which the Jews alone among all imperial subjects opposed. Far from suppressing the rioting, the Governor withdrew the Jews' rights as citizens and declared them "aliens and immigrants."

The worst persecution of Jews in the history of Alexandria erupted. Jew-ish houses were set afire or smashed; four hundred were leveled to the ground. In the port the ships of Jewish merchants and shipowners went up in flames or were sunk. Jews who could not hide or flee the city were beaten and stoned; others were driven back into their burning houses. Flaccus had thirty-eight elders, members of the Jewish council, brought in fetters to the theater and scourged before the eyes of the Greeks. Under pretext of hunting for hidden weapons, soldiers invaded the Jewish quarter. They, too, tormented and abused the inhabitants.

In the middle of September these excesses suddenly ceased. Flaccus, on orders from the Emperor, was arrested and banished to an Aegean island. He was punished not for his actions against the Jews, but because he had fallen into Caligula's disfavor for other reasons. But the situation con-tinued delicate for the terrorized Jewish community of Alexandria, and the statues of the emperors still stood in their houses of worship. A petition to

Caligula concerning the violation of their traditional rights had gone un-
answered. The Jews therefore decided to send a delegation to Rome, and
asked the philosopher Philo to act as its spokesman.

They could not have found a better advocate, or a man with greater
prestige. Philo of Alexandria, the foremost thinker in the widespread community of Jews, had imbibed the spirit of Hellenism but nevertheless remained faithful to the religion of their fathers. Philo was so deeply familiar
with the writings of Plato, had made Plato's language so much his own, that
it was said that Plato writes like Philo, Philo like Plato. Along with his
ardent love of philosophy he preserved an unshakable attachment to Judaism, which he was attempting to reconcile with Greek thought. His writings later exerted considerable influence upon the Christian Fathers.

The anti-Jewish party in Alexandria likewise sent representatives to
Rome. Among them was Isidorus, the chief instigator of the violence, and
the notorious Apion. After making the two embassies wait for a long time,
Caligula at last granted the requested interview. He had the envoys of both
parties come to the garden of a villa on the outskirts of Rome, where he was
inspecting new buildings and newly laid-out gardens. Patiently, both parties
followed the Emperor around as Caligula issued his orders in connection
with landscaping or building. When the Jewish representatives were at last
permitted to greet him, Caligula remarked: "So you are the blasphemers
who are unwilling to acknowledge me as a god." The envoys responded
that sacrifices for the well-being of the Emperor were regularly made in the
Temple at Jerusalem. "All very well," Caligula replied. "But you sacrifice
for my welfare, not to me myself." Whereupon he strode on. After a while
he turned once more and asked: "And tell me, why do you refuse to eat
pork?" But suddenly the Emperor became serious: "I want to know what
rights you possess and what kind of political constitution you have." Philo
had scarcely begun his explanation when the Emperor shifted his attention
back to the landscaping. The Jewish delegation was dismissed without
having had the chance to deliver its petition. "These men are not so much
guilty as to be pitied, for they do not believe in my divinity," Caligula
remarked to his courtiers when the Jews had left.

Nothing had been clarified, nothing decided. The Jewish delegation
began making arrangements for their return voyage to Alexandria. But
before their departure from the capital alarming news reached them:
Caligula had ordered his statue to be set up in the Temple of Jerusalem.

In Eretz Israel the news of this blasphemous decree struck like a thunder-
bolt. Caligula, who was becoming more and more obsessed with delusions
of divinity, seemed to have been seized by a boundless hostility toward the
Judeans who refused to acknowledge him as a god even though he had

shown his benevolence to them by his coronation of Agrippa. He ordered all resistance to his decree to be crushed by force. Petronius, the Governor of Syria, was instructed to march to Judea at once with two legions. A fearful slaughter seemed in the offing.

In the spring of the year 40 Petronius arrived in Ptolemais, ancient Accho, near the border of Judea. Thousands of Jews were awaiting him. Their spokesman implored him not to carry out the Emperor's order. Otherwise an uprising was inevitable. "You will only be able to carry out the decree when not a single one of our people is left alive," the Governor was told. In Tiberias, the capital of Galilee, to which the Governor then marched, thousands of Jews again assembled at his camp, pleading with him not to carry out the order. The fields were left untilled; the whole country was like a seething cauldron.

Confronted with this situation, Petronius displayed considerable sympathy for the petitioners. He delayed executing the order and wrote to the Emperor, describing the people's temper and expressing hope that Caligula would change his mind.

Meanwhile Agrippa had hastened to Rome. He, too, begged Caligula to rescind the fatal command—and the Emperor relented. By an unfortunate coincidence, however, on the day the Emperor made this concession, Petronius' letter arrived. In a burst of rage, Caligula sent a letter to the Governor commanding him to commit suicide. The ship bearing this message was delayed by a storm at sea. Before it arrived, Petronius had already received news that Gaius Caligula had been assassinated. The praetorian tribune Chaerea had put an end to the life of the "divine emperor."

With Claudius as the new emperor on the throne of the Caesars, Judea breathed easier for a while. Claudius ordered the restoration of Jews' ancient rights both in their native land and in the Diaspora. Out of gratitude he also appointed Agrippa king of the entire kingdom that Herod I had once held. For Agrippa had been instrumental in winning support for Claudius from a number of senators who were disposed to restore the republic after the death of Caligula. The new Emperor, on Agrippa's urging, also confirmed the Alexandrian Jews in all their former civil rights. They retained their autonomy as a community, and their religious freedom. Claudius decreed "that the nation of the Jews be not deprived of their rights and privileges . . . but that these rights and privileges which they formerly enjoyed be preserved to them, and that they may continue in their own customs. And I charge both parties to take very great care that no troubles may arise after the promulgation of this edict."

Punishment was also meted out to the instigators of the persecution of Alexandrian Jews. Claudius personally called them to account. The dangerous demagogues, Isidorus and Lampon, were tried in the Emperor's presence. Fragments of Egyptian papyri in the Greek language—which came to light in 1895—testify to the outrageous language the two trouble-makers used during the trial. Both were condemned to death and executed.

The new Emperor was determined to have public tranquillity in his lands. In an edict sent out to all provinces Claudius decreed: "I think it just that in no Grecian city should the Jews be deprived of such rights and privileges as they enjoyed under the great Augustus. It will, therefore, be fit to permit the Jews, who are in all the world under us, to keep their ancient customs without being hindered. And I charge them to use this my kindness to them with moderation, and not to show a contempt for the observances of other nations, but to keep their own laws only." This edict was to be publicly displayed in all the cities of the empire, and "in such a place whence it may be plainly read from the ground," as the Roman legal formula had it.

For the last time Judea enjoyed a few years of unclouded happiness. Agrippa reigned for only four years, during which he distinguished himself by loyalty to his people, his country, and the faith of his fathers. He won the love of the Jews by both his mercy and his firmness of character. On A.D. 44 the King suddenly died at Caesarea, at the age of fifty-four. The country bitterly lamented his premature passing. But for non-Jews in Judea this day of mourning was a day of rejoicing. In Caesarea, the Roman garrison town, Greeks and Romans held noisy feasts. The taunts of the pagans mingled with the lamentation of the people—harbingers of the night that was about to descend upon the people of Israel and the land of Judea.

TERROR UNDER THE PROCURATORS

The King was dead; with him died the dream that Judea might preserve a remnant of independence as a vassal of Rome. In A.D. 44 Eretz Israel was once again placed under the government of Roman procurators.

The Emperor, Claudius, had initially had different intentions. Upon hearing of Agrippa's unexpected death, he wanted to proclaim his friend's son, Marcus Julius Agrippa, as the new King of Judea. But he was advised against taking this step on the grounds that the Crown Prince was too young—only seventeen—and completely inexperienced. He would be unable to cope with the unrest in Judea, it was argued. And the country, that narrow bridge between Asia Minor and Egypt, was strategically too important to be entrusted to a youth in such restive times. The Emperor therefore decided to appoint a procurator once again—and at the same time to enlarge the area under his control. Henceforth Judea and Samaria, Galilee in the north, and Peraea in the south were placed under the same procurator.

The new procurators behaved like despots. These Romans, tough soldiers or cool administrators concerned only with enriching themselves in the provinces, understood nothing of the spirit and religion of the Jewish people. An almost unbridgeable gulf separated them from the Judeans who had been given into their hands. The painstaking care with which the Jews obeyed every jot and tittle of their law, the religious rituals that extended into so many aspects of daily life, their outrage against the least infraction of their customs—these were matters the Romans could not fathom. They did not understand why so much fuss had to be made about this little nation with its autonomy and its curious institutions. Why should Judea, of all places, not be treated like other Roman provinces, which would never have dared to make such demands upon great Rome?

It did not help that Claudius, and Nero, too, at the beginning of his reign, displayed a benevolent attitude toward the Jewish nation. Rome was far. Few of the mistakes and abuses of office on the part of the procurators reached the ears of the Caesar.

The reign of the last five procurators, which led to armed uprising by the people, began with Cumanus. The first disturbances appeared under his governorship. The solemn day of a Passover feast in Jerusalem, for which hordes of pilgrims from far and near had come to the Holy City, ended in a bloody massacre. In his mistrust, the new Procurator had posted a cohort in the colonnades of the Temple, outside the Tower of Antonia, to keep an eye on the huge crowd assembled for worship. The sight of the Romans in front of their sanctuary in itself irritated the Jews. An ugly incident raised their vexation to a pitch of indignation: "Suddenly, one of the soldiers," Josephus relates, "pulled up his garment, crouched down indecently, and presented his breech to the Jews, at the same time producing a sound such as might be expected." Furiously, the crowd demanded punishment of the legionary for his sacrilegious act. But, instead, Cumanus called out more troops to drive the Jews out of the Temple. The sudden appearance of the heavily armed men sowed panic among the worshipers. Thousands were crushed, trampled to death, or severely injured in the rush to escape through the narrow entrances and in the narrow streets. "Thus this feast became the cause of mourning to the whole nation, and every family lamented."

One day a Roman soldier conducting searches of houses, which degenerated into pillaging, tore up a scroll of the Torah and threw it into the fire. "Hereupon," Josephus relates, "the Jews were in great disorder, as if their whole country were in flames . . . and ran together with united clamor to Cumanus, pleading with him that he should not overlook this man who had offered such an affront to God and his law, but punish him for what he had done." In the face of the national outrage, Cumanus ordered the soldier executed; but when occasion arose shortly afterward he vented his wrath upon the Jews.

Samaritans had killed a Jewish pilgrim to the Feast of Tabernacles. Cumanus was asked to bring the murderers to account, but took no action. When the petitioners returned home without having accomplished anything, the people took the law into their own hands. Led by Eleazar ben Dinai, a band of Zealots massacred many Samaritans and set their villages afire. When Cumanus heard of this, he sent a troop of cavalry to aid the Samaritans. Most of the Jews and Galileans who were caught were mercilessly cut down. With great difficulty, moderate leaders of the Jews from Jerusalem dissuaded the populace from attempting an armed attack upon the Roman troops, whose partisanship had aroused popular feeling to a fever pitch. Ummidius Quadratus, the Procurator of Syria, who was called in to mediate the dispute, ordered both Samaritans and Jews to send delegations to the Emperor to hear his judgment. Cumanus, too, was called to Rome to explain his actions. The trial, in which the Procurator soon became a defendant, set loose a whole series of court intrigues. The Emperor decided in favor of the Jews; several of the Samaritans were executed. Cumanus was sent into exile.

As a result of these disputes with the Samaritans, an ancient method of communication, which had served to bring news swiftly from distant Babylonia, fell into disuse.

It was considered highly important that all Jewish communities in Judea and in the Diaspora should begin the High Holidays simultaneously. From ancient times, therefore, the day from which the reckoning was to begin was determined in Jerusalem by special watchmen who noted the first appearance of the crescent moon after the new moon. That same night a chain of signal fires was lighted, and it traveled with astonishing speed. A great fire first flamed up on the Mount of Olives opposite the Temple. As soon as it was seen from the next peak, a fire was kindled there, and so the signals ran to Mount Tabor in Galilee, from there to the six-thousand-foot peak of Hauran in East Jordania, and finally to a peak called Beit Baltis. Across the expanse of desert the signal fire could be seen on the borders of Mesopotamia. Here observers from the Jewish communities waited, and as soon as they spied the signals, they in their turn lighted signal fires on the roofs of the higher houses; the chain of glowing dots sped on through nocturnal Mesopotamia. Within a few hours all the communities "beyond the river" learned that that was the day from which to calculate the festival calendar.

One night, in order to deceive the Judeans, the Samaritans prematurely lighted a fire signal. The resultant confusion extended all the way to Babylonia, in view of which the Sanhedrin decided to abandon the ancient custom. Henceforth messengers were sent out with circular letters to all the communities, setting the dates for the festival. The texts of some of these ancient circular letters have been preserved. Gamaliel the Old, a grandson of Hillel, dictated one of them to his scribe. "Sitting on the steps of the Temple Mount," he began, "we inform you, our brothers . . ."

The "peacemakers" in the Sanhedrin, headed by Gamaliel, for a time regained control of that body. These scholars and disciples of the great Hillel followed his example in preaching patience and gentleness in spite of all the insults and injuries of foreign domination. But their influence was soon to fade; their voices, the last that urged the people to peace and patient endurance, soon went unheard.

That the brutal Cumanus was sent into exile proved to have been scarcely advantageous to the Jews. Their lot merely worsened under his successor, Antonius Felix. Clashes with patriots, hitherto an isolated phenomenon, became matters of almost daily occurrence. "Antonius Felix," Tacitus writes, "indulging in every kind of barbarity and lust, exercised the power of a king in the spirit of a slave." He mercilessly persecuted the Zealots, whom the Romans called robbers. Felix lured their leader, Eleazar ben Dinai, into a trap and sent him to Rome in chains; members of his band were crucified. The Procurator's reign of terror was answered by terrorism. A secret league of Sicarii—the "knife men"—arose. These conspirators murdered pro-Romans and lukewarm patriots. They began their campaign of terrorism by stabbing to death Jonathan, the high priest. On holidays, in the dense crowds in front of the Temple, the Sicarii would suddenly strike down their victims with daggers (Latin, *sicae*), which they kept hidden under their clothes. Almost invariably they succeeded in escaping unrecognized. The general feeling was that life was no longer safe.

In the midst of these mounting public difficulties a wave of religious enthusiasm spread rapidly. False prophets and alleged messiahs appeared and attracted large followings. They convinced the people that they could free them from the Roman yoke. One of these, who was called the Egyptian, assembled thousands of men in the desert, marched them to the Mount of Olives, and there urged them to liberate the Holy City from the Romans. The walls, he promised, would miraculously collapse at their approach.

Felix, the Procurator, sent out soldiers to break up this disorderly and ineffectual mob. Once more blood flowed.

With bitterness the people heard that Drusilla, young Agrippa's sister, had turned her back upon her family and the Jewish religion and had married Rome's hated Procurator. That was only a sign of the times. The most respected families of Judea had been corrupted by their lives in Rome, by the intrigues and extravagance of the court there. The prestige of the high priest had also vanished; his office had been debased, was bartered or purchased, and had become a bone of contention among rich families, who regarded it as a source of income for their kinsmen.

In the meantime the non-Roman foreigners in the country were growing more and more hostile to the Jews. The seacoast cities were inhabited by many Greek Syrians. Street battles blazed up between them and the Jews in the port city of Caesarea, the Procurator's seat. Felix took the side of the Syrians and sent troops against the Jews. His legionaries pillaged houses, and beat and arrested the tenants. The Procurator's practice was to punish first; only then did he send representatives of the Jews and the Syrians to Rome for adjudication of their conflict.

In Rome, meanwhile, Claudius had died—poisoned by his own wife—and Nero inherited the throne of the Caesars (A.D.54). A host of intrigues followed, in the course of which the Syrians from Caesarea attempted to win over the Emperor's former tutor, Burrus, by bribes. But Nero's mistress and subsequent wife, Poppaea, felt attracted by the religion of the Jews, and at her instigation Nero relieved Felix of his office in A.D.59. But otherwise the Emperor's decision favored the Syrians rather than the Jews, who were deprived of their equal rights in Caesarea.

Porcius Festus, the successor of Felix, continued the policy of mercilessly hunting down the Judean rebels, but active resistance to the Romans only increased. When Festus died after a governorship of only two years, Nero appointed Lucceius Albinus to the post. "There was no evil that he did not commit," a contemporary writes. "Not only did he embezzle public funds, rob a multitude of prosperous persons of their fortunes, and overburden the entire nation with imposts, but he also freed criminals for ransom. Only those who could not pay remained in prison. . . . Thus the jails were emptied of prisoners, but the country was filled with robbers."

Only a spark was needed to transform the smoldering unrest among a harassed, humiliated people into open rebellion. That point was reached with the accession to office in A.D. 64 of Florus, who conducted himself "as if he were an executioner appointed for the punishment of condemned men." As Tacitus puts it: "The endurance of the Jews lasted till Gestius Florus was procurator. In his time the war broke out."

The new Procurator demanded that seventeen talents from the Temple treasury be paid to him. When the Jews refused, Florus entered Jerusalem, where his legionaries slaughtered and pillaged. That was the signal for the uprising. One last time the peacemakers attempted to quiet the populace, to restrain the people from entering upon a hopeless struggle. A feud erupted in Jerusalem. The advocates of peace were subdued; the Zealots, led by the armed Sicarii, won the upper hand. Palaces went up in flames; the Roman garrison was massacred. Henceforth there was no turning back. The war against Rome had begun.

THE JEWISH WAR

Rebellion spread through the entire country with lightning speed. Simultaneously, a general struggle between pagans and Jews began. In Caesarea the entire Jewish population, some twenty thousand persons, was killed. In Ascalon, Ptolemais, and many other cities, Jews were attacked and killed. There was a massacre in Alexandria also. Tiberius Julius Alexander, the commandant of Alexandria, who happened also to be an apostate Jew and the nephew of the philosopher Philo, loosed his troops upon the Jewish quarter after a dispute between Greeks and Jews. It is said that fifty thousand Jews lost their lives on this occasion.

Cestius Gallus, the Syrian legate, could not stay out of the fight. He advanced into Judea with an army of thirty thousand men, burning cities and villages as he went, and marched toward Jerusalem. The Zealot leaders Simon bar Giora and Eleazar ben Simon attacked. They succeeded in routing the Romans and inflicting severe losses upon them in the pass of Beth-horon. Cestius lost some six thousand men in this campaign against the despised Jews. But the greatest shame of all, from the Roman viewpoint, was that the legion from Antioch had lost its eagle.

The victors returned to Jerusalem with rich booty of weapons and war gear. Every Roman garrison had been driven from the country; the commander of Syria was defeated; the brutal Procurator Florus had vanished. Judea and Galilee had cast off the Roman yoke.

Rome could not accept such a challenge without striking back. Nero dispatched his most capable general, Titus Flavius Vespasian, who had previously distinguished himself in the conquest of Britain, to head operations in Syria and punish the rebellious country. In the spring of 67 Vespasian arrived in Ptolemais with two legions at full fighting strength, numerous auxiliary troops, and heavy military engines. His son Titus was bringing up a third legion from Egypt by sea.

The Jews were no match for so formidable an army. Even before the autumn rains brought the campaign to a stop, all of Galilee—the bulwark of Jerusalem—and the northern lands were again in the hands of the Romans. Among the prisoners was Josephus, commander of the Jewish forces in Galilee. He found favor with Vespasian and remained in the Roman camp, acting as interpreter and negotiator. Subsequently, in Rome, Flavius Josephus wrote his *History of the Jewish War* in seven books, the twenty books of his *Antiquities of the Jews,* which began with the creation of the world and extended to the reign of Nero, and a defense of Judaism against the malignant attacks of Apion.

In the midst of the battles, when the whole country except for the vicinity of Jerusalem had been reconquered by the Romans, news of Nero's suicide reached the army. Three emperors in quick succession died by violence—Galba by assassination, Otho by suicide, Vitellius by execution. Then Vespasian, acclaimed emperor by the legions, sped back to Rome. He left his son Titus in command of the eastern legions, with orders to conquer Jerusalem.

The campaign lagged. It was not until the spring of 70 that Titus appeared with a large force and heavy siege engines before the strongly fortified city. The siege had begun.

Behind her mighty walls, Jerusalem heroically held out in spite of famine and ferocious factional conflicts. The battle-hardened Romans could only advance step by step, making use of their full range of siege tactics. At last, on the ninth of Ab (August 29), Titus was able to advance over heaps of corpses and ruins to the Temple itself. He had only a short while to admire its splendor. A hurled torch set fire to the ancient sanctuary, and the soldiers, in the din of battle and the heat of passion, did not hear Titus' repeated orders to quench the flames. Almost on the anniversary of the destruction of Jerusalem by Nebuchadnezzar, the great Temple collapsed in smoke and ashes.

For another month desperate resistance continued in the upper city, intrepidly defended by the Zealots Johanan of Gishala and Simon bar Giora. At the end of September the Romans broke through and planted their ensigns on the towers of the palace of Herod. Day and night the upper city burned. "And next morning the sun rose on the smoking ruins of Jerusalem."

This was the end. For four years a small nation had waged a heroic struggle against the masters of the world. After five months of siege the Holy City was in the hands of the enemy, a heap of rubble filled with corpses. More than a million Jews had been killed; some nine hundred thousand were taken into captivity. Once more the lament of an unknown witness of the first destruction of Jerusalem could be repeated: "How doth the city sit solitary, that was full of people! How is she become as a widow! She that was great among the nations, and princess among the provinces, how is she become a tributary! She weepeth sore in the night, and her tears are on her cheeks; she hath none to comfort her among all her lovers; all her friends have dealt treacherously with her, they are become her enemies" (Lamentations 1:1–2).

Titus ordered harsh measures to be taken against the survivors. He left it to his friend Fronto to determine their fate. Fronto ordained that all who were recognized or denounced as having fought should be nailed to the cross. But out of these, seven hundred of the strongest and handsomest youths were selected for the triumphal procession. All men older than seventeen were carried off to the quarries and mines of Egypt, condemned to lifelong slavery for Rome. Thousands of youths were sent to the provinces, where they died as gladiators in the circus and arena, fighting other men or wild beasts. Boys and women were sold to slave traders; the enormous supply depressed prices, so that Jewish slaves became cheap goods in the marts of Asia Minor.

Fronto likewise singled out the last Zealot leader to fall into Roman hands, the intrepid Simon bar Giora, to serve as the sacrificial victim for the triumph. Johanan of Gishala was condemned to life imprisonment. In the days during which Fronto was making his selections, another eleven thousand Jews died of starvation in the gruesome prison camps.

Then Titus issued the order to raze the entire city and Temple. Only the three tall towers called Phasael, Hippicus, and Mariamne were to be left standing—as a testimony to posterity of the fate of the rebellious city. The Tenth Legion was left behind to garrison the wasteland that had been Jerusalem. Titus sent the Twelfth Legion, which he could not forgive for its defeat under Cestius, to frontier duty on the Euphrates.

Emperor Vespasian expropriated all of Judea. He had the vineyards, fields, and pastures sold by Roman officials to the highest bidder. Meanwhile, Titus moved to Caesarea and ordered games to celebrate the victory. Jewish prisoners were compelled to fight wild beasts or one another in groups. Twenty-five hundred men were killed in a single bloody show staged by Titus for his brother's birthday. In Caesarea Philippi on Mount Hermon as well as in Berytus the pagan populace derived amusement from the sight of the defeated Judeans killing one another.

In Rome Titus celebrated his victory with a magnificent triumphal procession (A.D. 71). The Jewish prisoners of war marched in front of the chariot of the laurel-crowned General and the escort of senators, dignitaries, and soldiers. Among the trophies of victory were the golden shewbread table, the seven-branched candlestick, and a scroll of the Torah from the Temple in Jerusalem. Gigantic floats illustrated the events of the campaign, the battles, and the destruction of cities.

The procession stopped on the Capitoline before the temple of Jupiter. In accordance with the ancient custom, it waited there until a messenger should report that the leader of the defeated nation had been executed. Simon bar Giora was fetched out of the troop of prisoners; pulled along by the rope around his neck, and scourged as he walked, he was dragged to the edge of the Tarpeian Rock and sent tumbling into the abyss. Howls of rejoicing from the crowds announced that the execution had been completed.

Rome took such pride in her subjugation of little Judea that she had coins of gold, silver, and copper struck in memory of the victory. In fact, such coins continued to be produced for decades, into the reign of Domitian (81–96). They show the unhappy country as a despairing woman, bowed and fettered beneath a palm tree, and bear the inscription *"Judaea devicta"* or *"Judaea capta."* Similar coins were struck with Greek inscriptions. Both Vespasian and Titus declined the offer of *Judaicus* as an agnomen; perhaps they feared that the epithet would be misunderstood as signifying attachment to the Jewish religion.

The ancient cult objects from the sanctuary in Jerusalem were later turned over to the Temple of Peace, built by Vespasian and Titus; the scroll of the Torah was kept in the imperial palace. A representation of the scroll was incorporated into a relief on the Arch of Titus in the Forum Romanum, which may still be seen in the noisy, bustling city of present-day Rome.

Long after the noisy celebrations in Rome had ceased, a single bulwark still defied the Romans in occupied Judea: the fortress of Masada. On the steep rock above the Dead Sea a thousand Zealots with their wives and children took their last desperate stand. Under Eleazar ben Jair, a descendant of the family of Judah of Galilee, who had been one of the first Zealot leaders, these extremists swore to fight to the last and never to capitulate to the enemy. Vespasian's general Silva besieged the fort, employing all the resources of Roman technology in the enterprise. He had vast walls of earth thrown up around the entire fortress and brought ballistae and battering-rams from great distances. Finally, one of these mighty rams succeeded in pounding a breach in the wall of the fortress. But behind it the defenders had already built another wall, of crossed beams with earth filling the interstices. The blows of the ram only packed the earth harder in this second wall, so that it grew stronger the more it was assailed. At last the Romans contrived to set fire to the beams, and the whole structure threatened to collapse. The last hour of Masada was at hand.

At this moment—it was the first day of Passover in the year 73—Eleazar gathered the defenders of the fortress around him. He described the humiliations and sufferings that all, including the women and children, could expect at the hands of the Romans, and cried out to them: "Let our wives die before they are abused, and our children before they have tasted slavery. And after we have slain them, let us bestow that glorious benefit upon one another and preserve freedom as our glorious funeral monument."

Next day, when the Romans stormed through the flames into the interior of the fortress, they met no opposition. An uncanny silence surrounded them. Among the still-smoking ruins lay groups of lifeless bodies. They counted nine hundred and sixty dead—men, women, and children. The Zealots had killed their families and then themselves. So died the last heroes of the Jewish War, three years after the destruction of Jerusalem and the Temple.

The communities of the Diaspora were not spared the effects of the catastrophe that had descended upon the mother country. Sparks of the conflagration extinguished in Judea leaped to Egypt and North Africa. Bands of dispersed Zealots carried their unquenchable hatred of Rome abroad and did everything they could to stir up rebellions against the Romans. They very nearly succeeded in inciting mass uprisings in Alexandria also. In the year 73 fanatical patriots appeared in the Jewish quarters of the Nile metropolis and described the horrors and cruelty of the Roman occupation in Judea. The agitators found receptive listeners; the Alexandrian Jews still remembered the massacres under Tiberius Alexander. Bands of extremists began to form everywhere in the city.

At this point the elders of the community took vigorous countermeasures against the irresponsible extremists, and managed to bring the agitated masses of Jews to a rational view of their precarious situation. The adherents of the Zealots melted away; the Zealots themselves were pursued by Roman troops and six hundred of them were captured. Julius Lupus, the Roman prefect of Alexandria, had them tortured, hoping to wring from them a promise to be obedient subjects in the future. But they remained steadfast. When the vilest tortures could not shatter their determination, the Prefect ordered their execution. "Everybody was amazed at their courage, or perhaps we ought to call it madness," admits Josephus, who, in fact, hated these fanatical patriots as the source of untold misery to his people. "They preserved their own opinion in spite of all the distress they were brought to, as if they received those torments and the fire itself with bodies insensible of pain, and with a soul that in a manner rejoiced.

But what was most astonishing to the beholders was the courage of the children; for not one of these children was so far overcome by these torments as to name Caesar as his lord."

Reports of Zealot activity came from Thebes and other cities of Egypt. In the city of Cyrene and its vicinity the Zealot Jonathan, a weaver, had gathered together a band of two thousand rebels. The Roman governor Catullus scattered them. Many of the rebels were killed. Jonathan was brought to Rome in chains, sentenced by Vespasian to be scourged, and then burned alive. That was the end of the Zealot movement. A bare half century later, however, the old Zealot spirit flamed again, for one last time—and once more in Cyrene.

A single sizable group of Zealots was spared for a different destiny. From East Jordania they fled to Arabia, where they settled among nomadic tribes in the vicinity of Yathrib and formed their own community. For a long time all news of them was lost. But their descendants were destined to play a very special part in the seventh century—when, in the remote caravan city of Yathrib, which these Jews called Medina, the third world religion, that of Islam, was born.

All Jews in the Roman Empire were made answerable for the Jewish War and punished accordingly. The two drachmas they had annually contributed to the Temple in Jerusalem henceforth had to be paid for the temple of Jupiter Capitolinus. Thus an imperial order transformed a hitherto voluntary gift of piety into a compulsory tax for a pagan god.

II AFTER THE DESTRUCTION OF THE TEMPLE

THE RULE OF THE SCHOLARS

The Jewish state was shattered, Jerusalem destroyed, the Temple fallen. More than half of the country's inhabitants had lost their lives in battle or been scattered over the world as prisoners and slaves, or as fugitives seeking safety in remote lands. Judea lay devastated, her cities and villages in ruins. Only the widows and orphans, the enfeebled, the sick, and the wounded had remained. The fields went untilled, the olive groves and vineyards were overtaken by wild growth. There seemed nothing to hope for.

No other nation on earth has ever survived such a catastrophe as had descended upon Israel. All the others have vanished, erased from the roll of nations; only their names remain. But the people of Israel continued, despite the terrible bloodletting. The arms of the Romans had been able to repress the rebellion, but not the spirit that inspired this people. In defeat they preserved their unshakable faith in the One God who had always been part of the life of Israel and hitherto guaranteed its survival. The Zealots of political freedom had been silenced, but the zealots of spiritual liberty raised their voices more loudly than ever. From among the people men rose up who were determined to preserve the precious content of their ancient religion and adjust it to their new homeless existence.

A new era began in the history of the children of Israel—the dominion of the teachers of the Law, the scholars.

The rebirth began as if by a miracle even while the ruins of the Temple were still smoking. In the small town of Jabneh, south of the port of Jaffa, a "house of learning" had opened its doors. An aged scholar named Johanan ben Zakkai, hailed as the "glory of scholarship," gathered surviving friends and disciples, Pharisees and teachers of the Law like himself, in this small place of refuge. Thus, scarcely noticed at the time, there arose in a time of distress and despair a new spiritual and intellectual center of Judaism.

Legend has preserved a tale of how this came about. Johanan ben Zakkai, trapped in besieged and obviously doomed Jerusalem, was seized by fears for the future of Judaism. He became convinced that it was his task to flee and build the foundations for that future. But how was he to escape from the surrounded city?

At dusk one evening, the story goes, a funeral procession moved slowly through the streets of the ancient city. Disciples, it was said, were carrying their beloved teacher to the grave. Respectfully, everyone stood aside; even the guards of the Roman besiegers outside the city gate permitted the mourners to pass unhindered. Once behind the lines, the procession halted; the disciples set down the coffin, opened the lid, and the venerable rabbi Johanan ben Zakkai was helped out of it. This trickery had been his only recourse, for the Zealots had ordered that no man was to be allowed to leave Jerusalem alive.

The old man, the story continues, asked for an interview with the Roman commander, Titus, and pleaded: "Let me found a school in Jabneh." The request was granted. The Roman could not suspect what his consent would mean, what spiritual force he was releasing at that moment. Rome would one day succumb to the fate of empires, but Israel continues to live in its teachings, which Johanan ben Zakkai carried from Jerusalem to Jabneh.

No sooner was the small school opened than news came that the capital had fallen and the Temple had gone up in flames. For days dense clouds of smoke drifted on the winds above the tops of the Judean hills. They could be seen throughout the land and seemed to mark the end of a great age, of the almost two-thousand-year history of the children of Israel.

Johanan ben Zakkai and his disciples rent their garments and lamented. But the teacher did not despair, for he was convinced that the essence of the people and its religion was not so inseparably linked with the Temple and its altar that it must be destroyed along with them. Johanan encouraged his seemingly inconsolable disciples. Legend has handed down the words he is supposed to have addressed to them. "Acts of loving kindness replace the sacrifices, for it says in Scripture, 'I am pleased by good deeds and not by sacrifices.' " This great sage had looked far into the future in clearly defining the new mission of Judaism.

The news of the gathering of many scholars in the small town soon drew disciples from all sides. A vigorous intellectual life swiftly developed in Jabneh. Johanan ben Zakkai did not confine his work to forging intellectual bonds that would hold together the people of Israel. He also considered the need for some central authority for the smitten and scattered Jewish communities. In Jabneh he convoked a High Council of Elders, a new Sanhedrin to assume the religious and judicial functions formerly held by the Sanhedrin in Jerusalem. For the first time in the history of Israel, the Elders met outside the sacred court of the Temple.

Jerusalem itself had now become a garrison town for a Roman legion. With the destruction of the Temple, the high priest, the priesthood, and the Sadducees, whose existence had been founded entirely upon the worship in the Temple, lost all importance. They disappeared. Not that the people of Israel ever forgot the Temple—they have not done so to this day. But henceforth the place for the worship of God became the home, and for common worship and the teaching of Scripture, the synagogue. The words of Scripture, the teachings of Torah, became the center of Jewish faith and worship. And authority henceforth resided in the teachers of the Law, the rabbis, who took over the functions formerly performed by the priesthood of the Temple.

The rabbi (the word means "lord" or "master," and is the title by which Jesus is addressed in the New Testament) is not a priest with sacramental powers. He is primarily a searcher, an interpreter, a preserver, and a teacher of the Law, and, as such, the spiritual head of the community. The rabbis had long enjoyed great prestige among the people for their knowledge of the Law, for their expertise in religious and judicial questions—the latter because of the peculiarity of the Jewish religion, which includes the governance of everyday life by instructions to be found in the Torah.

The process that began in Jabneh and subsequently became so characteristic of Judaism—acceptance of the leadership of scholars—remained unique among the Jews. Neither origin nor title, neither connections nor material wealth henceforth decided a man's prestige, nor gave him entry to the circles of the rabbis, but solely his intellectual qualities. Any man of the people, no matter what his descent or occupation, could become a scholar, a rabbi, and hence a holder of authority. Jewish history is filled with innumerable examples of poor youths who by indefatigable study of the Law rose to the highest honors, and of men who won immortal fame although they earned their daily bread by the hardest work. The rabbi, the synagogue, the school—henceforth the life of the people was concentrated in them. An educational system was created that, as Cecil Roth has pointed out, reached a perfection that was not achieved in Europe until the late nineteenth century.

The prestige of the Sanhedrin grew rapidly. Throughout the Diaspora Jews soon accepted its decisions; thus a new link was forged with the homeland. The new Sanhedrin also determined the calendar of feasts, and messengers were dispatched from Jabneh to inform home and foreign communities of the dates.

The members of the Sanhedrin also served in the newly founded academy for the study of the Torah. For centuries—according to tradition, in fact, from the very time the Law was revealed upon Mount Sinai— there had existed an "oral doctrine," side by side with the written Torah, passed on and elaborated from generation to generation. There were commentaries on the written Torah—the Halakah—and instructions—the Haggada. A vast amount of learning had accumulated, and since it was forbidden to write it down, it had been passed on from teacher to disciple. Knowledge of this oral doctrine imposed demands on the memories of teachers and pupils such as we can scarcely imagine nowadays. The tradition of this oral doctrine—later written down as the Mishnah—was saved by Johanan ben Zakkai. In Jabneh he set about sifting it and systematically examining it.

Johanan ben Zakkai died at a great age between A.D. 80 and 85, mourned by his many disciples. After his death, they continued the work of the master. Two of them, Eliezer ben Hyrcanus and Joshua ben Hananiah founded schools of their own in Lydda and Peqiin, not far from Jabneh. Gamaliel II, a great-great-grandson of Hillel and also a highly learned rabbi in secular matters, who was familiar with Greek and an accomplished astronomer, assumed headship of the Sanhedrin, with the title of Nasi. He was recognized by Rome as the head and representative of the Jewish people, and accorded the title of patriarch. During the reign of Emperor Domitian he repeatedly traveled to the capital and pleaded for the abolition of anti-Jewish measures.

Domitian, the brother and successor of Titus, was extremely hostile to the Jews. "He collected the tax on the Jews with a peculiar lack of mercy," says Suetonius, "and took proceedings not only against those who kept their Jewish origins a secret in order to avoid the tax, but also against those who lived as Jews without professing Judaism. As a boy, I remember once attending a crowded court where the Procurator had a ninety-year-old man stripped to establish whether or not he had been circumcised."

Domitian also took the severest measures against Romans who showed an inclination to convert to Judaism. Sympathy for the Jewish religion cost a cousin of the Emperor, the Senator and Consul Flavius Clemens, his life. He was executed for "atheism" and his wife, Domitilla, a niece of Domitian, banished. Many other "Judaizing" Romans were sent into exile or condemned to death.

The Jewish religion strongly impressed many Romans, as some verses by the satirist Juvenal suggest. He mocked Roman fathers who were attached to Jewish customs: "When children are fated to have a father who celebrates a Sabbath, they will soon revere only the sky and clouds, avoid eating pork as if it were human flesh, because the father also avoided it. Soon, too, they dispense with the foreskin. . . ."

For a while conditions eased for the Jews in the empire after the violent death of the tyrannical Domitian, last of the Flavian line. Nerva, just and humanitarian, ordered the mistreatment to stop. Profession of Judaism was freely permitted. The "Jewish tax" continued to be collected, but with forbearance. "Charges connected with the Jewish tax are abolished," reads the inscription on a coin that bears the Emperor's portrait, along with a palm tree, the symbol of Judea. But Nerva remained in office only sixteen months (from September, 96, to January, 98). He was succeeded by the Emperor Trajan.

In Jabneh the work of the teachers of the Law and of the Sanhedrin continued. The scholars seemed to have a presentiment that there was no time to be lost if they were to prepare their defenseless people for survival by strengthening the structure of the Law.

Forty-five years after the fall of Jerusalem, however, their quiet work of construction was suddenly interrupted. Profoundly disturbing news reached Judea: The Jews of the Levant and Africa had risen in rebellion.

A victorious campaign of Trajan's into Babylonia, the heart of the "Mother of the Diaspora," had initiated the uprising. After his victories over the Dacians on the Danube, in what is now Rumania, Trajan had turned his attention to the eastern frontier of the empire. The lands between the Tigris and the Euphrates, then dominated by the kings of the Parthians, and still more distant India, lured the ambitious Emperor. He dreamed of matching the fame of Alexander the Great.

In 114 Trajan crossed the Euphrates with his legions. He conquered Armenia and advanced toward Mesopotamia. Ctesiphon, the capital of the Parthians, fell into his hands—magnificent reliefs on the gigantic Column of Trajan at the foot of the Capitol in Rome still show scenes of his Asiatic campaign. At first the Emperor met with little opposition. The Parthian kingdom was enfeebled by old age and torn by internal struggles for the throne. But in Babylonia his legions unexpectedly encountered fierce resistance.

The Jews, who lived in great numbers in this region and who had hitherto enjoyed complete freedom, had taken up arms. For them, Trajan was a successor of the tyrants who had destroyed the Temple and had killed and enslaved their brethren. The thought that they themselves might have to bow to the harsh yoke of Rome seemed unendurable and sharpened their militancy. In the provinces of Nisibis and Nehardea strong bands of Jewish troops were raised, and these advanced against the Romans. In northern Mesopotamia the kingdom of Adiabene, whose prince had embraced Judaism, rose up against the invaders. Cities and towns that Trajan had already occupied were stormed by the Jews and reconquered. The legions had to return on their tracks, and were involved in savage battles. The war that had seemed already won began to drag on. The city of Nisibis, one of the citadels of Jewry, was defended with ferocious courage; the Romans succeeded in taking it only after a protracted siege, and made the inhabitants pay dearly for their resistance. In Adiabene levies of Jewish soldiers fought fanatically against the superior might of the Romans.

The sparks of open resistance to Rome leaped from Babylon to the empire proper. The battles being fought in the lands beyond the Euphrates became a cue for a series of uprisings by Jews in the Roman Diaspora. The first to rise were the Jews in Cyrene. Then the rebellion leaped to Alexandria, to Libya, and to the island of Cyprus. In Palestine, too, there was much ferment, but not enough strength for an actual uprising.

From Mesopotamia to Africa the colossal empire of the Caesars found itself facing an unforeseen crisis. Rome had to battle Jewish soldiers in four theaters of war simultaneously. Trajan, who was staying in Babylonia at the time, was forced to mobilize sizable land and naval forces. The Emperor sent his favorite general, Lusius Quietus, a Moorish prince, to direct operations against the Mesopotamian Jews. Marcius Turbo, prefect of the fleet, was entrusted with the command in the Mediterranean.

Only after a long struggle could Rome once more claim to be master of the situation. Lusius Quietus suppressed the Jews in Mesopotamia with inhuman harshness. Trajan rewarded him by appointing him legate of Judea. On Cyprus the entire Jewish population had been annihilated. In Alexandria the principal synagogue went up in flames and the Jewish quarters were devastated. The once flourishing Egyptian community of Jews never recovered from this blow.

Even before the outbreak of Jewish rebellions in Egypt, in Cyrene, and on Cyprus, Trajan had been forced to abandon the Parthian war and give up all thought of converting Mesopotamia into a Roman province. Disappointed and severely ill, he died in Cilicia in 117. Not even his last wish—that Quietus should succeed him—was realized. His widow, Plotina, informed the army that Trajan had desired his kinsman Aelius Hadrianus to be the new emperor. Hadrian was acclaimed in due course, and Lusius Quietus, far from succeeding Trajan, was even relieved of his office as legate of Judea.

Hadrian brought peace to the empire. The wars under Trajan and the suppression of the Jewish uprisings had overstrained the military resources of the Roman world. Hadrian renounced the ambition to extend Roman conquests beyond the Euphrates. He devoted himself to the administration, which he reorganized, to the army, and to securing the borders. The limes on the Rhine and the Danube was reinforced. In Britain the great wall against the Picts was built. The Emperor traveled constantly; he spent no less than fifteen years in journeys through the provinces. In 131 Hadrian passed through Judea. For many years now Hadrian had enjoyed the nickname *Restitutor* (the Restorer), because he had erected so many splendid buildings and impressive monuments throughout the empire, and had enlarged cities and repaired the damage left by years of neglect. In Judea, too, he conceived a grandiose plan. After half a century the former capital of the Jews was still little more than a stony desert. Hadrian decided to convert it into a modern Roman city—the military colony of Aelia Capitolina—and to crown the Temple Mount with a temple of Jupiter.

Hadrian was surely thinking only of embellishing a provincial city, of proclaiming the glory of Rome. He did not expect that this new order would provide the pretext for the one serious war during the twenty-one years of his rule. Many legends and popular stories have surrounded the prelude to this war. The historian Dio Cassius states the facts dryly and tersely:

"When Hadrian founded a city of his own in Jerusalem, to replace the one that had been destroyed, calling it Aelia Capitolina and erecting a temple to Jupiter in place of their [the Jews'] temple, a great and tedious war began."

As long as the Holy City lay in ruins, the Jews could secretly hope that one day a new Jerusalem and a new Temple would arise. Now even this hope was about to be destroyed. Was a pagan city to take the place of the city of David, and a pagan temple to desecrate the site of the First and Second Temples?

No sooner had the Emperor reached Rome again after his visit to the East than the sword was drawn in Judea.

BAR KOCHBA'S REVOLT

In the winter of 1951–1952 a sensational find was made in the Holy Land, fifteen miles southeast of Jerusalem. In an almost inaccessible cave on the Wadi Merubaat, near the Dead Sea, fragments of writing in Hebrew characters were found: a proclamation and two letters from one Simon bar Koseba. These precious documents, probably written by Simon himself more than eighteen hundred years ago, are testimony to the patriot who headed the last desperate uprising in Judea.

What led to the uprising, and exactly how it took place, can no longer be determined. No pen has entered the deeds of Judea's last hero upon the tablets of history; it is as though a deliberate attempt had been made to blot his name from the minds of succeeding generations, who were to forget the craft of war. Even the report of Antonius Julianus, composed under Hadrian, has been lost; mere fragments of it are known. These testify eloquently to the courage and the reckless ardor with which the Judeans fought for their people and their religion. Otherwise there are merely a few terse remarks by the historian Dio Cassius and the Church Father Eusebius.

Legends have been woven around the figure of Simon bar Koseba, whose rebellion challenged the then weakened Imperium Romanum much as the Gauls of Brennus and the Carthaginian warriors of Hannibal had challenged the Roman Republic in the past. In the memory of his nation he survives as Bar Kochba, a warrior of gigantic stature and strength. One story tells of his kicking back with his knee the mighty stones cast by the Romans' ballistae and thus slaying many of the enemy. But nothing is known of his origins.

Many of the staid teachers of the Law considered his rebellion madness and advised against it. One of them, however, an important scholar, supported the movement with passion, and joined in the struggle for freedom. He was Rabbi Akiba, who believed profoundly in a political rebirth of the Jewish nation. It was this rabbi, also, who gave the popular leader the name that was destined to become so famous. The first time Rabbi Akiba saw Simon bar Koseba he was so impressed that he cried out:

"He is the messianic king." And he applied to Simon the prophesy of Balaam: "There shall step forth a star [kochba] out of Jacob, and a scepter shall rise out of Israel, and shall smite through the corners of Moab, and break down all the sons of Seth." With this promise of Israel's victory ringing in the people's ears, Simon from the town of Koseba in Judea became the "son of the star," Bar Kochba.

Bar Kochba gathered from far and near those who still had the heart for resistance. Bands of Jewish armed men streamed to his banner from lands beyond the borders of Judea. Samaritans and pagans, too, who chafed under the yoke of Rome, flocked to this charismatic leader. A tremendous levy was raised. Dio Cassius, surely with wild exaggeration, speaks of no less than five hundred and eighty thousand soldiers. Whatever the true number, the Roman governor could not cope with an evidently overwhelming force. Quintus Tineius Rufus had to withdraw, abandoning one fortress after the other to the rebels. Within a year Judea, Galilee, and Samaria fell into their hands. Bar Kochba seems also to have retaken Jerusalem; bronze and copper coins have been found bearing the inscriptions "Simeon" and "The Liberator of Jerusalem."

In response to the disquieting reports, Hadrian sent reinforcements to the theater of war. Legions were sent from Phoenicia, Egypt, and Arabia. Even from such distant provinces as Moesia and Mauretania units were ordered to Judea. The fleet stationed in the ports of Syria and Phoenicia was fully occupied with the transportation of troops. Since the uprising threatened to spread into neighboring provinces, two experienced generals were placed in command: Publius Marcellus, the governor of Syria, and Loliu Urbicus, legate of the province of Asia. They suffered the same fate as Rufus: Both were defeated.

The Emperor thereupon decided to send to Judea his most capable general, Julius Severus, who had won glory in Britain. With the appearance of Severus the tide turned; the intoxication of victory soon ebbed. Severus had under his command an exceptionally large levy of legions and auxiliary troops. He deliberately avoided pitched battles with the combat-happy Jews. Instead, he had his men attack only isolated strong points, surrounding them and starving out their garrisons. Step by step the Romans gained ground. They suffered severe losses in the process, but they managed to wrest fort upon fort and town upon town from the rebels. The struggle went on into a second and a third year. Inexorably, Israel was being bled of its strength.

Finally, the fighters for freedom were driven back to a narrow area around Jerusalem. The ancient capital with its razed fortifications and its buildings still in ruins offered poor prospects for defense. Bar Kochba, with his main force, therefore settled in the vicinity, in the town of Bether (present-day Battir), about six miles west of Jerusalem, resolved to fight to the last.

High up above the southern rim of the valley through which today the railroad from Jaffa to Jerusalem runs towers the summit of a mountain that dominates the plain below. The Arabs call it Khirbet el-Jehud—the Jews' ruin. Bar Kochba and his troops took their stand there. Severus had once again to depend on siege tactics. Remains of the *circumvallatio,* the encircling wall built by his troops, still stand as silent witnesses to the final struggle. An inscription discovered in the nearby village of Battir mentions detachments of the Legio V Macedonica and the Legio XI Claudia who fought here under the Roman general.

No historian has reported the last events at the mountain fortress of Bether. It was overcome around the year 135—according to tradition, on the same fateful day on which Jerusalem had fallen sixty-five years before. Bar Kochba and all his men met death.

The war had lasted for three and a half years. Half a million Jews had died or been killed. The Romans, too, had suffered frightful losses. Some of their legions and auxiliaries had been entirely wiped out in the course of battles and sieges. In announcing the victory over the Jews, Hadrian did not dare to use the traditional formula of victory: "All is well with me and the army." But as a tribute to the successful outcome of the campaign Hadrian was awarded the *ornamenta triumphalis,* and inscriptions glorified the *expeditio Judaica* under the "divine" Hadrian and his great general.

The land of Israel presented a ghostly aspect after the war was over. It was totally devastated and almost depopulated. The smell of death and decay poisoned the air. The Romans had forbidden burial of the dead; the sight of corpses was to serve as a warning to what remained of the population. All the cities, towns, and villages that had offered resistance lay in ashes. In Galilee, formerly covered with olive groves and vineyards, scarcely an olive tree or a vine was left. For the second time since the fearful losses of the Jewish War, the remnants of the population in the country had been nearly wiped out. Captured rebels, with their women and children, had been sold by the Romans at the slave market by Abraham's terebinth at Mamre and in the market in Gaza. Many others had fled to Egypt. For months after the cessation of resistance Roman squads continued to hunt down fugitives and stragglers from the Jewish forces who had taken refuge in caves.

Now at last Hadrian was able to carry out his plan to build a pagan city within Judea. The plow was drawn over the Temple Mount to wipe out all memory of the ancient sanctuary. In its place arose the Roman colony of Aelia Capitolina, populated by soldiers who had served out their time and by foreign settlers—Romans, Greeks, Syrians, and others. On the site of the Temple a temple of Jupiter Capitolinus was erected, and a statue of Hadrian was put up. The city acquired a theater, a circus, more temples and statues of gods and emperors, public buildings in the Hellenistic style. Nothing remained as a reminder of the city of David. At the southern gate, through which the road to Bethlehem passed, the Romans installed the image of an unclean animal—the head of a pig. And Jews were banned under penalty of death from entering Aelia Capitolina.

Even the name Judea was wiped out. Henceforth the land was called Palestine, after the onetime enemies of Israel who had inhabited the "land of the Philistines" along the coast. By decree of Rome there was no longer to be any semblance of a "land of the Jews."

Even these humiliations of the Jews did not satisfy Hadrian. He wanted to eradicate their spirit, to force paganism upon them. A campaign of religious persecution followed. As the Seleucid ruler Antiochus Epiphanes had done three centuries before, Hadrian seemed to believe that the existence of the Jews as a people could be terminated by banning their religion. By imperial decree obedience to the laws and traditions of the Jews was forbidden on pain of death. Neither circumcision, nor celebration of the Sabbath, nor instruction in the Torah was permitted. All other Jewish customs were likewise punishable. Supervision of these repressive measures was entrusted to Tineius Rufus, the governor who had been driven from the country by the first onslaught of the rebellion.

Rufus employed spies and informers, who lurked everywhere, denouncing all who still ventured to follow the pious customs of their fathers or, what was worse, secretly to maintain a school. This was the beginning of what the Talmud called Shaath ha'shmad, the "time of severe persecution," the "hour of danger."

The "vineyard" at Jabneh now lay orphaned; no one set foot over the threshold of the school. Those teachers of the Law who had survived had to make a grave decision. What was left of the people of Israel looked to them as the only ones who might offer guidance. They met in Lydda in all secrecy. For they had to decide a question of life and death—the question that was so inexorably to confront hundreds of thousands of Jews in the centuries to come. Was it permissible for a Jew, who was threatened with death because of his religion, to make a sham renunciation of Judaism in order to save his life?

The opinions of the teachers were divided. Some insisted that every Jew was obligated to give his life for his faith. Others rejected this austere counsel. Temporary defection imposed by threats of violence could not be regarded as apostasy, they held. After long and agitated debates the rabbis arrived at a compromise: Under duress, and to escape a martyr's death, observance of the Law could be suspended. But there were three exceptions: idolatry, unchastity, and murder.

This policy had to be carried out in the face of inhuman persecution by the Roman authorities. One tradition recounts an interrogation in a Roman court. "Why are you to be crucified?" "Because I ate unleavened bread on the Passover." "Why have you been condemned to the pyre and you to the sword?" "Because we read the Torah and permitted our children to be circumcised." Anyone caught with the prayer capsule (tephillin) on his forehead had his skull smashed. In their methods of torture, the Roman tribunals were pagan forerunners of the later inquisitional courts of the Church. Red-hot balls of iron were placed in the defendants' armpits, splinters driven under their fingernails and toenails.

Among ten teachers of the Law who died as martyrs was Rabbi Akiba, the aged supporter of Bar Kochba. He was caught giving secret instruction in the Torah, and was thrown into jail. The Governor, Rufus, gave orders to torture him. The Talmud (Berakkot IX) relates: "The hour when Rabbi Akiba was being led to execution happened to be the time for reading the Shema, and his flesh was torn with iron combs; but he took the yoke of heavenly dominion upon himself. His disciples said to him: 'Master, so far?' He replied to them: 'All my life I grieved over the verse in Scripture: "with your whole soul, even if he takes your soul," for I thought: When shall the opportunity be offered me, and yet I want to fulfill it. And now, when it is offered me, should I not fulfill it?' He then stretched out the word One [in the prayer "Hear, O Israel: The Lord our God, the Lord is One"] until he breathed out his soul. Then a voice resounded, saying: 'Hail to you, Rabbi Akiba, that you breathed out your soul on the One. . . . Hail to you, Rabbi Akiba, you are destined for the life of the future world.' "

Rabbi Hanina ben Teradion, likewise brought before the tribunal for teaching, was asked why he had opposed the commands of the Emperor. He replied: "Because the Lord so commanded me." Whereupon he was wrapped in a scroll of the Torah and burned to death slowly on a pyre of fresh willow wood. His daughter Beruria was carried off to a brothel.

Rabbi Huzpit, the interpreter in the Sanhedrin at Jabneh, had his tongue cut out. Rabbi Judah ben Baba, fearing the complete extinction of the Word, consecrated the remaining last pupils of Akiba. In order not to endanger a city, he withdrew with these six into a lonely valley in

Galilee. Roman informers tracked them down. The pupils fled, and were able to save themselves. Judah ben Baba was pierced by so many lances that his body resembled a sieve.

The deaths of the Ten Martyrs, as they were called, remained unforgotten; these ten represented a whole people. They are still mourned on the Day of Atonement (Yom Kippur) and on the day of memorial for the destruction of Jerusalem (Tishah b'ab).

The dreadful era of persecutions and martyrdoms ended after the death of Hadrian in 138. Soon after his accession to the throne of the empire, Antoninus Pius heeded the desperate pleas of the rabbis and revoked the edicts against the religion of the Jews. Henceforth the Jews were permitted to keep the Sabbath again, to practice circumcision, and to devote themselves to the study of the Torah. The happy news reached Palestine on the twenty-eighth of Adar (February–March). This date, too, was included in the calendar as a memorial day. Only the ban on Jews entering Jerusalem remained in force.

As in the days of the Jewish War, during and after the Bar Kochba rebellion thousands and tens of thousands of fugitives left Judea. New colonies formed, and the geographic boundaries of the Diaspora widened considerably. But the many new emigrants only strengthened the bonds that tied the communities abroad with the old homeland.

The Diaspora of Syria expanded. Antioch, with its large ancient community of Jews, attracted many of the refugees, as did Palmyra in the Syrian Desert—the old Tadmor of the Bible—which was linked to the lands on the Euphrates by the caravan road from the Mediterranean. The Jewish colonies in Asia Minor also swelled. There was a large community in Caesarea Mazaca, in Cappadocia, that was repeatedly visited by Palestinian scholars. Inscriptions on gravestones and memorial tablets recall the active Jewish community life of Smyrna, Ephesus, and many other cities. A whole stream of refugees poured southward to North Africa. But Alexandria was no longer their goal. The new exiles moved into the Roman provinces farther to the west. Important Jewish settlements sprang up in Africa Proconsularis, Numidia, and Mauretania— what are now Tunisia, Algeria, and Morocco. From Carthage to Caesarea in remote Mauretania there now existed a whole chain of communities, each with its own synagogue. Excavations have brought to light innumerable evidences from that period: remains of synagogues with inscriptions in memory of the heads of the communities, who bore the honorary title of *archisynagogus,* and gravestones, often incised with seven-branched candlesticks, from the necropolises. The texts are usually in Greek or Latin, but often with Hebrew words interspersed; the greeting "shalom" (peace) is common.

But even far from their old homeland the Jews living in the Diaspora were not destined to enjoy a long period of peace. With the rise of Christianity, the daughter religion of Judaism, a new, powerful, and inexorable enemy appeared. Paganism had destroyed the political existence of Jewry. Now the time was approaching when victorious Christianity would attempt what Antiochus and Hadrian had failed to do: to stamp out its spiritual existence as well.

THE MAKERS OF THE MISHNAH

It is astonishing that so much strength, such inexhaustible reserves, remained in the people of Israel after such terrible losses, such suffering. In A.D. 135, even while the homeland lay devastated, a scene of death and decay, the intellectual elite of the people rallied once more to defend their religion. Within a few generations they completed a work of profoundest importance. A task of inner reconstruction, of spiritual regeneration, which had been so violently interrupted, was taken up again with devotion and zeal, and was completed. The vast mass of oral doctrine was collected, arranged, and written down, so that it could be preserved forever.

The disciples of Rabbi Akiba—most of the survivors had escaped to Babylon—returned to Palestine. Even Simon, son of the patriarch Gamaliel, emerged from the hiding place where he had survived the years of catastrophe. Judea was deserted, scarcely inhabited; Jabneh was destroyed. But Galilee had suffered somewhat less than the south. The choice of the scholars fell upon the small Galilean town of Usha. All scholars of the Law were summoned to a synod.

The tannaim, or teachers, were as poor as the country itself. Almost all of them practiced some craft in order to feed themselves and their families. Rabbi Meïr, who excelled in spirituality and knowledge, lived by making fair copies of documents and of the Scriptures. Judah ben Ilai of Usha was a cooper; a barrel he had made himself served him for a teacher's chair. Jose ben Halafta of Sepphoris earned a wretched living as a tanner but, along with study of the Law, found time to write the historical work *Seder Olam* (*Order of the World*), a chronicle from the creation of the world to the Bar Kochba war. Johanan was a sandal maker. Simon ben Yohai was virtually destitute. Condemned to death by the Romans, hunted by their informers, he and his son had lived for twelve years in a cave, keeping themselves alive on wild fruits and absorbed in their studies.

The scholars and elders gathered in Usha were bent on restoring their ancient self-government and constitution. A new Sanhedrin was formed, and Simon ben Gamaliel was appointed to the vacant office of patriarch. His closest associate was Rabbi Meïr, and Nathan the Babylonian assisted him as head of the judiciary.

A quarter of a century later their work was crowned by that of a man who commanded authority and prestige in all three of the revived institutions, the academy, Sanhedrin, and patriarchate. He was Judah ha-Nasi (the Patriarch), son of Simon ben Gamaliel. He transferred his labors to Sepphoris, the capital of Galilee. When Judah died, in about 220, after more than forty years of scholarly endeavor, he left behind a gospel that has remained essentially unchanged to the present day. Under his editorship, after long preparation by other scholars, notably Akiba and Meïr, the oral doctrine was codified in its fundamentals.

It had at last become essential to put that doctrine down in writing, if it were not to be lost. This was not only because the body of knowledge had swollen to such vast proportions that very few men could master it completely. The experiences of the Jewish War and the Bar Kochba rebellion had shown how imperiled the oral doctrine was in times of severe persecution. It had been on the verge of being lost forever, and had been saved only by the few surviving disciples of Rabbi Akiba.

Now, set down in writing under the guidance of Rabbi Judah ha-Nasi, the codified oral doctrine existed alongside the Torah, as elaboration and supplement. It was known as the Mishnah, that is, "the Repetition," or "the Instruction." Even during Judah's lifetime his fellow Jews realized what an enormous service he had performed in writing down the Mishnah, which was to form the basis for Jewish culture and literature in succeeding generations. Judah ha-Nasi's fame exceeded even that of Johanan ben Zakkai and of Rabbi Akiba.

As the great Rabbi neared his end, after a severe illness, Jews from far away streamed to Sepphoris in Galilee. Anxiously, they waited the sad tidings. After Judah ha-Nasi had closed his eyes forever, at first no one had the courage to tell the people. At last Bar Kapparah, one of his disciples, took heart, stepped from the house of death in mourning robes, and announced: "Angels and mortals strove with one another for the Ark of the Covenant. The angels won, and the Ark of the Covenant is gone." All understood. Wailing filled the streets. Mourning crowds lined the way when the Rabbi's body was borne to Bet-Shearim for burial in one of the underground tombs where later so many noted teachers were to find their last rest.

FOUNDATION OF THE BABYLONIAN ACADEMIES

More than two thousand years had passed since Abraham's family had departed from Ur of the Chaldees for their first long migration into the Promised Land. Seven centuries had gone by since the Jews captured by Nebuchadnezzar "sat and wept" by the Euphrates when they remembered Zion. Now once again the ancient Land of the Two Rivers, the cradle of Oriental civilization, became a center of Jewish culture. From the academies and schools in Galilee the spark leaped, at the beginning of the third century, to Mesopotamia. Within a few decades the "Mother of the Diaspora" became the leading cultural center of the dispersed people, and in the near future, when darkness once again descended upon the homeland for more than fifteen centuries, Babylon assumed the role of the "new Jerusalem."

Far from the dominance of mighty Rome, the Babylonian Jews had been spared the conflicts that had shaken all the lands of the Mediterranean and plunged Eretz Israel into darkest night. Under the Parthian kings the Jews had enjoyed a peaceful life, with freedom to develop economically and socially. The "great lords of Iran"—bitter enemies of the Romans in the Orient—appreciated their Jewish subjects. They knew that the Jews in Babylonia hated the oppressors of their old homeland. More than once the Jewish communities lent vigorous aid to the Parthians in their wars against Rome.

Here the Jews, their numbers far exceeding all others in the Diaspora, were spread out in numerous communities over a vast territory—a huge reserve who were destined in critical times to preserve the old and make something new of it. In the most fruitful region of southern Mesopotamia, where the courses of the Tigris and the Euphrates approach closer and closer, most of the Jews lived in densely populated settlements. The landscape, cut by canals and ditches, resembled a great island meadow, covered with heavy-yielding grain fields, with lush orchards and truck gardens, shaded by groves of date palms—dates were so plentiful in this land that the saying, "A basket of dates for a denarius," became proverbial. In addition to tilling the fields, the Babylonian Jews raised cattle, engaged in trade, shipping, and all kinds of crafts, and were sought after as experienced canal builders.

Among all the cities, Nehardea took first place. On the shore of the broad Euphrates, where the Nahr Malka, the royal canal, joined the river, it was called the "Babylonian Jerusalem." And, indeed, its population was preponderantly Jewish. Only a few miles south of Nehardea a second heavily populated city rose beside the banks of one of the greater canals. This was the resplendent Pumbaditha. Farther upstream, on a baylike indentation of the river, was the city of Sura. If Pumbaditha enjoyed a reputation for splendid buildings and the cunning character of its inhabitants, Sura was celebrated for its poverty and honesty. "It is better to live on a dungheap in Sura than in the palaces of Pumbaditha," the proverb went.

A fourth city, Machuza, rivaled the three Jewish cities on the Euphrates. Machuza was situated on the bank of the Tigris close to Ctesiphon, the capital of the Parthian Empire. Built on a height beside a canal, protected by strong walls and a deep moat, it had been entrusted to its Jewish inhabitants, in spite of its strategic importance. Its foremost families were descended from converted pagans and hence were more secularly inclined, more devoted to a pleasurable life than to piety, unlike the majority of Orthodox Jews. The Orthodox secretly referred to them as "candidates for hell." Ctesiphon and the new city of Ardashiris also had large Jewish populations.

Among the inhabitants of these cities were many wealthy families, some of whom enjoyed luxuries that the great majority of their fellows scarcely knew existed. In the countryside and in the smaller communities, life was simpler, work harder, and piety therefore more intense.

All these Jews felt at ease in Babylonia. The land had become their second home. Their relationship to the rulers remained flexible; their obligations were limited to payment of a poll tax and a land tax. Otherwise they were left in peace. No one interfered with their internal affairs. They were ruled by their own authorities, whose recognized head was the exilarch, "ruler of the exiles." The holders of this dignity were considered descendants of the House of David, and were revered by the populace. They had considerable influence with the Parthian kings, were received with all honor at audiences and feasts in the royal palace, and were entitled to wear silken upper garments and golden girdles.

The exilarchs resided in resplendent palaces and frequently had large households, swarms of slaves and servants, retinues, and court scholars. They rode forth before the people in gilded carriages, entertained generously, and on holidays received the congratulations and gifts of the people. At the same time, these Jewish "princes of the Orient" carried a heavy load of duties. The exilarch was regarded as the supreme judge of all Babylonian Jews in criminal and civil suits. He decided the most important cases in person; local judges appointed by him dealt with the ordinary affairs of justice. As head of the administration, the exilarch also supervised public safety in all the communities, appointed officials to control trade in the market places, and collected dues and taxes for the treasury. He had the right to punish offenses with "stick and lash." In prestige and dignity the Babylonian princes were equals of the patriarch in Palestine, and in secular matters they held far greater power.

Their one great lack was cultivation and scholarship. Few of the Diaspora princes made a name as scholars; many of them, the tradition reveals, were even ill tutored in the religious law. Consequently, the teachers who fled to Babylonia from the homeland during the years of catastrophe made little impression. In spite of widespread prosperity, general security, and autonomy, Babylonian Jewry lacked a profound knowledge of the Torah and the kind of academic and cultural life that had been the distinguishing feature of the homeland. To be sure, religious instruction in the synagogues was modeled on that of Palestine; but in other respects intellectual life was not comparable with the heights it had reached in the old homeland.

At the beginning of the third century, however, the Diaspora in Babylonia seemed to awaken suddenly from a sleep of centuries. Two highly gifted men succeeded in stirring the communities on the Euphrates to vigorous new intellectual life: Abba Areka, later known as Rav, and Samuel Jarhinai. Both were natives, having spent their childhood and youth in Mesopotamia. But as grown men they had looked in vain for opportunities to study. Far and wide they could find no school of solid reputation, nor any universally respected teacher of the Law. Thirsting for knowledge, like Hillel before them, they turned their backs on their native land and drifted to Palestine, where Judah ha-Nasi was collecting and writing down the Mishnah, and where the academy of Sepphoris had reached the height of its glory.

Abba Areka and Samuel became disciples of the Patriarch Judah, and the two Babylonians soon won admiration and distinction among students and teachers. Abba Areka in particular shone for keenness of mind and dialectical skill. In the discussion of moot points of the Law he often engaged in long debates with his great teacher, and more than once his views triumphed.

As highly respected scholars, familiar with the Mishnah and the rich treasures of Palestinian learning, Abba Areka and Samuel set out for home again about the year 200, filled with hope and confidence and determined to raise the level of Jewish culture in Babylonia. Samuel returned to Nehardea, his birthplace, and reached his goal more swiftly than he had dreamed. Astonished at his comprehensive knowledge, the members of his community chose him to head the small and hitherto unimportant school in the city. Within a few years Samuel had transformed it into a famous academy.

His friend Abba Areka, upon his return, was offered the post of agoranome, or controller of trade, by the Exilarch. His task was to see to the maintenance of correct weights and measures and maximum prices in the market places of all Jewish communities in Babylonia. This required him to travel all over the country, even to the most remote villages and small towns beyond the Tigris. In the course of these travels Abba Areka learned, to his astonishment and dismay, of the alarming ignorance in which so many of the communities dwelt. Many of the requirements of the Torah had been forgotten, or were no longer regarded, among them commandments and prohibitions that everyone in Eretz Israel obeyed with scrupulous care, and whose most trifling details frequently formed the subjects of heated disputes among scholars. Abba Areka did what he could to remedy matters. He taught the people and advised the elders of the communities. These activities brought him into collisions with the Exilarch, who could not enjoy a subordinate's laying down the law. One day the Prince had him thrown into prison. But Abba Areka did not remain locked up for long; he was by then too well known and respected. A high-ranking magistrate reprimanded the Exilarch for punishing unjustly a man who was "so full of the juice of the date," that is, of the spirit. Moreover, Abba Areka had won the high regard of the King of the Parthians, Artabanus V (who ruled from 213 to 227), who had made his acquaintance while Abba Areka was traveling about. The ruler sent him valuable pearls as a gift.

After some twenty years Abba Areka gave up his post of agoranome, resolved to devote himself entirely to spreading the light of learning among his fellow countrymen. Since ignorance of the Law was worst in the vicinity of Sura, he chose to settle in that city. He founded an academy in Sura, modeled after the one in Sepphoris, in the year 219.

As soon as the school opened its doors it was besieged by students. They flocked from all the regions of Babylonia, even from distant Nabataea and Arabia Felix. The thirst for knowledge was acute; the people, so the tradition relates, resembled dried-out sponges.

Within a short time twelve hundred pupils had assembled. The modest structure that had been built for the school was altogether inadequate for such an audience. A large adjacent garden was added for lectures and disputations in the open air. Rav fed many poor pupils at his own expense, for he owned much land and was well-to-do. He also concerned himself with the ordinary folk of the vicinity, the peasants and craftsmen, giving lectures to them in the earliest hours of the morning or late in the evening after they had finished their day's work. Out of this sort of teaching arose something altogether unique for those times: the first genuine institutions for higher popular education, open to all classes of people. Everyone was accepted, no matter what his status or vocation, because the study of the Law was regarded as every man's right and duty. These schools, in charge of rabbis and scholars, became centers of an intellectual life in which an entire people participated.

The Kallá—literally, "the generality"—became famous and was frequently mentioned in Talmudic sources. Twice a year, in spring and autumn, when agricultural labors ceased, these gatherings were held. Seekers of knowledge poured toward Sura from all directions; there were men and youths of all occupations. Even the Exilarch put in an appearance amid the colorful, motley crowd. So many attended that all houses far and wide could not give shelter to the multitude, even though the tiniest huts were pressed into service. Hundreds camped in the open, by the shores of Lake Sura. Sometimes, according to the tradition, as many as twelve thousand people assembled during those months, March and September. The instruction lasted for a full month; not a day passed that was not filled from morning to night with lectures and elucidations. Often the discussions and the dialectic of question and answer went on late into the night. Along with examination of technical questions, instruction in the tracts of the Mishnah, and commentaries on commentaries, there were instructive lectures for the simpler folk on the meaning of the High Holy Days.

The great scholar of Sura carried learning to the people as had none other before him. It was proof of how they honored him that his pupils called him simply Rav—the word for "master" or "teacher" in the Babylonian dialect of Aramaic. Abba Areka not only stimulated scholarship in Babylonia; he also raised the prestige of the courts and laid the groundwork for a general improvement of manners and morals. Moreover, his interpretations and commentaries on the Mishnah prepared the way for the important work of the future: the Babylonian Talmud. In spite of his vast scholarly work, Rav also found time to write religious poetry. Many hymns are ascribed to him. The most famous of these, the Alenu, later became the evening prayer of Jews throughout the world.

Samuel, Rav's great friend and head of the school at Nehardea, was engaged in a fundamentally different kind of work. Deeply versed in secular as well as religious knowledge, he did not restrict his studies to the tradition and the interpretation of doctrine. A rare exception among the Torah teachers of his time, he applied himself to mathematics, the sciences, and medicine; he was also a practicing physician. An eye salve he had concocted was highly esteemed. Astronomy, however, was his favorite study.

"The orbits of the heavenly bodies," he once declared, "are as familiar to me as the streets of Nehardea. Only the comets perplex me." The rabbis of the Palestinian school frowned upon these astronomical efforts, for out of his own lore Samuel had made a calendar in which the holidays were precisely calculated. But he forbore to publish it, for from time immemorial the determination of holiday dates had been the privilege of the Sanhedrin in Eretz Israel; this custom was indeed one of the bonds that held the dispersed communities together.

Samuel also functioned as district magistrate in Nehardea, and enjoyed the reputation of a great authority on the civil law. It was he who formulated the principle that was later to dominate the thinking of the Diaspora in some respects: "The law of the State is Law." Long ago the prophet Jeremiah had offered the following rule for behavior in a foreign land to the exiles in Babylonia: "And seek the peace of the city whither I have caused you to be carried away captive, and pray unto the Lord for it; for in the peace thereof shall ye have peace" (Jeremiah 29:7). Samuel took this admonition from the days of the first exile and explicitly made it into a religious principle. Henceforth the laws of the country were to be as binding upon the Jews as their own Law in the Torah and Talmud. This willing acceptance of the laws of their host countries often became, later, the salvation of the Dispersed.

In the midst of the cultural renaissance initiated by Rav and Samuel, political changes suddenly threatened to destroy their work. The Persians, the former masters of Babylonia, rose against the Parthians, whom they hated. Ardashir, scion of an old Persian family, led the rebels. He conquered Iran and all the other territories of the Parthian Kingdom, including Babylonia. King Artabanus fell in battle against the rebels. In 224 Ardashir ascended the throne as the "king of kings of Iran." The New Persian Kingdom of the Sassanidae had begun.

Rav was distressed by the news of the death of Artabanus, the king who had been so well disposed toward the Jews as well as his personal friend. "Now the bonds are broken," he cried sadly. The great scholar of Sura had a premonition of woes to come for the Jews of the Diaspora.

In Persepolis, the ancient holy city of the Persians, the flames flared forebodingly in the Temple of Fire. The Magi, priests of the old Iranian Zoroastrian religion, had acquired great influence upon the new King and the affairs of state. These zealots of fire worship were bent on disseminating the cult of fire and faith in the dual principles of light and darkness among the unbelievers.

The Babylonian Diaspora was soon to feel the painful consequences of these changes. Political as well as religious persecutions followed. The Jewish communities were stripped of their independent judicial powers. Jews were banished from public office; they were even forbidden such jobs as supervision of rivers and canals. Strict prohibitions were issued concerning the festivals of the new rulers, when the Magi worshiped light as the visible image of their god, Ahura Mazda. On such days no hearth fire might be kindled throughout the kingdom, no lamp lighted. The fire worshipers forced their way into the homes of Jews, put out all fires, gathered the embers in their sacred fire vessels, and even carried off all supplies of fuel to the places where they offered official sacrifices. Burial of the dead was forbidden; the Magi regarded the earth as sacred and therefore not to be contaminated. Corpses were placed on high towers for the vultures to dispose of.

For more than a decade the fanatical Magi held the whip hand and imposed their will upon the land. Then at last the pressure relaxed, or, rather, yielded to the stubborn resistance of the densely populated Diaspora communities. The pleas and laments of the Jews at last found a hearing at the royal court. Shapur I, who ascended the Sassanid throne in 241, proved to be mildly disposed. He restricted the powers of the zealot priests and displayed open sympathy toward his Jewish subjects. Involved in an interminable war with the Romans, Shapur soon recognized that these Babylonian Jews had not forgiven the Caesars for the destruction of the Holy Land. They proved stout allies in his struggle with Rome. Moreover, as prosperous subjects they were able to contribute important financial aid to the equipping of armies and the prosecution of war.

Abba Areka lived long enough to see this turn for the better. He died peacefully in 247, after having headed his academy in Sura for thirty years. After his passing Samuel was recognized as the sole head of schools throughout Babylonia. Samuel had also succeeded in winning the favor of King Shapur I, and he remained on friendly terms with the ruler, often participating in banquets at court along with other Jews. Open-minded and ready to learn from anyone, Samuel shared with the Magi an interest in astronomy. He frequently discussed astronomical theory and observations of the stars with Ablaat, the Persian astrologist. Before he died in 257, ten years after Rav, he could feel that he and his associate had in the course of half a century fundamentally transformed Jewry in Babylonia. After long ages of subsisting in darkness, the "Mother of the Diaspora" had now moved to the side of Palestine as the preserver of Jewish tradition and builder upon those traditions. In the not too distant future she would stand alone, carrying on the heritage that had been expelled from its homeland by the Jordan.

THE LAST CENTURY OF PAGAN ROME

After the death of Marcus Aurelius (121–180) enormous unrest took possession of the colossus that was the Roman Empire. Rome's legions, for centuries accustomed to advancing in successful campaigns of aggression, found themselves suddenly driven into the role of defenders, fighting almost incessantly in wearing battles and skirmishes along the borders of the empire. The assaults upon Rome's dominance increased from all sides; various tribes of Germans waged them in the north, and the rulers of Mesopotamia in the east.

In the midst of this ferment of the last century of pagan Rome, Jewry was enjoying a breathing spell. For the time being, the Jews who had remained in the homeland, and those scattered throughout the Roman Empire, were granted a relatively quiet life. In the legal sense matters took a turn for the better for them. In 212 the famous *lex Antoniniana de civitate* was proclaimed: Roman citizenship was conferred upon all free inhabitants of the empire. Emperor Caracalla did not except the Jews; they, too, became citizens with full rights, sharing like all other peoples of the empire the advantages as well as the burdens of citizenship.

Privileged as they had always been, as the only people exempted from making sacrifice to the Roman gods, their religion tolerated, subject to no occupational restrictions, the Jews in the empire now enjoyed unclouded liberty. Their conditions were no different from those of all other peoples of the empire.

Elgabal, Caracalla's successor, was equally well disposed toward the Jews, so much so that some Romans mockingly said that he had had himself circumcised and abhorred pork.

Alexander Severus, the emperor (222–235) of Syrian origin, treated the Jews with emphatic friendliness. He made no secret of his admiration for the ethical greatness of Judaism, and alongside the Roman gods in his private temple he kept a statue of Abraham. He also had inscribed on his palace and on public buildings the famous maxim of Hillel: "What you would not have done to yourself, do not do to others." At the Emperor's orders heralds proclaimed this maxim even in army camps, as a warning to the legionaries who might yield to predatory impulses. During his campaigns against the Persians, Alexander Severus repeatedly displayed his favor to the Jews in Palestine. He restored some measure of self-administration to them, with the patriarch once more holding the right to judge in capital cases, and the Jewish judges in general deciding all civil disputes among their coreligionists—much to the displeasure of the Greeks and Romans in the country. The Emperor's pro-Semitic policies also discomfited the inhabitants of Antioch and Alexandria. They sneered at the Emperor as a "Syrian high priest."

In 235 Alexander Severus was killed by his own soldiers on the Rhine. A period of anarchy followed; ten emperors were acclaimed and killed within barely two decades. "Today's Caesar pushed yesterday's from the throne," the saying went.

During these troublous times Rome was not worrying about internal affairs in remote provinces. The arrangements of Alexander Severus were left untouched, and the authorities in Palestine made good use of the situation. Once again the patriarchate rose in prestige, enjoying a last glimmer of its ancient glory. While still a youth, the grandson of the great Judah ha-Nasi, Rabbi Judah II Nessia, assumed that high office and held it for more than half a century (c. 230–286), virtually heading a national government. Judah II did not have the stature or the amazingly versatile talents of his grandfather. He was not particularly distinguished for scholarship, but then, he made no claim to legislative authority; rather, he asserted the administrative powers of the patriarchate.

Judah II established his residence in Tiberias, on the pleasant shores of the Sea of Galilee, to which the academy of scholars had also moved. The Roman governor in Caesarea fully recognized his authority. "Even now," the Christian writer Origen states, "when the Romans rule and the Judeans pay their tribute, the double drachma, the ethnarch [patriarch] still exercises extensive power, along with Caesar. The secret tribunals still judge by their own law, and sometimes death sentences are passed, although they are not empowered to pass such sentences, at least not without the Procurator's knowing about it. I have discovered this for myself, since I remained for a long time in the land of this people."

Many aspects of the Patriarch's life-style offended the more austere teachers of the law. Judah II often spoke Greek among friends and family, and took an interest in Greek literature. Sometimes, too, there was unpleasantness about the extravagance of his court. The Patriarch was surrounded by "princely splendor, has an honor guard and many of the signs of sovereignty." Small though the court was, it cost money, and the populace lived more poorly than ever. One day when the Patriarch complained about the burden of high Roman exactions, the teacher Resh Lakish replied sharply: "Do not take and nothing will be taken from you."

But Judah II contrived to win great prestige. The people revered him, both within Palestine and beyond its borders. Generally progressive in his attitudes, he made efforts to bring the customs and prohibitions of the people up to date. For example, during the Jewish War the purchase of olive oil from pagans had been forbidden. This prohibition had remained in force for over a century and a half, until Judah II abolished it. His decision met with general approval; the teachers Samuel and Rav followed suit for the communities in Babylonia.

Judah II also strove to raise the level of schooling and to spread knowledge among the populace. "The whole world," he declared, "lives on the breath of small school children. Not even a work such as the building of a temple should distract men from the holy cause of instructing children." On his orders, teachers constantly traveled about the country, looking into the state of schooling in cities and small towns.

In the meantime, scholars were continuing along the paths that Judah ha-Nasi had laid down. It had taken three centuries to complete the mighty work begun by Hillel and Shammai, rescued in the hour of mortal danger by Johanan ben Zakkai, and first committed to writing by Judah ha-Nasi. The most precious heritage of the past aside from the Torah, the "oral doctrine" had been poured into a firm mold, set down in writing as the Mishnah, and thus saved for the future. For many hundreds of years that was to be the last contribution of the spirit to come out of the ancient homeland in Israel.

But the project was still not completed. For another three centuries and more, the scholars who succeeded to that heritage labored to develop and expand it. The tannaim (teachers) were followed by the amoraim, the "speakers" or "interpreters" of the Mishnah. That great compilation of religious law had left many questions open, for even Judah ha-Nasi could not have dealt with all cases and precedents. The teachers therefore set about adding critical explanations and commentaries, called, in Aramaic, Gemara, or "completion." Among the items included were records of the debates in academies and schools of the old homeland and in Babylonia. These discussions were conducted with learning and perspicacity, and often with refinements of sophistry. Explanations sometimes ran off into wild divagations. In the Gemara historical materials are mingled with legends, proverbs with parables, medical counsel with astronomical and scientific lore. The whole vast mass of material, the Mishnah together with the Gemara, constitutes that enormous and wholly unique work called the Talmud.

Two commentators on the Mishnah who lived in Galilee during the lifetime of Patriarch Judah II towered over all others: Johanan bar Napacha and Resh Lakish, his brother-in-law. Both were extraordinarily gifted as scholars but presented a contrast in character and fate, in effectiveness and creativity.

Johanan was by nature mild, sensitive, and open to the currents of the age, a sage who appreciated Greek culture as well as his own. Resh Lakish was physically powerful, single-minded, and intensely pious, and a stickler for the letter of the law. Here were two contradictory temperaments such as Hillel and Shammai had been, and their encounter, the conflict of their views, was to promote a wider and deeper analysis of the bulky collection of precedents and opinions incorporated into the Mishnah.

Johanan surpassed Resh Lakish and all other scholars in mental agility—the sources have wonderful tales to tell concerning his intellectual feats. In his earliest youth he had heard the lectures of the great teacher Judah ha-Nasi, sitting in the "seventeenth row," as he precisely recalled. During his early years he had endured misery and privation, and had spent a long time in restless wanderings until the urge came to him to devote himself entirely to learning. He finally established a school of his own in Tiberias. To his pupils and disciples he lectured indefatigably on the Mishnah, comparing texts, resolving apparent contradictions.

Resh Lakish found his way back to scholarship only after a lifetime full of adventure—for a time he had actually performed in arenas as an animal tamer. The turning point came when he and Johanan, who had been old schoolmates, met again. Johanan gave Resh Lakish his beautiful sister to wife and summoned him to Tiberias. Within a short time Resh Lakish acquired a reputation as one of the most acute interpreters of the Law. He often proved superior to his brother-in-law in manipulation of the dialectic. Once started on this course, he became wholly devoted to study. "If you are unfaithful to scholarship for a single day," he would often tell his pupils, "it will repay you with double unfaithfulness."

Johanan, ably assisted by Resh Lakish, laid the foundation for what has since become known as the Palestinian Talmud. The fame of the academy in Tiberias attracted people from far beyond the borders of the country. Among these were many students from Babylonia who had come to study the ancient traditions in the land of their origin. The enthusiasm Rav and Samuel had stirred in the communities along the Euphrates was beginning to bear fruit. These young Babylonians were perhaps too clever, for the Palestinian scholars were not always delighted with them. One day Resh Lakish let his vexation get the best of him, and said to the Babylonians: "Disperse! At the time you could have been a wall for Judea, you remained at home. What do you want here now?"

The schools of Galilee were still the intellectual centers of Judaism at this time. But the outlines of future developments could already be discerned. Rabbi Johanan's foremost disciples proved to be Babylonians: Rabbi Eleazar ben Pedat, whom his countrymen would later call Teacher of the Land of Israel; the twins Ami and Assi, who later would head the academy in Tiberias; Rabbi Simon bar Abba; and Rabbi Hiya bar Abba. None of Rabbi Johanan's Palestinian disciples could approach them in learning or skill in debate.

At this time, also, Judaism was encountering an ever more powerful opponent in the new religion that had sprung from its own womb: Christianity. The first significant centers of Christian life had already sprung up in Palestine itself. In Jerusalem, which was still closed to Jews, a Christian congregation had established a firm foothold. The bishop of the Palestinian Christians resided in Caesarea—in other words, a form of church organization was already in existence. Origen, one of the first major Christian thinkers, made his home in Palestine. He had come from Egypt to learn Hebrew, so that he could study the Bible in the original. Rabbis instructed him, one of his teachers being Hillel, a brother of the Patriarch. Origen associated with these men for decades.

The Diaspora communities in Africa became the target of strong attacks by the Christians. In what are now Algeria, Tunis, and Morocco tensions steadily mounted. Tertullian, the Church Father, waged a vehement campaign against the Jews in North Africa, and his successors proved equally virulent. Commodian, the Bishop of Carthage, fiercely denounced Jews and Judaizing, and called the sad lot of the Jewish people a deserved punishment for their denial of Christ. His utterances show him to have been seriously concerned with battling the "Jewish temptation." "Why do you go running into the synagogue?" he cried out to the pagans who sympathized with Judaism. "Do you wish to be half Jew, half heathen? You were blind, and now you are in the midst of blind men, you fools. The blind man can only draw his blind fellow after him into a pitfall."

Under the twin assault of Greeks with deeply rooted anti-Jewish feelings and Christians with new-found fanaticism, Judaism in Egypt was reduced to insignificance. Christianity won the upper hand. In Egypt and North Africa, in Syria and Asia Minor, in Greece itself—wherever Greek was spoken—Christianity became the dominant religion. The proselyte movement, the conversion of pagans to Judaism, virtually ground to a halt. The few Jewish cells that remained scattered here and there lived in isolation, concerned chiefly with preserving their ancient traditions. The really vital, energetic, and progressive centers of Judaism were now limited to Palestine and, above all, Mesopotamia.

But both these countries were affected by the power struggles between Rome and the New Persian Empire. After endless campaigns the Persian ruler, Shapur I, succeeded in penetrating into Syria and Asia Minor. Emperor Valerian advanced at the head of an army, determined to wrest these conquests from the Sassanid. But Rome met with a signal disgrace: The Emperor was defeated near Edessa in 260 and was taken prisoner.

In this hour of weakness and peril the Romans were saved by Odaenathus, an Arab prince from the oasis of Palmyra. With a private army of Saracens he expelled the Sassanidae from Syria, crossed the Euphrates, and boldly advanced deep into Mesopotamia. This campaign, in which Odaenathus penetrated as far as the New Persian capital of Ctesiphon, took a heavy toll of the Jewish communities of Babylonia.

Units of Jewish soldiers hurled themselves bravely at the invaders from Palmyra and inflicted heavy losses upon them. Nevertheless they could not stop the Saracen army, who made them pay terribly for their loyal defense of the country on the side of the Sassanidae. Prosperous, largely Jewish Nehardea was captured by Odaenathus, who gave permission to his Saracen hordes to sack the city. After a frightful slaughter among the populace, Nehardea was burned and razed. The famous academy of Samuel, the scene of his lifework, was reduced to rubble. He himself was spared the sight; he had died a few years earlier. But along with many others the great sage's daughters were taken prisoner and carried away to Sepphoris in Galilee. The Palmyrans held this valuable human booty for ransom; they knew they could obtain larger sums that way than in the slave markets, for it was well known that Jews would spare no sacrifice to buy the freedom of captive coreligionists.

Odaenathus, the oasis princeling, was well recompensed for his aid to Rome. Henceforth he was allowed to call himself Consul and Army Leader of the Orient. Overnight Palmyra had become a mighty power, holding dominion over Asia Minor, Syria, and Palestine. But the destroyer of Nehardea did not enjoy his new prestige for long. He was assassinated by envious kinsmen. After his death his wife, Zenobia Augusta, succeeded to his throne—with even more ambitious plans in her head. A woman of unusual vigor, cultivation, and intelligence, she had determined to become Empress and the "Semiramis of Palmyra." She succeeded in extending her sphere of influence as far as Egypt, and in launching a vast building program that transformed her Palmyra into one of the most magnificent cities of the Orient. She assiduously promoted art and science and attracted cultivated Romans to her court.

Palestine did not share in this splendor. In fact, it was a dreary time for the land that had once been Judea. Jewish traditions mention Ze-

nobia, but they have nothing favorable to say about the inhabitants of Palmyra or its rulers. Rabbi Johanan, a contemporary of Odaenathus and
Zenobia, once remarked: "Blessed is he who will live to see the fall of
Tadmor." (Tadmor was the native, Palmyra the Greek and Roman name.)
There are dark tales of persecutions of Jews under the "Empress," and of
petitionary visits by envoys of the Patriarch to her court. Jewish guerrilla
bands seem to have harassed Zenobia's troops whenever they passed
through Palestine.

The collapse of this remarkable dream-kingdom, which shone like a
mirage in the desert, was as sudden as its rise had been. In 273 Emperor
Aurelian put an end to the tiny city-state that had tried to create an empire around itself. Zenobia, in golden chains, was brought to Rome to be
paraded in his triumph. Rabbi Johanan saw his wish fulfilled in his lifetime, for the Roman soldiers destroyed much of the city. In the following centuries earthquakes and the decline of trade completed the downfall; Palmyra was forgotten and its great ruins rediscovered by the European West only in the late seventeenth century.

Palestine, which had already seen so many powers rise and fall, survived the short-lived drama of Palmyra's explosive expansion and contraction. But the energies of the motherland, once seemingly inexhaustible,
were fast fading. That fruitful womb, which for fifteen centuries had produced kings, generals, and soldiers of liberty, towering prophets, match-
less poets, and great teachers of morals and laws, seemed now exhausted.
Within a few years the last of the great men left the stage: Rabbi Johanan
bar Napacha died in 286; his friend and associate Resh Lakish had been
carried off only a short while before. Patriarch Judah II died in the same
year. Schools and the institutions of self-government began to founder.
The homeland, toward which the eyes of Jews in the Diaspora had hitherto been directed, no longer exerted this force. But all intellectual creativity
had not come to an end. It continued to flow vigorously "beyond the
river"—by the Euphrates. The academies of Babylonia were ready, prepared to take up the torch.

For forty years Huna (died 297) headed the academy at Sura. Thanks
to his uncontested authority, Babylonia achieved full intellectual independence. Huna accomplished what even his teacher, Rav, had failed to do; he
made the "Mother of the Diaspora" equal in dignity to Eretz Israel. "In
Babylonia we consider ourselves to be exactly as if in the Holy Land."

Nahman bar Jacob had opened a school in Machuza on the Tigris.
Hisda of Kafri, Shesheth the Blind, and Hama bar Hanilai were among the
most famous of the scholars. Amends were made for the loss of Nehardea; soon after its destruction Pumbaditha on the Euphrates became a new

center of scholarship, in which the best teachers from Samuel's famous academy were reunited. Under Judah ben Ezekiel (whom friends called the sharp-witted) it became the intellectual center of northern Babylonia as Sura had become for the southern part of the country.

These two sister academies were destined for an extraordinarily long life. "With brief interruptions the schools of Sura and Pumbaditha dominated intellectual life during the following eight centuries," Cecil Roth remarks. "They were, so to speak, the Oxford and Cambridge of Mesopotamian Jewry. But we must conceive of a state of affairs in which scholarship enjoyed all the prestige and reverence that was paid to religion in the Middle Ages. We must consider that the heads of the best academies were no less powerful than the archbishops of Canterbury and York in medieval England, and we must remember that the masters of the Law did not hesitate to oppose the civil power—and sometimes with striking success."

The cultural level of the Babylonian Jews was remarkably high, for there was compulsory schooling for all boys from the ages of five or six on. Instruction began in the home and extended to the "university"; the graded educational system took in all children, youths, and adults. Every town had its school, for "A town that has no school children to show for itself," says the Talmud, "can easily go down to destruction." Work loads, as we would term them today, were strictly regulated; no teacher was permitted to instruct more than twenty-five pupils. If the number increased, he had to procure an assistant. In the elementary schools everyone was taught reading and writing. Supplementing the secondary schools and the academies that were meant for scholars was a popular system of higher schools for the ordinary man. "The class of scholars," Simon Dubnow remarks, "formed, in Jewry, the highest aristocracy, with whom neither the nobility of birth nor that of wealth could compare."

In Palestine, meanwhile, the glories of the past had fled. The Patriarch's court was modest indeed. His scholars were as poor as the whole country, as destitute as the rest of the people. In order to remedy things, the Patriarch sent "apostles" into other countries to collect contributions and gifts for the homeland. But interest in study continued to diminish under the harsh conditions of life. Only a few pupils sat in lecture halls that had once been thronged.

Judah III was as bent on improving education as his predecessor, Judah II, had been. He sent scholars traveling about the country to inspect schools and to take measures where buildings had fallen into disrepair or the level of instruction had sunk too low. But the scholars had many sad experiences. Tradition has preserved one significant tale. One day the emissaries came to a town and looked about in vain for the teacher. Finally they asked: "Where are the guardians of the town?" Hurriedly, a few of the armed guards of the town were called and brought before them. "These men are not the guardians of the town, but its destroyers," the envoys exclaimed angrily. "We mean the scholars and teachers who serve the word of God, for it is written: 'If God does not guard the city, the watch watches in vain.' "

Rabbis Ami and Assi, native Babylonians, taught at the academy in Tiberias, along with Rabbi Hiya bar Abba, a fellow countryman from Mesopotamia. In Caesarea, Rabbi Abbahu, a man of considerable secular learning who was held in esteem by the Romans, taught in a community of some size. Not especially distinguished as a scholar, he was famous for another gift; he was an eloquent, stirring preacher. He had, it was said, a particular talent for comforting the people by his sermons, which were built around some phrase in the Scriptures.

As a roving lecturer, Abbahu could always count on larger audiences than could Hiya bar Abba. Abbahu's sermons appealed directly to the public, which could not always follow Hiya's intricate arguments. Hiya complained bitterly about the neglect of his teaching. But Abbahu consoled him. "Behold," he said, "your teaching is like the valuable gems that only rare connoisseurs appreciate; my sermons, on the other hand, resemble baubles that everyone likes." Abbahu was a gentle and forbearing man who remained modest all his life, even after he had won such wealth in his secular occupation—he manufactured women's veils—that he could afford Gothic slaves and couches with legs of ivory in his home. Abbahu often comforted his people for the insults they received in the theater at Caesarea, where vulgar jokes at the expense of the manners and habits of the Jews were a commonplace. Samples of these jokes have been preserved; they suggest a rather laborious sense of humor. One skit ran: "Why is the camel mourning?" "Because the Jews who are strict in their observance of the sabbatical year do not even eat weeds; they feed on thistles. The camel is mourning because they have taken away his favorite food."

In another skit Momus, the Greek god of mockery, appeared on the stage with shorn head. "Why is Momus mourning?" "Because oil is so dear." "Why is oil so dear?" "Because of the Jews. They consume on the Sabbath everything they earn on weekdays. They don't even have enough wood to cook all the food, so they have to burn their beds and sleep on the ground at night, rolling in the dust. Then to get rid of the dust they use a lot of oil. That's why oil is so dear."

Abbahu stalwartly defended Judaism against the increasingly violent attacks of the Christians. He cited verses of the Bible to counter the Christian dogmas of divine sonship and the Ascension. "God is not like an earthly king," Abbahu argued. "He has neither a father nor a son nor a brother. This is the meaning of the Biblical verse: 'I am the first, and I am the last, and beside Me there is no God.'" The Christians attempted to support the dogma of the Ascension by referring to Enoch, of whom it says in the Bible: "And Enoch walked with God, and he was not; for God took him" (Genesis 5:24). Rabbi Abbahu replied by citing many passages in Scripture which showed unmistakably that the phrase "God took him" was used in the sense of "God caused him to die."

Abbahu regarded the Scriptures as the possession of his own people, sprung from their womb, and he never tired of defending them. This was still permissible—a generation later and he would have had to pay for his courageous words with death.

At this particular time, however, another great protector of the Jews held the throne of the Caesars, a ruler who stretched his hand over them and guaranteed them what, on the whole, in spite of the wars between Jews and Romans, had become a firm tradition in the Roman Empire's policy toward the Jews: freedom of conscience and unhindered exercise of their religion. The new Emperor's name was Diocletian.

After fifty years of anarchy (235–285) following the death of Alexander Severus, the principle of strong rule was once again reasserted under Diocletian. This son of a slave succeeded in checking the threatening collapse of the vast empire. Following the pattern of Oriental despotism, he instituted a form of administration new to the Roman world: absolute monarchy.

The Jews of Palestine and of the Diaspora watched these upheavals with close attention. As always, there were some who found in the Bible predictions of contemporary political events. According to some interpreters, the fourth beast of the visions in the book of Daniel signified the Roman Empire. "Three of the first horns were plucked up by the roots" (Daniel 7:8), the vision reads. Had not three emperors been overthrown —Carus, Carinus, and Carausius—before Diocletian was able to win the purple for himself?

Diocletian cruelly persecuted the Christians, whose missionary efforts seemed to him responsible for the decay of the Roman state religion. But he left the Jews unmolested. In 286 he issued an edict requiring all nations of the empire to sacrifice to the Roman gods, but the Jews alone were exempted from this coercion of conscience.

Under the strong hand of Diocletian, the years passed in peace and security for the Jews. Except for two stipulations, there were no sanctions upon the Jewish communities of the Diaspora or the homeland. The two exceptions were the requirement that the Jews pay the *fiscus judaicus,* as they had done ever since the fall of Jerusalem, and the ban on their setting foot inside their former capital. But the Jews were not long to enjoy these favorable conditions. In 305 Diocletian, after having reigned for twenty years, laid down his office and retired to Dalmatia. In his beautifully situated palace in Spalato near Salona he watched the liquidation of his work. The structure he had patched up with so much effort was nearly shattered in a series of civil wars among his old comrades in arms and coregents. Barely a decade later came the great turning point. In the same year, 313, in which Diocletian, the last bitter persecutor of the Christians, closed his eyes forever, a new era in history began. Christianity entered into an alliance with the emperors, became the religion of state, and set about assuming the heritage of pagan Rome. The age of Christian Rome was dawning.

CONSTANTINE THE GREAT

One of the most momentous battles in history was fought outside the gates of Rome in the autumn of the year 312.

Two powerful men among the rival successors to Diocletian met for the test of strength: Constantine, who after the death of his father in 306 had been acclaimed Augustus of the entire West, and the Emperor Maxentius, who commanded Italy and Africa. After a bloody struggle on October 28, Maxentius fell near the Pons Mulvius, which crosses the Tiber in the northern part of the capital. Constantine was the victor and master of Rome. Christian tradition looks upon this battle as the great turning point in its history, from which awareness sprang the legend that before the battle Constantine had a vision of a cross in the sky, and was promised: "In this sign you will win."

In fact, Constantine owed his victory to a considerable extent to the Christian soldiers in the ranks of his army. A decade later, with their help, he defeated his Eastern coregent, Licinius, and became sole ruler. He then transferred his capital to Byzantium on the Bosporus, and named it both New Rome, to suggest its dignity, and Constantinople, to commemorate himself.

The Emperor could not help observing the vast growth of the new religion in every province of the empire. Instead of combating it, as Diocletian had done, he made peace between the state and the hitherto persecuted Christians. With Constantine, Christianity began its evolution into the religion of the state. In 313 the Emperor issued his subsequently famous Edict of Milan. It promised all citizens of the Roman Empire freedom of conscience. For Christians the imperial decree meant that at last their religion had officially attained equality in law with paganism.

The edict of toleration also included the Jews. It merely confirmed once more what was already established by law: Judaism was a *religio licita,* a legal religion. Its official representatives, the patriarchs and elders, the heads of schools and synagogues, continued to enjoy the same rights that were now being granted to the Christian clergy.

The weapons of violence, with which pagan Rome had hitherto suppressed Christianity, had not been able to prevent its victorious advance. "What an astonishing process this was," writes Heinrich Graetz, "that a Jewish child from Nazareth was able to subject thrones and empires to himself. Who can fail to recognize this as a historical necessity, by which the old, worn-out world was consigned to its grave and a new world permitted to arise? Judaism might well have rejoiced in this victory of the spirit over armed might, if victorious Christianity had made a reality out of its founder's gentleness. But its dominion . . . only brought new, grave, and protracted trials upon Judaism."

Tolerance toward the Jews lasted only a short time under Constantine. The first anti-Jewish decrees followed just two years after the Edict of Milan. Henceforth Judaism and Jewry were to be subject to attacks that in harshness and duration have no parallel in all of history. Jewry was to find its cruelest enemy in Christianity, which owes its origins to the Jewish religion, derives its highest ethical doctrines from the spirit and the thought of great sons of Israel, sings the Psalms and repeats the ancient prayers of the Jews. Christianity, having risen to power in the secular state, did everything it could to break the spirit of the Jews and to convert them. The Jewish religion became, for Christians, the "unholy cult" of a damned, "blasphemous nation"; the members of that nation were condemned as "deicides," "Christ-killers."

The pattern of many centuries, of the Middle Ages and down to the very recent past, was first laid under Constantine.

In 315 the Jews unexpectedly received a reprimand from the supreme seat of government. Under penalty of being burned alive they were forbidden to proselytize for their religion among Christians, or to molest any of their own fellows who had already been converted to Christianity. The imperial decree read: "We herewith inform the Judeans, their chiefs and patriarchs: If after publication of this law anyone shall dare to molest with stones or in any other way one who has left their harmful sect [*eorum feralem sectam*] and converted to the cult of God, as to our knowledge frequently happens nowadays, is to be given over to the flames and burned along with his accomplices. But if anyone of the people shall join their abominable sect [*nefariam sectam*] or attend their gatherings, he will be subjected to the deserved punishment together with them [who converted him] " (Codex Theodosianus XVI, 8, 1). Thus the religion of the people of Israel was publicly contemned. But this was only the beginning. In 321 an ancient, guaranteed privilege of the Jews was annulled by law: their freedom from the Roman decurionate. Exercise of this office in the municipal administrations constituted a heavy burden for those forced to accept it. On the whole, men of wealth were selected, for they were personally responsible out of their own fortunes for every error or delinquency in the collection of taxes for a city.

"We permit all authorities," the text of the decree ran, "to summon Jews to the curia. But in order that they receive some compensation for abandonment of the former custom [*i.e.,* freedom from this office], we grant that two or three of them at any given time may be exempted from the call." Ten years later other decrees somewhat lightened the burdens thus imposed. Constantine ordered that "rabbis, archisynagogi, synagogue elders, and others who hold office in the synagogues shall be free of all personal obligations."

The two religions were still not differentiated from one another with sufficient clarity. The Church Fathers feared that Christians might fall under Jewish influence. The religion of the People of the Book still constituted a strong rival, which had to be repressed with every means at the disposal of those early builders of the Christian Church. The extent to which the Church endeavored to make a sharp line of division, and to eliminate the last traces of a connection with Judaism, is evident from some of the proceedings at the First Ecumenical Council of Nicaea.

More than two hundred bishops and other members of the clergy assembled in the year 325 in the small town of Nicaea near the imperial residence of Nicomedia in Asia Minor. Constantine himself had convoked the Council to settle the differences between the Arians, followers of the Alexandrian presbyter Arius, who did not recognize Jesus as the equal of God, and the followers of Bishop Alexander, whose views were destined to become the orthodox position of the Church. Torn between these doctrines, the Christian East had fallen into virtual anarchism. A split Church could not justify the hopes that the Emperor had placed in Christianity. Hence Constantine had determined that the dispute must be settled, the rent unity repaired, before the forum of the entire Church.

In the midst of the discussions on the dogma of the Trinity and the Credo, in the midst of the raging disputes over the theological question of whether the Son of God was like in essence to the Father, the Council made a decision that forever separated the new religion from the old in the celebration of its highest feast day. Easter, the oldest and most meaningful of all the Christian holy days, had hitherto been celebrated by the Christian congregations in Asia at the same time as the Jewish Passover, on the day calculated and announced according to the ancient custom by the Sanhedrin in Palestine. Henceforth, the Christian feast was to be separated from the Jewish calendar; this demand was put forth by the Western, Roman Church, and was accepted. Henceforth, the Council decided, Christians would celebrate Easter independently of the Jewish Passover. The day was set as the first Sunday after the full moon of the spring month.

"It would be unworthy," the text of the Council's decision argued, "for us to follow for this holy feast the custom of the Jews who soiled their hands with the most monstrous crimes and remained spiritually blind. Henceforth we wish to have nothing more in common with the people of the Jews, who are hostile to us, for our Saviour has shown us another way. . . . It would indeed be contrary to good sense to permit the Jews to boast that we are not able to celebrate the Passover without their instructions."

Bishop Eusebius, the principal spokesman of the Council, in his *Ecclesiastical History* puts these words into the mouth of the Emperor Constantine. But whether or not Constantine spoke them, they corresponded to the general views of the Church, which then proceeded to enforce the new dictum. All the Eastern Christian congregations, in Asia Minor, Syria, and even in distant Mesopotamia, which went on celebrating Easter along with the Jews on the night of the fourteenth of Nissan, were condemned as "Judaizing" and threatened with excommunication.

The laws concerning the Jews tended at the beginning of Constantine's reign to vacillate between sternness and tolerance, but toward the end all ambiguities vanished. An edict issued in 335 once again sternly forbade the Jews to molest any of their fellows who had converted to Christianity. At the same time they were forbidden under threat of dire punishment to circumcise their heathen or Christian slaves, or to win such slaves over to their religion. If a slave was converted, the Jew lost his property right and was required to release the slave.

Who or what was the motivating force behind all these anti-Jewish legislative acts? Was it the Emperor, or was it the Christian Church?

Constantine had not been raised as a Christian. In the years of his struggle against Maxentius he had been a declared devotee of Apollo. According to one legend, he received baptism only on his deathbed. "Constantine could not have known all that is implied by 'Church,'" the historian Alfred Heuss comments, "nor could he have had the remotest inkling of what we would call establishmentarianism. For the former, he was too little a Christian; for the latter, he would have had to be a seer capable of looking ahead over many centuries. By nature and training only one thing was clear to Constantine: that his acceptance of a god as the imperial protective deity by no means excluded the existence of other gods or another faith altogether. Thus he was tolerant, not because he had views on tolerance, but because as a man sprung from pagan antiquity he could not conceive being otherwise. Such had long been the characteristic attitude of antiquity, and it was the normal, natural view for Constantine. Hence his decision to accept the new religion could not have been coupled with the intention to subject the whole Roman Empire to Christianity. In the course of the years, he came to see that the Christians had quite a different opinion on this matter. He was therefore compelled at times to abandon the course of impartial tolerance and to make concessions to Christian impatience."

Palestine, too, was affected by the Christianization of Rome. Under Constantine, to be sure, the pagan name Aelia Capitolina vanished, and the city was once more called Jerusalem. But Jerusalem was converted into a Christian Holy City after the Emperor's mother, Helena, had visited there on a pilgrimage. The temples to heathen gods were razed and replaced by Christian churches. The temple of Venus, under whose foundations the tomb of Christ was believed to be, gave way to the Church of the Holy Sepulcher. Hordes of Christian pilgrims poured into the country from all parts of the empire. But the Jews were still forbidden to set foot inside their former capital. Constantine expressly renewed the decree issued by the pagan Emperor Hadrian. Only once a year an exception was made: On the fast day of the ninth of Ab the Roman guards at the gates of Jerusalem let Jews pass through.

In the year 337, while preparing for a campaign against the Sassanidae, Constantine died. Under Constantius, the second Christian Emperor, who ruled (337–362) the eastern half of the empire despotically, the situation of the Jews continued to worsen. In 339 Constantius signed a law forbidding all marriages between Jews and Christian women, on pain of death. Even more serious for the Jews were the provisions of the new slave laws. The penalty for conversion of slaves to Judaism stiffened. In 339 Constantius ordered that circumcision of a Christian slave—which might mean conversion—was to be punished by death or banishment. This measure was supplemented by another that proved to be a severe economic blow to the Jews in the empire. The religious influence of Judaism was still considered a grave danger to Christianity, for Jews were now forbidden, under penalty of confiscation of all their goods, to buy or to keep Christian slaves. It became illegal for them to purchase or to own even pagan slaves.

The Christian Church had no objections at all to slavery in itself—although a Biblical injunction forbids the lasting enslavement of brethren—*i.e.,* coreligionists—without their consent, limiting it to six years (Deuteronomy 15:12 ff.). Humanitarian considerations did not underlie this measure. Eusebius, Bishop of Caesarea, candidly gives the reason: The descendants of those who had crucified the Son of God must not be permitted to be masters over slaves whom Christ had freed. Since the entire economic life of the time was founded on slave labor, this decree prevented the Jews from practicing many occupations that were open to all other citizens of the empire. It drove the Jews out of many of their former positions and trades. In agriculture, in craft manufacture, in shipbuilding, the work was inconceivable without slaves. For many Jews, the decree meant financial ruin.

To make matters worse, in the year 350 difficult times once more began for the land of Israel. Rome was again drawn into a weary struggle with her archfoe, the Sassanidae. King Shapur II tried, like his predecessors, to seize the border territories of Mesopotamia. To meet this threat Constantius dispatched a strong army under the command of his coregent, Gallus. Numerous Roman units under the command of the legate Ursicinus established their headquarters in Palestine. Humiliations and provocations of the Jewish inhabitants followed. Soldiers were quartered in their houses. In addition, they had to feed the legionaries. Even on the Sabbath they were forced to bake bread for these unwelcome lodgers. Everywhere, the Jews saw their religious feelings offended. Crushing taxes were imposed on the country and collected with merciless harshness. In addition to all these troubles were the excesses committed by Christian fanatics. Once again, the Jews resorted to rebellion. The uprising began in Galilee. It spread out from Sepphoris and Tiberias to Lydda in Judea. Armed with captured weapons, Jewish rebels attacked Roman garrisons.

This time the Romans succeeded in regaining control of the situation before the movement could spread throughout the country. All villages and towns that had participated in the rebellion were destroyed. Thousands of Jews were killed. Once again many fled abroad; many took refuge in caves, especially the caves near Tiberias. "When we escaped into the underground passages," a rabbi who had fled with his fellow fighters reported, "we had torches with us. When they burned darkly, we recognized that it was day; but when they flamed more brightly, we recognized by that token the time of night." The distress and oppression in Palestine did not change after Gallus, on the Emperor's orders, was executed and Ursicinus fell into disgrace in 354.

In 357 another edict was promulgated creating a further barrier against conversions to Judaism. It read: "If after publication of this law anyone shall change from a Christian to a Jew, and shall demonstrably join their [the Jews'] impious assemblies [*sacrilegis coetibus*], we command that his whole property be confiscated for the state treasury." The right to proselytize was to be reserved for the dominant Church.

During these difficult years the patriarch Hillel II (*c.* 330–365), the son of Judah III, resolved on a significant step. He voluntarily surrendered one of the privileges of the patriarchate that had hitherto helped greatly to uphold the supremacy of the Palestinian center among all the Jews of the Diaspora. In 359 Hillel announced a system that would permit all Jewish communities to calculate the calendar independently and determine the times for the regular feasts. The rules of the calendrical system devised by Hillel were so easy to handle, and corresponded so closely to astronomical observations, that in its essentials it has proved applicable down to modern times. But astronomical significance aside, Hillel's act was a basic step toward complete decentralization of Judaism's community organization. Hillel, however, was more concerned with the perpetuation of Judaism in uneasy times than with the dignity of his office.

A change of rulers brought an unexpected respite to the era of distress that had descended upon the Jewish people. Constantius was succeeded in 361 by Julian, to whose name Church historians have added the epithet "the Apostate." The new lord of the empire set about restoring the pagan religion. Determined to check any further incursions of Christianity, Julian revoked the privileges of the Christians, made it illegal for them to convert pagans by force, and closed down their places of instruction. The old Roman tolerance returned. Julian guaranteed freedom of belief to all religions and sects. He restored to the Jews their ancient unrestricted rights of citizenship, freed them from all special imposts, and promised to rebuild "the holy city of Jerusalem."

From Antioch, where Julian was preparing to take the field against the Sassanidae, an imperial edict was published in 362, addressed "To All the Jews." It read: "In former times you were made to feel the yoke of slavery, particularly by new taxes imposed upon you without warning. You were compelled to deliver untold quantities of gold to the imperial treasury. I myself have witnessed many of your misfortunes, but I learned even more when I found the tax rolls, which had been arranged for your disadvantage. . . . I myself have consigned to the flames these tax rolls, which were stored in my archives, and have commanded that you shall no longer be slandered as blasphemers. Throughout my empire you will be relieved of your cares, and after the happy completion of the war against the Persians I shall once again build up the holy city of Jerusalem and have it renewed at my expense as you have long desired to see it rebuilt. . . ."

The Emperor seemed totally in earnest about this promise. During the advance into Mesopotamia he dispatched his friend Alypius, an administrative official from Antioch, to Jerusalem to make a start on the planned reconstruction of the Temple. The governors in Syria and Palestine received orders to lend their full support to Alypius. At the glad news of the Emperor's intentions, contributions had begun arriving from many Jewish communities throughout the Roman world. Building materials were delivered, and armies of workmen were already beginning to clear the great heaps of ruins from the site of the old Temple. But a strange incident suddenly interrupted the work: Flames shot out of the depths and killed several of the workmen. Presumably, accumulated gases, compressed by the weight of the ruins, had suddenly been released and had caught fire. The populace regarded this episode as an omen, the work immediately ceased—and was never resumed. For Emperor Julian never returned from the campaign in Mesopotamia against the Sassanidae.

The theater of war, in which the bloodiest battles between Rome and Persia raged, shifted to the territory of Jewish Babylonia. Shapur, a city inhabited by many Jews, went up in flames. Roman siege machinery transformed Machuza—a prosperous suburb of the capital, Ctesiphon—which had a thriving academy, into a heap of rubble. But in spite of many successes, Julian did not succeed in accomplishing his aim—the conquest of Ctesiphon. Struck by the arrow of a Christian soldier in his own army—so legend tells the tale—he died on a June day in the year 363. He certainly never said, "Thou hast conquered, Galilean," but, in effect, that was the upshot. Julian had not succeeded in forcing the wheel of history to run backward. No power on earth could any longer check the tremendous development that had begun with the spread of Christianity and its recognition within the empire.

For the Jews, the passing of Julian meant the fading of the last ray of hope for a peaceful, unharried existence.

At this time the work on the Mishnah, the body of commentary and interpretation of the Gemara, came to an abrupt end after five generations of Palestinian scholarship. The unstable conditions in the country, the closing of schools, and the shortage of competent teachers meant that the project could not be completed in Eretz Israel. The old spirit of scholarship had died; intellectual life was stagnating. Tradition has preserved not a single name of a prominent scholar of that period. Thus, around the year 360, the canon of the Jerusalem Talmud became settled, in spite of its many lacunae. The sources do not tell us who decided that the collection was finished. Born in an unfortunate time, the *Talmud Yerushalmi* never achieved the importance of the Babylonian Talmud (*Talmud Babli*), which was completed a century and a half later. Rather disregarded, it languished in obscurity until in the twelfth century the halakoth, the religio-legal decisions of the Jerusalem Talmud, were taken up once more by the great Maimonides and thus brought back into the mainstream of Jewish intellectual tradition.

With the death of Julian, the last remnants of the heathen past soon vanished from the empire. In Rome, the goddess of victory and her altar were removed from the hall of the Senate. Under Theodosius I (379–395) Christianity at last became the official state religion of the empire. Before long, the Jews once again felt the sting of Christian intolerance. Emperor Theodosius himself had to intervene repeatedly to protect the Jews and to prevent his fellow Christians from abusing the rights that had been guaranteed them for so long. Frequent reports came to the imperial court of assaults upon Jews' religious worship, of the pillaging and destruction of their synagogues. Theodosius pointed out to his subjects that there was no law prohibiting the Jewish religion (*"Judaeorum sectam nulla lege prohibitam satis constat"*) and took energetic measures to stop the outrages. He threatened severe punishment for any attacks upon Jewish houses of worship and for any interference with the Jews in the free practice of their religion. Theodosius also took care that Jewish self-government was not infringed, and ordained that the decisions of "their famous men and illustrious patriarchs" (*"virorum clarissimorum et illustrium patriarcharum"*) were to be binding upon all Jews.

Thus the Jews were once more under the protection of the law. But the pressure upon their freedom of conscience persisted. And the defamations continued. The defamation was sometimes reflected in government decrees; the texts of some describe them as a "band persisting in their superstition." Marriage between Christians and Jews was once again forbidden.

Ambrose, the great Bishop of Milan who was later to be reckoned among the "Fathers of the Church," challenged the Emperor in regard to the

Jews. Around the year 388 the Bishop of Edessa had had a synagogue burned down in Callinicum on the Euphrates. Theodosius I ordered the Bishop to rebuild the structure at his own expense and to punish the actual incendiaries. When Bishop Ambrose heard of this, he took strong issue with the Emperor. In his view the "honor of God" was at stake. A member of the Christian hierarchy must not be compelled to build a Jewish synagogue, a "place of irreligion and wickedness." "I declare," Ambrose wrote defiantly, "that I myself would have set fire to the synagogue, indeed, that I would have given the men the order, so that there would no longer be any place where Christ is denied." Theodosius did not trouble to answer this letter. But the Bishop of Milan did not let the matter rest. One day, when Theodosius was in Milan, Ambrose interrupted the church service in the Emperor's presence and launched into a tirade on the question of the destroyed synagogue. He thus applied moral pressure upon this Christian ruler and forced him to withdraw his order and grant total immunity to the criminals.

In Constantinople and in Antioch a famous preacher loudly raised his voice against Judaism. This was John, later Archbishop of Constantinople, to whom Church history has given the epithet Chrysostom—from *chrysostomos* (golden-mouthed). While Ambrose was intent on shearing the Jews of state protection, Chrysostom opposed the peaceful concord that obtained between Christians and Jews.

The Bishop of Constantinople had angrily observed how strong the "Jewish temptation" still was among the people, how many followers of the Christian Church openly sympathized with the synagogue worshipers. In Antioch many Christians were wont to attend the Jewish services on the Sabbath and other holidays. In legal contests they often brought their cases into the Jewish courts; in sickness they sent for Jewish doctors. Chrysostom regarded such conduct as dangerous to the Church. In thunderous sermons he lashed out against the Christians who succumbed to Jewish customs and manners. "Among the miserable and unfortunate Jews," he warned on the eve of the Jewish autumn festivals, "a whole succession of holidays is beginning now—New Year, Tabernacles, fast days—and many of our people are going to gape at these ceremonies, while some have the effrontery to take part directly in the ceremonies and the fasts! . . . I know only too well that many hold the Jews in respect and regard their ceremonies as holy. Therefore I make haste to tear out this ruinous view by the root." Outside the Temple of Jerusalem, Chrysostom argued, Jewish worship had lost all meaning; with the destruction of Jerusalem the Jewish religion had forfeited all right to its existence. "What has hindered the rebuilding of the Temple," he asked, "if not the divine power itself? Are not riches in plenty at their disposal? Does not their Patriarch, who collects contributions everywhere, possess inexhaustible treasures? Are there only few of them in Palestine, in Phoenicia, and elsewhere? . . . They have built synagogues in many cities, but it is beyond their strength to reconstruct the one place that conferred power upon their nation and provided the backbone of Judaism."

Chrysostom was particularly insulting toward Jewish houses of worship. "Between the synagogue and the theater there is no difference," he maintained. In both foregathered "bands of effeminate men and wanton women. . . . The synagogue is not only a house of indecency and a theater, but also a robbers' den and a lair of wild beasts. . . . Even though no idols stand there, the demons feel all the more at home. . . . There are gathered the murderers of Christ. . . ." In a pagan temple the godlessness of idolatry was at least obvious to all, whereas in the synagogue it battened in concealment. Christians must take care not to let their wives go to the synagogue. "They will bring home the devil within their souls." On another occasion he berated the synagogue in these terms: "Let anyone call it brothel, home of vice, refuge of the devil, citadel of Satan, corruptor of souls, abyss of corruption and all mischief—whatever he may say, it will be less than it has deserved." As Professor Karl Thieme has observed: "From such slanders out of the mouths of ecclesiastical authorities it was clearly no very long way to burnings of synagogues."

John Chrysostom did his best to whip up enmity against the Jewish citizens of Constantinople. Nevertheless, much of the population long remained in peaceful and unclouded relations with the Jews. His sermons were preserved in writing, however, and continued to exert an effect for centuries to come. Included within the body of literature known collectively as patristic writings, they are studied to this day in theological seminaries.

The learned Church Father Jerome (c. 340–420) described the plight of Jewish pilgrims in Jerusalem with no trace of compassion: "Until the present day those faithless inhabitants who killed the servants of God and especially the Son of God have been forbidden entrance into Jerusalem. They are allowed in only for lamentation, and must purchase with money the permission to bewail the destruction of their state. . . . On the anniversary of the day on which the Romans aforetimes took Jerusalem and destroyed it, the wretched people can be seen arriving, women and old men feeble with age, dressed in rags, pouring in, their very exterior and clothing betraying the wrath of God. The hordes of wretches crowd together, and there where . . . from the height of the Mount of Olives the sign of the Cross gleams, a wretched people who, however, are not worthy of pity, mourn the ruins of their Temple. Their eyes are still full of tears, their hands still shaking, their hair still disarranged, and already the guards demand their reward for permitting them to go on shedding more tears. . . ."

One might have expected the subsequently canonized Jerome, who had spent forty years in Palestine as abbot of a Christian monastery in Bethlehem, to have taken a somewhat different tone. He was, after all, more familiar than most Christian theologians with the sources of the Jewish Scriptures and the customs of the people. Talmudists from Lydda and Tiberias had taught him Hebrew and helped him to understand the original text of the Bible. Bar Hanina, one of his teachers, used to visit him in his cell only at night, as his *nocturnus praeceptor*. This was at Jerome's request, for fear of the opprobrium that was attached to association with Jews.

Jerome's studies, and the instruction of Jewish scholars, later made it possible for Jerome to compose his famous Vulgate, the Latin translation of the Bible, which remained the sole text of the Scriptures acknowledged by the Roman Church throughout the Middle Ages. Jerome made use of rabbinical traditions in his interpretations of the Old Testament. He leaned on his Jewish teachers for the "Hebrew truth" of the Bible. Nevertheless, even such a man as Jerome did not find his way to these "elder brothers," and emphasized his orthodoxy by protesting his hatred of the Jews.

The greatest mind among the Church Fathers, St. Augustine, repudiated in no uncertain terms the charge of deicide that had been leveled against the Jews from the fourth century on. But he also composed—as did most of the other patristic writers—a polemical treatise against the Jews: *Tractatus adversus Judaeos*. The Judeans in their abasement, he wrote, were "witnesses to their wrongness and our truth." In his *The City of God* St. Augustine placed the Jewish people outside of Christian society. The Jewish historian Heinrich Graetz was scarcely wrong when he wrote, in the nineteenth century: "This creed of hatred for the Jews did not remain the private opinion of a writer. It became the oracle for all of Christendom, which drank in the writings of these venerated, canonized Church Fathers as if these were revelations. In centuries to come this creed incited kings and rabble, statesmen and monks, crusaders and herdsmen against the Jews, spurring them to invent instruments of torture and gather the faggots for the stake."

Theodosius I was the last of the Roman rulers to reign alone over the entire Imperium Romanum. His death in 395 opened the way for a great crisis, which was to lead, eighty years later, to the end of the Western Roman Empire.

In those very decades before almighty Rome ceded her dominion over the world, the condition of the Jews reached its nadir. The legislation of the first Christian rulers, from Constantine to Theodosius I, had reflected a certain inconsistency toward the Jews, alternating between severity and protection against excesses. But from Theodosius II to Justinian came a series of decrees reducing all adherents of Judaism to the status of a merely "tolerated" group outside the society of other Roman citizens and subject to grave legal disabilities.

Theodosius II, emperor of East Rome, issued one decree forbidding the building of any new synagogues. This ban was later renewed, in 423 and 439, in decrees directed against the "abominable heathens, Judaeans, and heretics"; the most that was permitted was the repair of synagogues in a dangerous state of dilapidation. This law was a painful blow to Jewry. Many Jewish communities, moreover, were compelled to suffer passively when incited mobs of Christians destroyed their synagogue or robbed them of the building, which would then be converted into a church. Injustices of this sort inflicted by hate-filled fanatics were legalized by the highest authority of the state. The Jews were helplessly exposed to all attacks and excesses, and could regard it as fortune in misfortune if a house of worship was "only" partially damaged, for then at least they could restore it and still have it for their own. Completely smashed synagogues, or those that had collapsed from age, were lost forever.

Other decrees renewed the ban on Jews' having Christian slaves. In 417 and again in 423 Theodosius II forbade the Jews, under all conditions and for whatever purposes, to purchase slaves of the Christian faith. "For we consider it unjust," the text of the edict explains, "for the pious servants to be tainted by the dominion of godless buyers." Such measures further drove the Jews from agriculture and many crafts and trades dependent on slave labor.

In the year 418 both emperors, Theodosius II in the East and Honorius in the West, ordered the exclusion of Jews from military service. Jewish *agentes in rebus* (men who combined the offices of couriers and police) and *palatini* (palace guards), "if they have already taken the military oath, may serve to the end of their legal term. But Jews who have long been performing actual military service shall be . . . dismissed at once without consideration for previous merits (*nullo veterum meritorum patrocinanti suffragio*)." Thousands and tens of thousands were dismissed from the army without compensation and without the usual benefits due to veterans.

Theodosius II extended his power even into the realm of familial rights.

An edict prohibited the Jews from disinheriting children who had converted to Christianity—"who have departed from the darkness of their superstition into the light of the Christian faith." Parents were no longer allowed to pass over the apostates in their wills or even to reduce their share of the inheritance "even if the children have committed a crime." Baptized children were entitled to demand their fair share of the inheritance in court. The legislators justified this infringement of parental rights—so alien to the traditions of Roman jurisprudence—by reference to the "honor of the chosen religion."

In 425 Jews were barred from the law courts. "We deprive Jews and pagans," the law declared, "of permission to plead in court cases and to hold offices in the state, since we are unwilling to see men living in the Christian state subordinated to them."

An edict issued on January 31, 439, in Constantinople against those "persisting in the Jewish superstition" decreed: "No Jew . . . shall hold offices and dignities, nor shall he be permitted in the municipal administration, nor shall he exercise the office of a defender of the city. We hold it a sin that the enemies of the heavenly majesty and the Roman laws should be executors of our laws . . . and that by virtue of the authority of acquired rank might judge and decide at their discretion upon Christians, frequently, indeed, upon bishops of our holy religion. That is an offense to our faith."

The accent of the new regulations lay upon exclusion of the Jews from all the positions they had formerly held in which they could exert influence. But in the later Roman Empire many municipal offices were burdens rather than privileges, and there was no intention of exempting Jews from these. They were still liable to difficult services and expense in the interest of the government, "so that it will not seem as if by this law we have conferred the benefit of a liberation upon the disgraceful people whom we wish to chastise."

A single act, a single word on the part of the Jews would have sufficed to save them from this position of pariahs—baptism. State and Church held this "golden door" wide open to them. But they did not take the step; they did not abandon their religion. A single people, although scattered from the Pillars of Hercules to the Bosporus, they accepted of their own free will the harsh conditions of their lives, just as later they accepted persecution and death, rather than betray their faith. Only a few individuals here and there chose apostasy.

Under Theodosius II, Archbishop Cyril of Alexandria—a Church Father who distinguished himself by his persecutions of heretics and non-Christians

—went so far as to expel the Jews from his city. In 414 Christian mobs, incited by his sermons, broke into the synagogues and seized possession of them. The Jews were driven from Alexandria, where they had made their homes for so many centuries. The mob pillaged their houses and shops. Only a single member of the large Jewish community—Adamantius, a teacher of medicine—went unscathed. He accepted baptism. All the rest submitted to banishment. In vain Orestes, Prefect of Alexandria, complained against the Bishop. The court at Constantinople did nothing about the excesses of the fanatics. Indeed, it nearly cost Orestes his life for daring to put in a good word for the Jews. Monks from Mount Nitra near Alexandria attacked the Prefect, who was severely wounded by a stone hurled at him.

In the small town of Magona on the island of Minorca the Jews were not so firm in their faith. After vicious street battles Severus, the Bishop of Minorca, achieved his end—all the Jews accepted conversion. But they were a rare exception.

Government officials in the provinces repeatedly attempted to take the Jews under their protection, but their efforts failed. When anti-Jewish riots began spreading throughout Syria, when synagogues were desecrated and robbed of their utensils or confiscated and turned into Christian places of worship, Asclepiodot, Prefect of Antioch, vigorously interceded with the Emperor in behalf of the Jews there. Theodosius II responded favorably, and by the decree of February 15, 423, ordered that the synagogues be returned and repaired and that redress be made for stolen liturgical articles. But the monk and hermit Simeon (this was before he had chosen to spend the rest of his life on a pillar) intervened with the weight of his reputation for holiness. At the request of the "sorrowful bishops," so the *Lives of the Saints* put it, "he wrote [to the Emperor] fearless words, full of terrible threats." His threats amounted to a prophecy that God would punish the Emperor for the favor he had shown to the "unbelieving Jews." "The Emperor, upon reading the letter, trembled with fear and did penance. He immediately issued orders to have it proclaimed everywhere that his previous decrees were . . . invalid."

In the midst of these harsh years, what measure of Jewish autonomy had survived in Palestine was also extinguished. The patriarchate came to an end forever.

Under the onslaught of Christianity the onetime Promised Land of the children of Israel had changed profoundly. The landscape of their great history was now filled with churches and monasteries. Strangers swarmed in the land, monks and pilgrims. In this changed environment the Jewish patriarchate seemed like a foreign body. Because the Jewish patriarch was the living symbol of an autonomous Jewish Palestine, he had to be eliminated. A pretext was soon found.

Patriarch Gamaliel VI had felt that he could overlook the anti-Jewish decrees of the Emperor. He had built new synagogues, and also sat in judgment on disputes between Jews and Christians. In the autumn of 415 Provincial Prefect Aurelianus received an order from Emperor Theodosius. The "diploma conferring the dignity of prefect" was to be taken away from Patriarch Gamaliel. Fourteen years later, when Gamaliel died leaving no male offspring, the Emperor abolished the office. The patriarchate was no more.

For more than three centuries after the end of the Jewish War, patriarchs, in times of terrible difficulty, had guided the spiritual and secular affairs of Jewry. There had been fifteen patriarchs in succession from a single house: two Hillels, three Simeons, four Judahs, and six Gamaliels. Now the name of this highest Jewish dignity passed into the possession of the Christian Church: In 451 the Council of Chalcedon granted the Bishop of Jerusalem the title of patriarch.

"O Lord of the world," runs a Jewish sermon spoken in the Holy Land during those years, "in former times you were wont to grant me an interval of light between one night and the others: thus between the night of Egypt and of Babylon, between the night of Greece and of Edom, but now one night follows immediately after the other."

THE BABYLONIAN TALMUD

The last vestige of Jewry's existence as a state had vanished from the Christian East. Palestine had lost the precedence it had hitherto enjoyed. It was now Babylonia's turn to assume the leadership. The great Diaspora community "beyond the river," with its princely leader and its flourishing academies, became the center of Jewish life.

In spite of a despotic government, the Jews of Babylonia under the Sassanidae enjoyed domestic liberty. Persecutions occurred, but they were rare, limited to brief eruptions of religious fanaticism.

King Yazdegerd I, a contemporary of Emperor Theodosius II, practiced tolerance toward both Christians and Jews during his reign (399–420). The fanatical Zoroastrian priests had no influence on this ruler. At state functions and on holidays the Jewish Exilarch and the heads of the Jewish academies appeared among the guests of honor at court. There are tales of Yazdegerd displaying special favor toward the Jewish prince before the eyes of his highest dignitaries. At one reception he went up to Exilarch Huna bar Nathan and straightened his belt, a symbol of honor in Persia. "You are a people of priests and a holy tribe," he remarked loudly enough for all to hear, "and therefore should wear your belt like the priests."

Many decades of study and discussion in the academies and communities of Babylonia had borne fruit. The wealth of traditions and commentaries on the Mishnah had swollen to gigantic proportions. The time was ripe to collect and sift the mass of legal prescripts and interpretations evolved by several generations of scholars.

Rav Ashi (352–427) took this enormous task in hand, and a conjunction of fortunate circumstances enabled him to proceed with it. He enjoyed wide authority and longevity. Because the Babylonian communities had a long period of peace during his lifetime, he was able to continue his labors for more than half a century.

Famed Sura on the Euphrates was his headquarters. After almost two centuries the school there had become dilapidated, and its rooms were far too small to house all who came from far and near to study under Ashi and share his labors. He had a new and larger academy built. Then he set about creating an unprecedented, far-reaching program of instruction. His cycle of lectures, planned for years ahead, was directed entirely toward one great task: to create a uniform code for his people by uniting the Mishnah and the Gemara. Each year, when all the pupils were assembled in spring and autumn, he would go through a section of the Mishnah and all the pertinent commentaries. Thirty years of intensive, creative teaching were to pass before the entire body of material in the Mishnah had been propounded, elucidated, discussed, and transmitted. When this was done, Rav Ashi began at the beginning again, surveying for a second time, with a new generation of scholars and students, the enormously varied material. When death at last came to the teacher at a great age, he had completed the second round. Rarely had so long and so fruitful a creative period been granted to any scholar.

Rav Ashi left behind him a unique lifework: the firm foundations for the Babylonian Talmud.

The work was not actually completed and rounded out until seventy years after his death. It was as if Rav Ashi had labored so hard because he sensed the onset of dire times. Sure enough, a quarter of a century after his death a period of persecutions began in the Sassanian Empire.

Under Yazdegerd II (King from 440 to 457) the fire worshipers rose up and oppressed both Jews and Christians. The troubles reached their height after King Peroz (ruler from 457 to 484) had ascended the throne.

The new ruler was completely under the sway of the Magi. Under the suasion of the fanatics, he ordered the closing of all Jewish schools and the abolition of separate Jewish judiciaries. The Jews indignantly resisted. In many places they clashed with the fanatical priests. In the city of Isfahan two Magi were killed in the course of one such battle. When Peroz heard of this, he ordered a total massacre of the rebellious Jewish inhabitants of the city. Only their children were spared. These are said to have been taken to the temple of Horvan and forcibly raised as fire worshipers. The reign of terror swept over Exilarch Huna V and many rabbis; King Peroz had them imprisoned and executed.

These were the first serious persecutions in many centuries on Babylonian soil, which had become a second homeland to the Jews. Panic seized the Jewish population. Great numbers of them fled from their communities, whose long years of peace had been so abruptly ended, and sought to escape Babylonia. Many made their way to Arabia. One sizable group of exiles had a strange and adventurous fate: They found their way, after long wanderings, to India! About the year 490 Joseph Rabban, a wealthy and learned man, reached the fruitful coast of Malabar in southwest India, accompanied by many other Jewish families. Legend has it that they there encountered coreligionists who had settled there long before, in days when Jews had first reached China also.

The new arrivals from Babylonia were given a friendly reception. Land was assigned them for their dwellings, and they were permitted to live by their own laws. King Airvi, the Indian sovereign of Cranganur, accorded regal honors to Joseph Rabban by allowing him to ride on an elephant, to sit on rugs, and to have drummers and trumpeters run before him. The privileges of the Jewish immigrants were inscribed on a copperplate. The story goes that seventy-two descendants of Joseph Rabban headed the Jewish colony.

The sufferings of the Babylonian Jews lasted for a full decade; the terror did not stop until the death of King Peroz. Babylonia, however, continued to be rent by power struggles long after his demise. There was an interregnum, followed by civil wars and anarchy. But the Jewish communities were able to restore their ancient order, and the schools resumed their work. Under Rabina bar Huna, the principal (488–499) of the academy in Sura, scholars completed collecting all the material of the oral teachings and preserving it in writing. With the death of Rabina bar Huna, the vast structure of the Babylonian Talmud was finished—just as the fifth century was drawing to a close and in distant Europe Gothic and Frankish kingdoms were arising out of the ruins of the Roman Empire.

DESTINY IN THE WEST

". . . and ye shall be left few in number. . . ."

Deuteronomy 4:27

I UNDER NEW MASTERS IN EUROPE

AFTER THE STORMS OF THE MIGRATIONS

Around the year 400 there burst from the mountains and steppes of Central Asia tribes of mounted men who pushed toward the West and unleashed a remarkable series of chain reactions. Pressed by the Huns, uncounted hordes of "barbarians" surged like a mighty tidal wave, overwhelming all resistance, into all the provinces of the Roman Empire. They poured into Italy, into Gaul, into Spain, and into North Africa.

Along with the other peoples in the heartland and the provinces of the empire, along with Latins, Celts, and Iberians, the widely scattered Jewish communities were swept into the turbulence and savage fighting of the times. It almost seemed as if this were the fate that the prophet had once predicted: "The earth reeleth to and fro like a drunken man . . . the transgression thereof is heavy upon it, and it shall fall, and not rise again. And it shall come to pass in that day, the Lord will punish the host of the high heaven on high, and the kings of the earth upon the earth" (Isaiah 24:20–21).

But how many storms of world history the ancient people of God had already weathered! They knew that "One nation arises, the other vanishes, but Israel remains forever."

Decades of fighting and unrest descended upon Italy. In 410 Alaric, the war lord of the Visigoths, entered Rome and unleashed his pillaging soldiers upon the city in which since time immemorial no foreign conqueror had set foot. The news of the fall of the Eternal City sent a shock throughout the world. St. Jerome, hearing of it in Bethlehem, lamented: "The bright beacon of the globe is extinguished; overcome the city which once overcame all the earth." Rome's fall marked the beginning of the end; soon Italy and, along with her, the entire Western Empire succumbed to the populous Germanic tribes that washed over Europe.

In 422 Attila's Huns devastated Upper Italy. In 455 the Vandals poured into the country and thrust on far south. Their bands, too, under the leadership of Geiseric, plundered the city on the Tiber. The sacred vessels and treasure from the Temple of Jerusalem, preserved in Rome since the unhappy outcome of the Jewish War, fell into their hands. One tradition relates that Geiseric took along this precious booty, together with Roman idols, on his invasion of Africa. Thus it reached Carthage, which the Vandals re-established as the capital of their kingdom.

The death agony of Imperial Rome continued until the last Roman ruler, Romulus Augustulus, was removed from the throne. In 476 Odoacer, leader of the barbarian mercenaries in Italy, made himself, in effect if not in title, King of Italy. Thirteen years later he was overthrown by King Theodoric the Great. The rule of the Ostrogoths in Italy ushered in a period of peace and order after a century of bloodshed and confusion.

For the Jewish communities in the country the firm hand of Theodoric meant a time of peace and security. The pressure to which they had been continually exposed under the last Roman emperors lessened. Theodoric, a heretical Arian in the eyes of Catholics, proved to be just and tolerant toward the Jews. He recognized the right of their communities to self-administration—contrary to the principles of the *Codex Theodosianus,* which still remained formally in force. He let it be known to the Jews that he gladly condoned their "preservation of their ancient rights." In fact, he extended their independent jurisdiction. One of his edicts reads: "In view of the fact that the Jews live according to their own laws, they must possess their own magistrates to settle their disputes. Among them these judges simultaneously serve as religious authorities."

Sizable Jewish communities already existed in Rome, Naples, and on the island of Sicily. Many new ones sprang up under the tolerant rule of the Ostrogoths, especially in northern Italy: in Milan, Verona, Genoa, and other cities.

Under the new masters life was once again secure for the Jews. The Ostrogothic King defended them against religious fanaticism as earlier Christian rulers had notably failed to do. In Rome, one day the slaves of a rich Jewish family rebelled against their masters and killed them. The authorities promptly punished the guilty slaves, whereupon a Christian mob took terrible vengeance. Jews were attacked in the streets and a synagogue went up in flames. Theodoric, informed of these events, flew into a rage. He denounced the Roman Senate for slackness and ordered sternest punishment of the culprits.

In Ravenna, his capital, he also intervened in no uncertain terms when a Christian mob, allegedly roused to indignation by "Jewish mockery" of some church ceremony, set synagogues afire. On Theodoric's orders, the Catholics in the city were required to rebuild the Jewish synagogues at their own expense. Those who refused were threatened with corporal punishment. The King was determined to have order in the land, and was especially concerned with repressing Catholic fanaticism, which also made difficulties for himself as an Arian. Yet Theodoric himself was no friend of the Jews; as a Christian, he desired their conversion. That is plain from the text of his decrees, which were drawn up for him by his learned adviser and secretary, the Roman Senator Cassiodorus. The Genoese Jews, who had asked permission to renovate their old synagogue, were informed: "Why do you desire something that you truly ought to avoid? Although we grant you the permission, we reprimand your desire, which springs from confusion. However, it does not lie in our power to command belief, for no one can be made to believe against his will."

Cassiodorus, who later became a monk and the author of many ecclesiastical writings, repeatedly debated with the Jews, and mustered all the arts of oratory in his efforts to convert them. "Hear, O Judeans, listen, you obstinate ones!" he addressed them. "Go to the Catholic pastors. They will open your ears, and with God's aid you will be saved from your eternal deafness." Yet even he heaped insults upon them, calling them scorpions and lions, wild asses, dogs, and unicorns.

In the other lands of the West, from the Rhine through Gaul into Spain, the Jews found themselves confronting new rulers when the turbulence of the migrations had subsided. Visigoths, Burgundians, and Franks had set up their kingdoms upon the ruins of the Gallic and Iberian provinces of the Roman Empire. Newly converted heathens, Arians like the Ostrogoths, these peoples were independent of the Byzantine and Roman churches and therefore did not impose upon the Jews the harsh provisions that had been embodied in the codes of Roman law. Under the new rulers the Jews enjoyed complete freedom.

The first of them had set foot in Europe, far from their ancient homeland, many generations before. Some voluntarily, some driven by destiny, as merchants, fugitives, or slaves, they had drifted into wealthy Gaul and Spain. As soon as they regained their freedom (and many slaves and prisoners did so quickly; because of their peculiar customs, their dietary restrictions and Sabbaths, they made inconvenient servants), they enjoyed full citizenship rights. Even while Rome was still a republic, in the time of Caesar, they had entered the Roman world, following Greek colonists, from the Diaspora communities of Asia Minor, Syria, and Egypt. These voluntary immigrants were followed by hordes of Jewish soldiers, carried off as prisoners by Vespasian and Titus after Rome's victory over Judea. Jews settled first in the coastal cities; they then spread into the interior. In Gaul there were numerous Jewish communities whose inhabitants lived on the best of terms with the native populations. They were especially numerous in Marseilles, which was called the Hebrew city; they also settled in Narbonne and in the Auvergne, where a mountain—Mons Judaicus—was named after them. They dwelt in considerable numbers in Arles, Avignon, Orléans, Bordeaux, and, farther north, in Paris and in the country of the Belgae.

The new conquerors treated Jewish subjects as Romans, not as a special subjugated class. In the Frankish and Burgundian kingdoms Jews were unrestricted; they engaged in agriculture and viniculture, pursued crafts and trade, held public office in the cities, and served as tax collectors. They sailed the rivers and the sea in their own ships. They practiced medicine and law. They held commanding positions in the army and because of their reputation for bravery were sought after as mercenaries. During the struggles between Clovis, King of the Franks, and Theodoric's generals, Jews performed military feats in the siege of Arles.

Throughout these years nothing troubled their peaceful relations with all classes of the population. Even ecclesiastical dignitaries associated with them on a friendly basis, went to their houses, and had them as guests in their own. In secular questions bishops would consult Jewish advisers and in sickness be treated by Jewish physicians.

Sidonius Apollinaris, the Bishop of Clermont, one day recommended his Jewish adviser to the Bishop of Tournai. These people, he remarked in his letter, were wont to conduct their affairs honestly. Hence the Bishop of Tournai could with good conscience make use of the industrious Jew— even though he must condemn the Jew's unbelief. As a matter of fact, Sidonius added in his own justification, a good Christian ought rather to employ a Jew, if only because the Jew might thereby become a convert to the true faith and so make amends for his errors. This missionary impulse on the part of the clergy became almost an obsession, and every conversion was hailed with jubilation. Thus Sidonius warmly congratulated the Bishop of Nantes, whose sermons had persuaded a Jew named Promotus to accept baptism.

The peaceful relationships between the Jews and the population of Gaul were not immediately clouded when Clovis, the Merovingian King, converted from Arianism to Catholicism in 493. Gradually, however, at first one by one but then in a larger chorus, voices of intolerance began to be heard in Gaul. The majority of the people had so recently been converted to Christianity, or to its Catholic form, that their religious adherences were by no means solidly established. Consequently, contact with Jews endangered their faith. The clergy knew what these "stiff-necked" people would reply if asked why they did not let themselves be baptized. And who among the newly converted would be able to counter the arguments of the Jews in a debate on questions of the faith? Even the simplest among the Jews had learned reading and writing in their early youth, and had studied the Holy Books. For centuries the Jews had had compulsory schooling for boys from the age of five or six on, and before they reached that age they had been given instruction at home, for it was the law among the Jews that "As soon as the child begins to speak, the Father must teach him the holy language and instruct him in the Torah." The masses of the Christian populace were illiterates, and were destined to remain so for more than a millennium to come.

It was essential, therefore, to take steps to protect the Christians from Jewish influences, and to erect a barrier between the two religions. At the same time, the Christians felt obliged to redouble their own efforts to bring the Jews into the Church—under pressure, if need be—and to set curbs upon the public exercise of their religious customs. Seven church councils in Frankland dealt with the Jewish question in the course of the sixth century. Step by step the clergy approached its goal.

In 517 a decision of the Council of Epaone in Burgundy forbade all laymen to dine with Jews, and renewed the existing ban for the clergy. A Council of the Church held in Vannes in Brittany as long ago as 465 had already forbidden members of the clergy to dine with Jewish families, or to feed Jews at their own tables.

In 533 the Council of Orléans banned marriages between Christians and Jews. Christians violating this prohibition were threatened with excommunication. The Council of Clermont renewed this ban, which, no doubt, was fairly often violated in practice. At the same time it was decreed that henceforth no Jew must be allowed to function as a judge in cases at law involving Christians. In 538 the Council of Orléans took even sterner measures. One decision struck the Jewish population at a particularly sensitive point: No Christian slave who fled into a church or to a Christian family was to be handed over to his Jewish owner. Instead, the purchase price of the slave had to be paid to the Jews in compensation. But slaves who had been converted by their masters to the Jewish religion were to be released without any compensation.

At this same Council of 538, finally, it was decreed that "for four days, from the day of the Lord's supper [Holy Thursday] to the second day of the Easter holiday, no Jew is permitted to be seen among Christians or on any occasion to mingle with the Catholic population."

In practice little attention was paid to all these measures. Even members of the clergy disobeyed them, and ordinary Catholics did not break off their friendly association with Jews. As yet, the decisions of the councils had little force. The Church was not yet so firmly anchored in the state that it could enforce its decrees. Indeed, not until the second half of the sixth century did the Catholics at last gain the upper hand in the Kingdom of the Franks.

In Spain, too, where the Visigoths at last built a kingdom after the turmoil and the devastation of the migrations, Jews had been living for centuries. Here they were far more numerous than in the onetime Gallic provinces of the Roman Empire. Their settlements were to be found throughout the country. The first Jewish immigrants in Roman times had subsequently received heavy reinforcements: Persecuted Jews from the Diaspora in North Africa, Carthage, and many other cities had made their way across the Strait of Gibraltar to the ports of Cádiz and Cartagena. Thence they had spread into the fruitful regions of Andalusia and deeper into the interior of the Iberian Peninsula.

The names of several Spanish cities preserve the memory of great communities. Granada in former times was called the Jews' City because it was populated exclusively by Jews; ancient Tarragona, which had been founded by the Phoenicians, also bore this name. In Córdoba on the Guadalquivir there existed a Jews' Gate from ancient times, and at Saragossa there was a Jews' Citadel. In northern Spain a gravestone of a young Jewish woman named Miriam testifies to a settlement of Jews. It is inscribed in three languages, Hebrew, Greek, and Latin—evidence that the Spanish Jews had come from Greek-speaking countries and had learned Latin under Roman rule without abandoning their own sacred tongue.

Even before Christianity had become the religion of state, even before the Council of Nicaea, the Church in Spain concerned itself with the Jewish question. At a Council in 306 called by the Bishop of Córdoba the workings of superstition are already evident. Canon 49 of this Council stated: "Owners of land are to be reminded not to summon any Jews to the blessing of the fruits produced by God's grace, so that they will not rob our benediction of its effectiveness. If anyone should violate this prohibition after it has been published, let him be totally excluded from the community of the Church." Canon 50 declared: "If a priest or any orthodox believer joins Jews at table, let him not be admitted to Communion until he mends his ways." And Canon 16 prescribed: "Catholic girls may not be married to Jews or heretics, since the orthodox may not be permitted to live in communion with unbelievers. Parents who flout this prohibition are to be subject to excommunication for the period of five years." "An orthodox believer who has committed adultery by forbidden intercourse with a Jewish or pagan woman," states Canon 78, "is to be placed under the ban of the Church."

Friendships between Jews and their Christian neighbors were thus forbidden and subjected to ecclesiastical punishments. But dicta as these were merely an overture to the cruelties to be inflicted upon Jewry in Spain centuries later.

In the meanwhile, the new Visigoth rulers were better disposed toward the Jews. Under the Arian Visigoth kings, Jews were let alone. They enjoyed civil and political equality, formed detachments of soldiers who guarded the passes of the Pyrenees against invasions of Franks and Burgundians, and held all kinds of public offices.

This favorable situation for the Jews in Spain lasted more than a century.

JUSTINIAN CODIFIES ANTI-JEWISH LAWS

Architects praise his name when conversation turns to the most magnificent domed church in the world, majestic Hagia Sophia in Istanbul on the Sea of Marmara. Lawyers venerate him as the creator of the most important legal work of antiquity—the justly famous Corpus Juris Civilis. Historians wax enthusiastic over the military campaigns of his great generals, Narses and the invincible Belisarius. But who, today, when the name of Emperor Justinian is spoken, thinks of all the distress that this Byzantine ruler inflicted upon the Jews who lived within reach of his power during his lifetime, and upon their grandchildren and great-grandchildren for long centuries after his death?

In 527, almost a full century after Theodosius II had abolished the patriarchate in Palestine and thus extinguished the last remnant of Jewish autonomy, Justinian became Emperor of the Eastern Roman Empire. And under this father of the law, persecution and humiliation of the Jews became the norm. The laws passed on his behest stripped Jews of even more of their rights than had already been forfeited under his predecessors. His imperial edicts interfered seriously with Jewish religious life. Yet the Jews had in no way, either by rebellion or acts of violence against the holders of power in Byzantium, or against Christians or their Church, provided a pretext for such actions. What, then, was the reason for these harsh new measures against them?

It would seem that their unshakable loyalty to their faith had aroused the indignation, and, indeed, the rage, of the Christian rulers in Byzantium. Everywhere, throughout the provinces of the empire, Christianity had triumphed over the pagans; and everywhere the Church had repeatedly encountered the Jews. They alone resisted all efforts at conversion; they alone by their attitude and their very existence provided a "bad example." Justinian was determined to punish this obstinacy and break this people to his will. He approached the problem with a certain cruel cleverness. He would humiliate the Jewish people—the "deicides"—and thus brand them in the eyes of the entire population as inferior.

Justinian's first step was to revive all the restrictions on the Jews that had been decreed between the time of Constantine and that of Theodosius II. Like all heretics, Jews were forbidden to hold honorary offices in the state or in local administrations. Prosperous Jews, however, were compelled to participate in the municipal government, to be members of the burdensome and expensive decurionate. The benefits connected with such office —freedom from punishment by the scourge or by exile—were explicitly denied them. "Let these people bear the whole burden of municipal government," the Emperor declared in a decree of 537, "and groan under those burdens, but they are not permitted to enjoy any associated honors. They are to remain in the same wretched predicament in which they have left their souls."

Justinian, too, made it a principle of law that no Jewish witness was to be regarded as credible if his testimony ran counter to that of a Christian.

Determined to reduce the influence of the synagogue, the Emperor struck at some of the fundamental practices of the Jewish religion. The Council of Nicaea, it will be recalled, had already forbidden Christians to celebrate their Easter at the same time as the Jewish Passover. In 546 Justinian added a prohibition that went much further, in that it affected the Jews themselves. Under the threat of severe penalties, he forbade them to celebrate the Passover with services and the traditional eating of unleavened bread if the time of Passover fell, according to their calendar, before the Christian Easter. Similarly, imperial decree forbade all Jewish communities in the Byzantine Empire to include Talmudic interpretation of the Scriptures in their services. "We entirely forbid what is called *deuterosis* [literally, repetition; *i.e.,* interpretation], since neither is it contained in the Holy Books nor is it handed down from above by the prophets; it is nothing but an invention of men who babble of earthly things and remain strangers to divine things. Although they [the Jews] unfold the scrolls, pronouncing holy words and not concealing what is contained therein, they add empty chatter borrowed from outside the sacred writings, contained in no book, but conceived for the destruction of simple souls." Carrying penalties of physical punishment and confiscation of property, this decree represented a grave invasion by the state into the spiritual life of all those who professed the Jewish religion. The prohibition of *deuterosis* was directed not only against the sermons at Jewish services, but also against the study of the Talmud in the schools that were usually attached to Jewish synagogues.

Further decrees and statutes proceeded from the Byzantine court "in the interest of what is best and most pleasing to God." The Jews, when praying their Shema Yisrael in the morning and evening service, were forbidden to pronounce the verse, "Our God is one"—as if this asseveration were a blasphemous protest against the Trinity. They were also forbidden to speak the words: "Holy, holy, holy is our Lord Zebaoth." The Jewish rabbis had added an explanatory phrase to this verse—since it was also used by the Christians as a proof of the Trinity. On Sabbath days, moreover, the Jews were forbidden to read publicly or to interpret the passages from the prophet Isaiah that promised future consolation and elevation from the dust of downtrodden Zion: "As one whom his mother comforteth, so I will comfort you; and ye shall be comforted in Jerusalem" (Isaiah 66:13).

Paid guards were posted in the synagogues to supervise the praying of the "Hear, O Israel"; they were particularly present on Sabbaths and feast days, to see to strict obedience to the imperial edict. Under the circumstances, the Jews had no choice but to submit, at least outwardly. But they devised ruses: They spoke the forbidden prayers under their breath, so that the imperial watchers could not hear, or else they gathered secretly for prayer at other times of the day, when the guards were absent.

These unfortunate decrees were destined for a long life because Justinian was such a great lawgiver. On instructions from the Emperor a committee of jurists, under the presidency of Tribonus, the greatest legal scholar of the day, set to work on the tremendous task of drawing up a code of Roman law. In the year 534 one of the most important lawbooks of all time was published—the famous Corpus Juris Civilis.

With it, Roman law—the great heritage of the pagan empire and its generations of lawyers and judges—was revived and assured permanence. That law has properly been praised as one of the greatest monuments of the human mind's talent for organization and reason's pursuit of order. The Code was destined to influence much of Occidental civilization. But the Corpus Juris Civilis also harbored the seeds of evils that were to darken the history of an entire people. Within the monumental body of law comprising the Justinian Code and the Novels were the laws relating to the Jews—which were thereby given a lasting life that they did not merit. Along with other general procedures of Roman law they later found their way into the lawbooks of European states; they became the model for all those indignities that were to weigh so heavily upon Jewry in the Middle Ages. The legal degradation of the Jews, their reduction to second-class citizens, set the tone for legislation of the entire Middle Ages, and its effects persisted into the nineteenth century.

It was a staggering political program Justinian undertook, nothing less than reviving the entire empire and asserting sovereignty over the whole of it. North Africa, lost to the Vandals, was to be reconquered, and the rule of Byzantium extended into the shattered lands of the West Roman Empire.

With powerful Byzantine forces, Belisarius, Justinian's great general, launched the assault upon North Africa. Carthage was taken; the powerful Kingdom of the Vandals, founded by Geiseric a century before, was conquered and forever destroyed. Among the spoils of victory, some chroniclers said, were the sacred utensils from the Temple at Jerusalem. These were transported to Constantinople, where, finally, they were lost from sight.

Almost as soon as the Byzantines became masters of the country, the Jewish communities felt the heavy hand of the East Roman Emperor. Brutality and persecutions began. In the city of Boreion Jews were forcibly brought to baptism, and their age-old synagogue was made into a church. Justinian himself instructed Propraetor Salomo, the governor of the new province, to transform Jewish houses of worship into Christian churches.

From Africa the Byzantines took the leap across the Mediterranean to their second goal—the conquest of Italy. They were determined to drive the heretical Goths from the peninsula. In 535 Belisarius subjugated all of Sicily and the southern tip of the Italian mainland. In forced marches he approached Naples, and in 536 he and his army were drawn up before the strongly fortified city below Vesuvius on the Bay of Naples.

Belisarius' call for surrender split the Neapolitans into two parties. Large segments of the population wished to submit and open the gates to the Byzantine general. But the Jews, sensing what awaited them under Justinian, joined with patriotic Neapolitans in opposing surrender, and the siege began. Determined to defend the city to the utmost, the wealthy among the Jews contributed their fortunes to the defense. Other Jews placed their granaries, the center of the city's thriving grain trade, at the disposal of the defenders. For a time all of Belisarius' assaults broke against the stubborn

Jewish resistance. Jews protected the unfortified waterfront of Naples. The struggle lasted for three weeks; then the Byzantines contrived to take the city by a ruse. Byzantine soldiers made their way into the city at night through the water conduits, whose location was betrayed to them by a Greek. Even then, the Jews continued the struggle along the waterfront until the entire city had succumbed to the enemy's superior forces.

Toward the end of 536 Belisarius took Rome without fighting. Unexpectedly surrounded there by the Gothic army, he broke out of the encirclement, marched to Ravenna, and captured that nearly impregnable city. Using the Ostrogothic capital as their headquarters, the Byzantines began the conquest of northern Italy. For two decades Totila, King of the Goths, maintained his hold during the shifting fortunes of war, in the course of which cities changed hands several times. At last the military craft of General Narses, the successor to Belisarius, completed the final conquest of Italy. In 555 the country was placed under a governor, called an exarch, who established his residence in Ravenna. Italy was once more a part of the Roman Empire. Or, to phrase the same thing in terms of a new reality, Italy became a province of the Byzantine Empire.

The Jews had vainly given their blood for the Goths, the masters of the country. Under the rule of Justinian they could scarcely expect a different fate from that of their brethren in the reconquered Kingdom of the Vandals.

As it turned out, however, the policies of Constantinople could never be imposed as rigorously in Italy as in the Orient. The Byzantines found themselves compelled to share their power in the Italian peninsula with partners who rapidly became forces to be reckoned with: the highest-ranking of the Roman bishops, the Popes. Gradually the Popes had strengthened their position in Rome and increased their prestige. The West Roman Church, however, did not as yet participate in secular politics. The Bishop of Rome, "St. Peter's successor," was not yet encouraging the secular rulers of the country to undertake anti-Jewish measures or inciting the population against members of the Jewish religion.

GREGORY I: A POPE SHOWS THE WAY

In 590 the gifted statesman Gregory I, subsequently known as Gregory the Great, acceded to the throne of St. Peter. The reign of this Pope and Church Father was to exert a tremendous influence upon future relations between the Latin Church and that of Byzantium. In his attitude toward

Jewry as well, this "father of the medieval papacy" set an example most of his successors were to follow.

Moderate and fair-minded, Pope Gregory I did all in his power to prevent poisoning the atmosphere. He wished to avoid any greater tensions in the relations between Christians and Jews precisely because he was much concerned with the latter's conversion. Within the framework of the laws he wished to have the Jews receive justice, and he repeatedly emphasized that the laws must be abided by strictly. In his pastoral letters, in which he frequently touched on the "Jewish question," and in his other numerous writings in which he advised or made decisions on questions of Christian behavior toward the Jews, he shows, however, that he had an exact knowledge of the ordinances relating to the Jews that had been fixed by Justinian's Code. To him, too, these ordinances were binding. Freedom of worship in existing synagogues was permitted the Jews, but they were not allowed to build any new houses of worship. The point was that the Jews must be prevented from wielding any religious influence outside their own communities. Christians must be protected from the "contagion" of Judaism. Jews were forbidden to undertake any missionary activity. Christians were not allowed to practice any Jewish rites.

Gregory went a step further than any predecessors in his endeavors to eliminate Jews from positions in which they might influence Christians: He made it illegal for Christians to consult Jewish doctors; the clergy was strictly forbidden to employ Jewish clerks; secular rulers were warned against seeking the advice of Jews or employing them in positions in which they would hold power over Christians.

At the same time, Gregory the Great was an opponent of all fanaticism. He vigorously opposed physical persecution of the Jews, strongly reprimanded all arbitrary acts, and upheld the autonomy of Jewish community government. "Just as it is not befitting to permit the Jews in their communities to go beyond the boundaries of what is permissible by law," he declared in a circular letter, "so also the rights they already hold should not be diminished." The introductory phrase, *"Sicut Judaeis non debeat,"* became famous. All subsequent papal bulls issued in favor of the Jews began with the same words, and were soon called, for short, *Sicut non.* "We forbid," the circular letter continued, "burdening and oppressing the Jews, contrary to the existing ordinances, and permit them to live under the same conditions as Romans and to hold their property without restrictions, except that they must not own Christian slaves."

But although the Pope thus formulated his principles in unmistakable terms, high clergy in the provinces nevertheless were guilty of outrages against Jewish communities. Gregory had to intervene several times in

response to complaints from the Jews. In Terracina, a town in the Campagna, a Bishop Peter expelled the Jews from their synagogue. He alleged
that the loud recitation of the Jewish prayers interfered with the Christian
services in the nearby church. Gregory had a commission look into the
case and ordered that, if the position of the synagogue was truly disturbing, a place be assigned to the Jews for building a new one. At the same
time he warned the Bishop against henceforth interfering with the Jews'
fulfillment of their religious obligations. "Instead of attracting the Jews
by mildness and sermons on salvation," he pointed out, "you repel them
by threats and terror."

Another bishop, Victor of Palermo, took over all the Jewish buildings
in his city—synagogue, schools, library, and hospital. The Pope was informed at once, but before the matter could be investigated, the Bishop
consecrated the buildings as churches, for he was well aware that to transfer Christian churches to Jews was considered blasphemy. Gregory I had
no choice; he could only reprimand the Bishop. But at the same time
he ordered Bishop Victor to pay full compensation to the Jewish community for the confiscated buildings and to return the books from the
library and schools.

The Pope also disapproved of the excessive zeal of a newly converted
Jew who had forced his way into the synagogue of his former community
in Cagliari and installed therein a crucifix and pictures of Jesus and Mary.
Gregory I sharply reproved the convert's conduct in a letter to the Bishop
of Sardinia. He sent orders that the crucifix and the images, which offend
the religious feelings of Jews, must with all due reverence be at once removed from the synagogue. "Just as the law forbids the Jews the building
of new synagogues," his argument ran, "it also guarantees them preservation of the old ones." When Gregory learned that in Naples Christians
were disturbing Jewish services on holidays, he wrote to Bishop Paschalis
instructing him to take measures in the future against all disturbers of the
peace.

Gregory's intervention in such matters sprang from his ecclesiastical
policy, not from any benevolence toward those he defended. He, too, had
no sympathy at all for the "people of God." In his letters dealing with
the Jews he constantly uses the words "superstition," "perdition," "per-
fidy." But Gregory was convinced that the "remnant of Israel" could
gradually be won over to the Christian faith by peaceable methods.

In order to bring the Jews into the Church, he offered rewards and all
sorts of inducements. Jewish peasants and tenant farmers on Church
lands in Sicily were relieved of part of the real-estate tax or the rent for
their land if they accepted conversion. Perhaps Pope Gregory was not

entirely at ease about this measure, for he admitted: "Although these Jews thus converted for material advantages may not prove to be especially faithful believers, their children will probably be better Christians."

Nevertheless, it remained for Gregory the Great a firm principle that no sort of violence and no pressure must be employed to persuade the Jews to convert. "If we wish to win new converts for Christianity," Gregory wrote to Bishop Paschalis of Naples, "we must proceed with kindliness and must not use harshness; for otherwise vexation will repel even those whose souls might by reason have approached close to Christianity." In the same letter the Pope placed great weight on winning the Jews over by circumspection, "so that they will not flee from us, but follow us." In letters to Bishop Virgilius of Arles and Bishop Theodore of Marseilles he expressed his regret that Jews "are being led to baptism more by force than by preaching," for there was reason to fear that "those converted by force actually remain attached to their old faith." And he informed Duke Landulf of Benevento: "We have never heard that our Lord Jesus Christ forced anyone by violence into his service, but rather he won men by simple persuasion; he allowed them their free will and did not deflect them from their error by threats, but by spilling his blood for them. One who has not come to baptism of his own accord, but against his will, cannot have the true Christian faith."

How correctly Gregory the Great understood this was to be proved later, in the frightful tragedy of those Jews who were baptized forcibly in the seventh century, under the rule of the Visigoths in Spain, and, eight centuries later, by the cruel fate of the marranos. All efforts toward forcible conversion of the descendants of the people of Israel failed—but then, so did all peaceful attempts to persuade them to abandon their faith. The tragic, monstrous error of all the following ages into the nineteenth century was the Christian conviction that this goal could be attained. No power on earth was able to shatter the loyalty of Jews to their One God.

The law against the possession of Christian slaves by Jews had not been enforced for many years. Meanwhile, in the tempests of the migrations and the incessant wars of disturbed times, the trade in prisoners and slaves had swelled considerably. Its economic importance was incontestable—the slave markets provided the supply of human labor urgently needed in agriculture and industry. No one regarded this as objectionable, nor did Gregory the Great. But he was concerned for the souls of Christian slaves whose as yet unfortified faith might be subject to the religious influence of Jewish masters. Hence he insisted that the law be obeyed to the letter. Upon learning that Jews in the city of Luna owned Christian slaves, he wrote to the Bishop and bluntly told him: "That is against the law. The slaves must be freed."

Rigid enforcement of this law brought total ruin to the Jewish slave traders in Italy. At one blow they lost a fortune in property—namely, the many Christian slaves they owned. Many slaves who were still pagan had themselves baptized in order to win emancipation. It was easily done, for Gregory had commanded: "Every slave of a Jewish master who flees into the Church for reasons of faith must be left at liberty, whether he was a Christian before or became converted afterward, nor need the Jews be paid compensation from the funds for the poor."

In Sicily, where the slave trade was a large-scale enterprise, the papal measures favored the Greek slave dealers. All Jewish competitors vanished. In agriculture the papal order was equivalent to barring Jewish owners and tenants from running vineyards, olive plantations, and orchards, since such operations were impossible without hordes of slave laborers. The Jews were affected in all branches of manufacture, and even in their own households. "No wonder," Professor Rudolf Pfisterer remarks, "that the Jews sought to evade these decrees by having one member of a Jewish family—a son, for example—become a Christian and thus escape these ruinous laws. Such was the case with the Jew Basilus, whose son Felix became a Christian; the father then turned his Christian slaves over to his son, in order not to suffer loss. Gregory therefore pointed out in a letter to the bishops that they must be on guard against such deceptive maneuvers. But was this attacking the evil at the root?" The case of Basilus is the first of the sort for which there is historical documentation, and shows clearly where such laws led. Those affected were forced to devise evasions and thus become violators of the law, incurring public obloquy and exposing themselves to punishment.

Gregory the Great kept an eye on infractions of the Jewish laws outside Italy and did not fail to warn the rulers of the Franks in Gaul and the Visigoths in Spain. He addressed an urgent appeal to Brunhild, Queen of the Franks, who had not yet forbidden Jews to keep Christian servants and slaves. The Queen would, Gregory said, "show herself a worthy worshiper of Almighty God by freeing believers from the hands of their enemies." A special letter of praise went to King Reccared in Spain for having sternly refused a petition by the Jews to rescind the ban, which had recently been proclaimed in the Visigothic Kingdom.

Toward the end of the sixth century a significant religious change took place: The long contest between Arianism and Catholicism was finally decided. Country by country, the new Germanic states, from Italy to Spain, turned away from the Arian belief, which thereby became the Arian "heresy." Catholicism became the dominant creed. "This was the hardest blow that could have struck the Jews of Europe," Professor Edmund Schopen has observed. "For henceforth they stood defenseless against the hostility of Catholic Christianity, which had completed the break with the austerity of Jewish monotheism."

From the moment that Catholicism triumphed, after the masses of the population had been baptized and their Germanic rulers had solemnly professed Catholicism, the situation changed abruptly. The decisions of the councils held under the Christian Roman emperors were now enforceable. From the Po to the Ebro, Jewish communities began being stripped of their ancient rights. Persecutions were initiated.

The first excesses, forced baptisms, began in France while Gregory the Great was still living. In 576 Bishop Avitus confronted the Jews of Clermont with the alternative of baptism or expulsion. After three days of hesitation some five hundred declared they would accept baptism— although this was only sham acceptance. The rest fled to Marseilles. The secular power in France shared the zeal of the clerics. In 582 King Chilperic, under the influence of the famous Bishop Gregory of Tours, took measures to force the Jews to baptism. In Burgundy, Christians destroyed the synagogues. When King Guntram came to Orléans in 585, representatives of the Jewish community begged him for permission to rebuild their synagogue, which had also been destroyed. "But, God willing, the King will probably not condescend," Bishop Gregory wrote.

Gregory the Great, informed of all this by Italian Jews who traveled frequently in France, directed warnings to the bishops of Arles and Marseilles, reiterating his policy of mildness and persuasion to win the Jews to Christianity. But if he had had any influence upon the clergy and the Merovingian kings of France, it did not last long after his death in 604. In 614 a synod of bishops held in Paris decreed that Jews were no longer to be admitted to positions of authority or to military service. The ruler, too, was no longer to entrust Jews with official tasks. All Jews already employed in administrative positions, as well as their relatives, were to be forced to baptism. The Frankish King Chlotar II endorsed the decisions of this synod. His son, King Dagobert I (who reigned from 629 to 639), called upon Jews who had immigrated from Spain either to accept baptism or to leave the country. Dagobert is also said to have ordered the expulsion of all Jews who refused baptism, even if they had long been settled in the kingdom of the Franks. He is supposed to have been prompted to this step by Emperor Heraclius of Byzantium, with whom he was allied.

A similar hardening policy toward the Jews was evident in Burgundy and in the Lombard Kingdom of northern Italy. But the reaction appears to have taken its most virulent form across the Pyrenees.

A DARK CENTURY IN SPAIN

In 587, a year after his accession to the throne, Reccared I, King of the Visigothic Kingdom, renounced Arianism and became a Catholic. Henceforth king and Church worked together more intimately than in any other country of Europe. Virtually every decision of a Church council became a law of the state, signed jointly by the ruler and the bishops. A policy of harshness against pagans, Arians, and Jews was instituted, its aim being the establishment of a unified Catholic Spain in which there would be no place for adherents of any other religion. The Roman-Byzantine laws against the Jews were now applied to the Jews of Spain—bans on their possession of Christian slaves, on marriages between Christians and Jews, and on Jews' holding any posts in government. But there was strong resistance within the country to these measures. King Sisebert, who ascended the throne in 612, recognized that the law on possession of slaves was by no means universally enforced. Moreover, in spite of massive pressure from the Church, the attempts at conversion were also failing.

A new edict was issued, once again demanding that Jews be prevented from having any Christian employees. "The glory of orthodoxy consists," the text reads, "in assuring that no power over Christians may be allowed to the detestable falsehood of the Hebrews (*Ebreorum execranda perfidia*). The corrupting power of the Jews is an abomination to Christians, and therefore the godly common people must be placed under the protection of Catholic love. We confirm by this law that henceforth, from this first happy year of Our government, no Jew shall be permitted, no matter by what legal title, to keep a Christian in his service or under his guardianship, whether such Christian be a freeman or a slave or a servant for hire or any other subordinate."

A single door was left open: baptism. But the Jews did not avail themselves of that recourse; they would rather put up with the severe economic loss, which robbed many of them of their livelihood. Disappointed at his failure to win souls, and determined to break the resistance of the Jews, King Sisebert issued an ultimatum in 613: baptism or expulsion from the country. Instructions were sent to secular and ecclesiastical authorities to enforce this order without mercy.

Faced with this dreadful choice, Spanish Jewry was split in two. Many decided to stay, especially those in agriculture who had for generations owned farms and vineyards. They yielded and submitted to baptism. Here, too, however, it was only a pretense; they were firmly resolved to keep secretly to the religion of their fathers. In time, they hoped, the persecutions would come to an end and they would once again be able to profess Judaism openly. Many, however—the strong and inflexible whose consciences rebelled at the thought of secret reservations, and, above all, those whose occupations in the crafts or in trade permitted them greater mobility—left Spain. Hordes of emigrants crossed the Pyrenees into the Kingdom of the Franks, where, shortly afterward, they were to meet the same fate under King Dagobert. Some of the deported made their way to North Africa, where whole communities of them were able to begin a new life.

The Christian clergy had raised no public protest against the King's Draconian measures. Had they already forgotten Pope Gregory's warnings against attempts to impose baptism by force? Isidore of Seville, the leading bishop of Spain, has recorded his personal opinion of the King's conduct: "At the beginning of his reign he displayed with regard to the conversion of the Jews to the Christian faith much zeal but little intelligence, for he applied force against those who should rather have been attracted by the spirit of the religion."

The terrible pressure did not persist beyond Sisebert's lifetime. Swintila, the next King (622–631), proved to be a mild and just ruler. Many of the exiles returned to their former homes. The sham Christians were permitted to return to Judaism. But this breathing spell lasted a bare decade. The tolerant ruler was overthrown by a conspiracy. Under King Sisenand (631–636) the Church avenged itself for the defeat it had suffered. A Council called in Toledo under the presidency of Isidore decreed: "Henceforth the Christian faith must not be imposed by force upon any Jew. But those who were forced to baptism and admitted to the sacraments of the Church under the most pious ruler Sisebert must henceforth remain Christians."

The children of baptized Jews were taken from their parents and educated in monasteries or handed over to Christian families. A Jew married to a Christian was given the choice between baptism or divorce. Baptized Jews were forbidden to associate with their former fellows. Any baptized Jew caught secretly engaging in the rites of his old religion suffered loss of freedom; he became a slave. Christians who accepted gifts from Jews and in return befriended them were threatened with excommunication. "For," the Council argued, "it is essential to shield from the Body of Christ those who take the enemies of Christ under their protection."

The nobility nevertheless continued to ignore these decrees and to extend their patronage to the Jews. Not even the royal power could compel them to change their ways. Yet the rulers attempted to pursue their harsh course. At his coronation in 636 Chintila swore to obey all the canons directed against the Jews. The forcibly baptized, fearing further troubles, delivered penitential letters to the ruler, in which they promised to be good Christians and no longer to associate with Jews. These protestations did not help them. They were lumped in with the others when King Recesuinto launched his campaign against the Jews soon after his accession in 649. At the Eighth Council of Toledo in 653 he declared: "I desire to inform you concerning the mode of life and customs of the Jews, because I am only too well aware of how gravely the land under my rule is tainted with this leprosy. While Almighty God has eradicated all heresies in our country, this blasphemous sect alone has not been exterminated, and therefore it must either be brought to the right path by the power of our piety or struck to the ground by the rod of vengeance. Among that people I behold, on the one hand, those who cling undeterred to the rotting traditions and laws of their vile superstition, while the others, although redeemed by the waters of Holy Baptism, to my sorrow have so gravely entangled themselves in the sin of apostasy that their blasphemous conduct must arouse even more indignation than the conduct of those who have not yet been purified by the holy water of the new life. Therefore I beg you, venerable and blessed ones . . . to draw up a decree conceived in the spirit of sincerity and truth, in honor of my Lord and Saviour Jesus Christ . . . without respecting persons and without being distracted by promises from whatsoever source. . . ." In despair, the baptized Jews once more signed pledges "not to hold any intercourse with the despicable community of the unbaptized Jews." The punishment for disobedience was to be death "by fire or stoning."

The Ninth Council of Toledo in 655 ordered the most stringent enforcement of the decree that its predecessor had duly passed. Baptized Jews were commanded to attend every episcopal Mass and to be in church on all Jewish feast days, under penalty of scourging if they failed to appear.

King Recesuinto proved to be a Visigothic Justinian. The various ecclesiastical canons and royal decrees of his predecessors were codified and preserved in the *Lex Visigothorum*. Included was even a mandate dealing with denunciation: "Let no one who learns of the performance of vile sectarian acts, or who knows the name of him who has performed them, dare to keep his knowledge secret. Let no one neglect to publish what he has seen and to reveal what he has overheard."

Like the *Codex Theodosianus* and the *Codex Justinianus,* this new Spanish lawbook was to have a sinister power far into the future. More than a millennium later the French philosopher Montesquieu wrote: "We owe to the Visigothic Code all those rules, principles, and notions by which the Inquisition is guided to this day, so that the monks of later times had only to copy the laws concocted long ago for use against the Jews." It must be remembered that the Spanish Inquisition was still a powerful force in the eighteenth century.

Since the new measures again did not accomplish their intended purpose, a policy of outright terrorism was resolved upon to force Spanish Jewry to abandon its faith. In 681, at the Twelfth Council of Toledo, Ervigius (King from 680 to 687) urged the bishops: "I implore you, gather your strength, gather your strength at last! Tear the snares of the unjust, purify the godless customs of the impious, condemn the faithless, and, what is of most importance, tear out by the roots the Jewish plague!" With the consent of the bishops, the latest and most drastic of the new laws was passed: The Jewish religion was prohibited. All Jews of Spain were commanded to undergo baptism within a year. "If any Jew . . . restrains his sons or servants from accepting baptism from the priest, or tries to evade it himself and advises his family against it, and after the passage of a year from the publication of this law has not yet participated in the grace of baptism, let such a criminal be punished with a hundred blows of the lash, decalvation [plucking of the hair from the head], and expulsion from the country, his property to be at the mercy of the King."

In the face of this threat many Jews fled abroad, chiefly to Africa. Others went into hiding within the country; this was possible because governors and local nobles took them under their protection. Unwittingly, the King and Council were by their fierce laws contributing to those forces that would soon bring about the downfall of the Visigothic Kingdom. In 694 King Ergica once again summoned a Council at Toledo. Alarming news had reached him that across the Strait of Gibraltar the Arabs were beginning preparations for another campaign of conquest. After their victorious march through the lands of the ancient East and all of North Africa, their next goal could only be Spain.

"It has recently been made known to us by reliable testimony," the King reported to the bishops, "that Spanish Jews have entered into negotiations with foreign Jews from countries overseas to conspire against Christians." The Seventeenth Council of Toledo decreed that henceforth all Jews in Spain were to be serfs of the King. Their children were to be taken from them at the age of seven and handed over to Christians for their rearing.

A few years later the terror under which the Jews had dwelt for so long came to an abrupt end. In July of the year 711 the Visigothic Kingdom collapsed under the Arab assault. In the sun-drenched plain near Jerez de la Frontera hordes of Arabs and Berbers from North Africa under Tarik, in whose ranks Jewish detachments fought furiously, annihilated the Visigothic army. The Iberian Peninsula fell into the hands of the Moslems, and a new era began for the Jews of Spain.

II UNDER EMPERORS AND CALIPHS

THE SECOND DAUGHTER RELIGION

The storm of conquest that swept over the Iberian Peninsula shortly after the year 700 and destroyed the rule of the Visigoths was only a part of the world-wide upheaval that was to change the course of history and to relieve Jewry of oppression for hundreds of years. That upheaval had begun barely a century before, many thousands of miles from Spain, in the heart of the Arabian Peninsula. At almost precisely the time that the first anti-Jewish edicts of the Council of Toledo under King Sisebert had inaugurated the bitter sufferings of the Spanish Jews, the conquering religion of Islam had been born in the scorching deserts of Arabia. Like Christianity, it had sprung from the womb of Judaism, a second daughter religion.

To Mohammed and his countrymen the Jews were not foreigners. They lived among the Arabs in the vast spaces of Arabia, between the Red Sea and the Persian Gulf, where time seemed to have stood still. Far from the scenes of world-shaking events, amid expanses of sandy wasteland marked only by lonely, perilous caravan trails, where no great army would ever dare to venture, the Arabs led unchanged a life such as their forefathers had led since time immemorial. They enjoyed untrammeled freedom, clinging to their age-old customs, and grouped in tribes and clans among which amity and bloody feuds forever alternated.

The mists of legend veil the time when wandering Jewish tribes first set foot in that ancestral home of the Arabs. Were they seafaring Israelites under the mighty kings of Judah, under David or Solomon, whose fleets plied the Red Sea to the famous land of gold, Ophir, and who established Jewish colonies for the trade with India at the once famous commercial towns of Marib and Sana in southern Arabia? Or had they come even earlier? Perhaps, as an ancient tradition has it, a multitude of Jewish fugitives arrived in northern Arabia after the destruction of the first Temple by Nebuchadnezzar, King of Babylonia. No one can say for certain. In any case, the wars between the Jews and the Romans certainly brought a Jewish population into the Arabian Peninsula—Zealots who had fled after the fall of Jerusalem. Dwelling among the Bedouins and nomads of a thinly populated desert, they were able to preserve the spirit of liberty and bellicosity that had forced them to flee.

Three important Jewish tribes of northern Arabia sprang from these fugitives: the Banu Kainuka, the Banu Nadir, and the Banu Kuraisa. They lived in Yathrib (Medina), the capital of the Hejaz, as the region was called, and in the vicinity—an area of palms and rice fields watered by small brooks. Farther north, the town and countryside around Khaibar were inhabited by a large Jewish colony. Barely a day's journey away, many smaller Jewish settlements stretched in a long line by the side of a fruitful wadi, the so-called Valley of Villages.

Since the Jewish tribes were frequently attacked by Bedouin robbers, they protected their village communities with strong walls, and for emergencies built forts on mountains difficult of access. In language, in many customs, and in habits, they could scarcely be distinguished from their Arab neighbors. Quite a few of them led a nomad Bedouin life; others were caravan traders. The majority practiced agriculture in oases and watered valleys. Tradition has it that they introduced the date palm into Arabia. Some were famous as goldsmiths and craftsmen.

In courage they were the equals of their warlike neighbors; they practiced generous hospitality like Arabs, stood loyally by their allies, and vied with their neighbors for excellence in poetry. Arabic tales have preserved the memory of many of their heroes and poets. The Jewish prince and poet Samuel ibn Adiya won proverbial renown for his honesty and high principles. "Faithful as Samuel," was the Arab phrase. Folk songs glorify a much-admired act of his. Pursued by enemies, the Arab poet Prince Imru-l-Kais confided his weapons and valuables to his friend Samuel, and continued his flight. Soon his pursuers appeared, besieged the Jewish poet's castle, and demanded surrender of the Prince's possessions. When Samuel refused, they threatened to kill his son, whom they had captured. Samuel would still not be swayed. "Do what you will," he replied. "Never will I break my word to my friend. Treachery is a collar that never rusts.

My son has brothers." The pursuers executed his son before the walls of the castle.

Only a few Jews lived in Mecca. But they were very numerous far to the south of the peninsula, in Yemen. In Arabia Felix, however, they never formed coherent communities. Many families wandered about as nomads, or were engaged in growing spices. Others had settled as merchants in the ports, then centers of world trade from which goods from India and Persia were transshipped to Egypt and Byzantium. The immigrants differed from the native tribes in one respect only: their religion. In Arabia, too, they clung unswervingly to it, observed the dietary laws, strictly honored the Sabbath, and celebrated the holidays of their people.

Yathrib was considered a center of Jewish scholarship; the town had its school and its teachers of the law, although not much is known about these scholars. For their learning, however, the Jewish tribes enjoyed great prestige among their pagan neighbors. All the Jews could read and write, whereas few Arabs were literate. The Arabs owed to the Jews their calendar, which was reckoned according to lunar months. Soon after A.D. 400 the Jewish nineteen-year cycle of intercalation, which served to adjust the solar year to the lunar year, was adapted on the Arabian Peninsula. The Arabs called the intercalation nasi, a word that retained memory of the annual proclamation of the holiday calendar to the Jewish communities by the Nasi, the patriarch of the motherland.

Many of the stories from the Scriptures, embellished by poetic imagination, circulated among the sons of the desert. Biblical tales were told everywhere, at wells in the caravansaries and on long, grueling rides across the desert as well as at nocturnal fires in the oases. The two principal Arab tribes even traced their origin and distant kinship to the Jews to statements in the Bible. The northern tribe, which lived in the Hejaz, regarded the desert warrior Ishmael, son of Father Abraham, as their ancestor, and called themselves the tribe of Ishmaelites; the southern tribe considered themselves descendants of Joktan, the son of Eber (Genesis 10:25–26). Under these circumstances it is scarcely surprising that a good many sheiks developed an interest in Judaism and became converts. Since the Arabs were in any case circumcised, the change of religion presented few difficulties. The warlike tribe of Banu Kinanah, kin of the prestigious Koreishites, a Ghassanid tribe in Mecca, and members of tribes who lived in Yathrib converted to the Jewish religion. The beginning of the sixth century saw the emergence of a small Jewish kingdom in southern Arabia.

Abu Kariba, Prince of the Himyarites in Yemen, had launched a campaign along the thousands of miles of caravan trail from the south, leading his forces all the way to Yathrib. Jewish soldiers fought side by side with

Arab friends and fellow inhabitants to defend the town against the numerous enemy cavalrymen, and harassed the foe by violent sallies from the town. The siege dragged on in the face of this tough resistance, when Abu Kariba suddenly fell severely ill. Two Jewish scholars, hearing of their enemies' misfortune, called on the Prince and used their knowledge of medicine to restore him to health. While attending him, they pleaded with him to make peace. Many legends about their conversations with Abu Kariba later sprang up. But the kernel of the story is this: The Yemenite Prince not only was persuaded to call off his attack, but he also accepted the Jewish religion, along with his entire army. The two Jewish sages accompanied him back to Yemen and, according to his wishes, converted all his subjects. This happened about the year 500.

Abu Kariba's grandson and successor (518–525), Prince Dhu Nuwas, took the Hebrew name of Yussuf (Joseph) and became so ardent an advocate of Judaism that he was prompted to rash acts that brought about his own destruction and that of his realm.

Learning of the sad plight of Jewish communities in the Byzantine Empire, Prince Yussuf resolved to force the Christian Emperor to treat his Jewish subjects justly. He therefore ordered several Christian merchants who had come to his capital on business to be seized and executed. Christian traders far and wide were terror-stricken. News of this high-handed deed soon reached Byzantium. A challenge of this sort could not go unpunished. But Emperor Justin I was involved in a war with the Persians, and Yemen was far away. He decided to write to the Christian King of Ethiopia, who was a good deal closer to Arabia.

Elesvaa, the Christian Negus, equipped an army and a fleet. Justinian, the Emperor's young coregent, brought reinforcements to the Ethiopians on ships from Egypt. The combined force that crossed the Red Sea to Yemen could not be withstood. In 525, after a disastrous battle, the Jewish Prince's land and capital, his wife, and all his treasures, fell into the hands of the Christian enemy. Yussuf, seeing all lost, took his own life; before the eyes of his pursuers he rode his horse over a high cliff into the sea.

In 570, forty-five years after the destruction of this little Jewish state, a child was born to Abdullah and Aminah, members of an impoverished Arab clan in the heart of the peninsula, a boy destined to be the greatest son of his people, founder of a religion that was eventually to embrace one seventh of the world's population. And as it happened, Judaism exerted an enormous influence upon Mohammed, "the prophet of Mecca and Yathrib."

History reveals little of Mohammed's youth. The boy grew up in Mecca, the ancient trading town at the intersection of important caravan roads, and also the holy city of all Arabs. Peace prevailed in this international market place; all open quarrels were banned from the town. Here thousands upon thousands of merchants met annually; here, too, came pilgrims from every corner of the huge peninsula. Mecca sheltered a whole pantheon of Arab gods; but from ancient times an invisible god, the father of all gods, had also been recognized: Allah. The pilgrims venerated him in a building called the Kaaba, which held a sacred large black stone.

Like most of the inhabitants of his native city, Mohammed became a merchant. In the market places of Mecca and on his many journeys—first with the caravans of his uncle Abu Talib, then with those of his first wife, Kadijah, across the Hejaz and sometimes all the way to Syria—he became acquainted with the stories of the Old Testament and the Talmud; he also heard something of the Gospels and some Christian legends. Jews, moreover, came frequently from Yathrib, and there were even some Christians living within the walls of Mecca. What made the deepest impression upon Mohammed was what he heard of the Jews' belief in a single God who was master of all the world, and of Abraham, the patriarchs, and the prophets.

Mohammed was about forty years old when he underwent a great spiritual crisis. He withdrew into solitude and gave himself to dreams and visions. In a cave close to his birthplace he had a decisive experience: The archangel Gabriel, so he claimed, appeared to him and revealed divine truths. On the basis of this, Mohammed became the founder of a new religion. Strict monotheism such as pervaded the Old Testament became the chief tenet of the new teaching. "There is only One God and Mohammed is his Prophet," became the creed of Islam. According to Mohammed, God's revelation to the world was a progressive manifestation that took place in six stages: through Adam, Noah, Abraham, Moses, Jesus, and Mohammed. After Mohammed no further prophet would be needed; he was the last, who proclaimed in the Koran the absolutely perfected Word of God.

The Prophet began to preach the idea of One God, Allah, in his native city. But Mecca was the center of Arab idolatry, and only a few poor and uninfluential tribesmen accepted his revelations. The rich merchants mocked and attacked him. Mohammed's denunciations of idolatry antagonized many of the Meccans, who feared a falling off in pilgrimages to the sanctuary, with which the city's mercantile interests were so closely associated. The powerful pagan clan of Koreishites began to harass him. In 622, his life in danger, Mohammed fled from Mecca.

He took refuge in Yathrib, for he had already succeeded in arousing enthusiasm for his doctrines among some pilgrims from that city. Moreover, he appears to have been convinced that the influential Jewish tribes, the People of the Book, who were the oldest witnesses to divine revelation, would naturally side with him. Perhaps some apostates from Judaism may have nourished that hope. In Yathrib—later to be known as the City of the Prophet, Mohammed tried to enlist the sympathy of the Jews. To please them, he appointed Islam's annual day of fasting, Ashura, to fall on the same day as Yom Kippur, the Jewish Day of Atonement. "It is even more fitting for us to fast on this day than the Jews," he declared. Also to please them, he ordained that the kiblah, the direction in which the face was turned during prayer, should be toward Jerusalem rather than toward Mecca.

Mohammed's hopes were disappointed. Only a few Jews joined him. The majority rejected all his doctrines. Thereupon the Prophet's regard turned to hatred. He broke forever with these Jews who would not follow him, and he became their bitter foe. "Now that Allah has given you a Book for a confirmation of your former revelation, you have disavowed it. . . . Then let the curse of Allah come upon the misbelievers." The Sura of the Cow in the Koran is full of invective against the Jews.

The Prophet's great goal became Mecca. He was determined to seize the Kaaba. In 623 he changed the direction of prayer: Henceforth all believers were to turn toward the ancient sanctuary of Mecca rather than toward Jerusalem. He also abolished fasting on the Jewish Day of Atonement and instead introduced it in the month of Ramadan, sacred to the Arabs from ancient times. Moreover, he commanded that, in clear distinction to the Jewish Sabbath, the day of rest of all Arabs was to be Friday. Thus Mohammed was at one and the same time completing his break with the Jews and bringing his religion into harmony with the oldest traditions of Arabia. Islam was assuming the shape of a national religion of the Arab people.

Mohammed's victory over his powerful enemies in Mecca, whose superior forces he defeated before the gates of the city, marked the turning point in the evolution of Islam. Henceforth the power of "Allah's sword" would win adherents to the new religion.

The Jews were the first to feel the Prophet's power and animosity. In the course of a four-year war Mohammed crushed all the Jewish tribes living in Arabia. The Banu Kainuka in Medina were the first to suffer. They were followed by the tribes of the Banu Nadir, in the vicinity of the city, and the Banu Kuraisa. In the spring of 628 Mohammed took the field at the head of fifteen thousand men against the great Jewish community of Khaibar. It, too, succumbed, after desperate resistance. Toward the end of the year the last sizable Jewish community, Taima, at the farthest northern tip of the Peninsula, was likewise subjugated. The downfall of the free Jewish tribes of Arabia was complete. Many of the Jews fell in battle, others were either executed or tortured to death, and the remainder were either forced to emigrate or plundered of all their goods and subjected besides to payment of heavy tribute. In addition, many of their farmlands and date groves had been destroyed.

The story goes that a Jewish woman who wished to avenge the death of her brother had to pay for her attempt with her life. Sainab, the young widow of a Khaibar Jew who had fallen in battle, put a strong poison into the roast of mutton she served Mohammed. But the Prophet spat out the first morsel almost as soon as he had taken it into his mouth. Called to account, Sainab said: "You have inflicted unspeakable suffering upon my people. I therefore thought: If you are only a bloodthirsty oppressor, I shall give my people peace by using this poison; but if you are a prophet, God will warn you against it and it will do you no harm." Mohammed had her killed instantly. He is said to have felt the aftereffects of the poison for many years afterward, and even his ultimately fatal illness is ascribed to it.

Just twelve years after the fall of Khaibar, the few surviving Jewish communities suffered the same fate as all the others. Caliph Omar expelled them from Arabia and gave their lands and plantations to his soldiers. All the bravery of the Jews had come to nothing, pitted as they were against the overwhelming forces of Mohammed, which were commanded by such capable generals as Abu Bekr, Omar, and Ali. These three later became Islam's world-conquering caliphs. The sword that the Maccabees had once wielded in defense of the faith, and which they had passed on to the Zealots, who, in turn, bequeathed it to the Jews of Arabia—that sword was wrested from the last Jewish heroes for many centuries by the warriors of Islam. This was to be the last time Israel resorted to weapons in defense of its religion. Henceforth Jewry submitted to its fate, became passive. The warriors became patient sufferers who accepted the heaviest persecutions of the coming centuries without offering resistance. Their Law, to which they now became wholly devoted, remained their only shield.

The anti-Jewish suras of the Koran contained dangerous tinder for fanaticism, but for a long time that tinder seldom kindled. Having achieved the status of a world power, Islam proved to be tolerant. Unbelievers were despised, to be sure, but for the most part they were not persecuted. Under the dominance of Islam the Jews, quite contrary to their experience in the

Auto-da-fé in Spain. Painting by Alonso Berruguete (*c.* 1480-1561), in the Prado, Madrid.

BELOW: Auto-da-fé in Madrid for the wedding of Charles II of Spain, June 30, 1680. At this public execution eighteen marranos were burned alive, along with other "heretics."

Calendar for A.D. 1276 for calculating Jewish Holy Days. The outer circle shows the twenty-eight-year sun cycle, the inner circle the nineteen-year moon cycle.

Armillary sphere constructed in Spain by Jewish astronomers under Alfonso X. The major piece of apparatus in the observatory, it was the most advanced astronomical measuring device of the Middle Ages.

The astronomer Abraham Zacuto, Vasco da Gama's adviser

Astrolabe with inscriptions in Hebrew

Johann Reuchlin, humanist and first
Christian scholar of Hebrew,
who prevented the burning of the Talmud
in Germany

Departure of the Jewish community from Frankfurt as a result of the Fettmilch
uprising, August 23, 1614

Cossack hetman Bogdan Chmielnicki, whose rebellion against the Polish nobility in 1648 brought on one of the most frightful persecutions in the history of Eastern Jewry

Torture of Francisca de Carvajal at her interrogation, 1590. All the members of the marrano family of her brother Governor Luis de Carvajal, who secretly professed Judaism, fell victim to the Spanish Inquisition in Mexico.

Isaac Aboab de Fonseca,
who left Amsterdam for
Pernambuco, Brazil, in 1642,
to become the first rabbi
on the American continent

Johannes Buxtorf the Elder,
Hebrew theologian and
scholar of Basel

The old and the new synagogue in Fürth, Bavaria, where an important Jewish community arose after the expulsion of the Jews from Nuremberg in 1499. A view from the year 1705. On the far right can be seen a wedding party on the way to the synagogue. The bride and bridegroom walk under the canopy called a chuppah.

View of the interior of the old synagogue in Fürth. In the background is the pulpit (almemor), from which the Torah is read aloud.

Passover meal (Seder). Painting by Dirk Bouts, *c.* 1450.

Synagogues of the German (left) and Portuguese (right) Jews in Amsterdam.

Christian West, on the whole enjoyed favorable conditions. Moslem civilization developed a high culture, and the children of Israel made notable contributions to it.

IN THE REALM OF ISLAM

Mohammed died in 632. Scarcely a decade later, the flag of the Prophet waved over the best lands to the north and northeast of Arabia. In their first onslaught the warriors of Islam, bursting out of the boundaries of the peninsula, had snatched Palestine, Syria, and Egypt from mighty Byzantium and conquered Babylonia from the Persians. Before the Byzantines and Persians realized what was happening, the soldiers of the "Holy War," crying, "There is no God but Allah!," had changed the world situation forever. Overnight, Jewish communities from the Nile to the Euphrates found themselves subject to new masters.

In 638 Jerusalem fell; in spite of tenacious Byzantine resistance, Caliph Omar ibn al Katab (who ruled from 634 to 644) marched into the city at the head of his fanatical army. For the second time, the passionate followers and the secular power of a religion sprung from Judaism were taking possession of the Holy City. There are no Jewish accounts of the capture of Jerusalem, but a few confused legends have been preserved by Moslems and Christians. It is said that after Caliph Omar had ridden into the city on a camel, he prayed and read aloud the beginning of the Seventeenth Sura, "To the Israelites," which speaks of the miraculous night journey of Mohammed from the mosque at Mecca to the Remote Mosque—*i.e.,* the Temple in Jerusalem. After the Caliph had finished his prayer, he sent for Kaab, a Jew who had converted to Islam, and asked him, "Where do you advise me to build a place of worship?" Kaab indicated the Temple Rock, now a gigantic heap of ruins from the temple of Jupiter. The Jews, Kaab explained, had briefly won back their old capital a quarter of a century before—in 614 a surprise advance of the Persians had overrun Syria and Palestine—but they had not had time to clear the site of the Temple, for the "Rums" (Byzantines) had recaptured the city.

A Christian chronicler—the Alexandrian Bishop Eutychius—has left another description of the taking of the city. Upon entering Jerusalem, he says, the Caliph had beheld Patriarch Sophronius coming to meet him. When Omar asked him to suggest a site for erecting a mosque, Sophronius replied: "Commander of the Faithful, I shall show you a place on which you will build your mosque, a place which the Greek kings could not build on. It is that rock where God spoke with Jacob, and Jacob called it Gate of Heaven, but the Israelites called it the Holy of Holies. It rises in the center of the earth and was a sanctuary to the Israelites; wherever they might be they would turn their faces toward it in veneration." The Bishop added that the rock had been a place of ruins as far back as the time that Empress Helena, mother of Constantine the Great, built churches in Jerusalem. The Byzantines, he said, had deliberately left the ancient site of the temple as it was, and had even thrown garbage on it, so that a great heap of rubble formed.

After his explanation the Patriarch led the Caliph to the ruins that covered the sacred site. Omar is said to have taken a handful of the rubble and thrown it into the Vale of Kidron. Seeing this, the other Moslems followed his example, and soon a tremendous rock with a deep hole in it came to light. "Let this stone become a house of God," the Caliph declared, and laid a cornerstone. The site Omar selected for the mosque was high on the ancient Temple Mount—a symbol of Islam's victory within the former capital of Jewry and the Holy City of Christendom. Omar himself did not live long enough to carry out his plan. But half a century later Abd el-Malik (Caliph from 687 to 691) saw to the construction of the splendid domed building—one of the outstanding examples of Islamic architecture—which was visible from all the hills round about and stands to this day towering impressively above the city of Jerusalem: the famous Dome of the Rock.

Immediately after the capitulation, the centuries-old restriction was abolished. Omar permitted the Jews to enter and remain in Jerusalem. They were also allowed to worship unhindered at the holy places—much to the anger of the Christians. For during the negotiations for surrender of the city, a delegation led by Patriarch Sophronius, so an Arab chronicler relates, had made retention of the old ban an express condition of the capitulation.

The sites of the famous old Jewish academies—Lydda, Jabneh, Tiberias, and Sepphoris—also fell into Moslem hands. In 640, strongly fortified Caesarea was wrested from the Byzantine Emperor Heraclius. After tenacious resistance, it was won by guile: A Jew named Yussuf led the Arabs into the city by way of underground passages. Singing the Moslem hymn, "Allah Is Greatest," the soldiers of General Muawiyah suddenly appeared in the midst of the city, to the horror of the inhabitants.

The same year that Jerusalem fell, the Caliph's warrior bands, under his commander Chalid, conquered all of Babylonia. By this time the oppression of the Persian kings had so alienated the Jews that in many cases they aided the Arab conquerors. When soon afterward the Arabs succeeded in taking Egypt—Alexandria capitulated in 641—a sigh of relief passed through Jewry throughout the Near East. For the first time since the brief reign of Alexander the Great, the Jews from the Nile to the Euphrates were living within a single united kingdom whose rulers were well disposed toward them.

The communities in Babylonia regained a large measure of freedom. Their aid must have been valuable to the Mohammedans, for Caliph Omar rewarded them generously. Once more they were granted the right to live under a prince of their own, with political and judicial powers; once more they had virtually an autonomous commonwealth.

General Ali (who later became Caliph) confirmed Bostanai, the youthful descendant of the Exilarch, in his dignity as head of the Babylonian Jews. He even gave him Isdadvar, sister of the defeated Persian ruler, King Yazdegerd III, as his wife, and permitted him to sign his documents and decrees with a seal ring—a high distinction.

Under Bostanai a period of unusual brilliance began for the exilarchate; works of art show the Oriental pomp of his office. The Exilarch lived in a palace; he maintained swarms of servants and a bodyguard. When he visited the Caliph, he was accompanied by an escort of mounted men, both Mohammedans and Jews. Heralds preceded the procession to announce his approach. The Prince dressed in glittering garments of royal magnificence. At court he was received standing; even the Caliph rose to greet him, and invited him to take his place on the raised throne that stood opposite his own. A whole series of legends became attached to the name of Exilarch Bostanai; these served to perpetuate the memory of the first Exilarch under the dominion of Islam, whose descendants were to hold the office for more than three centuries.

Before long, intellectual life received new impetus in Babylonia. The heads of the centuries-old academies at Sura and Pumbaditha rose to the status of supreme spiritual dignitaries; the resplendent title of Gaon (Excellency) was conferred upon them. Ali bestowed upon the head of the Sura academy the privileges that were henceforth to distinguish that office.

The Caliph's grant was an act of gratitude. During the bitter struggles that had broken out among the Moslems for recognition of the new legitimate "successor" to Mohammed, the Jews had favored Ali and lent him their support. Abdullah ben Saba, a Jewish convert to Islam, had succeeded in winning great numbers of Moslems in Babylonia, Syria, and Palestine to the cause of Ali. After the capture of the city of Peroz-Shapur in 638, the chronicle relates, a crowd of Jews numbering many thousands came pouring toward the town from Sura. Mar Isaac, principal of the Talmudic academy, congratulated Ali in the name of the Jews. The General received their homage with pleasure and gave the scholar the title Gaon. With Gaon Mar Isaac, there began a new period in Jewish history—the Age of the Geonim.

In other countries, as well, a new, free life began for the Jews under their Moslem rulers. With the spread of Islam its initial fanatical intolerance disappeared. Political rationality alone forbade the caliphs from subjecting the vast numbers of unbelievers whom they had conquered to the same kind of harsh treatment their predecessors had meted out to the Jewish tribes of Arabia. Let Arabia, the motherland, remain purely Moslem, free of all unbelievers. But unless the caliphs intended to depopulate their vast new dominions, they would have to show a good deal of latitude. And so they did.

As did the Christian Church through its canon law, Islam also set up a host of prohibitions and restrictions upon members of other religions— many of the ordinances sound like copies of the anti-Jewish laws in the Christian empire. Unbelievers were not permitted to bear arms or ride horses. They were supposed to wear special dress. The building of new houses of worship was forbidden to them. They were excluded from public office. And the severest punishment awaited any who dared to vilify the Prophet or to attempt to seduce a Moslem from his religion. But free exercise of their religion was permitted to all, and no one ever suffered physical violence merely for his beliefs.

In actuality, most of these edicts were soon ignored. What remained in practice and was enforced with full harshness was the ordinance based on the Ninth Sura of the Koran: "Fight those to whom the Book is given, if they do not . . . believe in Allah . . . if they will not acknowledge the true religion—unless they pay the head tax humbly with their own hands." This became the ruling principle of Moslem policy toward all non-Mohammedans: All were considered to owe tribute, and the tributes were oppressively heavy, often reaching the limit of what could be borne. But if they were paid, the "unbelievers" enjoyed the full protection of the law.

In 661 Ali was assassinated, and the famous Ommiad dynasty was born. Surrounded by jubilant warriors, Muawiyah, great-grandson of a kinsman of Mohammed, was proclaimed Caliph. At his accession the empire of the Moslems already extended from North Africa to Persia; under him it made still more advances, and reached its greatest size and power.

The goal of the new Caliph was the imperial city on the Golden Horn. But the Byzantine Empire was still capable of mighty resistance. When tremendous levies of land troops and repeated assaults could not take Constantinople, the Ommiads decided to attack from the sea. A gigantic fleet was equipped and dispatched to the Bosporus. For four years—from 674 to 678—the walls of the Byzantine capital were bombarded and assailed by sea-borne troops. But this vast undertaking also failed. The Byzantines succeeded in annihilating the Moslem fleets with the aid of Greek fire, their secret mixture of explosives, which would burn even on water. The Caliph's vessels went up in flames. That victorious defense of Constantinople saved the West from being drowned in the Arab tide.

Although the thrust had failed in Eastern Europe, where Byzantium presented an insuperable barrier to Islam, there seemed to be no stopping the onrush of the Moslems in Africa. They swept westward from Egypt, and in the same century conquered all of North Africa. In 670 they founded, in the region of ancient Carthage, Kauruan, the city that was later to become the cultural center of African Jewry. After prolonged battles with the bellicose Berber tribes, Morocco, too, fell into the hands of the Arabs around the year 700. The coast of the Atlantic had been reached, and only a narrow strait separated Islam's territory from Europe.

In 711 the Mohammedan general Tarik landed a powerful army on that famous rock which still dimly echoes his name—Gibraltar, or as the Arabs dubbed it, Jebel-al-Tarik. After the destruction of the Visigothic troops at Jerez de la Frontera, near present-day Cadiz, and after the death of King Roderick, the fate of the Visigothic Kingdom was sealed. The Arab caliphate extended all the way to the Pyrenees; a great Christian country had been conquered by the Moslems. Only Asturias, a small Christian kingdom in the northern part of the peninsula, succeeded in holding its own.

In the course of their conquest of Spain, the Arabs were everywhere supported by the Jews, who regarded them as liberators from the heavy oppression of the Visigothic rulers. As soon as the Moslems had taken a city, their generals left behind only a few troops to garrison it. They entrusted the city itself to the Jews. When Tarik appeared before Toledo at the head of his army, he found only a feeble guard on the walls. The onetime grandees of the country, the nobility and the bishops, had already made their escape. While the Christian populace took refuge in churches, the Jews opened the gates to the Arabs. Jubilantly hailed by the Jewish community, Tarik made his entry into the capital of the Visigoths on Palm Sunday of the year 712. He entrusted men selected from among the

Jews with the task of guarding Toledo for him. This policy was followed by Musa, the governor of Africa, who crossed into Spain with a second army and conquered more cities in northern Spain.

A wave of alarm passed through the countries of the Christian West. The victorious march of the Arabs seemed invincible. After they had conquered Andalusia and reached the Pyrenees, all of Europe felt threatened. Bands of Moslem raiders were already pushing through the Basque passes into Gaul. They defeated the Duke of Aquitaine and penetrated as far as Septimania. The coastal regions along the lower Rhone were already swarming with Arab infantrymen and cavalry until, at last, the vigor of the Frankish majordomo stopped any further thrust into the heart of Europe. At the Battle of Tours Charles Martel checked the Arab force under Abd-er-Rahman ibn Abdullah, the Caliph's governor in Spain. The dangerous pincers movement from east and west, which for a time had threatened the whole Christian Occident, was thus thwarted and Europe liberated from the threat of encirclement.

The victory of Islam had profound consequences for the whole development of world history. Its influence upon the history of the Jews was destined to be equally great. The conquest of the Iberian Peninsula for the first time established a bridge between the Diaspora communities of East and West. The great reservoir of Jewish population in the Orient entered into vital contact with settlements of Jews in the far reaches of the Occident. It was now possible for anyone to travel freely from the Jordan or even from the Euphrates by way of Egypt and North Africa all the way to the Pyrenees. A great gate had been flung open for the Jews, and long-repressed forces began to stir, furthered by the wealth of stimuli that emanated from the Arab Empire. In years to come, Spain was to see a unique spiritual and cultural flowering resulting from this contact.

The first sign of change was migration. After long ages of stagnation and immobility, a tremendous movement began. Hordes of Jews—scholars and doctors, merchants, artisans, and farmers—followed in the wake of the Arab victors. New arrivals from Asia and Africa even penetrated the lands of the hitherto remote "people from the Rhine," the "Anshe Rhenus."

During the caliphate of the Abbassides, who came to power in 750, a period of unclouded peace and unusual intellectual and cultural progress began in the Mohammedan Empire. A Jew even took part in the choice of the new Moslem capital. Al-Mansur, the new Caliph, wished to abandon Damascus, for so long associated with the now exterminated Ommiads. He instructed the astrologers Naubacht and Manasseh of Persia to select the site for his new capital and to survey it. Baghdad, the City of Salvation on the Tigris, was built according to their plans. Manasseh happened to be a Jew who had converted to Islam and received the name Mashallah, "As God Wills"; he won renown through having made a collection of all the sources of ancient astrology—Babylonian, Egyptian, and even Indian. The Persian Jew Abu Masher, known as Abulmassar, made such good use of this material as to be hailed as the "greatest astrologer among the Arabs." His compendium was widely distributed throughout Europe. But while in the Occident observation of the stars remained the "handmaiden of astrology," the science of astronomy developed under the Arabs.

Under the new rulers in Baghdad, no profession was closed to "unbelievers," and no restrictions were placed on the exercise of their religion. The Jews, unhampered, began to take an active part in the cultural rebirth of the Orient. They lost no time acquiring the Arabic language, in place of the Aramaic, which had hitherto been the language of communication among them. The Arabs' enthusiasm for language and poetry influenced the Jews, and awoke them to a new appreciation of their own language. A renaissance of Hebrew poetry began, affecting also the services in the synagogue.

The Jews had long been familiar with Greek literature in their own Aramaic translations. In the Arab Empire they very early assumed a task of the highest importance for the future of culture. As early as 683 the Jewish physician Messer Gawaih of Basra, on the Persian Gulf, translated Syrian medical works into Arabic. He was only the first in a long line of Jewish translators who henceforth transmitted to the Moslems the treasures of antiquity's scientific literature, thus preserving them for humanity.

Two centuries after Emperor Justinian had closed the academy of Athens, last refuge of the Greek spirit, so that the tremendous heritage of Hellenistic science was lost to the Christian West for three quarters of a millennium, that science awoke to new life. Caliphs and philanthropists eager for knowledge sent forth their messengers to obtain all the extant philosophical, astronomical, mathematical, and medical writings of the Greeks. In Baghdad and many other cities in the Arab world, great collections of classical manuscripts were formed—the works of Apollonius, Archimedes, Euclid, Plato, Aristotle, Galen, and Hippocrates. Among the men who were employed to sift these manuscripts and translate them into Arabic were both Syrian Christians and many Jewish scholars. These men contributed enormously to the subsequent intellectual upsurge in the Arab world. During the centuries that followed, science reached hitherto unimaginable heights under the Moslems. Great numbers of Jews worked in Arab academies. Lists of their names were compiled only in the nineteenth

century; distorted by Arabic script, many of these names have been difficult to restore to their original form. But there can be no question that
the contribution of these Jews to astronomy, mathematics, and medicine
was formidable indeed.

Babylonia, meanwhile, the ancient "Mother of the Diaspora," remained
the intellectual center of the world's Jewry. From Babylonia, knowledge
of the Talmud, which so carefully governed the whole of Jewish life,
reached the remotest communities of Jews. The organization of the communities in Babylonia became the pattern followed by all other Jewish
groups that attained to autonomous self-government. Honored by the people, venerated as a descendant of King David, the Exilarch still ruled as
secular head of the Babylonian communities. He resided in Baghdad,
supervised the self-governing Jewish townships or quarters within towns,
saw to the punctual collection of taxes, and was counted among the highest
dignitaries at the Caliph's court. For all practical purposes the Exilarch
was considered the prince of a nation obligated to tribute, and since that
tribute, in the form of taxes, was quite sizable, he was a welcome guest to
the Moslem rulers.

In keeping with his princely rank, the Exilarch was installed in office
with due solemnity and pomp. His appointment had to be confirmed by
the heads of the academies of Sura and Pumbaditha. Election and inauguration were governed by a precise ceremonial. "When the public has
decided upon the appointment of a particular person to the office of
Exilarch," the account of the Babylonian scholar Nathan ha-Babli informs
us, "the heads of the two academies meet with the younger members of
the academies and with representatives of high society and the elders, in
the house of one of the leading men of Babylon, the choice of house signifying one of the highest honors that can be paid to anyone. On the following Thursday an assembly in the synagogue takes place. There the
Exilarch is welcomed, and the shofar sounds to inform all the people,
common and great folk, what has taken place. All who have heard the
news send a gift suitable to their wealth to the newly elected Exilarch. The
representatives of the people and the rich send him splendid garments,
jewels, and silver and golden vessels. On Thursday and on Friday he,
for his part, holds great banquets at which all sorts of foods, drinks, and
sweets are lavishly served.

"Early on the Sabbath morning he goes to the synagogue, accompanied
by the most venerable members of the community. There a wooden platform stands ready for him, entirely covered and draped with magnificent
silks and purples. . . . The Exilarch sits down on a raised place prepared

for him. The head of the Sura academy follows him, bends his knee before him, and after receiving the response to his salute takes his seat on the platform by the Exilarch's side. The head of the Pumbaditha academy does the same. . . . The Chasan in his prayer shawl speaks . . . certain prayers required for the consecration of the Exilarch, and the choir of boys loudly cries, 'Amen!' Then either the Exilarch himself delivers a sermon on the quotation from the Bible for that Sabbath, or he leaves this task to the head of the Sura academy. . . .

"After the Exilarch has left, the people accompany him to his house, singing songs in his praise and marching before and behind him. The heads of the academies do not accompany him, but the students do; they lead him to his house and then linger with him for seven days. . . ."

Once a year, in the third week after the Feast of Tabernacles, a kind of court reception took place at the Exilarch's house—or, rather, palace. The heads of the schools, with their faculties, and representatives of the communities called upon him. On the Sabbath a ceremonial similar to that at the time of appointment was repeated.

The Exilarch's ventures into the outside world and his receptions at the Caliph's court were likewise regulated by a dignified and firmly fixed ceremonial procedure. "If the Exilarch has something to do outside his home," an eyewitness has recorded, "he rides like the court dignitaries, richly dressed, in a resplendent carriage, with a retinue of fifteen persons and a slave running behind his vehicle. The Jews who meet him hasten toward him to shake his hand and greet him. Like all other dignitaries, he never appears in public without a retinue. If the Exilarch has anything to inform the Caliph of, or to petition him for, he requests an audience. Upon his entrance to the palace all the Caliph's servants come running toward him, whereupon he takes from his purse coins kept in readiness for this purpose and distributes them among them, until he reaches the Caliph's chambers, to which the respectful servants lead him. Stepping before the Caliph, the Exilarch falls to his knees, but the Caliph signals to a servant to help him rise and lead him to the place designated for him. The Caliph then inquires after his health and asks about his business, whereupon the Exilarch, after requesting permission to speak, begins with a prepared address of greeting, recalling venerable customs and seeking to persuade the Caliph with mellifluous words, until the Caliph yields to his plea. After he has received written approval of the matter he requested, the Exilarch takes his leave of the Caliph and returns home in a glad and confident frame of mind."

In spite of all this ritualized deference, however, the Geonim actually surpassed the Exilarch in importance and in the respect they enjoyed among Jews throughout the world. The highest religio-legal authorities in Jewry resided in Sura and Pumbaditha, whereas the Exilarch embodied strictly secular authority in a limited part of the Moslem world. The heads and faculties of the academies that had been so famous for centuries remained the guardians and interpreters of divine law and of Jewish traditions. Once more the Jews, though scattered so widely throughout Asia, Africa, and Europe, presented an example unique in history, of a people living under a single spiritual discipline. Wherever questions of Jewish law and religion arose among the communities of the Diaspora, appeal was made to the sages of Mesopotamia. The decisions of the Babylonian academies formed part of the famous literature of *Responsa,* and were considered, like the adjudications of the Sanhedrin of Eretz Israel in former times, the highest legal authority. They served as guidelines to legal scholars and judges in all the countries of the Diaspora. The questions and answers touched upon every imaginable field of interest to Judaism: exegesis of the Torah, explanations of the Talmud, marital ordinances, the laws of economic life. Along with the actual teaching work in the academies, the Geonim more and more engaged in correspondence with remote parts of the world, even with the "Far West"—Spain and Germany.

Twice a year, as had been done as far back as during the lifetime of Rav, the Kallá was held: the academic weeks to which scholars and students flocked from great distances. The Gaon presided over these conferences. Members of the college of scholars took their seats in seven rows in front of him, ten to each row, each occupying a seat in keeping with his rank. Up front were seven scholars who bore the title of honor, Reshe Kallá—conference leader—and, beside them, the three chaberim, the members of the presidium. The seventy scholars together with the Gaon formed the Great Sanhedrin. Behind them sat the students, many hundreds of them.

The program was extremely varied. Students were examined in those sections of the Talmud that had been studied the previous semester. New laws were discussed and decided upon. During the sessions queries from all over the world were debated. Every decision or opinion was set down in writing and signed by the head of the academy in the name of the whole body. Marked with the seal of the academy, these "responses," prefaced by a solemn formula of greeting, were sent to the inquiring community.

Months, sometimes years, might pass before the decision reached the recipient, for the letters had sometimes to pass along difficult caravan routes and by hazardous sea voyages. The inquirer might be thousands of miles away from Babylonia and have only the vaguest notion of where it was located. No secular power stood at the disposal of the Geonim to enforce their decisions upon fellow Jews living at such distances. And yet the decisions were accepted and obeyed; all the Diaspora communities voluntarily submitted to the authority of the Jewish scholars by the Euphrates. The Jewish community in Mesopotamia, with its Exilarch, as the last holder of the secular power once enjoyed by the House of David, and the Geonim of the academies, as the guardians of ancient traditions of scholarship, seemed to those distant communities of Jewry to represent the glory of times long past, the last remaining symbols of the power and greatness of Judaism. Contributions from far away were sent to Babylonia as once they had been sent to Jerusalem—so that the Exilarch could have an establishment worthy of his station, and so that the Talmudic academies need suffer no want. Such tributes came even from Spain and France, and in all the synagogues of the Diaspora the Exilarch and the Geonim were included in the Sabbath prayers. The pain of being dispersed among the peoples was alleviated by the thought that by the distant rivers of Babylonia there still existed a great Jewish commonwealth.

Around the middle of the eighth century Jewry throughout the Islamic Empire was shaken by an intellectual breach within its own ranks. A movement hostile to the Talmud developed, and spread alarmingly: Karaitism.

The heresy was started by Anan ben David, a learned and ambitious man who had been excluded from succession to the exilarchate. Profoundly disappointed, this descendant of patriarchs left Babylonia and moved to Palestine, where he gathered around himself the first Karaite community. Anan rejected the authority of the Babylonian Geonim, and, in fact, that of all rabbis who followed the traditional interpretations of Jewish law. He rejected the Talmud on the ground that it falsified Judaism by its additions to the Torah and by having wandered too far from the literal text of the Scriptures. Only the Bible could be accepted as authority, Anan declared; religious life must be governed by the literal meaning of the texts.

This new doctrine again brought to the surface the ancient and long-forgotten split between Sadducees and Pharisees. Long ago the Sadducees had condemned the "oral doctrine" of the Pharisees on the ground that Jewry could and should live by the laws of the Bible alone, without modifications, additions, or commentaries. Sadduceeism had faded out after the destruction of the Temple; the rabbinate had triumphed. The zealous activity of the scriptural scholars among the rabbis had produced those vast supplements to the text of the Bible that were ultimately set down in the Talmud.

The new Karaite movement spread with astonishing rapidity. From Mesopotamia and Palestine it reached into the neighboring countries, became established in Egypt, and penetrated all the way to Spain. Opponents of the Talmud were soon raising their voices throughout the entire Arab Empire. But this dangerous challenge, which for a time threatened to shatter the unity of Judaism, was doomed to failure. Karaitism splintered into innumerable sects and, as a power in its own right, more and more subsided into insignificance. But Judaism emerged from the struggle reinvigorated and enriched with new ideas. For the dispute with the Karaites had once more moved the Bible into the center of interest, rescuing it from the neglect of past centuries, during which the teachers had been concerned almost exclusively with the Talmud. A new concern with understanding of Scripture arose, and the study of Scripture was revived. With great conscientiousness scholars now set about for the first time trying to restore the original text, which had suffered distortion from careless copying. A new Biblical science was born.

It had also become essential for Judaism to deal with the increasingly powerful influences of the flourishing new science and philosophy of the Arabs. Scholars at the academies began taking an interest in humanistic knowledge. Long before the Christian West paid any attention to the greatest thinker of classical antiquity, Jews were studying Aristotle and engaging in violent controversy over his doctrines. In the East, a Jewish philosophy of religion came into being. One of its creators was Saadia ben Joseph (882–942), the "greatest of all Geonim," under whom the work of the academies experienced its last period of glory. This scholar, who became head of the Sura academy in 928, was a man of universal learning and a great pioneer. Saadia translated the Bible into Arabic, prepared exegeses and commentaries, composed poetry for the synagogue, and also devoted himself to the philosophy of religion. In his principal work, *Belief and Philosophy,* he discussed, as Philo of Alexandria had done before him, the relationship between religion and philosophy, maintaining that the Jewish religion could be reconciled with the most advanced knowledge and ideas. He demonstrated by bold logic the creation of the universe from nothingness and the presence and unity of God, and thus showed the possibility of supporting faith by reason.

With the passing of Saadia, one of the finest minds Jewry has ever produced, Babylonia seemed to have fulfilled its great historic task. When Gaon Saadia died in 942, the Gaonate at Sura came to an end. After more than seven hundred years of teaching and scholarship the famous academy closed its doors forever. Its sister institution, the academy at Pumbaditha, retained its prestige for a few decades more, because of the presence of two famous men, father and son: Sherira and Hai.

Sherira took care of the many queries from distant communities. One such precious document has been preserved; it is a letter responding to an inquiry about the composition of the Babylonian Talmud, and provides, among other things, the names of the heads of the Babylonian academies. Indeed, it forms the principal source for the history of the Gaonate period. During his lifetime Sherira transferred the office of Gaon to his son Hai. Hai died on March 28, 1038, and was succeeded by Hesekiah, who held office for only two years. On orders from the Caliph he was executed, and with his cruel death in 1040 the Gaonate of Pumbaditha also came to an end.

The "Mother of the Diaspora," the cradle of the Babylonian Talmud, thereafter lost its spiritual hegemony over Judaism, never to recover it. The twilight of oblivion began to settle upon Babylonia. But the current of spiritual and intellectual life had long been flowing strongly elsewhere. Thousands of miles from the ancient centers in the Orient, a new chapter had begun in the life of the Jewish people.

"Truth has departed from Pumbaditha and Sura," Samuel ibn Nagdela (later known as ha-Nagid—"the Prince") lamented. "Hai has gone down into the grave leaving no son. Never again will the Torah come into its ancient port. But he has children in the lands of the Arabs and in those of Edom [the Christian regions of Europe], whom he raised in the spirit of the Talmud and taught to be masters. . . ."

TOLERANT CAROLINGIAN AND SAXON EMPERORS

The eighth century ushered in a climate of hope and promise for Israel in the Occident. At the beginning of the century the conquest of the Visigoths by the Arabs had terminated the oppression of the Spanish Jews. Within a few decades the situation of the Jews north of the Pyrenees also changed decisively. The rise of the Carolingians brought a period of peace and unmolested life to Jewry in the other countries of Europe also.

Charlemagne (742–814), to whom Europe owed its rebirth and its rise to the status of a world power, broke with the intolerance of his predecessors. Pious and devoted son of the Church though he was, he regarded the Church as an instrument of state policy rather than the reverse. He did not hesitate to bend Church canons and conciliar decisions to his will, if such steps were essential to the ends of his government. In the general lines of his policy, he followed in the footsteps of his father, King Pepin.

In 759 the Franks under Pepin had taken the city of Narbonne in Septimania, which had been under Arab occupation. The Jews living in the city were permitted to retain all their rights and liberties. Charlemagne continued this course, disregarding the canons of Church synods held in Frankland. Indignantly, Pope Stephen III wrote to Bishop Haribert of Narbonne: "Overcome by grief and woefully alarmed, we have received word from you that the Jewish people, who have always been rebellious toward God and hostile to our customs, live on Christian soil in full equality with Christians, calling freehold fiefs in cities and suburbs their own, and that this is done on the basis of the privileges formerly granted to them by Frankish kings. Christians till Jewish vineyards and fields; Christian men and women live under one roof with these traitors and day and night taint their souls by words of blasphemy. These unfortunates must daily and hourly humble themselves before these dogs, serving them in all their whims. . . . Justice alone demands that the promises given these traitors be declared null and void, so that the death of the crucified Saviour shall at last be avenged. . . ."

There is no indication that the Pope expostulated on this theme to the King of the Franks. Stephen did not dare, especially since Charlemagne himself was at this time protecting Rome from the attacks of the Lombards.

Charlemagne took the Jews under wardship. He assured them protection of their lives and honor, practice of their religion, and secure possession of their property. The slave trade was explicitly permitted to them, and they were allowed to own pagan slaves; nor was it permissible to baptize such slaves in order to wrest them from the hands of the Jews. Jews were also permitted to employ Christian workers, provided that their laboring ceased on Sundays and Christian holidays. Jewish judges settled disputes among Jews. In return for this protection the Jews paid an annual tax to the Emperor, which amounted to a tenth of their income. Concerned for the economic interests of his empire, Charlemagne favored the Jews in all respects, and also encouraged their immigration into his dominions. He recognized very clearly the advantages to be gained from an industrious and enterprising Jewish population, with its widely diversified abilities and knowledge. Because of their far-flung connections, the Jews were one of the principal forces of international commerce. They were needed more than ever in these times, especially for any dealings with the world outside Europe, whether in diplomatic missions or in foreign trade. For all around the West a gigantic Iron Curtain had fallen.

The Arab Empire had erected a mighty barrier around all Christian lands in a great arc extending from the Atlantic to the Caucasus. Since the victorious advances of Islam, Central Europe had been cut off from Africa, Egypt, and the Near East. The once lively trade across the Mediterranean had dwindled to a trickle. Where merchant vessels had formerly sailed the sea, the Caliph's fleet dominated the waves and pirate ships of the Saracens made all the coasts unsafe. The stream of goods from the Orient had almost ceased; pepper and spices had become precious rarities. The Church itself was conscious of the difficulties; incense and even oil for consecration were hard to procure.

The Jews alone were still in a position to mediate between the Christian West and the Moslem East. Jews lived everywhere in the realm of Islam, and Western Jews could turn to them for aid in negotiation and travel. Moreover, foreign languages were virtually unknown in the West. But the Jews were multilingual; an Arab account testifies that they knew "Persian, Greek, Arabic, and also the languages of the Franks, Spaniards, and Slavs." Africa and the Levant were familiar to them from ancient times. In addition, the Jews were among the first Europeans who established vital contacts with the Far East, long before the days of Marco Polo and William of Rubrouck. Nearly four centuries earlier than these celebrated travelers, pioneering Jewish merchants had regularly traveled to China and India. In late Carolingian times they had organized a trading network connecting the heart of Europe by land and sea with the Far East. Facts culled from a mosaic of separate traditions, and supplemented in recent years by archaeological finds, now enable historians to draw at least the outlines of a world-wide commerce, adding a new page to the economic history of the early Middle Ages. Indeed, the new knowledge seems bound to correct many prevailing views, particularly in regard to the position and importance of the Jews during those times.

We owe the most important evidence to an Arab chronicler of the end of the ninth century. Ibn Chordadbe, Chief of Police and Postal Administration in the province of Jibal, in what is now Iraq, wrote in the *Book of Roads and Kingdoms*: "This is the road of the Jewish merchants called Radanites. . . . They travel from west to east and back again, now by land, now by water. From the west they bring eunuchs, slavewomen, boys, silk, furs, and swords. They take ship in the land of the Franks, on the shore of the western sea, to go to Faram [Pelusium, in Egypt]. There they load their wares upon the humps of camels

and take them by land to Kulsum [Suez], a journey requiring five days.
From Kulsum they proceed by water across the eastern sea [the Red Sea]
to Aljar and Jidda [in Arabia] and then continue on to Sind and China.
On the way back they carry musk, aloes, camphor, cinnamon, and other
products of the Orient with them, returning to Kulsum and Faram, whence
they once again cross the western sea. Some take the road by way of
Constantinople, to sell their wares there, while others sail directly back
to the land of the Franks."

Ibn Chordadbe's list of the wares brought to Frankland is far from
complete. The imports included many more products of the Orient:
balsam, saffron, ginger, nutmeg, pearls, enamel, and, above all, incense
for the churches and pepper.

This circuit of Jewish importers and exporters followed four principal
routes.

The first was primarily a sea route. From Frankland—the Arab name
for all the Christian countries of Europe, including Italy—Faram was the
first destination. This city, on the right arm of the Nile delta, anciently
known as Pelusium, could trace its history back to earliest Biblical times.
Its walls, Strabo relates, measured two and a third miles in circumference.
In the time of the pharaohs, however, it was called Sin (Exodus 16:1)
and in the words of Ezekiel was considered "the stronghold of Egypt"
(Ezekiel 30:15). On orders of Pharaoh Necho, Diodorus of Sicily tells
us, the first efforts to build a canal to the Red Sea were begun—a work
that the Persian King Darius continued and King Ptolemy II is said to
have completed.

All the goods had to be loaded on camels at Faram, for the overland
journey to Kulsum, then one of the Caliph's strong naval bases. There
the long ocean voyage began. The merchants touched at Jidda, the port
built for holy Mecca, and then continued on down the Red Sea. July was
known to be the most favorable month for sailing out into the Indian
Ocean from Aden. Sped along by the western monsoon, ships could
reach the mouth of the Indus in forty days. The return voyage was
equally speedy if it were timed to coincide with the eastern monsoon,
which blows around the end of December or early in January. On such
a voyage to India the brother of Maimonides, the great philosopher, died
in the year 1161.

From India all other markets of the Far East could easily be reached
aboard Chinese junks—Java, Sumatra, Indochina, and Canton. But every
voyage was an unpredictable adventure, full of incidents and hazards. At
the beginning of the ninth century Ishaq, the "son of a Jew" from Oman,

on the Persian Gulf, was arrested in Sumatra and released from imprisonment only after he had paid twenty thousand dinars.

The second principal trade route of the Radanites started in southern
Italy. The ships sailed eastward to Syria, where the goods were loaded on
camels and taken overland by way of Antioch to Haran. From this Biblical town, known since the days of the patriarchs, the journey continued
across the Euphrates and up the ancient caravan route to Babylonia, along
ways that the tribe of Abraham from Ur in the Chaldees had taken when
the Hebrews for the first time entered the Promised Land. The merchants
crossed through the densely populated region of Babylonian Jewish communities—visiting en route the cities of the academies, Sura and Pumbaditha—going as far as Oballa (today called Basra), which likewise held
a sizable Jewish population. Its name occurs repeatedly in the *Responsa*
of the Geonim; it is mentioned, in fact, that members of this community
provided a fourth of all the contributions to the academy in Sura. From
this port on the Persian Gulf, the voyage to India began.

The third of the great trade routes reached the Far East entirely by
overland travel. From Frankland the merchants crossed Spain to North
Africa, where they followed the coastal roads along the Mediterranean
as far as the Nile. From Pelusium they took the ancient roads through
the Holy Land to Damascus and on by way of Palmyra to Baghdad.
Thence the journey was full of perils and hardships, so much so that it
was scarcely undertaken by merchants other than the Radanites. From
the Tigris the route followed the famous Chorasan Road, which led to
the eastern regions of the caliphate. Then it pursued lonely paths to
Samarkand and, through deserts, wastelands, and wild mountain valleys
and across high passes buried in eternal snow, to China.

The fourth great route lay farther north. It, too, was entirely overland,
and proceeded through difficult country to the same destination. From
Prague it passed through the lands of the Slavs, through the Kingdom of
the Khazars, which was ruled by Jewish monarchs, and on across the
Caspian Sea, the Oxus, and the mountain range of Central Asia.

All four of these routes terminated in China. That enormous empire
had reached its greatest extent under the famous Tang dynasty (618–
907). Its frontiers reached to Persia; its culture and civilization were
flourishing. And even here, in the Middle Kingdom, the Radanites from
remote Europe encountered fellow Jews.

For there were Jewish communities in China!

In 1605 Father Matteo Ricci, a Jesuit living in China, made an astonishing discovery. One day when he went to the city of Kaifeng—which
had been the capital of China from 907 to 1127—he suddenly came upon

a Jew. Astonished, he inquired what fate had brought him to the Far East, and received a reply he found almost incredible. "He said," Ricci noted in his account, "that they had an old tradition to the effect that after King Tamerlane captured Persia, he also conquered China, and that many Mohammedans, Christians, and Jews came to the country with him."

Father Ricci found a large community of Jews. Could the story they told about their immigration under Tamerlane possibly be true? It proved possible to date precisely the remains of a great synagogue in the town: the forecourts, enclosed by high walls, had been built in the thirteenth century. But the Mongol conqueror had lived a century later. Therefore the inhabitants of Kaifeng must have been in the country before Tamerlane. Soon other evidence accumulated, which left no doubt that Jews had lived in the Middle Kingdom far, far earlier. Suleiman, an Arab merchant of the ninth century, notes in an account written before 900 that he had met Jews in all the larger cities of China, and that they spoke Hebrew and had accorded him lavish hospitality. There is mention, moreover, of "Jewish tribes" in China in the narrative of Eldad ha-Dani, a Jewish merchant who after many adventures returned to Kairouan from China in 880. He had been carried off to China as a prisoner, and a fellow Jew had bought his freedom. There are also Chinese accounts of Jews in Canton at this time.

Ancient Chinese documents contain frequent mention of Jews, but these have never been systematically combed. Only after this basic work has been done will it be possible to write a history of the Jews in China. Perhaps then something of the mystery surrounding the "Ten Lost Tribes of Israel" will be clarified. The scholar M. N. Adler has commented: "In view of the fact that the trade routes to China and India in former times were not sea routes alone, but also led through Media, Mesopotamia, and Persia, it is not at all impossible that parts of the Ten Tribes of Israel found their way to China."

Although the Talmud is utterly silent about China, it contains many references that point to early Jewish associations with India. It mentions teakwood and ginger; it relates, in connection with the death of Rav Judah, that he had at one time come from India to Babylonia and converted to Judaism. The heads of the Talmudic academies were astonishingly well informed about India. Gaon Saadia speaks of "fakirs who know how to defy the heat of fire." Gaon Hai mentions famous "Indian writings." He also answered inquiries from that distant land. In one of his responses to a community in India he greets them with the epithets "Scholars, Scribes, and Teachers."

In 820 Jacob ibn Tarik, whose Hebrew name was Aben Sheara, returned to Baghdad from Ceylon bearing with him astronomical writings. There are also reports of a "Joseph from Spain" who is said to have brought Indian numerals from the land of the Ganges in the eighth century and introduced the use of them in Andalusia and thus to Europe. He also translated the Indian Panchatantra from Sanskrit into Arabic, from which language it became known throughout Europe as the *Fables of Bidpai*. And Abraham ibn Ezra, who lived in the twelfth century, repeatedly mentions Jewish communities in India.

To this day descendants of the children of Israel dwell in India. They are the Beni Israel—only rediscovered by missionaries at the beginning of the nineteenth century—descendants of fugitives from the Spanish Inquisition and dark-skinned Jews from Babylonia. Benjamin of Tudela, the Jewish travel writer who visited the Near East and India in the twelfth century, writes of meeting thousands of Indian Jews who were "all black."

The Jews of China and India were frequently forgotten for long periods and then rediscovered again. They vanished from the consciousness of Western Europe along with the Radanites; for when the commercial empire of the Radanites collapsed, all information about their great trading routes was lost.

It was in about the year 900 that the Radanite commerce came to a sudden end. The fall of the Tang dynasty in 907 abruptly severed all relations with the West. Under the onslaught of the Slavs, the Jewish Khazar Kingdom between the Caucasus and the Black Sea disintegrated. Other roads were blocked by Tatar raiding parties. The Jewish communities in India and China were once more cut off from the world of the distant West, and entered upon a slow period of decay.

During their heyday, however, the Jewish Radanites were blockade runners. They helped to overcome a shortage of spices and drugs that was growing acute in the West. That such articles reached the West at all after the Arab conquest of Spain was owing to their enterprise. But they were never able to bring in Eastern goods in such great quantities as they had done before the Arab blockade. An old list of the monastery of Corbie on the Somme, dating from Merovingian times, suggests the volume of imports from the Near and Far East in the seventh century. The list records:

pepper	120 lbs.	costusroot	10 lbs.
ginger	70 lbs.	galingale	10 lbs.
cloves	10 lbs.	sage leaves	10 lbs.
spikenard	15 lbs.	sponges	10 lbs.
incense	10 lbs.	indigo	3 lbs.
myrrh	3 lbs.	thyme	2 lbs.
mastic	10 lbs.	cinnamon	15 lbs.

This is only part of a much longer catalogue. Not all connections with the Orient were cut off after the Radanites ceased trading. In 973 Sidi Ibrahim ben Achmed at-Tartushi, traveling from Córdoba on a diplomatic mission to the court of Otto I of Germany, offered a merchant in Mainz some foreign coins—gold pieces from Samarkand coined some fifty years before, according to their date. The Arab visitor from Andalusia noted with astonishment, soon after his return to Spain: "It is strange that in this city in Frankland, on a river called the Rîn . . . there are spices that occur only in the farthest East, although Mainz is in the farthest West. I saw there pepper, ginger, cloves, spikenard, costus and galingale roots. . . ."

But let us return to the days of Charlemagne.

Arles on the Rhone served as the most important emporium for export goods, which were then placed aboard freighters in the ports of Marseilles and Narbonne, where many Jewish shipowners lived. In the Carolingian capitularies (as the decrees of Charles and his successors were called) and other documents of the time, the phrase "Jewish and other merchants" frequently recurs.

Jews also played a part in the reviving political relationships between Occident and Orient that marked the reign of Charlemagne. The first Jew mentioned by name in German records is Isaac of Aachen, to whom Charlemagne entrusted a notable task at the end of the eighth century. In 797 Isaac was commissioned to go as interpreter with an embassy to Caliph Harun al Rashid in Baghdad. Isaac alone survived the hardships of the expedition and returned in July, 802, to Aachen to bring the Emperor the Eastern ruler's replies to his greetings and messages. Among the presents from Harun al Rashid that Isaac had brought with him was a sensational zoological specimen that aroused tremendous excitement and astonishment: an elephant. Isaac had managed to carry out his difficult assignment and to bring the huge, precious animal all the way from Baghdad over the long caravan trails and across the Mediterranean and the Alps safely to its destination. The event seemed a matter so remarkable at the time that the Carolingian Royal Annals (formerly called Einhard's Annals) report all the circumstances of the trip, thus preserving the tale for posterity. The Annals relate that "the Jew Isaac, whom the Emperor had sent to the King of the Persians along with his envoys Lantfrid and Sigismund, returned with munificent presents. Lantfrid and Sigismund had both died en route. . . . In October of this year the Jew Isaac came from Africa with an elephant and landed in Portovenere; and since he could not cross the Alps because of the snow, he wintered in

Vercelli." Next year, "on July 20 Isaac arrived [in Aachen] with the elephant and the other presents the King of the Persians had sent, and delivered all to the Emperor. The elephant was named Abul Abbas."

The rights and protection the Jews received under Charlemagne were to be extended and confirmed under his successors. His son Louis (Emperor from 814 to 840) continued to favor them, despite that devotion to the Church which earned him the epithet the Pious. Louis even permitted them to serve as tax farmers, contrary to the prescripts of canon law, which expressly forbade any Jew's wielding official power over Christians. Again out of consideration for the religion of the Jews, Louis ordered that the day for weekly markets be shifted from Saturday, the Jewish Sabbath, to some other day. He was the first Christian monarch to place the Jews under his direct guardianship, and he appointed an official, the Magister of the Jews, who was to make sure that no one infringed upon their rights. He conferred charters upon whole communities as well as upon individual Jews granting them the ruler's personal protection. Anyone in possession of such an imperial charter was not to be molested or slandered; no one could challenge his rights to his property or impose special imposts of any sort upon him. In court a Jew's testimony was to be held equal in value with a Christian's. Jews were not subject to ordeals, *i.e.,* trials of guilt by fire, battle, or boiling water. Anyone who killed or physically injured a protected Jew would be called to account by the Emperor in person.

This policy of tolerance proved good for the Carolingian Empire. The economy experienced an amazingly rapid expansion throughout the empire.

From southern France, where the Jewish population was especially dense, the Jews spread out over the northeast. Communities formed in Champagne, in Lorraine, and in the Rhineland. There were sizable ones at Metz and Trier, and in Coblenz, Speyer, and Worms. Many of the new settlements sprang up on the very same sites where Jews had lived half a millennium earlier—long before anything like a Carolingian Empire existed and, in fact, long before the Germanic tribes had settled down. Among these earlier communities of Jews had been many landowners who under Roman law could be conscripted for the honorary offices of municipal government. At the head of the Jewish communities were "rabbis, archisynagogi, elders," and other officials. An edict of Emperor Constantine's dated December 11, 321, addressed to the magistracy of Cologne, testifies to this matter. This precious document, the oldest evidence for the presence of Jews on the Rhine, has been preserved and today rests in the Biblioteca Apostolica Vaticana in Rome. Excavations have brought to light a further astonishing fact: The later Jewish town was located within the old Roman wall, from which it is deduced that the Jews in Cologne must have lived there uninterruptedly, surviving the tempests of the great migrations.

Topographical researches in Regensburg indicate that the core of the Jewish quarter there was similarly inhabited by Jews as early as Roman times. In Trier, chance digging brought to light a ceramic lamp embossed with a seven-branched candlestick such as had been customary in Jewish houses since Biblical times. This, too, has been dated to the beginning of the fourth century. The overwhelming probability is that the same conditions prevailed in other Roman sites along the Rhine and the Danube, wherever army camps or fortifications were growing into towns. In the city of Metz around the year 350 a certain Simeon, who was of Jewish extraction, became Bishop of the city. In 1432, in connection with some dispute, the town council of Mainz referred, by the bye, to "the Jews during the time they have been in Mainz, namely fifteen hundred years and longer, which is before the see of Mainz was founded. . . ." Presumably this comment was based on some ancient municipal records.

But there is a gap between the time of these very first Jewish communities and the age of the Carolingians. No one knows what their fate had been during the intervening stormy centuries. Only from the time of Charlemagne on can we speak properly of a history of the Jews in Germany.

From Marseilles, up the Rhone, and then up the Rhine, a vigorous trade flowed through the Jewish settlements in Lyons, Mainz, and Cologne. It reached as far north as Nijmegen, thus connecting the Mediterranean with the North Sea and England. In the ninth century many Jews lived in Magdeburg and Merseburg, settled in Augsburg and Regensburg, and finally penetrated into Poland and Bohemia, where the famed Jewish community of Prague grew up. Wherever they established themselves—in northern Europe, in the lands of the Slavs, in the Danube countries— a stream of goods began to flow.

In the cities the Jews lived in alleys or streets in the immediate vicinity of the school for the boys, the bathhouse, and, above all, the synagogue, which had to be close enough to be reached in a few steps on the Sabbath. But they never lived in isolation from other citizens. In old Cologne the town hall stood *inter Judaeos,* that is to say, wall to wall with Jewish houses. Peaceful and neighborly relations prevailed between Jews and Christians. There were no economic disparities, for the Jews, too, were landed townsfolk who tilled their fields and vineyards and, like all the rest, practiced crafts and trades.

The people respected them; neither as persons nor in their religion were they objectionable. Quite often Christians attended services in the synagogues, which the new communities had built in many cities. Christian clerics had no hesitation about consulting learned Jews over questions of interpreting the Scriptures. Bishop Hrabanus Maurus of Fulda spoke openly of having obtained information on Jewish traditions from a rabbi for use in his commentary on the Bible.

At court, too, the Jews enjoyed great prestige; they were admitted to the Emperor's presence and could associate freely with him and his retinue. Under Charlemagne and his son Louis the foremost intellectuals in Europe flocked to the Carolingian court: the Franks Angilbert and Einhard, author of a biography of Charlemagne; Paul the Deacon, historian of the Lombards; the Italians Peter of Pisa and Paul of Aquileia; the Visigoth poet Bishop Theodulf of Orléans; the architect Odo of Metz; and the Anglo-Saxon scholar Alcuin. Science, poetry, and historical and philosophical speculation flourished at the so-called Palace Academy.

In this atmosphere of openness to the wide world and esteem for the things of the mind, which constituted the "Carolingian Renaissance," the religion and history of the Jews was regarded with interest and respect. Empress Judith, Louis's beautiful and intelligent second wife, made no effort to hide her bias in favor of Judaism. The heroes in Israel's history especially inspired her with deep veneration. When the learned Bishop Hrabanus, well aware of this, sought to win her favor, he dedicated to her his translation with commentaries of the books of Esther and Judith. He praised the two Hebrew women, of whom he wrote, "the one is a queen like yourself, and the other bears your name."

Under Charlemagne and Louis the Pious a golden age of tolerance had dawned for the Jews, of a sort they had not enjoyed earlier nor were to enjoy in Central Europe until modern times. But peace and mutual respect between Jews and Christians were not to remain undisturbed for long. The mutual rapprochement of members of the two religions, the high social position many Jews enjoyed, the favor displayed toward them at court, and their popularity among the common folk seemed to the Catholic clergy to hold great dangers. Tolerance, and especially the disregard of canon law by the Carolingian rulers when they granted the Jews occupational and religious freedom, vexed the adherents of strict ecclesiasticism.

Even while Emperor Louis was still living, the forces of reaction raised their voices for the first time. Agobard, Archbishop of Lyons, launched a passionate and stubborn struggle against the privileges already accorded to the Jews. Against the background of that struggle could already be discerned the claims of the ecclesiastical authority to precedence over state and society, those claims that would animate the coming great contest between the papacy and secular government. "He who acts against the Church commits a sin against God," Agobard proclaimed. A trivial incident provided the Bishop with a welcome pretext for his attack.

A slave girl belonging to a respected Jew of Lyons had run away from her master and in order to gain freedom had had herself baptized by Agobard (c. 825). The Jews regarded this baptism as an infringement of the rights guaranteed them by the Emperor. The owner demanded that the runaway be returned to him. Agobard refused, whereupon the Jews appealed to Eberard, the Magister of the Jews. Eberard wrote to the Bishop, threatening to force him to return the slave girl if he refused to do so voluntarily.

Agobard was not concerned about this particular slave. He wanted to make an example in order to revive the ancient principles of canon law, which had curtailed the liberty of the Jews—principles whose strict observance Pope Gregory I had so emphatically insisted on.

Agobard now wrote a long letter, addressed to numerous high dignitaries at the court, urging them to influence the Emperor toward a reduction of the Jews' privileges. Above all, he inveighed against the ruling of the "most pious and most Christian Emperor" that pagan slaves could be converted only with the consent of their Jewish masters. "Inspired by the desire to respect the commandments of the Church," Agobard declared, "and at the same time fearing to act contrary to the imperial decree, we see ourselves exposed to a double peril: If we obey this decree in disregard of the canons of the Church, we would be dishonoring God; but if, on the other hand, we obey the canons, we may fear the wrath of the Emperor, since the Magister of the godless Jews is constantly threatening that he will denounce us to the magistrates of the court, who will bring us to trial for thus acting of our own accord."

The clerical party did not succeed in swaying the ruler. But the Bishop's obedience to the Church won out over his loyalty to his sovereign. He did not abandon the struggle, and sought by every means possible to attain his goal more deviously. He began delivering anti-Jewish sermons from the pulpits of Lyons. At the same time he issued an order binding throughout his province: All Christians were henceforth obligated to obey the laws of the Church without exception. They must not associate with Jews, buy meat or wine from them, share their meals, or enter their service.

When the Jews heard of these arbitrary ordinances, they complained at court. An imperial decree was issued to the Governor of Lyons, insisting that the rights of the Jewish population were to be upheld; he was

to take measures to assure their protection (A.D. 826). A direct letter to
Agobard threatened him with punishment if he did not cease preaching
against the Jews. The Bishop, convinced that he was in the right, refused
to obey; he continued so stubbornly on the same course that the Emperor
at last sent out a commission empowered with full authority to bring the
rebellious Archbishop to his senses. Eberard, Magister of the Jews, appeared in Lyons accompanied by these officials. He informed Agobard
of the Emperor's anger and urged him henceforth not to disobey the
laws of the state.

Unyielding, determined to make the case a test of where the true power
resided, the Bishop again appealed to the Emperor's advisers. It was incomprehensible to him, he wrote them, that a Christian ruler should condescend to take such actions in defense of Jewish interests. The actions
of the imperial commissioners would inevitably cause the people to
think that the sovereign preferred Jews to Christians. The rule forbidding
the baptism of slaves of Jewish masters was "godless" and contrary to holy
canon law. "This matter may not be left to the arbitrary will of the godless,
whose falseness keeps from the doctrines of Christ all who live under
them, and, in addition, continues privately and publicly to offend all believers. This matter is troubling not only to us, but also and even more
to those who could so easily be won for Christ. . . . The souls who
might increase the shepherd's flock . . . remain in the toils of the devil
because of the obstinate resistance of those who deny God, and these are
even strengthened by the Emperor's protection."

In a letter personally addressed to the Emperor, Agobard attempted
to appeal to his conscience, conjuring up the perils allegedly threatening
all Christendom "by the impudence of the Jews, by their crimes, and by
their patrons at court." He maintained that "the envoys of Eberard proved
terrible to the Christians and mild to the Jews. . . . They have only reinforced the party which is persecuting the Church. They command the
Governor of the province to take the Jews under his protection against
me. . . . The Jews have celebrated immoderate triumphs. . . . The demands of the Jews have been so completely confirmed that they dare to
deliver sermons to the Christians on what they should believe and hold
true, and they curse God and the Saviour in the presence of Christians.
This perversity finds support from the envoys, who are said to have
declared that the Jews are not so contemptible as many believe, but are
dear to you, your Majesty. . . . Highly placed persons ask them for
their prayers and blessings, thereby confessing that they regard the Jewish
law higher than the Christian. . . . The Jews . . . proclaim the glory of
their forefathers and contrary to law have been permitted to build new

synagogues. It has come so far that ignorant Christians prefer Jewish rabbis to our priests. . . . Since the Jews are living among us . . . it is incumbent upon us to regard most earnestly the ordinances of the Church that tell us when we must be on our guard against them and when we may meet them on a human basis. Therefore I must emphasize once again what the Frankish Church and its leaders, kings as well as bishops, have decreed concerning the separation of the two religions, in documents that accord with the authority and the acts of the Apostles, and which go back into the Old Testament. From these documents it is apparent with how much detestation these foes of truth must be regarded."

Agobard argued for strict observance of the ancient decrees of the Catholic Church, dating back to Emperor Justinian, concerning the social, economic, and intellectual separation of Jews from Christians. He maintained that the wall dividing Jews and Christians in Merovingian times must be rebuilt—this after it had been conclusively demonstrated that the Christian population could live in perfectly good concord with the Jews. (It may be observed, incidentally, that reviving the ban on the holding of slaves by Jews would have been in the interest of Christian landowners, who were beginning to be bothered by the competition of Jewish agriculture. Deprived of essential labor, the Jews would have to abandon farming and viniculture, and to sell their lands.)

The Emperor continued to reject Agobard's pleas, whereupon the Archbishop appealed to the public. He published his letter to Emperor Louis as a pamphlet entitled *De insolentia Judaeorum* and issued a pastoral letter entitled "On Jewish Superstition," in which he cited all the canons of the Church that had reference to the Jews. In his zeal he was carried away into metaphors that sound surprising indeed from the pen of a high dignitary of the Church. Thus, he wrote in 828 to Bishop Nibridius of Narbonne: "It is unworthy of our faith that a shadow should fall upon the children of light through their intercourse with the sons of darkness. It is unfitting that the Church of Christ, which should be brought stainless and without flaw to her heavenly spouse, is disfigured by contact with the impure, senile, and reprobate synagogue. How strange it seems to see the immaculate virgin betrothed to Christ sitting down to dine together with a whore."

"What is interesting about such remarks," Josef Kastein has commented, "is not the crude and coarse tone, but the general tendency. It is suggested that the religion of an entire people is threatened by a few thousand Jews. . . . Availing itself of the slogan that religion is in danger, the Church employs its most dangerous tool: the uncultivated masses of the people. The same argument is repeatedly hammered into brains that are receptive to anything. Inevitably, they grasp it some day and change from neighbors to enemies of the Jews."

When Agobard finally realized that he could not change the mind of the humane and progressive Emperor, he took his revenge. He entered into a conspiracy directed against Empress Judith, joining with Louis's sons in their attempt to dethrone their father. The plot was foiled, and Agobard was deprived of his office and had to flee. Later, the Emperor, in his generosity, restored the archiepiscopate to him.

Emperor Louis the Pious retained his tolerant attitude toward the Jews until the end of his life. Only a few months before his death he made a marginal note upon a license to three Jewish landowners: "Although the apostolic doctrine requires us to be charitable only toward professors of the faith, it in no way forbids charity toward unbelievers; rather, it recommends that we seek to imitate divine mercy and make no distinction between believers and unbelievers."

Not even the apostasy of his own confessor caused the Emperor to reconsider. In 839 this confessor, Deacon Bodo, became a convert to Judaism; he assumed the name Eleazar, married a Jewish woman, and retired to Saragossa, in Spain. All Europe gossiped about the affair. Since Bodo had been so close a friend and familiar of the Emperor, the anti-Jewish elements gleefully seized upon the case. Archbishop Amalar, Agobard's successor in Lyons, issued a circular letter, "Against the Jews," which gave a sinister account of the case of this Christian pastor who had been entangled in the "diabolic" snares of the Jews. "And now he lives in Spain, in the midst of the Saracens and allied to the Jews by family bonds. He has become wholly a Jew in his wretched superstition and his mode of life, crouches in Satan's synagogue, thickly bearded, and together with the others blasphemes against Christ and his Church."

What had prompted Bodo to his change of religion he himself subsequently described in letters to some friends. He had made a pilgrimage to Rome, only to be horrified by the behavior of the high clergy in the very citadel of Christendom—behavior that also was mocked savagely in a satire about a supposed female Pope.

With the death of Louis the Pious, the empire created by Charlemagne splintered. A period of political upheavals followed the decay of central administration. As the influence of the clergy grew, the first signs became manifest of the future great conflict between secular and ecclesiastical powers.

Nevertheless, there were no changes in the legal position of Jewish communities after the Treaty of Verdun in 843, which divided the empire among the sons of Louis the Pious. The policy of tolerance practiced by the first two Carolingian emperors was continued. The rulers balked at all the efforts by the Church to reinstate the old laws of Christian Roman times that had so severely limited the freedom of the Jews. Aside from a few isolated incidents, persecutions and humiliations of Jews were unknown. In the young states that sprang from the ruins of the empire, the Jews helped lay the foundations for the future development of Europe. They participated as pioneers in the colonization of new areas of settlement—in the East as far as the Elbe and Oder, and deep into the regions later known as Austria and Bohemia. They also contributed the versatile knowledge of an ancient people toward the evolution of commerce and the economy in general. The West was beginning to stir from centuries of torpor and decline, and the Jews on the whole enjoyed a peaceful life and aided these stirrings for a whole quarter of a millennium—until the Crusades.

In the Kingdom of the West Franks, Charles the Bald, the son of Louis the Pious and Judith, came to the throne (843–877). He chose as adviser a Jew named Judah, whom he called "my faithful servant," and Zedekiah, a Jewish physician. Zedekiah was the first in a long line of Jewish doctors of whom we hear throughout the Middle Ages and long afterward, everywhere in Europe. Emperors, kings, dukes, Popes, and high ecclesiastical dignitaries entrusted their health to them, and there is scarcely any period in Jewish history, no matter how devastating—even periods of the worst persecutions—in which Jewish doctors were barred from secular and ecclesiastical courts. During the Renaissance the Jewish personal physicians of the Popes were even permitted to treat other Christian patients, although this ran strictly counter to the canons of the Church. They were much-sought-after specialists, and no wonder, for any kind of solid medical knowledge was a rarity in the Christian West.

Chochmat ha-refua—the art of healing—has been a specialty of the Jewish people from time immemorial. It is occasionally mentioned in the Bible as a profane science (Exodus 21:19; II Chronicles 16:12; II Kings 20:7). Hygiene was a component of the Law, in which priests were always instructed. Priests were likewise charged with cleaning persons and houses of leprosy (Leviticus 14). The Talmud, too, contains detailed information on medical matters, and reveals significant knowledge of the body and its organs, of internal diseases, and of elementary surgery. Throughout the empire of the caliphs, from Mesopotamia to Africa and Andalusia, Jews were regarded as the foremost teachers of a highly developed medical science. They also made names for themselves as translators of the works of Hippocrates and Galen. The oldest medical work in the Hebrew language, the *Book of Healing,* was written in about 650 by the Jewish physician Assaf ben Berechia. During Arabic rule in Spain a large number of Jewish doctors won fame in both medicine and pharmacology. Abdulmenis wrote an authoritative book on drugs; Moses ben Eleazar treated the subject of gynecology. Originally, Jewish medicine was based upon the knowledge and experience of the ancient East, but Jews in the Mohammedan sphere later engaged in careful medical research, and from those times to the present Jews have made signal contributions to medicine.

"Salerno's name has become immortal throughout the whole world for healing the sick and for teaching the healer," wrote a student who returned to Germany in 1162. There, by the Bay of Paestum, as early as 846 Arabs and Jews had founded the first university in Europe specializing in medicine. One of the first teachers to be mentioned is "Ebraeus Solonus." One of the oldest medical publications was the *Antidotarium* of Sabbatai ben Abraham, known as Donnolo, written in Hebrew. The famous University of Bologna was founded more than a quarter of a millennium after the one in Salerno, in 1119; then followed that of Padua and, in the twelfth and thirteenth centuries, those of Oxford and Cambridge.

But to return to the ninth century: Archbishop Amalar of Lyons, although in other matters an enemy of Agobard, continued his predecessor's policy of hostility to the Jews. We have already mentioned his letter "Against the Jews"; in it he once again evoked the perils that menaced the Christian people and their religion through the presence of Jews. On the whole, he repeated the charges of Agobard; but he added a denunciation of those Christians who ignored Christian holidays and observed the Sabbath in common with the Jews.

"For this reason," Amalar wrote, "in the current year, cursing their wickedness and imbued with the desire to guard the people who have been entrusted to us by God against the danger of contagion, I have three times caused it to be announced publicly that all shall obey the statutes of the Church, withdrawing from the Jews; that Christians may not serve them either in the towns or in the country; that the Jews must do all their work themselves with the help of their pagan slaves. I have also forbidden Christians to partake of their food and their drink. And I have also issued many other strict injunctions in the effort to eradicate this evil. . . ."

Others among the high clergy held similar views. Archbishop Hincmar of Reims, one of the Emperor's favorites, and the archbishops of Sens, Bourges, and other cities, likewise fulminated against the Jews. At a

Council held in 848 in Meaux, near Paris, the decision was taken to request the Emperor to reaffirm the old canonical laws. He was to be reminded of the edicts of Emperor Theodosius and even the decrees of the Visigothic kings and councils of Spain. But Charles refused to have laws imposed on him by the clergy, and he ordered that the Council be dissolved. Subsequently, when the bishops met again, they were forced to drop the motion. Amalar had no more success than had Agobard. The rights of the Jews remained inviolate; their lives went on peaceably. Only in two cities in the southern part of the West Frankish Kingdom did they experience repeated humiliations.

In Béziers the Jewish inhabitants were annually molested and mistreated by Christian churchgoers at Easter time, after the Bishop's Passion sermons. Since the Jews defended themselves, there were many cracked heads. And in Toulouse the Jews were subjected to a different type of shameful abuse. Thrice a year—at Christmas, on Good Friday, and on Ascension Day—one member of their community was publicly slapped. Complaints from the Jews were of no avail. The Archbishop of Narbonne decreed that the custom was to persist. Moreover, the man selected for the slapping had to say three times: "It is well that the Jews bend their neck beneath the blows of Christians, since they refused to kneel before Christ." This ugly humiliation persisted into the eleventh century.

Throughout the rest of southern France peace prevailed. The Jews owned fields and vineyards and industriously plied all branches of agriculture, crafts, and commerce. They often rented large estates as tenant farmers, but many of them were also landowners, thus enjoying all seigneurial privileges. The larger Jewish communities all owned synagogues and schools, a bathhouse, bakehouses, a guildhall, a building for weddings and dances, and a hospital and cemetery. On the western edge of the city of Narbonne there was a "villa Judaica" whose inhabitants owned the nearby vineyards and salt mines. Béziers, Nîmes, Arles, and other cities had Jewish suburbs. Only once were the Jews of France menaced: Under Robert the Pious, second ruler of the Capetian dynasty, there were popular outbreaks against them in many places.

In the year 1007 reports reached Europe about persecutions of Christians in the Holy Land and the desecration or destruction of many churches there under the Egyptian Caliph Hakim. A rumor sprang up that the Jews had incited the Mohammedans to these actions. Persecutions began in many cities of northern and central France. In Limoges the Bishop offered the Jews the alternative of converting to Christianity or leaving the city; the entire community departed. In Rouen the authorities ruled all Jews who refused baptism to be outlaws. Many were slain; women drowned themselves to escape baptism. Only the courageous intervention of Jacob ben Jekutiel prevented further bloodshed. He declared to the city authorities: "The right to baptize Jews is not yours, but the Roman Pope's alone. I will go to Rome, and let it be as the Pope decides." The authorities accepted this proposal, and Jacob ben Jekutiel succeeded in persuading the Pope to denounce the forcible baptisms. A bishop from Rome informed the clergy of Rouen, and of the other cities in which similar incidents had taken place, of the papal decision.

Until the Crusades the Jews also lived peacefully in Germany. The emperors of the Saxon dynasty displayed the same benevolence toward them as had the Carolingians, and as the Salians would subsequently. During this period the clergy also proved thoroughly tolerant.

Emperor Otto I (who ruled from 936 to 973) "gave" to many bishops the Jews living in their dioceses. The bishops thus assumed all the rights and duties of lords; they became the chief magistrates over the Jews and were also responsible for their security. In 965 "Jews and other merchants" were placed under the hand of the Bishop of Magdeburg. Otto II conceded to the diocese of Merseburg "everything that is enclosed by the city wall, including the Jews and merchants." The bishops of Worms, Cologne, Mainz, and other cities likewise had authority over the Jewish populations transferred to them. The Jewish communities living under these new lords flourished, for the high ecclesiastical officials showed no inclination to restrict the activities of the Jews who were proving so useful to the economy of their dioceses and contributed significantly to filling their treasuries. The profit was sufficient to persuade the bishops to forget the letter of canon law.

About the year 1000 a family by the name of Kalonymos, from the Tuscan city of Lucca, settled in Mainz. One member of this family had twice saved the life of Otto II in Italy. A chronicle relates that a Jew named Kalonymos accompanied the Emperor on his campaign in the south. In 982, after defeat in a battle against the Arabs and Byzantines at Cotrone in Calabria, Otto suddenly found himself separated from his forces and in acute danger. The Jew lent him his horse, and the Emperor was able to ride to safety. A second time, in a precarious situation, Kalonymos again enabled the King to flee. The grateful ruler offered his rescuer a boon, and Kalonymos asked to be allowed to settle in Mainz, where his family had trade connections. Heads of the communities in Mainz and Speyer and a number of respected scholars were later counted among the descendants of Kalonymos. Excavations in the old Jewish quarter of Mainz have turned up, in the cellar of a palatial dwelling, lead custom seals stamped with the imperial eagle. It is surmised, from this and other evidence, that the house once belonged to this famous family.

Throughout this whole period the chronicles cite only a single persecution of Jews in Germany. This was not initiated by the people but by a ruler, Henry II, last Emperor of the Saxon house. In the year 1012 an imperial decree suddenly descended upon the Jewish community of Mainz: Anyone who resisted baptism must depart from the city. Only a few yielded; all the rest departed. No contemporary account gives the reason for this harsh order. Had it been prompted by the fact that a priest named Wezelin, confessor to a relation of the Emperor's, unexpectedly converted to Judaism? Or had the Emperor been wrought up by rumors circulating in Germany concerning alleged Jewish intrigues against Christians in the Holy Land? No one knows.

The suffering was, fortunately, brief. A year later Rabbi Simon ben Isaac, head of the affected community, obtained permission for the expelled group to settle in Mainz again. The forcibly baptized were also allowed to resume their former faith.

On the other hand, the general esteem in which Jews were held toward the end of the eleventh century is clearly reflected in the story of two incidents. In 1084, when Bishop Rüdiger of Speyer was about to attach an adjacent hamlet to his bishopric, he knew what ought to be done to foster the development of a town. He invited Jews, and in September, 1084, granted them "the best rights that the Jewish people had in any city of the German Reich." They were assigned sites for their homes and granted special privileges. For their presence, he declared, "could only tend to the greater glory of the region." Bishop Rüdiger provided the new settlement with a charter entitling the Jews to practice trade unhindered throughout the territory of the city and in the port. They were permitted to hold land, to own buildings, gardens, and vineyards, and to employ Christian servants, even nurses. The new Jewish community had its own judiciary.

The Bishop's expectations were not disappointed. Many Jews, particularly from Mainz, were drawn to hospitable Speyer. A decade later, thanks to the industrious Jewish community, the diocese possessed a new and important center of commercial life on the Rhine. When Emperor Henry IV visited Speyer in February, 1090, Rüdiger personally introduced him to the elders of the community, among them Judah ben Kalonymos, David ben Meshullam, and Moses ben Jekutiel. The Emperor confirmed them in all their rights and in their "farms, houses, vineyards, fields, slaves, or other movable and immovable property." On his journey through the Rhineland the Emperor also granted a charter of extensive rights to the Jews of Worms. He received the "Jewish bishop" Salman in audience. Henry IV was particularly well disposed toward the Jews because they had aided him, along with the other citizens of Worms, in a dispute with the Bishop. "In order to reward the citizens of Worms for their loyalty," the Emperor released them from all customs duties. Some time earlier a similar imperial charter had been granted to the Augsburg Jews.

Jewish communities were to be found in towns from Lorraine far to the east across the Elbe and Oder and as far as Bohemia. In Prague and in nearby Vysehrad toward the end of the century there lived "Jews rich in gold and silver, more prosperous than the merchants of all other nationalities." Many of them were also living in Moravia; one named Podiva built a castle of his own at the border, to which he gave his name. And in the newly founded Kingdom of Poland the city of Poznan had a sizable community of Jews, whose members enjoyed all liberties. For the rulers of Poland were as tolerant as those of Germany.

JEWISH ACADEMIES ON THE RHINE

About the year 1000 there emerged out of the mists of history the figures of important Jewish scholars in the West. New centers of learning had been established in the heart of Europe—Jewish academies on the Rhine. Far from Palestine and Babylonia, Talmudic scholarship struck roots on another continent. When the lights began to go out in the Orient, where they had been shining for nearly three thousand years of Jewish history, they were lit anew on the soil of the Occident.

Far off in Babylonia, Hai, the last important Gaon of the famous academy at Pumbaditha, was teaching at the same time that a great scholar in the Rhineland was at the height of his creative work. The latter was Gershom ben Judah, born in 960 at Metz in Lorraine. In the newly opened academy of Mainz, Rabbi Gershom found a position of great influence. He gave an enormous impetus to Talmudic studies, and was soon regarded far and wide as the supreme authority. His prestige brought about a change of high significance to the future. Whereas for centuries the Jews of the Rhineland had appealed to the academies at Sura and Pumbaditha for the word on difficult questions, they now submitted their questions to Gershom. The intellectual dominance of the Babylonian academies was over. The European Diaspora had at last become spiritually and intellectually independent of the Orient.

Gershom's greatest contributions were the ordinances (takkanot) that aimed at adjusting Jewish life to the new conditions of Europe. One of these was his ban on polygamy. Although not forbidden by the old law, polygamy had long since become a rarity among the Jews of the Orient, and had continued only here and there among the Jews living under Moslem rule. It was completely incompatible with the customs of the West and had in practice vanished entirely. In order to strengthen familial bonds, Rabbi Gershom ruled that a husband could not dissolve a marriage without the wife's consent. He also strongly upheld the secrecy of letters, a decision of great importance in those times, for letters were carried only by private individuals and frequently by travelers scarcely known to the sender.

Disregard of such rules, Gershom decreed, was to be punished by excommunication—which meant expulsion from the community and economic and social boycott. This was the most extreme punishment at the disposal of the rabbis. They possessed neither police powers nor any other means of secular pressure to enforce observance of their decisions. Nevertheless, the rulings were obeyed, as were the verdicts of authorized teachers, even in remote communities in foreign countries. All recognized the opinions of respected rabbis as the valid decisions of supreme spiritual authorities, and all submitted to them voluntarily.

Gershom became the great spiritual and intellectual leader of his generation. He was called Rabbenu—our teacher—and may be considered the father of rabbinism in Europe. So great was his fame that he has gone down in the history of his people as Meor ha-Gola, Light of Exile.

"Rabbenu Gershom, the just and holy man of blessed memory," wrote Rashi, his remarkable successor, "illuminated the eyes of the dispersed, and now we walk in his footsteps. The leaders of the Diaspora in Ashkenaz and Kitim [Germany and the coastal lands] are all his disciples."

A whole college of Talmudic teachers associated with Gershom's academy enlivened Jewish intellectual life in the German and French lands along the Rhine. The "scholars of Lorraine," the chachme Lothar, became famous far beyond the confines of their country. Gershom's pupils were soon at work in many cities: Jehudah ha-Cohen and Eliezer ha-Gadol taught in Mainz, Jacob ben Jakar and Isaac ha-Levi in Worms, still others in Metz and other cities. Among the many students who filled the lecture halls of the new schools was the man who would later exert the most lasting influence upon medieval Jewry with his great commentaries on the Bible and the Talmud: Rabbi Solomon ben Isaac, known by the Hebrew initials of his name as Rashi.

The great Rashi's life story has been embellished by many legends. The tales of his travels and his conversations with Godfrey of Bouillon, ruler of Jerusalem, belong to the realm of legend. But it seems remarkable indeed that Rashi was born at the very time that the Gaonate perished forever in distant Babylonia. He came into the world at Troyes in Champagne in the year 1040, in the same year that the last head of the academy of Pumbaditha was executed, on orders from the Caliph.

As a young man Rashi left his native town. The thirst for knowledge drew him to the academies of the Rhineland. Living in the most wretched circumstances—"in want of food and clothes," as he himself later wrote —he studied at the schools of Worms and Mainz. Among his teachers were Gershom's most gifted disciples: Jacob ben Jakar and Isaac ha-Levi at Worms, and Isaac ben Jehudah in Mainz.

At the age of twenty-five he returned to his birthplace and founded his own Talmudic school. In order to live he was forced to have some occupation, for the rabbinate was an honorary post, which did not provide a livelihood. Rashi became a vintner; he went to his teaching and his researches only after his day's work in the vineyard.

The young scholar soon won recognition for wisdom and erudition throughout Germany and France. Pupils streamed to his school; from far and wide communities now addressed their questions to Troyes. His old teacher Isaac ha-Levi wrote proudly from Worms: "The generation that counts you among its own is not orphaned. May the like of you increase in Israel."

Rashi opened up to the Jews of Europe the treasures of the Babylonian Talmud. Hitherto any understanding of the gigantic work had required prolonged study. Rashi was able to produce so lucid a commentary on it that now anyone could study it. Rashi's commentary on the Bible was also universally intelligible, even to the common man; for many centuries it served as a text in the schools for teaching the Scriptures. His commentary on the Pentateuch was later published as the first book printed in Hebrew—in 1475, in Reggio di Calabria. The commentary was diligently studied and also had a decisive influence upon Christian interpretation of the Bible. As in the days of the Church Fathers, Jews once again became the teachers of Christian exegetes. The Franciscan Nicholas of Lyra quoted Jewish scholars so frequently that he was nicknamed Rashi's ape. And Luther later made use of Nicholas' writings for his translation of the Bible.

When Rashi died in Troyes in 1105, he left behind a body of writings that contributed as scarcely any other has done to the spreading of Biblical and Talmudic knowledge among his people. After his death his sons-in-law completed his work. Along with other scholars they supplemented

and corrected the commentaries by additions—tossafot—for which reason
they were called Tossafists. Among them were Isaac ben Asher Halevi
(born c. 1090), a pupil of Rashi's, regarded as one of the foremost Tossafists, who headed the academy in Speyer, where Jehudah ben Kalonymos
ben Meir (died 1199) also taught. Prominent in Bonn was Ephraim ben
Jacob (born 1132), and in Mainz, Eliezer ben Nathan (born 1132).

Before the eleventh century came to an end the First Crusade brought
down upon the Jews a period of bloody persecutions. Rashi himself lived
long enough to witness the destruction of flourishing Jewish communities
on the Rhine. "We must not complain of the divine judgment although
criminal evildoers threaten us," he wrote in 1096. "For a long time we
have been numbed with fear. We have been unable to seek comfort even
in the healing study of the Torah. Tormenting is our grief."

THE GOLDEN AGE IN SPAIN

Two centuries after the Mohammedan conquest, an extraordinary renas-
cence of science, poetry, and philosophy ushered in what has been universally called a Golden Age for Jewry in Spain. What the Jews together
with the Arabs accomplished during those centuries was later to benefit
the entire Western world. Jews and Arabs became the teachers of Europe.
It was they who saved the precious heritage of antiquity, for much of
that knowledge was on the point of being lost forever. What was more,
they infused it with new life, so that it could continue to develop. Their
discoveries and experiments, their researches and bold new thinking gave
a strong new impetus to mankind's progress in philosophy and the natural
sciences, which for centuries had gone neglected in the West. Yet it was
not until their vast labors were completed that Europe became aware of
this great new body of thought, showed interest in it, and began with some
uncertainty and qualms—for the Christian West was not hospitable to
scientific research and untrammeled thought—to catch up with the intellectual advances made on the other side of the Pyrenees. Aristotle first
reached Europe from the Arabic Empire, where his writings had already
been reconsidered and commented on by Arabic and Jewish philosophers.
His impact on Europe had enormous bearing on the intellectual movement we call Scholasticism. Exact science, medicine, astronomy, and
mathematics made their first entry into Europe beyond the Pyrenees in the
form of translations from the Arabic into Latin.

When an Arab hears the word "Andalusia" and dreams of a paradise on earth, he thinks of Abd er-Rahman the Great (who ruled from 912 to 961), the still-remembered founder of the glorious and independent caliphate of Córdoba. "In the course of only twenty years," a historian of Islam remarks, "Abd er-Rahman III succeeded in creating out of the tangle of small, shattered principalities a mighty and flourishing kingdom. It was chiefly owing to this ruler that for almost a century Spain led the civilized world in both material prosperity and her highly developed culture."

The caliphate embraced the entire south and central portion of the Iberian Peninsula, including such flourishing cities as Seville, Granada, and Lucena, as well as ancient Toledo, the capital of Spain in the Visigothic age, and the wealthy ports of Almería, Murcia, and Valencia. But all these great cities were nothing compared to the "city of cities," Córdoba, the resplendent capital and residence of the Caliph in the heart of Andalusia. Its fame spread to all lands of the inhabited world.

"Bright ornament of the world, beautiful young capital, proud of her military might, famous for the delights she embraces, shining in superabundance of all earthly goods"—so Roswitha, the German nun who wrote poetry in the convent of Gandersheim, extolled Córdoba, and she was not exaggerating.

Outstretched along the green banks and gentle slopes of the Guadalquivir River, Córdoba, with its twenty-eight suburbs, was, in land area alone, the largest city of Europe in about the middle of the tenth century. In an age when no city other than Constantinople contained more than thirty thousand people, Córdoba had almost half a million inhabitants.

Here, in the metropolis on the Guadalquivir, the unique flowering of Spanish Jewry had its beginning. The city became the greatest testimony to the abilities that slumbered in the Jewish people—abilities going beyond study of Torah and Talmud—and that could emerge if the world around them gave them a chance. Three centuries in Arab Spain provided one example. The next occasion was not to present itself until almost a thousand years later, when, after the Age of Enlightenment and the French Revolution, the European Jews, once more emancipated, were to manifest their remarkable talents.

In Córdoba one man emerged from the ranks who began the long and glorious development: Hasdai ben Isaac ibn Shaprut. His father, Isaac, the head of a prosperous, respected family in the Córdoban Jewish community, could not have dreamed what destiny awaited the son who was born to him in the year 915. Isaac himself was a lover of the sciences who supported needy students and provided funds for gifted but impoverished scholars and artists. He played the Maecenas on a small scale. Isaac wished his son Hasdai to be a scholar also, and he was not disappointed. Hasdai proved both gifted and thirsty for knowledge. He studied medicine, mastered the Torah and Talmud, and shone in philosophy. He also devoted himself to languages, mastering Hebrew, Arabic, and Latin, the language of the Christian world.

When he was only twenty-five, he came to the attention of the Caliph. Abd er-Rahman III called Hasdai ben Isaac ibn Shaprut to his court to serve as his personal physician. Before long, the Caliph was entrusting entirely different tasks to him: affairs of state and government business. Hasdai rose rapidly and became what we would today call a minister of commerce and finance. He also served the Caliph as a diplomat and as the architect of his foreign policy. The Caliph's Spanish empire was being threatened by the Oriental caliphate of the Fatimids. Hasdai sought the support of the Byzantine Empire. His diplomatic endeavors were crowned in 949 when Emperor Constantine VII sent a large embassy to Córdoba. The most precious gift they brought with them, to the delight of the Caliph, was a richly illustrated volume of Dioscorides, the famous compilation of ancient medicaments. But the rare work proved to be a book of seven seals, for no one in Andalusia knew Greek. Hasdai asked the court in Constantinople for a translator. In 951 a monk named Nicholas arrived in Córdoba and translated the book into Latin. With Hasdai's assistance it was then translated into Arabic. The work of Dioscorides became the basis for the development of pharmacology in Spain. It provided the foundation for the great work of Ibn al-Baitar (1197–1248), the greatest of the Arab botanists, who recorded more than one thousand and four hundred vegetable drugs, as well as animal and mineral medicaments, along with precise prescriptions for their use.

Hasdai's diplomatic talents also enabled him to mediate the dispute that had arisen between the Caliph and the German Emperor Otto I. A letter from the Caliph to Otto I had contained a few sentences that stirred indignation at the imperial court, since they were taken to be contemptuous remarks about Christianity. The angered Emperor sent an embassy to Córdoba, led by an Abbot Johann. It reached Hasdai's ears that the letter borne by the ambassadors contained unfriendly remarks about Islam. Before the fateful audience could take place, Hasdai persuaded the Abbot to solicit another letter from Otto I, couched in a different tone. "Never," Abbot Johann wrote subsequently, "have I encountered a man of so keen intelligence as the Jew Hasdai."

Hasdai also succeeded in establishing peace with the Christian rulers of León and Navarre, who had been troubling the caliphate by their repeated raids. As the climax of these peacemaking efforts, the kings of these principalities came to Córdoba in person for negotiations.

Moslem Spain, the chronicle relates, "witnessed a strange procession. Surrounded by the grandees and priests of their retinue, the Queen of Navarre approached Córdoba, accompanied by her son García and the unfortunate King Sancho, who because of his weakness leaned on the arm of Hasdai." Abd er-Rahman received the Christian rulers in a summer palace of fabulous splendor, and agreed to the favorable conditions of a treaty for which Hasdai had already skillfully laid the ground. "A dignitary of the Caliph," the poet Donash ben Labrat wrote in praise of Hasdai's diplomatic triumph, "led Sancho to the hostile people. He it was who also . . . lured there with well-turned speeches the grandmother Tota, who wore the royal crown like a man. . . . He took from the foreigners . . . ten fortresses. . . . In East and West his name is equally great."

Despite the cares of his high office, Hasdai did not forget his coreligionists abroad. He regularly sent rich gifts to the academies in Sura and Pumbaditha, and entered into correspondence with Dossa, the son of Gaon Saadia, who supplied him with a biography of his famous father. He also corresponded with Donash ben Tamim, the learned physician of the Caliph of Kairouan, who composed for him an astronomical essay on the Jewish festival calendar and presented him with his books on medicine and grammar.

Posterity also owes to Hasdai's enterprise some exact information on the Jewish Kingdom of the Khazars. From Persian ambassadors, Hasdai one day received news that greatly astonished and excited him. The envoys told him of a distant kingdom near the Volga and on the shores of the Caspian Sea where a Jewish king ruled. Hasdai at first doubted the tale, but he obtained confirmation of it from Byzantium. "From Constantinople to that land the voyage by sea requires fifteen days. By land, however, many peoples live between our two kingdoms. A king named Joseph reigns over the people of the Khazars, from whose land ships with fish, hides, and many other kinds of goods come to us. They are a powerful nation whose warrior bands and armies march at certain times."

Determined to establish contact with that distant kingdom, which he thought might represent a relic of the Ten Lost Tribes of Israel, Hasdai wrote a long letter in Hebrew to the unknown king. "The land that we . . . inhabit . . . we remnants of Israel in exile," he informed the Khazar King, "is called in Hebrew Sepharad, in the language of its Ishmaelite inhabitants, al-Andalus. The capital of the kingdom is called Kortuba. The name of our King is Abd er-Rahman; he is called Commander of the Faithful. His name is universally known, and he has not his like among all former rulers. Our land is fruitful, rich in springs, rivers, and cisterns. It is a land of grain, of wine, and of oil; it is also rich in fruit and spices, covered with vegetable gardens and orchards, and from its soil spring all kinds of trees, bearing fruit as well as producing silk, for which reason we have silk in abundance. Merchants and traders from all lands stream to our realm from the distant islands, from Egypt and other great kingdoms. They bring aromatics and gems with them. Our King heaps up treasures of gold, silver, and all precious things. His army is more numerous than that of any other king of olden times. His annual income, which comes to me, amounts to a hundred thousand gold ducats; that much is brought in by the foreign merchants alone, whose business affairs fall under my supervision. All rulers of the world to whom the fame of our King's greatness and power reaches send him gifts to secure his good will, among those being the kings of Ashkenaz [Germany], of Gebalim or al-Saklab [the Slavs], of Constantinople, and many others. . . ."

After a lengthy description of the caliphate of Córdoba, Hasdai comes to the point: "I crave to know the truth, whether there really exists upon earth a place where harried Israel can govern herself and is subject to no one. If I knew that this was in fact so, I would not hesitate to renounce all honors, to lay down my high office . . . and travel over mountain and valley, by water and by land, until I had reached the place where my lord the king of the tribe of Israel commands. If I were destined to behold his greatness, his glory, and the brilliant retinue that surrounds him, as well as the peaceful existence of the remnant of Israel, my soul would overflow in gratitude to God who has not turned his mercy from his poor people. . . ."

Hasdai concluded his letter with the following words: "I have one more plea that lies on my heart. May you inform me whether you know anything about the Final Miracle, which we have awaited so long while we wander from country to country. Dishonored and humbled in exile, we must listen mutely to those who say: 'Every nation possesses its own kingdom and you alone lack even the shadow of a kingdom on earth.'"

By a long, roundabout route, passing through the hand of Jacob ben Eleazar in Germany, the letter actually reached the chagan or khan of the Khazars, Joseph. Years later, in 955, a reply arrived in Córdoba. Hasdai read it with astonishment.

The Khazars, he learned, were not descendants of Israelite tribes, but of pagan origin; they were kinsmen of the Turks. In the year 740, after a disputation among representatives of Christianity, Mohammedanism, and Judaism, King Bulan had become a convert to the Jewish religion. Thereafter the chagans of the Khazars ruled as adherents of that faith. Joseph listed the Hebrew names of all his predecessors: Obadiah, Hesekiah, Manasseh, Hanukah, Isaac, Zebulon, Moses, Nisi, Menahem, Benjamin, and Aaron. Obadiah had founded synagogues and schools throughout the country and had had the people instructed in the Scriptures. Nevertheless, Christianity and Mohammedanism were still widespread throughout his country.

"You ask me about my country. . . . I inform you that I hold court by the River Volga. Along this river dwell many peoples in towns and villages, in open and fortified places. . . . All of them pay tribute to me. The boundary runs from the Volga to the Caspian Sea. The inhabitants of the coasts of that sea live at a distance of a month's journey, but all owe tribute to me. . . . You ask me also about my residence. Know that with divine aid I dwell on the above-mentioned River Volga, on which my three chief cities are situated. In one of them lives the Queen Mother. That is my birthplace. It is fifty square parasangs in area and built in the form of a circle. . . . In the third I myself dwell with my ministers, slaves, and servants . . . and bar the way of the Russians. That is my residence in wintertime. From the month of Nisan on, we move out of the city, each to his vineyard, his fields, and his work."

Joseph went on to boast that Byzantium respected his kingdom as a great power, and that the Slavs under the successors of Rurik paid tribute to him. "In your letter you say that you would wish to see me face to face," Joseph's letter concluded. "I, too, would like to behold you and be a witness to your wisdom and nobility. If this wish were to be fulfilled, you would be like a father to me and I your son, and my whole people would faithfully follow your counsels."

But the Jewish minister in Córdoba was not fated to meet the Jewish King of the Khazars. At the time he wrote the letter Joseph could not imagine that the mighty Khazar Kingdom was destined to tumble within a few years, and that he himself was to be the last of the Jewish chagans. About the year 966 Duke Sviatoslav of Kiev stormed the capital on the Volga and laid waste the surrounding countryside. The last possessions of the Khazars in the Crimea and on the Sea of Azov were lost barely three decades later. The rise of Russia had begun.

Hasdai created a new home for Talmudic scholarship in Spain. Jewish chroniclers have described this achievement; Jewish poets have hailed it in verse. Even Arabic historians paid their homage. "Hasdai ben Isaac," the Arabic writer Ibn-abi-Usaibia comments, "was one of the best of Jewish scholars, perhaps the most skilled in knowledge of the Law. To his Jewish brethren in Andalusia he opened the gates of theological science, chronology, and the other branches of knowledge. Until he came forth they were compelled to apply to the Jews of Baghdad for questions of the Law and in all matters concerning the calendar and the times of feasts."

A legend, written down by Abraham ibn Daud in Toledo in about the year 1170, tells the romantic tale of the journey of four wise men from the distant Orient. In Sura, not long after the death of Saadia in 942, the academy had been closed. But the Surans could not resign themselves to the downfall of their venerable academy, and did all in their power to revive it. Four young scholars were sent out to ask for contributions of money from rich Jewish communities. But as fate would have it, none of the four ever returned.

During this period a flotilla dispatched by the Caliph of Córdoba cruised off the coasts of southern Italy. Its admiral, Ibn Rumahis, had strict orders to capture all vessels sailing between Byzantium and Italy. One day, when his men boarded a ship that had sailed from Bari, he captured four Jews among the passengers on board. Their names were Hushiel, Shemaiah, and Moses ben Enoch; the name of the fourth is not known. All were sold as slaves. Shemaiah was bought in Alexandria by Jews who took him to Cairo, where he became head of the community. Hushiel was ransomed by his fellow Jews in another African port; he went to Kairouan, where he was made chief rabbi by the large community that lived there. But heavy sorrow was in store for Moses ben Enoch, whose wife and small son had also been captured with him. On the return voyage to Spain the Admiral began casting eyes on Moses' beautiful wife, and he was so persistent that she saw no way to escape him. In her quandary she asked her husband in Hebrew whether those who died in the waves of the sea would also share in the resurrection. Unsuspectingly, Moses replied with the verse of the Psalm: "God speaks, I will bring them back from the depths of the sea." No sooner had he spoken than she threw herself overboard. The brokenhearted husband was taken to Andalusia with his son, Enoch. There the Jewish community of Córdoba purchased freedom for them both (c. 950). No one suspected that here was a learned rabbi until chance brought him to the attention of his fellow Jews.

Wretchedly dressed, resembling a beggar, he one day entered the school. Rabbi Nathan was at the moment discussing a difficult passage in the Talmud. From a modest remark that Moses made during the lecture, the others recognized his learning. To the astonishment of all, he proved able to solve even the most difficult questions with ease and knowledgeability.

That same day, it is said, Rabbi Nathan declared to the congregation: "Henceforth I am no longer your judge. This office belongs to that poorly dressed wanderer; he alone is worthy to be the dayan [judge] of the community of Córdoba."

The wealthy community in fact elected Moses ben Enoch as its chief rabbi, and before long he assumed the headship of all the communities in the caliphate. Rich gifts were piled upon him, and even a carriage was placed at his disposal.

When Admiral Ibn Rumahis learned that his former slave was held so dear by the Córdoban community, he wanted to rescind the sale in order to demand a higher price. The Jews therefore appealed to the Caliph, and Hasdai personally informed the Caliph of the affair. Abd er-Rahman intervened in the case. He was glad, the chronicler informs us, that the Spanish Jews now had, in Moses ben Enoch, a scholar upon whom they could rely, so that they would no longer be dependent on the Babylonians. For the Caliph had disapproved of the large annual sums being sent from Córdoba to the Gaonate—that is, into the country of his enemy, the Caliph of Baghdad. Hasdai himself was delighted—for he had long hoped that Spanish Jewry could establish an intellectual center of its own.

The heart of Andalusia, the capital of the mighty caliphate, became the seat of an important independent academy. Under Rabbi Moses the modest Talmud school grew into a famous center of learning. Córdoba became the Sura of Andalusia. Students from cities in Spain and Africa thronged to the new school in such numbers that the buildings could scarcely hold them. Their desire to study in the Andalusian academy was all the greater because not only was the Talmud taught there but also considerable secular knowledge could be gained.

While Christian Europe sank back into the ignorance from which the Carolingians had sought to liberate it, and while the spirit of learning was suffering a steady decline in the Oriental caliphate, the Spanish caliphate witnessed a remarkable cultural efflorescence. Nowhere else in the world could so many cultivated men be found as in the capital of Andalusia. And what had begun under the great Abd er-Rahman was continued by Hakim II, his gifted son and successor (961–976), with even greater zeal and enthusiasm. Himself a poet and admirer of learning, the young Caliph determined to make Andalusia surpass all other countries in the things of the mind. He spent vast sums to collect rare and valuable books. In Kairouan and Cairo, in Baghdad and Basra, his emissaries were intent on buying up manuscripts and copies of ancient works, as well as the first publications of scholars pursuing new researches. Soon the library in Córdoba was such as could not be matched anywhere in Europe. The chroniclers relate that it contained no less than four hundred thousand volumes. Many thousands of students attended the Moslem academy.

Hakim, who like his father held Hasdai in high honor, could scarcely have found a more talented and enthusiastic aide for his soaring aspirations. But while he helped Moslem learning to prosper, Hasdai did not forget to promote generously the sciences and literature among his fellow Jews—and in this he was supported by the enlightened Caliph. Hasdai invited talented Jewish scholars and poets to Córdoba, among them men who were engaged in studying the Hebrew language, and who were enriching it in many respects. Menahem ben Saruk, whom Hasdai brought from Christian Tortosa, where he had been living in destitution, was the first to open new paths for the study of Hebrew. About the year 950 he completed the first Hebrew dictionary, entitled *Machberet*; its existence much stimulated and facilitated subsequent linguistic research. His work was widely known in France and Italy also. Donash ben Labrat (*c.* 910–980), who had studied under Gaon Saadia in Baghdad, was living in Fez in Africa when Hasdai's invitation reached him. He had already distinguished himself for his grammatical researches, and he showed himself an innovator in introducing Arabic meters into Hebrew poetry. His poems are full of ardor and vigor. Others who came to Córdoba were the poet Isaac Gikatilla; Joseph ibn Abitur, who at the Caliph's request translated Talmudic texts into Arabic; and, in about the year 1000, Jehudah ben David Chayug, Menahem's greatest disciple, to be known to posterity as the Father of the Grammarians. He was the first to recognize the three-consonant root structure of Hebrew words.

The prosperity of the Córdoban Jewish community had its part in making the city the center of Jewish scholarship. Liberal contributions supported the schools and, above all, the academy. Close to one thousand wealthy Jewish families, whose magnificence matched that of the Arabs, lived in the city. They wore silken garments and elegant turbans. Like their Moslem fellow countrymen, they rode in resplendent carriages or on richly caparisoned horses, and in their personalities they acquired a chivalric quality, a grandeur, that set them apart from Jews of other countries.

But the days of the proud caliphate of the Ommiads in Andalusia were numbered. Berber warriors from northern Africa, hired as mercenaries for border battles with Christian principalities, had for years poured into the country, and in the end proved its nemesis. In April, 1013, the African leader Suleiman penetrated into Córdoba with his army, and for days the brilliant metropolis was given up to pillaging and destruction. The large Jewish community was also affected, of course. Panic-stricken, many families fled the city. In his great old age, Enoch, the son of Moses ben Enoch and his successor as chief rabbi, was an eyewitness of these melancholy scenes. But he did not long survive the terrible blow to this world-famous Jewish cultural center. As he was making ready for the service in the synagogue on the day of the Feast of Tabernacles, 1014, he suddenly collapsed and died.

The caliphate of Córdoba disintegrated in the course of a ferocious civil war. A number of small Moslem states succeeded it, each ruled by an emir. Seville and Granada, Almería and Saragossa, each had its own ruler. The Jewish scholars and poets, politicians and businessmen who had fled Córdoba found new havens in these cities—especially in the cities ruled by Berbers, who manifested distinct sympathy for the Jews. In many of the towns and cities of Andalusia Jewish intellectual life resumed and began to climb to new heights. And Jews continued to play a role in the counsels of state. For example, Samuel ibn Nagdela (993–c. 1063), a scholar from the famous Talmudic academy of Córdoba, became vizier in the Kingdom of Granada. After the pillaging of Córdoba he had found refuge in Málaga, where he earned a bare living running a small spice shop until chance altered the direction of his life. The shop was situated close to the palace, and one of the Vizier's favorite slave girls had requested the shopkeeper Samuel to write some letters for her. They were composed in such classical Arabic that they stirred the interest of the Vizier, Ibn Alarif. He sent for Samuel, and to his astonishment found the modest shopkeeper a scholar with a comprehensive knowledge of many fields. Samuel was not only an eminent Talmudist; he was also remarkably well versed in secular knowledge, was intimately familiar with Arabic literature, philosophy, and philology, spoke and wrote seven languages, and, in addition, was a gifted poet. "Your place is not in the shop, but at the Emir's court," Ibn Alarif decided, and he took the Jewish scholar with him to Granada.

Samuel's keenness and circumspection were quickly recognized at court, and soon he was being consulted in all important political matters. The Vizier fell fatally ill one day, and on his deathbed he proposed his learned counselor as his successor. Emir Habbus took his advice and appointed Samuel vizier of his kingdom. In 1027 the new minister of state moved into the splendid governmental palace in Granada. As it turned out, the ruler could not have made a better choice.

For twenty-eight years Samuel wisely and skillfully guided the affairs of government in the largest Moslem kingdom in Spain. During a period of much unrest, in the midst of rivalries among the mutually hostile Arab and Berber princes, he managed to guard the peace and prosperity for the Kingdom of Granada. When Emir Habbus died in 1037 and a quarrel over the succession erupted among the notables at the Granada court, Samuel successfully arbitrated and helped the Emir's son Badis to succeed. Badis was by temperament tyrannical, but was greatly indebted to Samuel, who managed to exert a salutary influence on him.

There were many adherents of other parties and many fanatical Moslems to whom the Jewish Vizier was a thorn in the side. But Samuel managed to disarm even his bitterest foes by leniency and kindness. He composed his commands and ordinances in the style of the Koran, and embellished them with Islamic maxims. Even an Arab who was ill disposed toward Samuel could not help admitting "that this unbeliever, although God has withheld the true faith from him, distinguished himself by his knowledge and his tolerance. The breadth of his intelligence and the charm of his manners united with an exceedingly firm character. He had a masterly understanding of the art of disarming his enemies and converting them into his friends. How perfectly he knew the languages and the literatures of both peoples; how brilliantly he wrote Arabic. Moreover, he was foremost in mathematical knowledge, surpassed his contemporaries in astronomy, was a master of geometry, and had not his like in logic and polemic. . . . He spoke little, but with extraordinary cogency, and his thoughts were full of profundity."

In addition to his administrative tasks as vizier, Samuel also held the office of chief rabbi of the Jews of the kingdom, headed the academy in Granada, wrote commentaries and an excellent introduction to the Talmud, and delivered lectures on it. He conducted a lively correspondence with important scholars, and also exchanged letters with Gaon Hai in Babylonia and Nissim of Kairouan. He supported both Spanish and foreign academies by generous donations, provided scholarships for impoverished scholars and students, and had copies of the Bible and Talmud made for poor communities. His generosity extended to Africa, Sicily, and Egypt, to Mesopotamia and Palestine. In his palace he established a library containing precious codices of the Talmud. Among the treasures were even a few copies from Sura. "In Samuel's time the kingdom of science rose up once again and the constellations of knowledge shone," a chronicle praised him. "God gave him a high intelligence, so that he would love knowledge and the care of it, and would glorify religion."

Poetry, too, flourished more luxuriantly than ever before during his lifetime. Samuel himself wrote many poetical works, of which only fragments have been preserved. He was also among the first to treat of secular subjects—he wrote one of his poems in 1042 in the military camp at

Lorca on the night before the battle between the armies of Granada and Seville. "In the days of Hasdai the poets began to chirp," the saying went, "but in the days of Samuel, to sing loudly."

Samuel ha-Nagid—"Samuel the Prince"—died, mourned by all, in about 1063. His son Joseph inherited his dignities, being both vizier and rabbi. Like his father, Joseph had amassed a great deal of secular and cultural learning and was adroit, generous, and a patron of science. But he lacked modesty and prudence. His domineering ways and sumptuous life-style vexed the Moorish populace, whose antagonism soon became open hostility. Within court circles, hatred for the Jewish Vizier mounted and was fed by his frequent practice of nepotism.

Abu Ishak, an Arabic poet who felt that his career had been ruined by Joseph, voiced his resentment in a public appeal directed at the Emir and the people. "In Granada I saw that the Jews hold a leading position," he wrote. "They have divided the capital and the provinces among themselves. Everywhere one of this accursed race stands at the head of the government. They raise the taxes, revel in luxury, and strut about in splendid garments. . . . The chief of these monkeys [Joseph] has adorned his house with the costliest marble facings and installed fountains of clearest water in his halls, and while we wait at his door he makes mock of us. . . . O God, what a misfortune. Hasten to slaughter him; offer this fat ram as a sacrifice. Do not spare his kinsmen and friends either. . . . Think it not dishonorable to annihilate them."

Emir Badis paid no heed; he continued to place full confidence in his Vizier. But the Berbers were more easily provoked. A series of conspiracies against Joseph culminated in a popular uprising. For when in December, 1066, war bands from neighboring Almería unexpectedly invaded Granada, the rumor spread that the Jewish Vizier had invited the enemy into the country. An enraged mob stormed Joseph's palace, killed him, and dragged his corpse to the city wall, where it was impaled on the gate. On that same day more than fifteen hundred Jewish families in Granada were massacred. Among the few who barely escaped with their lives were the Vizier's widow and son.

Hysteria swept over the entire country, and the Jews had to flee the land in which they had lived in peace for five hundred years. The outbreak in Granada was the first persecution of Jews on the Iberian Peninsula since the rule of Islam had begun.

The refugees found asylum in other Moslem states. Many of them settled down in the Kingdom of Seville, whose ruler (1049–1069), Emir Motatid, was known as a broad-minded lover of poetry and science. From far and near he had been inviting distinguished men to his country.

The Jewish scholar Joseph ibn Migash had been living at his court for many years. Emir Motamid, Motatid's successor (1069–1091), appointed as his court astrologer Isaac ibn Albalia (1035–1094), an astronomer and Talmudist from Córdoba, and conferred on him the dignity of Nasi, prince of all the Jewish communities in the emirate of Seville.

A lively intellectual life also prevailed at the emirate of Saragossa, whose ruler, Moktadir, appointed Hasdai Abu-Fadl as his vizier in 1066. The Vizier wrote in Arabic poetry that met with an enthusiastic response. "To hear Abu-Fadl sing," an Arabic writer testified, "is to fall transported into a wonderland. He brings forth not poems but works of magic."

Bahia ibn Pakuda, a celebrated teacher of ethics, acted as rabbi of the community in Saragossa. In his work *The Duties of the Heart,* written in Arabic and destined for great popularity, Bahia praised the "duties of the heart" as of equal importance to fulfillment of ritual obligations. Another famous Saragossan was the philosopher and poet Solomon ben Judah ibn Gabirol (1020–1058), whose hymns, prayers, chants and lamentations have remained unforgotten. His fame as a philosopher was established by his essay *The Fountain of Life.* It was to exert a powerful influence on the Christian theology of the Middle Ages. Catholic scholastics, who deemed it a classical work, read it in Latin translation (*Fons Vitae*) and ascribed it to a Church Father named Avicebron. Thomas Aquinas, Albertus Magnus, Duns Scotus, and, later, Giordano Bruno drew upon it, never dreaming that the author was a Jewish philosopher. Only in modern times was it discovered that Solomon ibn Gabirol was the author; he had called himself Avicebron in the original Arabic text, which was later lost, and this name had been retained in the Latin translation.

The Christian kings of Castile also took Jewish subjects into their service, entrusting them with high offices in the state and with diplomatic missions. Political considerations, rather than any change of heart in the descendants of the anti-Semitic Visigoth rulers, accounted for this tolerance. The *Reconquista,* the reconquest of Spain from the Moslems, had just begun. Ferdinand I, King of Castile from 1035 to 1065, had won the upper hand to the extent that the emirs of Saragossa, Toledo, and even Seville were paying tribute to him. But it seemed scarcely advisable to take measures against the Jews. For so long as the southern part of the peninsula was still in Arab control, the Jews were needed, especially for the conduct of diplomatic assignments in Andalusia. Many of them spoke both Arabic and Castilian fluently; they were fully acquainted with the manners and customs of the Moslems; and they seem everywhere to have been the natural intermediaries between Christian and Arab governments.

Alfonso VI, King of Castile from 1075 to 1109, shrewdly recognized this necessity. He entrusted the Jewish physician Amram ibn Shalbib with collecting the annual tributes from his Moslem vassals, and conducted all negotiations with them through Amram. He also invited the Jewish scholar Cidellus to come to his court as adviser on all questions involving the Arabs. Hearing of this, the Pope loudly proclaimed his indignation.

The Pope at this time was Gregory VII, the famous Hildebrand. In 1078 Gregory, at a Council in Rome, had revived the ancient canon that no Jew might hold a position of superiority to a Christian. He sent a swift rebuke to Alfonso VI: "We remind you in no wise to tolerate Jews having command over Christians or in any way receiving preference to them. To subordinate Christians to Jews or to force them to obey Jewish judges—would not this mean to humble the Christian Church and exalt the synagogue of Satan? In showing compliance to the enemies of Christ you deny Christ himself."

The letter accomplished nothing. King Alfonso had no intention of dispensing with the valuable services of the Jews. Ibn Shalbib remained in office, as did all his coreligionists. In fact, he was entrusted with a portentous and exceedingly risky mission—no less than persuading Emir Motamid of Seville to cede Córdoba to Castile. In 1083 he set out, accompanied by five hundred Castilian knights, reached Seville, and was received in the palace. But when the Jewish ambassador conveyed King Alfonso's demand, the Emir flew into a rage. The unfortunate emissary was ordered executed and his retinue thrown into prison.

But these highhanded measures were repaid. The following year Castilian troops invaded the emirate of Seville and devastated the countryside far and wide. Only two years later, in 1085, a further success of Christian arms alarmed the whole of Moslem Spain. After a five-year siege Sultan Kadir surrendered Toledo to the Castilians. The ancient Visigothic capital of Spain was once more in Christian hands. The Moslem princes of Andalusia, too weak themselves to halt the dangerous advance of the Castilians, asked for help from their fellow Moslems in North Africa. Yussuf ibn Tashfin, leader of the Berber sect of the Almoravides, crossed the Straits with a large army and marched into Andalusia. Reinforced by contingents of Moslem Spanish troops, a mighty array advanced north from Seville against King Alfonso.

The two armies met at Zallaka, near Badajoz, on October 23, 1086. In both the army of the Cross and that of the Crescent there were Jewish soldiers; there were forty thousand on the Moslem side alone, in yellow uniforms and black turbans. But since the day was a Friday, the battle was postponed. It was decided that there would be no fighting on Friday, the Moslem Sabbath, nor on Saturday because of the Jewish soldiers, nor on the Christian Sunday.

Battle was joined at last on Monday, and ended with complete victory for the Moslems. The Castilian King escaped with a mere remnant of his forces. Andalusia had been saved for Islam; the advance of the Christian states had been checked for the time being. But the victory was short-lived for the emirs of the many small Arab and Berber states. They had invited their own enemy into the country. Before long, southern Spain was racked by internal struggles. Yussuf ibn Tashfin seized control, reducing all the emirs to the rank of his subordinates.

The new Almoravide rulers of Andalusia were not religious fanatics. They permitted the Jews to live in peace, and even compensated them for their ordeal in Granada. Those who had suffered under Emir Badis had all their possessions restored. Once again they were able to live in harmony with the Moslem populace, and the Almoravides continued to make use of the services of educated Jews. Ali, second Caliph of the new dynasty (1106–1143), gave his Jewish physician and poet, Solomon Almoalem of Seville, the title of vizier. Similar prestige at court was enjoyed by another Jewish physician, Abraham ibn Kamnial of Saragossa, of whom it was said: "In the days of affliction he is the shield and refuge of his people. He lives in Spain, but the works of his mercy extend to Babylonia and Egypt."

Seldom has an age produced so many gifted men, seldom has any been so fruitful and creative, as was the era that now dawned for the Jewish people. While across the Pyrenees the First Crusade was bringing destruction upon the Jewish communities of Western Europe, in Spain the Golden Age of Jewry reached its greatest flowering. Jewish poetry and philosophy ascended to new heights.

In 1085, the year the ancient capital of Spain fell into Christian hands, Judah Halevi was born there. As a boy he went to Arab Spain. In Lucena he studied under Isaac ben Jacob Alfasi, who towered above all other scholars as a Talmudic authority. Afterward Judah Halevi moved on to Granada to continue his studies. Gifted in many directions, he chose to practice medicine after returning to his native Toledo. But he revealed his greatest talent as a poet. Since the age of Biblical poetry had come to an end, no such lyrical notes had been sounded in Jewish literature. His theme was the unquenchable longing for the Holy Land; his elegies lamented the fate of his people, the never-ending misery of Israel's exile. "Is there not in East or West one place where we might live in peace?" Halevi cried. "How much longer, O God, must I burn in the consuming flames between Edom and Arab, whom you have set above me for my judges?"

He spoke with passion of the ancient homeland, lost and shattered Zion:

> Oh city of the world, with sacred splendor blest,
> My spirit yearns to thee from out the far-off West,
> A stream of love wells forth when I recall thy day,
> Now is the temple waste, thy glory passed away.
> Had I an eagle's wings, straight would I fly to thee,
> Moisten thy holy dust with wet cheeks streaming free. . . .[1]

Halevi's poems, more than three hundred in number, made him the darling of his people.

Halevi also won fame by his religio-philosophical work *The Cuzari,* or *Book of the Khazars.* The Arabic title, *Book of Proofs for the Defense of the Humiliated Faith,* suggests what was in Halevi's mind. In a dialogue among a Khazar king, a philosopher, a Moslem, and a Jew, he expounded his ideas on philosophy and Judaism. He traced the limits of philosophy, arguing that reason, not even the insight of an Aristotle, could not replace divine revelation. "Do not let yourself be tempted by the wisdom of the Greeks, which surely blossoms but sets no fruit." Philosophical speculation can easily lead men astray. It is not given to philosophy to comprehend the whole spiritual being of man, as can Holy Scripture. Religion alone can legitimately govern the conduct of life. *The Cuzari,* later translated from the Arabic into Hebrew, Spanish, Latin, and German, is still considered among the most important works in medieval literature.

After his philosophical book was completed, Halevi was seized by overwhelming longing for the land of his forefathers. In vain his friends attempted to dissuade him from undertaking the dangerous journey to Palestine, which had been conquered by the Crusaders. After the death of his wife, nothing could hold him back. In 1140 he set out from Toledo on the long pilgrimage. All along his way, he encountered admirers. In Córdoba, where the aged Rabbi Ibn Zadik (author of the noted religio-philosophical work *Olam Katan,* or *Microcosm*) then lived, he was hailed enthusiastically, and a similar reception awaited him in Egypt, where he arrived after an eventful sea voyage. In Alexandria he was cordially welcomed by Rabbi Aaron ibn Alamini, the famous physician, and in Cairo by Samuel abu Mansur, head of Egyptian Jewry.

The last trace of his movements is lost in Damascus, and the ultimate

---

[1] Translated by Emma Lazarus.

fate of the great poet has remained unknown. Legend tells that when Halevi saw Jerusalem in the distance, he threw himself to the ground and began to sing his famous elegy: "Zion, dost thou still ask after the fate of the damned. . . ." At that moment a horseman came galloping along and trampled upon him, so that Halevi died with the immortal words of his greatest ode on his lips. To this day his "Zionide" is recited in the synagogues on the fast day of the ninth of Ab.

Judah Halevi surpassed all his contemporaries, including Moses ibn Ezra of Granada (c. 1070–1138) and Abraham ibn Ezra of Toledo (1092–1167). Moses ibn Ezra, known as the Master of Penitential Prayers, wandered hither and yon writing mournful verse about unrequited love and also left behind several hundred prayers and hymns. Abraham ibn Ezra was a man of many parts who, in addition to his treatises on grammar, astronomy, and philosophy, wrote an important commentary on the Bible as well as witty, sprightly verse; for more than twenty-five years he traveled about Continental Europe, England, and the Orient.

The great period of Hebrew poetry came to an end with the deaths of these three men. Their successors were talented versesmiths rather than great poets. Judah Alharisi (c. 1165–1225), the last gifted poet of the great Spanish period, put it bluntly: "After the passing of Solomon ibn Gabirol, who wore the royal crown of poetry, of poetry's prince, Abraham ibn Ezra, her general, Judah Halevi, and her prophet, Moses ibn Ezra, the springs of song have dried, the age of glory is done, the angel of God vanished. Never again have such poets arisen, never again have such songs been sung. For we only glean the ears they left, follow their track, and cannot catch up with them. The older generations fed on branless flour, but only the flourless bran is left for us."

But if poetry had reached and passed its pinnacle, philosophy's great day was still to come. First, however, an annihilating blow struck Jewish life in Moslem Andalusia—in the very same year that the Second Crusade began in Europe. The happy age under Islam came to an abrupt end.

The disaster came from the south, from Africa. The fanatical and anti-Jewish Almohades brought a third Moslem invading army into Spain under the banner of the Prophet. In North Africa these stern warriors of Islam had already driven out the tolerant Almoravides. Now zealotry began to rage from the borders of Egypt to the Atlas Mountains. They proclaimed that all who would not embrace Islam must leave the country. A wave of persecutions struck the Jewish communities; all the synagogues were destroyed. Many Jews in their distress accepted a sham conversion. Many others preferred to flee from Africa.

Led by Ab al-Mumin, the African fanatics carried their "holy war" across the Straits into Spain. Terror broke over Andalusia. "After the rebels had devastated all the dwellings of Israel in the whole territory between Tangiers and Mahdia," relates Abraham ibn Daud, an eyewitness of the events, "they came across the sea to Spain in order to deal with the Jews in the same manner here."

In 1147 Seville fell into the hands of the Almohades, and in 1148, Córdoba; Málaga and Lucena followed. Not a single Jewish community of Andalusia was spared, not a single Jewish synagogue escaped destruction or desecration. In Granada the inhabitants put up a brief, desperate resistance. Moslems, Christians, and Jews, led by Ibn Dahri, took up arms unitedly and met the Almohades in a series of bloody battles. But they succumbed to superior force. Panic-stricken, threatened by death, many Jews pretended conversion to Islam, although they intended to return to the faith of their fathers at the first opportunity. But the great majority sought escape. Hosts of fugitives streamed northward; long columns of Jews tramped along all the roads toward the Christian kingdoms.

"Woe, how cruel is the disaster that Heaven has cast down upon Spain," mourned the poet Abraham ibn Ezra. "How lamentable is Maghreb [Africa], where courage has been stripped from all. Full of tears I recall Lucena, the congregation of the good and the pious, where the Gola [Diaspora] lived in a safe home. Now the day of horror has come; the people are scattered, the congregation widowed. The house of the soul's worship has become a temple of shame; the hand of the enemy has not spared the rolls of the Holy Scriptures. I must shed tears for the lot of beautiful Seville, for the pride of her nobles and sages. . . . How Córdoba is laid waste, the city of wise and strong men. Jaén and even Almería have been stripped entirely of their Jews. There is no longer refuge on Majorca and none in Málaga for all the tormented, for all the pillaged Jews. . . . The people mourns, the harried, oppressed, persecuted people . . . and continually beseeches the Lord: 'Look down upon us from Heaven!' "

Unexpectedly, the distressed fugitives found a refuge. The border fortress of Calatrava, a Castilian military base, lay at the point of a deep salient into Arab territory. King Alfonso VII had appointed as its commander Rabbi Jehudah ibn Ezra, a nephew of the poet Moses ibn Ezra. Calatrava became the asylum through which the exiles passed. Rabbi Jehudah "loosened the bonds of the fettered, fed the hungry, gave drink to the thirsty, provided garments for the ragged," and cared for all the refugees until they had reached the precincts of Toledo.

Once again Israel had been driven from a homeland long familiar—

the southern part of the Iberian Peninsula, where Jews had lived for three quarters of a millennium. Not a single Jew who openly confessed his faith was any longer to be found in Moslem territory. The schools and synagogues lay deserted; weeds grew in the Jewish cemeteries. Those who had escaped with their lives henceforth dwelt under the descendants of the Visigoths.

The attitude of Christian kings toward Jews had not changed. They granted the persecuted people asylum in Castile, León, Aragon, Navarre, and Portugal. No exceptional laws hampered Jewish religious life or restricted their occupations. In place of Córdoba and Seville, Granada and Lucena, new communities came into being in Gerona and Barcelona. Toledo became the seat of Jewish learning, and the new arrivals soon swelled the community there to a population of ten thousand. The synagogues of Toledo, it was said, were "of a beauty with which no others could be compared."

Sharp clashes with the Almohades began along all the borders of the Christian states. These fierce warriors soon retook areas previously conquered by the Christians. The Jews readily followed the call to arms against the Islamic fanatics, from whom they could expect only persecution. Many young Jews volunteered for service under the Christian kings. Prosperous Jews contributed sizable sums to the defense of the Christian kingdoms.

At the court of King Alfonso VII (who reigned from 1126 to 1157), Jewish scientists and diplomats enjoyed great esteem. Jehudah ibn Ezra, who had previously commanded the fortress of Calatrava, served as royal treasurer. Alfonso VIII (King of Castile from 1158 to 1214) in his turn employed educated Jews in important government affairs. Only once did an anti-Jewish act occur in Toledo, and for that the King was only indirectly to blame. The Spanish annals give a discreet account of the case of Rachel, who was called La Formosa for her beauty. Alfonso VIII, who was married to an English princess, fell so head over heels in love with this beautiful young Jewess that "for her sake he forgot wife, people, and country." The affair continued for seven years. Then a conspiracy in the court put a violent end to the relationship. One night the palace in which Rachel lived was set afire, and she died in the flames.

In Aragon, Catalonia, and Navarre the Jews likewise enjoyed royal protection and lived in safety. In Barcelona documents record Jewish ownership of houses, gardens, and vineyards. The Jewish community there was hailed by the poet Jehudah Alharisi as "the community of princes and dignitaries." In Tudela on the Ebro the King of Navarre had even assigned the Jews a castle of their own for emergencies. From this community came Benjamin of Tudela, whose voyage of exploration through the entire known world won him fame. For thirteen years, from 1160 to 1173, he traveled through Europe, Africa, and Asia, describing lands and customs, historical and geographical data. His journey took him from Barcelona across southern France, Italy, and Greece to Cyprus and Rhodes, then on to Palestine and across the lands of the Euphrates into Persia. He returned by ship across the Indian Ocean, visiting the coastal cities of Yemen, from which he brought news of Jewish communities in India, and traveled on through Egypt. In exploration of vast areas of Asia Benjamin preceded Marco Polo by a whole century. His *Itinerary* was frequently translated and is a mine of information on the ethnology, geography, and commerce of countries then scarcely known to the Western world.

At about this same time Rabbi Petahia ben Jacob of Regensburg undertook another such tour of the world. He started out from Prague, crossed Poland, Russia, Tatary, and the lands of the Turkomans to the Orient, whence he returned by way of Greece after an absence of ten years. His account, too, was much read and translated.

After the terrors of the Almohad invasion a period of peace returned to Spain. The *aljamas* (Jewish communities) were able to enjoy an untroubled life and to cultivate poetry and the sciences unhindered. But the intellectual life of Spanish Judaism did not attain its crowning glory on the Iberian Peninsula. The man who towered above all the scholars of the Arabic-Spanish school completed his monumental lifework in Egypt. He was Moses Maimonides, whom his people honored with the title of the Second Moses.

Moses ben Maimon was born in 1135, the son of an ancient family of scholars in Córdoba. His father, a rabbi and Talmudist of the school of Alfasi, early instructed his remarkably gifted son in Hebrew and Arabic literature. The boy had just reached thirteen when disaster fell upon his native city: The Almohades conquered Córdoba and drove the Jewish community into exile. A life of wandering and privations began, flight from city to city. But ignoring all discomforts, the young man continued to study eagerly. He acquired a tremendous range of knowledge—in mathematics and astronomy, in natural science and medicine—which was later to earn him his livelihood. From Arabic sources, he absorbed the philosophical system of Aristotle, of which he remained a faithful follower all his life. Moses was only sixteen when he wrote his first important book, a lexicon of the concepts of logic, and at twenty he began a commentary on the Mishnah. In about the year 1160 Moses and his family landed in North Africa. They settled down in Fez for a time, but even there they found themselves under pressure from Moslem fanatics. After a stay of several years they were forced to flee again, in order to escape religious coercion. They reached Acre in Palestine by ship; from there they traveled by way of Jerusalem and Hebron to Egypt. After some twenty years of wandering they at last found rest in Fostat, in Old Cairo.

Their trials ended with Moses Maimonides being appointed physician to the vizier of Sultan Saladin. Thus he was relieved of concern for his daily bread and could devote himself entirely to his scholarly labors. He finished his commentary on the Mishnah. Next he set about on the tremendous task of disentangling and bringing rationality and order into the Talmud, which nearly a thousand years of lawgiving had rendered an almost impenetrable labyrinth. The fruit of ten years' work (1170–1180) was a huge book that had epochal effects upon world Jewry: *Mishnah Torah* (*Repetition of the Law*). Moses had succeeded in systematizing and clarifying the whole gigantic complex of traditional doctrines—laws, religious dogmas, and ritual prescripts—into a new, organized legal code. Everything was so arranged that even the poorly educated reader could without difficulty find what he was seeking. *A new handbook based on objective principles of logical order had been created.*

By this time the great scholar's reputation had spread throughout the world; his name was venerated in Orient and Occident. Appeals for advice and instruction came to him from every quarter of the known world. He comforted distant communities in Yemen, on whom intense religious persecution had descended, encouraging them to persist loyally in their faith. The persecutions had not come unexpectedly, he pointed out, for the Prophets had predicted them. "Because God has especially distinguished us, the sons of Israel, by his grace, the peoples hate us," Maimonides wrote to them. "Not for ourselves. Do not be discouraged by the plenitude of your sufferings. It serves only to test you and to show that the descendants of Jacob alone, the grandsons of those who received the Law on Sinai, are in possession of the true religion."

He admonished the communities in French Provence to abjure astrology, which bordered on idolatry, he said. As head of the Cairo community he held lectures on the Talmud, which attracted hearers from far and wide. Along with his medical work and his duties as rabbi, he sat from morning to night over his studies and his writing. He composed a treatise on poisons and a summary of medical writings that were highly esteemed by medieval doctors. At the request of the son or nephew of Saladin, he published a primer on hygiene. Seldom had a scholar's life displayed such variegated and fruitful activity.

"Much as I would rejoice to greet you in my home," Maimonides wrote to Samuel ibn Tibbon, the great translator, in southern France, "I must nevertheless advise against your undertaking the long sea voyage. The only profit from your visit would be to have seen me, and to have been received with all honors by me. But I could not even devote an hour of familiar intercourse to you. I will describe to you my mode of life: I live in Fostat, and with the Sultan in Cairo; these places are a good two Sabbath walks apart [about a mile and a half]. I have exceedingly laborious service under the Sultan. Daily at dawn I must visit him. Quite frequently, when he himself feels ill, or when one of his wives or his courtiers has fallen sick, I do not get away from Cairo that day. At best, I can only return to Fostat in the afternoon. When I arrive, tired and hungry, I find all the anterooms full of people, Jews and Moslems, high and low, who are waiting for my medical aid. I scarcely have time to dismount from the mule, wash, and have a bite to eat. Then I must write out prescriptions and cures for them. The going and coming often continues until late into the night. Sometimes I am so weak from fatigue that I can no longer say a word. Only on the Sabbath do I have time to devote myself to the congregation and the Law. Thus my days slip away."

Nevertheless, at the age of fifty-five he still found time and strength to draw up the sum of his wisdom. In his *Guide for the Perplexed* (1190) he boldly undertook to make a synthesis within Judaism of the religious and philosophical approach to the cosmos, to reconcile faith and reason. Maimonides assumed, writes Josef Kastein, that if "religion is truly to lead to clear knowledge of God, it must accord with the demands of reason. For reason, as well as faith, is a source of revelation. The latter he considered to be embodied in the Bible, the former in the philosophy of Aristotle." Maimonides, in the spirit of Aristotle's philosophy but deviating from him at crucial points, created his own metaphysics. He was convinced that "the entire universe represents nothing but the realized ideas of God."

The *Guide for the Perplexed* was swiftly translated from the Arabic into Hebrew and Latin. It was read everywhere, and both Jewish and Moslem scholars debated the pros and cons of the book. It created a storm among the strictly orthodox rabbis of Provence, who denounced it as dangerous to the faith.

During the lifetime of Maimonides the important Arabic philosopher Ibn Rushd (1126–1198), later known as Averroës, similarly examined the philosophy of Aristotle in its relationship to the doctrines of the Koran. The works of these two towering intellects were subsequently to exert the most powerful influence upon the thinking of medieval Christians.

"It was Maimonides who first reconciled the work of Aristotle with the theology of the Bible in a higher sense," the historian of literature Gustav Karpeles has observed. "Maimonides served as a model for the Scholastics, showing them how to approach those views of the ancient sage that contradicted their religious ideas. From Maimonides they were able to learn an independent attitude toward Greek and Arabic philosophy. And, in fact, the influence of Maimonides can be clearly traced in Albertus Magnus and Thomas Aquinas, just as the Franciscan Duns Scotus shows the influence of Avicebron-Gabirol and the philosopher Ibn Daud. When we credit Albertus Magnus with rewriting Aristotle by asserting the Church's differing views in regard to the eternity of the universe, by holding to the Biblical teachings on the Creation and maintaining the doctrine of personal immortality, we must not forget to add that he received precisely these anti-Aristotelian ideas from Maimonides. Indeed, on the most important points—Creation and prophesy—he borrowed directly . . . from the abbreviated translation of whole sections of the *Guide for the Perplexed*. The influence exerted by Rabbi Moses of Egypt . . . extends to the definition of the concept of God. The formulation and proofs of that concept were faithfully copied by Thomas . . . from the *Guide for the Perplexed,* which was already available to him in Latin translation. Similarly, the doctrine of the evil existent in the world, which passed from Thomas to Leibniz and modern philosophy, is in its origin Maimonidean, as is Scholastic ethics, which, whenever it rose above Aristotle . . . rested upon a clear distinction that Maimonides had already made . . . between ethical virtues and the virtues of knowledge."

For the Jews in the heart of Europe, however, Maimonides came at the wrong time. Even as he composed his *Guide for the Perplexed,* disaster and persecutions had already begun. In times of trial, prayer and the Holy Scriptures alone could yield the necessary strength, not philosophical speculations.

Incessant work had undermined the health of the great thinker. After some years of illness, Maimonides died in his seventieth year, on December 13, 1204. His remains were taken to Tiberias in the Holy Land. A general fast was ordered, and his burial was marked by the reading of that passage from the Bible describing the capture of the Ark of the Covenant by the Philistines. "With Moses ben Maimon," a contemporary wrote in obituary, "the Jewish people have for the second time lost the Ark of the Covenant."

He died when his people needed him most. In times of terror, when the long medieval night of suffering was beginning to gather over the Jewish communities, Jewry had no leader, Judaism no authoritative voice.

FORERUNNERS OF HUMANISM AND
THE RENAISSANCE

The treasures of ancient knowledge and new learning that had accumulated in the lands of Islam had swelled to vast proportions. The entire heritage of antiquity, increased by centuries of active research and study, was available in the libraries of Arab academies and Jewish schools. All fields from natural science to philosophy were comprehended. About the turn of the century this heritage, introduced by Christian, Arab, and Jewish scholars, began to seep into the countries of Western Europe. The first response was often incredulity and astonishment. General interest in it awakened slowly but steadily mounted, until at last these cultural "imports" had swelled to a broad stream. The result was that "discovery of the world and of man" which spurred Scholastic thought and prepared the way for the great intellectual awakening of Humanism and the Renaissance that terminated the Middle Ages and brought on the dawn of the "Modern Age."

Provence, situated at the gates of Spain in southern France, seemed predestined to become one of the great mediators between Orient and Occident. Its cities—Marseilles, Narbonne, Montpellier, Arles, and Aix—rich from sea-borne commerce, and harboring a large Jewish population, had long been in vital contact with the Spanish-Arabic world. An enlightened spirit prevailed among the Provençals. Speculation, literature, and the exact sciences flourished there as they did nowhere else north of the Pyrenees. In Provence the great works of translation were done. Two places above all won fame: Narbonne and Lunel, near Montpellier, where two gifted families of scholars over several generations translated the works of the Golden Age. These families were the Tibbonids and the Kimhids.

Judah ben Saul ibn Tibbon (1120–1190), a refugee from Granada, had settled with his family in Lunel, where he practiced medicine. He had a thorough knowledge of Arabic and other branches of learning. At the suggestion of the chief rabbi, Meshullam ben Jacob, a man deeply schooled in the Talmud and philosophy, Tibbon undertook to translate the works of Jewish-Arabic philosophers. Between his thirtieth and his seventieth years, he had translated the works of Gaon Saadia of Babylonia, the popular edifying tract *The Duties of the Heart* by Bahia ibn Pakuda, the much read *The Cuzari* of Halevi, the treatises of the grammarian, lexicographer, and philologist Mervan ibn Janach (c. 990–1050), and works of the great philosopher Solomon ibn Gabirol.

In his testament Judah ibn Tibbon exhorted his son Samuel (1150–1230), likewise a physician as well as a writer on philosophy, in this manner: "My son, never cease to concern yourself with the Law and with medical science, and only in small measure with business. Study diligently the profane books; in them you will find what is needful for practical life. Make it your habit to look over the medicinal drugs and herbs, and in your medical practice apply no method unless you are familiar with its workings. Continue to attend your teacher's lectures on the Talmud, and begin to instruct people only when you return from the academy, that is, in the nighttime. And teach to reliable pupils everything you have learned from me and your teachers, so that your science will become fixed in you by communicating it to others and by discussion."

Samuel, who inherited a fine library, surpassed his father in the art of translation. He corresponded with Maimonides, who gave him permission to translate his sensational *Guide for the Perplexed* from Arabic into Hebrew. Samuel also translated several works by Maimonides' greatest contemporary, the Arab philosopher Ibn Rushd.

Samuel's son Moses ibn Tibbon (died 1283) continued the family tradition, providing many translations from Arabic into Latin. Around 1232 his brother-in-law Jacob Anatoli entered the service of the Hohenstaufen Emperor Frederick II in Naples. That cultivated monarch paid him an annual salary for preparing translations of Aristotle's works. In Naples Anatoli completed the translation of a number of astronomical works that he had already begun in Provence. In addition, he lectured on Maimonides, whom he hailed as the equal of the Prophets. In his *Introduction for Pupils* he compared the three tiers of Noah's ark with three bodies of human knowledge: the exact sciences, physics, and metaphysics.

Through their translations the Tibbonids not only circulated philosophical ideas but also created a style for the writing of philosophical Hebrew. The Kimhi family carried this further, by becoming great students of linguistic phenomena.

Joseph ben Isaac Kimhi (who worked *c.* 1105–1120) had migrated from Spain to Narbonne; he translated philosophical writings and wrote verse, commentaries on books of the Bible, and a grammar of the Hebrew language. His sons, too, became distinguished scholars; the foremost of them was David. His Hebrew grammar and his *Dictionary of Roots* were works of fundamental importance, whereby later generations of Christian scholars and theologians acquired their knowledge of Hebrew.

These two families, which for three generations performed prodigies of intellectual labors, were by no means alone. In Palermo and Naples, and in the cities of Provence, linguistically gifted Jews continued the work of translation that had been initiated in Toledo under the kings of Castile. The vigor of intellectual life in the twelfth century—the profound and encyclopedic knowledge common among Jewish and Arab scholars of the time—remains all the more impressive when we consider the difficulties under which scholarship labored before the age of printing. Long before the Renaissance the curriculum for Jewish schools in Italy included poetry, philosophy, and the natural sciences. In Spain and in Provence it comprehended (aside from the religious subjects: Hebrew, the Torah, the Talmud) secular poetry, Aristotelian logic, Euclid's *Elements,* arithmetic, mathematical writings from Nicomachus to Archimedes, optics, astronomy, mechanics, medicine, nature, and metaphysics. Boys from the age of fifteen pursued this course of study.

In Provence the University of Montpellier grew up as a sister institution to the great medical school in Salerno. Jewish teachers at Montpellier lectured on the whole of Arab medical science, and gave courses in practical medicine that extended from surgery to ophthalmology.

Alongside Provence, southern Italy was at this time the second great bridge from Orient to Occident. Emperor Frederick II employed many other Jewish translators besides Anatoli at his court. The mathematics and natural science of the Arab world, as well as its philosophy, were studied and translated there. In decades of devoted labors Faraj ben Salim translated the colossal *al-Hawi* by the great Persian physician ar-Razi (known in the West as Rhazes), which summed up the whole body of medical knowledge from the times of the earliest Greeks to the year 925.

Jehudah ben Solomon Cohen ibn Mosca corresponded (1226) from Toledo with Emperor Frederick, and was later invited to his court. Ibn Mosca produced an encyclopedic work on Aristotelian foundations, *Teaching of Wisdom.* As an appendix he added the questions he had received from the philosophical Emperor and his own responses. At the request of King Alfonso X, Ibn Mosca also translated a famous Arabic astronomical work by Ali ibn Rijal into Spanish. Levi ben Abraham (1259–1316) of Villefranche, a close friend of Moses ibn Tibbon, who encouraged the project, wrote *Garland of Grace,* an encyclopedia of all the sciences. He divided it according to the famous pillars of Solomon's temple, into two major areas: Jachin was the gateway to arithmetic, geometry, astronomy, physics, and metaphysics; Boaz, to the religious and philosophical questions of prophesy, the mysteries of the Law and of Creation. Much to the annoyance of orthodox rabbis, Levi ben Abraham also wrote a didactic poem, *Scent Bottles and Amulets,* in which he somewhat daringly expressed opinions on the origin of philosophy, metaphysics, and morality. Shemtob ben Joseph Palquera, in Spain, was the author of a treatise (1262) on the relationship between body and soul. His *Book of the Seeker* affords a good account of the curriculum for higher learning. A scholar who turned to the "master of science, learning, and piety" was advised: "After the written and oral teachings study the *Mishnah Torah* of Maimonides and the commentary on the Mishnah. You are thereby equipped with enough religious judgment for dealing with doubtful cases. . . . After the study of the Law devote yourself to the sciences, first of all to those that are the preparation for physics and metaphysics. Then you will understand how to be God-fearing and to comprehend God." Only after he had studied for five years was the student to turn to the exact sciences. He would give a year each to arithmetic, geometry, optics, music, and astronomy; the final subject was logic.

Thus there were fortunate isles on the fringes of Europe where highly cultivated Jews corresponded with an emperor and discussed the proper place of philosophy and the exact sciences in the curriculums of Jewish schools, and where they created a great variety of works dealing with all areas of religious and secular knowledge. The time was ripe and more than ripe. Rich treasures stood ready. The peoples of Western Europe had only to reach out for them. But the powers that governed these peoples interposed their veto; to them, all such learning was a peril to the Faith. A ban was placed against importation of the intellectual achievements of the rest of the world. And Europe turned another way, began a slow march through long, dim, and dark centuries.

III THE MEDIEVAL INFERNO

IN THE SHADOW OF THE CRUSADES

"And there broke over us a terrible darkness"—these words sound like a premonition of his people's future fate. But Samuel ben Jehudah, who wrote them in the year 1096, could not possibly have foreseen the extent of the horrors that were to descend in the coming centuries. With the First Crusade as a bloody overture, long years of terror and persecution crushed the Jews of Europe.

Toward the end of the eleventh century, news from the Orient aroused great feeling in Christian Europe. Pilgrims returning from Palestine reported that Moslems had desecrated Christ's sepulcher and other Holy Places. At the Council of Clermont on November 26, 1095, Pope Urban II called upon sovereigns and knights to liberate Jerusalem—"the center of the earth and second paradise"—from the unbelievers. All who would take part in the Crusade were promised forgiveness of their sins.

Whole nations were seized by the frenzy. Men and youths from all classes of the people set out. Thousands upon thousands left home and family, sewed the sign of the cross to their garments, and seemingly could think of nothing but joining the war against the unbelievers. Along with knights who dreamed of glory in battle were peasants for whom the distant war provided a welcome chance to shake off serfdom and the burdens of debt. Adventurers and soldiers of fortune joined the movement, lured by the riches of the Orient. Thieves, vagabonds, and prostitutes attached themselves to the crusading armies, scenting loot or booty.

By the spring of 1096 a first great army of Crusaders had assembled. But before the commanders—Duke Godfrey of Bouillon from Lorraine and Duke Robert of Normandy, among others—could arm and organize these forces, anarchic elements among them launched out on quite a different crusade within their own countries. Their target was the Jews. "A fierce, ungoverned, merciless people rose up, composed of Franks and Germans," wrote a Jewish chronicler of the times. "Marching through cities with Jewish populations, they said to one another: 'Now we are setting forth to take our revenge upon the Ishmaelites, but even here we come upon the Jews whose forefathers crucified our Saviour. Let us first of all take revenge upon them. Let the name of Israel be annihilated if they refuse to be like us and acknowledge Jesus as the Messiah!' " The concept of the Jews as "deicides," framed as long ago as the fourth century, took possession of the imagination of Christians.

The Jewish community in Rouen in Normandy was the first victim. Crusaders dragged the Jews to the church and killed all who would not accept baptism. In other French cities the same lot befell the Jews. The irregular Crusaders marched from France across Flanders to the Rhineland—but the terrible tidings sped ahead of them. The Jews of Mainz sent messengers to their imperial protector, Henry IV, pleading for help. Henry, who happened to be in Italy, issued an order to all his dukes and bishops to protect the Jews. But he did not have the power to enforce his order. The hordes of Crusaders crossed the Rhine and made an onslaught against the German Jews, pillaging and murdering. Speyer, the newly founded community that shortly before had received privileges and assurances of protection from the Emperor, was the first victim. On May 3, a Sabbath, Crusaders and local Christians fell upon their Jewish fellow citizens. Eleven men who refused baptism were killed. When the mob began to storm the synagogue, in which many of the Jews had taken refuge, armed men sent by Bishop Johann intervened and restored order. The Bishop punished some of the local instigators by sentencing them to have an arm cut off, and gave asylum to the Jews in his own palace.

At the news of the bloody incidents in Speyer, a group of Jews in Worms barricaded themselves within Bishop Adalbert's palace, but most remained in their houses. When the Crusaders appeared, a rumor was suddenly spread that the Jews had killed a Christian. On May 18 the attacks began. Jewish families who had not sought safety were slaughtered; the scrolls of the Torah in the synagogues were destroyed. A few Jews submitted to the enforced baptisms. Many committed suicide. Mothers killed first their sons, then themselves, dying with the prayer on their lips: "Hear, O Israel: The Lord our God, the Lord is One."

By May 20 it was the turn of all the Jews in the episcopal palace. When the Crusaders gathered threateningly before the gate, the Bishop urged the Jews to accept baptism in order to save their lives. The Jews asked to be given time for reflection. When the period of reprieve was over, the Bishop had the doors thrown open to the room into which they had withdrawn. A terrible sight presented itself: Not one of the Jews was alive; they had all committed suicide. The Crusaders did not even spare the dead—"they stripped them naked," a contemporary account relates, "and dragged and tumbled the bodies. . . . The number of the slain on those two days approached eight hundred; all were cast naked into the grave." One man who had been baptized by force, a youth named Simcha Cohen, drew a knife and stabbed three of his oppressors. The mob tore him to pieces.

Other bands of Crusaders, led by Count Emmerich of Leiningen, moved toward Mainz. The members of the large Jewish community in the city appealed for aid to Archbishop Ruthard, and received permission to come to his palace until the danger was over. More than a thousand Jews turned their valuables over to Ruthard and took refuge in the court and solar of the spacious palace, guarded by the Archbishop's soldiery. But when Emmerich and his hordes appeared on May 27 and demanded that the fugitives be turned over to them, the guards withdrew and the Archbishop suddenly vanished—"for they wanted to kill him also, because he had spoken in favor of the Jews."

What took place is described by Solomon ben Simon, one of the few eyewitnesses who survived that frightful day. "When the sons of the Holy Covenant beheld the innumerable horde, they began to arm; old and young took up weapons. . . . From their hardships and fasting, however, they were so weakened that they could not resist their enemies. . . . In the inner courtyard of the episcopal palace the armed Jews posted themselves at the gate to fend off the murderous ruffians, and so a battle was fought at the gate. But they were no match for the foe, who pressed through into the courtyard. When the Jews saw that their lot was sealed . . . they encouraged one another: 'Let us bravely and with good heart endure all that the holy Faith imposes upon us. . . . No doubt the enemy will soon kill us. . . . What matter, if only our souls pass unharmed into the eternal light of Eden. Blessed is he who suffers death for the Name of the One.' Then all cried in chorus: 'Now there is no time to lose. The enemy is pressing forward. Let us without delay sacrifice ourselves to the honor of God.' . . . When the enemy forced their way into the yard, they saw the following scene: The devout men sat with our rabbi, Isaac ben Moses, wrapped in their prayer shawls, in the middle of the yard. The

Rabbi was the first to hold out his neck, and at once his severed head fell to the ground. The others meanwhile sat in the yard, prepared to fulfill the will of their Creator. The enemy hurled stones and arrows at them, but our people did not stir from the spot, and all were killed. At the sight of this those who were in the inner rooms decided, rather, to take their lives with their own hands. . . . Father sacrificed son; brother, sister; mother, daughter; neighbor, neighbor; bridegroom, bride. Each sacrificed, then to be sacrificed himself shortly afterward. The blood of parents mingled with that of children, of brothers with sisters, of masters with disciples, of bridegrooms with brides, of infants with nurses. . . . Who has ever seen or heard of the like?"

During the next several days wagons carried thirteen hundred corpses out of the Archbishop's palace and out of the city. Sixty Jews who had hidden in the cathedral made their escape, but they were later caught and slain. Two of the few who had accepted baptism were seized by despair: Isaac ben David, one of the heads of the community, who had yielded to save his mother's life, and Uri ben Joseph. They set fire to their own houses, rushed into the synagogue, and also set it afire. Both perished in the flames. A gigantic conflagration spread through the city and consumed a large part of Mainz.

In Cologne the Jews found protection. Many Christian inhabitants hid Jewish families in their houses. Bishop Hermann III had groups of them secretly taken out of the city to villages and manors that belonged to him in the vicinity. When a band of Crusaders entered the city early in June, they found the houses of the Jewish community deserted. Infuriated, they smashed everything, wrecked the synagogue, and destroyed the scrolls. But within three weeks they had tracked down the places of refuge. Cologne Jews hidden in Neuss, Welfinghausen, Xanten, Maerz, Geldern, and Altenahr suffered the fate of all the others. Many families plunged into the Rhine in despair. The number of suicides rose to terrifying proportions. With a spiritual courage bordering on the superhuman, the Jews withstood the temptation to save their lives by baptism, and suffered death for their faith.

In Trier alone were there mass baptisms. "As they approached Trier," a chronicle relates, "a few Jews who lived there . . . took their children and thrust the knife into their bodies, saying they must send them to the bosom of Abraham so that they would not become the plaything of the Christians' fury. Some of the women filled their bodices and sleeves with stones and threw themselves from the bridge into the river. The rest, who still yearned for life, gathered up their possessions and fled to the palace, where Archbishop Egilbert was staying, and tearfully pleaded for his protection. He seized this opportunity to admonish them to accept conversion. . . . After this admonition a rabbi named Micha stepped forward and asked the Archbishop for instruction, which the latter gave, explaining the Catholic faith. Thereupon Micha said: 'I call upon God for witness that I believe what you have declared and that I renounce Judaism; when the times have become more peaceful, I will investigate it all more closely. But now baptize us quickly, so that we escape our persecutors.' All the other Jews spoke similarly. Then the Archbishop baptized him and gave him his name, and the priests who were present baptized the rest. In the following year these others fell away from the faith again, whereas the Rabbi remained faithful to the Bishop and persisted in the faith." Metz also witnessed forced baptisms. In Regensburg Crusaders and citizens drove the Jewish families into the Danube, laid a wooden cross upon the water, and forced them to dip under it.

For three months cruelties and death were inflicted upon the Jewish Rhineland communities. "On the third day of the third month," a Jewish elegy runs, "there was no end of the lamentations. . . . I will pour forth torrents of tears over the dead of Speyer. . . . And I will bitterly bewail the community of Worms. . . . And let my lament sound for the victims of Mainz. . . ." From May to July of the year 1096 some twelve thousand Jews were killed in the Rhine provinces.

The Crusader bands moved into Bohemia, their trail marked by murders, pillaging, and forced baptisms. The Jews of Prague were dragged to baptism, and all who resisted were killed. When the baptized Jews of the Prague community began emigrating to Poland and Hungary, so that they could return openly to their religion, Bohemian Prince Vratislav II ordered that they be stripped of all their possessions. "You brought no riches with you from your Jerusalem to Bohemia," he declared. "Naked you came into the land, and naked you must leave it."

Meanwhile Emperor Henry IV had returned from Italy. Angry and filled with abhorrence for what had happened, he responded to the pleas of Moses ben Jekutiel of Speyer by ordaining that all Jews baptized by coercion should be permitted to return to Judaism with impunity. This act aroused the indignation of the Pope. "We have heard," Clement III wrote to the Bishop of Bamberg, "that the baptized Jews have been permitted to apostatize from the Church. This is something outrageous and sinful, and we require you and all Our brothers to ascertain that the Sacrament of the Church is not desecrated." But the Emperor refused to be swerved. Moreover, he began a strict investigation into the murder of Jews. Archbishop Ruthard and his men were punished because they had enriched themselves from the property of Mainz Jews.

The bloodbath that had so suddenly washed over the Jews after centuries of tranquillity and the hatred that had erupted from the ranks of their fellow citizens left permanent traces. For the first time a wide rift had opened between Jewry and Christendom in the West. Among the Jews, penitential prayers and elegies heavy with sorrow for the dead preserved the memory of this period of terror.

None of the irregular bands of Crusaders who had wreaked this havoc reached their goal, the Holy Land. They were scattered and annihilated en route. "After the atrocities they had committed," the Christian chronicler Albert of Aachen wrote, "Emicho, Clarenold, Thomas and this whole intolerable company of men and women, laden with Jewish booty, continued their journey to Jerusalem and marched toward Hungary. . . ." The Hungarian King's troops crushed them when they began to devastate the country. "All this," Albert of Aachen comments, "was surely God's hand against the pilgrims who had sinned before his face with lechery and shamelessness, and who had slaughtered the homeless Jews, enemies of Christ though they are, more out of greed than fear of God."

The main army of the Crusaders reached the Holy Land in three years. On July 15, 1099, Jerusalem fell. The "Franks," commanded by Godfrey of Bouillon, succeeded in storming the city after a six-week siege. All non-Christian inhabitants were slain. Moslems and Jews alike fell to the fury of the Christians. "The steam of blood rose to the knees of the riders, up to the reins of the horses, and the corpses of the slain were piled high in the streets." The Jews had barricaded themselves in their synagogue, but their resistance lasted only three days. Jerusalem became a Christian city, capital of the Kingdom of Jerusalem, whose power soon extended through Judea and Galilee and took in the coastal strip from Jaffa to Tyre. Many inhabitants of the Jewish communities in these regions emigrated to Egypt, others to Syria and Mesopotamia.

For almost half a century the Christians held fast in the land. Then Moslem warriors from Syria began seriously threatening the Kingdom of Jerusalem. In 1146 Pope Eugene III and St. Bernard of Clairvaux once more summoned Christendom to a Crusade. Emperor Conrad III declared his willingness to take the Cross. A papal bull promised that all who participated in the Holy War would be remitted their debts.

One of the most zealous sponsors of the new Crusade, Abbot Peter of Cluny, began to inveigh against the Jews. "Why should we seek the enemies of Christ in distant lands," he wrote to the King of France, "when the blasphemous Jews, who are much worse than the Saracens, live among us and revile Christ and Christian sanctities unpunished? . . . I do not demand that these accursed people be surrendered to death, for it is written: 'Thou shalt not kill!' God does not wish them to be exterminated; rather, like the fratricide Cain, they are to continue living in great torment and shame, so that life will be more bitter to them than death. They are dependent, wretched, oppressed, timid, and must remain so until they have turned to the way of salvation. You ought not to kill them, but to punish them in a manner befitting their baseness." He proposed that the property of the Jews be confiscated to finance the Crusade.

In the Rhineland, the monk Radulf went from city to city preaching the conversion or extermination of the Jews. "Avenge the Crucified One upon those of his enemies who live here in our midst, and then go to fight the Turks."

In August, 1146, this preaching yielded its first results: tumults and attacks on Jews in the Rhineland. In the vicinity of Cologne and Speyer an enraged mob killed several Jews. Even high ecclesiastics were helpless to check the viciousness. In Mainz, where Archbishop Henry I granted asylum to some persecuted Jews, the mob forced its way into his palace and killed them before his eyes. Bernard of Clairvaux vigorously opposed Radulf's incitements in a letter that he had distributed throughout France and Germany. But passions were already unleashed. It seemed as if nothing could calm the popular temper.

In Halle and Magdeburg Jewish families were driven from the cities. In Würzburg a horde of Crusaders attacked the Jewish population. More than twenty Jews were killed; the rest owed their lives to the Bishop of Würzburg, who sheltered them in his fortified palace.

In the spring of 1147 the persecutions spread to northern France. Jews in Ham, Sully-sur-Loire, and Carentan were slain. On May 8 gangs attacked the Jewish community in the town of Ramerupt. They stormed the house of the famous head of the French Jews, Rabbi Jacob Tam, plundered household goods, and tore the Holy Scriptures to shreds. Only energetic intervention by a knight prevented the mob from killing the Rabbi.

The Jews would have suffered far more but for the protection afforded by Emperor Conrad III and some princes of the Church. Cardinal Arnold, Bishop of Cologne, put the fortress of Wolkenburg near Königswinter, "the strongest castle in all of Lorraine," at the Jews' disposal and allowed them to arm themselves. The Emperor ordered that Jewish fugitives be given asylum in Nürnberg and other fortified cities. This was a necessity, for no Jew was safe on the highways. The Jews were able to breathe more easily only after the French and German Crusaders had departed in August, 1147.

With the Third Crusade (1189–1192) disaster befell the Jews of England who had entered the country in the train of William the Conqueror. In London, the first outbreak against them took place during the coronation ceremonies for Richard Cœur de Lion in Westminster Abbey. On Sunday, September 3, 1189, visitors, citizens of London, and Crusaders assembled in front of the Abbey to witness the coronation. Delegations arrived to salute the new monarch; among these were emissaries of the English Jews. They were suddenly stopped a few steps from the site of the coronation. Two of them who had already made their way through the crowd into the courtyard of the Abbey were beaten by the guards and thrown out again. A rumor spread among the onlookers that the King himself had ordered the Jewish representatives to be turned away. Excitement quickly spread throughout the city. Everywhere mobs fell upon the Jews, killing them, plundering and setting fire to their houses. Many important rabbis who had come for the coronation were killed, among them Rabbi Jacob of Orléans, a noted Talmud scholar.

The King did not hear about the bloody incidents until he was sitting down to the coronation banquet. He at once sent out messengers to bring the people to reason. But peace could not be restored until the following day. All through the night, in the glow of fires from burning houses and synagogues, the massacre continued. Outraged, Richard ordered strictest punishment of the guilty. But those responsible could not be found.

Richard's subsequent proclamation that the Jews must not be molested was of no avail. What had happened in the capital was repeated in the provincial towns. In Norwich, Bury, Stamford, Dunstable, Lynn, and other towns, bands of Crusaders and local inhabitants participated in excesses against Jewish communities. A hostile temper toward the Jews spread through all of England; much of the populace became infected by fanaticism.

No sooner had the King left England in 1190 to join the Crusading army than a new wave of persecution broke over the Jews of York. When the attacks began in this northern English city, the threatened Jews sought refuge in the royal castle. Crusaders and citizens laid siege to the castle until the last supplies of food inside the walls were exhausted. Then the elders conferred about the hopeless situation. Rabbi Yom Tov ben Isaac of Joigny said to his fellows: "It is plainly the will of the God of our

Fathers that we do die for his holy Law. And lo, death is at our door, as you see. . . . Since, then, we ought to prefer a glorious death to a life of deepest shame, we must choose the most honorable and easiest kind of death; for if we fall into their hands we shall die in mockery at their arbitrary choice. Therefore, since our Creator Himself now asks again for that life which He gave us, let us render it willingly and devoutly back with our own hands, nor let us await the ministration of our enemies' cruelty to restore that which God demands. For many of our race in their many tribulations are known to have acted in this praiseworthy fashion, providing us with the example of a most fitting choice."

On March 17, 1190, on the night of the "great Sabbath, the Rabbi and most of the members of the York community parted with their lives. Fathers slew their wives and children and then killed themselves. Next morning the doors were opened. The castle was deathly still—scarcely a living soul was left inside it.

William Longchamp, Richard's Chancellor and administrator of the kingdom in his absence, ordered an investigation. But it proved fruitless; the agitators and Crusaders had vanished and could no longer be located.

"No nation has ever undergone such sufferings for God," the French Scholastic Peter Abelard wrote in 1135. "Scattered among all the nations, having neither king nor secular prince, the Jews are oppressed with heavy taxes as if they must buy their lives anew every day. To mistreat Jews is regarded as work pleasing to God. For Christians can only explain such imprisonment as the Jews suffer as the result of God's hatred of them. The lives of the Jews are in the hands of their fiercest foes. Even in sleep they are not spared terrifying dreams. Except for heaven, they have no safe refuge. When they wish to travel to the nearest town, they must pay large sums of money to buy the protection of the Christian princes who, in truth, desire their death in order to seize their inheritance. The Jews are not permitted to own fields and vineyards because there is no one to guarantee their possession. Thus the only livelihood that remains to them is usury, and this, in turn, excites the hatred of the Christians."

Abelard, who thus compassionately depicted the lot of the harried Jews, remained a voice crying in the wilderness. Persecuted himself by the Church, he could sympathize with the victims of persecution. But he went unheard. The religious passions and fanaticism that had been stirred by the wars against the unbelievers did not subside; indeed, they intensified to proportions hitherto unknown in the Western world. The Crusades were followed by the darkest period of the Middle Ages for the Jews—

three centuries in which the centers of Jewry throughout Western Europe were destroyed.

Within less than a century after the First Crusade, all the successes of the Occident had been eroded. The holy war against the Christian Kingdom of Jerusalem, proclaimed by Saladin, ended in victory for the Moslems. The defeat of the Crusaders at the Battle of Tiberias delivered almost all of Christian Palestine into Saladin's hand. On October 2, 1187, the warriors of the Prophet entered Jerusalem.

The Third Crusade, led by three monarchs—Frederick Barbarossa, Richard Cœur de Lion, and Philip Augustus of France—did not succeed in reconquering the lost territory. Acre alone, after a bloody battle, was retaken, and the Christians re-established a foothold in the coastal area.

Petahia ben Jacob of Regensburg, the great traveler and travel writer, had encountered a single Jewish family when he visited Jerusalem a few years before—between 1175 and 1180. "As soon as the Ishmaelites conquered the city, it filled with Israelites also," wrote the poet Jehudah Alharisi, who made a pilgrimage to the Holy City after Saladin's conquest of it. "Why did not the Jews settle here when the city was in the hands of the Christians?" he asked a returning Jew, and was informed: "Because they were always saying that we had killed their God and had offended them. If they could have seized us here, they would have devoured us alive." But after the "Ishmaelite king" took Jerusalem, "his cry rang out everywhere: Let all of the descendants of Ephraim who wish to do so return to the city from Ashur [Mesopotamia] and Mizraim [Egypt], and from all the places whither they have wandered." Under Moslem protection a sizable Jewish community once again gathered in Jerusalem. Some three hundred rabbis from France and England immigrated into Palestine in 1211. Sultan Aladil, Saladin's brother, received them with honor and permitted them to build new synagogues and schools in Jerusalem. Talmudic scholarship, the keen methods of Tossafism so highly developed in the heart of Europe, had now been transplanted to the Orient.

Once again the Christian hosts set forth. But the fourth and last of the great Crusades changed its destination. The fleet equipped by Venice landed the soldiers of the Latin West on the Bosporus. In a bloody fraternal struggle Latin Christendom defeated and subjugated Greek Christendom. Constantinople was taken by storm in April, 1204, and a Latin Empire was founded on the Golden Horn.

BADGES AND LAWS FOR JEWS

The long and violent struggle between the two universal powers, the spiritual and the secular, ended after the Crusades with the decisive victory of the Roman pontificate over the empire. The papacy had reached the summit of its power; the Holy See sought, often successfully, to impose its will upon all monarchs and princes as well as their subjects. Innocent III, who wore the tiara from 1198 to 1216, dominated Europe with an iron hand during his papacy.

"Innocent," a Byzantine concluded, with some exaggeration, "was the successor not to Peter but to Constantine." The decisions made in Rome during this period determined events and life in the Christian West for a long time afterward—and especially concerning the lives of the Jews. For the triumph of the Church wreaked more hardship upon the Jews of Europe than upon any other groups.

Pope Innocent III had used the power of the Church to wage a Crusade within Europe itself against the Albigensians—a war that led to the founding of the Inquisition and the burning of heretics. This Pope, with a host of papal legates and a legion of secular and monastic clergy at his command, was the creator of an ecclesiastical policy that more and more narrowed down the possibility for Jews to survive. As a consequence of that policy the Jews were degraded to the lowest class in society, debased to a pariah group within the Christian order. "The goal was not the extermination of the Jew as a human being," Professor Karl Thieme has pointed out. "Rather, it was to make the Jew regret his persistence in his religion until he abandoned it, or else to punish him for his 'obstinacy' in clinging to it."

At the beginning of his reign Innocent, like his predecessors, while clearly not favoring the Jews, took them under his protection. In 1199, when violence on the part of Crusaders had again become a common occurrence, he issued a bull declaring that the Jews were neither to be baptized by force nor robbed, injured, or killed without the process of law. They were not to be molested on their feast days, and their cemeteries were to be respected.

But even the opening phrases of the bull undermined the total effect and contrasted strongly with the phraseology of all his predecessors. The initial formula since Gregory the Great had been: *"Sicut Judaeis non debeat esse licentia . . ."* Now it ran: *"Licet perfidia Judaeorum sit multipliciter improbanda . . ."* "Although the false doctrine of the Jews is in many ways to be condemned, believers must nevertheless not oppress them too greatly, for through them the truth of our own faith is confirmed."

In his messages addressed to bishops and secular rulers, a stern policy toward the Jews emerged more and more clearly. "The Jews, like the fratricide Cain, are doomed to wander over the earth as fugitives and vagabonds and to cover their faces in shame," he wrote in 1208 to the Count of Nevers, who had been displaying kindness toward the Jews. "Christian princes are in no circumstances to show them favor, but, on the contrary, to reduce them to serfdom. Wrongly do those Christian rulers act who admit the Jews into their cities and villages and avail themselves of their usurious services to extract money from the Christian populace. It even happens that these rulers arrest Christians for neglecting payments to Jewish creditors, and, what is worst of all, tolerate it that in this way the Church loses her tithe." Innocent III strongly reproved King Philip Augustus of France for having recalled Jews who had been previously expelled. The Pope protested indignantly that church goods were pawned to Jews and that the Jews were permitted to employ Christian servants and workmen.

The Crusade in southern France against the Albigensians, who rejected the papacy and the Catholic Church, also smote the Jewish communities. In Béziers, one of the centers of "heresy," the Crusaders summoned by the Pope set a record for savagery. Legate Arnold, a Cistercian monk, wrote to Innocent, "We regarded neither estate, nor sex, nor age; almost twenty thousand of the citizens were put to the sword. After the great slaughter the city was pillaged and burned, and divine vengeance raged within it in wondrous wise." Even orthodox Catholics had not been spared. Whether or not the Crusaders really asked the Legate how to distinguish heretics from Catholics, and whether or not Arnold really answered, "Kill them all, God will know his own," almost all were killed. Certainly Jews could expect little mercy in these circumstances. Two hundred of them, their own chronicle relates, were killed; many were led into captivity.

For three decades the holy war against the heretics raged. It was conducted on the intellectual as well as the military front. A ban was placed upon philosophical writings from Spain; among them were the works of Gabirol. Ancient canons of the Church that applied to the Jews, some of them dating back to the time of the Merovingians, were revived in 1209 at the Council of Avignon. From Spain to England the Jews felt the heavy hand of the Pope. And worse was in the offing. The Jews heard with apprehension the news that sped rapidly through all the countries of Europe: Innocent III had summoned the Church hierarchy to a Council in Rome. Jews remembered only too well the Lateran Council of 1179.

It had accused the Jews of co-operating with the heretical Albigensians and had revived the ancient anti-Jewish laws of the Early Christian Church, which had fallen into desuetude for seven centuries. Once again Jews were strictly forbidden to employ Christians, and Christians were forbidden to enter the service of Jews. These prohibitions extended even to midwives and nurses for the sick. "Believers" were not to be allowed to live among "unbelievers"—the first step toward the future ghettos.

The fears of the Jews proved justified—the new Council went much farther than its predecessor. The Fourth Lateran Council of 1215 prepared the way for the downfall of Jewish communities throughout Europe. It forbade Jews to practice Christian occupations—thus forcing them into total isolation from Christian society. "The Jews were branded as a species of submen," Professor Edmund Schopen has commented, "who, to be sure, were not to be persecuted by violence, but with whom Christians were not permitted to associate."

The rule that Islam in its early, fanatic phase had imposed upon all "misbelievers" in the Orient, both Jews and Christians, was now taken up by Innocent III at the Fourth Lateran Council and imposed upon Jews in the Christian West. One canon prescribed that Jews, "whether men or women, must in all Christian countries distinguish themselves from the rest of the population in public places by a special kind of clothing." The reason given for this was to prevent "criminal" sexual intercourse between Christians and Jews. "So that," the text declared, "henceforth in case of such criminal intercourse no mistake can be alleged as an excuse." In November, 1215, a papal bull gave these decisions of the Council the force of canon law.

The dreadful Jewish badge had been created—that dishonoring sign which for six centuries was to expose the Jews to public contempt everywhere they went in Europe.

The bull confined itself merely to ordering the distinguishing mark. The legislators of each country were to execute this decree as they saw fit. Princes and provincial councils henceforth discussed the type, shape, and color of the identifying mark. The most bizarre badges were devised. Two of Innocent's successors, Popes Gregory IX and Innocent IV, repeatedly reminded rulers to pay strict attention to the requirement and to allow no exceptions to the wearing of badges. Gradually, these "Cain's marks" became a common sight in all of Europe, their wearers identifiable everywhere at a distance.

England chose a badge depicting two stone tablets inscribed with the Ten Commandments. In France, St. Louis ordered a badge to be made of red felt or saffron-yellow cloth, cut in the shape of a wheel and worn on the upper garment, one in front and one in back, "so that those thus branded may be recognized from all sides." In vain the Jewish communities, especially those of southern France, which enjoyed the respect of their neighbors, attempted to resist the humiliating sign. But a contemporary remarks that they could not do so for long. "Our people felt the heavy hand of the judges, who made investigations everywhere in Provence and extorted much money. Many fine persons in Marseilles and Avignon were compelled to display badges on their clothing in public. From this the Jews of Avignon especially suffered a great deal."

Germany instituted the *rotella,* a patch of yellow cloth in the shape of a wheel or an O. In some countries a simple badge was considered inadequate, and the wearing of a hat of a specified color was also prescribed. The synod of Vienna in 1267 forced the Jews to wear especially humiliating headgear; the *cornutus pileus,* a high, pointed—and, moreover, horned—cap, so that Jews could be recognized at a distance. The effects of the Council's decision were felt far to the East; in 1279 the Buda synod decreed a badge consisting of a wheel of red cloth for Hungary and southern Poland.

The Jewish badge and Jewish cap were not the end of it. Other ordinances designed to humiliate Jews in public were devised. In some places it was regarded as the privilege of the rabble to pelt the Jews with stones at Easter; in other places, representatives of the Jewish community were made to accept blows or slaps in public at this season. In Crete Jewish houses, too, had their special mark. Jewish communities were frequently expected to provide a man for the ugly task of public executioner; the Jewish cemetery often became the site of the gallows. Jews were forbidden to enter public baths, or admitted only on the days reserved for prostitutes.

As if all these indignities and humiliations were not sufficient misfortune, the Jews also entered a period of frightful economic distress. As a result of the Lateran Council they lost all "positions of authority." Gradually, they were driven out of all important open occupations. Trades they had followed for centuries were closed to them, until at last they arrived at the lowest step on the social ladder, tolerated only in occupations universally execrated—as peddlers and small pawnbrokers.

Since the days of the Roman Empire Jews had been active in agriculture, commerce, and crafts. Thanks to techniques brought from their homeland in the Orient, they had made important contributions to European agriculture in the cultivation of the vine and the olive, in methods of irrigation. They had introduced Far Eastern spices and Chinese silks to Europe and had demonstrated new ways of bleaching and dyeing cloth.

Their ships had imported sugar and rice, grain and fine woods. They had, as we have seen, enriched European culture by their own works and by their translations.

But all these contributions now counted for nothing. Christian society no longer had any place for them. No Jew could henceforth practice a Christian occupation. That meant the end of all previous ways by which Jews had earned their livelihood. A profound social upheaval began for Jewry.

They were driven from agriculture, in which they had been active ever since the time of the great migrations. Forbidden to hire labor, they had to abandon the land. Moreover, they were soon everywhere hampered by the additional decrees making it illegal for a Jew to possess any land as freehold property. In the cities, too, their chances for livelihood were reduced to a minimum. The guilds determined who could engage in any artisan's work, and what prices the artisan must buy and sell for. Only Christians could be members of guilds. The towns' Jewish ordinances became lengthy lists that grew steadily longer. Sometimes religious scruples, but more often the desire to eliminate Jewish competition, determined the new regulations. Jewish merchants and traders had been forced out of their lucrative field ever since the Crusades. The vastly increasing exchange of goods with the Orient had been seized by the Italian commercial republics. Venice refused to admit Jewish merchants and even forbade the transport of goods belonging to Jews. Rabbi Jacob Tam was speaking only literal truth when he lamented: "We have been left with no trade for earning our living and paying the great taxes that kings and princes impose upon us."

As occupation after occupation was closed to the Jews, as they were more and more excluded from Christian society, there remained to them only one activity, which Christianity theoretically despised, regarding it as wicked and sinful: the lending of money at interest.

The Church's campaign against the taking of interest had reached a climax at the Third Lateran Council in 1179. The Council threatened every Christian who dared to lend money at interest with refusal of Christian burial. Irrespective of the interest rate, all such lending was condemned as "usury." Only non-Christians could skirt the consequences of this condemnation.

Until the twelfth century the chief moneylenders had been Syrian merchants and monasteries. Now these two groups had either to withdraw entirely from the money market or, if they preferred evasion, as they frequently did, to avail themselves of non-Christian intermediaries—in other words, Jews. Henceforth Jews took over the functions of supplying credit, which even the most primitive society or economy requires. For the Jews, in their hopeless predicament, the lending of money offered a broad field of activity, although one that was new to them.

They by no means had any natural inclination toward this occupation. Classical antiquity offers few examples of Jewish financiers. In Europe Jews were almost unknown in this field before the end of the eleventh century. One of the first Jewish loans mentioned in historical sources occurs in 1107: In order to ransom Duke Svatopluk, who had been imprisoned by Emperor Henry V, the Bishop of Prague pledged valuable church utensils in pawn to Jews of Regensburg.

From the religious point of view there were objections to this new type of enterprise. The Bible strictly condemned the exacting of interest (Exodus 22:24). In the Talmud this ban had been extended by the commentators; initially, it affected even the profit from commercial ventures in which a person invested his capital without himself actively taking part in the enterprise. The occupation of usurer was condemned as wickedness by the Talmudic lawgivers. One Talmudic maxim states: "Usury works just like the bite of a serpent, which is not felt until the bitten place has swollen; usury, too, gives pain only when it has already swollen and increased." There were other maxims of the Talmud to the same effect: "He who lends money at interest and he who receives it commit the same sin," "Gamblers and usurers may not be heard as witnesses in court." The Talmud even cautioned against lending money at interest even to those outside the faith—this despite the clear stipulation in Deuteronomy 23:21: "Unto a foreigner thou mayest lend upon interest; but unto thy brother thou shalt not lend upon interest. . . ."

In Europe this antagonistic attitude toward taking interest, and especially toward making a business of it, had been retained throughout Jewry. The *Sefer Chassidim,* the *Book of the Devout* (thirteenth century), stated the general viewpoint: "If anyone has another means of livelihood he ought not to lend money at interest." The rabbinical authorities looked askance upon moneylending. But they finally had to yield to the difficulty of the times, for in all Christian countries except Spain and southern Italy the Jews were more and more forced, in spite of their inner resistance, to become dependent on moneylending as an occupation.

Although the field was new to them, they once again displayed their remarkable versatility and talent. European trade and a mercantile economy were expanding in the wake of the Crusades, and the Jews began to fulfill a function of tremendous importance for the time, and for the future. "As in all the fields of endeavor into which the Jews entered," Edmund Schopen comments, "in this one, too, they developed the germinating money system into a new branch of the economy, well organized and rational. Thus the Jews in late medieval Europe became the founders of the banking system. . . . Nevertheless, even though they had thus shifted course, the same fate awaited them. After the Jews had transformed such dealings from the despised and disgraceful doings of the 'usurer' to a regular profession that filled an important role in the economy, and . . . after they had developed the methods of finance and banking despite continuous risks, the merchants of northern Italy imitated them, and with the immensely larger capital resources of their 'Lombard' community took over the large transactions, which yielded enormous profits, so that the Jews had to remain content with insignificant small loans to the petty nobility and burghers."

As givers of credit the Jews became indispensable to the dignitaries of Church and State. They financed the wars and building projects of sovereigns. The Church, which had pronounced so sharply against the taking of interest and hence condemned the Jews as "sinners," gladly and frequently availed itself of their services. In England nine Cistercian monasteries, the cathedrals of Lincoln and Peterborough, and the Abbey of St. Albans were built, thanks to loans granted by Aaron of Lincoln.

The dominance of Jews in the world of finance reached its pinnacle in the thirteenth century. But there were grim aspects to the picture. The sovereigns who were both their patrons and their clients began to regard them as inexhaustible sources of money, and to fleece them mercilessly. Moreover, their legal position deteriorated. After the Crusades the Jews in Germany, who had at one time been as free as any other members of the population, sank legally to the status of "things." They became property, just as animals had been first in Roman law and subsequently in the legal system of those European countries which adopted Roman law, or parts of it.

Originally, the Jews had possessed the privileges of foreigners. They were accorded special rights like other groups in the population, like the clergy and the merchants. As we have seen, they enjoyed the protection of rulers and from the time of Louis the Pious on held charters or letters confirming that status. But in the twelfth century this situation began to change, and the change for the worse continued in the thirteenth. Frederick Barbarossa had declared that the Jews under his protection belonged to "our exchequer." Under Frederick II they became sheer property. In 1236 he declared them *servi camerae* (servants of the chamber), which usually meant the treasury of the king's private household. They were, in a sense, chattels who could be dealt with as their possessor thought fit. They could be taxed; their property could be confiscated at any time, and the rights held in them could be disposed of or lent, sold, pawned, or given away. This was not mere theory; the German emperors did in fact deal with the Jews they owned as if they were personal property. In the policy of monarchs who were rapidly consolidating their strength, this royal prerogative proved to be a highly useful instrument.

Unfortunately for the *servi camerae,* the financial demands of three masters—emperor, local lord, and town—gave them no peace. Economically, they were forced to the wall. To add to unbearable burdens, the Church entered the field, demanding its tithe from the Jews. Thus the Jews became a constantly drained source of income, repeatedly forced to raise new sums, of which they themselves were permitted to retain only a fraction. All secular and ecclesiastical magnates who had the funds to be creditors, if only temporarily, were indirect participants in their banking and loan affairs. This situation inevitably proved the nemesis of the Jews. The more the lower nobility and urban patricians fell into debt to them, the more unpopular they became. The populace in any case had no comprehension of the vital part played by the Jews as providers of credit. The resentment fostered by indebtedness soon turned to hatred and inevitably led to violence. Naked economic motives often lay behind the assaults upon Jewish communities; religious zeal was frequently mere pretext. Quite often the attackers were the very ones who owed large sums to their victims. Massacres were often followed by destruction of the promissory notes kept in the homes of the "usurers." If the Jewish creditor was killed, and the note burned, the debtor had gained both the borrowed money and the interest.

The Jews of France and England were subject to the worst exploitation. One Sabbath day, January 19, 1180, Philip Augustus of France had all the Jews arrested; they were conveniently assembled in their synagogues. Their property and all their valuables were confiscated and they themselves were cast into prisons. They were released only after they had raised a huge ransom. This extortion was merely a prelude. That same year the King annulled all the claims of Jewish creditors. The Christian debtors, however, had to pay a fifth of the sums they owed into the royal treasury. A hermit of Vincennes, so it was said, had persuaded the King to take this step as an act pleasing to God. For the Jews it meant complete ruin; the King had reduced them to beggary. But Philip Augustus went a step further: His edict of 1182 banished all Jews from the Crown lands. They were permitted to sell only their movable goods, and to take the proceeds with them. All their real property—houses, fields, and vineyards—the King himself appropriated. He gave the abandoned synagogues to the Church to be transformed into Christian houses of worship. Sixteen years later, in 1198, Philip Augustus readmitted the Jews.

England's rulers put their exploitation of the Jews on a systematic basis. By royal decree, all financial transactions had to be registered with the Exchequer of the Jews. Copies of all deeds of indebtedness were deposited here. The business enterprises of the Jews as well as their whole fortunes were subject to strict state control. Thus, even if records were lost in the course of attacks on Jewish communities, the royal exchequer would suffer no loss.

John Lackland (King from 1199 to 1216) granted the Jews extensive liberties in a charter of 1201—in return for payment of a sizable sum. But his attitude soon changed, and he began squeezing the Jews dry, stopping at neither imprisonment nor torture to obtain money from them. In 1210 he imposed upon English Jewry a tribute amounting to the tremendous sum of sixty-six thousand marks—roughly equivalent, in present-day purchasing power, to one million and seven hundred and sixty thousand dollars. Wealthy Abraham of Bristol was commanded to deliver ten thousand marks of silver. When he refused, the King ordered that each day another of the unfortunate man's teeth should be broken out. After a week of such torture, he yielded.

Under Henry III (who reigned from 1216 to 1272) the position of the Jews deteriorated to the point of complete economic ruin. The ruler supported his extravagance by exacting repeated subsidies from the Jewish communities. Tribute followed upon tribute, and the Jews were given no breathing space in which to recover. The special tax rose from four thousand marks in 1226 to six thousand in 1230 and eighteen thousand in 1252. In 1239 an edict was issued requiring every Jew to surrender a third of his wealth. In 1241 a Jewish "parliament" was summoned to Worcester in order, as it was put, "to confer with the King on all matters concerning his and their interests." In fact, the assembled elders of the Jewish communities were informed that they had to pay the King an extra twenty thousand marks, and that each of them would be held personally responsible for the raising of this sum. Many were imprisoned along with their families until the money was delivered. Ultimately, the predicament of the English Jews became so intolerable that they saw emigration as their only hope. In 1254 Elias of London presented himself to the King's brother, Richard of Cornwall, on behalf of his fellow Jews. "It is evident to us," he said, "that our lord the King wishes to destroy us. We therefore implore him in God's name to permit us to go hence, granting us a safe-conduct for departure from his kingdom. . . . We wish to go away and never return, abandoning our houses and possessions here. . . . It cannot be unknown to the King that he is asking of us something that with the best will we cannot perform even if he were to have our eyes put out, our throats cut, and our hands cut off." The plea was refused. The King had no intention of letting the Jews, seemingly so inexhaustible a source of income, depart from his lands.

CHARGES OF RITUAL MURDER

One of the most monstrous and fateful of charges against the Jews, deriving from pagan times, suddenly reappeared in the Christian West: the false accusation of ritual murder.

Once upon a time the Romans had accused the early Christians of murdering children in order to use their blood for ritual purposes. Among the unsophisticated masses of the Roman Empire the tale had been believed. Now it suddenly began to haunt all of Europe, this time directed against the Jews.

The chronicles of England record the earliest case. In 1146 the Jews of Norwich were accused of having kidnaped, tortured, and killed a Christian boy before the Passover. But for the time being this remained an isolated fantasy. It was only after the tragedy that took place in the French city of Blois that such slanderous charges developed into a veritable mass psychosis.

Late one evening a groom was leading his horse down to the Loire to drink. As chance would have it, a Jew, suddenly appearing before him in the darkness, gave him a terrible fright. The superstitious groom ran to the prefect of the city with a wild story of having seen the Jew throw the body of a Christian boy into the river. Count Theobald of Chartres, informed of the alleged incident, ordered all Jews in the town to be taken into custody. On the advice of a priest, there was a thorough investigation. The judges decided to let a trial by water decide the case. The groom was placed in a boat filled with holy water, and the boat was pushed out on the Loire. Because it did not sink, the truth of the charge was considered proved. The town's Jews were dragged to a wooden tower, around which faggots were piled. A herald announced that any who wished to be baptized would be pardoned. None spoke up. On May 26, 1171, the fire was kindled; thirty-four men and sixteen women were burned alive in the tower. Their last song sounded from the flames; dying, they sang the prayer Alenu.

News of this frightful event came as a crushing blow to all Jews. Rabbi Jacob Tam declared the day the martyrs of Blois had been burned a day of mourning and fasting to be observed annually by the Jewish communities of France, England, and the Rhineland. It was as if the Jews had a premonition that there were more such horrors to come.

Before long, the accusation was raised in many places in Germany and Austria. In the winter of 1181, near Vienna, three boys who had been playing on the frozen river vanished. All searches proved vain. Then several Christians came forward and swore that they had seen Jews lure the boys into a house and slaughter them. The Jews were tried; three hundred died at the stake. When the ice melted in the spring, the bodies of the drowned children were fished out of the Danube, intact.

In 1199 the slander claimed more victims in Erfurt. In 1235 members of the Jewish communities in Lauda and Bischofsheim, charged with the same crime, ended on the scaffold. The end of that year was marked by a particularly sinister tragedy. Near Fulda on Christmas Eve a miller who had gone to town with his wife came back to find his house burned down. The charred bodies of his five children were found in the ruins. Crusaders had just turned up in Fulda, and the rumor spread swiftly that two Jews had killed the miller's children in order to use their blood in medicines; then, to cover the traces, they had set fire to the house after their crime. People claimed to have seen them making off with the blood in leather pouches. Thirty-two Jews of the Fulda community were arrested and tortured until two of them provided the desired "confession." Three days later, without waiting for further trials, the Crusaders killed all the arrested men. Emperor Frederick II happened to be staying in nearby Haguenau. The remains of the children were brought to him to demonstrate the alleged crime of the Jews. The Emperor realized the folly of the charge, and commanded: "Since the children have died, let them be buried." But in order to calm the people, whose excitement had risen dangerously at the sight of the bodies of the "holy martyrs," he ordered an official investigation. A commission consisting of secular and ecclesiastical lords—bishop, monks, dukes, and counts—looked into the case. After making thorough inquiries they came to the following decision:

"Neither in the Old nor in the New Testament is there any text to show that the Jews desire human blood. On the contrary, they guard themselves against being tainted by any blood at all. This is evident from the book that in Hebrew is called Berechet ["Bereshith," the first word of Genesis, used to signify the first book of the Pentateuch], and is in harmony with the prescripts of Moses from the laws that in Hebrew are called Talmillot [Talmud]. There is little likelihood that those to whom even the blood of clean animals is forbidden would have any taste for human blood. Against this charge are its frightfulness, its unnaturalness, and the natural human feeling the Jews display toward Christians also. Moreover, it is not probable that they would risk their lives and property. We have therefore declared the Jews of Fulda . . . completely innocent of the crime with which they have been charged."

In July, 1236, Emperor Frederick confirmed the conclusion of the investigators. A copy of the decision was placed in the archives of the city of Cologne, where it has remained to this day. Frederick pronounced all the Jews of Germany innocent of the charge, and forbade everyone to repeat the slanderous allegation. But even the imperial command could not prevent further dissemination of the baleful calumny. Unsolved murders of Christians continued to lead to vicious assaults upon the Jewish communities living in the vicinity. Quite often murderers would carry the bodies of their victims to Jewish houses to divert suspicion from themselves.

Avarice went hand in hand with superstition when charges of blood crimes were raised against the Jews. That is evident from a papal letter of the period. On July 5, 1247, Innocent IV addressed a circular letter on the subject to the archbishops and bishops of Germany.

"We have heard the fervent supplications of the Jews," Innocent wrote, "that some ecclesiastical and secular dignitaries, as well as other noblemen and officials in your towns and dioceses, have invented godless accusations against the Jews, using these as a pretext to plunder them and to seize their possessions. These persons seem to have forgotten that the testimony for the Christian religion is found precisely in the ancient writings of the Jews. Whereas Holy Scripture commands, 'Thou shalt not kill,' and even forbids them to touch the dead on the Passover, Christians are raising against Jews the false accusation that on this festival they eat the heart of a murdered child. If the corpse of a person killed by an unknown hand is found anywhere, the death is ascribed to the Jews, with evil intent. All this is only a pretext to persecute them in the cruelest fashion. Without judicial investigation, without any legal conviction of the accused or their confession, indeed, in disregard of the privileges graciously granted to the Jews by the Holy See, they are godlessly and unjustly robbed of their property, subjected to the pangs of hunger, imprisonment, and other tortures, and condemned to a shameful death. In the power of such princes and rulers the Jews have to suffer far more than did their ancestors under the pharaohs in Egypt. Because of such persecutions these unfortunates find themselves compelled to leave those places where their forefathers were settled from ancient times. Fearing total extermination, they have now appealed to the Holy See for protection. Since We do not wish unjust torments to be inflicted on the Jews, whose conversion God in His mercy is still expecting, We command you to treat them amicably and benevolently. If in the future you hear of such illegal oppressions, see to it that the law is obeyed and do not permit any persons to molest the Jews unjustly."

But this papal remonstrance proved equally vain. The terrible accusation continued to spread. Even among scholars there were those who believed the charge of the Jews' blood-guilt. The Dominican Thomas of Cantimpré, a pupil of Albertus Magnus, was one of them. In 1263, in his much-read book on bees, *Bonum universale de apibus,* he asserted that the Jews would continue to spill the blood of Christians every year. Because, when Jesus stood before Pilate, they had called Christ's blood down upon themselves and their children, God had punished them with an ugly flow of blood which only stopped when they converted to Christianity. But they believed that they could be freed of their secret ailment if Christian blood were spilled.

Some secular rulers opposed the libel as vigorously as the Popes. Respected rabbis were given opportunities to refute it publicly; Christian theologians systematically demonstrated its untruth. But neither warnings nor threats, neither imperial prescripts nor papal bulls helped, nor did all the efforts at enlightenment. In 1283 the ritual murder lie turned up in Mainz. Two years later the Munich rabble did not wait for the results of an investigation into such a charge; they massacred all the Jews they could lay hands on. A hundred and eighty persons who had fled into the synagogue were burned along with the building. In Erfurt, Colmar, Krems, Magdeburg, and Weissenburg, in Paris, Bern, Würzburg, and Poznan, in Prague, Trent, Boppard, Budweis, and many other places, thousands of Jews died, the victims of psychosis and superstition. Some fifty alleged ritual murders, each of which took its toll in the blood of the Jewish community, have been recorded up to the end of the fifteenth century alone—and the records are indubitably incomplete. And as Cecil Roth has remarked, the relics of the alleged victims were venerated by the populace. Miracles were attributed to them at their shrines.

The fantastic accusation lived on into the twentieth century, when even in supposedly civilized states Jews could still be charged with ritual murder.

DISPUTATIONS AND TALMUD BURNINGS

Jewry suddenly found itself exposed to a burst of increasingly violent and passionate attacks. The entire Christian world in Europe seemed to be conspiring against the minority living in its midst. Along with outbreaks of crude violence, often inspired by the most senseless rumors and either subsiding or leading unpredictably to fresh persecutions, the struggle against the intellectual aspects of Judaism also intensified. Even where the Jews as individuals were spared, their sacred books might not be.

There had always been religious disputations between Jews and Christians. The tradition for these had never quite ceased since the latter days of classical antiquity—in spite of the ban on formal arguments over religion, which Emperor Justinian included in his famous collection of laws. Such disputations were conducted publicly, and often tolerantly; both sides presented their arguments freely, and no coercion was imposed upon the Jewish debater, even where questions of Christian dogmas and the messiahship of Jesus were involved.

On both the Christian and the Jewish side a whole apologetic literature arose, often in the form of a dialogue with a fictitious opponent. The Christian theologian Rupert of Deutz wrote a well-known *Dialogue Between a Jew and a Christian* in which "the Jew, as well as he is able, refutes the Christian from the letter and the meaning of the Law. . . ." Among the works of Joseph Kimhi, the great Provençal grammarian, was a handbook intended for disputations with members of other religions and baptized Jews "who try to distort and twist the meaning of Holy Scripture by symbolic interpretation in the Christian spirit."

With the onset of the thirteenth century this spirit of free inquiry changed. Verbal battles were suddenly settled by physical arguments. More than once rabbis were beaten by excited crowds. Consequently, the Jews began to avoid public dialogue with Christians. The *Sefer Chassidim* (*Book of the Devout*) explicitly warned against Jewish participation in such disputations.

But the Church, too, was no longer interested in debates with the Jews—although for a different reason. It had been demonstrated all too frequently that many members of the Christian clergy could not cope with the arguments of their Jewish adversaries. In the Rhineland in 1227 uneducated priests—*sacerdotes illiterati*—were forbidden to engage in religious discussions with Jews. Similar ordinances were issued in Vienna, Freising, and Bamberg. In 1233 Pope Gregory IX issued a general ban forbidding Jews to challenge Christians to disputations; the stated reason for this ban was "so that simple folk will not be led into error."

The Dominicans, however, who were in charge of the Church's struggle against heresy and dissent, went over to the offensive. In France they staged a trial of the Talmud.

The affair began in 1239 when Nicholas Donin, an apostate Jew who had become a Dominican monk, denounced the Talmud to Gregory IX.

The book, he asserted, contained vilifications of Jesus and of Christians, as well as immoral doctrines. Donin drew up a tract of thirty-five articles summarizing the "errors, blasphemies, and defamations" of the Talmud. He presented his tract to the head of the Church in Rome.

The Pope ordered an investigation. He charged the bishops of France and England, Castile and Aragon, to confiscate all copies of the Talmud in their lands, and to hold a trial. In England and Spain the papal request was disregarded. But in the France of Louis IX—St. Louis—the Jewish communities were compelled, under threats of dire punishment, to deliver up their books. On June 24, 1240, the trial of the Talmud began in Paris, in the presence of Queen Mother Blanche. The panel of judges consisted of bishops and Dominican monks. The verdict was foredoomed: The Talmud was proclaimed a blasphemous, harmful book and sentenced to burning.

For two years the Jews were able to delay execution of this sentence. But in 1242 the burning was held at last. Twenty-four carts piled high with volumes of the Talmud were taken out to a public square in Paris and the precious loads were consigned to the flames. Rabbi Meïr ben Baruch of Rothenburg wrote an elegy that became part of the liturgy: "Ask, you who have been consumed by the fire, what has become of those who shed tears over your terrible lot . . . ?" In Jewish communities the world over, the flaming death of the sacred books was lamented.

Innocent IV, Gregory's successor, was not yet content. "Give orders," he wrote to St. Louis in 1244, "that these books be consigned to the flames throughout your entire kingdom, wherever they are found." The hunt for Talmudic volumes was resumed; after Paris, the Jewish communities in the French provinces had to surrender their books. In 1248 a commission of censors met once again. Among its members was the famous Dominican Albertus Magnus. Once more the Talmud was condemned; once more the public pyres consumed quantities of confiscated books and tracts.

Across the Pyrenees in Aragon, which had become one of the strongholds of the order, the Dominicans attempted a different type of offensive. They decided that they would be able to force the Jews to abandon their religion. A Dominican convert from Judaism, Paulus Christiani (Fra Pablo), persuaded King James I to organize a religious disputation. An official invitation was sent out to "Rabbi Moses ben Nahman, Master of the Jews of Gerona," called Nahmanides, one of the greatest Talmud scholars of his age, and a cabalist also.

The disputation began on July 20, 1263, in Barcelona, in the presence of the King and his nobles, and of bishops and monks. For five days it went on, shifting from palace to synagogue and back, and at times being held—the clergy were so sure of their cause—in a public square before the assembled populace.

Three subjects had been proposed for the debate. Among them was the key question of whether the Messiah had already appeared, or was destined still to come. Nahmanides asked for full freedom of speech, and was granted it, by the King's grace—one of the rare cases in which this was still being done. As it soon turned out, the challenger was no equal to the great Rabbi either in knowledge of Torah and Talmud or in the precision, logic, and persuasiveness of his arguments.

"The sceptre shall not depart from Judah," Paulus Christiani quoted from the Bible, until the saviour comes, and asserted that this event had already taken place, since the Jews had long ago lost their land and their sovereignty. Nahmanides countered that his people had already lost their sovereignty before, at the time of the Babylonian exile—but surely the Christians did not think the Messiah had already appeared at that time? Moreover, had not the prophet predicted, Nahmanides asked, that in the time of the Messiah peace would come upon earth? Was that already the case? Wars were supposed to end forever—"so it is said," Nahmanides declared, turning to the king, "and it is likewise said that the peoples will beat their swords into plowshares and not learn war any more; but how unfortunate would that be for you, O King, and for the knights around you here, if the time had already come for you to forget the making of war."

Fearlessly, Nahmanides defined the differing conceptions of divinity which divided Judaism and Christianity. "But what you say concerning the nature of deity is very painful to us. You, my lord and king, are the son of a Christian man and born of a Christian woman. All your life your priests and monks have impressed upon your mind a notion of deity that corresponds with the dogma of your faith. Yet this notion is contrary both to reason and to nature; and the prophets by no means believed that the Creator of heaven and earth would become flesh within the womb of a Jewish woman, would ripen in it for nine months, then come into the world as an infant and grow up to be turned over to his enemies, condemned to death and executed, so that he might at last be resurrected and return to his original state of divinity. Such notions are literally inconceivable to the rational mind of a Jew, as indeed to that of any human being. Therefore all your eloquence is vain, for at this most essential point reconciliation between us must fail."

The great religious disputation ended after four sessions—without the success that Fra Pablo had hoped for. Nahmanides had conducted his part of the debate with such skill that the King remarked he "had never attended so brilliant a defense of an unjust cause."

Nahmanides soon thought it wise to leave the country, in order to escape the clutches of the Inquisition; according to another story, he was banished from Aragon at the instigation of Pope Clement IV. He had prepared a truthful account of the disputation for the Jewish communities, which so enraged the Dominicans that they asked the King for permission to confiscate and burn all copies. Nahmanides bade good-by to his community and his family in Gerona, and set out on the long journey to the Holy Land. In 1267, by this time seventy years of age, he reached Palestine. He found the country deserted; in 1260 the Mongols had destroyed everything. His first letter was addressed to his son:

"I am writing this letter in the holy city of Jerusalem. . . . The devastation and emptiness is great. . . . Jerusalem is more destroyed than any other city, the land of Judah more than Galilee. But even in this state of destruction it is a blessed land. . . . There are no Jews here . . . except for two brothers, dyers by trade. . . . We have succeeded in finding a deserted house that is built on marble pillars, with a fine arch. This we have taken for our synagogue. . . . We have sent to Shechem to fetch some scrolls of the Torah that were . . . safely hidden there when the Tatars invaded. Thus we shall now be able . . . to hold services regularly. For people are always coming to Jerusalem, men and women from Damascus, Aleppo, and all parts of the country, to see the sanctuary and to mourn for it. May He who has granted us to see Jerusalem in its devastation grant us also the happiness of beholding it rebuilt and restored when the divine glory returns to it. . . ."

In 1270 the great Talmudist and cabalist died in Acre. He was buried in Haifa.

Nahmanides found his peace in the land of his fathers, far from Europe, where his brethren in Spain and other countries were facing times of even greater suffering.

Jewish badges and occupational bans, superstitious libel and slandering of their religion—the Jews found the enmity toward them growing ever more intense among the surrounding Christian population. And that population was being reminded constantly of its obligation to assume an anti-Jewish posture. In sculptures over the portals of cathedrals, in paintings in churches, in carved ivory covers of Bible paraphrases, there appeared the symbolic figure of a woman, Synagoga, the condemned and rejected counterpart to Ecclesia. A veil or bandage covered Synagoga's eyes, signifying her blindness to Truth, or else a devil would be shooting an arrow at her eyes. As a sign of shame she was represented with the Jewish hat and yellow dress; her mount was a miserable, feeble donkey or even a pig. Sometimes Synagoga was shown as a murderess, using a lance to inflict a mortal wound on Christ. She was also shown as an exile, banished by Christ, standing on the brink of hell's maw, the tables of the Law drooping from her hands, in the midst of a group of lost souls.

Dialogue between Church and Synagogue had ceased. Ecclesia appeared to be the radiant victor. As the Middle Ages advanced, miracle and mystery plays made the synagogue more and more the object of abuse. The actors represented Jews as hypocrites, blasphemers, obstinate enemies of Christianity. From the church, Passion plays moved to the market place and became spectacles full of malignant attacks upon the people of God—holding the Jews up to ridicule for speaking a jargon interspersed with Hebrew, or representing them as infamous usurers, or mocking their customs and rites and even the Talmud.

During this period there appears the mysterious figure of a Jewish minnesinger: Süsskind von Trimberg. Wandering from castle to castle, the Jewish minstrel sang his songs among the Christians. Twelve of his poems have been preserved. The famous Manesse manuscript of songs also contains a picture of him—with a pointed yellow Jew's hat and long beard. He sang of constancy of spirit and of virtuous wives, extolled kindness and generosity. One of his verses runs: "I praise him as a noble man who nobly acts, not him who merely boasts a patent of nobility. Do we not see roses blooming among thorns and wickedness flourishing among noblemen?"

We know few details of this Jewish minnesinger's life. One day, however, Süsskind von Trimberg abandoned his art. Among the few statements of his that have come down to us is the following: "I mean to flee the courts of the lords, grow a long beard and gray hair, and henceforth live the life of the ancient Jews, for the lords have withdrawn their favor from me." In Arab Spain Jewish poets had their honorable place at the courts of sultans and viziers. There they were celebrated and honored. In Christian Europe honors were never shown them.

THE CHARGE OF DESECRATION
OF THE HOST

No sooner had Emperor Frederick II died than chaos broke out; the great interregnum began, the "terrible time." Uprisings and civil wars shook all the lands that formed the Holy Roman Empire, particularly the German states. The Jewish communities were particularly exposed to the general disorder. Secular and ecclesiastical lords, although they might make efforts to protect the Jews, were powerless to enforce their will. To be sure, a decree was published in 1265 ordaining that attacks upon the Jews were "against the will of God, for the sake of Whose martyrdom and in memory of it Holy Church keeps the Jews alive." Such attacks were also "to the disadvantage of the empire and its treasury," and were henceforth to be punished as breaches of the prince's peace.

Nevertheless Jewish martyrs died by the hundreds—broken on the wheel in the Alsatian city of Weissenburg (1279), put to the rack and hanged in Coblenz and Pforzheim (1267), the entire Jewish community burned alive in its synagogue at Sinzig. Ruffians who had distinguished themselves in the burning of Jews were called by a special nickname: Jew roasters.

The interregnum finally came to an end after more than two decades. Rudolf I of Hapsburg, elected King in Frankfurt in 1273, restored order in Germany at any rate. Rudolf, a rather impoverished count by origin, was deeply concerned that the Jews in his kingdom be left in peace. He needed a great deal of money to discharge war debts and to build up the power of his house, and he was well aware of the sizable sums that could be obtained from the Jewish communities in quiet times. His demands, however, were so great that the Jews were totally impoverished. From Mainz, Worms, Speyer, and many other cities, Jewish families began to emigrate. Rudolf, reluctant to lose so important a source of income, issued a decree forbidding emigration. "All Jews," the decree stated, "are without exception serfs of our crown and belong, together with their property, to us alone or to that lord to whom we have ceded our rights in fee. If therefore some Jews run away without our special permission, in order to settle beyond the sea, thus escaping the power of their lawful lord, it is right that all their property, movable and immovable, should become ours."

This royal decree proved nemesis for the most respected rabbi of the age—Meïr ben Baruch. This scholar presided over a well-attended Talmud school in Rothenburg ob der Tauber. His judgments and decisions were known far and wide. But he had decided to move to the Holy Land, along with his family. He reached Lombardy safely, but there fate caught up with him. An apostate Jew named Knippe who was escorting the Bishop of Mainz back from Rome, chanced to pass Meïr ben Baruch on the road. He recognized the Rabbi and denounced him. The great scholar was arrested and taken before King Rudolf, who had him imprisoned in the Castle of Ensisheim in Alsace. The shrewd Hapsburger was well aware that German Jewry would not shrink from any sacrifice to purchase the celebrated Rabbi's release. And, in fact, the Jewish communities raised no less than twenty thousand marks, which sum they meant to offer to the King as a ransom. But Rabbi Meïr refused to sanction this; he did not want to provide the King with opportunities for extortion. And so he remained in prison for the rest of his life. When he died, in 1293, the authorities refused to let the Jews have his body. All petitions proved vain. Not until fourteen years after the Rabbi's death did a wealthy Jew from Frankfurt am Main, Süsskind Wimpfen, succeed at last in buying release of Rabbi Meïr's bones. He had them buried in the Jewish cemetery at Worms.

Despite pledges of royal protection, the ritual murder story continued to crop up. There was one such trial in Mainz in 1283, another in Munich in 1286, a third in Oberwesel in 1288. But in addition to these, a new charge had appeared—that Jews were desecrating the host, profaning the sacramental wafer. Among the superstitious folk, fables began to circulate concerning the miracle-working host—*hostia mirifica*. Jews, it was said, stole or bought consecrated hosts in order to pierce them with knives out of hatred for Christ, or to crush them in a mortar. Thus treated, the hosts, it was said, exuded blood of miraculous healing properties.

An innocent natural phenomenon became the proof for this fantastic accusation. Microbes (such as *micrococcus prodigiosus*) sometimes settle in starchy foods, especially those that are no longer quite fresh, and multiply rapidly. They excrete a strong red dye that could indeed be taken for blood.

Rumors of such desecrations of the host led to frightful massacres of Jews in southern Germany in 1298. In Röttingen the Jews were accused of having stolen an oblate from the church and having crushed it. A nobleman named Rindfleisch stepped forward and declared that he had been chosen by heaven to avenge the crime and destroy all the guilty. A gang gathered around him, killed all the Jews in the town, and then marched on from place to place, killing and pillaging, through Franconia, Bavaria, and Austria. They left Rothenburg "red with the blood of Jewish martyrs." After three successive attacks upon the Jews, more than five hundred dead were counted. In the large Jewish community of Würzburg, only a few were left alive of the more than one thousand inhabitants. In Nuremberg several hundred Jews, supported by Christian fellow citizens, vainly defended themselves in the citadel. They were all slain on August 1, 1298. Among the six hundred and eighteen dead of the city was the famous Rabbi Mardochai ben Hillel, a disciple of Rabbi Meïr. Innumerable Jews took their own lives rather than fall into the hands of Rindfleisch's band of brutes. One chronicle notes that many "men and women with obstinate minds, together with small children, set fire to all their household goods and plunged into the flames." In vain the persecuted Jews begged the authorities for protection. Only in Augsburg did they succeed in ransoming themselves, and in Regensburg the town council energetically came to the defense of the Jewish community and saved it from annihilation.

From the spring to the autumn of 1298, one hundred and forty-six Jewish communities were set upon. The laments written at the time give the number of dead at some twenty thousand. The massacres were finally stopped by Albrecht von Hapsburg, who after a protracted civil war won power in 1298. He imposed heavy fines on all the towns that had not protected their Jewish communities—so that the royal treasury could obtain compensation for the loss of its serfs.

The horrors they had witnessed were stamped forever upon the memories of the surviving German Jews, and were incorporated into the songs sung in their synagogues, laments that sprang from inexpressible grief and sadness. Eleazar ha-Kohen, who had lived through the time of horrors, wrote in despair:

"Oh Heaven, are we worse than other peoples? Is our endurance like that of a stone, or is our flesh of bronze, that we bear such evils? Twelve hundred and thirty years have already passed since the enemy visited destruction upon us, and still he rends us with his sharp claws. He devises all conceivable agonies to annihilate us; he takes up the sword, fire, and water. Small and large, women and children, old men and youths, brides and bridegrooms, all are burned and slaughtered. . . . Ask all who walk upon this earth: Has ever any people had to suffer so much?"

Rabbi Meïr of Rothenburg had had to lament the burning of the Talmud in France; in Germany his brothers mourned the burning of human beings. Amid the cries of woe an occasional voice was heard calling down the judgment of God upon the scenes of such horrors: "Annihilate their land with a hail of sulphur and salt; avenge my sufferings upon this atrocious people. . . . Pay them back for their triumphant savagery, for the blood of the innocent that has mingled with the filth of the streets."

Even before the century was out that had brought such misery upon the children of Israel throughout Europe, the destinies of the Jews in England came to an abrupt end. Edward I violently closed the chapter in their lives in Britain that had only begun with William the Conqueror. In 1275, three years after he acceded to the throne, King Edward issued a new law concerning the Jews, *Statutum de Judaismo,* which deprived them of their last chance for livelihood. He forbade them "for the glory of God and the common welfare" to lend money at interest. Any loan agreements already made were declared null and void. (Edward acted in response to the Pope's urging. In 1274 at the Council of Lyons Gregory X had once again called upon the Christian world to take strict steps to check "usury.") For the Jewish communities of England, the new statute meant total economic ruin. In their distress many of them resorted to counterfeiting, a device much practiced in those days by Italian money-changers and Flemish wool traders. Two hundred and ninety-three Jews paid with their lives; accused of debasing the King's coinage, they ended on the scaffold in London in 1278.

Edward I carried out one last act of extortion. In the spring of 1287 he ordered the heads of all "his" Jews' families to be locked up. They were set free only after the communities had raised twelve thousand pounds for ransom. Three years later the bitter farce was over. The Jews were no longer needed; their economic utility as a source of income to the state had reached the zero point. On July 18, 1290—the day of recollection of the destruction of Jerusalem—Edward I signed the decree of banishment. All Jews had to leave England by All Souls' Day (November 2). Any who were found in England after that date would be punished by hanging.

Most did not wait for the deadline; the exodus began in October. The unfortunates gathered by the thousands in all the ports, terrified that they might not be able to obtain a place aboard a ship in time. Sixteen thousand five hundred Jews in all left the country whose prosperity they had promoted, and whose industry and trade they had enormously stimulated. Their homes and real property were confiscated, their synagogues converted to churches. The King wanted to let them leave in peace, but the populace harassed them up to the time they embarked. One captain, moreover, after he had pocketed the passage money, refused to take aboard a large group whom he was supposed to pick up from a sandbank in the Thames during low tide. He let them drown as the high tide came, taunting them to ask their Moses for help, since he could part the waves. King Edward, however, had the captain hanged for this atrocity.

Some groups of Jews wandered to Germany, Flanders, and Spain. But the great majority turned to France for refuge—never suspecting that sixteen years later they would once more have to be on the move.

For more than three and a half centuries England remained a virtually empty page in the book of Jewish history. Only in 1657 did Cromwell permit some Jews to settle in London again. In the intervening period we occasionally hear of Jews who visited England briefly, of a few who settled there once more, and of some who became converts to Christianity. For these there was a *domus conversorum* in London; its inmates regularly received small subsidies, the idea being to encourage the change of religions.

Joseph Süss Oppenheimer, Heidelberg financier who became court factor to Duke Karl Alexander of Württemberg. After his sovereign's death, he was condemned to death and executed.

ABOVE: Rabbi Jonathan Eibeschütz, who was thought to be a secret adherent of Sabbatai Zebi

LEFT: Interior of the Altneuschul, Prague's famous synagogue, built c. 1260

The philosopher Baruch Spinoza

BELOW, LEFT: Sabbatai Zebi, the false Messiah. Portrait from the year
1666.   AT RIGHT: Manasseh ben Israel, rabbi of Amsterdam, who persuaded Cromwell to readmit the Jews to England. Etching by Rembrandt, 1636.

the *commune clameur du peuple,* began negotiations with the exiles to persuade them to return. It was the fault of bad counselors, the King said, that the Jews had been banished. At first the harried people, now so suddenly wanted again, hesitated. They did not trust the peace, and demanded royal guarantees for their security. Acceptable conditions were settled, and in 1315 they were permitted to return home, with the duration of their stay fixed for the present at twelve years. But only a portion of the exiles availed themselves of the opportunity.

Those who returned began rebuilding their shattered communities. They received their synagogues and their books, with the exception of the Talmud. Royal officials helped with the restoration of their former possessions. But starting life anew in France was a slow business, for most of the returned refugees were totally impoverished. The great age of French Jewry, with its vigorous intellectual life, was a thing irretrievably of the past. The peace, in fact, lasted a bare five years. Then the "march of the shepherds," the notorious *pastoureaux,* descended upon the Jews who had trusted the royal word.

In 1320 King Philip V was preparing a new Crusade to the Holy Land. In the midst of the excitement that shook the nation, a young shepherd living near the Garonne suddenly had a vision: A beautiful virgin had summoned him to gather warriors and march against the unbelievers. Glorious victories would be his. Innumerable shepherds and peasants followed his call, and, as always, the religious zealots drew in their wake all kinds of lawless folk. A horde many thousands strong, led by two defrocked clerics, set out on a Crusade in their own country. Proclaiming war against all unbelievers and slaughtering all Jews, the horde rampaged through northern and southern France. The only Jews who were spared were those who accepted baptism. In Gascony, in the district of Bordeaux, around Toulouse, Albi, and many other cities, Jews were slaughtered by the hundreds. The Christian populace did not oppose the "shepherds" with any vigor until Pope John XXII commanded, from Avignon, that something be done to check them. Then gangs moving on Narbonne were dispersed. Other bands of the shepherd army succeeded in escaping across the Pyrenees to Navarre and Aragon, where they continued their bloody work. One hundred and twenty Jewish communities in France and northern Spain were devastated within the span of a year.

The following year brought fresh disaster. Lepers in Aquitaine, in revenge for meager rations, had poisoned some wells. Under torture one of the arrested lepers came forth with the confession that he had been instigated to the deed by Jews, who had supplied the poison. Some Jews were therefore stretched on the rack until they confessed to what the

EXPULSIONS AND KILLINGS

The example that Edward I had provided in England proved to be contagious. Sixteen years later the same fate overtook the French Jewish communities. In 1306 Philip IV, surnamed the Fair, issued secret instructions for all the Jews to be arrested on a single day. The King's motive was simple; he intended to refill the royal treasury—emptied by wars with Flanders and his feud with the Pope—by confiscating all Jewish property.

On July 22 his henchmen struck. All Jews, young and old, men, women, and children, without distinction of status or age, were seized and thrust into jails and dungeons. They were then informed that within a month they must leave the country, leaving behind all their movable and immovable possessions.

Most of the expelled Jews lingered close to the borders of France. Some went to Palestine, among them Estori Farchi, who later wrote a treatise on the topography of the Holy Land. "They have torn me from my school," he grieved. "At night I had to leave my father's house and wander from land to land, from country to country, whose languages were strange to me."

Meanwhile, throughout the country the loot was converted to money; all the confiscated valuables were brought to the King. Effects of lesser value were sold to the populace at absurd prices. "Commissioners on Jewish affairs," appointed from Paris, went about auctioning off Jewish property. In addition to land and houses, all synagogues and famous old schools, including those of Rashi and his disciples, went under the hammer. In Paris there was a synagogue that no one was interested in buying; the King presented it to his coachman. In Narbonne the Cordada, the ancient seat of the well-known Kalonymid family, was sold. Huge sums flowed into the treasury—in the district of Toulouse alone Jewish property yielded more than seventy-five thousand livres. Moreover, Philip took over all the promissory notes in the tills of the Jews so that debts, far from being erased, had now to be paid directly to the King. The populace henceforth was dependent exclusively on Christian lenders, who apparently gouged the people mercilessly once they were free of Jewish competition. A popular song of the time went: "The Jews were far more generous than the Christians." Many of those who had hitherto reviled the Jews now began to grumble.

Sure enough, ten years later, Philip's successor Louis X, in response to

Berlin's oldest synagogue, built 1712-1714

Interior of the Berlin
synagogue after its
consecration in 1714.
Engraving from
a tapestry.

Moses Mendelssohn, famous philosopher of the Enlightenment, early advocate of the emancipation of the Jews

The Ephraim Palace, Berlin. Veitel Ephraim, court jeweler to Frederick William I and later Master of the Mint to Frederick the Great, was given the palace as a reward for his services in financing the King's wars. The palace was torn down after 1933.

Gotthold Ephraim Lessing,
German dramatist and critic,
who fought prejudice against
the Jews

Synagoga, symbol of the Old
Testament, represented on the
Cathedral of Strassburg (1230-
1240) as defeated and rejected,
with blindfolded eyes and
flagstaff broken in three places

A "Jews' sow" on the parish church in Wittenberg

Elijah ben Solomon, gaon of Vilna, father of Talmudic research and one of the bitterest opponents of Hasidism

Rahel Levin Varnhagen,
who conducted
a famous salon in Berlin
c. 1800

Henriette Herz, wife of
the philosopher Marcus
Herz, whose salon
served as the literary
and artistic center of
Berlin at the end of the
eighteenth century

Heinrich Heine,
poet and wit

Ludwig Börne,
one of the leaders
of the literary
movement known as
Young Germany

torturers wanted to hear. Massacres followed. In July, 1321, more than five thousand Jews were arrested, tortured, and then burned alive, supposedly for the crime of poisoning the wells. The complete innocence of the Jews was revealed only after Philip V ordered an investigation in order to establish his claim to the property of the victims.

But instead of punishing those to blame, Philip imposed a fine of one hundred and fifty thousand livres upon all the Jewish communities of France. Ruthless collections of this enormous sum forced the majority of the Jews to leave the country again. From 1322 on, only a few Jews remained in France.

Insecurity, exploitation, and persecution were the lot of the Jews across the Rhine also. "All Jews belong to us with their bodies and their possessions," Louis the Bavarian declared in 1343. "We can do with them whatever our will and pleasure is." And that is precisely how he behaved. No previous German emperor had ever treated the Jews quite so arbitrarily. Louis sold Jewish communities to princes and cities, or else he pawned them. Documents reveal how unscrupulously Louis dealt with "his dear *servi camerae*," as he preferred to call them, for the purpose of filling his coffers. In many cities the Jewish communities owed taxes to several "owners"—in Strassburg, for example, they paid taxes to three "protectors": the emperor, the city magistrate and the bishop. As if the oppressive burdens on the communities were not enough, Louis also imposed an individual poll tax on all Jews in the empire.

Louis could tax, but he could not provide the protection he had solemnly assured "his" Jews. The empire seethed with hostility toward the Jews. The endemic antagonism between city and countryside within the empire was often discharged at the expense of the unarmed, helpless minority. Gangs from Bavaria, who called themselves "Jew killers," began raids into Franconia in 1336. They attacked the Jewish communities in Mergentheim, in Rothenburg, and in the vicinity of Nuremberg. A down-at-heels nobleman, who was called King Armleather because he wore a piece of leather around his arm, exhorted the people to avenge the death of Jesus. "The peasants dropped whatever they were doing, came with axes, shovels, swords, flails, hunting spears, and whatever they had. With the five thousand men at his disposal King Armleather so terrified the Jews that many killed themselves and their children. The murderers threw others from high places or strangled them, casting the bodies into water or piling and burning them. Several thousand Jews were slain." The bands raged through Swabia and as far as Styria in Austria. Other groups, led by a tavernkeeper named Johann Zimberli, ranged through

Alsace and the Rheingau. In more than a hundred towns and villages, attacks on Jews were recorded.

Cities even organized such raids on an official basis. In the Bavarian town of Deggendorf on the Danube an alleged desecration of the host provided a welcome pretext. The town council secretly planned the whole thing. On a set day—September 30, 1337—the tocsin began to clang. That was the agreed sign. Sir Hartmann von Deggenburg, at the head of his retainers, rode in through the open gate of the town and together with the citizens attacked the defenseless Jews, killing them, pillaging their possessions, and burning down their houses. As a permanent memorial to this gallant feat a church was built where the host was displayed as a holy relic, along with the "Jews' bodkin" with which the wafer had supposedly been stabbed. For centuries the church attracted pilgrims. An inscription recorded the event: "Anno 1337, the day after St. Michael's Day, the Jews were slain, the town them burned who God's body spurned. Men and women saw the deed. Then God's house was built with speed."

Once more stories of miraculous oblates began cropping up everywhere. Only in Vienna and Regensburg did the populace protect the Jews from persecution. Duke Albrecht II of Austria appealed to the Pope, bluntly stating that the tales of the desecrated host were merely a pretext for plundering the Jewish communities, for there was never any proof of the supposed crime. Pope Benedict XII thereupon ordered that no such accusations were to be tolerated unless the most incontrovertible evidence was offered. But even the head of the Church could not control the superstitious delusions of the populace.

The Emperor did little to counter the breaches of peace and the killing of his "serfs of the chamber." The most he did was to impose fines for the damage done to his property in the course of the anti-Jewish excesses. Purchasing amnesty was not very expensive; in fact, the citizens often profited, as the following imperial decree makes clear:

> We herewith declare . . . that in return for our renouncing all our claims in connection with the killing of the Jews of Mühlhausen, or with the losses and harm caused to the Jews, the town is to pay us one thousand pounds in old Basel currency. But in order to make it possible for the citizens to raise the required sum, we relinquish to them the entire property of the Jews killed within the town: houses, farms, pledges, and other possessions. . . . After payment of the thousand pounds all citizens and inhabitants of Mühlhausen are to be relieved of all obligations with regard to the murdered Jews.

BLACK DEATH AND THE STAKE

Shortly before the middle of the fourteenth century a great darkness, of the spirit and of the physical conditions of life, swept over the continent of Europe. The catastrophe that descended upon the Jewish communities at that time was more devastating than anything that had gone before. Their sufferings and disasters surpass belief.

In 1348 the greatest and most horrible epidemic in history spread through Europe: the plague, imported from the Orient. The Black Death carried off millions of people; whole cities and provinces were emptied. A third of the population succumbed.

Men went out of their minds before this peril. Helpless, distraught, half mad with fear of death, they faced the ghastly and inexorable approach of the contagion. Everywhere appeared the weird processions of the flagellants, carrying enormous crosses, lashing their naked backs until they streamed with blood, wailing penitential psalms. There was no explaining the riddle of this spreading mass death. And then suddenly a monstrous rumor began to circulate: The Black Death had been caused by the Jews; to exterminate Christians they had poisoned all springs and wells.

The insane charge was believed; the self-evident fact that Jews, too, were succumbing to the plague was simply ignored. Superstition was too deeply rooted in the Christian masses; they had already heard too much about ritual murders and desecration of the host by the "deicides." Hysteria drove the populace to mass crime. Christians became "destroying angels to the Jews," delivering thousands upon thousands of helpless people to torture, the executioner's ax, or the stake—as if they meant to annihilate the whole of Jewry from the face of the earth.

Now for the first time the fateful accusation of poisoning springs and wells arose in France. In May of 1348, in a town of southern France the entire Jewish community—men, women, and children—were burned along with Jewish scrolls of the Scriptures. The rumors leaped the Pyrenees into Spain. In Barcelona a mob killed some twenty persons and plundered Jewish houses. A few days later the community of Cervera was attacked; eighteen Jews were killed, the rest forced to flee the town.

By July the papacy had taken note of the new wave of persecution. From Avignon Pope Clement VI issued a bull threatening excommunication for the killing of Jews without trial, for forcing baptism upon them, or for robbing them of their goods. The bull quieted southern France for a time, but it had no effect in the rest of Christendom.

In Savoy the first "proof" was provided. Duke Amadeus ordered Jews suspected of poisoning arrested. They were incarcerated in the castle of Chillon on Lake Geneva and tortured until two of the group, half insane with pain, made confessions. They told an utterly preposterous story of a conspiracy of the Jews with the Moorish king in Granada to exterminate all Christendom by using poisons consisting of dried snakes, scorpions, human flesh, consecrated hosts, and Christian hearts. That sufficed. The secretaries recorded the confessions and placed an official seal on them. Everywhere in Savoy during the month of September pyres were ignited and great numbers of Jews burned.

From Lake Geneva the rumor that the guilt of the Jews had been proved passed quickly into Switzerland. The frightful scenes of Savoy were repeated. Bern requested the judicial documents from Savoy, and then put its own Jews to the rack and the stake. In Zurich, Winterthur, and St. Gall, Jews were burned, baptized, or expelled. In Basel, despite the protest of the town council, a mob forced a number of Jews to crowd into a wooden house on an island in the Rhine and on January 9, 1349, set the building on fire.

In September, 1348, the Pope had intervened once more in favor of the persecuted. Clement VI declared the Black Death a scourge of God and painstakingly explained to Christians that the Jews were innocent of the crimes charged to them. The clergy, too, were once again admonished to protect the Jews, and anathema was threatened for those who violated the papal injunction. But again the Pope's efforts were in vain.

Nowhere was the extirpation of the Jews practiced with more thoroughness and cruelty than in the Holy Roman Empire of the German nation. In vain did Emperor Charles IV issue warnings and dispatch letter upon letter enjoining all and sundry against harming his *servi camerae*. There were men of insight in Germany who kept their heads, but they were few. Konrad von Megenberg of Vienna pointed out in 1349 that the Jews would have endangered their own lives if they had poisoned wells, and that in Vienna alone so many Jews had died of plague that their cemetery had had to be enlarged. In Strassburg, Mayor Konrad von Winterthur, a magistrate named Gosse Sturm, and a guild master named Peter Schwarber intervened in favor of the Jews. Sensible men in the council of burghers in Freiburg and Cologne took the part of the unfortunates. But they were outvoted. Toward the end of 1348 the Jews of Alsace were declared outlaws. That sealed the fate of their communities.

On February 14, 1349, all the Jews of Strassburg were burned to death in their own cemetery "on a wooden platform, about two thousand of them; but those who let themselves be baptized were granted their lives. Many small children were taken from the fire and baptized against the will of their fathers and mothers." The citizens divided the spoils of the "Jew burning" among themselves. "Their money was the poison that killed the Jews," observed Closener of Strassburg, and another contemporary chronicler added: "Do you wish to know what brought the Jews to destruction? It was the avarice of the Christians." In Colmar the "Jews' hole," where the burning took place, has been preserved to this day. In Benfeld the Jews were consigned to the flames or drowned in the marsh. Other Alsatian towns followed suit; then it was the turn of the oldest German communities, those of the Rhineland. In Worms on March 1 the Jews themselves set fire to their houses, and on July 24 those in Frankfurt am Main followed their example. In Mainz the Jews offered armed resistance. When they had to yield to overwhelming force and there no longer remained any hope of rescue, the encircled Jewish families sacrificed themselves as "burnt offerings." Their hymns of lamentation rang out forcefully from the flames and smoke. Six thousand died on one day, August 24, 1349. On that same day the ancient Cologne community was destroyed.

Like the roaring fires of hell, the flames leaped across all of Germany. From the Alps to the North Sea, from the Rhine to the Oder, in innumerable towns the Jews were burned or burned themselves in their despair. Everywhere, the hatred and superstition of the mobs outweighed the desire of princes or a few city fathers to protect the hapless Jews.

In the cities and towns of Bavaria and Swabia the killing raged until the autumn of 1349. In Augsburg, in Würzburg, in Munich, and even in Nuremberg, which had been spared the plague, community after community went down to destruction. Of the larger Bavarian Jewish communities, only the one in Regensburg was spared. There the city fathers, especially Mayor Berthold Epoltspecht, vigorously aided the Jews. In Vienna, too, they were again protected by the authorities—but in no other city.

The balance sheet of the catastrophe was frightful—the greatest horror in the history of Europe had descended upon the Jews. In more than three hundred and fifty Jewish communities murder in its most brutal forms had raged unchecked; countless martyrs had been drowned, strangled, hanged, burned, broken on the wheel, or buried alive. Sixty large and a hundred and fifty smaller Jewish communities were devastated, burned to ashes, exterminated down to the last living person. The survivors had fled to the east. German Jewry, the leading community in Europe outside of Spain, had been annihilated, the majority killed, their property distributed among lords, towns, and citizens. Even the grave-stones in their cemeteries were filched and used as building stone.

The merciless pursuit ended only when the land had been cleared of Jews. Blackened heaps of ashes remained as reminders of the places in which they had lived and been slaughtered or died by their own hands —thousands upon thousands, young and old, praying and singing their psalms. No threats, no agony, had sufficed to break their unconquer-able spirit. In spite of the massacres, there had not been a single case of mass apostasy from Judaism. The victims died rather than accept baptism.

There were some Christian chroniclers who could not shake off the impression such firm faith had made upon them. "Joyously, singing, as if they were off to a wedding, they went to their deaths," wrote the canon Jean de Belans of Liége. And a contemporary Dominican monk observed: "As if they were engaged in a dance, they hastened to death, throwing first the children, then the women, and finally themselves into the flames, so that they would not violate their faith by human weakness."

It is hard to imagine that this inferno would not set an unbridgeable gulf between Christians and Jews, between the persecuted and their vic-tims, for ages to come. It is hard to imagine that the two groups could ever again live together in peace and harmony. Yet a few years later—the last disputes over the distribution of Jewish property scarcely ended—the cities of Germany scrambled to invite the Jews back again. Forgotten were the oaths sworn by burghers and magistrates during the plague period that no Jew would ever again be permitted within their walls. Even the clergy was eager once again to "have Jews." The Bishop of Augsburg requested the Emperor's permission "to receive and settle Jews." All seven electoral princes of Germany, both ecclesiastical and secular, made the same ap-peal, which was granted. In 1336 the Golden Bull issued at the Diet of Nuremberg contained an article conceding to the electoral princes the right to exploit mines of metal and salt. It also stated: "Likewise they are granted to right to possess Jews."

The reason for this turnabout was simple. Economic life had suffered by the extermination of the Jews. After their disappearance, the authori-ties of the empire and the towns discovered that they had forfeited an in-exhaustible source of income. The populace, impoverished by years of plague, had also been deprived of any sort of credit. When in 1352 Elec-tor Ludwig of Brandenburg invited the Jews to settle in his lands, he made it plain why. After the destruction of the Jews the whole financial situation of his country had been thrown into disorder by the lack of liquidity. The Jews were indispensable; they were needed to manage taxes and duty, trade and the credit system. For that reason the doors were everywhere thrown open to them again. But the blow that had been inflicted upon German Jewry could not be undone.

Many German Jews who had meanwhile settled in Austria, Bohemia, and Poland refused to return. Moreover, the conditions of readmission were scarcely tempting. Jews were forbidden to buy their own houses; they could only rent. And they would be permitted to live only "where the citizens think it is best and nowhere else," that is, in restricted Jews' quarters or Jews' streets. They would not be free to transfer to another town. Former inhabitants would be accepted as immigrants only for a limited period of settlement; they would be merely tolerated.

Only small groups of Jews accepted these humiliating conditions. Between 1350 and 1370 some came nevertheless. They no longer had anything. Their capital was gone, all their possessions looted or confiscated. Most of them, excluded by occupational limitations from any other work, depended on petty commerce in clothing, spices, and poultry, on peddling, which provided the barest of livelihoods. Jewish artisans were permitted to work only in Jewish quarters and only for fellow Jews. A very few of the more prosperous Jews could once more engage in moneylending, the only profitable occupation open to them. The statutes of Munich provided that "The Jews may not engage in any other work but the lending of money on interest, for that is their business."

In France, where for financial reasons the rulers had likewise permitted the Jews to return in 1360, the restrictions were not so harsh. Jews were allowed to own fields as well as houses. Their furnishings, livestock, granaries, and wine cellars were protected by law, as were their sacred books. The greatest amount of protection was extended to their commerce. These wider privileges resulted in the immigration into France of Jews from many countries.

In Germany, wherever Jewish life resumed, it remained on a depressed, impoverished level. The terrible harshness of their experiences had marked the Jews for good. They were no longer the same; their former energy and pride were gone. Their eyes took on a look of sadness, as if reflecting the lamentations they sang in the synagogues. And Christian society continued to impose such galling restrictions upon them that their spirit had little opportunity to revive. They were held down to the bare minimum at which they could still exist, without any hope of improvement. Peddling, even for those who plied that trade from morning to night, never provided enough of a livelihood for an escape from poverty. The same was true for petty pawnbroking. The effects of sheer necessity showed even in the degradation of Jewish cuisine. "The Crusades, with their massacres of Jews and subsequent impoverishment," writes Salcia Landmann, "also had consequences for the cuisine of German Jews that marked it forever afterward. Deep into modern times poverty left its traces upon German-Jewish recipes. Even the festive Sabbath bread, the white barches or challah, was made with few eggs and frequently with an admixture of potatoes."

Everywhere the Jews went they still encountered suspicion, contempt, and mockery. The authorities imposed, more sternly than ever before, observance of the special clothing for Jews: the yellow badge and pointed cap as warning signs to the populace that one of the pariahs was about. Jewish ordinances grew longer and longer, with one word predominating: *verboten*. Everything was forbidden them. The whole object was to humiliate and harass them, and to cut off all relations between them and Christians.

Their appearance changed, their physical development and bearing. It is only from the late Middle Ages on that the world has known the sorry, bent-backed Jew—who, moreover, was destined to become a figure of mockery, the basis for hateful caricatures. As yet, there has been no anthropological and sociological study of how environmental influences could possibly have caused such a physical change and deformation of the human body. The Jew's whole personality changed as well. As Professor Edmund Schopen has put it: "In the long run this condition had to shatter that proud assertiveness and aristocratic self-assurance which under normal conditions are attributes of the Jewish character. The Jew acquired the slyly subservient, falsely obliging, almost mockingly hypocritical manner that the defenseless must necessarily and bitterly adopt toward the brutal possessor of power to whom they feel inwardly superior."

The brilliant intellectual life of German and French Jews had been shattered. In France, where for more than two centuries—beginning with the great Rashi and continuing down to the last of his disciples, the Tossafists—study of the Talmud had reached exceptional heights, alarming ignorance now prevailed among the new immigrants. Mattathias ben Joseph Provenci founded a school in Paris once again and gathered around him pupils whom he instructed in the Torah and Talmud. He also had new copies made of the Talmud, for so many had been destroyed. Through Mattathias' efforts it became possible once again to train new rabbis.

In Germany persecutions and expulsions had so thinned the ranks of the rabbis that in many places the small Jewish communities had to make do with ignorant men. Meïr ben Baruch Halevi, a respected rabbi from Vienna, made herculean efforts to provide candidates with adequate training for the rabbinical posts. In 1381 the rabbis of the Rhine districts met in Mainz to reconstitute the largely lost knowledge of ancient Jewish ordinances. On both sides of the Rhine there were efforts at a new beginning.

Life slowly revived in the now thinly populated Jewish communities. For a few decades they were granted peace; then the diabolic persecutions resumed. "In 1384 the burgraves of Nuremberg arrested the Jews and imprisoned the prosperous ones in the Reichsburg," a chronicle reports, "while they thrust the poor into the cellar of the town hall. The Jews were released only after they had paid a ransom." Emperor Wenzel saw nothing wrong with this method of robbing the Jews by "legal" procedures. Twice, in 1385 and 1390, he annulled all debts owing to Jewish creditors.

For the Jews in France even harder blows were reserved. The anger of the populace with high taxes was discharged in attacks upon the Jews. In 1380 and 1382 there were riots in Paris. Noblemen in debt to Jewish moneylenders stirred up the people. Jews were killed and their houses burned. For four days the massacre continued, and the disorder spread soon afterward to other cities. Agitation against the Jewish moneylenders steadily increased; and the clergy contributed its mite toward arousing hatred for the "unbelievers." The King attempted to protect them. But then word of a new Jewish "crime" excited a storm of indignation. The wealthy apostate from Judaism Denis Marchant had been persuaded to return to the faith of his fathers; coreligionists had helped him escape from France. For this offense all the Jews in the capital were arrested and imprisoned. A tribunal of royal officials and clerics sentenced seven, charged as accomplices, to scourging. In April, 1394, the culprits were publicly whipped in the squares of Paris.

On September 17 of that same year—it happened to be the Day of Atonement—Charles VI decreed expulsion of the Jewish population from all royal lands in France because of "grave crimes against the Holy Faith as well as abuse of the privileges conferred upon them." They were permitted to take their property with them. Six weeks later royal gendarmes escorted them to the frontier. Some of the exiles sought refuge in the south: in Lyons, in Provence, and in the Dauphiné, lands not directly subject to the Crown, or in the papal territory around Avignon; others emigrated to Germany and Italy. Only a few turned their steps toward Spain.

Thus, in 1394, ended the story of Jewry in France; it was not to begin again until modern times. Thus Jewish history was terminated in both England and France by an act of official expulsion. This point was never reached in Germany and Austria; instead, the sufferings of the Jewish communities stretched on amid persecutions and a long series of local routs.

As at the time of the Crusades and the wars against the Albigensians, the Hussite wars once again led to intensification of anti-Semitism and brought disaster to many Jewish communities. To cover his military expenses Emperor Sigismund (who reigned from 1411 to 1437) collected the "third penny," as it was modestly called, from the Jews; in reality, it amounted to one third of their wealth. On their march to the "holy war" the imperial troops incidentally fell upon the Jews. At Sigismund's command Jewish communities even had to pay the costs of the Council of Constance, which condemned John Huss to the flames.

The Jews of Austria were affected worst of all. It was whispered about Vienna that Jews supported the Hussites with money and arms. A debate on this subject was held by the theological faculty of the University of Vienna. Students rampaged through the Jewish quarter. In 1420 the rumor of a recent desecration of the host incited fresh hysteria. The incident had taken place in the city of Enns during Easter. A Jew named Israel was alleged to have bought a consecrated wafer from the sexton's wife, with the intention of profaning it. Duke Albrecht V ordered the suspect persons to be brought to Vienna so that they could be questioned under torture. No confession could be forced out of any of them, except the sexton's wife. Nevertheless the verdict was guilty, and Duke Albrecht confirmed it. Two hundred Jewish men and women from Enns were publicly burned at the stake on a meadow by the Danube on March 12, 1421. Their children were forcibly baptized and placed in monasteries. At the same time the Duke banished all Jews from Austria and confiscated their entire wealth. A poet celebrating the heroic deeds of Albrecht of Hapsburg, who became German Emperor in 1438, wrote: "I have warred on the Turks and encircled the Hussites, but first I burned my Jews." Even the inscription on his gravestone mentioned, at his express wish, this burning of the Jews.

Austria's expulsion of the Jews was imitated in other countries. In 1424 the Jews had to leave Zurich and Freiburg im Breisgau; in 1426, Cologne; in 1432, Saxony; in 1435, Speyer; in 1438, Mainz; in 1440, Augsburg.

Frequently, economic motives lay behind these expulsions. Driving out the Jews meant eliminating troublesome competition in industry and trade, while the burghers at the same time enriched themselves by not repaying the money they had borrowed from the Jews. The clerical reaction stimulated by the Hussite wars also contributed to the wave of expulsions. Mendicant friars and monks of the preaching orders were waging a relentless struggle against the heretics, and included Jews in that category. Pope Martin V, in 1422, and subsequent heads of the Church issued several bulls condemning the persecutions of Jews, but to no effect. The Council of Basel, which lasted from 1431 to 1448, struggling to fortify as well as to reform the Christian faith, once more solemnly confirmed the entire body of Church canons against the Jews—all the decrees issued from the time of Pope Gregory I on. It added two new restrictions: Henceforth no Jew could be admitted to a university degree, and all were to be required to listen to conversion sermons, by force if necessary. Hordes of Franciscan and Dominican monks began preaching in Jewish districts and streets. Threats and persecutions intensified. But none of the zealots was as baleful as John of Capistrano (1386–1456), a fanatical Franciscan monk. Sent forth to supervise the implementing of the conciliar decisions, he became the "scourge of the Hebrews." As papal legate he marched at the head of a Crusader band from Sicily through Italy and in 1450 crossed the Alps to Bavaria, Austria, Silesia, Hungary, and Poland. He left a trail of anti-Jewish excesses— imprisonments, confiscations, expulsions, and executions by fire, as well as the removal of children under seven from their parents so that they could be forcibly reared as Christians.

In 1450 the Jews of Bavaria were arrested, stripped of their wealth, and finally expelled. In 1453 an alleged desecration of the host in Breslau led to an inquisitorial trial that Capistrano himself conducted. After torture had produced a confession by two defendants, forty-one Jews were burned alive on July 4, and all the others were expelled and forced to give up their children. On August 13 there were similar harrowing scenes in Schweidnitz and Liegnitz. Wherever Capistrano appeared, persecutions and expulsions began. His frightful work extended deep into Bohemia and Moravia.

In the midst of these tragic events there came from Italy news of a ritual murder trial that became a European *cause célèbre*. This was the Trent trial.

On Maundy Thursday in 1475 a two-and-a-half-year-old child named Simon, son of a poor tanner, disappeared in the city of Trent. A Jew named Samuel found his body on the bank of the Adige. To avoid any possible misinterpretations, he ran straight to Bishop Hinderbach and reported his discovery. Just at this time Bernardino da Feltre, a countryman and fellow monk of Capistrano, had preached against any collaboration between Christians and Jews. Inevitably, the charge was immediately raised that the Jews had tortured and killed little Simon and thrown his body into the water. Without further ado Bishop Hinderbach had many Jews arrested, and initiated an Inquisition proceeding against them. After an interrogation of fifteen days the tortured defendants provided the desired confession and were subsequently burned. The body of little Simon had meanwhile been embalmed and put on display; monks announced that Simon's bones were working miracles. At once Trent began drawing pilgrims from far and wide.

Doge Mucenigo of Venice and the Duke of Tyrol protested against these procedures. Pope Sixtus IV ordered Bishop Hinderbach to break off his investigation of other Jews. A delegate was sent to examine the records of the trial. Upon receiving the report, Sixtus declared that he was not convinced of the guilt of the Jews, and issued an encyclical calling upon the ecclesiastical authorities to protect the Jews against the ominous consequences of the accusation. Similarly, the Doge extended official protection to the Jews in the city of Padua and the county of Friuli. In his order he stressed that the charge of ritual murder had been wantonly instigated by the "preachers." Nevertheless, Bishop Hinderbach's so-called trial continued. In December, 1475, and in January, 1476, four more Jews were executed. The Pope intervened again in 1476 and demonstrated the innocence of the Jews. Sixtus IV refused to canonize Simon as a holy martyr. But a century later Pope Gregory XIII did so. In the year 1965, however, the Congregation of Rites, which concerns itself with canonizations, ruled against the evidence set forth in the verdict of Trent —a significant sign of our times.

News of the Trent trial, now circulated with astonishing speed by printed broadsides and sheets of woodcuts, stirred all of Germany and provided new fuel for hatred. The citizens of Frankfurt set up a statue on the bridge over the Main representing a martyred child and Jews with the devil. Underneath was the verse: "As long as Trent and the child are named, the Jews' rascality will be famed."

In Regensburg, too, the ritual murder charge turned up, and Bishop Heinrich ordered the arrest of several Jews. On the basis of the confession extorted by torture he was ready to proceed against the entire community. Guards barred the gates of the Regensburg Jewish quarter. All the Jews would probably have been massacred if Emperor Frederick III, convinced that the charges were lies, had not intervened. Yet he was forced to impose the imperial ban on the refractory town before all the imprisoned Jews were at last released, in 1480, and the inquisitorial investigation was quashed. Hostility against the Jews remained, and in 1519 Regensburg expelled the whole community.

Meanwhile the Jews had been banished from a large part of the empire. "For the honor of God and the Holy Virgin," all the important commercial cities had purged them from their midst. Forever wandering, they moved from town to town, but nowhere could they find a place where they were permitted to stay for long. Thus ended the fifteenth century, in which a John of Capistrano had offered the suggestion that the conflict between Christians and Jews could be solved by placing all the Jews on ships and sending these "enemies of the faith" out on the high seas.

MOURNFUL END IN SPAIN

By the beginning of the thirteenth century fateful events had taken place on the soil of Andalusia, in the course of the prolonged struggle between Crescent and Cross. In 1212 Christian Spain celebrated the greatest victory of the *Reconquista*. In July of that year the troops of the kings of Castile, Aragon, and Navarre inflicted an annihilating defeat upon the army of the Almohade Caliph at the Battle of Las Navas de Tolosa. The Moslems were never to recover from that defeat. Thereafter the Almohade Kingdom rapidly declined. Ferdinand III, who ascended the throne of Castile in 1217, succeeded within little more than a decade in seizing the most important districts of southern Spain from the enemy. In 1236 he conquered Córdoba, and in 1241, Murcia. Two years later the fortress of Jaén fell, and in 1248, after the Christian fleet defeated the Moslem navy at the mouth of the Guadalquivir, the last strongpoint surrendered: Seville. Granada alone continued to be a small Arab holding in the newly Christian territory. And thus the situation remained for almost two and a half centuries.

Ferdinand III, who later acquired the epithet the Saint, was just toward the Jews, although he did not like them. He was mindful that during the campaign against Seville many had fought bravely in the ranks of his army. After the city was taken, he rewarded the Jewish warriors with estates. He also turned three mosques over to the Jews of Seville for use as synagogues. The grateful Jewish community presented him with a silver bowl inscribed in Hebrew and Castilian: "The King of Kings will open the gates; the earthly king will march in."

The clerics did not conceal their annoyance. Reproachfully, they reminded the King of the canons prohibiting new synagogues. When in other conquered towns the Jews actually built new and splendid houses of worship, the clergy reported these outrages to the Popes. Honorius III and then Gregory IX and Innocent IV addressed letters of admonishment to Ferdinand. The King preferred to ignore them, at the cost of being considered a disobedient son of the Church. The measures against unbelievers demanded by the clergy would have affected Moslems as well as Jews. That seemed impolitic. Victory was too new, and North Africa swarmed with strong Berber forces. Reasons of state prescribed tolerance. The hour of the clergy had not yet come.

After Ferdinand's death the number of "unbelievers" at court actually increased. His son and successor, Alfonso X (who reigned from 1252 to 1284), was with justice nicknamed the Wise. He became a great patron of science, particularly of astronomy. And someone with an interest in that science could turn only to Arabs and Jews. A whole staff of non-Christian scholars soon surrounded the Christian ruler in Burgos. A period of fruitful scientific activity began. Whatever Arab manuals of astronomy could be found were translated into Castilian. Jehudah ben Mosca, Samuel ha-Levi and Don Abraham of Toledo prepared translations for the King. Samuel ha-Levi, incidentally, also constructed a much-admired water clock for the King. At the urging of Alfonso's Jewish advisers, the building of an observatory was begun. The King was resolved to have it better equipped than any of the observatories in the Arab world—and the Arabs were the acknowledged leaders in astronomy. An armillary sphere of the Arab type was built: an astronomical measuring instrument consisting of several rings that represented the chief circles of the firmament—equator, ecliptic, tropics, polar circles, and meridians. The magnificent instrument should have created a sensation in all of Europe. But no one knew of it beyond the Pyrenees. Scientific astronomy was still virtually unknown in the West, and remained so for several centuries afterward. Only later did the Western world learn from the writings of Jehudah ben Mosca of the remarkable instrument and of the astronomical measurements it had made possible.

Other important work in astronomy was done by Don Isaac ibn Cid, the head of the synagogue, whom the wise King called his "wise man." He drew up astronomical tables that represented improvements on the ancient Ptolemaic system, and dedicated them to the ruler. These famous Alfonsine Tables long served as an indispensable aid to astronomy. They were still being used in Europe at the time of Copernicus to calculate calendars and almanacs. It was not until 1551 that Erasmus Reinhold of Wittenberg undertook to replace them by his own Prussian Tables.

The King was said "to have forgotten the earth for the sky." A letter from Pope Nicholas III recalled him to the laws of this world. Like his father, Alfonso X had installed Jews in offices of state and entrusted them with administration of Castile's finances. Don Meïr de Malea served under him as *almojarife,* which meant royal tax and customs farmer—practically speaking, his treasurer. Don Meïr's sons, Don Zag and Don Joseph, held the same position in their turn and saw to it that huge sums annually poured into the royal treasury. Moreover, Alfonso, trusting the experience of his ancestors, appointed Jehudah Kohen his personal physician. The Pope took him to task for violating conciliar decrees in thus according Jews power over Christians. Such conduct, the Pope prophesied, would bring disaster upon Castile.

Perhaps in order to show good will, Alfonso X ordered that all the pertinent canons of the Church, as well as the ancient Visigothic decrees, be incorporated into the laws of Castile. The new code, composed in the vulgar tongue, Castilian, was actually published. But for the time being that was all; in practice, Alfonso ignored the code. It would have produced chaos and excited great opposition among Arabs as well as Jews, who for centuries had been accustomed to a good life in the Christian kingdoms, where they were respected, honored, and entrusted with high positions. Nevertheless, the new laws had not been codified in vain. One day they would be enforced, paragraph by paragraph.

Few in Spain, let alone anyone across the Pyrenees, took note of all that Alfonso the Wise did for science by enlisting the aid of Arab and Jewish scholars. He remained the sole Christian ruler of Spain who attempted to preserve and further an entirely new science and a humanistic culture far in advance of its age. For in the rest of Europe, the tendency was to repress intellectual freedom and the progress of knowledge. And Spain, too, was approaching an era in which human abasement would reach a depth whose like had hardly been known in all previous history. The misfortune was all the greater because Spain was peculiarly situated to provide a noble example for the times and the future. Three religions, three cultures, three peoples had encountered one another on the soil of Spain. Here a population consisting of Christians and Jews had lived peacefully together, in mutual tolerance and respect, as if on some blessed island, for many centuries. Stimulated by contact with the Arabs, a unique culture had bloomed. Philosophy, science, and poetry had reached heights unmatched elsewhere in the world.

Tolerance, humanity, and progress were swept aside by formidable powers that determined the future of the Iberian Peninsula. These powers had an entirely different goal, which they pursued relentlessly: to establish one sole religion, one sole state, and one sole culture sustained by an all-dominant Church. "Christian Spain for the Christian Spaniards" became the watchword to which all other considerations had to yield. The policies that Visigothic kings and synods had initiated half a millennium before were taken up once more and carried to their fateful end.

A century after the death of Alfonso the Wise the time had come. The balance of forces had shifted. The clergy had grown powerful, more powerful than ever before, and had acquired allies who worked in unison with it, although from entirely different motives: the nobility, vexed by the high positions the Jews held in the government, and the urban middle class, vexed by Jewish competition. A "holy war" against unbelievers could begin; but, for the present, not against the numerous Moslems living in the Christian parts of Spain. The attack began against the weakest enemy: the Jews. Who would take offense if the Jews were injured? There was no earthly power ready to come to their defense. Shortly before the end of the fourteenth century, the most frightful of times for Spanish Jewry began with a first merciless blow.

In 1391 Henry III had just ascended the throne as a child of eleven. A fanatical priest named Ferdinand Martinez, deputy for the Bishop of Seville and confessor to Queen Mother Leonora, began inciting the populace. He sent out letters calling upon everyone in his diocese "to raze to the ground the synagogues in which the enemies of God and the Church practice their idolatry." In Seville he himself conducted the operation. On May 21, 1391, he addressed a gigantic crowd and whipped them up to a fever of hatred for the Jews. An assault upon the Jewish quarter at the foot of the Alcazar was already beginning when the city guard intervened and at the last moment prevented violence. But three months later came a new assault. At break of dawn on June 6 armed Christians unexpectedly broke into the Jewish quarter, set fire to the houses, and massacred the people. Some four thousand Jews were killed; many others were sold into slavery to the Arabs. Only a few succeeded in escaping. All the rest, numb with terror, submitted to baptism. The Jewish community of nearly six thousand families was annihilated. A cross was fastened to its synagogue. Among the forcibly baptized was Don Samuel Abravanel, who had held high office at the court of King Henry II. He took the name of Juan Sanchez de Sevilla, but subsequently emigrated to Portugal, where he returned to Judaism.

The bloodbath of Seville was only the beginning. Kill all who refuse baptism—that was the slogan promulgated by Martinez. Like a destroying river of lava, the persecution rolled across all of Spain. In Córdoba the smoke of the burning *judería* rose into the sky. The corpses of two thousand men, women, and children were heaped in the ruins of destroyed houses and magnificent old synagogues. On June 10 it was the turn of the Toledo community. "For the sanctification of God's name" the rabbis took their own lives. Many followed their example; but once again the number of those who submitted to baptism was considerable. In Castile alone nearly seventy *juderías* were destroyed. Everywhere, the bloody terror produced new "converts."

Soon the same fate struck the Jews of Aragon. In Valencia on July 9 a mob broke into the Jewish quarter, screaming: "Martinez has come to baptize you." When the Jews defended themselves, a massacre ensued. Their houses were pillaged and destroyed. Of five thousand Jews, not one was left, although many accepted Christianity to save their lives. A month later the same fate descended upon the community in Barcelona. In vain, large numbers of Jews fled into the citadel. Townsfolk, reinforced by peasants from the vicinity, stormed the fortress. The residential area was burned to the ground. Palma, capital of Majorca, suffered a similar visitation. Three hundred Jews were killed; eight hundred escaped into the citadel and under cover of night succeeded in taking ship to Africa. Many fled from Castile to Portugal and were allowed in by permission of the King. Moses Navarro, chief rabbi of Portugal and the ruler's personal physician, had shown the King a copy of a papal bull forbidding forcible baptisms and acts of violence against Jews.

In less than three months the flourishing communities of Jews from the Pyrenees to the Strait of Gibraltar had been shattered. Tens of thousands had died, many thousands had fled. But something else had happened that hitherto had occurred only rarely: Everywhere thousands of Jews had accepted mass baptism in order to escape death. The number of converts far exceeded that of the martyrs.

This represented a new phase in the history of Jewry. For the first time the resistance of the Jews had been broken in the face of tribulation. When the terror abated for a time, a profound gulf remained between the two groups who had hitherto formed one community. Alongside Jews who had survived the massacres and remained unswervingly loyal to their faith there now lived, though torn from their midst and separated from them, the converts—the *conversos,* as they were called. To be sure, many had merely submitted to baptism without accepting Christianity. Secretly they remained faithful to their old religion and lived by its laws. But this concealment forced them into a desperate situation, which was ultimately to be the ruin of themselves and their descendants. For in the long run they could not hide their curious conduct from the Christians. Before long, they were being regarded with the greatest suspicion. They were dubbed marranos, a word meaning either "swine" or "the damned."

As had happened so often before, one of Judaism's bitterest and most dangerous enemies arose from the ranks of the apostates. He was the former rabbi Solomon Halevi of Burgos, who as a Christian assumed the name of Paul de Burgos. He rose to be primate of Spain, and was a member of Castile's Council of the Regency. In letters to eminent men—Don Joseph Orabuena, chief rabbi of the communities of Navarre and physician to Charles III, Don Meïr Alguadez, who held similar posts in Castile, and many others—Paul de Burgos attempted to heap ridicule upon Jewry and its customs. The Jewish scholars did not fail to reply. A sharp disputation flared. Foremost among the men who courageously opposed the neo-Christian zealot was the philosopher Don Hasdai Crescas of Saragossa.

The "holy war" had severely damaged the economy. The vigorous commerce with European and African countries suddenly halted after the destruction of so many Jewish communities. The survivors were pillaged of their goods and completely impoverished. Many Spanish coastal cities suffered from an economic depression. The consequences of the madness could also be seen in the royal treasure chambers. Large sums from Jewish special taxes no longer poured in. The baptized were no longer liable for these levies, and income from the remaining ruined Jewish communities had dwindled sharply. This state of affairs prompted Henry III of Castile, despite the opposition of the clergy, to order in 1395 the reconstruction of the destroyed Jewish communities. But the premature death of the King in 1406 spelled an end to this project. For on his deathbed Henry III had appointed, as executor of his will and tutor of his infant heir Don Juan, the anti-Semitic Bishop Paul de Burgos. Between the latter and the regent, the pious Queen Mother Catalina, the clergy acquired unchallenged power at court.

In 1408 the collection of laws made by Alfonso X was fetched out of the archives and its anti-Jewish provisions revived. All Jews were to be removed from high positions. The "holy war" was continued. Meïr Alguadez, physician to the late lamented King and a staunch protector of his fellow Jews, was put out of the way. In 1410 he was involved in a trial staged at Segovia for desecration of the host. His accusers extorted a confession from him on the rack: that he had hastened the King's death. Meïr Alguadez died a ghastly death; the executioners rent him limb from limb. And in 1412 the Ordinance of Doña Catalina was issued, a decree that struck down at one blow all the Jews of Castile. They were henceforth permitted to live only in special streets, had to desist from all crafts and the medical profession as well, and were required to wear the Jews' badge. Stern punishments—imprisonment and confiscation of wealth—threatened all who attempted to flee the country. The Ordinance was intended to force more Jews to baptism.

At the same time a new scourge of the Jews had arisen: the Dominican monk Vincent Ferrer. Surrounded by a band of flagellants, he paraded through the country preaching "holy hatred" against the unbelievers. He drove the Jews into their synagogues and forced them by threat of death to conversion. The monks garnered a rich harvest for the Church; some twenty thousand Jews were baptized in Castile and Aragon.

No stone was left unturned in the campaign to force the Jews into the Church. Benedict XIII, Spain's Antipope, hoped to win them from their errors by disputation. Once again an apostate was behind this enterprise: Geronimo de Santa Fe, the papal physician and a baptized Talmudic scholar formerly known as Joshua of Lorca. With the approval of King Ferdinand I, in 1412 all the Jewish communities of Aragon were instructed to send their most learned rabbis to Tortosa.

On February 7, 1413, the most remarkable public disputation in history began. Geronimo de Santa Fe took the role of prosecutor. Among the Jewish spokesmen were the physician and poet Don Vidal Benveniste of Saragossa, the philosopher Joseph Albo, and the keen and learned Rabbi Astruc Halevi of Alcañiz.

"When we entered the Pope's residence," a Jewish eyewitness has recorded, "we beheld a large courtyard adorned with colored hangings. This was the place for the disputation. There were seventy seats for the cardinals, bishops, and archbishops, who wore gold-embroidered garments. Of the other ecclesiastical dignitaries, townsfolk, and representatives of the government, there were about a thousand men present. We were seized by great fearfulness. . . . Now the Pope addressed us: 'Know, Jewish scholars, that I have not come here and instructed you to appear here in order to dispute on which of the two religions is the true one, since I do not doubt in the slightest that it is mine, whereas your Torah no doubt was true once in the past, but has since been abrogated. Here we wish only to consider the arguments of Geronimo, who is prepared to demonstrate, on the basis of the Talmud of your ancient teachers, who were wiser than you, that the Messiah has already appeared; and you, for your part, are to address yourselves to this question alone.' " By thus placing the Christian dogmas beyond discussion, the Pope put the rabbis on the defensive from the start.

Right at the beginning there was a nasty clash. Geronimo began by quoting Isaiah 1:18–20: "Come now, and let us reason together, saith the Lord. . . . If ye be willing and obedient, ye shall eat the good of the land; but if ye refuse and rebel, ye shall be devoured with the sword. . . ." Vidal Benveniste pointed out that this quotation amounted to a threat. "You are right," the Pope replied, "but this ill custom should scarcely surprise you —for Geronimo is one of your own."

It quickly became apparent to the rabbis, from the "prosecutor's" next remarks, that a fair exchange of views was not in prospect. They asked to be allowed to leave, but the Pope insisted that they go on with the disputation.

The great debate went on from February, 1413, to November, 1414. There were sixty-eight sessions, almost all of which revolved around the proposition that the Messiah had already come. Geronimo, however, took every occasion to denounce the Talmud. He claimed that it permitted children to strike parents and men to blaspheme against God and to practice idolatry. The Jewish representatives could not retort, for it was worth their lives to profess their opinions openly. Any criticism of Christian dogmas would only have brought disaster upon themselves and their fellows. Consequently, they confined themselves to refuting the attacks on their opponent's ground.

The disputation ended as might have been foreseen: Geronimo maintained that he had defeated the Jews. But the hoped-for mass baptisms throughout the country did not follow. In his wrath, the Pope ordered that all copies of the "blasphemous Talmud" be confiscated and destroyed. His order, however, went unexecuted, for in 1415 the Council of Constance decided that Benedict XIII "must be hacked off as a withered branch on the tree of the Catholic Church." Vincent Ferrer, whose methods the Council also condemned, died soon afterward. In 1418 Martin V, the Pope elected at Constance, once again explicitly prohibited all conversion by compulsion. In 1421 he sanctioned the appointment of Jewish financiers and court physicians. Decades of peace—a breathing spell—followed for the harried Jews. With new hope the Jews of Spain resumed the interrupted work of reconstruction.

They found a strong leader and protector in Abraham Benveniste, who at the Castilian court bore the title of court rabbi—*el rabí de la corte*. The tasks facing him were enormous. The parlous economic conditions of the entire country had to be overcome, and the ruined intellectual and social life of the Jewish communities revived. There were not enough synagogues, schools, or teachers. The majority of the Jews were destitute. There were a few families who still possessed wealth and lived in luxury— and, naturally, the eyes of the anti-Semites were fixed upon these few rather than upon the impoverished masses of Jews.

"It was no honest life that many representatives of our congregation led," Solomon Alami testified. "I mean those eminent persons who puffed themselves up at the royal courts. The kings raised them to high offices, entrusted them with the keys to their treasuries; but the wealth they acquired made them haughty, and they wished to forget their former poverty and humbleness. They had palaces built, hitched magnificent mules to their carriages; their wives and daughters began adorning themselves like aristocratic ladies and displaying their jewelry. . . . These people were full of contempt for scholarship, work, and craftsmanship, in their idleness preferring haughtiness and pomp. . . . At the same time they were filled with mutual envy and slandered one another before the kings and grandees, without realizing that by so doing they were only plunging themselves into ruin. . . . But small folk were exploited and plundered by them. Their only aim was to shift the burden of taxes from themselves to those who had nothing. By their whole conduct they dishonored themselves in the eyes of their foes, who waited only for the opportunity to get rid of them and to drive them in disgrace out of the palaces of the kings and the grandees."

In 1432 Abraham Benveniste summoned the rabbis and elders to a meeting in Valladolid. Among other decisions of the assemblage was a condemnation of slanderers and a call for just taxation, which would strike rich as well as poor. There was also a warning against luxury and the rage for adornment. "May our men and women never forget that they pine in the galuth and do not stand upon their own soil."

Not two generations had passed since the first bloody wave of forced baptisms before the terrible consequences unfolded. The tragedy of the marranos began. When the city fathers of Perpignan had exclaimed, "Let the Jews become Christians and the whole tumult will end," Juan I had made a prediction. Baptism of the Jews without their free consent was "a terrible crime," the King declared, "for if they do not convert completely and with a good will, the confusion afterward will be worse than before." That prediction now came true.

In 1467 there was a bloody clash in Toledo that brought to light the nasty situation resulting from the enforced baptisms. For some time an increasingly vehement conflict had been raging between Old Christians and New Christians over dominance in the municipal government. Ultimately the entire population of the city was split into two feuding parties. One feast day in July a quarrel in front of the cathedral suddenly erupted into civil war. Armed bands of Old Christians forced their way into their opponents' residential district and began a general massacre. Whole rows of houses were burned to ashes and more than a hundred marranos were killed.

Six years later the storm broke out against the New Christians in Córdoba. During a procession on March 14, 1473, word suddenly went round that a marrano's daughter had emptied dirty water from a window on a saint's image. For three days the cry, *"Viva la fe de Dios,"* rang through the city, while the mob went on a rampage against the New Christians. In vain the commandant of the city, Alfonso de Aguilar, himself related by marriage to a marrano family, tried to check the wave of terrorism with his troops. The contagion spread to other places in Castile. The following year there were attacks on marranos in the northern part of the country. Segovia became the scene of a frightful massacre. All the New Christians were expelled from some cities.

The reasons behind these terrible excesses were not hard to discern. The New Christians, no longer despised, no longer handicapped by occupational restrictions, had suddenly found all the doors of society open to them. By the simple act of accepting baptism they could engage in any work they pleased, could rise in commerce and agriculture, in Church as well as State. As Jews, even in spite of unfavorable circumstances, they had held high offices and done well in their occupations. Who could blame them for now making the most of the multitude of new opportunities that were open to them? They did so, and the result was something that had not been considered by those so furiously determined to convert the Jews. Baptism had not diminished their abilities and gifts; the many thousands who had been driven into the Church by threats rose with incredible rapidity. They were to be found in every occupation, in every class of society. Everywhere they held important and profitable positions. They intermarried with the nobility. Law, government, the army, the universities, even the Church, were flooded with them.

The reaction was inevitable. Envy and hatred flared against the New Christians.

But there was another reason, fraught with far more danger, that prompted the Church to proceed against them. The overwhelming majority of the *conversos* had been baptized but never really converted. They adhered outwardly to all the prescribed customs of the Christian Church. Couples were married by priests; parents had their children baptized; all attended Mass and went to confession. But at the bottom of their hearts most of them remained faithful to Judaism and secretly observed their old laws. They kept the Sabbath holy as far as they were able. An observer standing on the hills above a town could see the many chimneys from which no smoke rose on a Saturday. Many also followed the dietary laws. One marrano, it was said, used the pretext of illness to eat unleavened bread, matzoth, every day so that he would also be able to eat it on the Passover without stirring suspicion. Thus the marranos led a double life, in constant fear of discovery and denunciation. This continued even when a new generation of marranos had grown up, born and raised as Christians.

In the long run this state of affairs could not remain concealed. The Church discovered, to her alarm, that the enemy was now securely lodged within her own ranks. Marranos occupied high ecclesiastical offices; quite a few of them held the episcopal staff. How wise had been Gregory the Great's admonition to seek the conversion of the Jews only by love, never by violence. Subsequent Popes had repeatedly stressed that principle as the policy of the Church, but the Spanish clergy had flagrantly disregarded it. The consequences were only now becoming apparent. The object of the "holy war" had been to drive the Jews into the Church. Now a "holy struggle against the enemy within" began, with the object of driving them out again. The Church of Spain knew only one way to cope with this peril. She used the same means as before, murder and terror.

In 1469 Isabella of Castile married Ferdinand of Aragon; in 1474 she ascended the throne of Castile. The clergy found the new rulers most receptive to its plans. Thanks to a pact between Church and throne, this country of three religions became a hell on earth for the adherents of two of the three.

It represented an irony of fate that Jews, and marranos in particular, had innocently helped to promote the marital alliance that was to have such dire consequences for them. In Aragon the marrano statesman Alfonso de la Caballeria overcame the obstacles that for a while had blocked a union between the ruling houses. In Castile the much respected Rabbi Abraham Senior of Segovia played an important role in the negotiations preceding the betrothal. Isabella was so grateful to Abraham for his services that she settled a large annual salary upon him.

From the moment she ascended to the throne, however, Isabella's spiritual advisers kept urging her to wage the struggle against apostasy by "legal" measures. All heretics were to be tried before a special tribunal. That meant introduction of the Inquisition, which could only be done with permission from Rome.

The Pope was willing to concede a national Inquisition for Spain—but he demanded participation by the Roman Curia. Isabella and Ferdinand would not agree for purely material reasons. They feared that the Church would lay claim to the booty that would result from these trials, which they were eager to add to their own treasury. Tomás de Torquemada, Isabella's confessor, finally prevailed upon the Pope to give way. The King was to appoint the members of the tribunal and garner the wealth of all the condemned into the royal treasure chamber.

In November, 1474, Pope Sixtus IV issued his bull on the establishment of the "national" Inquisition in Spain. But it was not until the end of the year 1480 that the terrible wheels began to turn. The first tribunal was appointed in Seville. Instructions were published detailing all signs of a leaning toward Judaism. Some of those signs were the wearing of fresh linen on Saturday, the Jewish Sabbath, or washing hands before prayer, or preferring certain kinds of meat and wine, or reading aloud the Psalms but omitting the words "honor to the Father and the Son." All Christians were called upon, under threat of the severest punishments, to denounce anyone who appeared to be acting suspiciously in any way. Every denunciation remained anonymous, with the result that informing and denouncing became the order of the day. Searches of homes and arrests followed. Fifteen thousand marranos accused of "Judaizing" were thrown into prisons. In the crypts of the monastery-fortress of Seville there began the interrogations under torture. The victims were subjected to inhuman torments, and made to confess not only their own alleged sins, but to betray their Judaizing relatives and friends. A confession made on the rack and confirmed once again afterward was considered sufficient proof of a charge. But if the defendant afterward retracted his confession, he was tortured still more cruelly.

Amid solemn ecclesiastical ceremonies, on February 6, 1481, the first auto-da-fé took place. In that "act of faith" six marranos were burned.

For the first time the city of Seville beheld one of those uncanny processions that for centuries were to be part and parcel of life in Spain— for the Inquisition was not abolished by law until the nineteenth century. In resplendent robes the clergy, bearing crucifixes, and the grandees, dressed in black and carrying banners and flags, marched along with the candidates for death in their dresses of rough sacking painted with red crosses. Their route, lined by gaping crowds, led to the municipal center, where a special execution ground had been established: the *quemadero,* on which the gigantic pyre was placed. Members of the court, the nobility, and the clergy took their places on tribunes to watch the proceedings. The Inquisitors read aloud the death sentences. Then the secular power carried them out. The royal executioner performed his office—for the Church abhorred the spilling of blood: *"Ecclesia abhorret a sanguine."* The heretics were burned alive. But those who showed repentance were accorded a special mercy; the executioner strangled them first, and only their dead bodies were delivered over to the flames.

On March 26 seventeen more victims of the Inquisition were consigned to the flames on the *quemadero* in Seville. By November, 1481—in a space of only ten months—the smoke of three hundred burned marranos rose to the sky from this one execution ground.

A cry of horror rang through all of Spain, and its reverberations reached Rome. In January, 1482, the Pope addressed a letter to Ferdinand and Isabella. Sixtus IV sharply reproved the Inquisitor's procedures—people had been yielded to torture and death solely on the basis of denunciations, he declared, without proper legal trial. Three months later the Pope once again attempted to check the arbitrariness of the tribunals. In his bull he bluntly stated that most of the trials were impelled "not by zeal and concern for the salvation of souls, but by avarice" (*"non zelo fidei et salutis animarum, sed lucri cupiditate"*). These efforts were vain. Ferdinand ignored the papal injunction for orderly and just procedures.

The events in Seville were only a rehearsal for what now began in the whole of Spain. In September, 1483, Tomás de Torquemada was given the office of Grand Inquisitor. Promptly, more "spiritual tribunals" were established in other cities in Castile. Then came Aragon and Navarre. Throughout Spain, arrests and torture ensued on a mass scale; flames of innumerable vast pyres consumed their human victims. "Of the horror that now began," Josef Kastein wrote in December, 1932, "one cannot give details without seeming to be pandering to the instincts for sensation. No age, no nation, no church, ever carried out such a program of bloodthirsty torture of human beings, except perhaps for the slaughter of the Incas by the Spanish conquistadors."

Within a short time the count of the victims reached almost thirty thousand. The tribunal of the Inquisition in Saragossa did not even grant the penitent the "mercy respite" required by the statutes. Even the dead were not exempt. The statute devised by Torquemada empowered the tribunals to sit in judgment even on the deceased—for they often left fortunes that could be confiscated if they were condemned posthumously as apostates or heretics. Their bones were dug up and burned, and their whole property reverted to the royal treasury.

Year after year the Inquisition ate like a corrosive acid deeper into Spanish life. A destroying process had been set in motion. It led inevitably to the ruin of the country, and its effects deeply branded the character and the psyche of the whole population of Iberia.

During these years the Jews themselves lived undisturbed, merely eyewitnesses of the terrible fate that was descending upon their former coreligionists. For the Inquisition had no charges against them; they could not be treated as heretics because they were unbelievers, outside the Church.

The rulers continued to employ Jews in official capacities. Thus a weird situation came into being: Jews occupying high office went in and out the same royal courts that secretly harbored a plan for exterminating not only all "Judaizing" Christians but also all the Jews in the country. Ferdinand and Isabella had entrusted the finances of their kingdom to Isaac Abravanel. Abraham Senior was responsible to the royal couple for collection of all the taxes on Jewish communities. Unknowingly, these two men paved the way for a war that was to be the nemesis of Spanish Jewry. The Jewish minister Abravanel procured the funds that Ferdinand needed for his campaign against the Moors in Granada. Abraham Senior took care that the full amount of special taxes imposed on the Jews for this war was punctually collected.

The last struggle between Cross and Crescent on the soil of Spain dragged on for ten years. The Christian armies levied from Aragon and Castile made slow progress against the one remaining Moslem base in the southern part of the peninsula, the tiny kingdom of Granada. In 1487 Málaga fell. Toward the end of the year 1491 Granada at last surrendered. On January 2, 1492, Ferdinand and Isabella made a solemn entry into the magnificent capital of the once mighty Arab rulers. The goal for which generations had fought was at last attained: Islam had been expelled from the Iberian Peninsula. Only one thing was lacking to realize the Visigothic ideal of one nation and one religion—the expulsion of the Jews.

Eight centuries earlier, with the victory of the Mohammedans over the Catholic Visigoths, Spain had become a country of three religions. The moment the last Moslem bastion fell, intolerance held sway again. On March 31, 1492, Ferdinand and Isabella, in the Alhambra, issued their "General Edict on the Expulsion of the Jews from Aragon and Castile." It read:

> In Our kingdoms there are not a few Judaizing, evil Christians who have deviated from Our holy Catholic faith, which fact is due chiefly to the intercourse of Jews with Christians. . . . According to the report presented to Us by the Inquisitors, there is no doubt that intercourse of Christians with Jews, who seek to mislead them to their damnable religion, causes the greatest harm. . . . It has led to the undermining and debasement of Our holy Catholic faith. . . . We have therefore resolved to expel all Jews of both sexes forever from the borders of Our kingdom. We herewith decree that all Jews living within Our domains, without distinction of sex or age, must depart by no later than the end of July of this year from all Our royal possessions and seigneuries, together with their sons and daughters and their Jewish domestic servants. And let them not dare to set foot in the country again, for the purpose of settlement, or transit, or for any other purpose whatsoever. If, however, disregarding this command they shall be caught in Our domains, they will be punished by death without trial and with confiscation of their wealth. From the end of July on, therefore, let no one in Our kingdom, under penalty of confiscation of all goods for the royal treasury, presume openly or secretly to grant a Jewish man or woman shelter. . . . We permit them to take out with them by land or by sea, from Our kingdom, their property with the exception of gold, silver, coined money, and other objects subject to the general ban on exports.

A stroke of the pen sealed the fate of the Spanish Jews who had been living in the country for more than a thousand years and had made vital contributions to its culture and economy.

Abraham Senior and Isaac Abravanel tried at the last moment to prevent the promulgation of the edict. They pleaded with Ferdinand and Isabella and promised to raise a huge sum in compensation—thirty thousand gold ducats. As one chronicle recounts, Ferdinand was on the point of yielding when Torquemada entered the room holding a crucifix. The Grand Inquisitor approached the royal couple and said: "Judas Iscariot betrayed Christ for thirty pieces of silver, and now you would abandon him for thirty thousand. Here he is, take and sell him." Whereupon he laid the crucifix down before Ferdinand and Isabella. The plea of the Jewish leaders was rejected.

Royal heralds proclaimed the edict throughout the country. It affected some two hundred thousand persons. All they possessed had to be sold hastily at ludicrous prices. Some sold their houses for a mule, their vineyards for a bale of cloth. Spies kept a sharp watch lest any Christian violate the ban against giving the slightest help to those condemned to banishment. The treasury confiscated the Jews' schools and hospitals; their synagogues were later converted into churches and monasteries. To this day magnificent former synagogues converted into churches are among the sights of the ancient capital of Toledo—among them, El Tránsito, once built by the Jewish statesman Don Samuel Allavi as a gift to his community, and Santa María la Blanca.

The lamentation increased as the day of departure approached. For the last time the Jews visited their cemeteries. The great trek to the frontiers began; vast processions of people, loaded down with humble possessions, thronged the roads, heading in all directions—to the Kingdom of Navarre in the north, to the ports in the south, hoping for a place aboard a ship that would take them to Africa, Italy, or Turkey, and to Portugal in the west.

Two days before August 2, 1492, the day of mourning for the destruction of Jerusalem, Spain was empty of all who professed the Jewish religion. Among the exiles were not only scholars and teachers, financiers and merchants, but also a great many of Spain's vintners and successful farmers, artisans, armorers, and metal workers. A significant portion of the middle class was gone. The economy soon felt the blow; in many once busy places commercial life slowed to a standstill. Soon there was an acute shortage of doctors throughout Spain. The high degree of commercial and cultural achievement that the country had reached never returned after the expulsion of 1492. The sciences, philosophy, and intellectual life in general never again reached the heights that had been attained during the Arab-Jewish period. The Spanish economy would have collapsed entirely had it not been for the baptized Jewish families who remained in the country. When toward the end of the sixteenth century a mass flight from the cruel toils of the Inquisition began among the marranos also, the economy of Spain was doomed. So was that of Portugal, where events followed a parallel course.

EXPULSION FROM PORTUGAL

The largest current of the refugees from Spain—some one hundred thousand of them—took the nearest and safest road to the west. The lanes and highways that led to Portugal's borders were black with long lines of tramping human beings. Full of hope, they turned their footsteps toward the land in which their coreligionists had lived peacefully for centuries, protected by the kings, active in all occupations. Since the twelfth century, when the Portuguese King Alfonso Henriques had appointed the brave and prudent cavalry leader Jachia ibn Jaish his majordomo, Jews had repeatedly held office in the government and Jewish scholars and physicians had been esteemed at court.

João II, who had been reigning since 1481, had turned even more often to Jewish experts in recent years, for he was considering dispatching ships from Portugal to discover a sea route to India by way of the West African coast. Jews made significant contributions to the scientific preparations and technical equipment of the great expeditions that were to win glory for the Portuguese seafarers. Martin Behaim, the German geographer who had been summoned from Nuremberg, collaborated with Moses, an astronomer and the royal physician, and Joseph Vecinho, a mathematician. Together they prepared new and improved astronomical calendars and star tables for the expeditions. Vecinho considerably improved the astrolabe, the indispensable instrument of navigation for measuring the altitude of the sun or stars. Moreover, years before the departure of the ships, Rabbi Abraham de Beja and Joseph Zapateiro de Lamego had visited Asia on commission from the King to obtain important geographical information. In 1487 Bartolomeu Dias, eminently well advised and equipped, was able to set out on his great voyage to the Cape of Good Hope, which opened up the sea route to India.

The hopes of the expelled Jews from Spain were bitterly disappointed. Portugal became only a brief way station on their flight, which led only to new oppressions and sufferings.

At the pleading of an embassy of thirty elders from the Jewish communities of Castile, King João II had permitted the refugees to enter his country. But their stay was limited to eight months, and even that had to be paid for by a large donation to the royal treasury. In return, the King promised to provide the fugitives with ships for voyaging to other lands. Exception had been made only in the cases of wealthy Jews who transferred their capital to Portugal, and specialists; shipwrights, metal workers, and especially armorers were allowed to remain indefinitely. The King urgently needed such craftsmen for his African venture.

The King's promises were not kept. In vain tens of thousands of hapless refugees waited impatiently for the promised ships. The few vessels that belatedly arrived were not sufficient. Those fugitives who finally were able to board vessels in Lisbon and Oporto were treated brutally by captains and crews. They were put off willy-nilly anywhere at all on the African coast. Those who had been unable to obtain ships, and had remained in the country after the eight-month period was up, were out of hand declared royal serfs and sold into slavery. Children were mercilessly snatched from the arms of their parents. Hundreds of the refugees were sent to the tropical island of St. Thomas, where most of them perished.

In the midst of these calamities, João II died in 1495. His successor, Manuel I, who reigned from 1495 to 1521, restored freedom to all the enslaved refugees who had been unable to leave Portugal in time. Once more the Jews began to hope. In addition, the King summoned a famous Jewish scholar to his court—Abraham ben Samuel Zacuto, the great mathematician and astronomer, who had formerly taught in Salamanca and who in 1473 had made a name for himself with the publication of his astronomical tables *The Perpetual Almanac*. Zacuto was consulted as scientific adviser for an expedition that was to prove a sensational success: that of Vasco da Gama. In 1497 the Portuguese navigator rounded the Cape of Good Hope; in 1498 he crossed the Indian Ocean and landed near Calicut on the Malabar Coast of India.

The favor shown to the Jews during this period lasted only a short time. Political considerations soon turned Manuel, too, into an enemy of the Jews. For Manuel had great plans; he thought to bring the entire Iberian Peninsula under his scepter by marriage. Manuel sued for the hand of the eldest daughter of Ferdinand and Isabella. The rulers seemed inclined to consent, but they had the Infanta set a condition: She would not set foot on the soil of Portugal before the country was cleaned of the "accursed" Jews.

After close consultation with his advisers and grandees, the King accepted the Spanish demand. He was not going to sacrifice his dynastic aims for the sake of the Jews.

On November 30, 1496, the marriage contract between Manuel and the

Spanish Infanta Isabella was signed. Its clauses, dictated by Spanish fanaticism, sealed the fate of all the Jews in Portugal. The edict was issued on December 25, 1496, requiring all Jews, both the refugees from Spain and those who had been settled in the land for centuries, to leave Portugal within ten months. By the end of October none of them must remain. For, so the edict declared, echoing the Spanish decree of expulsion of 1492, "The Jews persist in their hatred of the Holy Catholic Faith; they commit crimes against the religion and deflect Christians from the path of truth."

Manuel had deliberately given the Jews a longer reprieve than had the Spanish rulers. He was conscious of their value as useful subjects, reluctant to lose them from his country, and hoped that many Jews would finally accept baptism if they had time to reflect on the alternative. When they did not, Manuel ordered all Jewish children and youths between the ages of four and twenty to be seized and forcibly baptized.

Frightful scenes took place in the days before Easter of the year 1497. The King's bailiffs began their hunt, dragging their victims to the churches. Many parents killed their children and committed suicide. "I saw," reported Bishop Fernando Coutinho, who had vainly advised the King against taking this action, "how many were dragged by the hair to the baptismal font, and a father overwhelmed by grief walking beside his son crying to God to witness that his child would die with him in the faith of Moses."

Meanwhile, the date of departure was approaching. More than twenty thousand Jews thronged to the quays in Lisbon, the King having ordered that they could leave only from this one port. But the expected ships again did not arrive, the time limit passed, and the edict was issued to baptize all who remained. Many, in their distress, gave sham consent. But the majority attempted to flee; they rushed into the water. A band led by Simon Maimi tried armed resistance. They were overpowered and dragged off to dungeons. But all violence proved fruitless, and Manuel called off the atrocities. His purpose had been to keep the Jews; his strategy had failed, and now he had to let them go. The following year the last of the Jewish families boarded ships and departed from Portugal.

From 1498 on there were no Jews living in Portugal who openly professed the religion of Moses. But the country, like Spain, was full of thousands who had been forcibly baptized. The "solution" of the marrano question by torture and auto-da-fé was attempted in Portugal, too, for more than two centuries. In Lisbon, Coimbra, Evora, and other cities the Inquisition burned hundreds of secret Jews. Restrictions were not placed upon the activities of the tribunals until after Antonio José da Silva, one of the foremost of Portuguese dramatists, was burned at the stake for this charge. As late as 1766 religious trials were held in Lisbon. Officially, the Inquisition was not abolished in Portugal until 1820. The steadfastness with which many Portuguese marranos clung to their faith was demonstrated by an amazing fact: A whole community of secret Jews survived in the mountains of northern Portugal and were not discovered until after the beginning of the twentieth century, when they openly returned to their ancient religion.

Like her larger neighbor on the peninsula, Portugal had undermined her own prosperity by the expulsion of the Jews. In spite of her favorable position on the North Atlantic, in spite of her great overseas possessions, she succumbed to economic and intellectual decay.

A chapter in the post-Biblical history of the Jewish people that had begun so hopefully ended in darkness and inhumanity. The dispersed sons of Israel continued their wanderings among the nations.

THE FATE OF THE ABRAVANELS

The misery of the refugees from Spain and Portugal seemed without bounds. Where were they to go? Where in the world was there a place for them? None among the more than one hundred thousand fugitives could answer this question. For months they drifted about the Mediterranean, from port to port, hoping for a haven—in France, Italy, North Africa, Egypt, Turkey. Thousands died of hunger and disease; thousands were sold into slavery or killed. Sometimes they were permitted to land, only to be plundered and driven forth again. One account tells the story of a single Spanish Jew. On shipboard he lost all the members of his family. His wife was raped and carried away before his eyes. His children were taken from him. Whereupon he raised his hands to heaven and cried out: "Lord of the Universe, you have done a great deal to me to make me abandon my faith. But be sure that, in spite of all who sit enthroned above, I am a Jew and I shall remain a Jew."

One of the most eminent of the Spanish families was not spared such blows of fate. The destiny of the Jews for more than a century is reflected in the strange experiences of these Sephardim, these Spanish Jews of the Abravanel family who lived through all the heights and depths of a terrible age.

The Abravanels belonged to one of the oldest and greatest Jewish families of Spain. They boasted that they were descended from the House of

David, and they counted many scholars and distinguished men in their ancestry. In the fourteenth century Seville was their native city; there Judah Abravanel was attached to the royal service. His son Samuel became one of the richest men in all of Castile. When Henry II ascended the throne, he entrusted Samuel with high office. In 1391 there came the wave of anti-Jewish hysteria. Under threat of death during the excesses of the "holy war," Samuel converted to Christianity and adopted the name of Juan Sanchez de Sevilla. But his conversion was only a sham. When the disturbances abated, Samuel secretly emigrated to Portugal with his family and there returned to Judaism. The family's rise began anew with Samuel's sons. The Infante Don Ferdinand appointed Don Jehudah his treasurer. Don Jehudah's son Isaac, born in 1437, became the most famous of the Abravanels. A child prodigy, carefully educated, he acquired profound learning in theology and the sciences, familiarized himself with Arab as well as Jewish philosophers, and endeavored to unite the brilliance and wealth that were his birthright with the glory of scholarship and fame as a writer. His whole life long Isaac studied the glorious antiquity of Judaism and the meaning of its concept of God. His greatest wish, he once said, was to write a commentary on the Scriptures. But this was a task reserved for his old age.

Isaac's life took an unexpected turn. Alfonso V of Portugal (who reigned from 1448 to 1481) had taken a liking to the learned young man and invited him to join his court. He became the King's confidential adviser on questions of state and on familial matters as well, and was appointed finance minister. Soon Dom Isaac Abravanel also enjoyed the confidence and affection of the grandees and many dignitaries of the country. He was a close friend of Duke Ferdinand of Bragança, a member of the royal house.

"Without a care," he later recounted, "I lived in the house I inherited from my ancestors, in much-praised Lisbon, the mother of all Portuguese cities. God blessed me with wealth, honor, and all the joys of human life. My house was a gathering place for scholars and wise men, where we were wont to speak of books and writers, of the knowledge and the fear of God. I served at the court of King Alfonso, a righteous ruler, under whom the Jews were permitted to live free and unimperiled. I was close to him; he leaned upon me; and as long as he lived I went in and out of his palace."

This life under Alfonso was the last of the good days for the Portuguese Jews. No one forced them to wear demeaning badges or banished them into *juderías*. The prosperous among them rode on horses and mules, as was the custom of the country, their mounts richly caparisoned. They

dressed in long cloaks, sported silken vests, and carried swords. Dom
Isaac was regarded by his fellow Jews as a "shield and wall." Whenever
they met with any mischance, he came generously to their aid. After the
conquest of the African ports of Tangier and Arzila the returning soldiers
brought home a horde of prisoners whom they sold as slaves. Dom Isaac
later learned that hundreds of Jews were among them. He promptly contributed ten thousand gold doubloons to buy their freedom, and looked
into each of their cases, traveling about the country himself until the last
of them had been ransomed. He likewise made efforts, through the Portuguese Ambassador, to persuade Pope Sixtus IV to favor his coreligionists.

With the death of Alfonso V in 1481 this happy period came to an
abrupt end. João II, the new King, accused the Duke of Bragança of
treasonable relations with the rulers of Castile, and had him executed.
His relatives and friends were threatened with the same fate. Dom Isaac
had been called to an interview with the King when some of his con-
fidants warned him and advised him to flee. He took the advice, and,
although pursued by the royal cavalry, he managed to reach the Spanish
border. João II confiscated all his property. Beggared, Dom Isaac traveled
across Spain with his wife and three sons, and in 1483 settled in Toledo.
The Jewish community in the Castilian capital gave him an honorable
reception. A circle of scholars gathered around the exiled Portuguese statesman. He delivered lectures and once more devoted himself with great zeal
to his studies, for which he had previously had insufficient time. In only
six months, from November 1483 to April 1484, he wrote a commentary
in Hebrew on the books of Joshua, Judges, and Samuel.

The period of his literary activity proved all too brief. He had just
begun his commentary on the books of the Kings when a message from
the Spanish rulers reached him. Ferdinand and Isabella, having learned
of his presence in the country, invited him to their court. Once more the
scholar became a statesman, only to be involved in the tragedy of Spanish Jewry. For eight years he served as royal tax farmer, until the fateful
March 31, 1492, when the royal couple suddenly signed the edict of expulsion. When his efforts to bring about revocation of that fateful decision
failed, he was in no doubt where his loyalties lay. Though Ferdinand and
Isabella asked him to remain in office, assuring him their full protection,
Isaac Abravanel refused. Accompanied by his three sons, he turned his
back on Spain and along with many other refugees took ship for Naples.

At last the time seemed to have come for Dom (or, rather, ever since
he had left Portugal, Don) Isaac to resume the scholarly work that had
been twice interrupted by government service. He took up where he had
left off in Toledo and wrote a commentary on the books of the Kings.

But scarcely had he finished when a third career began. Ferdinand I, King of Naples, entrusted him with an important post at court. Before long he experienced once again the vagaries of fortune. In 1494 King Charles VIII of France invaded Italy to enforce the claims of the House of Anjou upon Naples. Abravanel had to flee with his king. He accompanied Ferdinand to Sicily. After Ferdinand's death he moved to Corfu. There pure chance brought him a great happiness: He met another refugee who possessed his commentary on the fifth book of Moses; his own copy had been lost in the course of his travels.

His wanderings were not yet over. In 1496 he was able to return to the liberated Kingdom of Naples, but until 1503 he lived in retirement, absorbed in his literary work, in the small town of Monopoli in Apulia. Then he moved on to Venice, where he served as adviser to the Doge and undertook several important diplomatic missions. He devoted himself to the cause of the republic with the same skill and earnestness that he had shown toward his first master in Portugal. In 1509 the eventful life of Don Isaac Abravanel ended.

The story of the Abravanels, however, did not end with his death. In the meantime his sons had made names for themselves and were famous throughout Italy. Judah (c. 1460–c. 1521), Don Isaac's eldest son, served as physician to the Spanish Viceroy in Naples after the expulsion of the French. Gonsalvo de Córdoba, who had conquered Naples for the Kingdom of Spain in 1504, protected him and repeatedly thwarted King Ferdinand's orders to expel all Jews from Naples as they had been expelled from Spain. But one day Judah had to flee; the Inquisition was after him. He went to Venice and there employed his time in enlarging his already vast knowledge of astronomy, mathematics, and philosophy. Although he had been in Italy barely ten years, he wrote in the language of the country a work that was to win him fame under his pseudonym, Leone Ebreo. His *Dialoghi di amore,* one of the most influential philosophical works of the sixteenth century, soon became favorite reading among all cultivated persons in Europe. It was translated into French, Spanish, Latin, and Hebrew. Toward the end of his life Judah lived in Genoa, engaged in a friendly battle of wits with the scholars of the Medicean age, few of whom could match him in versatility and breadth of knowledge. But all his achievements were overshadowed by one sorrow. His son, a victim of forced baptism, lived far from him in Portugal. A letter from Judah has been preserved in which he reminds his son "to remain always mindful of Judaism, cultivate the Hebrew language and literature, and imagine the grief of your father and the sorrow of your mother."

Isaac, Don Isaac's second son, lived first as a physician in Reggio di

Calabria. Later he went to Venice; it was he who persuaded his father to come there.

Samuel Abravanel (1473–1550), the youngest of the three, ranked as the most respected Jew in Italy; his coreligionists regarded him as virtually a prince. "Samuel Abravanel," wrote the marrano poet Samuel Usque, "deserves to be called Trismegistos—the Thrice Greatest. He is great and wise in the law, great in nobility, and great in wealth. With the goods that fortune has bestowed upon him he is always generous, and relieves the tribulations of his people. He sees to the marriage of orphans without number, succors the needy, endeavors to ransom prisoners. . . ."

Samuel had taught for a time at the Talmudic school in Salonika. He inherited from his father both intellectual gifts and extraordinary financial acumen. When he came to Italy the Spanish Viceroy of Naples, Don Pedro de Toledo, employed him as finance minister, in which capacity he served for many years. His wife, Benvenita, as broadly educated as himself, supervised the education of Princess Leonora, the Viceroy's daughter. Jewish and Christian scholars frequented Samuel's house. He remained in Naples until anti-Jewish measures were instituted in that city on orders from Emperor Charles V. Thereupon Samuel and his family left the city. He moved to Ferrara, where he died soon afterward.

Samuel was the last of the pre-eminent Abravanels in the sixteenth century. But their descendants continued the old tradition, producing many men of distinction. In 1650 one scion of the famous family lived in Amsterdam—Jonah Abravanel, a poet who among other works published a Spanish translation of the Psalms. The last of that branch, Hirsch Abravanel, chief of the rabbinate in Lissa, Prussia, died in 1863. But the family name still survives among the London Sephardim, and it also exists in Spain in the form Barbanel, probably carried down from the days of Don Isaac Abravanel in a marrano side branch.

THE SAVING CRESCENT

Of the great host of refugees from Spain and Portugal, tens of thousands landed on the North African coast. From the Atlas Mountains to Suez they tried to make a fresh start or to slip into old and settled Jewish communities. Ship after ship brought new bands of unfortunates who desperately sought asylum.

The largest group of all, a tremendous migration of expelled Jews and marranos, went still farther east, where as a consequence of great changes in the world balance of power the gates were thrown open to them and they were welcomed hospitably, to the Ottoman Empire.

When Constantinople fell to the onslaught of the Turkish conquerors on May 29, 1453, and the crescent banner was raised above the old imperial city—eleven centuries after its founding by Emperor Constantine I—good fortune was in store for the Diaspora community on the Bosporus. The Turkish sultans were as magnanimous toward the persecuted Jews as the Arabs had once been when they conquered the Iberian Peninsula from the Visigothic kings.

Samuel Usque, a refugee from Portugal, wrote jubilantly in his book *Comfort for the Oppressions of Israel*: "The great Turkish Empire, boundless as the seas that wash its shores, opened wide before us. The gates of freedom stand wide open to you, son of my people. Without fear you may profess your faith there; you can begin a new life, shake off the yoke of wrongful doctrines and customs that the nations have forced upon you, and return to the age-old wisdom of your ancestors."

Throughout the Ottoman Empire new communities of Jews sprang up and old ones expanded, on both sides of the Bosporus—from the Balkans through Asia Minor and down to Egypt, and finally in conquered North Africa as well. The sultans Bajazet, Selim, and Suleiman generously granted the Jews all liberties. Istanbul, where new bands of fugitives arrived daily, soon held the largest Jewish community in Europe. Their number grew to forty thousand; forty-four synagogues were built. Twenty thousand Jews settled in Salonika and began a new life. Settlements in Adrianople followed, and in Gallipoli. The influx of the Sephardim, the Spanish-Portuguese Jews, was heaviest of all. Compared with them, the number of immigrant Ashkenazim, the Jews from France and Germany, remained small.

Turkey soon began discovering how valuable these hordes of Jewish immigrants were to the life of the country. Industry and trade boomed mightily. Sultan Bajazet II is said to have commented on Ferdinand of Spain: "You are mistaken to call this king wise, for he has only ruined his own country and enriched ours."

The international commerce of the young Ottoman Empire expanded significantly. The trade of the Levant ceased to be a monopoly of the Italians and Greeks. Ports on the Adriatic, Aegean, and Black seas awoke from the sloth of ages and became thriving trade marts. Salonika, in particular, grew into the largest port of transshipment for the entire Mediterranean, and at the same time became a largely Jewish city. A rapidly expanding textile industry, created by the refugees, supplied the Turkish troops with uniforms. The mines in the vicinity of the city were worked by Jews. Jewish fishermen provided food for the population; Jewish stevedores unloaded the ships.

Never before had vocational opportunities been greater for the Jews, never had their religious liberty been more fully acknowledged, than during this period in Turkey. The immigrants entered all fields, for they were freed at last of those occupational restrictions that had hampered them in the Christian countries. The government and population prospered also, for the Jews had brought varied experience and valuable knowledge with them. Some continued in their old professions as doctors and interpreters; but Jewish craftsmen also plied their trades. The metal workers were especially in demand, for they were familiar with the methods and craft secrets of the famous armorers of Saragossa and Toledo. Jewish refugees established printing plants, hitherto unknown in Turkey, and began printing not only Hebrew but also Latin, Greek, Italian, and Spanish texts. Could the fugitives from Spain and Portugal and other Christian countries be blamed if they also instructed the Turks in the latest military developments? They established a modern armaments industry, set about manufacturing gunpowder, and made firearms and heavy artillery.

The chamberlain of the King of France, Nicolo Nicolai, who visited the Ottoman Empire in 1551, could not conceal his astonishment: "There are so many Jews throughout Turkey and Greece, but especially in Constantinople, that it is a great marvel. They increase daily through the commerce, money changing, and peddling, which they carry on almost everywhere on land and on water, so that it may be said truly that the greater part of the commerce of the whole Orient is in their hands. In Constantinople they have the largest bazaars and shops, with the best and most expensive wares of all kinds. In addition, one meets among them many skilled artisans and craftsmen, especially among the marranos, who some years ago were driven out of Spain and Portugal. These, with great harm and injury to Christendom, have taught the Turks to make implements of war. . . . Besides, they know most languages, so that they are employed as interpreters."

The Holy Land, too, was beginning to be repopulated. "How lovely are the tents of Jacob in Jerusalem," a Jewish traveler wrote enthusiastically to his family in Lombardy. "From early morning until late evening and from midnight to dawn the voices of worshipers and pupils resound in them. The city possesses two synagogues. The smaller belongs to the community of the Ashkenazim. . . . The other, which is larger, belongs to the Sephardim. In its vicinity is a large House of Instruction. . . ." But Jerusalem itself did not become the new center of Jewish life. The Holy City was too thronged with pilgrims of other religions, with Moslem dervishes and Christian monks. In Galilee, where a thousand years earlier the residence of the patriarchs and the famous Talmud academies had been located, a sizable community of Jews sprang up. This was Safad, situated on a steep slope rising above the flat northern shore of the Sea of Galilee. "Safad has abundance of grain and olive oil," a letter of 1521 to a prospective Italian immigrant stated. "In Palestine four types of craftsmen are most amply represented: weavers, goldsmiths, shoemakers, and tanners; there are also carpenters. Those who have the strength can hire out as day laborers; tailors, too, can earn their bread here. But he who neither has learned a trade nor possesses plenty of money will do better to remain in Italy, for he would regret moving and will have to return."

The heavy influx of Spanish immigrants made a profound impression linguistically. Spaniol, Spanish with Hebrew loanwords, displaced the Greek formerly spoken by the Jews of the Levant. It became the lingua franca of Jews throughout the Near East. Similarly, the Sephardic liturgy was adopted everywhere in Turkish Europe and Asia. A Spanish businessman, Gonzalvo de Ilescas, reported around 1550: "The Jews have transplanted our language to Turkey. They have faithfully preserved it down to the present day and speak it perfectly. In Salonika, Constantinople, Alexandria, Cairo, and other cities they employ Spanish alone in trade and otherwise. In Venice I met Jews from Salonika, very young people, whose Castilian was as fluent as mine."

Once again Jews served government; they played a vital role in the diplomacy and foreign politics of the Sublime Porte. Many of them became physicians and confidential advisers to the Turkish sultans and viziers. After the conquest of Constantinople Mohammed II entrusted the conduct of negotiations with Venice to a Jew; another Jew, named Jacob, became one of his ministers of state. Sultan Selim I employed Joseph Hamon (died 1518), a refugee from Granada, as his physician, and appointed Abraham de Castro administrator of coinage. Sultan Suleiman II took Joseph's son, Moses Hamon, into his service; Moses accompanied his master on his military campaigns and also prepared for him an Arabic translation of the Scriptures and of Jewish prayers.

Under the brilliant governments of Suleiman the Magnificent (who ruled from 1520 to 1566) and Selim II (Sultan from 1566 to 1574), when the Ottoman Empire had become the most powerful state in Europe, Turkish foreign policy was linked with the work of Jewish statesmen. Two names above all repeatedly turned up in the diplomatic correspondence between the Sublime Porte and the Christian governments and were soon on everyone's lips at courts throughout Europe. They were Joseph Nassi and Solomon Nathan Ashkenazi.

A typical marrano destiny had driven Joseph Nassi and his family across all of Europe before he arrived at the Bosporus and began his career in Turkish government service. He came from a family which had left Spain at the time of the expulsion and been subjected to forcible baptism in Portugal in 1497. As a New Christian under the name of Miguez, his father had served as physician to the Portuguese King. The introduction of the Inquisition into Portugal prompted the son, Juan Miguez, to emigrate to Flanders. In 1536 he was followed by his aunt, Doña Gracia Mendes, a banker's widow. Together, the two very successfully continued the banking house in Antwerp, and its business soon reached into France. They moved freely in aristocratic circles and won the favor of "Governess" Mary, the sister of Charles V. But before long the marrano family, which had remained inwardly Jewish, no longer felt safe. By now the spies of the Inquisition were sniffing about Flanders also. In 1549 the order went out for the arrest of Juan Miguez and Doña Gracia Mendes and the confiscation of all their property, but the two were able to escape from the Netherlands in the nick of time, and even to smuggle out their wealth. In a flight replete with adventures they made their way to Venice. Determined to be done forever with Christian Europe, they sought to emigrate to Turkey. But the Republic of Venice, sensing a rich catch, put difficulties in the way of their journey. On the ground that they were secret Jews, the Venetian Senate put a lien on all of Doña Gracia's wealth. The French King, Henry II, availed himself of the excuse not to repay a heavy debt to the bank, his creditors having been unmasked as Jews. Juan Miguez resolutely appealed to the protection of Sultan Suleiman. An official messenger from the Sublime Porte sailed to Venice and demanded that the family be permitted to continue its journey, and, moreover, that it be allowed to depart with all its property. The threat of the Sultan's displeasure sufficed. In 1552 the great financiers landed in Constantinople.

With their happy arrival in Turkey, the long years of harried life as marranos ended. The Christian masks were discarded. Gracia Mendes called herself Gracia Nassi; Juan Miguez also returned to his old Hebrew surname and was henceforth known as Joseph Nassi.

On recommendation from Moses Hamon he was invited to Suleiman's court. A new sphere for his talents opened out, and Joseph Nassi began another brilliant career. He soon became one of the most influential personages in the Ottoman Empire. Wherever he could, he tried to help Jews in distress. At his request Sultan Suleiman pressed Pope Paul IV to intercede on behalf of the marranos arrested by the Inquisition in Ancona, which then belonged to the Papal States. Joseph also became a close friend and adviser of the heir to the throne, Selim.

After Suleiman's death Joseph Nassi, under Selim II, virtually conducted the political affairs of the Sublime Porte. The new Sultan appointed him Duke of Naxos and of the Cyclades. Henceforth Joseph began his letters: "We, Duke of the Aegean Sea, Lord of Naxos." His influence was so great that many European rulers—among them, Emperor Maximilian II, the Duke of Orange, and other sovereigns—sued for his favor. No one with affairs at the Sultan's court could pass him by. When after new Turkish victories in Hungary an embassy from Emperor Maximilian II arrived in Constantinople for peace negotiations, the envoys had explicit instructions to give lavish gifts to the Duke of Naxos. Sigismund Augustus, King of Poland, engaged in a personal correspondence with the Jewish dignitary, and in one of his letters asked the "Illustrious Prince" to support his emissary in negotiations with the Sublime Porte. From the Netherlands, where the revolt against Spain and King Philip II was beginning, Duke William of Orange asked the Jewish Duke to persuade the Sultan to make war on Spain.

France and Venice felt his vengeance. Upon hearing that a gunpowder explosion had wreaked havoc in the arsenal of Venice, Joseph advised the Sultan to dispatch a fleet against Cyprus. Nicosia was taken in the first assault. In 1571 Famagusta fell after a difficult siege; the island, hitherto a possession of Venice, was to remain in Turkish hands for good.

The Sultan several times admonished King Charles IX to repay France's debt to Joseph Nassi, "this exemplary representative of the Jewish people." When Paris stubbornly withheld the borrowed one hundred and fifty thousand talers, the Sultan authorized the Duke of Naxos to confiscate French property. In 1569 several French merchant vessels docking in the port of Alexandria were detained as pledges.

After Sultan Selim's death in 1574, Joseph retired from politics and devoted all his energies to the welfare of his coreligionists. He supported a Hebrew printing press in Constantinople, was the benefactor of writers and scholars, and was the mainstay of several rabbinical schools. But he was not fated to carry out his most remarkable project: the establishment of a small Jewish state in the Holy Land.

At his request Sultan Suleiman had turned over to him the ruined city of Tiberias and seven neighboring villages as a site for Jewish settlers. Joseph had in mind an industrial colony that would serve as a haven for refugees from Europe. In 1564 Tiberias was surrounded with a new wall and the rebuilding of the city was begun. Mulberry trees were planted for the future raising of silkworms. Joseph imported wool from Spain, for he thought to set up weaving workshops. An appeal for settlers was sent out. The first groups of emigrants assembled in Italy. They boarded Turkish ships in Ancona and Venice and reached the Holy Land safely. But such was the opposition of neighboring Arabs that the building of the new settlement was increasingly hampered. And these were years in which Joseph was too occupied by his labors for the Sublime Porte, hence he could not personally preside over his project. The colony failed. After Joseph's death in 1579 his widow, Reyna, the daughter of Gracia Mendes, continued the printing press in Constantinople and for another twenty years actively promoted the dissemination of Jewish scholarship.

During Joseph Nassi's lifetime the diplomatic career of Solomon Nathan Ashkenazi had begun. A physician and Talmudic scholar whose birthplace was Udine, Italy, Solomon had traveled all over Europe and acquired great political experience, especially at the Polish court. He became the confidential agent of Grand Vizier Mohammed Sokolli. After the conquest of Cyprus he conducted the negotiations, as Ambassador of the Sublime Porte, that led to the peace treaty with Venice in 1573. When the Jewish diplomat and his retinue arrived in Venice, the Doge and the dignitaries of the republic gave him a magnificent reception. Ashkenazi seized the opportunity to speak for the Jews of Venice, and was able to dissuade the Venetian Senate from carrying out an already planned expulsion.

Solomon Ashkenazi also played a decisive part in the diplomatic negotiations conducted in 1572 among the powers of Europe after the death of King Sigismund II of Poland. He favored Prince Henry of the French House of Valois as successor to the throne of Poland, and it was largely owing to his efforts that Prince Henry was elected in May 1573.

Another Jewish statesman of distinction toward the end of the sixteenth century was Don Solomon Aben-Jaish (1520–1603). Like Joseph Nassi he had been born a marrano, had lived in Portugal under the Christian name of Alvaro Mendes, and had emigrated to Turkey in order to be able to return to Judaism. Called into the Turkish service, he soon played an influential role in international politics. He had close ties with William Cecil Lord Burleigh, the English statesman, and energetically furthered an alliance of the two states against Spain. He sent envoys to England to negotiate with Queen Elizabeth. For his services the Sultan conferred upon him the title of Duke of Mytilene, the capital of the island of Lesbos.

Solomon Aben-Jaish also entertained the plan for a Jewish settlement in Palestine. Again the Sultan was prevailed upon to place the territory around Tiberias at the disposal of the Jews. Members of Solomon's own family threw themselves into the project. They moved to Galilee and proceeded to take up the interrupted pioneering work. But again the courageous effort failed. The time was not yet ripe for it.

Although Tiberias proved a failure, Safad became the scene of a great revival in Jewish intellectual life. The work of two men there was destined to have an enormous effect upon the whole of Jewry.

Joseph Caro, born in Toledo in 1488, composed in Safad his subsequently famous *Shulhan Aruk* (*The Prepared Table*). Out of the vast and often contradictory halakistic literature he compiled a brief, systematic, and intelligible code of law. The four volumes contained a list of the daily duties, the regulations for the Sabbath and feast days, the ritual laws, the marital law, and the civil law. The first printed edition of this work was published in Venice in 1564. It enjoyed unprecedented success; although many commentaries and supplements were also composed for this last in a long series of lawbooks, none of the later books achieved anything like the same authority. Conduct of life according to the *Shulhan Aruk* became virtually obligatory for Jews.

At the same time a powerful religious current began to sweep over Jewry. Mystical tendencies that had always been present now came to the fore. Suffering and persecution drove tormented souls to seek more support than lay in moral codes. With passionate longing many Jews turned toward the supersensual and sought to penetrate the mysteries of the supernatural world. This contemplative Jewish mysticism is known as the cabala. The word means "reception" or "tradition," thereby stressing that the cabala is just as much a part of tradition as the Torah, and is likewise of divine origin. The cabala flourished in Gerona, Spain, under Nahmanides, and shortly after 1100 its teachings spread, orally at first, through France, Germany, and Spain. Toward the end of the thirteenth century, the *Zohar* (*Brightness*) appeared. This book was ascribed to Simeon ben Johai, a disciple of Akiba, a scholar who lived and wrote in Jabneh in the second century. In reality, it had been composed or compiled by Moses de Leon (1250–1305).

The technique of the *Zohar* was to seek secret divine revelations behind the simple literal meaning of the Biblical text. "Woe to the man who thinks the Torah contains everyday stories and the dialogues of simpletons. The wise pay no attention to the garment, but seek the body it covers; still others look into the soul, into the meaning of the Torah, in order to behold in the future world the soul of souls, that is to say God himself. . . ."

Safad, the site of the tomb of Simeon ben Johai, became a new center of the cabala under the leadership of Isaac ben Solomon Luria. His disciple, Haim Vidal, took careful notes of all the master's utterances, so that a literary testament survived his death in 1572. From Galilee the "practical cabala" began to spread with astonishing rapidity through Turkey, Italy, Germany, and all the way to Poland.

Toward the end of the sixteenth century signs of decay were becoming apparent in the Ottoman Empire. Power was repeatedly seized by rebellious Janizaries; the policies of the empire were more and more determined by harem intrigues. And with the passing of the glorious days of the powerful sultans, the part played by Jews in the service of the Sublime Porte likewise waned. In the provinces the Jewish communities began to feel the harsh hand of pashas who extorted heavy tributes from them. But no overtly anti-Semitic policies developed. The Jews had reason to be grateful to the Turkish Empire. In one of the darkest hours in their history, when there seemed scarcely any hope of a new life and most countries were closed to them, Turkey had generously thrown open its doors to receive the fugitives, and those doors continued to be held open.

REFUGE IN POLAND

The great flight to the east that carried the stream of refugees from Spain and Portugal across the Mediterranean to Turkey had its parallel in northern Europe. Poland, which became something of a great power in the sixteenth century when it formally cemented its union with Lithuania under the sons of Casimir IV, represented the second great haven of refuge for the harried and persecuted Jews and marranos.

For generations Poland was a land of promise to which ever-increasing hordes had turned in their distress. There were the thousands of the expelled; there were the fugitives fleeing from mass murder. In the Slavic lands Jews were not, as they were in the West, restricted to despised occupations; they could work in all branches of agriculture, industry, and trade. The Jews brought progress into a land economically undeveloped. They were equally welcome to the kings and the nobles, who granted them extensive liberties.

A large class of Jewish dealers in cattle and agricultural products arose. As against five hundred Christian wholesale dealers in these products in Poland, there were three thousand and two hundred Jews. There were also three times as many Jewish as Christian craftsmen, among them gold-smiths, silversmiths, blacksmiths, and weavers. Rich Jews served as customs collectors and tax farmers; the Polish rulers relied upon them for counsel on government finances and dynastic questions. Other Jews rented or admin-istered the estates of the nobility, or the Crown lands. Throughout the coun-try Jews could be found as overseers or stewards of large landholdings. They ran salt mines and timber holdings. The great majority of the Jew-ish population, however, lived by craftwork and peddling, by truck gar-dening, or, especially in Lithuania, by large-scale farming. Jewish com-munities or individual Jews could be found in almost every village and town from the Vistula to the Dnieper.

Of the former great communities in the West there survived only a piti-ful remnant, decimated and impoverished by a series of disasters that had visited them almost without a pause since the time of the First Cru-sade. In Poland, on the other hand, the number of Jews had steadily increased. From fifty thousand souls around 1500 it tripled by the end of the century, and a few decades later exceeded half a million. Since the disappearance of the great Diaspora community in Babylonia and the destruction of all the Jewish communities of Spain and Portugal, no other country could boast so enormous a concentration. The inexorably advanc-ing colonization of the Slavic countries by new bands of Jewish emigrants and fugitives from Germany, Austria, and Bohemia transformed Poland into a great new center of Jewry, the reservoir of the future. Most present-day Jews are descended from those who lived in Poland at the end of the Middle Ages.

The immigrant Ashkenazim brought their language with them from Germany and established it in Poland. While in the south, in European and Asiatic Turkey, the Spanish of the Sephardim from the Iberian Peninsula became the prevailing language of Jews, in the north, Jewish-German—Yiddish—became the lingua franca. It was a form of Middle High German mixed with Hebrew and Slavic words. Even among the Jews long settled in Poland it gradually displaced Polish. It was spoken in families, academies, and schools, and women—who received no in-struction in Hebrew—also used it in prayer. Next to Hebrew, Yiddish was considered virtually a sacred language. For centuries the two groups of Sephardim and Ashkenazim were differentiated by their speech, Span-iol or Yiddish.

Belatedly, the Polish Jews, the last among all the Jews of Europe and Asia, familiarized themselves with the Talmud. But although they came to it late, they studied it with all the greater passion. The Talmudic acad-emies in Cracow and Lublin, cities that were also the sites of important printing presses, became the most famous in Europe. Scholars from Italy, Germany, Moravia, and Silesia studied at them. Three scholars had helped establish the high reputation of the Polish academies: Shalom Shachna of Lublin (1500–1559), Solomon Luria of Poznan (1510–1573), and Moses Isserles of Cracow (1520–1572). Hordes of students rushed to sit at the feet of this triumvirate of great scholars. The students proved to be literally obsessed with the craving for learning. Poland became the supreme home of Talmudic studies. Nowhere else in the world was even the average pupil so well instructed. In addition, a uniquely cultivated laity developed. Literally every Jew endeavored to acquire knowledge of the Talmud.

"In no other country is the holy doctrine so widespread among our brothers as in the Kingdom of Poland," Rabbi Nathan Hannover wrote. "In every community there is a Yeshiva [Talmudic academy] whose head receives a generous salary so that he can devote himself without anxiety to directing the school and to his scholarly work. The communities likewise support the students by granting them a regular stipend every week. Each of these youths is in his turn expected to instruct at least two boys; in this way he acquires practice in exegesis of the Talmud and the elucidation of its problems. The boys are usually fed by means of a welfare fund or from the community kitchen. A community of fifty families, for example, provides for at least thirty young scholars with their boys, for each household takes in one scholar with his two boys. . . . In all the lands of the Polish king there is scarcely a family in which the Torah is not studied. Either the head of the family is a scholar, or the son or son-in-law has devoted himself permanently to study. At the very least the house shelters a young scholar. But frequently a single household will include all three of these. . . . After the close of the summer or winter semester the head of the academy, accompanied by his entire band of disciples, goes to the fairs, in summer to the Zaslaw or Jaroslaw fair, in winter to the fair at Lwow or Lublin. Here the youths or boys decide upon which Yeshiva they wish to attend during the next semester. Thus at each of these fairs hundreds of heads of schools, thousands of youths, and tens of thousands of boys meet, and this is without counting the vast numbers of merchants who come together from all countries. . . ."

Where else has an entire people ever devoted itself so intensively to religion, and offered such rigorous intellectual training to every boy from earliest childhood? That training of youthful intellects continued for generation after generation. Three centuries after Rabbi Hannover's account, in 1929, Professor Alfred Jeremias wrote: "It is altogether astonishing how the memory of twelve- and thirteen-year-old boys, who at this age receive the dignity of the bar mitzvah, is trained by study of the Talmud. It frequently happens that a very young boy knows the entire Pentateuch by heart, and the Psalms as well. In a cheder [school] in Warsaw I put some questions about a Bible passage to an unusually zealous boy of eleven. He stood up and commented like a little professor, giving most ingenious examples from the texts to explain the difficult matter."

On the whole, Poland long remained a land in which the Jews lived in peace. It continued to be the great asylum for the persecuted. To be sure, the nobility sometimes urged restrictions. The Church, too, from the very beginning saw danger in overly peaceful and neighborly relations between Poles and Jews. "In consideration of the fact that Poland represents a new planting in the soil of Christianity," a declaration of the Polish clergy as early as 1267 read, "it may be feared that the Christian population here, where the Christian religion has not yet been able to strike firm roots in the hearts of believers, may all the more easily be swayed by the false religion and the wicked customs of the Jews living in their midst." But even in the sixteenth century the Church did not yet have sufficient influence upon the government. Kings Sigismund I (who reigned from 1506 to 1548) and Sigismund II (ruler from 1548 to 1572) were more interested in the economic benefits the Jews brought to the country, and protected them against exclusions, expulsions, and persecutions. Not until the middle of the seventeenth century did misfortune come to the Jewish communities of Eastern Europe.

DAVID RËUBENI'S TIDINGS

As the trials of the Jews in the West reached a summit toward the end of the fifteenth century and hordes of fugitives pressed toward the East, the entire people were seized by a passionate longing for fulfillment of the Prophets' predictions. They began to hope that the time of the Messiah was approaching, and with it the end of their sufferings. Widespread distress gave birth to messianic prophecies and zealot movements, as had happened immediately before and after the destruction of Jerusalem. Hopes of a saviour produced inspired preachers, brave fighters and martyrs—but also adventurers.

In 1502 there appeared in Istria, near Venice, a cabalist named Asher Lemlin, a German Jew. He proclaimed himself the forerunner of the Messiah and called for penances, self-castigation, and charity. Salvation would be coming in a very short time, within half a year, he announced. In Italy, Austria, and Germany there were people who believed him and began to fast and pray, undertake penances, and give their money to the poor. The six months passed; the hopes proved vain. "Only our sins have delayed the Messiah," Asher Lemlin temporized—and disappeared.

More such "prophets" cropped up, however, even among sober and sensible scholars. Isaac Abravanel, the "head of the exiles," calculated the exact date: In 1531 Rome would be overthrown and Israel would triumph. Bonet de Lattes, the personal physician of Pope Leo X, made a different prediction; he placed the date of salvation as 1505.

Amid this general expectation, a mysterious figure from the Orient made his appearance and caused a commotion throughout Europe. In 1524 a tiny, ascetic, brown-skinned man who gave his name as David Rëubeni landed in Venice. His bearing was proud and imperious; he went about surrounded by servants; he spoke Hebrew. Incredulously, people listened to his account of his origins and the purpose of his visit. He was, he said, the younger son of the now deceased King Solomon. His elder brother, King Joseph, ruled in the Khaibar desert of Arabia over three hundred thousand subjects from the lost tribe of Reuben. A mission of the greatest political importance had brought him to Europe. Along the Nile in Nubia he had come upon the descendants of the other nine missing tribes of Israel. In concert with the Christians, these Israelites must expel the Turks from the Holy Land. The soldiers in Khaibar were ready for war, but they needed arms. Therefore he was on his way to Rome to see the Pope.

In the very year of his arrival Rëubeni appeared in Rome, making an entry like a sovereign prince. "I, David, son of King Solomon of blessed memory, from the desert of Khaibar, arrived before the gates of Rome on the fifteenth of Adar, 1524. . . . I rode on an aged white steed, my servants going before me, many Jews accompanying me. Thus on my mount I penetrated into the Castle of Sant'Angelo. Thereupon I was led before Cardinal Egidio of Viterbo, and all the cardinals and princes came to see me. And before Cardinal Egidio there was the learned rabbi Joseph Ashkenazi, the teacher of the above-mentioned cardinal, and in addition there came the learned rabbi Joseph Zarphati."

David Rëubeni succeeded in obtaining an audience with the Pope. Curiously enough, Clement VII took an interest in the stranger's plan and gave him a letter of recommendation to the King of Portugal.

In 1525 Rëubeni and his retinue arrived in Lisbon. King João III received him honorably and likewise listened with keen interest to Rëubeni's proposals. The Jews of Khaibar would aid Portugal against Sultan Suleiman and in the conquest of the Holy Land, Rëubeni reported. The King promised him ships and weapons. A regular plan of campaign was to be devised.

The presence of a Jewish priest in Portugal's capital aroused feverish excitement among the marranos. They felt new hope. Perhaps this was the Messiah. Jubilantly, they hailed David Rëubeni. Other newly converted Christians hastened to Portugal from Spain to see the phenomenon. A youthful enthusiast, a marrano named Diego Pires, circumcised himself, took the Hebrew name of Solomon Molko, and, with his head full of dreams and "wonderful visions," departed for Turkey. Preaching the imminence of the Messiah, he turned up in Salonika, Adrianople, and Safad, the center of cabalism.

In 1530 David Rëubeni had to leave Portugal. The case of Solomon Molko had stirred up the Inquisition. Rëubeni was accused of having entered into secret negotiations with the marranos, and was banished from the country. Henceforth his luck turned. On the return voyage to Italy a storm wrecked his ship off the Spanish coast. With difficulty, harried by the bailiffs of the Inquisition, he managed to escape to France. For a time he found refuge in Avignon, where the Pope still owned much land. He reappeared in Venice subsequently with a splendid retinue. There he negotiated with the Senate, trying to win the support of the republic for his campaign against Turkey.

Meanwhile Solomon Molko had returned from the Orient. The news that the troops of Emperor Charles V had penetrated into Rome and devastated the city seemed to him a sign of great significance. The downfall of Rome must be impending. In 1529 Molko landed in Ancona and hastened to Rome. Fasting and praying, experiencing repeated religious visions, he crouched on the bridge over the Tiber at the Castle of Sant'Angelo. Did not an ancient Jewish popular tale hold that the Messiah, unrecognized, would sit among beggars and cripples at the gates of Rome and wait for the day of salvation? Clement VII heard of Molko's presence; he gave him audience and talked with him. The Inquisition likewise turned its attention to him, and urged proceedings against this marrano apostate from Christianity. But the Pope granted him a safe conduct. Molko, nevertheless aware that his life was no longer safe, fled to Venice, where he met David Rëubeni again.

Once more, for the last time, Rëubeni and Molko astonished the world by their boldness.

In 1532 Charles V had convoked the Diet of the Empire at Regensburg. Suddenly the two Jews appeared there and announced their plans for a joint enterprise against the Turks. Molko there also met Rabbi

Josel of Rosheim, the spokesman for German Jewry. It was a confrontation of two worlds, this meeting of the religious zealot and the sober politician. "At this time a foreign proselyte named Solomon Molko has appeared," the diary of Josel of Rosheim records, "with strange notions to rouse the Emperor so that he will summon all Jews to battle against Turkey. When I heard what he had in mind, I warned him against stirring up the Emperor's heart, lest the great fire consume him. . . ." The warnings were vain. Molko insisted on an audience. There are no accounts of what happened at the conversation between the pious Emperor and the former marrano, but the pitiful end is known. "Solomon Molko . . . was placed in iron chains," Josel of Rosheim's notations continue, "taken to Bologna, and there burned for the sanctity of God and the religion of Israel. . . ." On the Emperor's orders David Rëubeni was taken to Spain; the Inquisition threw him into one of its dungeons, where he died years later.

IV THE WAY OUT OF
THE DARKNESS

REUCHLIN DEFENDS THE TALMUD

The sixteenth century in Germany, on the eve of the Reformation, began with a savage attack on the Jews and the Talmud. Leaflets with such titles as *Mirror of the Jews, Confession of the Jews,* and *Foe of the Jews* suddenly made their appearance in the Rhineland from 1507 to 1509, and found wide distribution throughout the German lands. These leaflets denounced the Talmud and a great many other Jewish books as anti-Christian and blasphemous. Even the phrase "smashing the thralldom of usury," later to be a watchword of the Nazis, became current at this time. The leaflets contended that the Jews must be forbidden to lend money at interest—let them earn their bread in dishonorable occupations such as those of executioner, knacker, and peddler. Moreover, missionary sermons must be delivered to the Jews. If they still refused to accept baptism, let them be expelled from Germany as they had already been driven from England, France, and Spain.

Once again Jewry was undone by an apostate from its own ranks. The author of these tracts was a baptized Jew, Johann Joseph Pfefferkorn, a former butcher. He had been expelled from the Jewish community in Moravia because of his apostasy. The Dominicans, however, had received him with open arms and provided him with a job as overseer in a Cologne hospital.

Uneasiness and anxiety seized the Jewish communities of Germany. They suspected that the support this apostate had found among the

Dominicans boded ill for the future. Cologne was one of the powerful centers of the order; the Inquisition, headed by Dominican Prior Jacob van Hoogstraeten, had its headquarters in that city.

Their fears proved justified. The Dominicans took up Pfefferkorn's arguments and began to carry out his program with all the means at their command.

Armed with a letter of recommendation from his ecclesiastical patrons, Pfefferkorn called upon Princess Kunigunde, sister of Emperor Maximilian I, a nun living in a Franciscan convent in Munich. Pfefferkorn had little difficulty winning her support. The princess wrote to the Emperor imploring him to put a stop to the Jews' slanders of Christianity and to order all their writings destroyed, with the exception of the Bible. Otherwise, she said, echoing her Dominican mentor, the Emperor himself would be guilty of the sins of blasphemy.

Pfefferkorn betook himself to Padua, where Maximilian was staying to conduct a campaign against Venice. In August, 1509, the Emperor gave him full powers to confiscate all Hebrew books and to destroy all those whose contents were directed against the New Testament and the Christian religion. The authorities were instructed to aid him in his measures against the Jews.

Pfefferkorn started his work at once in Frankfurt, whose Jewish community was the largest in Germany. Accompanied by representatives of both the ecclesiastical and the secular power—priests and officials of the Free Imperial City—he appeared in the synagogue on September 9, 1509, and read aloud the Emperor's edict. One hundred and sixty-eight volumes, most of them prayer books, were confiscated.

Pfefferkorn next proposed to have the Jews' houses searched in order to confiscate copies of the Talmud. But this plan was thwarted. Uriel von Gemmingen, the Archbishop of Mainz, vigorously protested the Emperor's infringement on his own ecclesiastical rights. Moreover, he wrote the Emperor, in a matter of such fundamental importance as the condemnation of Jewish religious books, the authorities could not rely on the statements of a convert with the worst possible reputation.

The Jews, for their part, also tried to defend themselves. The communities of Frankfurt and Regensburg sent a spokesman to Maximilian urging him not to believe Pfefferkorn's charges and not to make a mockery of the religious toleration previously granted them. The Emperor reconsidered his hasty step. He ordered the already confiscated books to be returned. Meanwhile, a commission was to investigate the contents of Jewish writings and make a report. The Archbishop of Mainz was requested to collect opinions from the universities of Mainz, Cologne, Erfurt, and

Heidelberg. At the same time the Inquisitor Hoogstraeten was to be consulted, and likewise Johann Reuchlin of Tübingen.

Anyone who would undertake to say whether the Jewish books were indeed blasphemous and inimical to Christianity would have to know Hebrew. Reuchlin, the great Humanist, the "phoenix of Germania," was one of the few Christians in Germany who had familiarized himself with the original language of the Scriptures. In this he was following the example of Italian Humanists such as Pico della Mirandola and Marsilio Ficino, who had sought instruction in Hebrew so that they could study the cabala, that repository of Jewish mysticism and magic. Reuchlin had learned the Hebrew language from Jewish scholars in Germany and Italy. In Linz, at the court of the aged Emperor Frederick III, his teacher had been the Emperor's physician Jacob Loans, in Rome the scholar Obadiah Sforno. Reuchlin had studied the books of the Old Testament, and commentaries on them, in Hebrew, and became a great champion of the language. He was, in fact, the founder of Hebraistics as an independent branch of knowledge.

"For if I live, with God's help the Hebrew language will be used," he wrote to his printer in Basel. "When I die, I shall have made a beginning which will not easily be destroyed." He entitled his first book on the cabala and the language of the Jews *De verbo mirifico* (*The Wonder-Working Word*). In it he wrote: "The language of the Hebrews is simple, incorrupt, holy, brief, and firm. In it God spoke with men and men with the angels directly and without interpreter, face to face, as one friend speaks to another."

Reuchlin knew what prejudices against the rabbinical writings he had to overcome. He had the courage to proceed, though well aware of the risks he was running. In 1506 he had published his *Elements of Hebrew,* the first textbook of the language. Anyone who wished to understand the foundations of the Christian religion was obliged to learn Hebrew, he contended. Nor did he shy away from the conclusions that followed from comparing the Hebrew text with the Latin translation accepted by the Church, the Vulgate—a tremendously intrepid step for his time. "Our text is thus, the Hebrew truth different," Reuchlin said fearlessly. "I love St. Jerome . . . but I worship as God only the Truth."

In 1510 Reuchlin presented his opinion to the episcopal commission. The very title of his treatise suggested its significance: "Whether It Is Godly, Praiseworthy, and Useful to the Christian Religion to Burn the Jewish Writings." The opinion dealt first with the Jews' legal position. Reuchlin maintained—the first to presume to do so publicly—that the

Jews were "fellow citizens of the German-Roman Empire" and should "enjoy the same rights and protection."

Ecclesiastical and secular authorities within the empire must respect this right, Reuchlin declared. Then he went on to the crucial question. The Jewish books could by no means be lumped together as writings of the same kind. They must be divided into numerous classes. Among them, as in every other literature, there were probably one or two "shameful books." Aside from these aberrations, all other books of the Jews should be preserved. Many of their works were also of the greatest importance to Christian theology, especially the classical commentaries on the Bible by Rashi, Abraham ibn Ezra, and the three Kimhis. Christians were indebted to the Jews for their best writings on the Old Testament; the works of the Jews were like a fountain that poured out truth and right understanding of the Bible. If everything that came from Rashi were removed from the voluminous work of Nicholas of Lyra, the most important of the Christian commentators, little would remain. It was a disgrace that Christian theologians distorted the Scriptures because they knew neither Hebrew nor Greek.

Hebrew books on philosophy, the sciences, and art, Reuchlin went on, in no way differed from books written in Greek, Latin, or German on these subjects. The books of the cabala, for instance, contained many elements of similarity to Christian doctrine, and should therefore be promoted. And if the Jewish books of prayer and liturgy were to be banned and burned, that would be infringing on the privileges that had been granted the Jews by charter from ancient times.

On the principal question of whether the Talmud was dangerous, Reuchlin honestly admitted that he could not make a judgment because he was not sufficiently acquainted with the Talmudic writings. But other learned Christians also knew no more of the Talmud, he continued, than the indictment presented by such opponents as Pfefferkorn. "If the Talmud were so damnable as is claimed," Reuchlin observed, "our forefathers, who were more earnest about the Christian faith than we are in our day, would surely have burned it hundreds of years ago." And even if the Talmud could truly be shown to contain anti-Christian passages, it should nevertheless not be burned on that account—because against things of the spirit only spiritual arms should be employed, not crude force. The writings of the Jews, Reuchlin summed up, should certainly not be confiscated and burned. Far better, on the contrary, to install two professors of Hebrew in every German university.

Reuchlin was almost alone in these liberal views. For the experts from

the universities of Mainz, Cologne, and Erfurt were ready to condemn
the books in a body. Mainz even included the Hebrew Old Testament
wherever it did not agree with the Vulgate. Cologne University called for
the burning of the Talmud, as did the memorandum from Hoogstraeten. Only Heidelberg University took a cautious middle position and proposed a continuing examination.

The Emperor, presented with the opinions, found himself embarrassed.
He could not decide which view to accept, and asked for further statements.

In the meantime, however, a bitter fray had begun. Pfefferkorn was enraged by Reuchlin's treatise. He retaliated with a new tract, *A Hand Mirror, Against the Jews and Their Writings,* in which he aimed his barbs
against the "Jewish advocate." Reuchlin's opinion, he insinuated, had been
written with "golden ink"—that is, the scholar had been bribed by the
Jews. The renegade denounced the great Humanist in the pungent language of the age as "Jew-lover, ear-blower, purse-sweeper and back-
stabber," and charged that he knew no Hebrew at all and had had his
writings ghosted by a learned Jew, "as if you were yourself a great learned
doctor and teacher of the Hebrish language."

Thus maligned, Reuchlin could no longer hold his peace. He appealed
indignantly to public opinion to judge between them. "This baptized Jew,"
he retorted in his polemic entitled *Mirror to the Eyes* (1511), "asserts
that divine law forbids us to associate with Jews. That is a lie. Rather,
the Christian is commanded to love the Jew as his neighbor—that
alone is rightful." Once more Reuchlin set forth all the arguments against
confiscation of Jewish writings, including the Talmud.

Reuchlin's *Mirror to the Eyes* was published just in time for the Frankfurt Fair, and thus was quickly circulated throughout Germany. It created
a sensation that a celebrated scholar such as Reuchlin should denounce
an accuser of the Jews. For the first time a man of reputation was publicly coming to the defense of the Jews and branding the endlessly repeated accusations against them as slanders.

Pfefferkorn replied with another villainous pamphlet, *The Fire Mirror.*
He had not arrived at any new ideas. Once again he recommended that all
adult Jews be enslaved or expelled, as had happened to them once before
in Egyptian bondages. Their children should be forcibly baptized. Influential groups came to the renegade's aid, and gathered forces against Reuchlin. The Dominicans, on Pfefferkorn's side from the beginning, denounced Reuchlin's anti-Church utterances. Theologian Arnold von Ton-
gern of Cologne wrote that his polemic smacked of heresy, and Hoogstraeten demanded that the universities of Liége, Cologne, Erfurt, and Mainz

provide official opinions on *Mirror to the Eyes*. All four academies attested that Reuchlin's book was too favorable to the Jews and must be destroyed.

Reuchlin refused to be intimidated. This time he appealed directly to Maximilian I. His opponents in Cologne, Reuchlin commented, were both ignorant and dishonest. But then, everyone knew what the storm was all about; as in Spain, inquisitional procedures against the Jews had only one purpose, to rob them of their property. "Permit them, my Lord," Reuchlin wrote, "to take away the Jews' money—then they would soon leave me in peace. Only allow the theologians of Cologne to drag the Jews before their inquisitional tribunals, to kick and pillage them—and they would soon restore my honor. . . ." Such harsh truths antagonized the Dominicans still more.

When the Sorbonne in Paris, the most respected university in the Western world, likewise came out for the suppression of *Mirror to the Eyes*, Hoogstraeten struck. In his capacity of "Inquisitor of heretical wickedness" (*"haereticae pravitatis inquisitor"*) for Cologne, Mainz, and Trier, he issued a summons for Reuchlin to appear in Mainz to answer an indictment for favoring the Jews and for suspicion of heresy. Reuchlin prudently remained in Rome and sent a lawyer to represent him.

The trial was held, and Reuchlin's book was officially condemned. Sentencing was set for October 12, 1513. The clergy of Mainz had been instructed to threaten harsh penalties for anyone failing to deliver copies of *Mirror to the Eyes* for public burning. This order applied to both Christians and Jews. On the other hand, three hundred days' indulgence was offered as an additional reward for attending the auto-da-fé.

On the fateful day the square outside Mainz Cathedral was black with people. Stands had been set up, filled with Dominicans and guest theologians from the universities of Cologne, Liége, and Erfurt. The great pile of faggots stood ready. But at the very moment Hoogstraeten was about to pronounce the formula of anathema, a messenger from Archbishop Uriel came rushing up and delivered a letter that abruptly silenced him. The Prince of the Church had raised objections; the book burning was canceled.

"Rejoice, in that you recognize yourself, yes, rejoice, O my Germany," Ulrich von Hutten exulted in his paean, *Reuchlin's Triumph*. Germany should prepare a glorious welcome for the victor over the Dominicans, her great, immortal Reuchlin, as soon as he returned from abroad, Hutten asserted. He struck out boldly against the accusers. Hoogstraeten, he declared, was forever crying: "Into the fire with writers and their writings. . . . Whether you think true or false, righteousness or unrighteousness, he always has fire ready for you. He devours fire, he feeds on it, he breathes flames!"

All Europe reverberated with the dispute. The most learned men on the Continent had taken Reuchlin's side. They were led by Willibald Pirkheimer and Erasmus of Rotterdam. Even sovereigns such as Duke Ulrich of Württemberg and Electoral Prince Frederick the Wise of Saxony supported him. And Aegidius of Viterbo, general of the Order of Augustinian Eremites in Rome, wrote: "The teaching [Torah] which was revealed to man in the burning bush was saved from the fire the first time when Abraham escaped the fiery furnace (into which, according to legend, Nimrod wanted to cast him) and saved from fire the second time by Reuchlin, since the Scriptures have been saved through which the Law first was illuminated, and whose destruction would mean the onset of eternal darkness. . . ."

The counterattack had set in, and the country was ready for it. Peals of laughter hailed *The Letters of Obscure Men* (*Epistolae obscurorum virorum*), which appeared from 1515 to 1517. This brilliant satire on the ignorance, arrogance, and corruption of the clergy, by Ulrich von Hutten and his fellow Humanists, decisively prepared the way among the cultivated minds of the age for Luther's Reformation.

The dispute continued. Reuchlin had appealed to the Roman Curia. Pope Leo X submitted the question to the Lateran Council meeting in Rome. In 1516 the majority of the Council fathers declared in favor of Reuchlin. Therefore, Pope Leo, instead of condemning the Talmud, encouraged the Christian printer Daniel Bomberg in Venice to prepare an edition of the entire work. The result was the first complete printed edition of the Talmud that had not been distorted by Christian censorship.

The Jews, who had followed the course of this bitter contention with grave anxiety, could well breathe a sigh of relief. They were profoundly grateful to Reuchlin, who had fended off the dangerous assault on their books. That meant a great deal—the safeguarding of the *status quo*. But no more. The battle of minds had not been fought for the Jews' sake, and nothing had changed the basic attitudes of even so freedom-loving a man as Ulrich von Hutten. He had been concerned to defend the Humanist Reuchlin, not the Jews. The actual sufferings of the Jews left even the finest minds in Germany quite unmoved. The attitude of almost all the Humanists—Reuchlin was a rare exception—was pithily expressed in Erasmus of Rotterdam's ironic comment: "If it is Christian to hate the Jews, all of us are only too good Christians."

Nevertheless, the interest in Jewish literature that Reuchlin had awakened never entirely subsided thereafter. He had succeeded in breaching the inveterate prejudice against rabbinical writings and in introducing the Hebrew language into the area of general education.

Reuchlin dedicated an edition of the Psalms to Daniel Bomberg, the printer of many Hebrew books. "I must also preserve your name for eternity," he wrote. "You have freed the Hebrew language from its dark prison. Under your protection I have published a small book destined to further the study of this language."

Echoes of the controversy lingered for a few years afterward. Then the attention of public and Church was diverted by more important events—which were soon to change the face of Europe. On October 30 of the year 1517 Martin Luther had nailed his ninety-five theses to the door of the palace church in Wittenberg.

LUTHER'S WRATH AGAINST THE JEWS

The tempests of the Reformation brought no change to the situation of the Jews. It might have been expected that Protestant resort to the Old Testament as the prime source and foundation of Christian religion would at last create a sense of fraternity toward the people of the Bible. But nothing of the sort took place.

At first, to be sure, it did seem as if there were a gleam of hope for the Jews. At the beginning of the Reformation, when Luther and his followers were themselves being denounced as heretics and the spokesmen of the Reformation thundered against "pagan, idolatrous popery," these newly hatched Protestants said a good many things that seemed to suggest a change in the time-honored prejudices against the Jews. Luther especially, as a young man, took strong exception to the late medieval treatment of Jews.

"Who will convert to our religion," he wrote in his interpretation of the Twenty-second Psalm, "even if he were the gentlest and most patient of men, when he sees that they are abused cruelly and hostilely, treated not Christianly by us, but more than bestially?" And in 1523 he wrote a pamphlet entitled "That Jesus Christ Was Born a Jew." Incisively, he denounced the wicked way the Jews had been dealt with: "For our fools, the Popes, bishops, sophists and monks, coarse dunderheads that they are, have hitherto dealt thus with the Jews that whosoever had wished to be a good Christian would probably prefer to become a Jew. . . . For they have treated the Jews as if they were dogs and not men, and have robbed them of their possessions. . . . And yet they are blood-kin, cousins and brothers of our Lord. God has distinguished no other people as he has them; to their hand he confided the Holy Scriptures. . . . But now we drive them only by violence . . . and maintain that unless they have Christian blood they stink, and I know not what follies else. . . . How shall we draw good will from them? Item, they are forbidden to work and labor among us and have human intercourse with us. If they are driven to usury, how can they refrain from it? If they are to be succored, we should not apply to them the Pope's law, but the law of Christian love, and meet them amiably, letting them carry on trades and labor, so that they have reason and opportunity to be with us and about us . . . and from their own observation come to know the teaching and life of Christians. . . ."

"To know the teaching and life of Christians" in order to be converted—that was what Luther had in mind. It was from missionary zeal that he wrote these seemingly generous words. Had not St. Paul, the Apostle whom Luther ardently venerated, prophesied the eventual conversion of Israel to the Christian faith? Luther was firmly convinced that he could win the Jews to his new teachings, especially since his version of Christianity was far more strongly founded on the Old Testament than the Church of the Roman papacy.

This audacious pamphlet stirred a sensation, all the more so because recent persecutions of Jews were fresh in men's minds. As recently as 1510 thirty-eight Jews in Berlin had been the victims of a ritual murder trial, having been tortured and then publicly burned for alleged desecration of the host and the murder of Christian children, and all the Jews of Brandenburg had been banished from that city. Nine years later the Jews had been expelled from Regensburg, where they had been settled since the time of the Romans—ever since the fifth century! Their more than three-hundred-year-old synagogue had been torn down, and four thousand gravestones in their ancient cemetery had been demolished.

When Luther's pamphlet became widely known, the Jews sent him a copy of the One Hundred and Thirtieth Psalm, "Out of the depths have I called to Thee . . . ," written in the German language with Hebrew letters. His words had moved them to hope and gratitude, but their steadfastness in the faith of their fathers remained unshaken. They did not convert to Christianity, and were no more drawn to Martin Luther's new form of it than to the old, despite his having for the first time translated the Old Testament from the Hebrew into German.

When Luther found himself disappointed in his expectations of the conversion of the Jews, his tone altered. Just as Mohammed, centuries before, turned from an admirer of the Jewish people into their implacable enemy, so Luther's original kind feelings increasingly changed to dislike for the "obstinate ones." Soon little was left but hatred. In 1537 he abruptly made it very clear that the Jews need hope for no improvement of their lot from the great reformer.

Electoral Prince John Frederick of Saxony, known as the Magnanimous, had decided to expel all Jews from his lands. Josel of Rosheim, "Commander of all Our Jewries in the Holy Empire," who had been officially appointed by the Emperor as spokesman for all German Jews, sped to Saxony. He was confidently counting on Luther's influence with the Electoral Prince, who was one of the reformer's devoted followers. Surely Luther, who had so warmly defended the Jews, would help make the Prince reconsider so inhuman a measure. But Luther refused even to receive Josel of Rosheim. He replied by letter that he had, to be sure, once spoken in favor of the Jews, and that he still hoped "God in his mercy will some day lead them to his Messiah." Nevertheless he now had reason to think that any support for the Jews would only cause them to persist in their obstinate resistance to all attempts at conversion.

The following year Luther publicly took a position against the Jews. In 1538 he published his *Letter Against the Sabbathers.*

Influenced by studies of the Old Testament, which Luther's translation had made accessible to all literate Germans, a small sectarian group had formed among the Protestants. They followed the example of the Jews in observing the Jewish Sabbath as their holy day instead of the Christian Sunday. Luther's *Letter* was a diatribe against them—but the fiercest of his thunderbolts was directed at the Jews. "This people was possessed by all devils," he declared, and final judgment had already been passed upon them for their obstinacy. To Doctor Martin they were "a frightful example of divine wrath" and surely condemned.

In the following years Luther preached more and more violently against the Jews from the pulpit and in his "Table Talks." His wrath assumed ever more passionate forms, and in 1543 he published *Of the Jews and Their Lies.* In this work he served up all the atrocity stories that had accumulated against the Jews—ritual murder and poisoning of wells, black magic, and treason against the empire for the benefit of the Turks. From these tales he concluded: "What should we Christians now do with this contemptible, damned people of the Jews? . . . I will give my true advice. First, that their synagogues or schools be set afire. . . . Second, that their houses similarly be razed and destroyed, for they practice the same ill things in them as in their schools. . . . Third, that there be taken from them all prayer books and Talmudics in which such idolatry and lies and curses and blasphemy are taught. Fourth, that their rabbis be forbidden on peril of their lives henceforth to teach . . . that safe-conduct and the right of the roads be entirely taken from them . . . that usury be forbidden them and all coins and precious things in gold and silver be taken from them, for all they have is what they have . . . stolen and robbed from us by their usury."

Several leading Protestants were outraged by this hate pamphlet. The Swiss reformer Heinrich Bullinger wrote to his Alsatian colleague Martin Butzer that in reading it he had the impression it was written "by a swineherd, not by a famous shepherd of souls. If today that famous hero Reuchlin were to be resurrected, he would declare that in the one Luther were resurrected the Tongerns, Hoogstraetens and Pfefferkorns." Yet Bullinger had addressed himself to the wrong person, for Butzer proved to be no less bitter an anti-Semite than Luther.

Luther's wrathful writings terrified the Jews. Josel of Rosheim wrote to the town fathers of the city of Strassburg that "the crude, inhuman book of Dr. Martin Luther, which heaps slander and venom upon us poor Jews," was inciting the populace to violence and murder. For the people could only gather from Luther's words that the Jews were beyond the law.

Philipp Melanchthon also seemed to be troubled. Nevertheless he sent Luther's pamphlet *Of the Jews and Their Lies* to the Landgrave of Hesse with the remark that it contained "much useful doctrine." The Landgrave promptly issued an order expelling the Jews from his country and forbidding them even the right of transit. Luther's own lord, the Electoral Prince of Saxony, followed his example. Such were the direct consequences of Luther's opinions; the indirect consequences persisted longer—down to the most recent past. "As Church Father Jerome infected the Catholic world with his virulent hatred of Jews," Heinrich Graetz has remarked, "Luther with his anti-Semitic testament poisoned the Protestant world for centuries to come."

COUNTER REFORMATION
AND NEW SUFFERING

During the Middle Ages the Jews had lived more happily in Italy, the home of the hierarchy and canon law, than anywhere else in Europe. That country had never witnessed such persecutions and massacres as were common in Germany, England, and Spain. Among the Italian rulers, none were more friendly toward the Jews than the Renaissance

Popes, especially the Medicean Popes, Leo X (Pope from 1513 to 1521) and Clement VII (Pope from 1523 to 1534), who, we will recall, received Rëubeni in audience. These men were more enlightened than their times; they benignly regarded Jewish learning as an essential component of cultural life, which for them was of the deepest interest. Clement VII even permitted a Jewish print shop to be established in Rome. But then, on the threshold of the modern age the light of tolerance suddenly was extinguished in this hitherto happy refuge. Had not the Jews provided the reformer with the original text of the Bible? Was it not through them that he learned the Hebrew language and was thus enabled to make Holy Writ accessible to the people? Just as the Jews in the past had been accused of complicity with the Albigensians and Hussites, so they were now considered coresponsible for the new "heresy."

The Catholic Church responded to Luther's Reformation by intensifying the inquisitorial techniques. The Society of Jesus, which was founded in 1534, stipulated that its members might have no Jewish ancestors back to the fifth generation (later, back to the third generation). The new spirit of reaction struck hard at the Italian Jewish communities. There was a resurgence of the medieval spirit; a policy of repression was instituted, and the new measures were destined to remain in force for two and a half centuries.

All printed works were subjected to papal censorship. Everything displeasing to the censors was placed on the Index of Prohibited Books. The Holy Office knew where to look for "harmful books." For in Italy the printing of Jewish books was flourishing as never before. Thousands of copies were being exported to all countries of the world. The printing presses in Mantua, Ferrara, and Venice could scarcely keep up with the demand, for during the long ages of persecution so many Jewish communities had lost their sacred and secular writings.

The pretext was easily found for the Holy Office to intervene. There was the tried-and-true formula that had been employed centuries before in Spain and France, and a short time ago in Germany. Three renegade Jews—Chananel di Foligno, Solomon Romano, and Joseph Moro—declared the Talmud corrupt and blasphemous, and drew up a formal denunciation, which was sent to the Pope.

Cardinal Giovanni Pietro Caraffa, the Inquisitor General, ordered the confiscation of all copies of the Talmud in Rome—the same Talmud whose printing Pope Leo X had looked so favorably upon. Pope Julius III upheld the Cardinal's decree. On August 12, 1553, he signed a sentence of execution, which was carried out on September 9. The "harmful books" went up in flames on the Campo de' Fiori, in the heart of Rome. Three days after this Roman auto-da-fé the decree was extended to cover the whole of Italy. The Jews were required to surrender, within three days, all their copies of the Babylonian and Palestinian recensions of the Talmud, on pain of seizure of their property. Throughout the Romagna, and in Milan, Bologna, Ferrara, Mantua, Padua, and Venice, pyres were erected and Talmudic writings destroyed by the hundreds and thousands. Only the *Sohar,* the cabalistic *Book of Brightness,* was exempted.

In 1555 Cardinal Giovanni Pietro Caraffa ascended the throne of St. Peter and took the name of Paul IV. On July 12, 1555, he published a bull whose first words were *"Cum nimis absurdum."* "Since it appears utterly absurd and impermissible," the text began, "that the Jews, whom God has condemned to eternal slavery for their guilt, should enjoy our Christian love and toleration only to repay our graciousness with crass ingratitude and insults, and, instead of bowing their heads humbly, to strive for power; furthermore, in view of the fact that their impudence, which has been brought to our knowledge, goes so far in Rome and other places lying within the domains of the Holy Roman Church that Jews venture to show themselves in the midst of Christians and even in the immediate vicinity of churches without displaying any badge, rent houses in the finest quarters of the city, purchase estates, employ Christian nurses and other servants in their households, and in various other ways trample underfoot Christian honor, we find ourselves compelled to institute the following measures. . . ."

All the Jews in Rome, as well as in all other cities of the Papal States, were required to move to a separate quarter walled off from the rest of the population. Later, this came to be called the "ghetto," a word of uncertain origin. No one was permitted to leave the ghetto during the night; the gate was closed from dusk to sunrise. Whatever the size of the Jewish community, it was permitted to have only a single synagogue. All the rest were to be razed. Every Jew had to wear a yellow hat, every Jewish woman a yellow kerchief. No Christian was henceforth to address a Jew as *"Signor."* Jews were forbidden to own real estate; the only occupation they were allowed to pursue was that of old-clothes peddler.

On July 26, 1555, all Roman Jews had to move to the ghetto near Trastevere—two thousand of them into a single main street with a few cross streets—and a high wall was hastily built around the area. Two gates, bolted and guarded during the night, completed the enclosure.

The marranos, too, were in jeopardy. In August, 1555, Paul IV without previous warning abruptly annulled the letters of protection issued by his predecessors to Portuguese New Christian refugees. The marranos were taken so completely by surprise that only a few succeeded in escaping the Inquisition, which struck immediately; all the rest were thrown into dungeons and brought before the tribunal. Twenty-four men and one old lady, Donna Majora, who remained steadfast, received the death sentence. They died at the stake. Sixty marranos displayed repentance and were deported to the island of Malta. Only vigorous intervention by the Turkish Sultan prevented even worse tribulation. Prompted by his aide Joseph Nassi, the Sultan issued a vigorous protest to the Pope, and obtained release of all the marranos who claimed Turkish protection.

"A frightful monster broke forth from Rome, so fearsome its shape and so horrifying its eyes that all Europe shook at the sight of it," Samuel Usque had written in Ferrara in the year 1552, when the Inquisition was just beginning its reign of terror under Cardinal Caraffa. "Its food is human flesh. . . . Wherever it appears, the light of day is darkened by its black shadow . . . and the earth becomes a single wild wasteland."

In 1559, when word went out that Paul IV lay dying, there was a riot in Rome. A mob stormed the dungeons of the Inquisition and freed all the prisoners, both regular heretics and marranos. A marble statue of Paul IV, on whom a Roman Jew had set his yellow hat to cheers from the crowd, was tumbled from its pedestal and smashed. But "order" was soon restored, and the leaders of the mob ended on the gallows.

In the States of the Church, the Talmud schools closed their doors. Cremona in Lombardy became a haven for Jewish scholars. But no sooner had a school and a printing press resumed functioning there than the "dangerous" Talmud was once more hunted down. In obedience to a hint from the Inquisitor General, Cardinal Ghislieri, the Spanish governor of Milan took steps. Columns of wagons laden with confiscated books proceeded to the market place of Cremona in 1559. Some twelve thousand volumes of the Talmud and of Talmud commentaries were piled up in a vast pyre and burned.

Seven years later Cardinal Ghislieri ascended the papal throne as Pius V. He promptly expelled all Jews from the Papal States. His bull, issued on February 26, ordered them to emigrate within three months. Only those settled in Rome and Ancona and in the French cities of Avignon and Carpentras were allowed to remain. The deported, over a thousand families, sought refuge in Ferrara, Mantua, and Milan. Tuscany, too, granted them the right of asylum. Once again Turkey provided a home for many of the homeless.

The Pope's action was imitated in other Italy city-states. The Duchy of Milan expelled the Jews in 1597. Florence established a ghetto. Mantua, Padua, and Ferrara followed suit. Everywhere the Jews were sooner or later enclosed in walled quarters with guards at the gates. These ghettos were destined to last down to the nineteenth century.

The confinement and humiliation of ghetto existence became a characteristic of the life of Jews throughout Europe. For the intolerance kindled by Pope Paul IV was not restricted to Italy alone. The Catholic states north of the Alps strictly followed the lines of papal policy toward the Jews. In the Hapsburg lands, in Bavaria, in all the states of the Catholic League, the instructions from Rome were obeyed. The situation of the Jews proved to be no better in the Protestant countries. Luther's position scarcely tended to bring about a regime of tolerance and humanity toward the Jews.

Their situation in both camps was unenviable. To be sure, bloody massacres of the kind that had marked the darkest periods of the Middle Ages no longer occurred, and physical abuse was rarer. But the merciless hatred continued; time and again they were expelled. Insecurity and injustice prevailed. They were driven hither and yon, often to be invited back only a few years after they had been expelled. Usually they returned, for where else were they to go? If envy and rivalry on the part of nobility, priesthood, and burghers drove them out, the financial needs of the rulers would soon commend their being tolerated once more, and the previous edicts of expulsion would be annulled. Harried and wretched, the unfortunates wandered from country to country, from city to city, back and forth, their destination depending on where a door had opened again. Such was their fate in the sixteenth century, and so it remained in the seventeenth.

After the outbreak of the Thirty Years' War (1618–1648) the general situation of the Jews improved once more—because they were needed again. "The Jewish communities of Vienna, Prague, and Frankfurt am Main represented an indispensable source of revenue for the financing of the war," writes Simon Dubnow. "Hence they had to be treated with the greatest tact by the emperors who led the Catholic League, by Ferdinand II and Ferdinand III. These emperors, consequently, constantly displayed their 'solicitude' for the Jewish population." In Prague Rabbi Lipmann Heller presided over the commission that was responsible for punctually raising war taxes in the Prague and Bohemian Jewish communities. Ferdinand II appointed Jewish financiers from Prague and Vienna "court Jews." Jacob Bassewi of Prague, who bore the title of liberated court Jew, enjoyed high esteem. Ferdinand ennobled him in recognition of his services to the state, and accorded him the name von Treuenberg. The Emperor staunchly fended off the Archbishop of Vienna's demands that he expel the Jews. He acceded to only one point, the compulsory sermon the Jesuits and the Archbishop demanded. Every Saturday night, on threat of punishment, two hundred Jews of Vienna and an equal number of Jews of Prague had to appear in a church near the ghetto to listen to a conversion sermon. Beadles saw to it "that if any Jew should seem to be sleeping, he is to be stirred up to attention to the sermon." These missionary efforts were totally wasted; not a single Jew was converted.

In the Protestant Free Imperial City of Frankfurt am Main the guilds demanded that the municipality expel the inhabitants of the ghetto. The Emperor intervened, bidding them not to molest his "imperial serfs." The guildsmen thereupon published a memorial contesting the ruler's rights to the Jews as *servi camerae*. They pointed out that in 1348 Charles IV had sold his rights to the Jews in both Frankfurt and Worms to the cities themselves. The town councilors, too, resisted the demands of the guilds. Riots erupted. An enraged mob of artisans stormed the Jewish quarter. The Jews had meanwhile armed and barricaded themselves in their houses, and a violent struggle ensued, in which there were wounded and killed on both sides. But at last the Jews had to give way before the superior numbers of the attackers. The pillaging of their houses went on well into the following day. Scrolls and books of the Torah were carried off or destroyed. The synagogue was desecrated and everything in it turned topsy-turvy.

The leader of the rioters, one Vincenz Fettmilch, a baker of honey cakes, rounded up the Jewish families who had fled, and assembled them in the cemetery. He announced that the guilds would no longer tolerate them in the city. "Thereupon followed the departure of the Jews on the twenty-third day of August, 1614. . . . There were 1,380 persons of them, young and old, whom Vincenz Fettmilch had assembled in the Jewish cemetery . . . and a great number of others in the houses of citizens and some who stayed in their own houses, and so the Jew streets were closed and not inhabited. . . ." A Jewish chronicler records: "They departed filled with joy and sorrow: happy to have saved their lives and at the same time full of sadness because they were naked and robbed of all their possessions." All the others, who had been in hiding, followed them within the next few days.

The Emperor ordered stern punishment for the rioters. Fettmilch and the other ringleaders received the death penalty. On the day of the execution all of the expelled Jews were allowed to return. And they came, for they were weary of wandering helplessly. Fettmilch, the source of all the trouble, "was executed, his head placed on the bridge tower, his body quartered, and the four quarters hung on gallows erected on the roads. His house . . . was also torn down and leveled to the ground. A happy change took place for the Jews, in that by the Emperor's orders they were reinstated in all honors on February 28, 1616, the same day as the execution of Fettmilch and his accomplices. . . ." An army detachment and imperial commissioners welcomed the Jews at the market place with trumpets and drums.

A new compact setting forth the Jews' rights and taxes was agreed on. The Emperor once again declared himself protector of the Jews and forbade the town council to impose any further burdens upon them without his permission. But although they were again tolerated, the conditions of their lives remained oppressive. The city of Frankfurt set the maximum limit of their numbers at five hundred families; no more than twelve new families could be added annually by marriages. Occupational restrictions and high exactions produced a desperate situation for the Jews of Frankfurt. "What are we Jews to live on," they wrote in a petition handed to the town council in 1636, "since amid the confusion of the present war all trade has come to a standstill? Our debts cannot be collected outside the city, and we are therefore compelled to earn our livelihoods within the city itself. But as you know, the ownership of fields and meadows is forbidden to us, although only very few of us engage in credit and exchange dealings. As a result the burden of our innumerable poor falls upon us; nevertheless the weight of the taxes grows ever more pressing."

Barely nine months after the riots in Frankfurt am Main, a similar tragedy took place in Worms, one of the oldest Diaspora centers in Germany. On April 20, 1615, workmen attacked the Jewish community of one thousand five hundred persons. They pillaged the Jewish quarter, burned the Scriptures, and devastated the cemetery. The Jews fled from the city, but turned in their need to Elector Frederick of the Palatinate, who was a good friend of the Jewish doctor Zacutus Lusitanus. The Elector sent infantry, cavalry, and artillery to the city, and quickly put an end to the uprising. Protected by soldiers, the expelled Jews were finally able to return, after nine months of exile, on January 9, 1617.

After the Thirty Years' War one of the cities that the Jews helped to re-establish was Mannheim. Elector Karl Ludwig, who had taken careful note of the importance of the Jews for the trade of the Netherlands, enlisted their co-operation for the rebuilding of the devastated Palatinate. He permitted them to practice all crafts and conferred upon them the rights enjoyed by all other citizens, including the right to build a synagogue. No other German city granted them such favorable conditions—or, indeed, anything resembling favorable conditions.

Two decades after the end of the Thirty Years' War, Austria's anti-Jewish groups attained their long-sought goal. There had been persistent attempts by the town-dwelling middle class to defame the "Jewish city," which enjoyed the Emperor's protection. When war with the Turks began in 1664, the rumor was spread that the Jews had secret contacts with the Turks and were supporting them. In 1665 the corpse of a Christian woman was smuggled into the Jewish quarter in order to provide the pretext for a ritual murder charge. Leaflets were distributed denouncing in words and pictures alleged "Jewish crimes." "Scholars and other rabble," to use the phrase of an official document, forced their way into the Jewish part of the city at Passover time in 1668 and harassed the community.

In 1669 Leopold I, himself a pious pupil of the Jesuits and fired to even greater religious zeal by his marriage to the Spanish Infanta, yielded to pressure. He established a "commission of Inquisition" to investigate the Jewish question. Among its most active members was Bishop Kollonitsch of Wiener Neustadt. The commission's statement pointed to the exemplary conduct of Spain in its proceeding against the "archfoes of Christianity." It cited all the most vicious calumnies concerning the Jews, including the charge of secret collaboration with the Turks, contended that the Jewish communities and synagogues were nothing but centers of anti-Christian conspiracies, and upheld the various memoranda that had previously been sent to the Emperor urging expulsion. The town council likewise supported such a measure. That sufficed. On February 28, 1670, Leopold I signed the fateful decree. Heralds went through the streets of the capital proclaiming the news to the people: All Jews must leave Vienna, as well as both Lower and Upper Austria, forever.

By July 28, 1670, not a single Jew was left in all of Austria. Once more a great Jewish community had been annihilated, its members rendered homeless by a stroke of the pen. Not one of the many thousands asked for baptism in order to be able to remain. Deeply impressed by this fact, a Swedish resident in Vienna, who had witnessed all the events, wrote to his government: "This alone is astonishing, that among three to four thousand souls not a single one was found who in this greatest of necessities . . . thought to change his faith . . . although to accomplish that was certainly one of the particular motives that prompted His Majesty to take this resolution."

In "grateful" memory of the expulsion of the Jews, the Jewish quarter was rebaptized. It was given the name Leopoldstadt, in the Emperor's honor. With his own hands the ruler laid the cornerstone for a new Christian church on the square in front of the synagogue—the present Leopoldskirche. A tablet set into the foundation states that the church was built in place of a "den of thieves."

The rejoicing of the Viennese soon ceased—for the economy of the city had received a grave blow. Only three years later the court treasury presented a report on the consequences to Emperor Leopold. Commerce had slackened, general prices were rising, the crafts were in a deep recession, while at the same time there was an acute shortage of credit.

The great majority of the exiles from Vienna went to Moravia to seek a new refuge. A small group, however, founded a new community in a city that was to play a significant part in the history of Judaism: Berlin. Sober utilitarian considerations threw open the gates of this rising city to the Jews. It was hoped that they would put an end to the prevailing and by now retrogressive barter economy and supply the mechanisms of money and credit indispensable to a modern city, as well as improve the income of the state and municipality. The Great Elector, Frederick William (ruler of Brandenburg, 1640–1688), had shrewdly observed the vital role the Jews were playing as bankers, business agents, and merchants in the economic life of the neighboring Netherlands. When Neumann, his resident in Vienna, sent confidential information of the forthcoming expulsion, the Prince saw his opportunity. He was prepared, he wrote, to grant domiciliary rights to fifty families—"wealthy and well-to-do persons who wish to bring their funds into the country and invest them here."

Three Jewish representatives—destined to become ancestors of leading Berlin families—went to Berlin to look into the conditions being offered. They found them acceptable. On May 21, 1671, Frederick William signed an edict admitting the Jews and granting them permission to gather for worship in one of their houses, although they were not allowed to build a synagogue, and also to employ a kosher butcher and a schoolmaster for their children. For the time being, the length of their residence was limited to twenty years, with the assurance that the time limit would be extended if the Jews gave no offense.

Only seven families settled in Berlin, the rest in other towns in Brandenburg. But almost as soon as they were established the populace began to murmur against the commercial freedoms that had been granted to them. In 1672 the Christian merchants of Frankfurt an der Oder, and the rural nobility, complained to the Elector about the admission of the Jews into Brandenburg. They reminded him that a century before the ancestors of the new immigrants had been banished. Frederick William rejected the complaint "because We continue to hold the opinion that the Jews by their commerce are not harmful but rather useful to Us and to the country." He refused to brook any interference with his policy. He was also the first German sovereign to permit Jews to attend a university. On behalf of his friend young Tobias Cohen, Frederick William instructed the Medical Faculty in Frankfurt an der Oder to allow the "Jewish youth" to go to the lectures, and provided him with a stipend for study. The Great Elector furthermore appointed Elias Gumperts his court Jew. He took in more rich Jews from Hamburg, Glogow, and other cities. Before long, more than a thousand lived in his dominions. A new edition of the Talmud was printed in Frankfurt an der Oder.

Thus, in the heart of Europe and in an environment of resentment, dependent on the good will of the sovereign, a new life had begun for a small Jewish community at about the time that a fearsome catastrophe descended upon the Jews living farther to the east.

THE MASSACRES IN THE EAST

The hitherto peaceful oasis of East European Jewry sheltered hundreds of thousands of souls by the middle of the seventeenth century. In 1648, the year in which the Peace of Westphalia finally put an end to three decades of warfare in Western Europe, disaster struck the Jews of the East. The communities living under Polish rule were struck by persecutions that surpassed even the sufferings of the Crusades and the years of plague.

For a century the Polish kings had been extending their dominion over the southern fringes of Poland, the Ukrainian river valleys of the Dnieper and Dniester. The kings and their nobles ruthlessly exploited these fertile regions. The native populace, living and working on vast seigneurial estates, had no rights whatsoever. They were regarded as serfs and bore almost intolerable burdens of forced labor and taxation. In addition, the tensions were increased by seething religious hatreds. The foreign masters were Roman Catholic, their crushed subjects Greek Orthodox.

The people scarcely ever saw the Polish magnates who ruled the land. These nobles seldom lived on their estates. Stewards or tenants, many of whom were Jews, administered the landholdings. The nobles had rented out their inns, mills, dairies, distilleries, and taverns to Jews, and had frequently entrusted them with the collection of taxes. The high rents compelled the Jews to extract the maximum profit from their enterprises. Under pressure themselves, they became the involuntary instruments of exploitation, and the ire of the natives was more and more directed against them. The situation was expressed in a folk song: "The Ukrainian Cossack, the hero bold, rides past the inn, but the Jew takes hold and will not let go. 'Rest, my Cossack, my Cossack come in, or how can I pay my master, the Pole, his rent?' And the Cossack loses his shining armor to him."

Hatred of the oppressors, the foreigners, the heretics, increased steadily. It erupted finally in 1648, when the Cossack hetman Bogdan Chmielnicki summoned the Ukrainians to a holy war for freedom and orthodoxy against the *panowie*—the Polish lords—and the Jews. "What wrongs you have suffered from the Poles and their tenants and brokers, the Jews, what deeds of violence and cruelty, you yourselves know best," he exhorted the populace in a manifesto. Tatars from the Crimea came to the support of the rebels. United Cossack and Tatar forces fell upon and defeated Polish troops in the Ukraine. That was the signal for an uprising throughout the country.

Everywhere bands assembled, raided farms and set manor houses afire, and slaughtered stewards and Jewish tenants. From the countryside, the fury spread to the towns. Only converts to the Orthodox religion were spared. In the towns and villages of Poltava thousands of Jews were killed. The Cossacks, mad with savage fury, committed inconceivable atrocities upon the Jews. An eyewitness, Nathan Hannover, relates: "The Cossacks stripped the skin off one man and threw his flesh to the dogs. . . . Others were buried alive. They stabbed infants in the arms of their mothers, and tore many to pieces like fish. . . . Sometimes heaps of Jewish children were thrown into the water to improve fords. . . . The Tatars, for their part, made prisoners of the Jews; but they, too, raped women before the eyes of their husbands and took away the most beautiful for slaves and concubines. The Cossacks everywhere behaved in no less cruel a fashion toward the Poles, especially toward the priests."

Like the flames of hell, the rebellion spread through the Ukraine, reaching from the Dnieper all the way to the vicinity of Kiev. Some three thousand Jews, fugitives from four communities, at least preserved their lives because they fell into the hands of the Tatars. They were taken to Constantinople for sale as slaves.

Before long, roaming bands of Cossacks and peasants made the western Ukraine also unsafe for Jews and Poles. The massacres extended to Volhynia and Podolia. The threatened people fled to fortified towns. But even here they did not escape their enemies. In the city of Nemirov several thousand Jews barricaded themselves behind stout walls. But Chmielnicki dispatched Cossacks who gained entrance by a stratagem. Disguised as Poles, they approached the town, and the gates were thrown open for them. Hardly a one among the men thus taken by surprise escaped death. The women were raped, the children drowned in the wells. The Russians living in the town took part in the atrocities. Only a few Jews, who had consented to baptism, survived.

Hordes of fugitives in the fortified town of Tulczyn in Podolia were similarly slaughtered. Having taken the town, the Cossacks drove all the Jews—some fifteen hundred—into a garden. They planted their battle flag and their spokesman announced: "Let whoever consents to baptism step beneath this banner, and we will let him live." Not a single Jew came forward; all were put to death.

The massacre in Polonnoye reached even more frightful proportions. A tremendous number of fugitives, among them nearly twelve thousand Jews, had poured into this city. The only ones left alive were those whom the Tatars had taken prisoner; these "fortunates" were sold as slaves.

As word spread of these brutalities, a mass flight began. Wild with fear, vast numbers of Jews rushed from town to town whenever the approach of Cossack hordes was reported. "In Zaslaw we learned that the Tatars and Russians had surrounded Polonnoye," an eyewitness described the panic. "At once all who could run abandoned their houses and most precious possessions and fled from Zaslaw, only six miles away from Polonnoye . . . in order at least to save their lives. Some turned to the Russian ducal capital of Ostrog, which sheltered a large Jewish community with many scholars. But I, together with my family and my father-in-law's family, fled to Miedzyrzecz, in the vicinity of Ostrog. In these two cities more than ten thousand families gathered. . . . But that same evening, with the beginning of the Sabbath, came the frightful news of the fall of Polonnoye and the slaughter of the Poles and Jews . . . as well as that . . . Cossacks and Tatars were marching toward Ostrog and Miedzyrzecz. The Polish *panowie* were gripped by dread, and boundless fear overcame the Jews. . . . Then the word was once again: Up and away! By no means all owned a horse and wagon, so that many had to go on foot with wife and child, leaving all their property behind. But even the owners of wagons found themselves compelled on the way to unload some of their baggage, in order to make better speed. On that Sabbath . . . vehicles moved in three uninterrupted rows along the seven-mile road from Ostrog to Dubno. . . . Soon we were overtaken by three riders, the Jew Moshe Zoref of Ostrog and two *panowie*. They called out to us: 'Hurry! The enemy is already in Miedzyrzecz, and we barely escaped with a whole skin.' At that an indescribable panic erupted among our brothers. In haste everyone began to throw gold and silver things, clothing, books, feather beds and pillows onto the road, in order to be able to flee unburdened at redoubled speed. In the resulting confusion many women and men lost their children, and many hurriedly sought to hide in caves in the woods."

While the Ukrainians and Tatars under Chmielnicki were spreading havoc through Volhynia and Podolia toward Galicia, hordes of Cossacks and rebellious peasants surged into Lithuania and White Russia. The Jewish homes in Pinsk and Brest went up in flames; the communities of Chernigov and Starodub were annihilated. Another eyewitness records the atrocities in the White Russian city of Gomel: "The rebels bribed the city prefect, who thereupon turned the Jews over to them completely. The Russians surrounded them with drawn swords, daggers, and lances, and addressed them thus: 'Why do you always hold fast to your God? . . . Abandon your God and you will at once be treated like lords. But if you persist in the faith of your fathers you will fall by our hands as have so many of your brethren in the Ukraine and Lithuania.' Thereupon the voice of Rabbi Eliezer spoke: 'Remember, brothers, the deaths of our fellows, who willingly sacrificed themselves for the holiness of the Name.' When the villains heard this, they flew into a frenzy and struck the unfortunates with clubs, so that they would die a painful death. In heaps, men, women, and children fell, and their unburied corpses became the food of dogs and swine." Official reports to Moscow from Mogilev and Smolensk stated that in Gomel "more than two thousand of the Jews, counting women and children, were cut down, of the Poles about six hundred men, but not a single one of the White Russians suffered loss of life or property."

John Casimir, who was elected King of Poland in 1648, could not quell the atrocities. A peace treaty was finally signed, however, after the Polish army had inflicted a decisive defeat upon the Cossacks in July of 1651. The right of the persecuted to settle again in Cossack territories was again confirmed. But the period of peace was brief. Further suffering descended upon the Jews. The few remaining communities had just barely re-established themselves when the fury of war once again swept over the country. Chmielnicki had arranged an alliance with the Russians, and Czar Alexis Mikhailovich suddenly made territorial claims upon Poland. In the summer of 1654 Muscovite troops and Cossacks advanced into White Russia and Lithuania. "For Russianism and Orthodoxy!" was their battle cry.

Everywhere the Muscovite generals drove out the Jews. In White Russian Mogilev an ukase issued in 1655 forbade forever their "sojourning or abiding." Vitebsk fell after bitter resistance from Jews and Poles. The Russians speedily carried off the captured Jewish population to Novgorod and Kazan. By the time Vilna, the capital of Lithuania, was taken in August, 1655, most of the Jews had already fled. Rabbi Moses Rivkes, who escaped along with his community in the nick of time, wrote: "Bands of Russians and Cossacks marched through all of Lithuania, devastating the cities and occupying Polotsk, Vitebsk, and Minsk. Wherever the Cossacks appeared, they fell avariciously upon the property of the Jews, whom they massacred in untold numbers. . . . We went to Samogitia, but found no peace there either, for now the Swedes were the ones who harried the populace."

The Swedes: to add to the woe, a third enemy had entered the country in the summer of 1655—King Charles X of Sweden. His troops advanced into the heart of the Polish Kingdom and by the spring of 1656 had occupied all of Greater and Lesser Poland. They themselves left the Jewish communities unharmed. But indirectly they were the cause of new disasters. For when Polish General Stefan Czarniecki with his bands of guerrilla soldiers threw back the Swedish troops, the undisciplined hordes promptly fell upon the Jews, who were charged with having made common cause with the Swedes. In Gniezno, Leszno, Plock, and many other towns the Jewish population was slain after abominable tortures.

In the autumn of 1655 Chmielnicki's bands once again appeared before the walls of Lwow. All the outlying districts of the city went up in flames. Chmielnicki sent an ultimatum to the town council: "The Jews, enemies of Christ and of all Christendom, must be handed over to us together with their wives and children." But the council steadfastly withstood the demand. The Jews of Lublin were not so fortunate. For days the Cossacks raged through the city and set fire to the Jewish quarter. Rabbi Samuel Auerbach, who escaped the massacre, wrote: "It is written: '. . . for Thy sake are we killed all the day; we are accounted as sheep for the slaughter' (Psalm 44:23). How these words apply to the martyrs of Lublin. Day in, day out, we were slaughtered more cruelly than cattle. . . . They drove a lance into the body of Abraham ben Jehudah, so that for an entire day he writhed in the agony of death with the iron in his bowels."

Death reaped a ghastly harvest in the eight terrible years in Poland from 1648 to 1656. The number of murdered Jews is estimated at three —if not five—hundred thousand. Some seven hundred Jewish communities vanished totally, or were left with only a few survivors. Nine tenths of the Jewish population in Volhynia and Podolia had been massacred or carried away as slaves, or had fled. Their homes were ashes. The sufferings of the Crusades, of the times of the Black Death, even the disasters of Spain had been far surpassed. The flourishing center of Jewish life that Poland had been was shattered. A contemporary wrote: "Since the downfall of the kingdom, Israel had not been struck by such a catastrophe."

Western Europe was witness to the consequences. The harried remnants who had succeeded in escaping the inferno turned up in Hungary, Moravia, and Bohemia, in the streets of Frankfurt, Hamburg, Amsterdam, Venice.

Everywhere the existing Jewish communities took the refugees in. More-over, all those whom the Tatars had carried off to Turkey were ransomed. Contributions to that end poured in from all of Western Europe.

The turning point in the history of Polish Jewry had come. Poland, for so many years the longed-for haven of Jews expelled from Central Europe, henceforth became a country of emigration. From 1648 on, the tide of Jewish wanderers began flowing back again—toward the west.

WITH COLUMBUS TO THE NEW WORLD

At the time these disasters descended upon the Jewish communities in Eastern Europe, momentous events, which were profoundly to affect the history of Jewry also, were taking place in the farthest West. They had begun a century and a half before, in the very year that the Spanish Jews were expelled.

On April 30, 1492, heralds had proclaimed throughout Spain the royal edict that all believing Jews must leave the country within three months. On April 17 Columbus had received from their Most Catholic Majesties, Ferdinand of Aragon and Isabella of Castile, the contract setting forth royal approval of his bold project. "In that same month," Columbus wrote, "in which the Spanish rulers determined to expel the Jews from the entire kingdom, they gave me my commission to undertake my voyage to the Indies."

The archives at Seville preserves to this day a document containing an account by the sailor Juan de Aragon from Moguer. At the end of July, 1492, he had served as cabin boy aboard a vessel that was to take expelled Jews to Africa. As the ship sailed down the Río Tinto and passed the quay of Palos, the exiles saw Columbus' three caravels lying with reefed sails, on the point of departure. The refugees aboard Juan de Aragon's ship could not suspect that members of their own people were aboard the caravels.

On August 2, 1492, all Jews except the marranos had left Spain. The following day, August 3, the three ships under the command of Columbus set out on their audacious voyage to the "Indies."

From the hour of its conception, the story of the New World's dis-covery was closely linked with Jewry. Marranos and Jews had taken a decisive part in the planning and execution of the epoch-making expedition.

Was Columbus himself a Jew? No one can say with certainty. There are a good many indications that he was, but unequivocal proof has so far not yet been provided. The controversy among the experts has been summed up as follows by Fritz Heymann:

"For several centuries scholars were convinced that the Admiral of the New World had been a son of the weaver Domenico Columbo of Genoa and his wife Susanna Fontanarossa. This son figures in the documents as Christofforus Columbo. . . . But in 1914 the scholar Celso Gracia de la Riega discovered documents in the town of Pontevedra in the province of Galicia in northwestern Spain that spoke of a Domenico Colón, his wife Susanna Fonterosa, and their children Cristóbo, Bartolomeu, Diego, and Branqua. The Fonterosas, who appeared to be Columbus' family on his mother's side, were newly baptized Jews. Since that time, diligent scholars have found Colóns and Colóms of Jewish descent in all the regions of Spain. It has been demonstrated in innumerable essays that the Admiral . . . never wrote Italian, but did write excellent Spanish, and that he tended to name newly discovered islands after the towns around Pontevedra. A violent dispute continues to rage over whether the explorer Cristóbal Colón was identical with the Genoese Christofforus Columbo or with the Spaniard Cristóbo Colón."

There is, however, no controversy over the Jewish descent of the men who supported his plan and ultimately helped to make his voyage of discovery a success. There were many of them.

For two years Columbus lived as a guest of Luis de la Cerda, Duke of Medica Celi. His patron had offered to outfit three ships, but Queen Isabella refused her consent. The Duke recommended Columbus to his cousin, Cardinal Pedro Gonzalez de Mendoza, Bishop of Toledo. The Cardinal and the Duke were related through the same Jewish grandmother. There had been pamphlets attacking the Duke on his descent, and the Prince of the Church had had to face a tribunal of the Inquisition. Be that as it might, the Cardinal wholeheartedly promoted Columbus' plans; he sat as chairman of a commission in Salamanca that carefully examined and approved the proposals.

Diego de Deza, Bishop of Zamora and confessor to King Ferdinand, quartered Columbus in his palace. "Ever since I came to Castile," the Admiral later wrote to his sovereign, "this prelate has protected me and furthered my good fame. Along with Chamberlain Cabreror, he is the reason Your Majesties possess the Indies." Bishop Diego de Deza was a grandson of the Jew Ruy Capon, and Juan Cabrero, the King's first chamberlain, was likewise the grandson of a marrano of pure Jewish extraction, Aragon's "minister of the interior," Sancho de Paternoy. In 1492 Cabrero succeeded with great difficulty in saving his grandfather from the stake and obtaining a commutation of the death sentence to life imprisonment.

Plausible traditions also report a meeting of Columbus with the influential Isaac Abravanel, as well as with Abraham Senior, the leaders of the Castilian Jews. He was supposed to have conferred with them in 1487 in Málaga, outlining his plans to them. They, too, were backers of his enterprise, until in 1492 Abravanel emigrated to Italy, while Senior submitted to baptism and adopted the name of Fernando Perez Coronel.

Among Columbus' highly placed patrons were also the marranos Luis de Santangel, the tax farmer who was virtually royal treasurer of Aragon, Gabriel Sanchez, another royal treasurer, and the vice-chancellor of Aragon, Alfonso de la Caballeria, scion of a famous Jewish family that had accepted Christianity.

The royal secretary, Juan de Coloma, was another of the supporters of Columbus. His wife belonged to the the de la Caballeria family.

On January 2, 1492, in the army camp at Santa Fe outside Granada, Luis de Santangel prevailed on the Queen to give her consent. He once again pointed out to Isabella the tremendous advantages that would accrue to the first country to find the shortest sea route to India. Immeasurable territories could be conquered, innumerable pagans converted. All the treasures of gold and gems described by Marco Polo would belong to the rulers of Spain. What glory for the crowns of Castile, Aragon, and León! In addition, since there were not sufficient funds available in the treasury to finance the enterprise, Santangel offered to advance a sizable contribution out of his own fortune: seventeen thousand ducats. This proved to be the decisive factor. The sum supplied by Santangel made possible the outfitting of the expedition.

Virtually all the nautical instruments and maps that Columbus took with him on his voyage had been made by Jews. Many of them were the creation of Jehudah Cresques, at one time head of the Nautical Academy of Palma on Majorca, later in Portuguese service under the name of Jacomo de Majorca, head of the School of Navigation at Sagres—the school whose founding by Henry the Navigator in 1418 marked the beginning of the Age of Discovery. Columbus also derived valuable information from Abraham Zacuto, the astronomer and mathematician, a child of the *judería* of Saragossa, who was forced to emigrate to Portugal in 1492. Columbus took along with him on his voyage Zacuto's *Perpetual Almanac,* a table of ephemerides. In the crew, too, there were several marranos, among them the interpreter Luis de Torres and the doctors Bernal and Marco.

Luis de Torres, a Jew baptized only shortly before departure, is said to have been the first to set foot on the new soil. He was also the first European who settled in the New World. When Columbus sailed back to Spain after the discovery of America, Torres decided to remain. He established himself in Cuba and began planting a crop hitherto unknown in Europe: tobacco. We are informed of these facts from the log book of the flagship, the *Santa Maria*. On the island of Cuba Columbus made the following notation in his own hand: "The Admiral decided to send two Spaniards into the interior of the country, the one named Rodrigo de Jerez . . . and Luis, who had been in the service of the Governor of Murcia, had been a Jew, and knew Hebrew, Chaldean, and even some Arabic. On the way home these two met many people, men and women, who carried a half-burned weed in their hands, those leaves which they are accustomed to smoke. . . ."

Luis de Torres died in Cuba. The account books for the "Indies" contain a brief final notation about him: "Paid on September 22, 1508, to Catalina Sanchez, wife of the deceased Luis de Torres . . . 8,645 maravedi as the wages of her husband, earned by him during the time that the island of Española [Haiti] was first discovered."

Luis de Santangel received the first report of the discoveries. Columbus had sent a message to him from the Azores, where he had put in on the return voyage. Ferdinand and Isabella first heard of the successful undertaking from the lips of their treasurer.

The second voyage of discovery to the New World, in 1493, was again financed by Jewish money. The funds the rulers made available at this time came from the sale of property confiscated from Jews who had been expelled the previous year. The archives still contain royal decrees ordaining the immediate sale of jewelry, wares, and estates so that the new voyage would not be delayed. The proceeds of the expulsion of the Jews were sufficient to pay for a third and fourth voyage for Columbus.

The King and Queen rewarded Santangel's and Sanchez's support of Columbus' expeditions by granting them valuable special privileges. Both marranos, although suspected of sympathy for Judaism, were protected from the clutches of the Inquisition, and Luis de Santangel received the first royal charter for the export of grain and horses to America.

A whole new world had been discovered. With fresh hope the marranos listened to the tales, and soon hordes of Jewish New Christian emigrants poured into the lands Columbus had claimed for the Crown of Castile. They had to board the ships secretly, for officially they were strictly forbidden to set foot in the new territories. But disregarding all bans and harbor controls, they made their way across the ocean, where they hoped to be able to begin a new life. Within a short time some had done so. Juan Sanchez of Saragossa was the first man to work as a merchant in the New World. The first industries in the American colonies were started by marranos. As early as 1492 Portuguese Jews settled in St. Thomas and began operating large-scale plantations. They imported sugar cane from the island of Madeira and established it with great success in the West Indies. They set up several sugar mills, and soon, following the custom that had developed there so quickly, were employing three thousand Negro slaves. Half a century later the new industry on the island was flourishing mightily. The harvest of sixty plantations flowed to the mills, and by 1550 production had already reached 3.75 million pounds.

But the marranos' and Jews' hope that they would be allowed to live and work in peace, so far from Europe, was not to be fulfilled. All too soon the arm of the Inquisition reached out to the new colonies in Central and South America. The kings of Spain appointed bishops as their Inquisitors—first in Cuba and Puerto Rico—and accorded them full powers to exterminate heresy. In 1515 the marrano Pedro de León, along with his family, was arrested on the island of Española and carried back to Seville for trial. Under Emperor Charles V the Inquisition made its entry into Mexico. In 1528, only nine years after the conquest of the Aztec Kingdom, the flames from the first auto-da-fé leaped up in the New World. The victims were a "Judaizing" colonist and conquistador who had fought at the side of Hernán Cortés in the conquest of Mexico: the marrano Hernando Alonzo. For the time being, however, the persecution was on a small scale.

Soon after 1536, when the Inquisition struck for the first time in Portugal, fresh bands of the newly baptized emigrated, chiefly to Mexico. Before long, there was no city in the New World in which they could not be found. They pioneered in all branches of economic life. They established plantations, started mines, and took up commerce with all parts of the Old World. In Peru, too, colonial trade developed with amazing speed under their auspices. A torrent of goods began to flow across the Atlantic Ocean.

There was almost inevitably a reaction. In 1571, under King Philip II, the first regular inquisitional tribunal was set up in Mexico. It was ordered to purge "the land desecrated by Jews and heretics, principally of Portuguese nationality." The auto-da-fé, celebrated with great pomp on February 28, 1574, was followed by a long succession of others. Everywhere in the New World the flames leaped toward the sky, and together with other "heretics" innumerable marranos fell victim to them.

At the end of the sixteenth century general feeling was further excited by a trial in which an entire family of emigrants from Portugal was wiped out.

Luis de Carvajal, a marrano, was considered so devout a Catholic that the post of governor of the Mexican Province of New León was conferred on him. As governor, he encouraged the settlement of the country. Among the many immigrants he brought over were quite a few marranos who secretly held to the religion of their fathers. A large community formed clandestinely. One day its rabbi married Francisca, the governor's sister. At this point the Inquisition struck suddenly. When the first arrests began, many of the secret Jews fled. But not a single member of the Carvajal family escaped. All its members were imprisoned and tortured. Luis de Carvajal, found guilty of not having denounced his sister, died in the dungeon, his relatives on the pyre. More autos-da-fé exterminated the community's remaining members. Their money, plantations, and mines were confiscated.

Within a quarter century the number of trials rose to no less than eight hundred and seventy-nine. In zeal the Mexican Inquisitions almost surpassed the notorious tribunal in Toledo. So thoroughly did it operate that in the following four decades there were only thirty secret Jews to be placed on trial. New mass trials began again in Mexico after 1646. The fury of the Inquisitors reached its height in the horrors of the Auto General of April 11, 1649—the greatest in the New World. One hundred and eight marranos perished in the flames.

A tribunal of the Inquisition was established in Peru in 1570. Its "purges" soon sent a wave of horror through the country. Autos-da-fé were held in 1595, 1600, and 1605, and on January 23, 1639, the capital of Peru witnessed the burning of seven marranos, out of a group of sixty condemned to the same death. One of these was Dr. Francisco Maldonado da Silva, who refused to renounce his faith despite torture followed by seventeen years of imprisonment. Another of the victims was Manuel Baptista Perez, the wealthiest merchant of Lima and a great patron of literature. For many years secret Jews had held clandestine meetings in his house for prayer and services.

The arrests and confiscations of the Inquisitors reached such proportions as to produce an economic crisis in Peru, and the bank had to cease its payments. With the annihilation of the marranos, the country's economic backbone was shattered.

Brazil also contained important Jewish settlements. From the very first hour of its discovery in 1500, the conquest and colonization of that vast land was closely connected with pioneering marranos and Jews. Pedro

Alvares Cabral's expedition, which gave the Portuguese their claim to this New World colony, had among its crew, as navigator and interpreter, Gaspar da Gama. Born in Poland, in his early youth he had been among those Jews sold into slavery by the Tatars. Vasco da Gama on his first epoch-making voyage around the Cape of Good Hope had encountered him in India and brought him to Portugal. The boy had been forcibly baptized and thereafter bore the Admiral's surname.

For years many Jews were able to cross the Atlantic because of Portuguese policy. After 1548 the tribunals of the Inquisition more and more frequently condemned suspect marranos to deportation—a piece of good luck in misfortune for the persons involved. For in the new settlements the exiles could return to their old religion with a freedom inconceivable in the homeland.

The vigor they brought to Brazil soon became apparent, and not only in commerce. A marrano served as first governor general: Thomé de Sonza, a man of sterling qualities, was sent over to the vast colony in 1549 to establish order in the administration. In addition, New Christians constituted the doctors almost everywhere in Brazil. The first great sugar plantations were owned by Jews. They also furthered the planting of cotton, tobacco, and rice. In fact, the marrano settlements soon began to flourish so mightily that in 1579 Portugal decided to confer inquisitorial powers on the Bishop of Salvador. All suspects, his instructions went, were to be sent to Europe for sentencing. A wave of interrogations, arrests, and confiscations followed.

This state of affairs lasted for nearly half a century. The turning point came in 1624. The Netherlands, in a long and bloody war of liberation against Catholic Spain, had won independence for themselves and freedom to practice the Protestant faith. They had developed into the strongest naval power in Europe. Their trading companies made many difficulties for the Portuguese in both the East and the West Indies. The West Indies Company was already reaching out toward Brazil.

The sorely oppressed marranos did not hesitate to take sides with the Dutch, whose country had generously taken in their expelled fellows from Portugal. Jews had already participated in the preparations for the Hollanders' Brazilian undertaking, among them Francisco Ribeiro, a Portuguese captain whose Jewish relations lived in Amsterdam. The Amsterdam marranos also supported the Dutch plans with all the means at their disposal. Spanish Jews, former marranos, participated in the West Indies Company, and the governing board of that company raised funds for the campaign. Jewish volunteers joined the Dutch troops and distinguished themselves repeatedly during the war. Nuño Alvarez Franco and Manuel Fernandez developed the plans that led to the capture of Salvador, and the conquest of Pernambuco succeeded thanks to the efforts of a group of Amsterdam Jews led by Antonio Vaez Henriquez. Under Francisco de Campos of Amsterdam, the Dutch were able to take the island of Fernando de Noronha.

Gradually, the Dutch succeeded in conquering the entire country. Their rule meant freedom for the New Christians of Brazil. For the first time in the New World a Jewish community arose that could openly profess its religion.

A stream of immigrants from the Old World poured toward Brazil. The number of prosperous Jewish settlements increased rapidly. The chief of these was located in Pernambuco. Sugar refineries were established; importing and exporting flourished. In 1642, along with numerous Jewish immigrants from Holland, two young scholars from Amsterdam arrived. They were Isaac Aboab de Fonseca, who became the "first American rabbi" in Pernambuco, and Raffael Moses de Aguilar, who served as cantor in one of the synagogues. With the glad news of reviving Jewish community life in Pernambuco, the great scholar Manasseh ben Israel, in Holland, encouraged his coreligionists to emigrate.

This period of freedom did not last long. In 1645 the Portuguese attacked Dutch Brazil. This was the signal for those Portuguese plantation owners who had remained in the country to rise in rebellion. The war lasted for nine years. Naturally enough, the Jews sided with those who had granted them freedom of religion rather than with those from whom they could expect nothing but oppression and the stake. In 1646 Rabbi Aboab rallied Jews from all over the country to come to the defense of Pernambuco. A fleet of eighteen ships under the command of David Peixotto, a Jew, brought aid to the famine-stricken city. But after a renewed siege it fell into the hands of the Portuguese on January 27, 1654. The last Dutch possession in Brazil had succumbed.

The Dutch did not forget their partisans during the peace negotiations. They insisted on full amnesty for the civilian populace, and expressly for the Jews. The Portuguese agreed to this condition, but broke their word. As soon as Brazil was under Portuguese mastery once again, the order was issued for the Jews to leave the country.

The end of Dutch rule in South America had fateful consequences for the future of the Jews in the New World. The refugees from Brazil became the founders of other Jewish communities in the Americas, which were subsequently to grow to great importance.

None of these new places of refuge, however, was located in the South American possessions of Spain and Portugal, the two nations that had brought so much suffering upon the Jewish people in Europe. An entirely new period of Jewish colonization now began.

Only Aboab, Aguilar, and a group of Amsterdam Jews from Pernambuco returned to Holland. The remainder of the deported Jews and marranos went to other regions in the Americas—chiefly to the West Indian archipelago and the adjacent coast: the Dutch, English, and French possessions in the Antilles and in Guiana. With their arrival a new period of flourishing colonial development began. Jewish settlements sprang up in Curaçao, Jamaica, and Cayenne. New arrivals from Brazil established the first modern sugar mill in Barbados. Sugar exports rose rapidly; by 1676 some four hundred ships annually, each with a capacity of one hundred and eighty tons of sugar, were sailing from the island. In 1664 Thomas Modyford introduced sugar production to Jamaica. By 1670 there were some seventy-five mills producing up to two thousand hundredweight of raw sugar. The following year Christian merchants complained; they wanted the Jews excluded. The Governor rejected their petition. "His Majesty could not have more useful subjects than the Jews and the Dutch," he countered.

The situation was the same in Surinam, where Jews had been living since 1644. The English accorded them privileges because, as they put it, "we have found that the Hebrew Nation is proved of utility and a Blessing for the Colonies." When Surinam changed owners in 1667 and the Dutch took over, nothing changed in that respect.

Much the same picture was presented by the more important French colonies. Jews deported from South America helped introduce large-scale sugar production into Santo Domingo. On Martinique, in 1655, Benjamin Dacosta established the first big plantation, and set up refineries. Nine hundred of his coreligionists, who had brought with them from Brazil eleven hundred slaves, took part in the project. On Guadeloupe the same process was repeated. All this was genuine pioneering work of enormous significance for the newly discovered lands—for the production of sugar became the core of the first economies in the New World. "France's shipping," a Parisian merchant testified in 1701, "owes its glory to the trade with the sugar-cane islands, and can be preserved and enlarged through that trade."

Another small band of exiles from Brazil sought a new home much farther to the north. They laid the foundation for what was subsequently to form the largest Jewish community in the world.

In 1654 twenty-three Jewish refugees landed in the port of New Amsterdam, the city on Hudson's river. Because the city was Dutch, the new arrivals confidently expected to be received hospitably. To their dismay, Governor Peter Stuyvesant proved to be distinctly unfriendly. In a report to the directors of the Dutch West India Company in Amsterdam, he brusquely objected to the admission of the Jews, since they "might infect New Netherlands." Several months passed, with the Jews waiting nervously for a decision. At last the reply from Holland arrived, dated April 26, 1655. It appeared both unreasonable and unjust, the letter to Stuyvesant stated, to refuse asylum to those who had taken so important a share in Holland's Brazilian enterprise and who had suffered great harm from their expulsion. "After close consultation, and in consideration of the petition of the Portuguese Jews [in Amsterdam] we have determined to grant to them the privilege to ply the waters of New Netherlands, to engage in trade everywhere, and to settle in all places, with the one reservation that those without funds among them are not to become burdens upon the Company or the Christian community, but are to be supported by members of their own race."

Such was the germ of the world's greatest Jewish community.

THE DUTCH JERUSALEM

"If one of the kingdoms rises against you, to deliver you up to annihilation, there is always another where you may find shelter," Samuel Usque had written in 1552 in his *Consolation for the Oppressions of Israel*. Even before the century ended, a new refuge unexpectedly opened up for the harried marranos: in the Netherlands.

The Dutch had waged a long and heroic struggle for freedom of religion, a tiny nation defying a world power, Spain. Soon after the seven northern provinces had thrown off the Spanish yoke and in 1579, in the Utrecht Union, proclaimed freedom of conscience, the first refugees arrived from Portugal, which King Philip II had recently incorporated into Spain.

In spite of the thousands of New Christians who had fled to Italy and Turkey, to Africa, and, finally, to the New World, during the fifteenth and sixteenth centuries, and in spite of other thousands burned at the stake by the Inquisition, there were still innumerable marranos in Spain and Portugal, the descendants of the forcibly baptized, waiting for the chance to renounce their high positions in the state and their ecclesiastical dignities and escape to tolerant countries where they could safely return to Judaism.

Accounts of contemporaries convey at least a sense of the state of mind of the marranos, which ultimately led them to remove to Amsterdam.

In 1590 a ship stole out from a port of Portugal with emigrants on board, the grandchildren of forcibly baptized Jews. The vessel was taken captive by a British warship engaged in hunting down the Spanish-Portuguese fleet. The captain, an English duke, was so enchanted by the beauty of one of the passengers, Maria Nuñes, that he wanted to marry her. He did not suspect that he had fallen in love with a secret Jewess; he assumed that she belonged to a family of Portuguese grandees. To his intense chagrin, she rejected his suit, for she was set against marrying any Christian.

Maria was brought to London with the rest of the prisoners, where her beauty caused so much talk that at last the Queen expressed the desire to meet her. She was brought before Elizabeth, who was delighted with the young marrano, and drove with her through the streets of London in an open carriage. But Maria Nuñes had her mind fixed on her original project, to reach the Netherlands. Finally she was released and permitted to leave, her supplications freeing all her comrades as well. The group arrived happily in Amsterdam, where they took up their old faith.

Another story tells of an incident three years later, when a storm in the Channel carried a ship with a group of secret emigrants off course to the city of Emden. They went ashore, and by chance noticed Hebrew lettering on a house. They had come upon the home of Rabbi Moses Uri Levi. Joyfully, they made themselves known and asked him to circumcise them. But the Rabbi refused, fearing the indignation of the Protestant populace. He advised them to continue their journey to Amsterdam; he would follow them there, he promised, and in the Dutch city take them back into the covenant of Abraham. This was done.

It is uncertain whether these two episodes actually took place exactly as described. It remains a historical fact that in 1593 a number of marranos from Portugal settled in Amsterdam. Jacob Tirado, a cultivated man whom they had chosen for their spokesman, negotiated with the authorities in Latin. The immigrants were also fortunate in having a highly respected personage in the city who gave vigorous support to their cause. He was Samuel Palache, envoy of the Sultan of Morocco, and a Sephardic Jew like themselves. He had established a place of worship in his home, and there they met regularly.

Almost inevitably, the seemingly secret conclaves of the newcomers aroused the suspicions of the Amsterdam authorities. They began suspecting in every arrival from the hated Philip's kingdom a papist or a Spanish spy. One day in October, 1596, when the "Portuguese" had secretly assembled to celebrate Yom Kippur, the authorities struck. Dutch police forced their way into the house of worship. The worshipers, still terrified of the Inquisition, took flight. The Dutch were no little astonished; instead of saints' images or Catholic sacred vessels, they found indecipherable writings—Hebrew books and Torah scrolls.

Jacob Tirado made a clean breast of the situation: The immigrants were Jews who hated the Catholic Inquisition no less than the Dutch. In addition, he explained, they had brought capital with them and had extensive commercial connections, which they were ready to use for the benefit of the country that had hospitably received them.

That same day the "Portuguese" were allowed to complete their services. A few days afterward the Amsterdam town council granted the marranos permission to profess their faith openly. In 1598 the first synagogue was built. Joseph Pardo, summoned from Salonika, took office as rabbi of the Jewish community.

News of the tolerant policy of the Dutch soon drew fresh bands of marranos to the country. And within a short time Amsterdam held one of the largest Jewish communities in all of Europe. Moreover, exactly at this same time the Netherlands began its dramatic economic expansion.

With every new inquisitional trial in Spain and Portugal, with every new auto-da-fé for convicted or suspected marranos, more persons secretly left the countries of eternal and unrelenting persecution and made their way to Holland. Ten years after the first settlement the Jewish community already comprised two hundred families; five years later, in 1608, a second synagogue was founded, and in 1618 a third. Economically and culturally, a remarkable upsurge took place within an astonishingly brief period. Released from fear and pressure, the marranos manifested a rare creative fertility.

The immigrants belonged chiefly to a class of learned men who in Spain or Portugal had served as doctors, scientists, and lawyers, or had held high positions in the state administration and even in the Church. Most of them knew Latin, were well read, acquainted with the sciences, and adept at social intercourse. Quite a few of them bore titles of high nobility. In the Netherlands, at this period one of the most cultivated countries in Europe, where Humanism was highly respected, learned Jews were soon on the best of terms with Christian scientists and artists. Many of them acquired Europe-wide reputations and corresponded with the most eminent of their contemporaries. Abraham Zacutus Lusitanus (1576–1642), a refugee from Lisbon and perhaps a great-grandson of the well-known astronomer Zacuto, was regarded as one of the foremost physicians of the age.

In the Dutch Jerusalem, as Amsterdam was often called, all the currents of Judaic literature met. Even among the very first settlers there were important writers. In their works sounded reverberations of the great tragedy they had witnessed in their former homeland. Jacob Israel Belmonte (1570–1629), one of the founders of the colony, recorded the sufferings of his people and the cruelties of the Inquisition. Rëuël Jessurun composed chants that were sung for the inauguration of the first synagogue.

A checkered destiny had brought Jessurun to Amsterdam. Born the scion of a marrano family of Lisbon—his Christian name was Paul de Pina—he had been raised as a Catholic, and proposed to become a monk. In Rome, however, he met Elias Montalto, later to be the personal physician to the French Queen Marie de Médicis. Montalto reminded him of the faith of his fathers, and of all those who had accepted martyrdom for its sake. Instead of entering the monastery, Rëuël, as he now called himself, turned his steps from Italy to Amsterdam.

Among the most important men in the new community was Manasseh ben Israel (1604–1657). He had come to Amsterdam as a child with his parents, who had fled from the Inquisition in Lisbon. Isaac Uziel, who had founded an academy, instructed him in the Torah and Talmud. A child prodigy, he soon wrote and spoke Hebrew, Spanish, Portuguese, Latin, Dutch, and English. He published theological, philosophical, and historical works, and in 1627 started one of the first Jewish print shops in Amsterdam. He also assumed the directorship of the Talmud school. Christian scholars thought highly both of him and of his writings. Men like Grotius, the "father of international law," Gerhard Johannes Vossius, "the greatest fount of learning in the Netherlands," Johannes Buxtorf of Basel, the "master of Hebrew and rabbinical studies," and even Queen Christina of Sweden—a great patron of scholars—corresponded with him. Rembrandt counted him a friend, painted his portrait, and used him as model for the well-known "Rabbi of Amsterdam."

Economically, a vast sphere of activity opened to the immigrant Sephardim, into which they stepped with great energy and skill. What Jacob Tirado had promised the Dutch authorities when he first negotiated with them took place: Along with the immigrants, sizable amounts of capital flowed into the country, to its great advantage. The devastating wars had impoverished the Netherlands. The prosperous Jewish families, with their manifold trade relations, brought a new and tempestuous spirit of enterprise into the country. Soon its effects were to be seen everywhere. Brief notations scattered among innumerable contemporary documents reveal how important a part the Jews played in the amazingly rapid rise of the Netherlands to a position of supremacy in the world market. The liberated marranos threw themselves into all branches of business, into industry as well as overseas trade, into banking as well as the colonization of new territories.

The banks, shipping concerns, and commercial houses founded by Jewish immigrants in Amsterdam and Rotterdam swiftly acquired great prestige. Jewish funds contributed to the establishment of the Amsterdam stock exchange and to the founding of the great Dutch overseas companies; Jews invested in the subsequently famous West and East India companies, and helped to finance trading ventures and voyages of discovery. One of the governors general of the Dutch East India Company was named Cohn. He was, "if not the founder of Dutch power in Java, certainly the person who contributed most to consolidating it."

When the Dutch conceived the plan of finding a northeastern sea route to China, wealthy members of the Jewish community equipped the celebrated expedition of the Polar explorer Willem Barents, which led to the discovery of Spitsbergen and Bear Island in 1596.

During the Thirty Years' War Amsterdam received a significant increment in its Jewish population from a different quarter. Jews from Germany asked for refuge, and in 1636 were admitted. These Ashkenazim could not compete with the enterprise of the wealthy and cosmopolitan Sephardim. They turned to humbler occupations. Many became diamond cutters and dealers in diamonds and precious stones, in which trade the Jews of Holland have remained up to the present.

After barely thirty years of existence, the young Amsterdam community was racked by a conflict that posed a serious question for the future of the Portuguese Jews. The erstwhile marranos proved to be exceptionally strict in their orthodoxy. They had imported orthodox rabbis who saw to stern obedience to the tenets of the religion and such matters as dietary laws. The pangs of conscience endured by generations of marranos now turned into religious fanaticism. In this atmosphere of impassioned piety, every stirring of free thinking was bound to smack of "heresy." But free thought could not be repressed indefinitely, and its advent resulted in the celebrated tragedies of Uriel da Costa and Baruch Spinoza.

Gabriel da Costa grew up in Oporto, the son of a wealthy marrano family, raised in the tradition of Spanish grandees. Dimly, his father remembered that he was descended from Jews, "those people who ages ago were expelled from Spain and went to Portugal." Young da Costa attended the Jesuit university in Coimbra and became a canon. But suddenly doubts of the truthfulness of Catholic doctrine germinated in the young man. He was seized by an irresistible urge to return to the religion of his fathers. Secretly, he chartered a ship, and under cover of darkness, accompanied by his mother and four brothers, he fled from Portugal. Arriving safely in Amsterdam in 1618, he and his family converted to Judaism; he himself changed his given name from Gabriel to Uriel. But

the new convert soon brought dissension into the community. He repudiated many of the traditions and opposed the rabbinate. When, in his zeal
for reform, he published his *Theses Against the Tradition*, the rabbis pronounced the cherem—excommunication—upon him. His writings were
impounded.

Expelled and homeless, rejected on all sides, despised by his own
brothers, Uriel da Costa spent nine years in exile from his community. In
1633 he returned to it, did penance, and was reconciled to the Jewish
community. But the peace was of short duration. He was no longer
capable of becoming an orthodox believer and piously carrying out all
the rites and customs. His freethinking temperament resisted all rigid doc-
trinal systems. In fact, he could accept only a natural, rational religion.
One day when he met two Christians who were on the point of converting
to Judaism, he advised them that they would only "be assuming an unbearable yoke." Once again Uriel da Costa was excommunicated. For
seven more years he endured the pain of solitude and contempt; then he
broke down and offered his submission.

Public penance was performed in the synagogue, before the assembled
Jewish community. Uriel da Costa declared his guilt and repentance. Then
he was scourged. The prescribed thirty-nine blows were administered.
He had to lie down on the threshold of the synagogue, and each member
of the community stepped over him. Only then was he considered readmitted. This drastic humiliation completely destroyed the unfortunate
skeptic's mental balance. He rushed home, locked himself into his room,
and wrote a stirring document: *Exemplar humanae vitae*. It was the story
of a Jew who could not find his way back to his brethren—his own
story. After he laid down his pen, the report of a pistol suddenly rang
out in the Amsterdam Jewish quarter. Uriel da Costa had put an end
to his unhappy life.

Twenty years after Da Costa's death, the intolerance of the Jewish community expelled from the synagogue one of the bravest thinkers and
greatest philosophers of all times: Baruch Spinoza.

Scion of a marrano family that had fled from Spain, Baruch Spinoza
was born in Amsterdam on November 24, 1632. He attended the Talmud-
Torah school there, and by the time he reached fifteen he possessed such
mastery of rabbinical learning that he far outstripped all his fellow pupils.
Even his teachers were awed by his scholarship. His interests ranged
widely, and he sought instruction in classical and modern literature and
even in the natural sciences. He plunged enthusiastically into the study
of philosophy, acquainted himself not only with the writings of Maimonides
and Hasdai Crescas, but equally well with the modern works of René

Descartes. The Cartesian principle of rational doubt of everything not demonstrably true commended itself strongly to him. Descartes's system of applying mathematics to all areas of life, and above all of using mathematical logic to derive the laws of ethics, produced a profound revolution in Spinoza's thinking. Soon he began to develop his own monumental structure of epistemology. Reason became for him the sole source of knowledge; he placed reason above all divine revelation and all religious or secular tradition. Henceforth, Spinoza began to shun the synagogue.

He became more and more estranged from the religion of his fathers. Soon an insuperable gulf opened between his own convictions and the requirements of Jewish orthodoxy. The Amsterdam community heard with horror that the young scholar in their midst was openly renouncing the religion of their forefathers, for whose sake the Jewish people had taken upon themselves so much suffering. The tragedy of Uriel da Costa had not been forgotten. This time the heads of the community tried hard to dissuade the potential apostate. Then they urged him to conform at least outwardly, not publicly to offend against the commandments of Judaism. But when their pleadings all proved vain, the college of rabbis in Amsterdam pronounced excommunication (July 27, 1656) upon twenty-three-year-old Baruch Spinoza. In so doing they expelled from their midst one of the greatest thinkers in their history.

Spinoza continued undeterred along his own path. He turned his back on Amsterdam and settled in The Hague. Henceforth he lived withdrawn, a philosophical hermit, his solitude relieved only by occasional visits from Christian admirers and friends. To earn his daily bread, he learned the art of polishing optical glass. That work provided him with a sufficiency; he rejected all offers of support. Though Elector Karl Ludwig of the Palatinate invited him to take the post of professor of philosophy at the University of Heidelberg, he preferred to remain in his quiet life. In November, 1676, four months before Spinoza's death, Leibniz paid homage to the great thinker by visiting him in his workshop.

The only work of Spinoza's published under his name was his *Philosophical Principles of Descartes,* issued in 1663. His famous *Treatise on Religious and Political Philosophy,* wherein he attempted to shake the foundations of traditional religious authority, was published anonymously in 1670. The storm of indignation that it aroused in the world of scholars made Spinoza even more cautious than he had been hitherto. Henceforth he did not venture to publish again.

Spinoza died on February 21, 1677, at the early age of forty-four, without ever having effected a reconciliation with the Jewish community that had expelled him. Among the few possessions he left—"a bed, a bolster, two pillows, two blankets . . ."—was a manuscript simply entitled "Ethics." This was Spinoza's immortal presentation of his rationalistic philosophical system, in which he translated the Jewish belief in God into the language of the mathematical age, and proclaimed the unity of God and Nature.

For a long while after his death a spate of denunciatory pamphlets and slanderous statements poured out upon the pure thinker who had lived entirely within God, merely seeing the divinity from another vantage point. Orthodox Protestantism also attacked him mercilessly. Thus Christian Kortholt, professor of theology at Kiel University, wrote: "Benedictus [in Hebrew, Baruch means "Blessed"] Spinoza, who ought more properly be called Maledictus, for the thorny earth cursed by God (Genesis 3:17, 18) has never born a more accursed man, whose writings are sown with so many thorns."

Such words were amply redressed a century after Spinoza's death, when he was rediscovered by Lessing. Thereafter, Baruch Spinoza held his place in the crystal palace of philosophy.

HAMBURG'S PORTUGUESE MERCHANTS

Holland did not remain the solitary new Jewish center in northern Europe. Considerations of economic life and commerce threw open other new places of residence for the Jews. Hamburg, the Hanseatic city that had previously been completely closed to them, early sheltered a colony of marranos—even earlier than Amsterdam, though the fact was unknown to the people of Hamburg.

The Hanseatic Lutherans rejected with abhorrence the idea of having Jews among them. In 1583, when a group of twelve German Jews headed by Isaac of Salzuflen asked for temporary rights of residence, the Hamburgers bluntly refused. But no one had any objection to some other newcomers who turned up in the city on the Elbe—the Portuguese merchants, or *Kommerzanten,* as they were called. These wealthy traders and entrepreneurs, representatives of foreign concerns, possessing large supplies of capital and connections throughout the world, seemed eminently desirable people with whom the Hamburg patricians associated without scruple. The Portuguese were welcome indeed; they stimulated the commercial life of the city. The physicians among them were likewise welcomed, for skilled and experienced doctors were not exactly common in Hamburg. Rodriguez de Castro, for example, who moved from Lisbon to

Hamburg in 1594, enjoyed great popularity. When plague struck the city, he saved the lives of many citizens, for he had had much experience in combating the Oriental epidemic. De Castro, schooled in Judaeo-Arabic medicine, which was far in advance of its time, argued as early as 1596— in his *Tractatus de peste*—that plagues were communicated by extremely small organisms. He also won fame as a gynecologist, practicing Caesarean section with a success rare indeed in those times. Among his patients were such personages as King Christian IV of Denmark, the Landgrave of Hesse, the Archbishop of Bremen, and many members of the high nobility.

For a while all went well. The "merchants of the Portuguese nation" were thought to be Catholics. When it turned out, a few years later, that these foreigners secretly held Jewish divine services and were in reality Jews camouflaged as Christians, a storm broke. In 1603 the outraged citizens demanded that the Hamburg Senate expel the foreigners at once. The local Lutheran clergy supported this demand. The commercially minded Senate, profoundly reluctant to lose these valuable entrepreneurs, found itself in a dilemma. Unlike the small shopkeepers, artisans, and clergy, the Senate was fully cognizant of the strangers' importance to the business life of the city. For was it not the "Portuguese" who had opened new connections for Hamburg with Spain, Portugal, and the New World across the Atlantic Ocean, and were bringing sugar, tobacco, cotton, and spices of all sorts to the marts?

To gain time and allow the tides of indignation to subside, the Senate promised to obtain theological opinions on the matter, so that it could decide whether toleration of Portuguese Jews was consonant with the Christian religion. Requests for opinions were sent to the universities of Jena and Frankfurt an der Oder. The Jena theologians ruled that Jews might be admitted only if they held neither public nor secret meetings for purposes of worship, remained uncircumcised, kept no Christian servants, and were kept out of any public office. Moreover, they must be required to listen to Christian missionary sermons. The Frankfurt theologians expressed the confidence that the foreigners would some day voluntarily turn to the Lutheran Church. The Senate was content. In February, 1612, it decreed that the "Portuguese" were forbidden to build a synagogue or to buy real estate. But they would be allowed to remain in Hamburg. They were also permitted to bury their dead in their own cemetery—which was situated in Danish territory near the city.

The Sephardic colony at that time counted one hundred and fifty souls —excluding employees and domestics. But their number grew steadily, to the great benefit of the city. The Portuguese Jews made ever greater contributions to the city's foreign commerce, to the rising importance and prestige of Hamburg. When in 1619 the Bank for Commerce and Industry was founded, thirty Jewish merchants were among the initiators. The names of twelve wealthy "Portuguese" who invested sizable amounts of capital have been preserved: Mardochai Abendana, David Brandon, Joan Francisco Brandon, Gonsalvo Carlos, Diego Cardoso, Abraham Dacosta, Francisco Gomez, Diego Gonsalvo da Lima, Henrico da Lima, Gonsalvo Lopez, Joseph Mendes, and Lope Nuñes.

In 1627 they secretly set up a modest synagogue, consisting of two rooms, and called the scholar Isaac Athias from Amsterdam to serve as their rabbi. Before long they were found out. Once again a storm of indignation broke loose; the scandal reached all the way to Vienna. Even the Emperor was aroused. Ferdinand II, an enemy of the Protestants, addressed an angry letter to the Hamburg Senate, denouncing it for permitting the Jews to have a synagogue in a city that tolerated no Catholics. But the "Portuguese" informed the Senate that they were resolved to move their commercial enterprises to another city should any attempt be made to impose new restrictions on them. The Senate had already heard that the King of Denmark was trying to lure the Portuguese merchants to Altona, promising them complete freedom to engage in all forms of trade and to buy real estate. Consequently, the Senate reversed itself and gave permission for worship in a synagogue.

The clergy remained obdurate, however. Its spokesman, Johannes Müller, pastor of the Church of St. Peter, constantly urged the closing of the "blasphemous" synagogue and the introduction of the Jewish badge. He also demanded that Jewish physicians be forbidden to practice. Müller obtained formal opinions from the theological faculties of Wittenberg, Strassburg, and Rostock universities. All three agreed that no Jewish doctor should be permitted to treat a Christian patient! When the pastor dedicated his anti-Semitic pamphlet, *Judaism: An Account of the Jewish People's Unbelief, Blindness, and Obstinacy,* to the King of Denmark, Christian IV wrote back to him that he had just appointed a second Jew, Benjamin Musaphia, to assist his personal physician, Daniel de Castro.

The "Portuguese" also aroused hostility by the splendid style of life they had brought with them from the land of their birth. "They go about adorned with gold and silver pieces, with precious pearls and gems," Pastor Müller fulminated. "They dine from silver vessels at their weddings, travel in carriages proper only to persons of high station, and, moreover, have riders going before them and a large retinue."

The truth was that the Sephardim had introduced to Hamburg a degree of pomp hitherto unknown in the city. Among their notables, aside from the owners of international commercial houses, were quite a few who had held high governmental office in Portugal, and bore titles of nobility. The wealthy Texeira family displayed princely sumptuousness. The father, Diego Abraham Texeira de Mattos, founder of a great banking house, settled in Hamburg in 1645, as resident of Queen Christina of Sweden. His elegant house on the Jungfernstieg was regarded as one of the sights of Hamburg. Texeira lived amid the luxury of a Spanish grandee. His servants wore embroidered livery; he went about the city in velvet-lined coaches. When Queen Christina came to Hamburg on a visit in 1654, the Texeiras brought her from Altona in a resplendent carriage. She stayed as their guest for two weeks. "It was a great vexation to Christians," a chronicler reported, "for her to prefer a Jew rejected by God to the Most Noble Christian Magistracy, and to dignify him with the honor of such majestic visitation." The chronicler omitted to report the Queen's reply when informed that her staying with the Texeiras was giving offense: "Jesus also spent more of his time in the company of Jews than of others." On later visits to Hamburg the Queen did not change her practice; she again stayed either with the Texeiras or with other Portuguese Jews.

The presence of the Sephardim caused the Senate considerable stress in other respects. There were several more clashes with the Emperor on their account. One began when Diego Abraham Texeira, soon after settling in Hamburg, openly converted to Judaism and had his two sons circumcised. Emperor Ferdinand III attempted to intervene. In 1648 he wrote to the Hamburg Senate demanding extradition of Texeira for "offending the divine majesty," so that the apostate could be turned over to the Catholic Inquisition. Meanwhile, his property must be sequestered. The Senate replied that it could not permit any inquisitional proceedings to be taken against a merchant of the Free City, no matter what his nation or religion. Queen Christina, the Swedish royal council, and various European sovereigns protested against the Emperor's demand. Eleven years later Emperor Leopold I tried again, lodging an indictment against Texeira in the Supreme Court of the Empire for "insult" to the divine Lord of the world. But for his friends in high places, Texeira would have been lost. The authorities in Vienna were determined to lay hands on the vast fortune of the Texeiras, and made repeated attempts to seize their prey. In 1663 the Imperial Resident in Hamburg demanded that Texeira, "to help meet present wartime expenditures," pay the enormous sum of one hundred and fifty thousand talers as a kind of personal ransom. Again the Senate stood firm. It rightly feared that compliance with any such demand would lead to similar exactions against other fugitives from Spain and Portugal, and would cause them to leave the city. The consequences were self-evident to the Senators. They were well aware that the marranos had helped Hamburg to compete successfully with Amsterdam, then the greatest commercial and naval city in the world. Even after Diego Texeira died in 1666 (he was buried in the Portuguese cemetery in Altona, despite stormy demonstrations by the city rabble), Vienna continued its attempts at extortion, pressing Diego's son, Manuel Isaac Texeira (1631–1705), to pay his father's "debt" to the imperial treasury. At last, in order to be let alone, he paid the Emperor a "fine" of eighty thousand talers. Queen Christina appointed the son her resident to succeed his father. At this time three other Jews were living in Hamburg as the plenipotentiaries of foreign powers. The banker Jacob Abendsur was resident of the Polish King; Jacob Kuriel and Duarte Nuñez da Costa represented the King of Portugal.

Meanwhile, after overcoming great difficulties, a group of German Jews had succeeded in establishing a foothold in Hamburg. The first of these were allowed to enter the city in 1654 as "envoys of the Portuguese nation." In the course of decades more and more of them moved into the city from the surrounding Danish towns of Altona, Wandsbek, and Glückstadt, where they had previously settled under the protection of the Danish King.

In contrast to the wealthy Sephardim, who were exporters and large-scale industrialists, the Ashkenazim were poor and engaged primarily in peddling or retailing. More than once the Christian shopkeepers and artisans, who felt threatened by these new competitors, demanded that they be "removed" from Hamburg.

It was not until nearly the end of the century, in 1697, that the Hamburg authorities officially recognized the Ashkenazim as a "High German-Jewish community." The memoirs of Glückel von Hameln, the widow of a dealer in gold and jewelry, have preserved a vivid picture of life among the German Jews in Hamburg during this period.

"My husband's first business was dealing with gold, running about from house to house to buy gold. He sold this to goldsmiths or to merchants. On every day on which there was a reading of the Torah, he fasted, until he started to make long journeys in which he underwent such hardships that even in his younger years he was already very sickly and had to do much doctoring for himself. But sick though he was, he never spared himself, and took great trouble to earn an honest livelihood for his wife and children, whom he loved beyond all else. . . . He was a veritable paragon of a devout Jew, as were his father and his brothers. When he was praying in his room and someone had come to take him to some place where something could be bought cheaply, I would not have the heart to go to him and tell him so."

In that same year of 1697 in which the German-Jewish community won legal recognition, Hamburg suffered a severe loss. On the insistence of the burghers, the Senate suddenly decreed new laws against the Jews —higher taxes and a ban on their owning larger houses of worship than they already had. Many of the Sephardim lost patience. The foremost among them turned their backs on the city. The Texeira family and many others moved to Amsterdam.

The cost of this to Hamburg's general welfare soon became apparent. The municipal authorities were obliged to display greater tolerance once more. In 1710 the remaining "Portuguese Jews" were accorded the right to appoint twenty bonded exchange brokers, in express recognition of their services in commerce with Spain. But it was too late; the prosperity that the Portuguese settlement had brought to Hamburg had already been checked.

CROMWELL INVITES MANASSEH

For more than three centuries scarcely any Jews had lived in the British Isles, after the expulsion of 1290. In the seventeenth century the country slowly began to open to them once again, although not all at once and not officially. Gradually, through a back door, as it were, they were re-admitted. Their hour came when England under Queen Elizabeth, and subsequently under the Lord Protector, Oliver Cromwell, became the fore-most power in Europe. There had been some small prelude—groups of Spanish and Portuguese marranos had entered England as merchants. But these had carefully retained their Catholic masks. To one of these secret Jews, in fact, England owed information of epoch-making significance: In 1588 Dr. Hector Nuñes brought Lord Burleigh the first news of the ar-rival of the Spanish Armada in Lisbon.

This timely warning enabled the English to meet the vast fleet on its way to England and begin the work of destruction that the storm com-pleted. A marrano was Queen Elizabeth's personal physician. She herself studied Hebrew. Rodrigo Lopez, the doctor, was involved in the Earl of Essex's intrigues, was falsely accused of attempting to poison the Queen, and was hanged in Tyburn in 1594. Small marrano communities that had settled in London and Bristol toward the end of Elizabeth's reign were banished from the country in 1609 by James I.

Nevertheless, under Charles I (King from 1625 to 1649), more mar-ranos turned up in London. They worshiped in the home of Antonio de Suza, the Portuguese Ambassador, who like themselves was a secret Jew. De Suza's son-in-law, Antonio Fernandez Carvajal, was counted among the most important men in the city; he was virtually the treasurer of the kingdom. In 1649 he was one of the five London merchants to whom the Council of State entrusted the supply of grain for the army. Carvajal owned his own ships, which sailed the sea routes to the Levant, India, and the American colonies. He imported large quantities of bar gold and silver, annually bringing silver worth hundreds of pounds sterling into England.

In the long run the English realized that the marranos were only sham Christians, and the question of officially tolerating them was raised. A favorable moment seemed to have arrived in 1649, after the Revolution. Cromwell's triumphant Puritans were disposed to be friendly toward the Jews, whom they viewed as the ancient people of God. They themselves, in their enthusiasm for the heroes of the Old Testament, were in the habit of taking their personal names from the Scriptures. In 1649 a bill was presented in Parliament to restore the Jewish Sabbath as the day of rest. Cromwell's officers proposed to form the Council of State of seventy members, like the Sanhedrin. As a Puritan, Oliver Cromwell dreamed of reconciling the Old and New Testaments; as a statesman, he was cognizant of the practical benefits of Jewish immigration. He believed that if he could attract Jewish and marrano merchants to London, English commerce would thrive.

At precisely this time Manasseh ben Israel, rabbi of the Amsterdam community, made overtures concerning the readmission of the Jews to England. In 1650 he addressed a petition to the Long Parliament, sending with it his apologia, *The Hope of Israel*. In 1655 a passport was sent to him. Accompanied by his son Samuel, he sailed to London in October, and presented to the government a "humble address" in which he enlarged on his proposals for admission of the Jews to England and their right to practice their religion freely. Although Cromwell strongly supported the petition, some members of the clergy opposed it. The merchants raised even more forceful objections. The Jews, they argued, would snatch all profits from the native merchants. Cromwell met their arguments by pointing out the contradiction: They claimed that the Jews were the basest and most despicable of peoples. How could they seriously fear that this despised people would outdo the famed merchants of England in industry and finance?

A compromise was finally arranged. Cromwell gave the marranos oral permission to remain in England and pursue their affairs. He dismissed the disappointed Rabbi Manasseh ben Israel with all honors, even conferring a pension of a hundred pounds sterling upon him. On the return

LEFT: Friedrich Julius Stahl (baptized 1819), professor of constitutional law, theoretician of Christian conservatism, and leader of the conservative faction in the Prussian upper chamber, the Herrenhaus

RIGHT: Karl Marx, son of a Jewish lawyer who was baptized

Sir Moses Montefiore, financier and philanthropist, who aided oppressed Jews in Syria, Russia, Rumania, and Morocco, and supported the colonization of Palestine

Gabriel Riesser, Vice-President
of the National Assembly

Eduard von Simson (baptized
1823), President of the
National Assembly at the time
of the adoption of the first
German federal constitution

LEFT: Benjamin Disraeli, Chancellor of the Exchequer and Prime Minister of England, a strong public defender of Jewry   RIGHT: Ferdinand Lassalle, founder of the Universal German Workers' Association (forerunner of the Social Democratic Party), 1863

Interior of the Great Synagogue in London at the beginning of the nineteenth century

Early automobile built by Siegfried Marcus, inventor of the gasoline engine. Given its trial run in 1875, the car had an internal combustion motor and electromagnetic ignition.

LEFT: Walther Rathenau, head of the Allgemeine Elektrizitäts-Gesellschaft, who organized the supplying of Germany with raw materials during the First World War and was Minister of Reconstruction and Foreign Affairs, 1921-1922. He was assassinated June 24, 1922. RIGHT: Albert Ballin developed the Hamburg-Amerika Line into one of the world's great shipping companies.

Fritz Haber, Nobel Prize winner, 1918. His process for producing ammonia from air assured Germany's supply of munitions during the First World War.

Airship invented by David Schwarz. Constructed of aluminum, it flew from Tempelhof Field in Berlin on November 3, 1897.

LEFT: Heinrich Hertz, who in 1886 generated electric waves for the first time, thus laying the foundation for radio technology
RIGHT: Paul Ehrlich, founder of chemotherapy.

Alfred Dreyfus, after his acquittal, being reinstated in the army with the rank of major and enrolled in the Legion of Honor (1906). The rehabilitation of Dreyfus marked the final defeat of the anti-Semitic movement in France.

Theodor Herzl in Basel, where
he convened the First Zionist
Congress (1897), thus founding
the Zionist world movement

LEFT: Albert Einstein developed the special theory of relativity in 1905,
the general theory of relativity in 1916; received the Nobel Prize, 1921.
RIGHT: Sigmund Freud, founder of psychoanalysis

Soldiers of the Jewish Legion at the Wailing Wall in Jerusalem. This troop of volunteers fought under General Allenby on the Palestine front during the First World War.

David Ben-Gurion, first Prime Minister, reads the proclamation of the new State of Israel in Tel Aviv on May 14, 1948. On the wall is a portrait of Theodor Herzl.

journey to Amsterdam, unfortunately, the untiring fighter for the rights of his people died—in 1657. But his mission had not been in vain. It soon bore further fruit.

In the spring of 1656 the marranos in London asked the Lord Protector for permission "to assemble for worship in our houses without fear of molestation," and to establish their own cemetery. The permission was granted. For the first time in more than three centuries and a half Jews could once again openly profess their faith in England. As yet, they did not have official, written permission; as yet, they were merely tolerated —but a new beginning had been made, three hundred and sixty-five years after their expulsion. Cromwell's unofficial sanction proved even more valuable than an official arrangement would have been. For when the Restoration abrogated Cromwell's laws and decrees, there were no edicts in writing concerning the Jews that might have been revoked. In 1664 King Charles II gave the Jewish community assurances of continuing benevolent toleration.

In France, too, meanwhile, marrano settlements had sprung up, especially in Bordeaux and Bayonne. A French letter of patent of the year 1550 read: "The merchants and other immigrants from Portugal known as New Christians may enjoy all the rights and benefits that are enjoyed by the other citizens of their cities." In 1636 the Bordeaux colony consisted of two hundred and sixty persons, among whom were prominent merchants, doctors, and lawyers of the city. "Without them the trade of Bordeaux and of the province would unquestionably be ruined," an official declared in response to an inquiry from Paris. Thanks to the vigor of the "Portuguese," banking and the wine trade, the foundations of the entire province's prosperity, throve in the city and the surrounding countryside. These French marranos had long since returned to their old faith and their old customs. Nevertheless, they were not permitted to call themselves Jews. Officially they were and remained "New Christians." They maintained close ties with the marrano communities that had been fostered by the Grand Dukes of Tuscany in the free ports of Pisa and Leghorn.

AUTOS-DA-FÉ IN SPAIN AND PORTUGAL

As we have seen, a sizable marrano Diaspora had grown up outside of the Iberian Peninsula. But while a new and vigorous life was forming in these dispersed communities, in Spain and Portugal the Inquisition was still taking its toll. Its ghastly practices had by no means ceased.

In 1680—two hundred years after the introduction of the Inquisition —Madrid was once again the scene of a tremendous auto-da-fé, arranged with maximum pomp in honor of the wedding of young King Charles II to the French Princess Marie Louise of Orléans, who was a niece of Louis XIV. Diego de Sarmiento, the twenty-fifth Grand Inquisitor since Torquemada, had notified all the tribunals of Spain to deliver their condemned heretics to Madrid in time for the festivities. Eighty-six victims, including many Judaizing marranos, were dragged to the stake. Heralds went about the city proclaiming the impending event to the populace. In one of the great squares of the capital, gigantic wooden stands were erected for the people, the court, and the royal guests.

Early in the morning of June 30 the sinister procession began to move slowly, through streets black with onlookers, from the Palace of the Inquisition. Charcoal burners carrying halberds led the parade. Behind them came the victims, barefoot, clad only in the sanbenito, the penitential garment of coarse cloth, on which a red cross shone in the sunlight. On their heads they wore paper caps painted with devil's masks, and each carried a burning candle. There followed Inquisition henchmen carrying placards, each showing a caricature of various deceased or runaway heretics, and coffins containing the bones of impenitents, the remains of deceased "sinners" who had died without absolution, which would be consigned to the flames. A long line of priests and monks of many orders, of knights, and of the "familiars" of the Inquisition followed, carrying church banners and crosses.

"*Viva la fe!*—Long live the faith!" the populace shouted as the procession entered the square that had been prepared for the execution. Gathered around the royal couple were the entire court, all the cavaliers, ladies, high dignitaries, grandees, and members of the lesser nobility. The victims were led to the pyre. Suddenly a girl's voice rang over the square. "Have mercy, Madame Queen! How am I to renounce the faith I drank in with my mother's milk?"

Francisca Negueyra, a seventeen-year-old marrano condemned to death, looked agonizingly toward the box where the new bride sat. But Marie Louise remained silent. The ceremony continued. Armed with a crucifix and a copy of the Gospels, the Grand Inquisitor went up to the King and administered the oath: that as a truly Christian ruler he would annihilate the enemies of the Church without mercy, and would always aid the Holy Inquisition. Charles II took the oath, followed by the dignitaries, the knights, the municipal officials. "Amen," the crowd murmured. The verdicts were read out, the penalties announced; the execution could begin. A torch was placed in the King's hand; he himself set the pyre alight.

The flames leaped up until well into the evening; the smoke carried the odor of burning human flesh over the city. Until the end, until the last victim was reduced to charred remains, the King, Queen, and retinue watched the executions. Eighteen marranos died in the fire, among them a sixty-year-old widow along with her two daughters and a son-in-law, and two women of thirty. The men, between the ages of twenty-seven and thirty-eight, were for the most part common people—tobacco dressers, goldsmiths, and shopkeepers.

"The courage with which the Jews went to their deaths aroused general amazement," wrote a French lady-in-waiting, Madame d'Aulnay. "Some rushed into the flames themselves; others let first their hands and then their feet burn, and endured it all with a steadfastness that astonished the King and made him express regret that such redoubtable souls should have shunned the light of the true faith." The Marquise de Villars wrote to her husband in France: "It was a horrifying scene. The cruelties committed in the course of the execution of these unfortunates mock description. Only a medical certificate or severe illness excused attendance at the auto-da-fé; lacking that, to be absent incurred the risk of falling into the odor of heresy. Some even took offense that I failed to express enthusiasm for what was taking place. . . ."

Portugal yielded nothing to Spain. While in the rest of the world a new age was dawning, the Catholic kingdoms of the Iberian Peninsula wallowed in the depths of the Middle Ages. The consequences were predictable: A general decline came hard upon the heels of the Inquisitors. A half century after the great auto-da-fé in Madrid a statesman said to the Portuguese heir apparent: "When Your Highness comes to the throne, you will find many fine towns and villages uninhabited, even Lamego and Guarda. If you ask how these places fell into ruins and how their manufactures were destroyed, few will dare to tell you the truth, that the Inquisition, by incarcerating so many for the crime of Judaizing and causing others to flee from fear of confiscation and prison, has devastated the towns and villages and destroyed the industries of the country."

The religious tribunals produced economic ruin. Spain and Portugal, the nations that had first taken the bold leap of discovery and conquest in the New World, lapsed into unimportance. Plunder and war could not provide the foundation for any lasting stature in the world. True, fleets laden with gold and silver, the booty of the New World, brought home tremendous wealth. From 1503 to 1660 Spanish galleons transported gold and silver bars from the American colonies approximating the value of one billion dollars. In spite of this, the mother country declined. The people who would have been capable of stimulating industry and trade were gone. Many thousands of Jews and marranos had been burned to death or cast into prisons; the rest had taken flight from the dread lands that had been their homes for centuries, in which they had once realized their Golden Age. Spain lost her world dominion. The new life, the life that was to have a bearing upon the future, developed in other countries—in all those to which the marranos had fled. As Cecil Roth has pointed out, the role of the marrano settlements, which extended to India and America, was enormous. "From the beginning of the sixteenth century they formed a network of trade relationships which can be matched in history perhaps only by the Hansa of the Middle Ages." The marranos dominated a large part of Western European trade. They had a virtual monopoly on the importation of gems from the East and West Indies. "The coral industry was a creation of the Jews, or rather, more precisely, the marranos. The trade in sugar, tobacco and similar colonial goods lay largely in their hands. . . . They were partly responsible for the establishment of the great national banks." Roth also points out that the shift of world trading centers from southern to northern Europe in the course of the sixteenth century can be attributed to the operation of the Inquisition.

All in all, it was scarcely hyperbole when a German economist, writing in 1911 on *The Jews and Economic Life,* declared: "Israel passes over Europe like the sun: Where it shines, new life springs up; where it departs, everything that had previously flourished molders."

SABBATAI ZEBI—THE FALSE MESSIAH

A decade after the horrors in the East, after the catastrophe that had descended upon the Jewish communities in the Ukraine and Poland, a messianic movement suddenly burst forth, causing tremendous upheavals in Jewry in both East and West.

The Messiah would come in the darkest hour, when conditions were at their worst—that had always been the belief of the Jews. In the seventeenth century there seemed to be a host of signs that the longed-for time had come, that salvation was nigh. The great expulsions of earlier centuries were still vividly remembered. Smoke from the pyres of the Inquisition still darkened the skies over Spain and Portugal. On the one hand, there was the spectacle of marrano families who had barely escaped with their lives seeking refuge in Holland, while on the other, there were the pitiable refugees from Eastern Europe. In Turkey there appeared multitudes of Jews carried off by the Tatars, prisoners offered for sale in the ports of the Levant.

According to the calculations of many cabalists, the fateful year 1648 was to usher in the time of wonders—the year 408 of the sixth millennium, according to Jewish reckoning. The fact that it had passed without some saving event—that, on the contrary, another frightful massacre had descended upon the Jews—only helped to augment the hopes that arose out of suffering. A veritable ecstasy of expectation ensued. Only a tiny spark was needed to bring about the discharge of the built-up psychological tensions.

At this time a man named Sabbatai Zebi was living in Smyrna, Asia Minor. Born in 1626, he had by the age of twenty gathered around himself a group of disciples who venerated him as a master of the cabala. He led an ascetic life, spent long hours in solitary prayer, fasted frequently, scourged himself, and bathed in the sea even in winter. Often he could be heard deep into the night singing songs of lamentation for Zion. The charm of this young fanatic appeared to be irresistible, the charisma of his personality overwhelming. Soon he was regarded with a respect that verged on awe. In 1648, when news came of the great wave of killings in Poland, Sabbatai Zebi decided upon a manifestation of unprecedented boldness.

In the synagogue, in the midst of the services, he suddenly cried out, "Shem ha-m'forash," the full name of God. It was the name that none was permitted to pronounce; only the high priest had ever used it, in the days when the Temple still stood, and only at the end of time would the Messiah speak it. Horrified at such rashness, the rabbis of Smyrna shrank from the speaker. Joseph Iskapa, formerly Sabbatai's teacher, pronounced excommunication upon the blasphemer, who had to leave his birthplace.

Sabbatai became an itinerant agitator. He turned up in Salonika, where he was again driven forth from the Jewish community. He wandered on to Morea, as the Peloponnesus was then called, and thence to Athens. He passed through Constantinople. After some time of restless wandering, Sabbatai Zebi arrived at the country of his dreams, the Holy Land. In Jerusalem he found followers among a populace given to mysticism and superstition. "Full of reverence," wrote the cabalist Abraham Cuenqui, who encountered Sabbatai in Hebron, "I looked upon this man, tall as a cedar of Lebanon, whose fresh, tanned face, framed in a black beard, shone in beauty. In a princely garment, bursting with strength, he presented a magnificent appearance. While he prayed first in the synagogue and then at the tombs of the patriarchs, I looked on spellbound, unable to turn my eyes from him."

The community of Jerusalem was in distress, and Sabbatai Zebi promised his aid. He went to Egypt to ask for contributions. In Cairo he learned of the strange, tragic story of a Polish-Jewish girl named Sarah. Ukrainian

Cossacks had taken her from her parents as a child of six and placed her in a convent, where she spent ten years. One night she fled. Fellow Jews discovered her in a cemetery, where she was hiding. They helped her to escape from Poland, and she reached Amsterdam. But the terrible psychological shocks she had experienced had left their traces. One day the distraught girl announced that she was destined to become the bride of the Messiah. She refused to stay in Holland. Impelled by vague restlessness, she made her way to Italy, and one day turned up in Leghorn.

After hearing this story, Sabbatai Zebi made up his mind to marry Sarah. She was, he declared, the wife destined for him by heaven. Messengers were dispatched to Leghorn and brought her to Cairo. The two were married in the home of one of Sabbatai's admirers, a wealthy man named Raffael Joseph Chelebi.

A young man named Nathan Ashkenazi of Gaza became an ardent follower of Sabbatai, a disciple who saw himself as the Messiah's "prophet." Nathan sent messages to the Jewish communities throughout the world. "Be it known to you," he wrote, "that our Messiah has come into the world in the city of Smyrna and bears the name Sabbatai Zebi. Soon his kingdom will be revealed to all. He will take the royal crown from the Turkish sultan's head and place it upon his own. . . . He will ride proudly into Jerusalem with our master Moses and all the great Jews of the past. . . ."

Threatened with excommunication by the rabbis, Sabbatai decided to return to Smyrna. By this time he had gathered a considerable following. His entrance into his native city in the autumn of 1665 resembled a triumphal procession. Cries rang out: "Long live our king, the Messiah." The whole city was thrown into an uproar. Men and women, young and old, even learned rabbis, began to fast and pray and castigate themselves. Sabbatai, singing psalms, followed by a great throng, paraded through the streets. Paul Rycaut, the English Consul in Smyrna, was an eyewitness and reported: "There were more than four hundred men and women who proclaimed the impending kingdom of Sabbatai. Even children who could barely speak pronounced the name of Sabbatai, the Messiah and son of God, with perfect clarity. Those of more advanced age swooned, whereupon, foaming at the mouth, they hailed the liberation and coming salvation of the Israelites, and spoke of visions in which Zion and the triumph of Sabbatai had been revealed to them."

News of the events in Smyrna traveled through the world with the speed of lightning. Samuel Primox, who had been attending Sabbatai since his days in Jerusalem, proclaimed the glad tidings in letters to the Jewish communities of Europe, Asia, and Africa. The frenzy rose to an inconceivable pitch. In the autumn of 1665 the great Jewish community of the Netherlands was thrown into ecstasy.

"Amsterdam seethed and roared," wrote Rabbi Jacob Sasportas. "Great throngs of people moved in prancing step, to the pounding of drums, through the squares and streets. The synagogues, too, were filled with thousands who had taken their Torah rolls in beautifully embroidered covers out of the chests and were carrying them about in the street. . . . Everywhere people were shouting the news to one another, undeterred by the mockery of the Christians." The great merchants of the Amsterdam community prepared a letter of homage to Sabbatai Zebi.

In Hamburg there were similar scenes. "What joy reigned," Glückel von Hameln wrote in her memoirs, "when letters from Turkey arrived. It was indescribable. The recipients went at once to their synagogue and read the letters aloud. Germans made a point of coming also. The young Portuguese . . . tied broad green silk ribbons around themselves—such was the livery of Sabbatai Zebi. They all went into their synagogues 'drumming and doing round dances.' Many sold their houses and everything they owned, and expected salvation to come any day. My late father-in-law, who lived in Hameln . . . sent two great casks filled with linen stuffs to us in Hamburg. Amidst the linen were packed all sorts of foods, such as peas, beans, dried meat, prunes, and similar things that keep well, for the old man thought that we would depart at once from Hamburg for the Holy Land."

Even such sensible persons as the banker Manuel Isaac Texeira and the physician Benedict de Castro believed the "tidings" that arrived from Smyrna. Jacob Sasportas, one of the few who remained clearheaded and skeptical, describes his impressions thus: "As I watched this spectacle, I wept silent tears, although it would have been worthy of laughter. I grieved at the credulity of these people, from whose mind all memory of our true prophets and our tradition had vanished." Sasportas was an exception even among the most learned Jewish scholars of his time. The madness swept throughout Europe, seizing Jewish communities as far apart as London and Venice, Avignon and Warsaw.

Toward the end of the year Sabbatai announced his decision to go to Constantinople. There, he declared, he would dethrone the Sultan, who was then master of the Holy Land. Before his departure Sabbatai divided up the crowns of the world among his closest followers. His ship, which reached the Dardanelles after a stormy passage, was met by Turkish police, and Sabbatai was arrested on the spot. Asked who he was, he replied discreetly, "A scholar from Jerusalem sent forth to collect contributions for the poor of Palestine."

In Constantinople, prison doors closed behind Sabbatai Zebi. But this did not disillusion his admirers. Rather, they regarded his imprisonment as the inescapable misfortune that would precede his triumph. Pilgrims appeared at the prison in such numbers that the Turkish authorities thought it advisable to remove him from the capital. He was sent to the fortress of Abydos. His prestige rose all the more. Ships from all lands arrived, bringing innumerable believers anxious to pay him homage. His prison became a virtual royal residence. Sabbatai, surrounded by his retinue, with Sarah at his side, greeted emissaries from communities far and near. Vast heaps of precious gifts accumulated. The influx of visitors steadily increased. But the end of the summer brought an unexpected turn of events. The cabalist Nehemiah Cohen arrived in Abydos from Poland, full of doubts and determined to examine Sabbatai. After a conversation of several days, the Polish scholar ceased to doubt; he became convinced that the man was a deceiver of the people who by Biblical law ought to be condemned to death. Hesitating no longer, Nehemiah went to the Sultan and denounced the "false Messiah."

Mohammed IV commanded that the prisoner be brought to Adrianople. There he confronted him with the alternative of death by torture or conversion to Islam. The unexpected happened; Sabbatai cast aside his "Jewish cap" and donned the turban. Sarah, too, accepted the faith of Mohammed. "Now go from me," Sabbatai wrote to his brother in Smyrna, "for the Highest has made me an Ishmaelite." Under the name of Mehamed Effendi, he henceforth served the Sultan; he became doorkeeper in the seraglio.

Just once, years afterward, he reappeared in the public eye. One day the Turks caught him preaching in an Adrianople synagogue—in order to convert the Jews to Islam, he alleged. They finally banished him to Albania. He died at the age of fifty, in the autumn of 1676, in Dulcigno.

In spite of his apostasy, in spite of the excommunication that the rabbis pronounced upon his followers, belief in Sabbatai Zebi did not cease entirely. Promoted by fanatics and frauds, his cult survived after his death. The "Sabbataians" continued down to the beginning of the nineteenth century.

The career of Sabbatai Zebi marked the end of an era. The Jews of the West were for the most part completely disillusioned. Their pride was shaken, and many years passed before they recovered from the blow. But medievalism was over for the Jews as well as for the rest of Europe. Before long a new age would be dawning.

THE COURT JEWS

"I have lived in Vienna for twenty-four years, and during this time I have refrained from all acts that might have brought me many advantages, but that would have made me untrue to my principles. I have done many services and handled many important missions and commissions for the late Emperor and his ministers, also obtained and advanced many millions of money in cash at times when the army would not have been able to maintain itself and operate otherwise, or the court would have suffered in its pomp and its activities, had I not raised such cash funds. With all that, I have never engaged in supplying provisions or in such affairs where the advantage would have lain more with me than the treasury. . ·. . For these things I have been rewarded by the Emperor and his predecessors by distinctions such as hitherto have never been accorded to a Jew. . . ."

The man who on November 28, 1705, proudly addressed these lines to Emperor Joseph I was named Samson Wertheimer.

Lion Feuchtwanger's novel *Power* has made famous the "case of the Jew Süss," although less is known about his actual accomplishments as a political economist than about his shameful torture and public execution amidst the gloating of the mob. It is not widely realized to what extent the "court Jews" in Germany and Austria during the seventeenth and eighteenth centuries were instrumental in creating the financial structure still employed by modern governments. Joseph Süss Oppenheimer was one of these court Jews, as was Samson Wertheimer. The latter bore the title of Imperial Chief Court Factor.

"The Viennese court," the historian Heinrich Graetz has written, "also invented another method of extracting funds for war from the Jews. It appointed Jewish capitalists court Jews, accorded them extensive commercial freedoms, liberated them from the restrictions to which other Jews were subject. . . ." Actually, such compacts were nothing new. But in the past they had been somewhat rarer and more in the nature of private arrangements. It was reserved for the absolutist rulers to make a system of their employment of Jews. After the Thirty Years' War, which splintered the territory of the German Empire into a multitude of small and minute states, the court Jew became an official and widely adopted institution. Court factors, as they were also called, were soon present in almost all the states, invited there by kings and dukes, by ecclesiastical as well as secular rulers, and even in principalities in which other Jews were not permitted to dwell. Not tolerance but the pressing need for money and revived mercantile interests prompted these invitations. The numerous rulers of states large and small had an unquenchable thirst for money—for government expenditures and personal luxuries, for the establishment of new manufacturing enterprises and for their many wars. The Jews were needed because they had developed into financial specialists, thanks to the medieval occupational restrictions and the church ban on interest. They were consulted as experts; their experience and competence in financial affairs soon spilled over into other realms, and they were asked to discharge many difficult assignments of all kinds. In wartime they were indispensable as suppliers for the armies. They arranged for the equipment and provisioning of mercenary forces, and raised the money needed for the war chest. In peacetime the court Jew was the financial administrator of the state. He procured the funds for the budget; he knew how to raise loans, to locate raw materials for new enterprises, to see to the establishment of factories, and to furnish the sovereign's favorites with finery and jewelry.

Significant changes took place in the lives of these favored court Jews. They no longer had to live in the ghetto or wear the Jewish badge. They could live wherever they pleased and travel about freely. They enjoyed the right to engage in trade on the same basis as Christian merchants. Many of them acquired great wealth, lived in grand houses, and had brilliant households. They received titles and honors. Sometimes a distinctly cordial relationship arose between sovereigns and their court Jews; princes would deign to attend weddings in the families of their Jews.

But these were exceptions, on the whole. Most court Jews never enjoyed unclouded good fortune. They remained dependent on the arbitrary will of their masters, on favoritism and whims. Their fortunes could be taken from them or their heirs on some pretext; they could be imprisoned, expelled, driven into flight, even—like the Jew Süss—sacrificed to popular discontent with the whole system. Their activities were unpopular, and their fall frequently took place more suddenly and dramatically than their rise.

In 1670, after the imperial decree of expulsion had been rigorously carried out, Vienna was "free of Jews." The Christian merchants and businessmen rejoiced. But it soon became evident that they themselves were incapable of filling the ensuing gap. Three years later the treasury presented a sobering memorandum to Leopold I. Such serious economic reversals had followed the expulsion of the Jews that the councilors could conceive of only one remedy: to readmit the Jews. Leopold was in a dilemma, and hesitated for some time. But humiliating though the step was, he had to yield at last. To save face, he did not rescind the order of expulsion, which had been promulgated with great pomp only too recently. Instead, he permitted exceptions; the ban was to be suspended in individual cases.

The court put out feelers, made inquiries among German banking houses. Once again the exiles were allowed to enter Vienna, at first individually, with important Jewish capitalists taking the lead. Granting concessions to them had simply become a political necessity, in peaceful periods and, as was soon to be demonstrated, especially in time of war. For shortly afterward a period of nearly incessant wars began—in 1674 against Louis XIV, in 1683 against the Turks—and Austria found herself more than ever dependent on those sources of lavish credit at the disposal of experienced financiers.

Among the first Jews who were permitted to return to Vienna were the learned and wealthy Samson Wertheimer, patriarch of a widely scattered family, and Samuel Oppenheimer. For thirty years, from 1694 to 1724, Samson Wertheimer served as chief court factor, banker, and financial agent for three emperors, Leopold I, Joseph I, and Charles VI. "Samuel Oppenheimer of Heidelberg and Samson Wertheimer of Worms were the men whose millions the German emperors employed in their wars against France and Turkey," Professor Alexander Dietz has observed. "They constituted an era in themselves for the history of German finance, like the Fuggers before them and the Rothschilds afterward."

Samuel Oppenheimer, the Jewish financier who had earlier provisioned German armies, received the title of Imperial Factor from Leopold I in 1674, and undertook to supply the army operating against the French. In 1676, along with Imperial Court Factor Georg Adrian Seeliger, he obtained large credits which, as he himself commented, "saved the imperial army from ruin, while much richer firms laughed and would not lend the Emperor a pfennig." In 1683, when the Turks stood menacingly before the walls of Vienna, and in subsequent years when the war continued in Hungary, Oppenheimer made vital contributions to the Austrian successes. He created exemplary order in the quartermaster's corps and supplied much of the money that Prince Eugene needed for his campaigns against the Turks. In a memorandum to the Emperor, the Hofkriegsrat, the imperial war council, commented: "He supplies better goods at lower prices than the town merchants. Whereas the latter in most cases take a negative attitude, Oppenheimer has accepted every assignment, often to his own detriment." Prince Eugene, who could appreciate these services more than anyone else, seized an occasion to demonstrate his gratitude. When Samuel Oppenheimer appeared at a reception in his palace one day, the victor over the Turks embraced him "before the assembled generals and the astonished courtiers."

In 1684 Oppenheimer finally settled in the capital, moving into a house on St. Peter's Square. He became chief banker of the imperial court, in that capacity repeatedly demonstrating financial genius. But his successes brought him no personal happiness. The populace, which hailed Prince Eugene, began to hate the man who had risked his fortune to save the West from the Turks. He was looked upon as a war profiteer, and the Hapsburgs did not pay the vast debts he had incurred in their behalf. Toward the end of the year 1692 the debts of the imperial treasury to Samuel Oppenheimer amounted to more than two million gulden. In that year the administration of the treasury was entrusted to Cardinal Kollonitsch, and thereafter all sorts of intrigues against the Imperial Factor were set in motion. He was repeatedly arrested. In 1700 a riotous mob stormed Oppenheimer's house, smashed everything in it, and destroyed his account books. The two chief instigators were hanged on orders from the Emperor, who still needed his Jewish banker. By the following year the treasury owed him 6.3 million gulden. Two years later Samuel Oppenheimer died. The fortune his son inherited consisted of bundles of promissory notes. But the treasury did not pay. When the heir ventured to sue, the Oppenheimer banking house was forced into bankruptcy. The records of the bankruptcy court show that Vienna continued to owe the Imperial Factor some one and a half million gulden.

The bankruptcy affected hundreds of other Jews; for many, it meant total ruin. A financial crisis ensued, for Oppenheimer had had to borrow much of the money he supplied to Austria from small- and middle-sized Jewish financiers and banks. The Viennese procedures that led to financial catastrophe was but one instance of a recurring phenomenon. "The principal reason for Jewish bankruptcies," Wilhelm Treue has observed, "was repeatedly the slowness or inability to pay on the part of royal debtors and their subordinates."

Joseph Süss Oppenheimer, administrator of the privy purse for Duke Karl Alexander of Württemberg, attempted to reform the finances of the duchy and to introduce the principles of mercantilism. He placed the traffic in salt, pepper, wine, and tobacco under government monopoly, with the result that considerable sums flowed into the treasury. Süss Oppenheimer set up a porcelain factory in Ludwigsburg and a silk factory in Stuttgart. He laid the groundwork for the first bank in southern Germany. But his measures were too modern for the times, and hence unpopular. He fell between the millstones of rising absolutism and an outmoded social system based on the estates, and became the object of widespread hatred.

The charges against him were numerous, but no misdeeds could actually be proved. He was accused of having minted coins of insufficient weight; an official commission of experts determined that the charge was false. It was alleged that he had enabled Jewish merchants to come into Württemberg and put them in the way of renting profitable ducal estates for a song. Oppenheimer was able to demonstrate that all his measures had been undertaken with the knowledge and full agreement of the Duke. To be sure, Oppenheimer had prompted the Duke to make extensive changes in the personnel of the Privy Council. But this had been done in the interest of reforms, which many of the conservative dignitaries opposed in every way possible.

Oppenheimer's enemies were hard put to it to find cogent reasons for condemning him to death. His lavish manner of life and his affairs with ladies of the court were hardly damning enough. But after his patron, the Duke, had died, the flimsiest grounds would do. Oppenheimer was arrested and thrown into prison. Stretched on the rack, he was tortured until he confessed to being guilty of all seven deadly sins. He was sentenced to death by the rope. After the sentence had been pronounced, he was called upon to convert to Christianity. "I intend to die a Jew," he replied. "I am a victim of violence and injustice." In September, 1738, Joseph Süss Oppenheimer died on the gallows, before a great crowd of spectators. His last words, "Hear, O Israel," were drowned in the shouts of the mob. After the execution Stuttgart once again expelled all the Jews who had meanwhile settled in the city.

What freedoms were accorded the Jewish court factors remained for a long time limited to this small group of the privileged whose lives presented a striking contrast to the wretchedness of the majority of Jews in the seventeenth and even the eighteenth centuries. Kings and archbishops, who eagerly availed themselves of the services of talented Jews in behalf of their personal and material interests, were totally indifferent to the miserable conditions in which thousands and tens of thousands of their court factors' coreligionists were compelled to live. Insofar as the Jews were concerned, the rulers of the much-praised Age of Enlightenment did nothing to change the traditional medieval restrictions and medieval views. The Jews remained without rights, completely at the mercy of arbitrary authority. They continued to form a class of pariahs; they continued to be despised. Guilds and many branches of commerce were still closed to them. They were still not permitted to practice crafts or agriculture, or to buy land. Whole provinces and many cities barred them from staying any length of time, and, in addition, extracted the shameful "body tax" from every Jew in transit. Wherever the right of settlement was conceded, it had to be bought at high price and was limited to a relatively few Jews. Thus, by every imaginable method, the economic rise of the Jewish people was artificially blocked. The period of bloody persecutions belonged to the past, and after the Thirty Years' War mass expulsions no longer occurred in Western Europe, though the Jews were still subject to arbitrary deportations from cities or locales. Official restrictions on births and marriages were now considered the better method to prevent an undesired increase in the Jewish population.

A long and difficult time still remained for Jewry in Western Europe before the French Revolution would open the gates of the Modern Age for them.

SUFFERING AND SUPPRESSION
IN AUSTRIA

The eighteenth century, celebrated as the "Century of the Enlightenment," opened on a somewhat less than enlightened note. In 1700 a Protestant theologian in Frankfurt am Main published a bulky manuscript. Johann Andreas Eisenmenger, professor of Oriental languages in Heidelberg, had felt called upon to rummage through the Talmud and the rabbinical writings in the old medieval fashion, searching once again for incriminating material against the Jews. His aim was to demonstrate the corruptness of the Jews and the inherent dangers of their religion. He had accumulated a vast quantity of material, curiosities, quotations, and stories taken out of context or wrongly translated, a compendium of the old lies and fables —even the ancient libel about the Jews' use of Christian blood. The long-winded title plainly stated the author's intentions. It ran: *Judaism Disclosed, or, A Thorough and Truthful Account of How the Obstinate Jews Blaspheme and Dishonor the Holy Trinity, God the Father, Son, and Holy Ghost . . . Making Mock of the Christian Religion. . . . Along with Many Other . . . Matters and Great Errors of the Jewish Religion and Theology, As Well As Many Ludicrous and Amusing Fables and Other Foolish Things; All Drawn from Their Own Books, and Indeed Very Many, Read with Great Toil and Unsparing Diligence, Vigorously Demonstrated by Citation of the Hebrew Words and Their Faithful Translation into the German Tongue . . . Prepared for the Edification of All Christians.*

Members of the Jewish community heard about the book with some anxiety, for Germany was still rife with anti-Jewish prejudice. They appealed to Vienna, where Oppenheimer and Wertheimer exercised considerable influence at court. The two financiers persuaded Joseph I that such a book was dangerous to the public peace. On the Emperor's orders, all printed copies of *Judaism Disclosed* were confiscated. Distribution of the book anywhere within the empire was forbidden. Nevertheless it came out again a decade later, in Prussia, where the author's heirs obtained permission to publish from King Frederick I of Prussia. The new edition, though actually printed in Berlin, bore on the title page Königsberg as the place of publication—the capital of East Prussia being outside the sphere of imperial censorship.

By this time other Christian scholars had long since been seriously engaged in thorough source studies of Jewish writings. In Basel two Hebraists, Johannes Buxtorf and his son, also named Johannes, had published a four-volume rabbinical Bible (1618–1619), a still useful *Lexicon . . . talmudicum* (1639), and a *Bibliotheca rabbinica* (1632). The French scholar Jacques Basnage (1653–1723) published the first history of the Jews that attempted to describe the events in an impartial spirit. His introduction took account of the prejudices of his contemporaries: "The Christian should not find it strange that we so frequently acquit the Jews of various crimes of which they are not guilty, since justice demands this. It is not partisanship to accuse of injustice and violence those who have practiced it. We do not intend to injure the Jews, but also not to ingratiate ourselves with them. . . . They have been accused of being the cause of all misfortunes that have occurred, and they have been charged with a vast number of crimes they never even thought of committing. Innumerable prodigies have been thought up . . . whereby hatred might be gratified under the guise of religion. We have gathered together a collection of laws published against them by councils and princes, by means of which the malignity of the one group and the repression of the other can be judged. Nevertheless, by a miracle of Providence that must arouse the astonishment of all Christians, this hated nation . . . everywhere persecuted for centuries, still exists all over the world. . . . Peoples and kings . . . have united in the intention of annihilating this nation, and they have not succeeded. . . . They live on in spite of shame and hatred, which pursue them everywhere, while the greatest of monarchs have so fallen that we know of them no more than their names."

In 1698 Wilhelm Surenhuys of Amsterdam translated the Mishnah into Latin. He spoke angrily of those who first derive profit from Jewish writings and then revile them—"like highwaymen who, after they have robbed an honest man of all his clothes, beat him with rods and send him away with mockery." Surenhuys lauded the Amsterdam Senate for taking the Jews under its protection. "You show favor to this nation that once surpassed all other peoples. The ancient glory and the dignity that this nation and the citizens of Jerusalem once possessed—all that is yours. For the Jews belong to you, not subjugated by violence, but won over by humanity. They come to you and are happy to belong to your republican governance."

Thus a goodly number of works by respected scholars endeavored to overthrow traditional prejudices. But the public disregarded these writings. On the other hand, Eisenmenger's tract, which served up the old falsehoods and slanders, became a best seller. The distinguished Orientalist Johann David Michaelis, though himself no friend of the Jews, had to admit: "I regard Eisenmenger's *Judaism Disclosed* as the product of . . . much diligence . . . but extremely hostile and unjust. If anyone were to write something of the sort against the three . . . established religions in the empire, it would be called a libelous lampoon. Suppose someone were to write a 'Popery or Lutheranism Discovered,' omitting all the good . . . and setting down everything that any of the worst writers let fall, or even things that were only said orally in the course of a disputation. Everyone knows what could be blamed on the Catholics in such a case—things their religion is nevertheless innocent of; but certainly we Lutherans would come off just as badly as the Anabaptists of Münster."

Eisenmenger's book was not only read with fervor at the time, but it also became a veritable mine from which anti-Semites picked their choicest gems well into the twentieth century. "Eisenmenger has been copied right up to the present," Professor Karl Thieme has remarked.

Once again the Viennese court factors were able to use their influence with the Emperor to help their troubled coreligionists. On January 14, 1711, the Frankfurt Jewish community had suffered a disaster. A fire started in the home of Chief Rabbi Naphtali Cohen and spread so rapidly among the closely clustered houses that almost the entire ghetto burned down. Most of the ghetto inhabitants were left shelterless. Nearly three thousand persons had to find emergency quarters in the bitter midwinter cold. Their plight was aggravated by threats and acts of violence on the part of the populace against the "incendiaries." Moreover, the city fathers refused to give the Jews permission to rebuild the burned-down quarter. In despair, the community again appealed to Wertheimer in Vienna. The Emperor, heavily indebted as he was to his court factors, could scarcely refuse their plea. Joseph I sent a decree to the city of Frankfurt admonishing the "proper authorities" to "refrain entirely from all baleful speeches against the Jews lest you incur Our disfavor and severe punishment" and "not only not to hinder the rebuilding of the Jews' Street, but to provide all possible assistance so that the Jewry . . . may as soon as possible once again be able to move into their former dwellings."

Soon after the death of Joseph I the Jews of Austria, especially of Vienna, were once again threatened with expulsion. In 1712 the Christian merchants delivered a petition to the new Emperor, Charles VI (who ruled from 1711 to 1740), complaining in all seriousness that "unless the Jewry is entirely removed from the city, the citizens will be reduced to beggary." Charles thereupon ordered the number of Jews in the capital to be drastically reduced. A hunt went up for all "nonprivileged" Jews; they were stopped on the street and made to show credentials. Jewish homes were repeatedly "visited." All those found in them without official permission were promptly driven from the city. New imperial "Jewish ordinances" soon affected the "tolerated" Jews as well. Henceforth in every family only one son, the eldest, would be permitted to marry. When a tolerated Jew had Jewish employees in his business, the wives and children of these employees were forbidden to reside in Vienna.

Before long, other laws followed, aimed at reducing the number of Jews by suppressing natural increase. Imperial commands of 1726 and 1727 for Bohemia and Moravia provided again that only one male scion of a Jewish family would be allowed to contract a marriage; he alone would be granted residence rights, while all his brothers and sisters had to leave the country. This decree inflicted celibacy or emigration—or else secret marriage—on thousands upon thousands of Jews. At the same time the Emperor decreed what was called "separation": Jews were banned from all parts of the city inhabited by Christians, as well as from the vicinity of Catholic churches.

After the death of Charles VI the situation actually deteriorated. Maria Theresa, his daughter and successor, was faced with a series of unfortunate wars. Austrian defeats were soon being blamed on the Jews, who, as so often before, could be made to serve the role of the scapegoat.

Ugly charges had been circulated as early as the First Silesian War (1740–1742). When Prussian, Bavarian, and French troops occupied many cities with Jewish populations in Silesia, Bohemia, and Moravia, it began to be said among the defeated Austrians that the Jews had given aid to the enemy. An incident in the Bohemian capital fed the rumor of treachery. In 1742 the famous rabbi Jonathan Eibeschütz left Prague after the French had marched in. He did so in order to take over the post of rabbi in Metz, but in order to leave he had applied to the French commandant for a safe-conduct for his journey. When Frederick II once more invaded Bohemia in 1744, and took Prague, the Austrians' suspicions were again aroused. By sheer chance, during the bombardment of the city not a single shell had struck the Jewish quarter.

No sooner had the Prussians departed than the ghetto was severely "punished." Austrian and Hungarian soldiers, together with the populace of Prague, broke into the Jewish houses on November 26, 1744, killing and pillaging. The excesses lasted for two days. Maria Theresa never issued so much as a reprimand. Quite the contrary. When stories of the Jews' alleged treason were brought to her, she believed them at once, without investigation, and resolved upon a drastic reprisal. On December 18, 1744, without consulting the Bohemian authorities, she signed a decree henceforth banishing all Jews from Bohemia. Every Jew in Prague was required to leave within a month, and by the end of June, 1745, all the rest of the Jews in Bohemia were to leave the country forever.

The Bohemian government tried to prevent this disaster. It sent a memorial to Vienna pointing out that the Jews had done nothing to deserve such measures. The Empress did not even answer. In response to further urgent petitions from the administrators of Bohemia, Maria Theresa "graciously" condescended to add a month to the term.

During the last days of February, the mournful spectacle began. More than ten thousand Prague Jews passed through the gates of the Bohemian capital in long columns. "It was an agonizing sight," the rector of the university wrote, "to see this people marching out with children and their sick, in biting cold." The official report of the Bohemian administration noted that two thousand persons, including the representatives of the Jewish community, were missing from the exodus. They were held as hostage until all outstanding taxes and dues had been paid in full—amounting to one hundred and sixty thousand gulden. When the sum had finally been raised, the rest had to go. One more time they assembled in their synagogues, went to their cemetery, then started out on the road to exile. The empty streets and houses of the ghetto lay still as death. "The former elders of this Jewish quarter," the report of the provincial administration noted, "with the greatest sorrow handed over the keys to their synagogues and schools, then their town hall and office of deputies . . . and with . . . tears and lamentations . . . commenced their emigration from the city on March 31."

For three years the Bohemian Jews wandered about the countryside, not knowing where to go. Meanwhile Maria Theresa had issued a similar order for the expulsion of the Jews of Moravia.

In Vienna, Baron Diego de Aguilar, a Spanish marrano, bent every effort to have these orders rescinded. Highly placed Jews in London and Amsterdam besought their own governments to protest this cruelty. They were successful—for the first time. On behalf of King George II, Thomas Robinson, the British Ambassador in Vienna, made representations in Vienna, and Baron Burmania, the Dutch Ambassador, did the same in the name of the Netherlands. These protests from her allies made Maria Theresa see reason, although her hostility toward the Jews remained undiminished. In September, 1748, four years after the decree of banishment, she renewed the right of residence for the expellees of Bohemia and Moravia, limiting the privilege to ten years.

In Vienna, however, where in 1752 the official census listed only four hundred and fifty-two adherents of Judaism, Maria Theresa vented her feelings in 1753 and 1764 by new decrees reminiscent of the darkest periods of the Middle Ages. Every Jew had to wear a yellow ribbon on his hat. No married Jew was allowed to shave his beard. Jewish factories, on the other hand, had to employ only Christian workers. "I know no worse plague in the state than this nation," Maria Theresa wrote on the margin of a document in 1777. "Therefore, as far as possible, they are to be kept away from here and their numbers kept down." Such sentiments did not, however, prevent the Empress from drawing on the services of a sizable group of Jewish experts, to the great profit of her empire and herself. She entrusted the Austrian tobacco monopoly to Baron Diego de Aguilar, although he openly professed Judaism. Among her bankers, financiers, and advisers were Isaac Arnstein (whose son was even ennobled), Berush Eskeles, Wolf Schlesinger, and many other Jews.

But, as fate would have it, an event took place during the reign of this anti-Jewish ruler that at one stroke more than doubled the number of Jews settled in the Austrian monarchy. With the first partition of Poland in 1772, Austria annexed the province of Galicia, thus bringing one hundred and fifty thousand more Jews under her sway.

UNDER PRUSSIAN RULE

In Prussia, the young and vigorously expanding state in the heart of Europe, anything but paradisiacal conditions prevailed. There, too, the Jews were subject to continual harsh pressure. But the Prussian rulers were not given to impulsive actions, like the sovereigns of Catholic Austria. Prussia's policy toward the Jews was governed by cool calculation. In this, as in so many other matters, Prussia leaned toward stern, virtually military discipline. Relations between the government and the Jews were defined in a series of sober, strict "regulations."

The Prussian rulers had been glad to have some Jews—but not too many. Those Jews who were rich, who could pay high taxes and duties, enjoyed protection. All the rest were regarded as undesirable. The laws applying to them had the undisguised purpose of frightening them away or driving them out, of restricting to the extreme their opportunities for settlement and for earning a livelihood. To keep their numbers to a minimum, Prussia followed the Austrian practice of forbidding more than one male descendant in a Jewish family to contract a marriage.

Soon after the turn of the century, things took a new course. Under the Great Elector and King Frederick I, living conditions for the Jews, in spite of all curbs, had been still bearable, by comparison with the general circumstances of the age. Under the "Soldier King," a general retrogression began.

Immediately after his accession to the throne, Frederick William I (who ruled from 1714 to 1744) curtailed certain rights that had been guaranteed the Jews of Berlin in 1671. Residence was permitted only to families who could prove a worth of at least ten thousand talers. Even in such families, however, only a single son or a single daughter would be permitted to marry, and in every case the permission had to be purchased at a high price. In addition to such "protection money" and special "dues," the bridegroom—on the King's explicit instructions—was obliged to buy the carcass of a wild pig killed in the royal hunts. There was the further ruling that all Jews residing in Berlin without permission were to come forward at once and identify themselves.

But that was only the beginning. At the insistence of the artisan and merchant guilds there was issued, on September 29, 1730, the "General Privilege and Regulation Concerning the Jews in His Majesty's Lands." The regulation forbade the Jews to practice any "civil" craft. Only seal engraving, embroidering in gold and silver, and glass painting continued to be permitted to them. Jewish commercial freedoms were restricted. The number of Jewish families to be tolerated in Berlin was fixed at one hundred. The Jews succeeded with difficulty in obtaining a slight softening of this restriction; a few additional families, most of them employees of the Jewish community organization, were allowed to remain. All the rest had to leave the Prussian capital. When Frederick William heard that the order had been carried out, he commented: "Thank God they are gone. Let the others be removed also, but I do not want them to settle in any other of my cities and provinces."

Frederick the Great shared his father's antipathy toward the Jews. "The more the Jews can be excluded from commerce, the better it is," he declared, and instructed his councilors "to be mindful and labor to the end that the number of bad and unimportant Jews in the small towns, especially those in the heart of the countryside, where even such Jews are quite unnecessary and rather harmful, should, whenever opportune and to the greatest extent possible, be removed."

Nevertheless, Frederick the Great himself was responsible for a rapid and enormous increase of Jews in his lands, for he "conquered" innumerable new Jews for Prussia. When he wrested almost all of Silesia from Austria by force of arms, many thousands of Jews in the newly conquered provinces hailed him, confident of better times. Those who had thus unexpectedly escaped the harsh oppression of Austrian rule hoped for improvement of their situation from the new sovereign. Rabbi Gomperz of Breslau welcomed the victors in verse written in both German and Hebrew. But the Jews were bitterly disillusioned. To their horror, the Prussian King gave orders that only twelve privileged families out of the large community in Breslau be permitted to remain. All the others—the "excessive, unnecessary Jewish people," as his order of 1742 read—had to leave the city at once.

On April 17, 1750, Frederick issued his "Revised General Privilege and Regulation for the Jews in the Kingdom"—a document the Jews felt to be so shameful and damaging that they vainly petitioned the King to reconsider it. Increase of the Jews, the preamble stated, worked to the disadvantage of the Jewish communities themselves, as well as to that of the Christian merchants. Out of his "most gracious paternal solicitude" the King in like fashion regarded the extension of Jewish trade as undesirable. Only two categories of Jews and their families were henceforth to be tolerated, the "regular" and "irregular" *Schutzjuden*—that is, Jews, enjoying royal protection. All the rest were to be banished. Only "regular" Jews would be permitted to act as independent entrepreneurs, and they alone might "produce a child . . . or marry a son or daughter. . . . But the irregulars are not allowed to produce a child nor to marry one off in their town." Thus, according to the ruler's will, all children in unprivileged Jewish families were condemned either to illegitimacy or to emigration.

The list of prohibitions and curbs was long. Jews could engage only in those trades "for which no professional associations and privileged guilds exist." They were forbidden to farm: "The Jews are not permitted to purchase or to own rural properties anywhere." Henceforth they were not allowed to buy houses of their own. In commerce they were even more limited than by the regulation of 1730. An unusually high percentage of Prussian Jewry was affected by the decrees, whose aim was to restrict either economic rise or population increase.

The wealthy Jewish financiers continued to enjoy full royal protection, however, for the King needed a great deal of money for his wars and his administration, and Prussia was poor. Frederick the Great enlisted them in his services everywhere; he rented the minting rights to them and employed them as intermediaries for the floating of government loans. He encouraged them to establish new manufactures and entrusted them with the supplying of military equipment. Moreover, when economic disaster threatened because of the enormous expenditures for the Seven Years' War, Frederick did not scruple to use the proprietors of respected Jewish banking houses for shady financial manipulations, including counterfeiting!

"After the conquest of Saxony," Professor Karl Kupisch reports, "the Berlin house of Ephraim & Sons received the assignment to produce debased coins; three years later the assignment was extended to all of Prussia. . . . Even before the war the King had taken the unsavory path of influencing the trade of neighboring countries by striking debased foreign coins. Thus Dutch ducats were manufactured for the trade with Poland. English subsidies had promptly been sent to the mints, to be recast into coins of threefold the original number. Now this counterfeiting of coinage became a system. The King made mock of the sovereign rights of other countries to regulate their own coinage. He had his Jewish court factors collect good money from Poland, Hungary, and Russia, melted it down, and sent the debased, counterfeit coins back to those countries." In this way Frederick stole enormous sums from the treasuries of his neighbors and foes in order to help meet his own war debts.

In impoverished Prussia, however, the people began to grumble, and their rage turned against the "Ephraimites," the "Jewish counterfeiters." They were the ones blamed for the debasement of the coinage; satiric verses were directed at them:

> Outside silver, inside tin,
> Outside honesty, inside shame,
> Outside Frederick, inside Ephraim.

The common people could not guess who the true perpetrator of the counterfeit coinage was—for Frederick the Great held his counsel. In return he presented to the banker Veitel Ephraim a house in rococo style in Berlin, the resplendent Ephraim Palace. Veitel Ephraim and his sons also had taken over the unprofitable production of gold and silver in Berlin. They had enlarged and improved the plant and developed it into the most profitable manufacturing enterprise in the capital. Soon it supplied the entire demand of the monarchy and also had large sales abroad. The Ephraim family, with their numerous enterprises, were among the biggest employers in the monarchy.

The court Jews who participated in the affairs of state could not very well complain; many amassed sizable fortunes. All other Jews suffered under burdens that became increasingly oppressive, especially during the second half of Frederick's reign. In addition to lump sum payments of "protection and recruit moneys," all Jews were required to deliver silver to the mint, and the quota was several times increased. The price paid for this silver was always below the market price, so that considerable losses were associated with these forced deliveries.

The highest taxes paid by Jews were for the right to marry. After 1763 Frederick graciously sold the right to "produce" a second child for the enormous lump sum of seventy thousand talers. In addition, the parents of newlyweds had to purchase wares from the royal factories to the value of fifteen hundred talers. These wares might only be sold abroad. In 1769 the King of Prussia was pleased to introduce the additional "porcelain tax"—upon the marriage of a son or daughter the Jewish family had to buy from the state factories, for purposes of export, porcelain to the value of five hundred talers.

In spite of all Frederick's efforts to reduce the number of Jews, in 1772 Prussia once again was faced with a sudden increase in her Jewish population—owing to the incorporation of part of the province of Poznan (Posen) after the first partition of Poland. With difficulty the King was dissuaded from deporting all Poznan Jews. He contented himself with severely restricting their freedom of movement, and enforcing the same punitive measures in Poznan as were current in Prussia.

Nevertheless, in a Prussia so ill disposed toward the Jews, there emerged from the obscurity of the ghetto a Jew whose name was to resound throughout the world and whose life was to constitute a first milestone on the road to the emancipation of the Jews.

V TWILIGHT OF THE GHETTO

MOSES MENDELSSOHN LEADS THE WAY

The Rosenthaler Tor in Berlin was the only entrance into the city through which traveling Jews were admitted. One morning in 1743 a puny Jewish boy presented himself at the gate. Asked by the gatekeeper what he intended to do in the city, he shyly brought out a single word: "Learn." Two decades later the boy had become a famous man—Moses Mendelssohn, the Jewish philosopher of the Enlightenment.

His life was as extraordinary as his achievements and his effect upon the world around him. Moses Mendelssohn was born on September 6, 1729, in Dessau. He was the son of a poor copyist of Torah scrolls, Menachem Mendel. Belonging by birth to the lowest rank of the rigidly stratified Prussian state, he would naturally have been destined for the same miserable career as thousands of his coreligionists—a despised and mocked peddler, tramping with a pack on his back through the villages of Prussia. But an obsession with learning that inspired him from his earliest childhood enabled him to pursue an entirely different course, despite endless privations and obstacles.

His devout father gave him his first instruction, teaching him Hebrew and the study of the Bible. But he soon took the boy to the local rabbi, David Fraenkel, for Talmudic studies. The usual curriculum did not satisfy this boy. Ardently, Moses began reading the medieval Jewish philosophers—especially Maimonides, whose *Guide for the Perplexed* fired his brain. He scarcely slept. Night after night he bent over heavy volumes, reading until the early hours of the morning by the dim light of an oil lamp. This strenuous regime shattered the health of a boy who was in any case not particularly strong. Later he remarked jokingly: "It is the fault of Maimonides that I have so misshapen a body. But for that reason I love him, for he sweetened many a dreary hour of my life and has compensated me tenfold for the harm to my frame."

When the teacher he revered, David Fraenkel, was unexpectedly called to serve as rabbi of the Berlin community, Moses felt he could no longer endure to stay in Dessau. With no money and no recommendations, the fourteen-year-old boy left his father's house and trudged to the capital of Prussia. He found a place to sleep in an attic. Often hungry and in rags, he continued his studies. He taught himself literary German and read all the German books he could lay hands on. Kindly patrons took notice of this gifted and eager student, and helped him further his education. Israel Zamosz, a Pole, gave him instruction in mathematics. Abraham Kisch, a young doctor from Prague, taught him Latin. Aaron Gumperz, another Prague scholar, helped him with English and French and introduced him to the philosophy of Leibniz and Wolff.

After seven hard years his difficulties were alleviated. In 1750 Isaac Bernhard, a wealthy silk manufacturer, offered him the post of tutor in his household; later he was to become confidential clerk in Bernhard's firm. At the same time his career in the great world began.

At this time Gotthold Ephraim Lessing had published a comedy entitled *The Jews,* which had caused something of a storm. Jews on the stage were acceptable, to be sure; but they must, as in life, serve as objects of mockery. Lessing had ventured for the first time to represent a Jew of noble spirit who acted unselfishly. This was unheard of, and the play was sharply criticized on this score, for anti-Jewish feeling was fixed even in cultivated circles. In the course of long centuries it had become too deeply implanted to be easily rooted out. Johann Andreas Cramer, editor and court preacher, went so far as to declare: "One who is not a Christian cannot be an honest man." Johann David Michaelis, one of the most respected of critics, articulated these doubts in a review: Could representation of such an honorable Jew be true to life? "To be sure, it is not impossible, but certainly highly improbable," he wrote, "that . . . such a noble spirit could form itself, as it were. The improbability obstructs our pleasure. . . . Even a modicum of virtue and honesty is so seldom found among this nation that the few instances thereof do not dispel our detestation as much as one might wish. . . ."

Deeply hurt, Mendelssohn wrote to his teacher Aaron Gumperz: "What a humiliation for our oppressed nation. What excessive contempt! The

common people among the Christians have from time immemorial regarded us as the scum of creation, as sores upon human society. But I
have always assumed that cultivated people held a fairer opinion. . . .
What temerity for a person who himself has a spark of decency to deny
an entire nation the probability of being able to produce a single honest
man! . . . Is it not enough that we have had to feel the bitter hatred of
Christians in so many different cruel ways? Are these injustices also to be
justified by slanders? Continue to oppress us, continue to force us to live
in fetters among free and happy citizens, even continue to expose us to the
mockery and contempt of the world—but do not attempt to deny us
virtue, the sole comfort of oppressed souls, the sole refuge of the helpless."

The letter fell into Lessing's hands, and he published the full text of
it in his *Theatralische Bibliothek*. "The author is a Jew," he observed,
"a person of twenty and some years who . . . has made great strides in
languages, in mathematics, in worldly wisdom, and in literature. I regard
him as already an honor to his nation. . . . With his sincerity and his
philosophic powers, he seems to me a second Spinoza, who will undoubtedly be as great as his predecessor except that he is unlikely to repeat
Spinoza's errors."

Lessing's comedy *The Jews* was, as he himself wrote, "the result of very
serious consideration of the shameful oppression suffered by a nation
which, I should think, should be held in honor by every Christian. In
former times so many heroes and prophets arose out of that nation, I
thought, and now people question whether a single honest man may be
found among it. I therefore conceived the idea of using the stage for the
experiment of showing people virtue where they least expect to find it."
The idea had, in fact, engrossed Lessing since his boyhood. As a twelve-
year-old schoolboy, he had had to translate into Latin a passage entitled
"On the Concept of Barbarism Among the Ancients and the Abolition of
This Prejudice by Christ." Young Lessing had added the comment: "We
must remember this sentence always, for it is barbarous to make a distinction among the nations, all of whom were created by God and endowed
with reason. Therefore we must not condemn the Jews, for God himself
said: 'Judge not, that ye be not judged.' Therefore only one who is inhuman
or cruel is a barbarian."

From the time of their first contact, Lessing and Mendelssohn fell into
a close friendship. Before long, Lessing helped his shy Jewish friend
achieve his first literary success. Mendelssohn had given him his manuscript of *Philosophical Dialogues* to read; on his own initiative Lessing
had it printed. The *Dialogues*—the first book by a Jew in the German

language—and *Letters on the Feelings,* which Mendelssohn published shortly afterward, aroused interest and sympathy. Moses Mendelssohn, who had never had regular schooling, who had only a few years earlier mastered the writing of German, had at one leap become a respected German writer.

A period of great creative productivity began for Moses Mendelssohn. In 1757 he wrote the critical introduction to the German translation of Rousseau's celebrated *Discours sur l'origine de l'inégalité parmi les hommes.* He contributed to the magazines published by Lessing and Friedrich Nicolai, the literary critic and book dealer. He was also constantly reviewing recent publications, which included works of the caliber of Rousseau's *Nouvelle Héloise.* One such review brought him to the brink of disaster. Frederick the Great considered himself something of a poet and published verses written in French. Commenting on these, Moses Mendelssohn had said it was a pity that the royal poet preferred a foreign to his native tongue. A preacher by the name of Justi at Frederick's court came upon the review and was incensed "at this Jew's disregarding proper reverence for the King's all-highest, sanctified person and impudently passing judgment on his poetry." The magazine was banned and Mendelssohn summoned to Sans Souci for a dressing down. But he wittily suggested an analogy that placated the King entirely. "Writing verse is like bowling," Mendelssohn said, "and anyone who bowls, whether he be king or peasant, must submit to having the pin boy say how well or ill he bowls."

Two years after this incident Mendelssohn enjoyed a unique triumph. The Berlin Academy of Sciences awarded first prize to his essay "On Certitude in Metaphysics" in a competition that had also been entered by Immanuel Kant. This distinction—won by a Jew on a theme generally lying outside the realm of Jewish scholarship—made his name well known among scholars. Thanks to this achievement, the now celebrated Moses Mendelssohn had succeeded in breaking through the social partition that separated Jews from Christians. Nevertheless, he still belonged to the lowest class of human beings in Frederick the Great's Prussia. It took a special appeal by an eminent admirer, the Marquis Jean Baptiste d'Argens, who was living at Frederick's court in Potsdam, to have Mendelssohn raised to the status of "protected Jew." Frederick the Great did not, however, confer this honor upon him as a hereditary privilege, but only for his lifetime.

His following increased still more when his *Phaedo,* a dialogue on the immortality of the soul, was published in 1767. *Phaedo* swiftly became the most read book of the age; within a short time it went through several editions in the original German, and was translated into the principal

European languages. Philosophers, artists, poets, statesmen, and sovereigns were edified by it. Mendelssohn was hailed as "the German Plato." The foremost literary men of Germany sought his acquaintance. Mendelssohn's house became the center for the members of Lessing's circle and the meeting place for the intellectual elite of Berlin society.

Something astonishing had happened. A Jew had succeeded, solely by his own merits, in attaining intellectual heights that elicited admiration from all cultivated persons. He had broken through all barriers and had made himself at home in the highest ranks of German intellectual life. He was revered for his achievements and his works. This fact in itself had enormous reverberations. It compelled society to examine its traditional misjudgment of the Jews. But radical as this was, it signified only a first step. For Mendelssohn's remarkable position remained an exception, involving a numerically small group of enlightened and highly educated persons. Outside these narrow limits, the old odium still attached to Jews. Moses Mendelssohn himself could not help sensing that everywhere, in court and in the streets, whenever he left the immediate circle of his friends.

After the publication of *Phaedo* the Berlin Academy of Sciences wanted to nominate Mendelssohn as one of its members. Frederick the Great, however, struck the name from the list with his own hand, and obstinately refused to confirm the nomination. He would not have the list of members of the Academy "defaced" by the name of a Jew.

In 1777, when Mendelssohn was visiting in Königsberg, he availed himself of the opportunity to meet Kant, with whom he had corresponded and who had repeatedly invited him to visit. A contemporary account describes what Mendelssohn had to endure when he appeared at the university: "A small, deformed Jew with a pointed beard and a hump entered the lecture hall, paying little attention to those present, but moving with timidly soft footsteps. He remained near the door. As usual, cries of mockery began, passing at last into clucking of tongues, whistling, and tramping of feet. . . . Students approached and asked him his business; he replied briefly and politely that he wished to stay in order to make the acquaintance of Kant. Only the latter's appearance at last muted the uproar. His lecture diverted everyone's attention to other matters, and the audience was so carried away that the appearance of the Jew was forgotten until, at the end of the lecture, he . . . pressed through the crowd to reach the Professor. No sooner had the students noticed this than the mocking laughter rang out once more, but instantly gave way to stupefaction when Kant, after regarding the stranger for a moment and exchanging a few words, shook his hand cordially and then embraced him. Like wildfire the word went through the throng: 'Moses Mendelssohn. It is the Jewish philosopher from Berlin!' And the students respectfully formed a line as the two sages left the lecture hall hand in hand."

Mockery and molestation remained the lot of Jews wherever they appeared. Even at home Mendelssohn was condemned to feel that when he went walking with his family. "At times," he noted in his memoirs, "I go for an evening stroll with my wife and children. 'Papa,' the innocent asks, 'what is that boy shouting after us? Why do they throw stones at us? What have we done to them?' 'Yes, Papa dear,' another child says, 'they always follow us in the streets and sneer: "Jews, Jews!" Do other people think being a Jew is such a disgraceful thing? How does it harm other people?' Alas, I cast down my eyes and sigh to myself. The human race, the human race—how have you ever let things come to this pass!"

Even among his closest friends, false notes were sometimes struck; even in this intimate circle Mendelssohn would sometimes be reminded that he was a Jew among Christians. Among the many cultivated persons who frequented his home was the Swiss clergyman Johann Kaspar Lavater, the founder of physiognomy. The Zurich pastor evidently cherished the plan of winning the famous Jewish philosopher over to Christianity, for one day, out of a clear sky, he made an overt attempt at conversion. A Genevan professor, Kaspar Bonnet, had written an apology for Christianity entitled *Examination of the Proofs for Christianity Against Unbelievers*. Lavater translated it from French to German and sent it to Mendelssohn with a dedication that had overtones of an ultimatum. He implored his friend "to refute this work or, if you find the proofs correct, to do what prudence, love of truth, and sincerity demand, what a Socrates would have done if he had read this work and found it irrefutable."

Mendelssohn was taken aback. Hitherto he had deliberately avoided entering into delicate religious questions. But now he could no longer remain silent. Lavater's challenge had been delivered in the full light of publicity. He would have to take a position, and he did so. In a public *Epistle to Deacon Lavater in Zurich* Mendelssohn tactfully but firmly rejected the invitation, and professed his adherence to the Jewish religion. "If after . . . many years of investigation the decision had not fallen completely in favor of my religion, I would necessarily have had to announce that fact. I do not understand what could possibly bind me to this seemingly overstrict and generally despised religion, if I were not convinced in my heart of its truth. . . . I shall not deny that I have detected in my religion human increments and abuses that, unfortunately, much obscure its radiance. What friend of truth can boast of having found his religion free of harmful human additives? We all know this poisonous breath of hypocrisy and superstition, and those of us who are seekers after the truth wish that we might purge the poison without harming the true and the good. But I am as firmly, as irrefutably convinced of the essentials of my religion as you . . . can possibly be of yours, and I herewith bear witness before the God of truth, your and my Creator and Preserver . . . that I shall abide by my principles as long as my soul does not assume a different character. . . ."

Mendelssohn's candor made a deep impression upon the public, and upon Lavater as well. "With sincere thanks," he wrote to Mendelssohn on February 14, 1770, "I have also received those passages of your letter that enable me to judge more correctly and properly to appreciate the purer Judaism you exemplify, and the mode of thought prevailing in your better rabbinical writings. You have made me very eager to know more about these. . . . Perhaps knowledge of the best system of Judaism would begin to remove many a stumbling block that now lies between it and Christianity."

The confrontation with Lavater reminded Mendelssohn of the great task that still remained—to lead his own coreligionists out of the narrowness of the ghetto. Culturally as well as legally, the condition of the Jews was wretched. Absorbed in his studies and his literary production, Mendelssohn had almost forgotten that; but now he suddenly realized the situation. "My nation has been kept at such a distance from culture that one might almost doubt the possibility of improvement." Access to education, to the arts and sciences, as he had learned from personal experience, could be obtained only through the medium of language. The Jews still spoke their German-Jewish dialect. They would have to learn cultured German instead of Yiddish. Mendelssohn resolved upon a momentous step, one that was to bring about a total revolution in Jewish intellectual life and to open new paths for Jewish literature. He translated the Pentateuch into German.

His translation of the first five books of the Bible was published in Berlin, along with a commentary in Hebrew. The impression it made was overwhelming—far beyond the borders of Germany. The book was eagerly bought in Holland, Denmark, England, and France. But indignation was great among German rabbis, especially among those originally from Poland, who adhered strictly to tradition. They went so far as to condemn the translation as blasphemous and to threaten excommunication upon everyone who studied the work. Their attacks, however, only resulted in greater popularity for "Moshe Dessau's" German Bible. History, moreover, proved that Mendelssohn had been entirely right. His translation marked the beginning of a German literature among the Jews, a literature that was to rise to remarkable heights in the course of the next century. In familiarizing the Jews with the German language, Mendelssohn's Bible offered them the key to the literature, science, and philosophy of the age. The German Bible served as an enormous stimulant, awakening the long-repressed cultural impulses of his people.

A severe nervous illness attacked Mendelssohn after his exchange with Lavater; his health, never very strong, was shattered. Nevertheless he continued, as far as his dwindling strength permitted, to do all in his power to raise his people from their despised state. He persuaded his friend Marcus Herz, a physician, to translate into German Manasseh ben Israel's famous essay addressed to Cromwell, *The Hope of Israel*. He himself prepared a preface in which he sharply castigated the prejudice against his people. In the Middle Ages, he wrote, untrue charges had been leveled against the Jews, such as the charge of ritual murder, desecration of the host, and similar senseless lies. In modern Western Europe, other but equally untrue accusations were being made. Opprobrium was cast upon the Jews for their alleged distaste for working with their hands, for their deficiency in art and science, and for their presumptive fondness for unearned profits in commerce and finance. "We continue to be banned from all arts and other useful trades and occupations; all ways for useful improvement are blocked to us; and our lack of cultivation is cited as the reason for our further suppression. Our hands are tied, and we are berated for not using them." His essay *Jerusalem, or, On Religious Power and Judaism,* written in 1783, pursued the same theme and ended with this appeal: "Regents of the earth! . . . At least smooth the path for a happy posterity to achieve that summit of culture, that general tolerance, for which reason still vainly sighs." Kant read it with the greatest enthusiasm and wrote to the author: "I consider it the annunciation of a great reform, impending and advancing, though slowly, which will affect not only your nation but also other peoples."

The times were ripe and more than ripe to cast off the chains of the Middle Ages. Mendelssohn, great forerunner of the emancipation of his nation, saw the bare beginnings of what was to come. He died on January 4, 1786, at the age of fifty-six.

In 1779 Lessing had published his drama *Nathan the Wise*—that great profession of a hitherto unknown religious tolerance and broader humanity. Lessing branded the idea that anyone could have "the best God" and try to impose this superior God upon the rest of the world as "pious madness." It took enormous courage to speak so bluntly. No one had ever before ventured to denounce the claims of Christianity in such terms, let alone to glorify a representative of Judaism as Lessing did his Nathan, who is presented as the ideal of virtue, wisdom, and conscience.

In 1781, two years after the publication of *Nathan the Wise,* a forthright political manifesto was published in Berlin that stirred no less of a sensation, and no less indignation, than had the moral message of Lessing's drama. It was a memorial by Christian Wilhelm von Dohm, archivist and member of the Prussian War Council, entitled *On the Civil Amelioration of the Condition of the Jews.* With the punctiliousness of an official writing a memorandum, this Prussian civil servant described the set of sanctions under which the Jewish population lived, and pleaded for improvement of their situation in the interests of the state itself. This was a staggering innovation. Dohm was the first Christian to urge publicly the granting of civil rights to the Jews.

"In some countries," Dohm wrote, "they have been wholly forbidden to reside. . . . In most other countries, however, Jews have been . . . allowed in only under the most burdensome conditions. Usually only a certain number of Jewish families are permitted to . . . settle, and this permission is generally restricted to certain places and must be purchased with a considerable sum of money. In very many countries a . . . fortune is the necessary condition for such toleration. A large number of Jews therefore find the gates of all cities closed to them. They are inhumanly turned away at all frontiers. . . . Their occupations are drastically restricted; . . . the foremost of employments, agriculture, is forbidden to them everywhere, and hardly anywhere are they permitted to own . . . real estate. . . . In almost all countries the Hebrew is entirely excluded from the crafts and mechanical arts. Only rare geniuses . . . retain the courage and serenity, amid so many crushing circumstances, to raise their eyes to the fine arts or sciences, and of these, considered only as occupations, surveying, physics, and medicine alone are open to the Hebrew. And even these rare individuals . . . can win respect from only a few noble souls; for the great majority, even the greatest merits of mind and heart never make amends for the fault of being a Jew. These unfortunates . . . whose activities are everywhere restricted, who can nowhere freely give rein to their talents, whose virtue is never credited, whose honor is never trusted —have no other way to earn their bread except by trade. But even that is impeded by many curbs and taxes, and only a few . . . have such wealth that they can undertake wholesale trade. Usually, therefore, they are limited to very small retail trade . . . to earn a meager livelihood, or else they are compelled to lend to others their money, which they themselves cannot usefully employ.

"These principles of exclusion, which bear the stamp of the Dark Ages, are as abhorrent on grounds of humanity as of policy. They are unworthy of the enlightenment of our times and should long ago have been discarded. Our solidly established state should welcome every citizen who observes the laws and by his industry increases the wealth of the state. . . . With all due modesty . . . I venture to suggest how the Jews could become happier and better members of their societies. To be so, they would have to . . . receive rights completely equal to those of all other subjects. . . . Concurrently, the Christians would have to endeavor to throw off their prejudices and loveless disposition. They would have to be taught in early youth to regard the Jews as their brothers and fellow men. . . . Preachers would have to be instructed to keep before their congregations these principles so concordant with the spirit of humanitarianism and true Christianity. And how easily will they follow such biddings if the spirit of love expressed in the parable of the Samaritan fills their hearts, and if they teach, like Christ's Apostles, that everyone who does right by all people is pleasing to God."

The consciences of cultivated Europeans were gradually awakening. Count Honoré de Mirabeau had Dohm's courageous book translated into French. But most of Dohm's German contemporaries regarded his views as far too bold, and he soon came under violent attack. On the practical level, nothing changed in Prussia. But Austria seemed suddenly on the point of a great advance, and took the first concrete action toward emancipation of the Jews.

In 1782 Emperor Joseph II (who ruled Austria from 1780 to 1790) issued a Patent of Tolerance. Its aim was to further the education and "utilization" of the Jews without conceding them civil rights. The act provided some relief; it abolished the body tax and the Jewish badge. Jews were permitted to engage in agriculture, crafts, and manufacturing and to send their children to the public schools. But in spite of the edict, which inspired the German poet Friedrich Gottlieb Klopstock to address an ode to the Emperor, the situation of the Austrian Jews remained oppressive. Their residence rights were still restricted; they continued to be merely "tolerated." In Bohemia and Moravia many cities were still barred to them; in the towns where they could reside they were limited to ghettos. All this was still a far cry from civil equality; the rule of religious intolerance prevailed. "It is our supreme will," the Patent of Tolerance announced, "that no latitude shall be granted to the Jewry living in Vienna in respect to outward toleration, but, rather, that in the future, as before, no public worship and no public synagogues shall be permitted. . . ."

By the edict of July 23, 1787, Joseph II ordered that all Jews living in the Hapsburg hereditary possessions were to assume civil surnames— a measure that was subsequently taken in all other countries affected by the French Revolution. Austrian officials, especially in Galicia, amused themselves by extracting heavy payments for pretty-sounding names derived from flowers, gems, or precious metals. The few prosperous Jews were permitted to name themselves after the places from which they came, or after materials such as steel, iron, and the like. The very poor, who could not pay anything, had to accept the names assigned to them, which were frequently made deliberately disgusting or ridiculous. In many cases their traditional names were simply varied: thus Samuel became Schmul; Isaac, Itzig; Mëir (which means "the Enlightened One"), Meyer; Emanuel, Mendel.

The object of Joseph's legislation was to solve the Jewish problem by assimilation. These measures would, it was hoped, gradually shatter the spiritual and intellectual life of the Jewish communities. The ultimate aim was baptism; conversion to Christianity was rewarded by gifts of property. These ameliorations were an experiment, and represented the farthest reach to which an enlightened monarch of the eighteenth century might go. The program remained a failure, for the Jews would not assimilate to the degree the authorities expected. Nevertheless, something had been done toward liquidating the cruel legacy of the Middle Ages, and a step had been taken along the road to emancipation.

IN THE CONFINES OF THE GHETTO

In 1776 the thirteen new United States of America framed their Declaration of Independence around a statement of the equality of all men. The result was that here, in the rebellious North American colonies, Jews were accorded the full rights of citizens, for the first time since the days of pagan Rome. In that same year of 1776, Moses Mendelssohn, the "Socrates of Berlin," had to pay a body tax at the city gate of Dresden in order to be allowed to enter the city. The impost was set at the same amount, as he himself phrased it, as "one Polish ox."

Whereas in the New World a new era had opened, conditions in the Old World were almost as reactionary as ever. Despite the Enlightenment, despite the enthronement of Reason, for the Jews the centuries seemed to have stood still. The walled ghettos still formed a feature of many of Europe's towns and cities, unchanging relics of the past.

So it was, for example, in the Free Imperial City of Frankfurt am Main. The authorities had refused to make any changes in the ordinances governing Jews. They were still confined within the ghetto, built during the Middle Ages, and by now more cramped and oppressive than ever.

"Imagine a long street," an observant visitor recounted in 1795, ". . . flanked by houses five to six stories high. Imagine these houses with rear wings, and these with still other rear wings, the courtyards barely large enough to allow some daylight to enter. Every corner of each house is full to the rooftop with narrow rooms and chambers, and into them, tier on tier, are crowded ten thousand persons who consider themselves fortunate when they can leave their caves and catch a breath of air in their dank and dirty street. . . . Then you have an approximate notion of the Jews' quarter. By day the street itself is used for all sorts of male and female occupations, for these wretched people have no working space in their dwellings."

Mockery and contempt were their lot whenever they ventured outside the ghetto. It was practically a Christian duty to jibe at them. "If a Jew passed down the street," wrote Ludwig Börne, who was himself born in the Frankfurt ghetto in 1786, "and a Christian called out to him, 'Show manners, Jew!' he had to remove his hat." Börne added sardonically, "This polite attention was intended to strengthen the love between the two religious groups." Such humiliations were commonplace everywhere in Germany.

The denizens of the ghetto were recognizable by their pale faces, their sickly appearance, their timid look, their bowed posture, their threadbare clothing. Confined within a narrow, fetid district, excluded from most work, from society, and from intellectual life, they led the most abject existence. Their very exterior reflected the mistreatment of centuries. They had deteriorated physically, had lost a few inches in height, had become abnormally timorous. Who could recognize in these hunched, frightened creatures the descendants of the courageous Maccabees, the cousins of proud Spanish dignitaries, the poets and philosophers of Andalusia? How could they help seeming repulsive and alien, even to the unprejudiced?

Toward the year 1760 Goethe, then a boy of eleven, visited the Frankfurt ghetto. His impressions remained with him all his life. As an old man he wrote in *Poetry and Truth*: "Among the ominous things that troubled the boy, and no doubt the youth as well, the condition of the Jewish town took a foremost place. It was really called the Jews' Street, since it consists of little more than a single street that in early times was apparently squeezed in between the city wall and the moat like an ani-

mal run. The closeness, the dirt, the swarming folk, the accent of an ugly
language—all these together made the most unpleasant impression when
one only glanced in through the gate in passing. It was long before
I ventured to enter, and I did not find it easy to return there, once I
had escaped the importunities of so many persons urgently huckstering.
At the same time there floated before my boyish mind the sinister old
fables about the Jews' cruelty to Christian children, such as we had seen
gruesomely depicted in Gottfried's Chronicle. . . . And there was no indication that they were any better thought of in modern times. Certainly
the large cartoon of which they were the butt, and which was still clearly
decipherable in the archway under the bridge tower, was a sharp warning against them; for it was not painted on anyone's private prompting,
but on orders of the municipality."

The Frankfurt town council had ordered this "large cartoon" to commemorate the Trent ritual murder trial. It showed a dead boy, his body
gashed in many places, lying on a table; shoemakers' awls were thrust
into the wounds. Below was the inscription: "In the year 1475, on Maundy
Thursday, the infant Simon, two and a half years old, was murdered
by the Jews." The wall painting, whose iconography also included a swine
stepping on a Jew, was restored in 1677 and 1709. It was located on the
way to the ghetto, and rarely could a Jew pass by without some Christian's
calling his attention to it. The painting continued to adorn the wall until
the bridge tower was torn down in 1801. For more than three hundred
years it had helped sustain an inhuman prejudice in a city where the
German emperors had been crowned since 1562 and which attracted visitors from far and wide to its famous fairs.

It must not be thought that this painting was exceptional. "Derisive
and accusing caricature of the Jews," writes Dr. Hans-Jochen Gamm,
"was specifically German. One of its characteristic motifs was the 'Jews'
sow,' which appears in sculptures and reliefs since about 1300. The
animal would be shown with Jews partaking of its milk and excrement.
Such 'works of art' are to be found, among other places, in the cathedrals of Magdeburg, Regensburg, and Freising, and in the parish church
at Wittenberg, the latter example having been described by Luther. From
early times the 'Jews' sow' nourished that belief in perverse customs among
the Jews which formed the basis for the whole anti-Semitic complex." Ismar Elbogen comments: "Visual images were strategically placed to perpetuate the shame of the Jews. Thus, among the favorite sculptures for
church doorways was the figure of the Synagogue, bowed and in chains;
cathedrals and town halls were regularly embellished with the Jews' sow
and other such symbols."

A sandstone relief on the choir in the Werner Hospital Church in Ober-wesel, renovated in 1727, depicts the legend of Werner von Bacha-rach, supposedly murdered by Jews in 1287. The same episode was also commemorated by the Werner Chapel—during the fourteenth and fif-teenth centuries one of the principal pilgrimage churches in the Rhine-land, which attracted pilgrims from as far away as Poland, Hungary, and Bohemia. A sculpture on the south portal of Strassburg Cathedral shows a devil dragging a manacled Jew down into hell, while another sprays filth into a Jew's face. The Church of the Holy Sepulcher in Deggendorf to this day contains pictures of an alleged desecration of the host in 1337.

Here and there something has been done about these relics of ancient prejudice. In Passau, for example, a Jew's knife and a Jew's bodkin had been on display in the Catholic church since a desecration trial in 1447. These mementos were removed a few decades ago. In the cathedral at Lincoln, England, an inscription concerning the supposed crucifixion by Jews of the eight-year-old boy Hugh in 1225 has been replaced by a plaque stating that invented stories of ritual murders were common in the Middle Ages, that the legend is but one of many, and that the al-leged victim of the Jews was buried in the cathedral. Such stories, the plaque continues, do no honor to Christianity, and people are told to pray: "Remember not Lord our offences, nor the offences of our fore-fathers." Professor Karl Thieme comments: "Considering that the ritual murder charge against the Jews had been emphatically dispelled in the Middle Ages after careful investigation by various emperors (among others, Frederick II, Rudolf of Hapsburg, and Charles V) and Popes (Innocent IV, Gregory X, Martin V, Paul III, and Clement XIII while he was still Car-dinal Ganganelli), and had been thoroughly refuted on the threshold of our century by the Protestant Talmudist Hermann L. Strack, it really would not be asking too much by now that similar signs of penitence, like that in the English cathedral, appear without delay wherever they are still needed."

Nevertheless it took even a man like Goethe a long while before he overcame the prejudices impressed on him in childhood. "The abhor-rence of the Jews that stirred in me in my earliest youth," he admitted in his maturity, "was really rather timidity in the face of enigma and ugli-ness. My contempt was more the reflection of the Christian men and women surrounding me. Only later, when I made the acquaintance of many intellectually gifted, sensitive men of this race, did respect come to join the admiration I cherish for the people who created the Bible and for the poet who sang the Song of Songs."

The lot of the Jewish communities within the lands under papal dominion was harsher and more oppressive than anywhere else. In Rome and
the Papal States, and in the papal possessions in France, the spirit of the
darkest Middle Ages ruled as mercilessly as ever over the "remnant of
Israel."

On the right bank of the Tiber, vulnerable to every flood, the Roman
ghetto lay like a sinister bear pit, only a few steps from the Vatican.
High walls sealed it off from the rest of the city. In 1732 its inhabitants
counted twelve hundred persons, crammed into two narrow streets and six
tiny alleys. The men had to wear a yellow beret, the women a yellow kerchief on their heads. Guards controlled the traffic of the inhabitants with
the outside world. Opposite the main entrance to the ghetto stood a large
wooden cross on which a verse from the Bible was inscribed: "I have
spread out My hands all the day unto a rebellious people" (Isaiah 65:2).
The gates were barred during the night and on all Christian feast days.

The community was impoverished. It staggered under an intolerable
burden of taxes imposed by the Curia. Fees had to be paid even for the
sermons to which the Jews were compelled to listen, and for permission to eat matzoth on the Passover. The sole legal occupations for Jews
were retail trade, peddling, and handicrafts. Of the latter, the common-
est was tailoring. "In summer," a traveler described the scene, "the tailors
can be seen, each in front of his door, sitting by the hundreds in the
streets. The women are busy making buttons and buttonholes. They are so
famous for this work that tailors from the rest of the city have these done
by Jewish women. . . . All in all, three quarters of the Jewish workmen
are tailors and only one quarter engage in other occupations." Attacks on
inhabitants of the ghetto when they appeared in the streets were nothing
unusual. It was a daily occurrence for stones to be thrown at Jews as
they passed by churches.

As if the situation were not bad enough, on April 20, 1775, Pius VI
issued a new "constitution for the ghetto." The twenty-four articles revived the strictest anti-Jewish canons of the Church. Corporal punishment
was to be inflicted upon any Jew who merely spent a single night outside
the Jewish quarter. It was illegal for Jews to stay anywhere in the vicinity of Rome, even if they needed "a change of air." They were, in fact,
forbidden to engage in any conversation with Christians. There were penalties for singing the Psalms aloud at a funeral, for erecting tombstones,
or for renovating synagogues in need of repair. Eight paragraphs were directed against "the godless Talmudic codices and other damnable, superstitious, cabalistic works." To fail to submit a newly acquired Hebrew
book to the censors for examination was to incur imprisonment up to

seven years. The French jurist Charles Dupaty, who visited Italy in 1783, concluded that nowhere was the predicament of the Jews as bad as in Rome. "The question is always asked: When will the Jews at last convert to Christianity? But I ask: When will the Christians be converted to tolerance? How long, Christians, will you go on acting as if you held a lease on divine justice?"

In 1786 the Jewish community in Rome had been brought to the brink of despair. It petitioned Pius VI to ease the lot of its members. A memorial listed all the burdens imposed on the ghetto, all the forbidden occupations, all the humiliations inflicted on the Jews. "Rise up, O Lord, rise up in mercy and cast a glance from your lofty throne upon the ghetto lying far below you, upon this wretched remnant of Israel which is nevertheless your people who implore you, weeping, and await comfort from your pity." But the entreaty fell on deaf ears.

The other Jewish communities scattered throughout the Papal States, such as those at Ancona and Ferrara, shared the same fate. Nor was it any different in the papal possessions in southern France. In Avignon and Carpentras the wearing of yellow Jewish hats was strictly imposed. Conditions were little better for the inmates of the ghettos in Venice and Padua, outside the Papal States. Only Tuscany constituted an exception. The harsh ghetto rules were not in force in Florence or Leghorn, and the Jewish badge had been abolished.

Conditions were very bad in the East also. The Jewish communities had never entirely recovered from the disastrous consequences of the Cossack uprisings under Chmielnicki. The steady decline of Polish Jewry continued inexorably. Moreover, new catastrophes were in the offing. In 1768 Cossacks from the Ukraine once again invaded Poland. The massacres they committed, culminating in the slaughter at Uman, completed the ruin of the Jewish communities in Podolia and Volhynia. Then followed the partitions of Poland in 1772, 1793, and 1795. Hundreds of thousands of Polish and Lithuanian Jews found themselves swallowed up by the Czarist Empire.

Out of the sufferings of this period a new and deepened religious fervor arose: the movement of that intensely devout group known as the Hasidim.

The founder of Hasidism was Israel ben Eliezer (1699–1760), called Baal Shem-Tob, the "good Master of the [divine] Name." The doctrine he first proclaimed in Podolia around 1750 kindled the enthusiasm of the common people. Not scholarship, not earnest study were what mattered, he preached, but strong faith sprung from simplicity of the heart. Such

devoutness he held superior to knowledge, and even the poor and ignorant could find their way through it to a close attachment to God. Thousands and tens of thousands were captivated by the new doctrine. Rabbi
Dov Baer (1710–1772), the "great maggid" (preacher), spread the doctrine
of Baal Shem-Tob throughout the East. The Jews of White Russia and
Lithuania welcomed it enthusiastically. But many rabbis considered the
denial of learning and scholarship virtual blasphemy. The most important
of them, the great gaon Elijah of Vilna, excommunicated the Hasidim.
Nevertheless the movement continued to spread. It brought about a decisive change. Jewry in the East had now embarked on a new course. Concerned solely with faith, the heart, the soul, moral purification, these
Hasidic Jews shut themselves off, locking their doors against the injustices of the outside world. Their object was not any improvement of their
lot, but inner renewal.

The fervor of the Hasidic movement has never entirely passed. Part
of its legacy are the *Tales of the Hasidim*. They were made famous in
retellings by Martin Buber, who is equally renowned as a religious philosopher and for his translation of the Bible.

From ardent piety, a turning away from worldly things, and distaste
for the intellect, little could come in the way of improving the social
predicament of Jewry. Any gains in that direction would have to be made
by the Jewries of Western Europe, where a fierce struggle for emancipation had been launched.

BEFORE LIBERATION

In England a first great advance had failed. Prospects had never been
brighter when once again all hope was smashed. In 1753, under Prime
Minister Henry Pelham, a Naturalization Bill had been presented to Parliament and approved. The bill provided for the granting of citizenship to
the Jews. But it aroused such violent and widespread opposition that the
government was forced to rescind it the following year.

In France, too, cultured circles had begun to take an interest in the
Jewish question. New voices were heard, harbingers of the approaching
upheaval. Men who were destined to play an active part in the coming
revolution spoke out in favor of the Jews. In 1785 the Royal Society for
the Arts and Sciences in Metz invited essays on the topic: "Is there a way
to make the Jews in France happier and more useful?" Seven of the nine
replies advocated emancipation. Three of the essays favoring emancipa-

tion won prizes. Abbé Henri Grégoire, a tireless fighter for freedom of conscience, called for total equality for the Jews. "O you nations," his essay concluded, "for eighteen centuries in succession you have trampled upon the children of Israel. . . . Is it you whom God has chosen for his instrument? . . . It was your ancestors in their ferocity who victimized this unhappy people. . . . Do you think it suffices to have left the Jews their bare lives, after having deprived them of all else that makes life worth living? Do you mean to bequeath your hatred for the Jewish race to your posterity as well? Behold, a new age is dawning. . . ."

Adolphe Thierry, a lawyer from Nancy and winner of the second prize, prefaced his essay with a verse of Racine's: "It is time to put an end to the shameful slavery of the Jews." The third essay, written by the Parisian librarian Salkind Hurwitz, who identified himself on the title page as a Polish Jew, concluded with the words: "Cease to make the Jews unhappy and useless. Restore to them those civil rights which in defiance of all divine and human justice and to your own disadvantage you have stolen from them."

The French press devoted considerable space to discussions of the prize-winning essays. Count Mirabeau also took a strong stand on the matter. In 1787 he published his treatise *On Mendelssohn and the Political Reform of the Jews.* "You desire the Jews to become useful citizens," he wrote. "Then banish from social life all humiliating distinctions; give the Jews access to all sources of livelihood. Instead of forbidding them to engage in agriculture, handicrafts, and the mechanical arts, urge them to take up these occupations. . . . Confer upon them the enjoyment of civil rights, and they will enter the ranks of useful citizens."

Voltaire, however, remained caught up in the time-honored prejudices. To the very end of his life he did not cease, in his writings and his correspondence, to deride and slander the Bible and the people of Israel. His famous *Dictionnaire philosophique* contains the following item: "The Jews are nothing but an ignorant, barbarous race who for ages have combined filthiest avarice with despicable superstition and inextinguishable hatred of all peoples among whom they are tolerated and from whom they enrich themselves." Personal reasons may have had something to do with this animosity. Voltaire had had business dealings with a Jew in which he himself had acted discreditably. The episode took place between 1750 and 1752 while Voltaire was the guest of his royal patron Frederick the Great, and the scandal was fairly well known. During his stay in Potsdam, Voltaire had engaged in some business affairs with the jeweler Hirschel. Apparently the French philosopher had stooped to fraud, obtaining diamonds by means of forged documents. The matter was brought to court, and only the influence of his friends in high places procured an acquittal for Voltaire. Frederick the Great, learning of the embarrassing affair in which his guest was involved, sent for the documents and was outraged. He vented his vexation poetically in a comedy, *Tantalus on Trial*.

Celebrated though Voltaire was, and feared for his sharp pen, there were people willing to oppose his slanders. Professor L'Advocat of the Sorbonne publicly decried Voltaire's ignorance of Jewish history. He named the long list of great Jewish poets and thinkers of the Middle Ages whose existence the philosopher had flatly denied. In 1762 Isaac de Pinto of Amsterdam took up the feud in his *Critical Observations*. "Is harm done by the pen less injurious than the flames of pyres?" he asked Voltaire. "Is not this evil more consuming than fire, since it is passed on to posterity? What can this unhappy nation expect of the rabble if barbarous prejudices are shared even by the most glorious genius of our enlightened age?"

In 1780 the Jews of Alsace sent a memorial to Louis XVI requesting the King to abolish some of the more intolerable burdens upon them. They were granted a single concession: In 1784 the body tax was annulled. "We have heard," the King pronounced, "that in Alsace and especially in the environs of Strassburg the Jews are required to pay a body tax that places them upon the same level as cattle. Since it contravenes the good will that we cherish without distinction toward all our subjects to permit a tax offensive to human dignity to remain in force for one group of them, we have found it good to abolish this same tax." Otherwise, things remained the same in France. In Paris the Jews continued to be harassed and humiliated in the most incredible ways. Every Jew who entered Paris had to report to a special Inspectorate for Swindlers and Jews (*Inspection des escrocs et des juifs*).

In Berlin Mendelssohn's friends continued to further the work of education that the philosopher had inaugurated. In 1778 the first Jewish Free School was founded in Berlin, based on plans by David Friedländer. It offered a staggering innovation: Not Yiddish but German was taught. The aim was gradually to replace Yiddish, still the dialect of the masses of Jews. In the course of ten years some five hundred pupils passed through this school. On the Berlin model, other reform schools sprang up in Dessau, Seesen, Wolfenbüttel, and Breslau. In 1783 Mendelssohn's disciples formed a Society of the Friends of the Hebrew Language and founded a magazine, *Hameassef* (*The Collector*). Naftali Herz Wessely, Marcus Herz, David Friedländer, and Herz Homberg were among this courageous band of enlighteners. They dealt with questions of natural science and history, made translations from contemporary German and French literary works, and published studies of Hebrew grammar and Biblical topics. All this represented a bold innovation, a formidable effort to raise the level of taste and cultivation among the Jewish populace. *The Collector* proved a remarkable success and continued to be published until 1811.

At the same time an unprecedented social situation arose in Berlin. The Prussian capital became a center for rapprochement between Jews and Christians. Cultivated persons of both groups began to meet and to exchange ideas. Jewish houses became the sites of salons subsequently famous in the history of German literature. In this matter, too, Moses Mendelssohn had taken the lead. From about 1754 on, he had daily devoted the morning hours—from seven to nine o'clock—to learned converse with his friend Lessing. Later his home became a center of literate talk. After Mendelssohn's death the enchantingly beautiful Henriette Herz came to preside over a famous salon. Her husband, the physician and philosopher Marcus Herz, there delivered lectures on Kant, whose friend and favorite pupil he was, and on physics. Some of the outstanding people in Berlin attended these lectures, including the future King, Frederick William III. Henriette Herz's salon was considered the meeting place par excellence of the literary and artistic circles in Berlin. Men such as Friedrich Schleiermacher, Friedrich von Schlegel, Wilhelm von Humboldt, Johann Gottfried Schadow, and Johann Gottlieb Fichte were among her regular guests. Mirabeau, too, frequently called upon her during his stay in Berlin in 1786. Before long two other gathering places came into vogue: the salon of Dorothea Mendelssohn, eldest daughter of the philosopher and subsequently Friedrich von Schlegel's wife; and the salon of Rahel Levin, who in 1814 married the prolific writer Karl August Varnhagen von Ense. Three clever Jewish women set the tone of Berlin society's intellectual and literary life.

Thus, in the intellectual realm, Mendelssohn's program had already achieved a significant success, although only in a limited circle. But the Jews continued to be a people of outlaws. To be sure, Mirabeau condemned the Prussian "regulation" as a *"loi digne d'un cannibale"*—"a law worthy of a cannibal." But Frederick the Great showed no disposition to permit the slightest change or amelioration for the masses of the Jews. He even refused the request of one rich Jew for permission to shave off his beard. The "Philosopher of Sans Souci" insisted on the strictest enforcement of his decrees aimed at limiting the occupations, freedom of movement, and natural increase of the Jewish people. To one proposal for improvement of the Jews' situation, the King replied in 1780: "I have long known that you unfortunately cherish a secret inclination for the miserable Jews. But, for my part, I think differently, for if you remove the malcontent Jews and in place of this abominable group take Christians into the economy, that will be for the country's best. Away with the usurious vermin who multiply so infamously; diminish the *crapule,* for I shall not change my mind about that; note it well, you adorer of these wretches!"

Under Frederick the Great's successor, Frederick William II, the administrative "serfdom" of the Jews continued, despite the new King's announced intention, on his accession, to "ameliorate as far as possible the situation of this persecuted nation." To be sure, Frederick William did, in 1787, abolish the body tax for the Jews of Prussia. A law drafted in 1790 held out the prospect that "after sixty or seventy years" the Jews, "except for a few religious differences of no concern or harm to the state, will be altogether equal with the Christians." David Friedländer, as spokesman for the Jews, rejected the statute because in practice it did not change their situation. Nevertheless, among the higher officialdom of the kingdom, the idea was beginning to dawn that something ought to be done about the Jews. "Experience has shown," a royal commission stated in 1793, "that the Jew is capable of exercising all social virtues. If his heart is not hardened by misery and persecution . . . he is able to display benevolence and nobility, unselfishness and self-sacrifice for the sake of his fellow citizens, without regard to religion. . . . There is indeed some reason to think that he is inclined toward excessive kindness." In spite of these opinions Frederick William II did nothing to modify the old Prussian "Jewish regulation."

One eighteenth-century document has been preserved whose author considered the Jewish question from a new angle. This was a private memorandum written by Prince Charles Joseph de Ligne. Born in Brussels of an ancient line of Belgian nobility, the Prince had entered the service of the Austrian army in early life. On campaigns in Bohemia, Galicia, and Poland, and later in the course of many diplomatic journeys throughout Europe, this attentive observer became conscious of the abnormal economic and social position of the Jews. In a *Treatise on the Jews* he expressed his abhorrence for the debasement that had been imposed on them.

"If the Christians possess neither the skill nor the kindness to liberate them from their present condition and make something reasonable out of them, then I would wish for their sake . . . that one of the Jews living in Turkey might contrive to win enough influence with the Sultan to restore to them the Kingdom of Judea. . . . The well-educated Jews, bankers, merchants, who sometimes are virtually noble barons living in the

Christian capitals, would renounce Jerusalem, while the others would no longer have to stay on to be ill-treated in Europe—which would suffer a well-deserved severe loss through the emigration of the Jews. . . . When I speak of a return to Palestine, I am referring only to the poor and to the class between rich and poor.

"Shall I paint a picture of them? They are always bathed in sweat because they must run about the public squares and taverns to peddle their wares. . . . They are pale . . . have an uncertain, anxious look; . . . their eyes are sunken. . . . In Avignon they must don a yellow hat; in Prague they are forced to wear yellow sleeves; and in Poland they are dressed in grenadiers' caps. Elsewhere they must cover their heads with a shaggy cap under an old, shapeless felt full of holes, or else don a pointed hat. Thus ten million Hebrews live in Europe. The humiliation imposed upon them by governments, their inescapable poverty, their poor food, the bad air of their synagogues and their streets keep them looking thus. . . .

"In all European capitals there are Jewish quarters. . . . They should be rebuilt new and clean and provided with running water in the gutters. . . . Give them work corresponding to their inclinations, and the swarm of them . . . will be transformed into a healthy, clean, handsome, and useful population. They are skilled in everything, and very fertile.

"Consider . . . the beauty of their wives and daughters, no matter whether these live in prosperity or misery. We think ourselves good Christians if we say: 'They have beautiful eyes, but look Jewish.' . . . Their religion, their customs, and their sad life restrain them from frivolity. The stringent prejudices of their laws and especially their manner of hiding their hair protect them from complaisance. Has anyone ever encountered Jewesses in brothels? . . . The Jews have their special virtues: They are never drunk, always obedient, tractable to commands, faithful subjects of their princes even during uprisings, and not irascible. They help one another . . . and the rich sustain the poor. . . . The Turks, less crude than we, do not regard the Jews as dogs. They reserve that name for us. They probably despise the Jews a little and make them pay well, but they do not revile them. With the exception of the turban and a few other small differences, in the Orient they are dressed almost like the rest of the population. . . . What a difference in appearance between a Jewish Turk and our own Jews, described above. Everything contributes to elevate the first and to humble the second." The treatise concludes, "A wrath that has lasted for eighteen hundred years seems to me to have continued long enough."

The Prince de Ligne remained a voice crying in the wilderness of a world unwilling to make the amends long overdue, on the ground of the Christian prescript to love one's neighbor, as well as on the ground of common humanity. Although the Prince de Ligne was a favorite of Emperor Joseph II, his plea made no more headway in Austria than Dohm's had in Prussia.

The exceptional regulations governing the condition of the Jews were rooted too deeply in the past to be easily done away with. That required a tremendous impulse from outside, a revolutionary event that would shake the foundations of all Europe.

That liberating event was in the offing.

THE BEACON OF THE FRENCH REVOLUTION

The eighteenth century culminated in the French Revolution, which spelled the end of many of the outworn institutions of Europe. For the Jews, too, it meant the end of the Middle Ages. On July 14, 1789, the storming of the Bastille brought down the old order. On August 27 the new government issued the Declaration of the Rights of Man.

The Jewish question had arisen in the National Assembly on August 22, when the principle of tolerance was being debated. Conservative deputies wanted to have Catholicism recognized as the dominant religion of the state. All other creeds were to be "tolerated." Mirabeau indignantly countered them: "Dominant religion! May this despotic phrase disappear entirely from our legislation. Unlimited religious liberty is to my eyes so sacred that even the word 'tolerance' sounds tyrannical to me." The Protestant pastor Jean Paul Rabaut Saint-Etienne concurred with Mirabeau, arguing that freedom of religion could recognize no exceptions: "I demand for the French Protestants, and also for all non-Catholics, what you claim for yourselves: freedom, equal rights. I demand this also for that . . . people who have now wandered, persecuted, for eighteen centuries, who would have adopted our morals and customs had our law only permitted them entrance into our midst. We have no right to reproach this people for their moral faults, for these are nothing but the consequence of our own barbarism, a consequence of that humiliating situation to which we ourselves have unjustly condemned them."

The broader tolerance won out. After heated debate, the decree finally adopted read as follows: "No restrictions shall be imposed on anyone because of his convictions, even religious ones."

The Jewish population rejoiced. But once again their patience was put to a cruel trial. The old restrictive laws had not yet been abolished. For two years they remained in uncertainty about their future. In its debates the National Assembly repeatedly touched on the question of civil rights for Jews. Yet even here the accent of eternal reaction was heard and there were those who wished to leave the ancient conditions unchanged. It was significant, however, that the great advocates of liberty took up the cause of the Jews: Robespierre, Mirabeau, Clermont-Tonnerre, even Talleyrand.

Nevertheless, no definite decision was taken. The headlong course of the Revolution constantly moved other matters, which seemed of greater importance, into the foreground. At last, in one of the last sessions of the National Assembly at the end of September, 1791, when deliberations on the Constitution had already been concluded, Deputy Adrien Duport rose to state: "In my opinion the freedom of conscience established in the Constitution no longer permits the making of any distinctions among the representatives of different denominations in regard to their political rights. Yet the question of the Jews still remains undecided, in disregard of the fact that Turks, Moslems, and members of other sects in France already enjoy political rights. I therefore demand that . . . a decree be issued at once to the effect that all Jews in France enjoy the rights of active citizens." The motion was passed that same day.

The civil equality of all Jews in France dates from that September 27, 1791. For the first time in modern history the members of the Jewish people were legally recognized as full citizens of a European state. "At last the day has come on which we behold the curtain rent that separated us from our fellow citizens and brethren," Isaac Berr, the tireless advocate of Jewish emancipation in France, announced in a circular letter to the Jewish communities of Alsace and Lorraine. "At last we have regained the rights that were taken from us more than eighteen centuries ago. . . . What a happy transformation hast Thou brought forth, O Lord!"

France's revolutionary armies carried the new principles into the countries of Europe they successively conquered. In 1795 the republicans of the Netherlands, in the presence of the French army of occupation, proclaimed the Batavian Republic. Along with all other inhabitants, the Jews received full civil rights. Belgium, too, declared their equality. A dramatic change took place in Italy. As the French troops marched into Piedmont, Lombardy, and Venetia, the old barriers fell. In Padua the order went out to raze the walls of the ghetto "so that every trace of the separation antipathetic to free men be abolished forever." In Venice the gates of the ghetto were lifted from their hinges and publicly burned. In February, 1798, Rome itself was liberated. While Pope Pius VI fled from the city, a Tree of Liberty was planted in front of the synagogue in the heart of the ghetto and the equality of the Jews proclaimed. In all of Italy there was only one more tragic manifestation of die-hard feeling. This was in Siena, where the Jews were massacred.

In Germany, too, emancipation came in the wake of the French. As early as the autumn of 1792 the revolutionary troops had occupied Mainz, Worms, and Speyer. Two years later they took Cologne. As fate would have it, the Jews were first liberated in those very cities in which the Crusader bands had raged seven centuries earlier, and in which Jewish communities toward the end of the Middle Ages had been entirely or partially destroyed. On September 12, 1798, on French orders the ghetto gates were removed in ancient Mainz. In Cologne, which had been closed to Jews ever since the expulsion of 1424, the French commissioner's proclamation warned: "Everything that is connected with slavery is hereby abolished. . . . You are to make an accounting of your religious beliefs to God alone, whereas civil rights are equal for all." In March, 1798, the first Jewish family, that of the banker Solomon Oppenheim, settled in Cologne. Others followed. A new community sprang up in the city where Jews had lived at the time of Constantine the Great.

Napoleon, heir and perpetuator of the Revolution in some ways, its destroyer in others, vacillated in his attitude toward the Jews. During his Egyptian campaign he had come into contact with them in their old homeland. In 1799, after his victory at Gaza and Jaffa, he issued a proclamation before the gates of Jerusalem, calling on the Jews of Asia and Africa to aid the French army. He promised to show his gratitude by restoring the Holy City. Six years later, after his victory at Austerlitz, when complaints about Alsatian Jews came to his ears, he declared: "It was the practice of feeble rulers to persecute the Jews. I shall better their lot." But Napoleon was irritated by reports from his ministries that the Jews constituted a "nation within the nation." This was something he could not allow. His Council of State decided to convoke a representative assembly of the Jews and insist on a binding declaration from them on their attitude toward the state. At the same time this act would revive "the civic morality of the Jews, lost during long centuries of a degraded existence."

In July, 1806, the Assemblée des Notables met in Paris on Napoleon's orders. It consisted of one hundred and twelve representatives of French Jewry. In answer to twelve questions, they affirmed that French Jews regarded the French as their brothers and France as their native land, that they would defend France with their goods and lives and obey her laws. They also gave their sanction to mixed marriages and renounced self-administration. Since they had been informed quite plainly that unsatisfactory replies would be the worse for them, they even went so far as to attest that the Catholic Church had always protected them. In February, 1807, Napoleon convoked another assembly, which he called the Great Sanhedrin, and which was meant to be a latter-day version of the ancient ruling body of the Jews. The whole affair was a political comedy. The "Sanhedrin" confirmed all the declarations of the Assembly. Having achieved his ends, Napoleon issued a decree, on March 17, 1808, which set severe limits on Jewish equality. The disappointed Jews rightly dubbed it the *Décret infame*.

Still, things definitely improved for the Jews in the various German cities Napoleon brought under French influence. At Kassel, in the newly formed Kingdom of Westphalia, King Jerome, Napoleon's brother, on February 9, 1808, received a deputation of the Jewish communities in solemn audience. "Tell your brethren," he informed them, "that they are to make fullest use of the rights conferred upon them. They can be as sure of my protection as the rest of my children." In 1810 the old regulations of Hamburg vanished when the French marched in. The Hanse cities of Lübeck and Bremen, which hitherto had barred all Jewish settlement, were no longer allowed to do so. In 1811 the Jewish community of Frankfurt am Main were accorded equality, although first forced to pay four hundred and forty thousand gulden as compensation for the annual special taxes. The townsfolk and archduke had stubbornly resisted the reform, and had finally exacted this "ransom."

Among all the German lands, only a single one acceded voluntarily to the new dispensation. Grand Duke Karl Friedrich of Baden was the first German prince to grant the Jews their new rights of his own accord. In 1808 he recognized them as citizens, imposing as his condition, however, that they should henceforth earn their living in the same manner as Christians, desisting from retail trade and usury.

PAPER EMANCIPATION

Twenty years after the French Revolution's Declaration of the Rights of Man, after the new ideas of liberty had already triumphed in many lands, Prussia hesitantly and reluctantly decided upon the emancipation of the

Jews. The act was undertaken with many reservations and only under pressure of the disaster that had brought about the total collapse of the state.

The tireless efforts of those Jews who had achieved status and wealth to remedy the hopeless situation of their fellows provoked a strong reaction. Violent anti-Semitic attacks began in Prussia. In 1803 a pamphlet was published entitled *Against the Jews—A Word of Warning to All Our Christian Fellow Citizens*. Its author, a Berlin magistrate named Grattenauer, once more went through the catalogue of crimes and horrors ascribed to the children of Abraham through the centuries. He called for the medieval yellow badge to be once more made mandatory, so that everyone could avoid the Jews like the plague. This pamphlet met with an almost incredible response and was bought up immediately. It had to be reprinted; within a few weeks it went through six printings. Grattenauer published a supplement in which he actually called for persecutions of the Jews. More such productions followed. In a treatise entitled *On the Civil Rights of Jews* a police superintendent named Paalzow contended that they were completely unsuited for economic life and could not possibly be tolerated in a Christian state. F. Buchholz in *Moses and Jesus* argued that no communication was conceivable between the representatives of stainless Christianity and the followers of the "bestial religion" of the Jews.

Others—Baron von Diebitsch and Professor Kosmann, for example—came to the defense of the Jews. Pamphlets pro and con flooded the market. The debate was threatening to arouse the most dangerous passions. At this point the government forbade the printing of any more pamphlets in Berlin. But the controversy raged on in the provinces, where the ban did not apply.

The excitement was quelled by an outside event—Napoleon's fresh preparations for war. The French army advanced inexorably upon German territory. In 1806 it defeated the Prussians in the Battle of Jena. French troops marched through Berlin. At the Peace of Tilsit in 1807 Prussia was stripped of all her land west of the Elbe and most of her possessions in what had been Poland. At this point Frederick William III recognized that modification of the absolutist regime and acceptance of some internal reforms had become an inescapable political necessity.

In the liberal governments under Baron Karl von Stein and his successor Baron Karl August von Hardenberg, the traditional guild and estate system was largely broken up and municipal self-government fostered. In the course of these reforms it became apparent that something had to be done about the most oppressed class in the country, the Jews. Toward the end of 1808 the new Municipal Act granted municipal civil rights to the "protected Jews." The King ordered a draft bill prepared, but disagreements flared once again in the ministries over their rights as citizens of the state. Progressive tendencies won out only after Hardenberg had become Chancellor in 1810. The new head of government left no doubts about his attitude. "I will not vote for any law for the Jews," he declared, "that does not contain the four words: equal duties, equal rights." In 1812 Hardenberg presented his program for emancipation to the King. Frederick William approved it except for one significant point: the admission of the Jews to government service. He himself was to determine whether and to what extent Jews would be allowed to serve in state offices. Otherwise they were granted the same civil rights and freedoms as Christians in Prussia, could occupy academic chairs and municipal offices, and were subject to military conscription like all other citizens.

The emancipation of the Prussian Jews was fated to be brief. Within three years their rights were retracted—with the fall of Napoleon. But first the King beneficently gave the Jews the opportunity to prove themselves at the front—after long centuries in which they had been regarded as "unworthy" to bear arms.

CONGRESS OF VIENNA AND RESTORATION

In 1813 Prussia, in alliance with Russia and Austria, began the great War of Liberation against the Corsican. On March 17 Frederick William III issued his "Proclamation to My People." The newly enfranchised Jews responded to the call. In addition to the conscripts, numerous Jewish volunteers flocked to the colors. Jewish soldiers took part in all the campaigns between 1813 and 1815; they fought in the Battle of Nations at Leipzig and at Waterloo. Many were decorated for bravery, one received the Order of Merit, seventy-two were awarded the Iron Cross, and twenty-three were promoted to the rank of officers for specially distinguishing themselves. There was even a Jewish woman, Luise Grafemus, born Esther Manuel, who fought heroically in an East Prussia cavalry regiment, was twice wounded, received the Iron Cross, and was promoted to sergeant; her husband was killed in France in 1814. Jewish doctors served at the front; Jewish women and girls acted as nurses in hospitals and camps. The Jewish community vied with their Christian fellow citizens in contributing large sums of money for the war.

Chancellor Hardenberg, who had so forcefully advocated emancipation, had the satisfaction of seeing his theory confirmed. "The history of this war against France has already demonstrated," he wrote to the Prussian Ambassador in Hamburg on January 4, 1815, "that they have proved themselves worthy by their fealty to the state which has taken them to its bosom. The young men of Jewish faith have been the comrades in arms of their Christian fellow citizens, and we have seen among them examples of truly heroic courage and of praiseworthy contempt for the dangers of warfare, just as the other inhabitants, especially the Jewish women, have joined the Christians in every kind of self-sacrifice."

In other German lands where they had been granted civil rights the Jews similarly proved themselves loyal citizens. In Mecklenburg the number of Jewish volunteers in proportion to population was actually three times the number of Christians. Young Jews from territories occupied by the French stole away to join the armies of the allies. After more than two thousand years, in spite of oppression and persecution, the spirit of their forefathers, of the Maccabees and the Zealots, still stirred within them. The willingness of the Jews to fight for their native land, and their suitability to bear arms, had often been denied. These doubts were no longer possible.

But the demonstration proved useless. In spite of the expulsion of the French, in spite of the success of the war in which they had taken so active a part, there was a terrible setback. Reaction raised its head. The solemn promises were broken, the freedoms and rights granted to the Jewish population were annulled.

Frankfurt was the first to backslide. No sooner had the thunder of cannon been stilled and the enemy routed from the city than the old mutterings against the Jews began. The old patricians once more came to power in the Free Imperial City, and in January, 1814, the Senate informed the Jews that their equal rights had departed with the French army. The Jews were once again to be *servi camerae,* restricted in regard to occupations and marriage, locked up once more in the ghetto.

Thunderstruck, the Jewish community resolved to appeal to the Congress of Vienna. Two deputies—one of them the experienced legal adviser of the Jewish community, Jacob Baruch, father of the famous writer Ludwig Börne—set out for Vienna. "The question now is," stated their petition, handed to the Congress in October, 1814, "whether three thousand born Germans, who have amply fulfilled all the duties of citizens, whose sons helped to fight for the salvation of Germany, shall be confirmed in the possession of the civil rights solemnly conferred upon them or cast back into their former state of oppression."

Further petitions of the same character arrived in Vienna as many other German cities followed the example of Frankfurt. In the spring of 1815 the Jewish question reached the Congress agenda. After involved debates, a proposal to confirm the rights already won by the Jews met with strong support. Hardenberg, in particular, had supported this proposal, against the resistance of Bavaria, Saxony, and Württemberg. The draft for a German constitution, presented by Wilhelm von Humboldt with the approval of Hardenberg and Metternich, contained the sentence: "All those professing the Jewish religion, insofar as they undertake to perform all the duties of citizens, are granted the same civil rights as other citizens, and wherever this reform runs contrary to the constitution of any state, the members of the League declare their willingness to remove these obstacles as far as possible."

The representatives of Prussia and Austria voted for this clause. But the majority were opposed to it. They refused to accept the pledge, hedged with reservations though it was, to introduce equality. Concessions had to be made to this group. A new formula was devised for the "Jewish paragraph" of the constitution of the German Federation. It now read: "The assembly of the Confederation will engage in consultations to see how, in as concordant a manner as possible, the civil improvement of adherents of the Jewish religion in Germany may be accomplished, and how in particular such persons can be provided with and assured the enjoyment of the rights of citizens in return for assuming all duties of citizens in the states of the Confederation. However, the adherents of this religion until that time will retain those rights that have already been granted them in the individual states of the Confederation."

Thus the commitment to devise a uniform solution to the Jewish question was postponed to a later period. But the various rights and liberties the Jews had already secured under French rule were guaranteed by this clause. For this reason the last sentence of the "Jewish paragraph" seemed unacceptable to the representatives of the Free Cities. Their Jewish inhabitants had attained civic equality by the action of the French government. The envoy for Frankfurt protested vehemently. Nevertheless, the Congress accepted the resolution—with one tiny, fateful change whose importance was not perceived at the time the vote was taken.

The deputy for Bremen, Senator Schmidt, had also recognized the troublesome aspect of the last sentence. He wisely did not protest, but contrived by a piece of clever trickery to frustrate the intention of the clause. His suggestion seemed so trivial that no one paid much attention to it. Remarking that the rights conferred by the French upon the Jews in North Germany could not reasonably govern the decisions of Germans, he proposed that the one word "in" need only be changed to "by" and everything would be in order. No one raised an objection, no one paid attention to what seemed to be the hairsplitting of an excessively legalistic deputy. Senator Schmidt's amendment was accepted.

The word "in" was eliminated, and "by" substituted for it. So it stood in the Federal Act by which the German Confederation was organized; so it was published and became law. The passage in Article 16 read: "The adherents of the Jewish religion will retain those rights that have already been granted them *by* the individual states of the Confederation." The insignificant "by" was all that was needed by the antiemancipation forces in the Free Cities.

Jews had been granted civil rights "by the states" nowhere else but in Prussia, Mecklenburg, and Baden. The ordinances of the French authorities, which had established emancipation of the Jews *in* the states and Free Cities, were thus rendered null and void. Lübeck was quick to see her opportunity; her merchants felt economically menaced by the sixty-six Jewish families who had settled in the city. In September, 1815, the Senate ordered the Jews who had settled in the city "on their own initiative" to depart at once. When the affected persons refused, pleading the rights that had already been granted them, the authorities countered with the exact wording of the paragraph in the Federal Act. They had their shops sealed and their wares confiscated. Impoverished, the expellees moved in 1816 to the neighboring village of Moisling. Bremen followed the example of Lübeck.

Frankfurt could not expel its Jews outright. Metternich had plainly given its deputies to understand that the "high powers" stood firm for the "preservation of all legitimately acquired rights of that class of inhabitants." The Frankfurt Senate took its revenge by plaguing the Jews in all sorts of ways—excluding them from assemblies of citizens, dismissing Jewish officials, forbidding them to practice a number of trades, withholding marriage licenses from Jewish couples. In short, the Senate behaved as if Frankfurters of the Jewish religion were still *servi camerae*. The Frankfurt Jews did not tamely submit; they began to fight for their rights. The legal dispute between them and the city continued for a whole decade; it involved the Congress of Vienna, the German Bundestag, and the faculties of jurisprudence in several universities—until it finally ended in a compromise.

In 1816 the Jewish community of Frankfurt addressed a petition to the Bundestag in which it vigorously protested the encroachments on its rights. The petition had been drawn up by young Ludwig Börne. The Frankfurt Senate, for its part, turned to the universities of Berlin, Mar-burg, and Giessen for legal opinions. Its reply in May, 1817, dismissed all the Jewish claims on the ground that the 1616 Frankfurt "Statute for the Jews" stipulated that the Jews must live in a separate quarter and be subject to various restrictions. Bolstering this reply was an opinion from Berlin University which argued that in the Middle Ages the Jews had been the *servi camerae* of the ruler; the administrative rights over them had been ceded to the city, which henceforth could impose any conditions it wished upon its Jews. The Jewish community retaliated with a historical argument of its own. If precedents were wanted, then the Berlin legal historians should not have stopped at medieval times but have gone back to antiquity, when the Jews had lived on the Rhine as free citizens of the Roman Empire.

Not until 1824 did the Senate yield to pressure from the Bundestag and grant "Israelitic citizens" equal rights with other Frankfurters in matters of private law. Certain important restrictions, however, remained in force, such as that of settlement and marriage.

Austria had protested against the Lübeck Senate's highhanded treatment of the Jews. But she herself behaved almost as badly. Francis I and Metternich forgot the Edict of Toleration issued by Joseph II and reverted to the harsh laws against the Jews of Maria Theresa. Thanks to Article 16 of the Federal Act, the rulers could deny any basic rights to Jews throughout the Austrian dominion. The Jews remained helplessly exposed to the state's arbitrary decisions. To be sure, Austria did not expel them as Bremen and Lübeck had done. But she insisted on the ghetto principle, establishing "settlement districts" beyond which they could not go. Tyrol was banned to them—as, for that matter, it was also to Protestants. In Bohemia, they were not allowed to live in mountain towns and villages; in Moravia, Brünn and Olmütz were open to them only for limited stays. The pressure was worst in Galicia, where enormous sums in special taxes were extracted from the Jews. The kosher meat tax was one of these; it doubled the price of meat for Jews, with the consequence that many poor Jews had to give up meat entirely. Vienna concocted an additional lighting tax for the lighting of candles on the Sabbath and holy days, or for weddings and funerals. There were special marriage taxes, which went up considerably with each successive marriage of a daughter or son; the object was to check the increase of a population who followed the commandment: "Be fruitful, and multiply."

All petitions for relief were rejected. In 1816 the Viennese representatives of Austrian Jewry appealed to Emperor Francis I, asking him to consider "whether it would not be appropriate to truth, justice, and fairness to remove entirely the yoke that still burdens half a million useful citizens and to grant Jewry their civil rights without any further restrictions." An Organization Commission was thereupon appointed to examine the Jewish question thoroughly and recommend reforms. But it advised that the existing system be retained and that all the rest be left "to the healing hand of time." On the basis of this, Francis I proclaimed the following policy: "The increase and spread of the Jews is by no means to be favored, and in no case is toleration of them to be extended to any provinces where they are not already to be found." The aim of any future reforms, moreover, could only be "to make the customs as well as the mode of living and occupation of the Jews harmless."

Thus nothing had changed, and reaction prevailed throughout the Hapsburg lands. Yet the Emperor and the court did not have far to look to see the grotesque consequences of their policies. Nowhere did the contrast between the civil degradation of the Jews and their actual economic importance appear so blatantly as in Vienna. The "tolerated" amounted to only about two hundred families, chiefly wholesale merchants and manufacturers, mostly producers of textiles. But the number of Jews living in the city amounted to between ten and twelve thousand. They were counted as "strangers," itinerants who had been granted rights of sojourning for only two weeks. The Jewish Office, created in 1792, supervised the administration of ordinances that no longer corresponded in the least to the facts of the situation and had become merely punitive nuisances. An army of spies was constantly poking about the city; zealous policemen staged raids, forced their way into private houses and hotels. Any Jew who had not paid the "customs tax" that entitled him to stay in the city two weeks was promptly transported with his family and belongings outside the city gate. Consequently, innumerable Jews who lived and worked in Vienna had to "depart" every two weeks. They left the city through one gate and reported to another gate as new "visitors."

Similar regulations prevailed in Italy also, the freedom won under French influence having been rescinded. The ghetto gates, burned only a few years before, were reinstalled and closed once more upon the Jews. Lombardy and Venetia, which the Congress of Vienna had made Austrian protectorates, now had the same reactionary policy as other Hapsburg possessions. It extended to the Kingdom of Sardinia, to Tuscany, and to most of the smaller principalities.

In the Papal States conditions were even worse. When news of the fall of Napoleon reached Rome in January, 1814, there was an assault upon the Jews. Clerics distributed handbills denouncing "Jacobins and Jews." In May, with the return of Pope Pius VII, whom the French had carried off to banishment in Fontainebleau, the Middle Ages returned to the

States of the Church. Clerical joined with political reaction. Not only were the Jews divested of their equal rights; they had also to leave their homes in the city and were once again confined in the narrow, unhealthy ghetto in Trastevere. As in the past, they were forced to listen to conversion sermons. The situation of the seventy-five hundred Jews in Piedmont was just as bad as that of their ten thousand fellows in the States of the Church.

Of all the European countries that had been under French sovereignty until 1814 and then returned to a reactionary policy, the Netherlands alone proved an exception. Nothing was done to abridge the equality that had already been accorded to the Jews. The restoration of the House of Orange in no way altered the prevailing liberal order.

TRIUMPH OF REACTION IN PRUSSIA

Of all the German states, Prussia was the most flagrant in breaking her promises of a better dispensation for the Jews. The first to know this were the Jewish soldiers returning from the War of Liberation.

They had fought side by side with Christians in the campaigns against Napoleon, had been killed, wounded, and decorated. At the outbreak of the war a civil service job had been promised to every veteran who returned disabled. The King of Prussia failed to keep his word. The applications of Christians for such jobs were approved, but there were no posts available in either state or municipal governments for Jewish veterans. Jewish war widows learned that they were not eligible for pensions. Even holders of the Iron Cross were denied government posts. Minister of Justice Kircheisen explained this decision on the ground that "the presumption of lesser morality is not dispelled by temporary bravery." Only by converting to Christianity would a wounded Jewish veteran qualify for the civil service.

The political winds had veered around, and with them went the principles of the King of Prussia. Soon the Jews as a group were to become cognizant of this, along with the common folk of Prussia. For the King's whole liberal program of a few years before was scrapped. With Prussia facing the great Battle of Nations, the monarch had appealed to the patriotism of his subjects by promising a parliamentary constitution after the war. Nothing, however, came of this promise. In the same fashion, Frederick William III, having promulgated the edict in 1812 granting civil equality to all Jewish inhabitants of Prussia, allowed the law to remain a dead letter.

The new Prussia of 1815 was larger than ever. Prussia had regained the provinces lost to Napoleon and added parts of Saxony, of the Duchy of Warsaw, of the Kingdom of Westphalia and the Rhineland. The Jewish population of Prussia, according to the census of 1816, had swelled to 123,823 persons. The government decreed that conditions in the new provinces were to "remain in the situation in which they were found at the time of the occupation." Since the newly annexed territories had belonged to a number of different states with widely varying Jewish ordinances, legal chaos ensued. Some twenty different laws concerning the Jews existed side by side, representing all sorts of shades and stages, from the still medieval Saxon and Polish laws to the enlightened French laws. In order to forestall emigration to legally more favorable areas, the Jews' freedom of movement was immediately abolished. A decree was issued that no Jew might move to a province "where a differing Jewish constitution exists."

Having thus assured stability in the new territories, the King and the government could turn their thoughts to the Jewish question within the original Prussian lands. What was to be done about the liberal edict? The equality already granted to the Jews could not be rescinded, for Article 16 of the Federal Act guaranteed the *status quo*. Officially, the edict of emancipation had to remain in force—at least to all appearances.

In 1816 the Prussian government conferred on the question. The liberal statesmen of the previous era, Hardenberg and Wilhelm von Humboldt, were no longer present. After the Congress of Vienna they had lost their influence at court and had had to resign their ministerial posts to men who thought in "restoration" terms, like their King. Three ministers categorically declared that the Edict of 1812 could not possibly be applied in practice. Minister of the Interior Schuckmann considered it incompatible with the "Christian principles of government" approved by the Holy Alliance. "There are certainly lawful and respectable individual Jews," the Minister explained, "and I myself know some; but the character of this race on the whole still continues to be composed of base vanity, filthy avarice, and cunning fraud, and it is impossible for a people that respects itself, with national spirit, to regard them as equals. If one were to insist on this, one would either bring down the nation to their level, or the law would be disregarded, with consequences of hatred and persecution." Wohlfahrt, the representative of the Ministry of Finance, argued: "It would be desirable if we had no Jews at all in the country. Those we do have we must tolerate, but endeavor incessantly to make them as harmless as possible. The conversion of the Jews to the Christian religion must be promoted, and with that all civic rights are linked. But as long as the Jew remains a Jew, he cannot occupy any governmental position in which as a representative of the administration he would have command over Christian citizens."

These, then, were the guidelines for the Jewish policy of the absolutistic State of Prussia. Lessing and Kant had apparently been forgotten overnight, the political theories of the Enlightenment thrown overboard, the ideals of humanity and tolerance discarded. The new political theory of Hegel had triumphed: the State is all.

The Jews had seen their great hopes dashed. But they remained confident and did not lose heart. They embarked on a tenacious struggle for recognition as free and equal citizens. It was to go on for six long decades—not until 1871 would it be crowned by victory in Germany.

A bureaucracy submissive to the King's will set about picking holes in the Edict of 1812 and annulling it piece by piece. Jewish jurists were refused admission to the bar; Jewish doctors could not obtain appointments to public health posts. No Jew could become a mayor of a town. Jews were barred from academic careers. "His Majesty the King has rescinded Paragraphs 7 and 8 of the Edict of 1812, wherein Jews regarded as natives are to be admitted to academic posts of instruction, because of the abuses that have arisen." The medieval alternative—conversion to Christianity or occupational exclusion—had once again become the maxim in the nineteenth century. Baptism, as Heinrich Heine put it, was to be the indispensable "ticket of entry to European culture."

Frederick William III was not alone in his prejudices. They were consistent with the outlook and mood of the cultivated class in his time. The enthusiasm accompanying the War of Liberation stimulated nationalism at the expense of cosmopolitanism. The struggle had been waged under the banner of romanticism; the longed-for "Kingdom of the Teutons" was to be built upon a foundation of Germanic Christianity, upon shared religion, language, and national feeling. The kind of patriotism that emerged was inimical to tolerance; along with enthusiasm for the nation went hatred for everything alien. The emphasis on *Volk* was coupled with religious intolerance, and, in fact, presaged later racist ideas.

As yet, the majority of the people were illiterates. But the kind of thing they heard from their "poets and thinkers" was blind chauvinism. Ernst Moritz Arndt proclaimed the ideal of Pan-Germania. He also spoke harsh, very harsh words against the Jews. "Our house, our children, our neighbors, our country, our people—these we ought to love and defend. A curse on the humanity and cosmopolitanism you prate of, that universal Jewish notion you present as the summit of human culture." In 1814

Arndt asserted: "Since the harried Jews are now streaming from all the regions of Europe toward the center, Germany, and are threatening to swamp her with their gabble and their pestilence, and since this flood threatens mainly from the East—namely, from Poland—the irrevocable rule follows that under no pretext and with no exceptions should foreign Jews ever be permitted to stay in Germany, even if they could prove that they bring treasure worth millions with them."

Johann Gottlieb Fichte's famous *Addresses to the German Nation* preached a passionate nationalism; Fichte regarded the Germans as the "original people" and German as the "original language." He harbored all the ancient prejudices against the Jews. "They ought to have human rights, although they do not concede these to us," this most noted of Kant's disciples declared. "But I see only one way to give them civil rights: to cut off all their heads in one night and put others on them in which there is not so much as a single Jewish idea. To protect ourselves against them I again see no other way but to conquer their Promised Land for them and send them all there." His 1793 essay on the French Revolution contained some strange rantings against the Jewish people. "Throughout almost all the countries of Europe," he wrote, "there is spreading a mighty, hostilely minded state that is engaged in constant warfare with all others and that in many a country exerts a terrible pressure upon the citizenry. I speak of Jewry. I do not think it so fearsome because it forms a cohesive body that holds itself aloof from its fellow citizens, but because this cohesiveness is built upon hatred for the entire human race. . . . This people has condemned itself and is condemned to retail trade, which enfeebles the body and deadens the spirit to every noble feeling. It is cut off . . . from any fellowship with us by the most binding element that mankind has, his religion. . . . Can anything else be expected of such a people than what we see: that in a state where the most absolutistic king may not take my father's hut from me . . . the first Jew who pleases can plunder me unpunished. You look on while all this happens . . . and speak sugary words of tolerance and human rights and civil rights, while you offend against the first of human rights. . . . Do you not remember being warned against the state within a state? Does it not occur to you that the Jews—who even without your efforts in their behalf are citizens of a state that is more firmly knit and mightier than all your others—will, should you also grant them citizenship in your state, trample the rest of you citizens completely underfoot?"

At the same time that Fichte was writing these words, he was on friendly terms with Dorothea Schlegel, the daughter of Moses Mendelssohn; and he made no bones about his esteem for Solomon Maimon, a Jewish philosopher and one of Kant's first adherents, who exerted great influence upon him. Moreover, as Rector of Berlin University Fichte took up the cause of an unjustly persecuted Jewish student named Brogi.

Fichte died in 1814, just after Napoleon's defeat. But his influence lived on, his writings were often reprinted, and his comments on Jewry have continued to the present day to provide quotations for the hate pamphlets of anti-Semites.

In the days of Lessing, Kant, and Herder, German scholars had come forward as advocates of humanitarianism. Those days were in the past. Another wind was blowing in the lecture halls of the universities. In 1815 Professor Friedrich Rühs, historian at Berlin University, which had been founded five years previously, published his treatise *On the Claims of the Jews to German Citizenship*. He proved a subtle spokesman for the German anti-Semites. Thus, he protested against the work of Dohm, the pioneer of emancipation, in these terms: "A foreign nation cannot win the rights that the Germans enjoy in part solely through their Christianity." To grant such rights would be injustice on the part of Christians toward themselves. "Everything must be done to lead the Jews by the road of gentleness to Christianity and thus cause them truly to assume German national characteristics, so that in the course of time the Jewish people as such should disappear." But these "gentle" methods were hardly original, for, as it turned out, Rühs recommended the tried-and-true impositions: subjection to the laws governing aliens, Jewish taxes, restrictions on their increase, supervision of their economic life, and marks of identification such as were used in medieval times. For the latter purpose he suggested a ribbon.

Rühs, however, was repelled by the idea of using force against the Jews. He would not strip them of their human rights. Not so his philosophical colleague in Heidelberg, Professor Jakob Friedrich Fries. The very title of his work, published in 1816, betrayed its tendency: *On the Endangering of the Welfare and Character of the Germans by the Jews*. The people hate the Jews, the philosopher pointed out, and the cultivated classes must take this circumstance into consideration. He preached "war on Jewry" and demanded that this "caste be exterminated root and branch." Fries's essay, parts of which were distributed in leaflet form, was so rabid that the government of Baden recommended to the "High Council of the Israelites" that it sue the Heidelberg Professor for defamation. Fries was one of the leaders of those fraternities that excluded Jewish students from membership.

A whole corps of hack writers soon gathered around Rühs and Fries, the leaders of this newly kindled dispute. Tracts and orations on the Jews soon flooded the bookstalls. That others spoke up who had remained loyal to reason and the heritage of humanitarianism was of small avail. August Krämer, a librarian in Regensburg, wrote a treatise in favor of "the Jews and their just claims upon the Christian states." He upheld the Jews' rights of citizenship and demanded that they be given complete freedom of movement. In 1816 and 1817 a learned pastor, Johann Ludwig Ewald, wrote vigorous replies to Rühs's views. The Jews must not be regarded as homeless wanderers but as citizens of the state who, in fact, were already members of respectable society. They were entitled to full opportunities; the state must place them on a basis of equality with other citizens, grant them admission to all occupations, respect their religion, and protect them from all attacks. Professor Alexander Lips, a philosophical and political scientist at Erlangen, wrote a study of the causes that had led to existing conditions. The origin of all misfortunes, he declared, was the idea of a dominant religion and a church that had presumed to inflict disabilities on believers in other faiths. "We inoculate the child with hatred of Jews; at later ages we diligently nourish that hatred; but we do not condemn the causes that engender it in us and the springs of it, which lie in our-selves, our own hatred, and our own spirit of exclusiveness. If something is to improve, it must be treated honorably. If we change toward the Jews, they will change also." Professor Lips repeated sentiments that had been heard in the eighteenth century but had been long forgotten: Just as Jewry must practice civic spirit, so Christendom must practice humanity and justice in order "to hold out our hand to our long-forgotten brothers."

But such voices of moderation were ignored, as were the defensive writings by a number of Jews. The hate campaign was stirring up so much emotion that Lips feared a disaster; its "symptoms are already loud and general," he warned. A few months later it came. In August, 1819, the ghost of the Middle Ages reappeared in many German cities. *"Hiero-solyma est perdita"*—"Jerusalem is lost." This was the new slogan and bat-tle cry coined by the academics. Abbreviated to "Hep," it became the watchword of the anti-Semites. Amid cries of *"Hep, hep, Jude verrecke!"* ("Hep, hep, perish, Jew!") a new wave of violence swept through the country.

The riots began in the Bavarian university town of Würzburg. On August 2 "patriotic" students shouted down Professor Brendel during a lecture—he had dared to take the side of the Jews. They drove him from the building and read a proclamation: "Brothers in Christ, up, up, as-semble, arm yourselves with courage and strength against the enemies of our religion; it is time to repress the killers of Christ, so that they shall not become rulers over ourselves and our descendants, for the Jewish pack are already proudly raising their heads. . . . Down with them, before they crucify our priests, profane our sanctuaries, and destroy our temples. We still have power over them. . . . Therefore let us carry out upon them the sentence they have passed upon themselves. . . . Up, all who are baptized; the holy cause is at stake. . . . Now, rise in vengeance. Let our battle cry be: 'Hep, hep, hep! Death and destruction to all Jews; you must flee or die.' "

Citizens broke into Jewish shops and pitched the goods out on the street. When the victims attempted to defend themselves, the mob killed several Jews. The army had to be called in to stop the bloodshed. The following day the Würzburg authorities decreed the expulsion of all Jews; four hundred had to leave the city. In Bamberg the operation was repeated; it spread to other cities of Franconia and Bavaria, extended to Baden, raged in Darmstadt, Mannheim, and Bayreuth. Everywhere the shouts rang out: *"Hep, hep! Jude verrecke!"* Meiningen expelled its Jews. In Karlsruhe, on the morning of August 18, stickers reading "Death and destruction to the Jews" were pasted on the synagogue and the houses of prominent Jews. In Heidelberg the municipal police refused to intervene. Only the energetic action of a courageous band of students and the outraged protests of Professors Daub and Thibaut prevented a massacre in the nick of time. In Frankfurt am Main the populace stormed the ghetto and smashed windowpanes. Houses—especially the home of the Rothschilds—were peppered with bullets. Jewish families fled. The Bundestag deputy hastily called for troops to be sent from Mainz. He had his special reasons; he knew that Bundestag funds were deposited in the home of Amschel Rothschild, son of the founder of the great banking house, and he feared for the money if the house were pillaged. The soldiers arrived in time to scatter the anti-Semitic rowdies.

The assault on the Jews rolled on as far as Hamburg. From August 21 to August 24, in accordance with a prearranged plan, the populace of Hamburg organized a "party," insulting Jews on the street and buffeting them out of public buildings. Those who defended themselves were admonished by the Senate "not to give occasion for disputes." In Prussia, however, "order" prevailed. The police had been instructed to prevent all excesses, and did so. In consequence, the anti-Semitic activities were limited to demonstrations in Düsseldorf, Danzig, Königsberg, and several other cities.

Scarcely had the riots subsided when there appeared a new and exceptionally outrageous pamphlet: *Der Judenspiegel.* Its tone was in keeping with its medieval title, *Mirror of the Jews.* The author, Hartwig von Hundt-Radowski, a novelist, minced no words in calling for violence. To kill a Jew, he maintained, was "neither a sin nor a crime, but merely a police action." He made "several proposals for satisfying the hep men." Large numbers of Jews should be sold to the English for work on their Indian plantations; of those who could not be disposed of, the men should be "emasculated and their women and daughters placed in houses of ill fame. It would be best, however, to cleanse the country entirely of this vermin, either by annihilating them or, like the Pharaoh of old and the people of Meiningen, Würzburg, and Frankfurt, by driving them from the land." The Prussian government ordered confiscation of the *Judenspiegel*. Nevertheless, it enjoyed wide clandestine distribution, along with other pamphlets of the same ilk.

THE STRUGGLE FOR RIGHTS

The ugly events of the year 1819 had long-lasting effects. For one thing, they distinctly colored the attitudes of governments. The assault on the Jews was taken as still another reason to delay the promised emancipation —was it not clear that the time was not yet ripe for it? But the German Jews refused to be deterred. They steadfastly continued fighting for their rights. "All who lack them so painfully must strive incessantly by word and deed for civil liberties. That struggle is especially incumbent upon us younger men, the sons of a century whose breath is freedom. . . . Faith in the power and the ultimate victory of justice and the good is our faith in the Messiah; let us hold fast to it." Such were the words of Gabriel Riesser, a Hamburg jurist who had experienced in his own life all the cruelties of injustice. He had been a child when his family was summarily expelled from Lübeck; in the course of time he had studied law and passed his examinations brilliantly. But he found all paths blocked by anti-Jewish laws. He could not be admitted to the bar or given a teaching position. Nevertheless his studies in German schools had imbued him with the ideals of European culture and an invincible passion for freedom. He vowed not to rest until Jewish equality had been achieved, and appointed himself the great advocate of his coreligionists.

"To reproach us for the fact that our fathers immigrated into Germany centuries or millennia ago is so inhuman that it is nonsensical," Gabriel Riesser reasoned. "We are not immigrants, we are native-born, and because we are, we have no claim to any homeland elsewhere. We are either Germans or we are homeless. . . . Anyone who denies me my claim to my

German fatherland denies me the right to my thoughts, my feelings, the language I speak, the air I breathe. Therefore I must defend myself against him as against a murderer."

Many of Riesser's fellows, especially the younger men, thought in the same terms. The German novelist Berthold Auerbach wrote: "We lean upon the morality animating the nation, and upon the German soul. I live in the happy and confident conviction that I express the views of the entire younger generation of Jews when I say: 'Test us in peril's baptism of fire and you will find us pure of all the slag of egotism and sly immorality. Give us the fatherland to which we belong by birth, morality, and love, and we will loyally offer up our goods and our blood upon its altar. Forget and teach us to forget the black wall that has parted us, and spare us the painful task of entering the lists against you because you so often join your patriotic strivings to the demon of anti-Semitism.' "

In a passionate article dedicated to the "legislative assembly of Germany," Gabriel Riesser took issue with the Heidelberg theologian Heinrich Paulus, who had called for baptism of the Jews as the "guarantee of German nationality." Riesser argued: "There is only one baptism that consecrates nationality: that is the baptism of blood in the common struggle for freedom and fatherland. . . . Our great desire is to belong to the German fatherland. It can and should and may ask of us all that it is entitled to ask of its citizens. We shall willingly sacrifice everything to it—except religion and loyalty, truth and honor. For Germany's heroes and Germany's sages have not taught us that someone becomes a German by such sacrifices." Thus Gabriel Riesser strongly opposed the type of assimilation that legislation and the practice of the authorities was furthering: assimilation by acceptance of Christian baptism. He had some premonition of the tragedy that a latter-day form of marranism would lead to. In his *Observations on the Conditions of the Jewish Subjects of the Prussian Monarchy* he pointed out one danger: "The ever-recurrent use of religion for outward advantage, the daily repeated cases in Prussia in which acceptance of Christianity appears to be the condition for achieving normal civic rights, must in the end lead to religion's being regarded as something external, the profession of it a civic act devoid of any element of truth and conviction. . . ."

In spite of such remonstrances, conversion was becoming more and more frequent. The policy of barring adherents of the Jewish religion from academic careers and from political office in itself promoted apostasy. During this period many of the most talented and capable turned their backs on Judaism forever. The longing to be acknowledged, to be recognized as whole men, had become stronger than the biddings of tradition. The years between 1812 and 1845 saw three thousand three hundred and seventy baptisms in Prussia alone.

The fate of the descendants of the great Moses Mendelssohn, the forerunner of emancipation, showed the way the wind was blowing. Three of his four children abandoned Judaism; his grandchildren were all Christians. Rahel Levin Varnhagen, the brilliant literary woman who was devoted heart and soul to Germany, accepted baptism. Ludwig Börne—born in 1786 as Löb Baruch in the gloomy ghetto of Frankfurt—had converted to the Protestant Church in 1818. "In order to help the Jews," he wrote, "their cause must be linked with justice and the claims for general freedom."

Convinced that it would be more effective to appeal to the peoples rather than to their governments, Börne—along with Heine—became one of the intellectual leaders of Young Germany, the literary libertarian movement whose goal was to liberate Germany from both romanticism and the "thirty-six tyrants" who ruled her multitude of small states. Heinrich Heine likewise became an apostate. In 1819 he had found himself in what he regarded as a blind alley. He was about to complete his studies of law in Göttingen. Because he was a Jew, governmental service, an academic post, and the profession of law were all closed to him. At the same time the young poet had experienced considerable disillusionment connected with his Judaism. The only way out of his dilemma appeared to be that "ticket of entry to European culture" referred to above—baptism. In 1825 he converted to Protestantism.

In 1819 Friedrich Julius Stahl, the son of a Bavarian Jew, underwent baptism and became the philosopher and theoretician of the Conservative Party of Prussia. As a professor in constitutional law at Berlin University he began developing his conservative, clerical views. His formula, a "Christian German State," provided the reactionaries with their intellectual weapons—and thus redounded against Jewish emancipation. Another jurist and philosopher of law, Eduard Gans, obtained a professorship in Berlin only after he had undergone baptism. In Trier in 1824 the son of a pure Jewish family, Karl Marx, was taken to the baptismal font by his parents. The list of baptized Jews was growing long.

Meanwhile, within the ranks of Jewry a great change had begun. Innovations and reforms in worship and instruction were being introduced to keep pace with the new age. Jews, after all, were no longer confined to the ghetto. Against the fierce resistance of the orthodox, rabbis began to preach sermons in the German language and to offer some prayers in German.

Choral singing was introduced and—for the first time in Hamburg in 1819 —the organ. Seminaries for the instruction of rabbis and teachers were founded, in order to meet the growing demand for broader knowledge.

Along with rabbinical scholarship of the traditional sort, something completely new and highly significant developed: the "science of Judaism." For the first time Jewish scholars systematically set about investigating the past of their own people, their history and the history of their religion and literature. Leopold Zunz created the concept and was the first to embark on the enormous task. His pioneering work was akin to what Jacob Grimm was doing in the field of German folklore. Soon a band of eminent men attacked the new problems. Abraham Geiger founded the *Wissenschaftliche Zeitschrift für jüdische Theologie,* a scholarly journal specializing in Jewish theology. Between 1820 and 1829 Isaak Markus Jost wrote his nine-volume *History of the Israelites from the Time of the Maccabees to the Present,* based on hitherto unexploited source materials. Three decades later Heinrich Graetz began publishing his eleven-volume *History of the Jews.* He had devoted twenty-two years of scholarly labors to producing this imposing work, the first general survey of Jewish history spanning more than three thousand years.

This new enlightenment movement, known as Haskalah, spread from Germany to Austria and thence to the East. Solomon Jehudah Rappaport of Lwow wrote the biography of the last Babylonian geonim, Saadia and Hai. Nachman Krochmal treated Jewish history from the philosophical viewpoint. In addition, the new literature of enlightenment led to a revival of Hebrew as a medium of scholarly communication and theoretical studies.

The upheavals of 1848, based on the widespread demand for democratic .and constitutional government, were a cause in which Jews could take heartfelt part. In Berlin Jews fought on the barricades. Of the victims of the March uprising, twenty were Jewish. Four Jews were elected as deputies to the Frankfurt National Assembly held in the Paulskirche: Riesser and the Berlin publisher Moritz Veit, along with Moritz Hartmann and Ignatz Kuranda, both from Austria. In the ranks of the other deputies were eleven baptized Jews, among them Eduard von Simson, grandson of Frederick the Great's "protected Jew," Joachim Moses Friedländer. Simson, who had converted in 1823, was elected President of the Frankfurt Parliament. He led the deputation, of which Riesser was also a member, which in 1849 offered Frederick William IV of Prussia the crown of Germany.

Gabriel Riesser, elected Vice-President by a vote of 220 to 43, delivered a passionate speech—in which he professed himself a Jew who was fully and wholeheartedly a German—calling for the end of all special laws for Jews.

"I claim the right to appear before you," he said, "in the name of a class oppressed for centuries, to which I belong by birth and to which—for personal religious conviction is not pertinent here—I shall continue to belong in accord with the principle of honor that has made me disdain to acquire iniquitously withheld rights by changing religion. . . . You have now, by solemn decree, assured the non-German-speaking peoples who live in Germany [the Slavs] equality before the law, equality of rights, equality in all those things that make Germany dear to Germans. Shall we Jews regard it as our misfortune that we speak German? . . . I myself have lived under conditions of the harshest oppression, and until recently could not have obtained the office of a night watchman in my native city. I may consider it a work—I should like to say, a miracle—of justice and of liberty that I am entitled to defend the noble cause of justice and equality here without having gone over to Christianity. . . . I grant that the Jews, sorely oppressed as they have been, have not yet attained the supreme good, the patriotic spirit. But Germany, too, has not yet attained it. The Jews will become ever more ardent and patriotic adherents of Germany under a just law. They will become Germans with and among the Germans. Trust in the power of justice, in the power of uniform and equitable laws, and in the great destiny of Germany. Do not think that exceptional laws can be made without creating a dangerous crack in the whole system of freedom, in which the seed of ruin will take root. It has been suggested that you sacrifice a portion of the German people to intolerance, to hatred; but you will never do that, gentlemen."

Riesser's words made a deep impression. The National Assembly in the Paulskirche voted for the complete equality of all citizens, including the Jews. "The enjoyment of civil and political rights is to be neither conditioned nor limited by religious denomination," it declared. But these "fundamental rights of the German people," so solemnly adopted in 1849, were never to become laws of the German Reich. For on June 18 of that year the National Assembly was violently disbanded.

Once again two full decades of waiting passed. In the meantime the Jews made every effort to participate in national life—even on the field of battle. In 1866 over a thousand Jews fought in the ranks of Prussian troops against Austria and the German Confederation. "It was as if they had agreed to disprove once and for all the old notion of their lack of desire or fitness for war," wrote Theodor Fontane.

In 1867 the dream was at last realized. The petitions for equality submitted by four hundred and twenty Jewish communities to the Constituent

Reichstag of the North German Confederation were given a favorable hearing. On July 3, 1869, Wilhelm I and Bismarck signed the so-called Tolerance Law. It consisted of only a single article, which stated bluntly: "All existing restrictions of civil and political rights based on differences in religious denomination are hereby abolished. In particular, qualifications for participating in local and state representative bodies and for holding public office shall be independent of religion."

In the war against France, which broke out the following year, six thousand Jewish soldiers took the field; four hundred and forty-eight were killed; three hundred and twenty-seven received the Iron Cross. In the Hall of Mirrors at Versailles Eduard von Simson as President of the Reichstag handed the crown of the German Empire to Wilhelm I. After the Franco-Prussian War, when Bavaria, Baden, and Württemberg entered the German Reich, the Tolerance Law also applied to the states of South Germany.

The long struggle was over, the keystone of emancipation set in place. The German Jews looked forward to a happy future. A new age appeared to be dawning for them.

THE DAMASCUS SLANDERS

The prospect of emancipation, which was slowly gaining ground in spite of stubborn resistance, emboldened the Jews of Western Europe for the first time in history to urge the cause of their more oppressed fellows in other countries and to come to their aid when they were imperiled. When two particularly crass cases of injustice occurred toward the middle of the nineteenth century, these Western Jews were quick to take action, to appeal to the conscience of the public.

In 1840 rumors of a ritual murder began to trickle in from the Near East. Once again the sinister charge had been raised. Damascus, the capital of Syria, was the home of some four hundred Jewish families, among them many wealthy and respected Sephardim. Father Thomas, a Capuchin monk who worked as a physician, was well known throughout Damascus. On February 6, 1840, he suddenly vanished, together with his servant. He was said to have been last seen in the Jewish quarter. The Capuchins of the monastery spread the rumor that the missing man had been murdered by the Jews—for "ritual purposes," so that his blood could be used in the preparation of their Passover bread.

On the instigation of the French Consul, Sherif Pasha, the governor of Damascus, ordered a search of the Jewish quarter. Along with several other Jews arrested at random, a poor barber was taken. Under torture— he received five hundred blows upon the soles of his feet—a confession was extracted from him. He accused seven elders of the community— David Harari, Moses Abulafia, Moses Saloniki, Joseph Laniado, and Harari's son and two brothers. All seven were arrested and cruelly tortured. But they remained steadfast and even under torture continued to avow their innocence. Sherif Pasha hit upon another means of obtaining a confession. He seized sixty-three Jewish children between the ages of three and ten, locked them up, and refused them food. But even at that, none of the desperate fathers and mothers could be induced to admit the base slander. The torture of the seven unfortunates continued. Laniado died, Abulafia converted to Islam. The torturers finally succeeded in wringing the desired confession from the five others. They acknowledged the ritual murder that had never taken place.

A few weeks later the horrible story cropped up elsewhere. On the island of Rhodes a young Greek was found hanged. Here, too, the Jews were immediately accused of murder, several were arrested, and confessions were extracted by tortures. A wave of hatred surged up in confused minds; there were attacks on Jews and desecrations of synagogues in Smyrna, Beirut, and the vicinity of Damascus.

The European press began reporting the story at length. In Rome the Capuchins set up a memorial in their church to the "martyr" Fra Tommaso. Jewish politicians protested to their various governments. In France, Adolphe (Isaac Moïse) Crémieux, lawyer and deputy, could obtain no satisfaction from Premier Adolphe Thiers, nor from King Louis Philippe. England, however, reacted differently. A joint protest demonstration of Christians and Jews was held in the Mansion House in London, in the presence of the Lord Mayor. Robert Peel demanded that the House of Commons pass a resolution in the interests of justice and humanity. Foreign Minister Lord Palmerston let it be known that a protest was being filed by the British Consul General in Alexandria. In Austria, Metternich ordered similar action. After a meeting in Philadelphia, the United States was also moved to issue a protest.

Perceiving that there was no time to be lost, French and English Jews joined in a common action. A meeting in London, under the chairmanship of the philanthropist Sir Moses Montefiore, President of the Board of Deputies, decided to send delegates to the Orient to free the innocent prisoners of Damascus and to denounce the blood slander.

After an audience with Queen Victoria, Montefiore himself set out on his mission. In France, Crémieux and the Orientalist Solomon Munk joined him. On August 4 they landed in Cairo, where they instantly sought an audience with Pasha Mehemed Ali, the governor of Egypt and Syria. They made their plea. Several weeks passed before they received the good news that Mehemed Ali had ordered the release of all the Jews arrested in Damascus. On September 6 Sherif Pasha had to release the prisoners. They were in dreadful condition, almost all having being permanently crippled by the torture.

In order to protect the Jews in the Turkish Empire against similar persecutions, the delegation went on to Constantinople. Sultan Abdul-Mejid I, who had already proved his sense of justice in the Rhodes affair, was receptive to Montefiore's and Crémieux's arguments. The first decree drafted by the Sultan, however, provided only for an "amnesty" for the Jews of Damascus. Montefiore refused to accept this, whereas Crémieux, who, unlike Montefiore, did not have the support of his government in Paris, seemed prepared to make do with it. The decree finally issued on November, 6, 1840, reflected Montefiore's firmness. It pronounced the accusation of ritual murder a crude slander. "In order to spare the Jewish nation torments and oppression in the future," the Sultan once again explicitly guaranteed to all Jews living in the Ottoman Empire the right to practice their religion freely and to enjoy full protection of their lives and property.

News of the happy outcome of these negotiations in the Orient aroused enormous enthusiasm in Jewry. Jews the world over regarded it as a sign of change after long centuries of haplessness, as the inauguration of a hopeful new era. On their return journey the delegates were hailed by Jewish communities all along their route.

Eighteen years later public opinion in Europe was once again agitated by the kidnaping of a Jewish child in the Papal States.

A Catholic maid in Bologna had secretly given emergency baptism to little Edgar Mortara, the child of Jewish parents, during a severe illness. Subsequently, she informed a priest of what she had done. Shortly afterward, in June, 1858, a monk and a policeman unexpectedly forced their way into the Mortaras' home, seized Edgar, who was by now six years old, and forcibly carried him off to give him a Christian upbringing. The mother nearly lost her reason from grief. All the steps the father undertook to recover the child proved fruitless.

News of this arbitrary act committed in the Papal States in the name of the religion of love reached the press. A storm of indignation arose among Christians and Jews. In an age when human rights and emancipation seemed to be already guaranteed, the case appeared almost incredible. The Jewish communities in free Piedmont protested. Ludwig Philippson, in the name of the German rabbis, addressed a petition to the Pope. There was a protest demonstration in London. But even representations by the Catholic monarchs Napoleon III and Franz Joseph did not sway Pope Pius IX. When a delegation of the Roman Jewish community laid a petition before the Pope in February, 1859, Pius reprimanded them as follows: "So this is the proof of your loyalty as subjects: that last year you stirred up all of Europe on account of Mortara. You poured oil on the flames; you incited the editorial writers. But let the newspapers write what they please; I shall only laugh at it." Even Moses Montefiore, who traveled to Rome to plead personally for the release of the little prisoner, made no headway. *"Non possumus—*I cannot," Pius IX replied.

When Bologna was detached from the Papal States shortly afterward by Victor Emmanuel II, the Mortaras began to hope anew. They appealed to the new government. But investigation showed that the boy had already been sent to Rome.

Edgar, when he reached his majority, never returned to the religion of his fathers. He became a priest and later served as a missionary.

The new *cause célèbre* led to the formation in 1860 of the Alliance Israélite Universelle, with headquarters in Paris. Crémieux, who in 1870 had been elected French Premier for the second time, assumed the presidency of the organization. The object of the Alliance was to help oppressed coreligionists and, by the founding of schools, to spread European culture in the Orient. Similar organizations were established on the same pattern in other countries—the Anglo-Jewish Association in England in 1871, the Israelitische Allianz in Vienna in 1873, the Hilfsverein der Deutschen Juden in 1901.

Crémieux and Montefiore continued their energetic efforts to raise the status of the Jews everywhere. When Charles of Hohenzollern-Sigmaringen acceded to the throne of Rumania in 1866, Crémieux called upon the new sovereign, described the harsh restrictions upon the Jews of Rumania, and asked the monarch to grant them civil equality. In return, Crémieux promised to obtain a loan of twenty-five million francs for the government. In Bucharest, Crémieux addressed the Rumanian deputies. "The decree on the emancipation of the Negroes," he began his speech, "bears the signature of the same French Jew, a member of the provisional government of 1848, who now stands before you and requests you to do for the Jews of Rumania what he himself has done with such joy for the Negroes of the French colonies." But his plea proved ineffective; conditions remained unchanged in Rumania.

Crémieux had decided that education held the key to the improvement of the Jewish lot in the Orient. As early as 1840 he had begun founding schools in Cairo. On his advice the Alliance established the first modern boarding schools in Turkey, despite the resistance of the strictly orthodox rabbis of the country, who were hostile to all innovations.

Montefiore devoted himself to the welfare of the Jews in Palestine. In order to provide work for them, he established a linen mill in Jerusalem. He also founded a Hebrew print shop, had homes built for the poor, and opened a school for girls. Active to the very end of his long life, Montefiore soon became as familiar a figure in the courts of Rumania and Russia as in the Jewish quarters of Palestine and Morocco, where some two hundred thousand Jews lived under conditions of harsh oppression. In 1875, at the age of ninety, he made his seventh and last pilgrimage to the Holy Land, whose poverty-stricken communities he had so often charitably aided.

The liberated, progressive Jews of the West felt responsible for their brothers in Eastern Europe, who still lived under medieval conditions, and for those in the ghettos of the Mediterranean world. They had virtually assumed patronage of these unfortunates in the confidence that for them, too, the day could not be far off when the hour of emancipation would come and their pariah existence would cease.

LIBERATION IN WESTERN EUROPE

The tide had turned at last. In country after country, after the revolutionary beginning of 1848, the fetters of the Middle Ages gradually dropped away. By 1870, liberal constitutions were proclaimed; the peoples of Europe had won representation in elected parliaments and citizens of the Jewish faith had at last achieved full equality. In some countries the change came peacefully; in others, under the impact of uprisings.

On March 13, 1848, the populace demonstrated in Vienna. "Hurrah for the Constitution! Away with the Jesuits! Down with Metternich!" Such were the slogans shouted by students, workers, and bourgeois in the streets of the old imperial city on the Danube. An excited crowd, which had been joined by many Jews, marched to the Landhaus and surrounded it. When many faltered in the face of troops, the Jewish doctor Adolf Fischhof exhorted the demonstrators: "Those who lack courage belong in the nursery." The troops opened fire. But the bloodshed unleashed the revolution. The people armed; a citizens' militia was created. Chancellor Metternich, his life no longer safe, fled to England. Only then did Emperor Ferdinand I yield and promise the people a constitution and the convoking of a parliament.

As a result of the March uprising, the Jewish community had lost several dead, among them a student named Spitzer. On March 17 the populace poured out for the funeral of the victims. The fallen Christians and Jews were buried side by side. At their common grave Rabbi Mannheimer spoke after the Catholic priest. "You have asked that the dead Jews may rest with your dead, in the same earth," he said. "But now grant those who have fought the same fight, and the harder one, that they may live with you on the same earth, free and untroubled as yourselves. . . . You are free men. Receive us as free men also, and God's blessing upon you." The following day Mannheimer spoke in the synagogue: "What is to be done now? For us? Nothing. Everything for the people and the country, as you have done in the last few days. . . . Not a word about emancipation of the Jews unless others speak that word for us. . . . No petitions, no pleas and laments about our rights. . . . First our rights as human beings. . . . First the right of the citizen . . . the Jews comes next. Let them not take us to task for thinking always and everywhere first of ourselves. Do nothing. Our time must also come, and will surely not fail."

There were more riots when the Emperor failed to keep his promise of calling a national assembly. On May 15 Jews once again fought in the ranks of the National Guard. One of the outstanding fighters in the student legion was Joseph Goldmark. Adolf Fischhof was elected by the people President of the Committee of Safety. At the end of October turmoil erupted anew. After a week of savage battles imperial troops under Prince Windisch-Graetz forced their way into Vienna. A court-martial passed the death sentence upon the ringleaders, in whose number was the young liberal writer Hermann Jellinek, a brother of Adolf Jellinek, the chief rabbi of Vienna. Fischhof, whose oratory had spurred the revolution, received nine months' imprisonment. Joseph Goldmark succeeded in escaping and emigrated to America. In place of Ferdinand, who had abdicated, Emperor Franz Joseph signed the new constitution on March 4, 1849. Among its other benefactions, it provided for equality of all religions: "The enjoyment of civil and political rights is independent of religious denomination." Eighteen years later the final barriers fell; the Hapsburg Empire at last kept its promises in full. The Fundamental Law of December 21, 1867, assured all inhabitants of the Dual Monarchy of Austria-Hungary full rights of citizenship without distinction of nationality or religion.

In Italy, too, 1848 was the turning point when the medieval strictures upon the Jews were finally set aside. As in Germany, it took the unification of the country, hitherto splintered in so many small principalities, to bring about that emancipation.

The *Risorgimento,* the movement for Italian unity and freedom inaugurated in Turin in 1847, began the struggle. In 1848 King Charles Albert of Sardinia granted his country a constitution, accorded the Jews all civil and political rights, and placed himself at the head of the nationalist movement. After his abdication in 1849 his son Victor Emmanuel II resolutely pursued the goals of the *Risorgimento.* Under the brilliant leadership of Cavour—appointed Premier of Piedmont-Sardinia in 1852 —the work of liberation proceeded step by step. Cavour found a capable associate in the Jewish jurist Isaac Artom. In 1859 Piedmont defeated Austria at the Battle of Solferino and wrested Lombardy from Austrian control. In 1860 Tuscany, Parma, Modena, and the Romagna joined the union by plebiscite. In that same year the guerrilla leader Giuseppe Garibaldi landed in Sicily with his Redshirts. His bold enterprise, in which many Jews enthusiastically participated, led to the fall of the Bourbons and the annexation of Sicily and Lower Italy along with Naples to the growing union. Under Victor Emmanuel, proclaimed King of Italy in Florence in 1861, the Jews were granted equality. The same rights were extended to Venetia when that province was taken from Austria in 1866.

Now only one last segment remained excluded from united Italy: Rome, the capital of the Papal States. Four years later there were glad tidings for the dwellers in the ghetto on the Tiber. On September 20, 1870—the year in which the Vatican Council had proclaimed the dogma of the infallibility of the Pope—the troops of Victor Emmanuel II marched into the Eternal City. Rome became the capital of united free Italy; the Pope, having lost his States of the Church, chose to consider himself the "Prisoner of the Vatican." The harsh exceptional laws reimposed upon the Jews by Pius IX in 1850 were abolished; the final act in the ancient tragedy of Roman Jewry had been reached. At the same time that the gates of the Vatican closed behind the Pope, the gates of the Roman ghetto opened for the Jews.

The members of the liberated Jewish community thanked King Victor Emmanuel II as "Italians, Romans, and Israelites." They vowed: "We now pronounce the name Israelite for the last time. Such is our duty of gratitude at this moment of transition to the sacred regime of civil equality. Under the scepter of Your Majesty we shall, outside of our temple, think only that we must be Italians and Romans, nor shall we be anything else."

England went her own organic and peaceful way, without reactionary setbacks. The island kingdom had no strict special laws concerning Jews. They could settle wherever they pleased and practice almost all occupations. Their relations to their Christian neighbors were good. In practice, they had been emancipated long before it was decided to legalize their condition. In 1830, after equality had been accorded to the Catholics, Robert Grant proposed to the House of Commons that full civil rights be conferred upon all Jews born in England. His bill did not pass. But in 1831 the restrictions pertaining only to the City of London, that no Jew could acquire citizenship or open a retail shop, were abolished. In 1833 another attempt at formal emancipation failed. The Commons voted for the bill presented by Thomas Babington Macaulay, but the House of Lords rejected it. That same year, however, the first Jew—Francis Goldsmid— was admitted to the bar, and two years later to a judgeship. In 1835 David Salomons, one of the founders of the London and Westminster Bank, was elected Sheriff of the city. In 1837 Moses Montefiore assumed that dignity. The bill of 1845 opened the doors of town halls to Jews—thanks to the efforts of Robert Peel.

Only a single barrier remained—the admission of Jews to Parliament. It was more than a decade before this disability was removed. In 1847 Baron Lionel Nathan Rothschild, Liberal candidate for the city, was elected to the House of Commons, but he could not be seated because he refused to take the oath as a member of Parliament according to the prescribed formula—"in the true faith of a Christian." Five times the same scene was repeated; elected anew, Baron Rothschild presented himself and was not admitted because he each time took the oath omitting the objectionable clause. It was not until 1858 that the Upper House after long debates finally yielded on this point. Rothschild took the oath with the words, "So help me God," and was seated in the Commons. In 1871, after Jews had long since been admitted to academic degrees elsewhere, Oxford and Cambridge dropped the requirement that attendance at these venerable institutions was contingent on membership in the Anglican Church. Thus the last remnants of religious restrictions were scrapped and the Jews in England fully emancipated.

As early as 1849 Denmark had introduced civic equality. The rest of Scandinavia followed suit, although more slowly. In Norway a heated struggle ensued over abolition of the law that made it a crime for Jews to enter the country. In 1851 Jews were admitted, but it was 1891 before they were allowed to hold divine services publicly. In Sweden—which had had no influx of Jews until 1775, when one Aron Isak came there from Germany—equality was also ultimately granted. Switzerland, where since the seventeenth century Jews had been permitted to settle only in the villages of Oberendigen and Lengnau, put an end to restrictions in the latter half of the nineteenth century. After protracted internal dissension and under considerable international pressure, freedom of movement was granted to the Jews in 1866. The new Federal Constitution of 1874 contained no mention of any restrictions whatsoever.

The last shadows of the Middle Ages had been dispelled from the heart of Europe. All members of the Jewish faith had become full-fledged Europeans, recognized as human beings, as citizens, as men of culture. Only the East still lagged far behind the times: Russia and Rumania.

In 1877 Rumania won her independence in the Russo-Turkish War. In 1878 the Congress of Berlin, presided over by Bismarck, rearranged the political affairs of the Balkans. A memorandum from the Alliance Israélite Universelle was presented to this Congress. It stated bluntly: "The situation of the sizable Jewish population of Rumania is ghastly. For ten years it has been exposed to the cruelest persecutions. Almost every year Europe is shocked by news of devastation, pillaging, murders, and mass expulsions of Rumanian Jews. In addition to these atrocities a series of laws exclude Jews from government service, public employment, free professions, and many branches of commerce and industry."

William Henry Waddington, the French Foreign Minister with an English name, proposed that Rumania's independence be recognized solely on condition that she assure members of all religions full and equal rights. Bismarck agreed to this proposal, as did the representatives of Austria and Italy, Prince Aleksandr Gorchakov for Russia, and Benjamin Disraeli, Earl of Beaconsfield, who was proud of his Jewish origin although he had been baptized at the age of twelve.

Nevertheless Article 44 of the Treaty of Berlin, providing that "the difference of religious profession in Rumania shall not serve as a reason for exclusion from the enjoyment of civil and political rights," remained a paper promise. Carol I of Rumania declared cynically soon after accepting the article: "The Jewish paragraph imposed by the Congress is a humanitarian generalization. It is entirely for legislation to regulate these conditions, and I am convinced that later, aside from the Alliance Israélite, no one will give a thought to how those stipulations are carried out."

The consequence was that two hundred and fifty thousand Jews remained without rights or protection. Serbia and Bulgaria, on the other hand, adhered to the prescripts of the Congress of Berlin. Greece had emancipated her Jews back in 1844; but only toward the end of the century were the rights guaranteed by the constitution gradually realized.

Far to the west Spain continued to abide by the expulsion edict of the year 1492 issued by their Most Christian Majesties Ferdinand and Isabella. All settlement by Jews remained officially forbidden. The expulsion was

not revoked until 1858. As late as 1961 there were no more than three
thousand Jews—mostly refugees from Hitler—in the country that four
hundred and sixty-eight years before had ruthlessly expelled some two
hundred thousand.

THE GREAT CONTRIBUTION OF THE JEWS

With the liberation of the Jews from the old fetters of occupational restrictions and discrimination, the world witnessed a unique phenomenon.
In Western Europe and in all lands that had granted freedom, the sons
of Israel underwent an astounding renaissance. They who for so long had
been condemned to stand aside wasted not a moment in utilizing the
multitude of opportunities that had hitherto been closed to them. Craving
knowledge, eager to learn, industrious and ambitious, and trained by
necessity, by the everlasting struggle that they had had to wage for a bare
existence for so many centuries, they were prepared to meet all challenges.
They displayed extraordinary talent and versatility in every imaginable
field, from politics to scholarship, from finance to industry, from music
to science and technology. The Jews who only yesterday had been crammed
into the ghettos found their way about their new environment with astonishing rapidity. Within a few decades they leaped from exclusive concentration upon the Torah and Talmud into the full intellectual life of the
West. They passed rapidly through an evolution for which Christians
had had centuries at their disposal since the Renaissance, Reformation,
and Enlightenment. Their long-repressed capacities, suddenly free to develop, richly rewarded the nations that seemed at last disposed to take the
long-despised pariahs into their midst.

Even in outward appearance they changed. "Crippled in body and
soul" they emerged from their narrow streets. Marked by suffering and
distress they entered modern society. With incredible speed their new
circumstances corrected the physical woes to which they had been exposed
generation after generation. The stooped posture, the weak frame vanished; the pale complexion became increasingly rarer. Jews as a whole
increased in height. Were these still the same people?

"It was thought to make them contemptible by treating them con-
temptuously for two centuries and denying them admission to all honors
and all honorable work, thus thrusting them all the more deeply into the
filthiest occupations," wrote Nietzsche, who condemned anti-Semitism and
foresaw a "dawn" of Jewry. "But they have never ceased to believe
themselves destined for the highest things, and the virtue of all sufferers

has never ceased to adorn them. The manner in which they honor their fathers and children, the rationality of their marriages and marital morals, distinguishes them among all Europeans. . . . In Europe they have passed through a school of eighteen centuries such as no other nation can boast. . . . In consequence of that, the spiritual and intellectual resources of present-day Jews are extraordinary. . . ."

Three epochs of Jewish history, said Leo Baeck, have shown a happy assimilation. In the first two—in the Hellenistic Age and in the Spanish-Arabic Middle Ages—Jewish scholars took a significant part in the great work of translation, which by way of Islam opened the sources and foundations of classical antiquity to the Western world and made possible the founding of universities and the blossoming of science in Europe. The third epoch was the German liberal period in modern times.

Even in brief, it is impossible to do more than suggest the magnificent achievements of emancipated Jewry in the nineteenth century, the pioneering work that Jews accomplished in art, literature, and music, as scientists and thinkers, as economists and industrialists.

It was scarcely surprising that Jews proved pre-eminent in finance. That, after all, had long been familiar territory to them, had perforce become their domain ever since the Church ban on lending money at interest and restrictions on other occupations drove them to money-lending. In this field, in which for centuries they had served kings, princes, and the high clergy as brokers and financial advisers, they could draw on long experience. They played their part in the new economic order as they had done in the period of rising mercantilism. The age of industrialism needed vast amounts of capital. Economic advances were dependent upon liquidity of money; capital had become the lifeblood of industry. The banking system created by the Jews of the Middle Ages reached the apex of its effectiveness; everywhere the banks established by Jewish financiers supplied the funds needed for the enormous expansion of production that followed from the new technology.

The Jews of the one-time ghetto city of Frankfurt occupied a key position in the rise of high finance. The story of the house of Rothschild is too well known to need repetition. Meyer Amschel Rothschild (1743–1812), the founder of the line, had served Elector Wilhelm of Hesse as court factor. His five sons became the government bankers in five European countries. They backed the conservative powers of Europe in the struggle against Napoleon; they helped to finance the building of railroads. In 1875 the English Rothschilds provided the funds for Benjamin Disraeli to purchase the Suez Canal shares owned by the Khedive Ismail Pasha, thus assuring England's dominant position in Egypt.

In England, toward the end of the eighteenth and the beginning of the nineteenth centuries the house of Goldsmid grew into one of the most important credit and loan enterprises in the country. David Sassoon, of a Sephardic family in Baghdad, founded a bank in Bombay, which grew to be the most influential financial force in India and, in fact, in the entire Near and Far East. His descendants won fame in the British moneyed aristocracy, in politics, and in literature. In France the Pereire brothers, descendants of a talented marrano family from Bordeaux, financed the building of the French and Russian railroads. Achille Fould became Finance Minister to Napoleon III; Baron Moritz Hirsch raised the capital for railroads in Turkey, Russia, and Austria. The Bishoffsheim, Stern, Oppenheim, Goldschmidt, Wertheim, and Seligmann families played a dominant part in the German capital market. Gerson von Bleichröder, "the last court Jew," as he was called, was the confidant of three kaisers and Bismarck's personal banker. When in 1871 the German Chancellor demanded an unusually high sum in war reparations from defeated France, the French President objected that it would have been impossible to raise such a sum even if the nation had begun saving at the time of Christ. Bismarck, who was accompanied by Bleichröder, replied: "For that very reason I have brought with me an adviser who begins his chronology with the creation of the world." Among the most prestigious private banks in Berlin was that belonging to Franz von Mendelssohn, a descendant of the philosopher. In Hamburg, M. M. Warburg's bank occupied a similar position.

Toward the end of the nineteenth century the importance of Jewish private banks began to diminish. More and more, stock companies assumed the task of financing industry.

During the early days of the Industrial Revolution in textile manufacture, iron fabrication, and mining, Jews had still not been free. Not until the emancipation laws had been passed could they enter the field as industrialists and manufacturers.

Simon Kremser—decorated with the Order of Merit for rescuing General Blücher's war chest in 1806—opened the first interurban transport company in Berlin in 1825. He equipped it with vehicles that were henceforth to be known as Kremsers. The cotton mills of J. Kaufmann & Sons set up the first four mechanical looms in Göppingen, Swabia. Subsequently, forty textile mills and an important shoe factory sprang up in and around that city. All their owners were members of the Jewish community. Ludwig Löwe supplied the Prussian army that fought the Franco-Prussian War with precision-made rifles. His son, Isidor Löwe, built his father's enterprise near Berlin into one of the largest German arms and tool companies. Philipp Rosenthal developed a modest porcelain-painting work-shop in Selb into one of the foremost porcelain factories in the world. Nathan Israel created Berlin's first department store. Albert Ballin was general director of Germany's largest shipping company, Hapag.

The role of Jews as technological pioneers has been largely forgotten. They made decisive contributions to the most significant inventions of modern times, the automobile and airplane, the telephone and radio.

For many years David Schwarz worked on plans for a rigid dirigible airship. No one took him seriously in Vienna, or in St. Petersburg. At last he found German financial backers. In 1897 the populace of Berlin saw a vision of Jules Verne made reality. Above Tempelhof Field floated a gigantic silvery monster, tethered by long ropes. It was Schwarz's air-ship, an aluminum shell filled with hydrogen. It rose up on its test flight and took off over the housetops. Because of a minor technical flaw—the strap for starting the propeller broke—it lost its motive power. A violent wind forced an emergency landing and the plane was destroyed. The inventor, David Schwarz, had not lived to witness the debacle. He had been felled by a heart attack the previous year when he received a telegram from the Prussian Minister of War asking for a demonstration of his airship. But among the spectators was a man already interested in the development of a dirigible airship—Count Ferdinand von Zeppelin. In 1898 he bought up all of Schwarz's patents.

In 1875, after fourteen years of tinkering, Siegfried Marcus of Mecklen-burg propelled his "automotive wagon" out of a workshop in Vienna. For motive power the vehicle possessed something totally novel: an internal combustion engine with electric ignition. The inventor made a first trial drive of his extraordinary vehicle on Vienna's famous Mariahilferstrasse. Next day the police forbade him any more such experiments—because of the noise. Disheartened, Marcus went no further with his invention, although he recorded the patents, no less than seventy-eight of them.

In 1870 Emil Berliner emigrated to America; in 1877 and independently of David Hughes he invented the microphone and made decisive improve-ments on Edison's phonograph. He was also the creator of the phono-graph record. Robert von Lieben, the son of a Viennese Jewish banker, discovered the application of cathode rays for amplifying, the technique that later made possible much of radio as well as sound movies. Gabriel Lippmann invented color photography. Moritz Jacobi discovered elec-trotyping; he also built the first motorboat. Sansone Valobra was re-sponsible for the safety match.

The brilliant Jewish achievements in medicine can scarcely be listed in limited space. There is Paul Ehrlich, cofounder of serum therapy, who developed Salvarsan, and August von Wassermann, who created the test named after him. Ferdinand Julius Cohn, the first Jew to be given a professorship at a Prussian university and one of the founders of bacteriology, was swift to recognize the importance of Robert Koch's discoveries before anyone else did. The bacteriologist Waldemar Mordecai Haffkine discovered the agent of bubonic plague and introduced inoculation against cholera and plague. Cesare Lombroso founded the psychology of criminality. Moritz Lazarus and his brother-in-law Heymann Steinthal created the new science of ethnopsychology.

Jewish names likewise belong on the roster of modern chemistry and the dye industry. Adolf von Baeyer, Jewish on his mother's side, produced synthetic indigo in 1878. Heinrich Caro, as director of the Baden Aniline and Soda Factory, was responsible for many discoveries and advances in the field of dyes and for the rapid expansion of the chemical industry. The German potash industry owed its origin to Adolf Frank. Fritz Haber discovered the method for obtaining nitrates from the air and thus came to the aid of German agriculture during the First World War, when it was faced with a dire shortage of fertilizers.

In physics Heinrich Hertz's work was pioneering in many respects; among other things, he provided proof that light is an electromagnetic phenomenon. Karl Gustav Jacobi was, after Gauss, the foremost mathematician of his age. Count Georg von Arco, of Jewish descent, turned from military service to physics and made significant contributions to radio technology.

As the century approached its end, two scientists had already begun on enterprises that were to open up vast new territories of the mind for the whole of humanity; Sigmund Freud and Albert Einstein.

As Professor Edmund Schopen has rightly pointed out, "The proportion of creative personalities and leading minds among Jews and non-Jews in the nineteenth century of bourgeois liberalism is something like fifteen to one." Hans Joachim Störig has remarked that "the Jews, less than one per cent of the world population, provide more than ten per cent of the Nobel Prize winners."

Their activity in the field of newspaper and book publishing has been crucial. Leopold Ullstein, who founded his famous publishing house in Berlin, came from the Jewish community of Fürth. In the United States, Adolph S. Ochs rescued the New York *Times* from bankruptcy and built it up to the great newspaper it has since become. Baron Paul Julius von Reuter, born Israel Beer Josaphat, in 1849 established in Aachen (and in London in 1851) the subsequently world-renowned Reuter's News Agency. In 1856 Leopold Sonnemann founded the Frankfurt *Zeitung*.

In public life and political theory Jewish creativity extends from the scientific socialism of Karl Marx to the social democracy of Ferdinand Lassalle. In art the names of Camille Pissarro, Max Liebermann, Amedeo Modigliani, Marc Chagall, and Jacob Epstein only begin to suggest the extent of Jewish participation in the evolution of modern art. In music, it is not even possible to name the countless Jewish virtuosos, and it is sufficient to mention such composers as Felix Mendelssohn-Bartholdy, Jacques Halévy, Giacomo Meyerbeer, Gustav Mahler, and—in the twentieth century—Arnold Schönberg, Erich W. Korngold, Kurt Weill, and Darius Milhaud.

"In all the countries of Europe," Carl Jacob Burckhardt was to write later, "the Jews, after their emancipation in the nineteenth century, integrated vigorously into the nation. Jewish citizens fell in with the nationalistic trend within Germany. It was thanks to three Jews that Germany found it possible to confront an entire world for four years during the first world war of the twentieth century: Walther Rathenau, who organized the German war economy; the chemist Fritz Haber, whose discovery of the nitrogen fixation process assured raw materials for the German munitions factories; and Albert Ballin, the creator of the great German merchant fleet. All three came to a tragic end."

AFTER 1871

After the exultation over the winning of the Franco-Prussian War and over the establishment of the German Reich, the fine promises made to the Jews were all too soon qualified. Severe disappointments followed hard upon the elation of victory. The *Kulturkampf* and political struggles, economic anxieties and social abuses produced dissatisfaction in large segments of the population—and, naturally, a scapegoat had to be found. From all sides charges and complaints against the Jews suddenly resumed.

In 1872 official Catholicism struck out against liberalism and Manchesterism, as well as against the "greed" of the *Gründerjahre,* that period during which so many stock-promotion schemes were being used to defraud the public. A Christmas address by the Pope sounded the new note. Pius IX, whose long pontificate since 1846 had been marked by antagonism toward the Jews, once more made them the chief target of his attack. The Jews were the enemies of Christendom and civilized society, he said; they worshiped Mammon.

In 1873 the fever of hasty corporation promotions and risky speculations ended in a stock-market crash. Many segments of the middle class, including many Jews, lost their savings. Even before the crash the Jew Eduard Lasker, leader of the National Liberals in the Reichstag, had been first to warn against the dangers of uncontrolled speculation in conjunction with French reparations payments. He had demanded action against the financial scandals he had uncovered. But nothing had been done.

For agitators, it was enough that some Jews had participated in the frauds. In the widely read family magazine *Die Gartenlaube,* a series of articles began, entitled "The Stock Exchange and Stock-Promotion Swindles," by Otto Glagau. Disregarding the fact that there were many Christians, including many of the nobility, among the promoters and speculators, the author placed the blame for the crash squarely upon the Jews. "Jewry," he asserted, "is interested exclusively in commerce, and in that realm only in haggling and usury. It does not labor itself, but lets others labor for it." The series ran for two years, from 1874 to 1875. Glagau's essays were studded with such gems as: "From the baptized minister to the Polish schnorrer, the Jews form a single chain . . . a race physically as well as psychically degenerate, controlling the whole globe by cunning and slyness, by usury and haggling."

Attacks began on the liberal newspapers edited by Jews, such as the Berlin *Tageblatt* and the Frankfurt *Zeitung.* "The Jews have seized the entire press," the conservatives grumbled. *Germania,* the Catholic organ of the Center Party, in 1875 blamed "the Jews" for the spread of secularization, charged them and the "Jewish" press with being the principal advocates of nefarious liberalism. They began voicing the thesis that the medieval persecutions of the Jews had sprung not from religious fanaticism, but from "the protest of the Germanic race against the intrusion of a foreign stock."

Years earlier, a great composer had become the spokesman of anti-Semitism in the arts—Richard Wagner. In 1850, using the pseudonym K. Freigedank, he had published an essay entitled *Jewry in Music.* In 1869 he republished it, with a slight change in title, and this time under his own name. He denounced Jewish music wholesale, charging the Jews with general artistic impotence, with being able "only to imitate, to copy, not to originate or create works of art." He endeavored to prove this thesis by the examples of Mendelssohn and Meyerbeer, the most noted Jewish composers of his time. Giacomo Meyerbeer, whom he thus viciously attacked, had arranged the premières of *Rienzi* and *The Flying Dutchman* in Berlin. During his Paris years Wagner had been a great admirer and imitator of Meyerbeer. In this same essay Wagner spoke his mind on the matter of citizenship for Jews. "Jewry has been able to take root among us solely by exploiting the weakness and faultiness of our conditions. . . . When we fought for the emancipation of the Jews we were in actuality fighting more for an abstract principle than for the concrete case. Indeed, all our liberalism was a not very clearsighted intellectual game, in which we waxed sentimental over liberty of the people without knowing this people. . . ." The theme recurs insistently in Wagner's later writings and even in his letters: "What a wonderful, incomparable phenomenon is the Jew: Protean demon of humanity's decadence now triumphantly secure, and, in addition, a German citizen of Mosaic religion, the darling of liberal princes and guarantor of our empire's unity." To King Ludwig II of Bavaria he wrote: "I most certainly regard the Jewish race as the born enemy of pure men and of all nobility in them, and am convinced that we Germans in particular will be destroyed by them. Perhaps I am the last German who is capable of maintaining himself against Judaism, which already dominates everything." In spite of this position, Richard Wagner counted heavily on Jewish admirers and backers. Joseph Rubinstein, Angelo Neumann, and Hermann Levi were among his intimates at Bayreuth—and proved highly useful to Wagner.

In Berlin the political struggle against the Jews was headed by Adolf Stoecker, a chaplain in ordinary. He founded the first petty-bourgeois movement, the Christian Socialist Party, in 1878 for the express purpose of combating socialists and Jews. From the pulpit and from platforms at mass meetings that soon drew huge crowds from the ranks of the middle class, he ranted against the "domination" and "arrogance" of the Jews. "Just because we have felt this blood poisoning we have at last torn free and at last, at last, raised our hands against this poison that devours the spiritual life of the nation, and have cried out: 'This must not go on.' But they, the Jews, are the poisoners . . ." he declared. And: "Revitalization of the Christian Germanic spirit, that is the way to oppose the rampant growth of Judaism in Germanic life, that furious increase that is worse than the increase of debt to a usurer."

Stoecker's campaign began in the same year in which Bismarck's policies turned conservative. The Chancellor now tolerated, without directly supporting, all the forces of reaction, which had unleashed a hate campaign against the Jews such as Germany had not experienced since 1819. Not once did Bismarck vigorously and publicly take steps, by way of warning, conciliation, or enlightenment, to oppose the more and more provocative agitation, the ugly slanders against Jewish citizens, the public denunciations of them in mass demonstrations and in Parliament.

The old anti-Jewish current, now swollen with dangerous fresh waters, carved itself a new bed. Arguments that had once been founded on religion were secularized and given a pseudo-biological basis. A new and allegedly "scientific" doctrine made its appearance. Wilhelm Marr, the baptized son of a Jewish actor, published *The Victory of Judaism Over Teutonism*. The Jewish question, he contended, was not a religious but a racial question. Marr, who also originated the concept of "anti-Semitism," founded the League of Anti-Semites in Berlin in October, 1879. Its avowed aim was: "Saving the German Fatherland from complete Judaization."

The kind of nonsense that was proclaimed in mass meetings, scurrilous pamphlets, and agitational speeches was carried into the halls of the universities and made acceptable to academics. In 1879 the *Preussische Jahrbücher* published a series of essays, entitled "A Word About Our Jewry," by Professor Heinrich von Treitschke, a spokesman for reactionary nationalism. "Up to the spheres of highest culture," he wrote, "among men who would reject with repugnance any thought of ecclesiastical bigotry or nationalistic arrogance, the words are spoken as if in chorus nowadays: 'The Jews are our misfortune.' " A fateful slogan had been coined.

Among the Liberals, Theodor Mommsen vigorously opposed Treitschke. In his *Another Word About Our Jewry* (1880) the famous historian pointed to the utter absurdity of the campaign against the Jews. He charged Treitschke with unleashing jingoism in united Germany and branded anti-Semitism a "monstrous abortion of nationalism." Theodor Fontane, too, argued that "Hostility toward the Jews is nonsense, aside from all moral questions." But even Mommsen could not dispense with the idea of a "Christian state" and admonished the Jews to "put aside their idiosyncrasy." "No Moses will lead the Jews back to the Promised Land," he wrote. "Entry into a great nation has its price." Like the Liberals, the Social Democrats firmly repudiated all types of anti-Semitism "because the exploitation of man by man is not a specifically Jewish occupation, but one peculiar to bourgeois society, and will end only with the downfall of bourgeois society."

The anti-Semites did not confine themselves to speeches. They immediately plunged into political activity. Headmaster Bernhard Förster (Nietzsche's brother-in-law) and former army officer Max Liebermann von Sonnenberg, members of Stoecker's group, addressed a petition to the Chancellor. It began: "For some time the minds of serious patriotic men of all classes and parties have been most deeply concerned about the rampant growth of the Jewish element of the population. . . ." They demanded curbs on additional Jewish immigration and the removal of Jews from all government employ. When the text of this petition was published, libertarian groups protested energetically. A proclamation signed by such noted scholars and scientists as Mommsen, Rudolf Virchow, Johann Gustav Droysen, and Rudolf von Gneist, as well as by representatives of Berlin business, denounced the anti-Jewish movement as a "national disgrace" and called for "opposing the confusion" and calming "the artificially kindled passions of the mob."

The Prussian House of Representatives became the scene of excited debates. Virchow pointed out that the anti-Semitic agitation constantly shifted ground from religious to economic to racist arguments. He called it a fraud and charged the government, which found its support in the Conservative Party, with complicity with the anti-Semitic agitators. Eugen Richter, leader of the Progressive Party, declared: "They complain about the Jews' stock-market speculation, but forget that German princes and dukes have taken part in it. . . . People's banks are the best instruments for fighting usury, but at the head of the Berlin People's Bank is Strassmann, a Jew and municipal representative. They are incensed about the Jewish press, but admit that by that they mean the liberal press in general. The administration persecutes the Social Democrats, who oppose only the propertied classes, but protects the Social Christians, who preach hatred against a race. I know very well that the Chancellor has his head and his hand in this game. Bismarck's friends, Treitschke and Busch, are all too active in the anti-Semitic movement. . . . We introduce our interpolation in order to clarify this matter, for we desire the suppression of a reactionary movement that is disgracing our country. . . . Beware of arousing savage passions in the undisciplined masses. Do not awaken the beast in man, for then it will stop at nothing."

The Jews were alarmed and horrified. Here was the same sort of temper that had culminated in the general onslaught against the Jews in 1819. The Rühses and Frieses who had raised their voices against them at the beginning of the century had found worthy successors in Stoecker, Marr, and Treitschke. Berthold Auerbach, author of the famous *Village Tales of the Black Forest,* wrote in November, 1880: "To have lived and worked in vain! That is the overwhelming effect upon me of this two-day debate in the House of Representatives. And although I tell myself that perhaps it is not really so bad, the horrifying fact remains that such crudeness, such lying, and such hatred are still possible. . . . The awareness of what is still harbored within Germans, and what can unexpectedly burst forth, is ineradicable."

The German-Israelite Community Association issued a circular letter, which cautioned: "Although this new wave of artificially kindled and fanned religious and racial hatred arouses painful emotions in every thinking and feeling coreligionist, let it not embitter our hearts against our Christian fellow citizens or lessen our devotion to our civic duties. Let us learn in this time of tribulation to recognize, appreciate, and venerate the true friends and supporters of humanitarianism, and let it also lead us to meditation within ourselves." The organization appealed officially to Bismarck. It asked the Chancellor to use his "great moral weight" to "point out the way of justice and humanity to confused and misled public opinion." Bismarck did not bother to reply. The Berlin Jewish community several times appealed, likewise in vain, to the Prussian Minister of the Interior, Count Botho zu Eulenburg, who finally evaded the whole matter by answering that the government could interfere only if public criticism violated the law, which was not the case.

Ludwig Bamberger, a National Liberal deputy of the Reichstag, wrote: "If there were still many Jews in Germany who did not regard themselves as Germans, Treitschke's charges would only confirm them in their feeling of alienation. . . . In no other country does the polemic assume the base and spiteful tone that pervades it in Germany. . . . The attack on the Jews is only a side issue in the present grand campaign against liberalism, which is no doubt the reason why Herr von Treitschke has been attracted to the question. . . . With no other people have the Jews lived together so closely, I might say identified themselves, as they have with the Germans. They are Germanized not only on German soil, but far beyond the borders of Germany. . . . The European Jews have more bonds with the German language than with any other, and language is spirit. . . . If we consider the special hardships that have made life in Germany difficult for the Jews, and to some extent still do, and that nevertheless they have all through the centuries managed to sustain themselves in Germany, we cannot but suppose that common elements in their basic character must have made Germany and the German nature particularly attractive to the Jews, just as the Jews have been most useful in supplementing elements in the German character. . . . It would seem that equality under the law has penetrated intellectually in Germany, but not yet emotionally. . . ."

The band of hatemongers and agitators who urged German people to a crusade against the Jews continued to grow. In 1881 Karl Eugen Düh-ring, an eccentric philosopher and political economist, published *The Jewish Question as a Racial, Moral, and Cultural Question*. Its basic thesis was as follows: "The Jews are the . . . basest coinage of the entire Semitic race and have formed a nationality particularly dangerous to other peoples." They had given the world nothing, he asserted, but instead had stolen everything from other nations, and their goal was nothing but exploitation and world domination. "Therefore there can be only one policy toward them, that of restriction, suppression, and exclusion."

The Orientalist Paul de Lagarde, conservative politician and an early exponent of full-blown racism, demanded that Christianity be severed from the Old Testament, and that the Jews be expelled. "It takes a heart as hard as crocodile skin not to feel pity for the poor, fleeced Germans and . . . not to hate both the Jews and . . . those who out of 'humanity' act as spokesmen for these Jews or are too cowardly to trample this vermin underfoot. Negotiations are not conducted with trichinae and bacilli; trichinae and bacilli are not 'educated'; they are disposed of as quickly and completely as possible."

The shift in position had been accomplished. The medieval arguments had been abandoned, the Christian motivation had receded, for it no longer had any power over the masses. The new line of argument sought plausibility in a "modern" way; it was based on so-called economic reasons. The Jew, so went its tenor, had no capacity for participating in modern civilization; on the contrary, his "racial" characteristics constituted a threat to it. Therefore he must be segregated from the rest of the population or annihilated. This line left Jewry no alternative at all. Chaplain Stoecker had at least permitted one door to remain open: "The Israelites are an alien people and can become one with us if they convert to Christianity." But racist anti-Semitism shut even that door. Whereas the medieval Church had repressed the Jews in order to force them to accept baptism, anti-Semitism aimed at their total elimination.

As early as 1862 Moses Hess had foreseen this situation. He wrote, in *Rome and Jerusalem*: "Even baptism will not free them from the curse of German hatred. The Germans do not so much hate the religion of the Jews as their race. . . . It is not possible to be simultaneously philo-Teuton and Judaeophil, as it is impossible to love German military glory and German popular liberty."

The anti-Semites' petition was handed to Bismarck in 1881 with two hundred and sixty-seven thousand signatures, including four thousand of university students. The Chancellor did not respond to it. A self-respecting government at the end of the nineteenth century could not revoke the rights embedded in the Constitution. Instead, officialdom silently applied what Mommsen had once called the "administrative brake." Without baptism it was almost impossible for a Jew to become an officer in the army or to obtain an appointment to a professorship, let alone any high post in government. This remained the situation until the First World War. The many students of law and medicine could only enter private practice, and did so in great numbers.

The anti-Semites did not win their demands. But the poison they had dispensed so widely, the "socialism of the stupid," as August Bebel called anti-Semitism, continued to infect society. Hordes of hate pamphlets and pseudo-scientific works against Judaism were published. Anti-Semitic congresses were held, and the German Socialist Party—one of the forerunners of Nazism—was founded.

In 1887 Theodor Fritsch drew up his "Anti-Semites' Catechism," which was elaborated into the notorious *Handbook on the Jewish Question*. In 1891 an attempt to hold a ritual murder trial in Xanten on the Rhine failed, with the prosecuting attorney himself calling for acquittal. But in the Reichstag Chaplain Stoecker declared: "I cannot imagine that Jewish religious ritual requires the murder of human beings, the use of blood, for any purpose at all. But the dispute concerns more than words. No one who knows history will deny that, for centuries, Christians, especially children, were killed by the hand of Jews out of fanaticism or superstition."

In 1898 Houston Stewart Chamberlain (who ten years later became Richard Wagner's son-in-law) published his *Foundations of the Nineteenth Century,* in which the whole history of civilization was regarded solely as a struggle of "virtuous Aryans" against the "vicious Semites." This son of an English admiral who became a German by choice and wrote in German, joined the procession of those who would stamp out tolerance and freedom of conscience.

To Chamberlain, the Teutons alone were "the true shapers of the destinies of humanity . . . either as founders of states or conceivers of new ideas and creators of original art." Turning all historical facts upside down, he dared to serve up to his readers the most blatant lies, such as "that the Jew . . . is the teacher of all intolerance, all religious fanaticism, all killing for the sake of religion, that he has always appealed to tolerance only when he has felt oppressed, that he himself, however, has never practiced it or been allowed to practice it, for his law forbade him to and forbids him today as it will tomorrow."

These divagations "of a bloodthirsty dilettante," as Professor Erich Adicks rightly called him, should have aroused nothing but ridicule in an intelligent nation. Instead, the book became favorite reading among the half-educated, and made passionate converts. Ernst von Wolzogen was scarcely exaggerating when he commented on this product of Bayreuth intellectuals in the *Literarisches Echo*: "We need only recall that the Wagnerians' favorite words are 'illusion, need, hero, world,' and that their authorities, aside from the Master himself, are Schopenhauer, Carlyle, Count Gobineau, and perhaps also Lagarde. . . ."

Thus, by the end of the nineteenth century, the ideology of anti-Semitism was fully formed. All the slogans, arguments, and watchwords were ready, to lead, after 1933, to the greatest mass slaughter ever committed against a helpless minority.

The anti-Semitic movement had long since spread to Austria-Hungary also. In 1882 a great ritual murder trial was held on the medieval pattern. Fifteen Jews from the Hungarian town of Tiszaeszlar were held in prison on remand for a full year before the court was forced to recognize the total innocence of the defendants and to acquit them.

In 1875 August Rohling, professor of theology at Prague University, published *The Talmud Jew,* which did a great deal to intensify the anti-Semitic atmosphere. Although Theodor Nöldeke and Karl August Wünsche demonstrated that the author had distorted more than four hundred passages in his text by either misleading translations or misinterpretations, the slanderous book was published in huge editions. At the municipal elections in Vienna in 1895 the Pan-Germans, who represented a brand of racist anti-Semitism, won an overwhelming majority. Dr. Karl Lueger was elected mayor of Vienna. Emperor Franz Joseph, who detested anti-Semitism, refused to recognize the results of the election, but in spite of his opposition Lueger was repeatedly re-elected until the Emperor gave way. Lueger remained Mayor of Vienna for fourteen years, and the city itself turned more and more into a center of Jew-baiting where the Jews were constantly vilified as an inferior race, aliens in the body politic, and dangerous enemies of the people. The flood of hate pamphlets and pseudo-scientific anti-Jewish "literature" published in Austria in those days made heady reading for an Austrian named Hitler, who later—having become a German citizen by administrative trickery—succeeded in leading Germany to the lowest depths of barbarism to which a civilized nation has ever sunk.

Even France, the homeland of emancipation, was not immune to the contagion. Shortly before the end of the century, France was swept by a surge of anti-Semitism. The affair of Alfred Dreyfus brought the country to the brink of civil war.

In 1854 Count Joseph Arthur de Gobineau had published his *Essai sur l'inégalité des races humaines.* It set forth a racial theory to the effect that only "Aryans," and especially Germans, could be considered culturally creative. Gobineau's arguments, though scientifically worthless, even then won a wide hearing. Three decades later anti-Semitism suddenly began to gain ground in France. In 1882 the Catholic bank Union

Générale, to which many members of the aristocracy had entrusted their money, went bankrupt. Blame was quickly assigned: The rascals were, of course, the Jews. The anti-Semitic doctrine spreading in Berlin and Vienna had just begun to reach Paris. In 1883 Ernest Renan, Orientalist and expert on comparative religions, vigorously denounced the anti-Semitic racial theory. But the forces of reaction were stronger. In 1886 Edouard Drumont published his *La France juive,* which soon became one of the most widely read books in France. The author's thesis was that every misfortune France had ever suffered was due to the machinations of the Jews. In 1892 Drumont began editing the daily newspaper *Libre Parole,* which featured constant attacks on the Jews. Thus the ground was prepared for an event that would clinch the case against them. When a Jewish officer fell under suspicion of espionage, French anti-Semites and the clerical-royalist party instantly closed in.

In 1894 Artillery Captain Alfred Dreyfus, an employee of the French General Staff, was accused of having betrayed military secrets to the German government. The similarity of his handwriting to that of a letter filched from the German embassy was the sole basis for the charge. Only three of five handwriting experts affirmed the identity of the handwritings. Nevertheless Dreyfus was found guilty by a military tribunal, publicly degraded, and sentenced to life imprisonment on Devil's Island. The outcome of the trial, which had been accompanied by a savage anti-Semitic campaign in the press, in the streets, and in the Chamber of Deputies, unleashed a wave of anti-Jewish feeling throughout the country.

But Dreyfus was innocent. A Major Esterhazy, not Dreyfus, had committed treason, and this was soon demonstrated. However, there was enormous resistance to a new trial. The military authorities refused to compromise the army for the sake of a Jew. But there were Frenchmen willing to fight for the rehabilitation of Captain Dreyfus. Emile Zola wrote his famous open letter to the President of the Republic, *"J'Accuse."* A controversy began that split France into two camps: the Dreyfusards, battling for justice and humanity, and the reactionary, anti-Semitic anti-Dreyfusards.

In 1900 Dreyfus was granted amnesty. Another six years passed before he was finally rehabilitated and named a chevalier of the Legion of Honor. But the long and bitter contest had had a purifying and clarifying effect on the country. In the words of Ernst von Schenk: "France had overcome anti-Semitism as a political temptation and had found her way to an attitude toward Judaism that was to make her a bulwark against racist barbarism."

THEODOR HERZL AND THE BASEL
ZIONIST CONGRESS

Shortly before 1900 there emerged from the ranks of the many thousands of assimilated Jews the man who fathered the political movement known as Zionism: Theodor Herzl.

He was born in Budapest in 1860; later his family moved to Vienna. There the young Herzl studied law, engaged in literary activity, and joined a student fraternity. In these respects his course differed little from that of many of his coreligionists. Yet he was blessed with more than usual charm. The playwright Hermann Bahr recalls: "When I came to Vienna University . . . Theodor Herzl was the pride and glory of the fraternity. . . . I still distinctly recall the effect he had on us all. His tall figure, his mockingly superior mind, and the chivalry of his manner were irresistible. We freshmen were therefore no little surprised to learn that he had been stricken from our midst by the unanimous decision of the fraternity convention. What had happened? The fraternity, in order not to lag behind fashion, had decided henceforth no longer to take in Jews, and to bar Herzl. . . .

"Herzl, however, did not permit this experience of his student days to warp his life. He soon became a staff writer on the *Neue Freie Presse,* at that time an enormously powerful newspaper, not only in Vienna, but also far beyond the borders of Austria. Herzl was its Paris correspondent, a much-envied position, for Vienna was constantly flirting with Paris. In the French capital Herzl was present as an eyewitness at the degradation of Dreyfus; at this time no one, including Herzl, doubted the Captain's guilt. He was struck only by the cruelty with which the act was performed: the way an officer broke the traitor's sword and the way a sergeant, a corporal, and finally the enlisted men successively tore off the insignia of his former honors and threw them at his feet. Herzl, who at the time regarded this procedure as well-merited punishment for treason, wondered to himself at the obvious pleasure the participants took in it, as if the degradation were a gala occasion. When the spectacle was over and Herzl was walking away with other journalists, he asked one of them: 'Why are these people all so happy about it? The traitor deserved his fate, he has received justice; but how can people rejoice when a human being suffers, even if he suffers justly? He is a traitor, but a traitor remains human.' His Viennese colleague said: 'No, that is not how the

French feel about it. They do not see him as a human being, but only as a Jew. And where the Jew begins, Christian pity ends. That is unjust, but we shall not change it; it has always been so and always will be so.' At that moment Zionism was born."

The experience affected Herzl as a profound shock. He wrote to his friend Arthur Schnitzler that a "basalt mountain" had grown up inside him. And in his diary for 1895 he noted: "For some time I have been engaged on a work of infinite grandeur. I do not know whether I shall carry it out. It looks like a mighty dream, but for days and weeks it has been filling my mind down to my unconsciousness, accompanying me everywhere, hovering above my ordinary conversations, looking over my shoulder at my ridiculously petty journalistic work, disturbing me and in-toxicating me. I cannot yet guess what will come of it. Only my experience tells me that it is remarkable, even as a dream, and that I ought to write it down—if not as a memorial for mankind, at least for my own later . . . thinking. And perhaps between these two possibilities: for litera-ture. If the romance does not become an act, perhaps the act can be-come a romance. Title: The Promised Land." And on June 16, 1895, he noted: "During the past days I have often feared I was going mad. Trains of thought whirl shatteringly through my soul. A whole life will not suf-fice to carry out all my plans. But I shall leave an intellectual legacy. To whom? To all men. I think that life for me has ceased and world history begun."

Theodor Herzl labored feverishly. Six months later his plan had as-sumed some concrete form. He communicated it to the influential phi-lanthropist Baron Moritz Hirsch—but did not arouse the response he had hoped for. In February, 1896, Herzl published his pamphlet *The Jewish State,* and accompanied it with an essay in the London magazine *Jewish Chronicle.* He wrote:

"There are two striking phenomena in our time: high civilization and low barbarism. By high civilization I mean the remarkable achievements of technology that have enabled us to conquer Nature; by low barbarism I mean anti-Semitism. . . . Everywhere, we Jews have honestly tried to assimilate into the nations around us, preserving only the religion of our fathers. We have not been permitted to. In vain we have been loyal and in some places fierce patriots; in vain we make the same sacrifices of lives and property as our fellow citizens; in vain we endeavor to add to our countries' glory in the arts and sciences, to increase their wealth by trade and traffic. In our countries, in which we have already dwelt for centuries, we are decried as foreigners. . . . Everywhere, then, we are good patriots in vain, just as were the Huguenots who were forced to emigrate. If we were unmolested . . . But I do not think we will be unmolested.

"We are a nation—the enemy has made us one without our desiring it, as has always happened in history. In oppression we stand together, and so we suddenly discover our strength. For we do have the strength to create a state, and, moreover, a model state. We have all the means that are necessary for this task. . . ."

Herzl's plan struck many of his coreligionists as the wildest of fantasies. He was laughed at, regarded as a utopian. The executive committee of the rabbis' association in Germany issued an official warning: "Religion and patriotism equally bid us to enjoin all those who have the welfare of Jewry at heart to abstain from Zionistic ambitions and especially from the planned congress." The Congress, which had been scheduled for the summer of 1897 in Munich, came to nothing because of the opposition of the Jewish community there.

Yet the Zionist Congress met, in Basel, on August 29. Two hundred delegates and three hundred guests and journalists attended. In his opening speech Herzl outlined the key elements in his political program. Zionism itself was to be the "homecoming of Jewry," even as it prepared the way for the "return to the Land of the Jews." "The object of Zionism is to establish for the Jewish people a publicly and legally assured home in Palestine," the Basel program declared.

Herzl's friend and partisan, Max Nordau, physician and writer, made a stirring appeal to the delegates, who, as Europeans, may have been sanguine about the progress of recent years. In a moving report he drew up the balance sheet of the nineteenth century: "Everywhere that Jews . . . settle in sizable numbers among the nations, there is distress among them. . . . That distress assumes two forms, one objective and one moral. In Eastern Europe, in North Africa, in Western Asia, especially in the areas inhabited by the great majority, probably nine tenths of all Jews, distress must be taken quite literally. It is a daily physical tribulation. . . . In Russia . . . the home of more than half of all Jews, our brothers are subject to a variety of legal restrictions. . . . They are forbidden to reside in a large part of the country. . . . From Rumania, with its quarter of a million Jews, we hear that our brothers there are likewise without rights. . . . The conditions our correspondent in Galicia reveals to us are frightful. . . . It is significant of the conditions in western Austria, with its approximately four hundred thousand Jews, that in Vienna fifteen thousand out of twenty-five thousand Jewish households cannot pay the synagogue tax because of their poverty. . . . From Bulgaria the same lament is heard; a hypocritical law holds that there is to be no discrimination because of religion, but the authorities simply ignore it. . . . In Hungary the Jews do not complain. They are in full possession of all civil rights. . . . But the hundred and fifty thousand Jews of Morocco, the Jews of Persia . . . do not even have the strength to rebel against their misery. . . . The countries I have cited determine the destinies of far more than seven million Jews. . . .

"The Jews of Western Europe are not subject to any legal restrictions. . . . But among them the other kind of Jewish distress is increasing—the moral kind. . . . I must say the painful words: The nations that have emancipated the Jews have succumbed to illusions about their feelings. In order for emancipation to exert its full effect, it would have had to be completed in the hearts of people before it was set forth in the law. But that was not the case. . . . The emancipation of the Jews has not come about from the realization that grave crimes have been committed against this race, that terrible injuries have been inflicted upon it, and that it is time to atone for millennial injustices; it has come about solely as the consequence of . . . French rationalism of the eighteenth century. . . . Thus the equality of the Jews was proclaimed in France . . . because logic demanded it. . . .

"The rest of Western Europe imitated the example of France . . . because civilized nations felt morally obliged to appropriate the accomplishments of the great upheaval. . . . The emancipation of the Jews was thus one more of those indispensable pieces of furniture in a civilized political household, something like the piano that must have its place in the parlor even if no member of the family can play it. . . . These words do not apply to one country alone. . . . In England the emancipation of the Jews is a truth. It is not merely written there; it is lived. . . .

"The Jew, in a kind of intoxication, hastened to burn all the bridges behind him. He now had another homeland, no longer needed the ghetto. He . . . adjusted at once and completely to the new conditions of his life. . . . He was now permitted to believe that he was nothing but a German, Frenchman, Italian, et cetera. . . . Then, after a slumber of from thirty to sixty years . . . anti-Semitism burst forth again in Western Europe . . . and revealed before the eyes of the horrified Jew his real situation, which he had not seen before. . . . He had been given the right to meet all the duties of a citizen, but the rights that go beyond the universal franchise, the nobler rights that are conceded to talent and competence—these rights were gruffly refused him.

"That is the present situation of the emancipated Jew in Western Europe. He has surrendered his Jewish peculiarity. . . . He has lost the home that the ghetto was, but the land of his birth refuses to be his native land. He has no soil under his feet, and he has no attachment to a whole into which he can fit as a welcome, equal member. Among his Christian fellow countrymen he can count on neither justice nor benevolence, because of his character or his achievements; and he has lost the connection with his Jewish fellow countrymen. . . . That is the moral distress of the Jews, which is more bitter than the physical distress. . . .

"The picture would not be complete if I failed to add another element. A legend in which even serious and cultivated persons believe, without their necessarily being anti-Semites, holds that the Jews have all the power and dominion, that the Jews own all the riches of the earth. . . . Certainly there are several hundred excessively rich Jews whose noisy millions draw a great deal of attention. But what has Israel in common with these people? . . . In a normal . . . Jewish society these persons . . . would assume the very lowest level in the respect of the community and at any rate never receive the titles of nobility and high decorations with which Christian society distinguishes them. The Judaism of the Prophets and tannaim, the Judaism of Hillel, Philo, Ibn Gabirol, Judah Halevi, Ben Maimon, Spinoza, and Heine, knows nothing of these moneybags. . . . These people are the chief pretext for the new hatred of the Jews, which has economics rather than religion as its basis. . . .

"The distress of the Jews cannot be a matter of indifference to anyone, no more to the Christian nations than to the Jews. It is a great sin to let a race whose talents not even its worst enemies have denied sink in intellectual and physical distress. . . ."

Herzl was elected chairman of the action committee. Until his death in 1904 he continued to strive for the realization of his great plan. He had two meetings with Kaiser Wilhelm II—once in Constantinople, then in Jerusalem itself—to ask him to use his influence with the Turkish Sultan for the furtherance of the plan. The Kaiser showed considerable enthusiasm. Jews friendly to Germany in Turkish territory could only be useful to him, he thought. He also saw an opportunity, as Chancellor Bernhard von Bülow wrote later, "to free his country of many elements he did not like." Bülow, who foresaw English and French protests, dissuaded Wilhelm, and nothing much came of the interviews beyond a meaningless official statement. In 1901 Herzl obtained an audience with Sultan Abdul-Hamid II himself. Meanwhile Jews had begun buying land in Palestine. Jewish immigrants, from Russia especially, embarked on the pioneering task of making wasteland fruitful again. They labored under almost inconceivable difficulties. In 1903 Herzl spent some time in St. Petersburg negotiating with Minister of the Interior Vyacheslav Pleve. That same year Joseph Chamberlain, England's Colonial Minister, made concrete offers to Herzl, including settlement rights in British East Africa. This Uganda project encountered strong resistance within the Zionist movement, however, and was rejected. The majority of the Zionists favored Palestine as the sole goal. When Herzl, only forty-four years old, died in 1904, a great movement had already emerged from his utopian vision. It had sprung up out of nothing within a few years. The aim that Herzl and his fellows had set themselves was ultimately to lead, though through many detours, to the State of Israel.

POGROMS IN RUSSIA

In Western Europe a new life had truly begun for the Jews with their emancipation—despite all setbacks. But the tempests of freedom that had torn down the gates of the ghetto in the countries west of the Vistula had not penetrated into the East. The pressure of medieval conditions, the weight of harsh restrictions and utter hopelessness, persisted throughout the realm that in 1795, after the third partition of Poland, had become the home of the overwhelmingly largest number of Jews. The news from the land of the Czars remained discouraging.

Since the days of Catherine II the policy had been to shut the Jewish masses into the interior of the empire. Strict ordinances limited them to territories in the southern and western governments; they were banned from the rest of the Russian Empire. Only a few privileged Jews were permitted to travel freely. Squeezed by special ukase into Pales—regions in which they were compelled to live—and deprived of all freedom of movement, hundreds upon hundreds of thousands of Jews lived on the edge of destitution, in inconceivable poverty. Even the districts assigned to them shrank steadily in the course of time; new ukases expelled them from the villages and packed them more and more into cities and towns. The autocratic rulers made every effort to force their Jewish subjects into "improvement," by which was meant conversion. The object was, again, complete assimilation.

Under Czar Nicholas I (who ruled from 1825 to 1855) the reactionary policy reached frightening proportions. As Cecil Roth has pointed out, the treatment meted out to the Jews had no parallel in history, its severity surpassing even that of the legislation of the Catholic Church at the time of the Counter Reformation. No less than twelve hundred legal provisions bearing on the Jews were promulgated between 1649 and 1881 in Russia, and of these no less than half came in the reign of Nicholas I.

The harassment was directed even against Jewish children. On August 26, 1827, the Czar signed a ukase providing that Jews as well as other Russian men be eligible for twenty-five years of military service. But a special statute decreed: "The recruits to be provided by the Jewish communities must be between the ages of twelve and twenty-five." Moreover, "Jewish minors, that is, those below eighteen years of age, are to be sent to special training institutions for military service." This training, which began at the age of twelve, was considered merely preparatory. It was not included in the period of twenty-five years of service, which began at eighteen. Thus Jews were subject to thirty-one years of military service.

The government mercilessly saw to it that the inhuman provisions of the ukase were fully enforced. As soon as a levying party approached, therefore, there were scenes of utter desperation among the Jews. Whole hordes of adolescents took flight; they hid in woods, wandered about the fields. A veritable hunt for the children began. Even younger boys, in some cases no older than eight, were seized by the recruiters. In the middle of the night raiding parties would descend on Jewish families; the boys would be snatched from their mothers and taken away. The draftees were dispatched to garrisons far from the Jewish Pales; many of them never saw their parents again.

Aleksandr Herzen, the Russian revolutionary, observed the dispatch of a band of Jewish draftees in 1835, when he was on his way to the Urals.

" 'You see,' the officer who was with me explained, 'a whole mob of the damnable Jewish brats, eight to ten years old, were picked up, and the order was first given to drive them to Perm, but then came a new order and now we're driving them to Kazan. . . . The officer who handed them over to me said it was an awful misery; a third of them broke down on the way. No more than half will reach the destination.' . . . Soon the little fellows were fetched and lined up in rank and file. It was one of the most piteous sights I have ever beheld. Poor, poor children. The twelve- and thirteen-year-old boys could still manage somehow to stay on their feet. But the children of eight and ten . . . pale, emaciated, terrified, stood in their heavy, ill-fitting military coats with stiff collars and looked up with helpless eyes, pleading for mercy, at the garrison soldiers who roughly straightened out their lines. Their lips were bloodless and the blue circles under their eyes spoke of fever and chills. So the poor children, deprived of all love and care . . . trudged toward the grave. I gripped the officer's hand and said to him, 'Have mercy on them!' and leaped into the carriage—a moment longer and I would not have been able to check my tears."

A new era seemed to be dawning for the Jews with the accession of Alexander II (Czar from 1855 to 1881). The young Czar, whom Disraeli once called the "kindliest prince who has ever ruled in Russia," instituted a consistent policy of reform. He abolished serfdom and began efforts to industrialize the country and to follow the example of the Western nations in other matters. Forty million serfs were emancipated. The special laws regarding military service were revoked, thus ending the plight of the Jewish child recruits. The period of military service was reduced to five years. The gates of institutions of higher learning opened to the Jews; they could attend universities, were admitted to the legal profession, and could even hold office as judges. All of Russia was thrown open to Jewish craftsmen and prosperous businessmen. Their connections with the banks of Western Europe prompted the Czar to turn to influential Jews for help with the economic reconstruction of his empire. "It was to the Jews that he entrusted the building of Russia's banking system," writes Max A. Dimont. "Samuel Poliakov, known as Russia's 'railroad king,' linked Russia's East and West with arteries of iron, for which he was knighted. Banking, architecture, medicine, industry became the occupations of Jews in Russia."

Thus Russia, too, was for the first time offering new opportunities to the Jews. But the number of those who knew how to avail themselves of them remained small; it amounted to scarcely more than five per cent of the Jewish population. The overwhelming majority, more than three million souls, continued to live in the Pales. And any hope that they, too, would be able to improve their condition in the foreseeable future was soon dashed. A reaction ensued, a time of renewed persecutions and misery more terrible than ever before.

On March 13, 1881, a bomb put an abrupt end to the life of Alexander II, the "Emancipator." Under his successor, Alexander III, the pendulum swung to the other extreme. A few weeks after the Czar's assassination the hounds of hell seemed to have been let loose. A wave of pogroms—the Russian word for "devastation"—poured over the unfortunate Russian Jews. "There can be no doubt," concludes the historian Simon Dubnow, who lived for many years in St. Petersburg, "that they were instigated from some central headquarters, for they broke out almost simultaneously at different places in southern Russia, and followed the same pattern everywhere, both in regard to the crimes of the mobs and the inaction of the police."

The fifteen thousand Jews in Elisavetgrad, in the government of Kherson, were among the first victims of the violence. The report of an official investigating commission describes the events: "On April 16 the tumults began anew at seven o'clock in the morning and spread with unusual rapidity throughout the entire city. Storekeepers, tavern servants, artisans, coachmen, household servants, adjutants, artillerymen—all joined the movement. The city looked strange indeed: the streets covered with eiderdown and smashed furniture, the doors and windows of houses broken in, a maddened mob pouring in all directions, screaming and yowling, continuing its work of annihilation without let or hindrance. . . . The troops dispatched to restore order had not been given definite instructions, so that they stood helplessly by, awaiting orders from their superiors or the police, as the mob stormed a still undamaged house. . . . Toward evening the riots grew worse, since the city in the meanwhile had been flooded with peasants from the vicinity who were bent on seizing Jewish property. The troops and police units . . . offered not the slightest opposition to these bands of pillagers."

The troops finally put an end to the frenzy of the mobs next day. In the meantime the Jews had suffered frightfully. Many had been killed, women had been raped, hundreds of houses and stores and many synagogues had been demolished. Property to the value of more than two million rubles had been stolen or destroyed.

That was only the beginning. More pogroms flared in other places: on April 26 in Kiev; shortly afterward in nearly fifty villages and market towns in the governments of Kiev, Volhynia, and Podolia; in the early part of March in Odessa, the metropolis of southern Russia; in the beginning of July in and around Pereyaslav in the government of Poltava. In the wide plains of the Ukraine from Kiev to the Crimea the dread cry of "Death to the Jews!" rang out. Some one hundred and sixty places in southern Russia were struck by sudden acts of violence. In December, 1881, persecutions began in Warsaw; fifteen hundred Jewish dwellings, stores, and synagogues were destroyed, with damage running into millions of rubles.

News of these frightful events shocked the Western world. In England there were vehement public protests. The *Times* ran a series of articles describing the horrors of the pogroms. At a public meeting in the Mansion House, the official residence of the Lord Mayor of London, Lord Shaftesbury declared that an appeal must be addressed to the Czar, admonishing him to play the part of a Cyrus for the Jews in Russia, not that of an Antiochus Epiphanes. Before the House of Commons, Prime Minister Gladstone expressed the regret and repugnance with which Her Majesty's government viewed the events in Russia. In St. Petersburg the American Ambassador protested to the Russian government in the name of the United States. A protest meeting in New York condemned the "medieval persecutions."

In Russia the pogroms sowed panic among the Jewish population. To the terrified people the only course seemed to be flight. Emigration committees formed with unprecedented speed and set to work. But thousands upon thousands of Jews were too frightened to await the formalities of emigration. They left everything behind them, and a vast flood of refugees began to pour toward the frontiers of Russia. Soon hordes of the hapless were backed up like water at a dam before the customs stations of Western countries. The ports St. Petersburg, in the north, and Odessa, on the Black Sea, swarmed with would-be emigrants.

An exodus had begun that surpassed anything in all previous Jewish history, even the expulsions from Spain and Portugal. When no improvements in Russian conditions developed in the course of the following years, when restrictions, persecutions, and expulsions only continued and increased—in 1891 thousands of Jews were deported from Moscow and other cities; in 1898 seven thousand were driven from the government of Kiev —the numbers of those striving to escape Russia steadily increased. For more than thirty-three years the departure of Jewish families from Russia continued without cessation. Even before the century ended, nearly a million Jews had left their former home in Eastern Europe.

All of Europe beheld the grievous consequences. The hordes of starving, impoverished victims turned up in all the capitals of the West. They were seen from Stockholm to Lisbon, in Paris and London, in Berlin and Vienna. In Germany and Austria they were given an unfriendly reception. These two countries in the heart of Europe, where anti-Semitic propaganda had done its work, remained coldly indifferent. Neither the accounts of the pogroms published in the newspapers nor the sight of the pitiable refugees brought about any change of heart. Instead of an impulse to help, there was rejection; voices were raised calling for a stop to any further immigration from the East. The commandments of charity were forgotten, even among the clergy.

The overwhelming majority of the refugees found new homes in other countries. Many went overseas from Dutch, Belgian, or Portuguese ports to Australia, New Zealand, South Africa, South America, and, above all, to Canada. A much larger group sought asylum in England. In London's East End alone immigration rapidly increased the number of Jewish inhabitants from forty-seven thousand to one hundred and fifty thousand. The new arrivals for the most part went into tailoring and dressmaking. In London, Leeds, and Manchester they introduced modern methods of large-scale manufacturing.

One country, however, took in more immigrants than any other. The principal stream of refugees poured into the United States of America.

U.S.A.: THE GREAT DIASPORA

As the first waves of refugees arrived by the shipload at the docks in Manhattan, more than two centuries had passed since those September days in 1654 when the first twenty-three Jews, after a long and perilous voyage from Brazil, set foot on the rocky island. In 1654 the modest Dutch settlement of New Amsterdam had occupied a small area at the southern end of the island. Now the island was completely covered by the vast metropolis of New York, with its endless avenues and streets, its sea of houses. Violent and incredibly rapid development had changed the city and the entire continent beyond it. From the shores of the Atlantic over the vast plains of the interior to the coasts of the Pacific Ocean, the most modern and free industrial country in the world had come into being.

As the new country grew, so did its complement of Jewish immigrants. Many had turned their faces hopefully toward the land that was the first in the world to give full freedom to its citizens. The New World had, as we have seen, been closely linked with Jewry from the time of its discovery, and Jewish immigrants participated side by side with Christians in the history and the building of the United States, in both war and peace.

A decade after the first landing of Jewish immigrants, Manhattan changed owners. New Amsterdam, conquered by the English in 1664, was rebaptized New York. The Jews became British. The Puritans who had emigrated from England proclaimed good-neighborly feelings toward the "children of Israel"; they had no prejudices toward Jews. Rooted as they were in the spirit of the Old Testament, they were fond of comparing their own flight to America with the exodus of the Jews from the land of the Pharaohs, and they regarded their own first settlement in Massachusetts Bay as a New Jerusalem. When Harvard University was founded in 1636, Hebrew was introduced into the course of studies on an equal basis with Latin and Greek. "In fact, there was even a proposal," Max A. Dimont has remarked, "that Hebrew be made the official language of the Colonies, and John Cotton once wanted to adopt the Mosaic Code as the basis for the laws of Massachusetts." Desultorily, without planning, Jewish settlements sprang up on the soil of the new colonies. The first Jewish settlers in Virginia in 1621 were followed by a number in Massachusetts in 1649 and in Maryland in 1658. In 1660 a new community began to flourish in Newport, Rhode Island. By 1733, when they also established a foothold in Georgia, there were Jews in all thirteen colonies. For the most part they dealt in the export of tobacco, sugar, and grain. The wholesale trade with Europe was organized from Newport by Aaron Lopez, of whom it has been said that "probably no merchant in America surpassed him in prestige and the extent of his enterprises." Among the Jews were both shipowners and slave traders, for the slave trade was taken for granted in those days. A Jew from Portugal was the first to introduce the manufacture of wax, indispensable to the making of candles, into America.

When the War of Independence broke out, there were Jews in both camps. Although they numbered only about two thousand, they volunteered, rose to positions of command, and helped to supply the armies. The supporters of the Revolution participated in the boycott of English goods; the most vigorous fought for the cause of the patriots. Among the latter were Francis Salvador, who "scalped the redskins," Major Benjamin Nunes, who served under Lafayette, and Jacob Franks, Benedict Arnold's adjutant. Haym Solomon has frequently been called the "banker of the Revolution"; it is said that he provided the Continental Congress with three hundred thousand dollars for the equipping of the army. Two sons of the distinguished Franks family fought in the Revolutionary army; the third remained loyal to England, as did the Hart and Pollock families of Newport.

The Declaration of Independence, with its opening statement "that all men are created equal, that they are endowed by their Creator with certain inalienable rights," had a special meaning for Jews. And the Constitution, in its Bill of Rights, embodied as a supreme principle freedom of conscience and of religion: "Congress shall make no law respecting an establishment of religion, or prohibiting the free exercise thereof." In the New World Jewry was granted what Christian Europe had withheld for more than a thousand years.

Originally, Spanish and Portuguese marranos had formed the majority of the immigrant Jews. But after 1700 more and more Ashkenazim entered the country; by 1750 they were already the majority. After the Congress of Vienna the stream of immigrants began to swell; they arrived in greater and greater numbers from Central Europe, especially from southern Germany. From ten thousand in 1820 the number of Jews living in the United States increased to a quarter of a million by 1880.

In 1825 an attempt was made to establish a Jewish state on American soil. Mordecai Manuel Noah, a newspaper editor, bought land on Grand Island in the Niagara River, planning to create the city of Ararat as a haven for Jewish refugees. But despite his efforts, the project failed.

During this period few of the immigrants to the land of liberty stayed in New York. They moved on to the South and West—to Louisville and New Orleans, Cincinnati and Cleveland, Chicago and St. Louis. Along with the adventurers and pioneers attracted to California by the gold fever in 1849, Jewish immigrants also reached the Pacific Coast. They were among the first settlers in San Francisco. Soon there were small Jewish groups in almost all cities.

When the Civil War broke out in 1861, ten thousand Jews hastened to the colors. They fought as professional soldiers and as volunteers in the armies of both North and South.

After 1871 the flood of emigration from Germany and Austria almost entirely ceased—a consequence of the emancipation that was at last firmly guaranteed by law. But the stream of immigrants continued as, year after year, from the time the Civil War ended, vessels brought Polish and Russian Jews. After 1881 the influx increased enormously; following outbreaks of Russian pogroms during the four succeeding decades, there began a vast migration of Eastern European Jews that swelled the Jewish population in the United States to an unprecedented total. Not too long after, another stream of immigrants began—of German Jews fleeing the brown terror after 1933. Some two hundred thousand were received into the United States in the nineteen-thirties and forties.

The majority of the Eastern European refugees who had arrived at the turn of the century concentrated in New York. The East Side of Manhattan, where they settled by the tens of thousands, was transformed within a few years into a bastion of Jewish life and culture. The language was Yiddish; newspapers and magazines appeared in that language; the Yiddish theater became famous. The second-largest settlement after New York grew up in Chicago. Large Jewish communities also formed in Boston, Baltimore, Cleveland, and Philadelphia. In Canada, Toronto and Montreal became sizable centers of Jewry.

Before many years had passed in the United States, an amazing change took place. The appearance, character, and manner of the immigrants were transformed with astonishing rapidity. They no longer looked like the people who had set foot on Ellis Island—wasted, worn, hungry, with fear in their eyes. No attentive observer could fail to notice "how the miserably poor, oppressed, intimidated inhabitant of the notorious Pale, the nebbich Jew, over whose head the Damoclean sword of brutal violence always hovered and who trembled like an aspen leaf before any policeman who came his way . . . changed under the impact of independence into a free, erect American Jew who does not stand for insults and who has become a citizen in the full sense of the word."

When the Spanish-American War broke out, many American Jews volunteered for service. They constituted the majority of the members of the volunteer regiment from New York, and in Philadelphia they formed a Jewish legion. Four centuries after 1492—the year of the expulsion of the Jews from Spain and the year that Luis de Torres set foot on the soil of the West Indies—historical destiny found the Jews fighting on the side of the power that finally expelled Spain from the New World.

Until the eighties the immigrants, chiefly German Jews, went into retail trade. "The peddler's tray became the drygoods store," writes Max A. Dimont, "and the drygoods store expanded into the department store. Most of modern America's giant department stores are outgrowths of these early Jewish peddlers' work and ingenuity." Millions of dollars from the Jewish fortunes created in those early days ultimately benefited the general public. "Families like the Guggenheims, the Warburgs, the Strauses, the Schiffs, the Rosenwalds have become bywords in American philanthropic and cultural enterprises." When the immigrants from Eastern Europe began arriving, Jews were suddenly present in almost all occupations. Eastern Jews worked as farmers, factory hands, craftsmen; they were quick to take any employment that was offered. Polish, Russian, and Rumanian peasants went into the steel foundries of Pittsburgh and into the automobile factories of Detroit. A sizable number turned to textiles, and by clever division of labor—the so-called Boston System—developed an important industry. The union founded by Jewish workmen, the Amalgamated Clothing Workers of America, grew to almost two hundred thousand members. The women in the industry formed the International Ladies Garment Workers Union. The children of these immigrants increasingly turned to intellectual and artistic professions. Out of the new generation emerged a growing number of Jewish lawyers and doctors, journalists and writers, painters, sculptors, and musicians.

For more than a century America provided an asylum from oppression and misery to the Jewish refugees from the reactionary and intolerant countries of Europe—as she did to countless other emigrants. She gave them and their descendants a new life. Within two generations the mass exodus from the Old World created in the United States the largest and most important Diaspora in Jewish history. And never before had the descendants of the People of the Book found a home in so free, progressive, and powerful a world power.

VI THE CATASTROPHE

The first month of 1933 marked the beginning of that course which was to lead Germany to deepest debasement and stain her name with the most monstrous crime in the history of the human race. On January 30 of that year Hitler became Chancellor of the Reich. For fourteen years Germany had attempted to live by the rules of a democratic system; now she publicly repudiated the principles of morality, justice, and religion. The German nationalists Alfred Hugenberg and Franz von Papen had helped install the brown-shirted demagogue in the seat of power. More quickly than they could ever have imagined, the government formed by Hitler turned into the Nazi dictatorship. The clique of Nazi leaders were all prepared to carry out the aims that had long been stated in their Party program: the elimination of all Jewish influence from politics, culture, and the economy, and "ejection" of the Jews from the state. The "Aryan spirit" was no longer to be imperiled by the "ferment of decomposition"—as Mommsen had once formulated it. An intensive campaign of incitements and lies was set in motion in the press and on radio; the pseudo-scientific "race theory" was introduced into all schools as a required subject, and was taught in all universities. The Nazis concentrated on the youth, raising them to regard the principles of anti-Semitism as the rock on which the future greatness of Germany would be founded.

The new rulers proceeded step by step, cautiously at first, on the assumption that if they acted too hastily, without sufficient psychological preparation, they could encounter resistance, either from the middle class, the army, or the Church. But these anxieties appeared to be unfounded, as was to become evident within a few months after the seizure of power. For when on April 1, 1933, the SA, the fighting storm troopers of the "struggle for power" period, staged a boycott against Jewish businessmen in all the cities of Germany, no protests were heard. A few days after this first test, on April 7, 1933, the "Law for the Restoration of a Professional Civil Service" passed the Reichstag with the acclamations of the nationalists. It provided for compulsory retirement of all civil servants of "non-Aryan descent." A long succession of harsh anti-Jewish laws followed. Two years later, on September 15, 1935, Hitler promulgated the Nuremberg Laws in the city that had been noted even in the Middle Ages as a breeding ground of anti-Jewish feelings. Included in these were the "Reich Citizenry Law" and the "Law for the Protection of German Blood and German Honor." They officially reduced the German Jews to second-class citizens. Marriages and extramarital sexual relations between "Aryans" and Jews were forbidden. Jews lost the franchise, could neither vote nor hold public office.

The struggle for full emancipation of the German Jews had lasted for some sixty years. Three years of the Hitler regime sufficed to wipe out all their gains. More than half a million persons were stripped of their rights at one blow. The worst affected were those Jews in intellectual and scientific professions. University professors, among them scholars of world repute, doctors, lawyers, architects, novelists, and journalists found the whole basis of their lives taken away.

But cultured Germany remained silent. The middle class displayed no signs of outrage; the university professors raised no storm of protest when their Jewish colleagues were driven from their teaching posts overnight. Nowhere was there open protest against the violation of justice, against measures that were a disgrace to a civilized nation.

The result was a new exodus. Intellectual, cultural, and scientific Germany suffered a bloodletting from which it has not recovered to this day. Soon afterward there was scarcely a country in the world at whose gates refugee German Jews had not knocked, seeking asylum. By the end of 1937 one hundred and eighteen thousand Jews had left the country in which their ancestors had lived for centuries. Some forty-seven thousand went to Palestine, fifteen thousand to the United States, twenty-one thousand to South America, and four thousand to South Africa. The rest found refuge in European countries—France, England, Belgium, the Netherlands, Czechoslovakia, Austria, Italy, and the Scandinavian countries.

During those years the outside world, too, seemed not to have realized the nature of the new regime. For in 1936 the world came to Berlin for the Olympic Games organized by the National Socialist government. Some two years later the Nazi government celebrated a whole succession of successes and "victories" that blatantly flouted international law. Initially, the world public might have told itself that the repressions, persecutions, and anti-Jewish laws in Nazi Germany constituted an "internal" affair. But the events of 1938 could hardly be interpreted this way. For now Nazi rule burst the bounds of the old Reich. Hitler sent his troops on sudden onslaughts against country after country. Terrorism and repression followed on the heels of invasion or annexation. After the Anschluss on March 13, 1938, Austria's nearly two hundred thousand Jews, of whom the greater number lived in the highly cultivated Jewish community of Vienna, found themselves overnight within the power of the Nazi government, and soon felt the brutality of the conquerors. All the German anti-Jewish measures went into force immediately, along with the Nuremberg Laws. A wave of terror was unleashed. Jewish stores were pillaged and confiscated, and synagogues turned into Nazi Party offices; mass arrests began. Prominent Jews, among them the head of the Rothschild family, were beaten and carried off to concentration camps, from which very few ever returned alive.

New streams of refugees began to move, the majority toward the east, into countries that were markedly inhospitable to the harried people. Rumania had from the start disregarded her laws concerning minorities. Acts of violence against the Jewish population and restrictions upon all phases of their lives were commonplace. Hungary began co-operating with Nazi Germany in 1938 and showed her good faith by instituting racial legislation patterned on the Nuremberg Laws. In Poland the Beck clique sought to apply the methods and ideology of the Nazis to political life. Only one country in Central Europe proved an exception. Czechoslovakia had treated her minorities in exemplary fashion. There the Jews lived as fully equal fellow citizens. But unfortunately the country was on the verge of dissolution under Nazi pressure. On October 1 Hitler's troops occupied the Sudetenland. A Nazi puppet state was set up in Slovakia. Hungary annexed large portions of the country. On March 15, 1939, Hitler annexed what was left of Czechoslovakia and another three hundred and fifty thousand Jews fell into the hands of the Nazi rulers. To complete the misfortunes of the Jews, in 1938 Italy signed a military alliance with her good friend Nazi Germany. To confirm the pact, Mussolini officially introduced anti-Jewish laws. Even in this country where Jews had lived continuously since Roman antiquity, they could no longer feel that their lives were safe, and began to emigrate.

Once more, ships crammed with Jewish refugees began to ply the oceans. The unfortunates wandered from port to port, hoping that somewhere they would find shelter. But the world reacted with something less than openhearted sympathy.

Alarmed by the reports of the terrible and humiliating fate of thousands upon thousands of fugitives, the President of the United States called an international conference on refugee questions. It met at Evian-les-Bains on Lake Geneva. Thirty-two countries sent delegations. But the results were dispiriting—there was no country willing to accept the homeless Jews. Everywhere was the general fear of being flooded with impoverished refugees who would become a grave economic burden.

Even before 1938 ended, the Nazi rulers demonstrated once again that they meant to be completely ruthless in their policy of making Germany *judenrein,* entirely free of Jews. The desperate act of a Jewish youth gave the Nazis the pretext they needed.

At the end of October the SS deported seventeen thousand Jews of Polish origin who had entered Germany between 1918 and 1933. They were taken to the eastern border, presumably to be "sent back where they came from." When Warsaw refused to accept them, some five thousand remained stranded in the no man's land at the border, crowded together under frightful conditions, with no shelter whatsoever. Among these unfortunates was a couple named Grünspan from Hanover. When their seventeen-year-old son, who was living in Paris, heard of the fate of his parents, he was possessed by the thought of revenge. He obtained a pistol, went to the German embassy on November 7, and fired two shots at Embassy Attaché Ernst vom Rath, fatally wounding him.

The assassination gave the Nazi leaders their chance to put into action a plan prepared long before. On the night of November 9, 1938, "spontaneous" anti-Jewish excesses took place, led by storm troopers. Germany witnessed a frightful pogrom. Everywhere the synagogues were set afire. While almost six hundred synagogues, community houses, and cemetery chapels went up in flames, the storm troopers destroyed Jewish shops and department stores. Jewish homes were attacked, their inhabitants driven from their homes and beaten. Some thirty thousand persons were carried off to concentration camps. The extent of the devastation was enormous. Jewish property valued at a billion marks was senselessly wrecked on that notorious "Crystal Night." But even this did not satisfy the Nazi rulers. As a penance for Herschel Grünspan's act in Paris, the German Jews were also fined a billion marks. Concurrently an order was issued that all remaining shops and businesses must be transferred to "Aryan" owners.

The civilized world shuddered; the foreign press recorded a storm of indignation. But in Germany not a voice was raised; no one dared to speak out against the criminal actions organized by the government.

Had all sense of justice, all ethical responsibility, been extinguished among the "nation of poets and thinkers"? Had they lost all courage? Had five years of Nazi rule sufficed to undermine all feeling for righteousness, to becloud and poison the minds and hearts of the people? Was it conceivable that nowhere, far and wide, did any group in the population make the slightest attempt to aid the Jews? The armed forces, those repositories of the honor of the nation, did not stir. "The generals stood by," Karl Jaspers has written in attempting to diagnose the condition of the German people at that time. "In every city the commandant had the right to intervene when crimes were being committed. For the soldier is there for the protection of all whenever crimes occur on such a scale that the police cannot prevent them, or fail to do so. The soldiers did nothing. At this moment they abandoned their erstwhile glorious ethical tradition. It did not concern them. They had cut themselves off from the soul of the German people in favor of a completely arbitrary military machine which obeyed orders."

On September 1, 1939, Hitler ordered the attack on Poland. The Second World War had been unleashed, bringing death, destruction, and infinite suffering upon the world. But it was also to bring total annihilation upon millions of defenseless Jewish people.

Within a few weeks Poland was overrun by the Germans. In the occupied territories lived approximately two and a half million Jews. The Jewish population in the parts of Poland taken by the Soviet Union amounted to about one million. Thousands upon thousands tried desperately to reach Russian-occupied Poland. But the Germans had sealed the borders. There was no longer any escape. The cessation of fighting was followed in the newly created *Generalgouvernement* of Poland by rigorous repression of the Jews. In November the yellow badge worn in the Middle Ages was introduced. There were mass executions of Jews and forcible expulsions from the cities. Ghettos were established, the largest in Warsaw.

In 1940 it was the West's turn. Four weeks after the surprise attack on Denmark and Norway in April, Hitler gave the order for the offensive against France. After a blitz campaign, half the country and the entire French Atlantic Coast fell to German occupation; the rest of the South of France was governed by the equivocal Vichy government, which was at Hitler's beck and call. The following year, in April, 1941, the Balkan campaign began. The attacks on Yugoslavia and Greece were swiftly carried to a successful conclusion with the conquest of Crete. Then Hitler, now master of the Continent, on June 22, 1941, ordered the assault on the USSR. The swiftly advancing German armies overran those territories in the south of Russia that were most densely settled by Jews—the area around Odessa and Kiev, where two thirds of the three million Jews of the Soviet Union lived. Along with these, one and a half million Jews from the Soviet-occupied parts of Poland and from the Baltic countries fell into German hands.

A merciless campaign of extermination against the Jewish population started in the East. But in the West, also, the persecutions continued in the invaded and conquered countries. All of Europe became the scene of increasingly vicious measures against the Jews. In every occupied country the Jewish populace felt the hatred and violence of the Nazi rulers.

On September 1, 1941, the wearing of the Jewish badge—a yellow patch bearing the star of David and the word "Jew"—was ordered for Germany, Bohemia, and Moravia; in the summer of 1942 this order was extended to France and other Western countries. Plans were developed to ship all Jews from the occupied territories to Eastern Europe. In October the first deportations from Germany began. Deportations from France and the other occupied countries were organized soon afterward. In March, 1942, the order went out to increase the number of deportees to one hundred thousand a month. From all over Europe long trains of human freight—sealed cattle cars containing Jewish men, women, and children—rolled toward the east, in the fiery heat of summer and in the icy cold of winter. Thousands of the unfortunates died before they ever reached their destination.

In a few occupied countries the inhabitants refused to permit their Jewish citizens to be mistreated or deported. In Denmark there were public protests. The population absolutely rejected the anti-Jewish measures; the King, it was said, declared that he himself would wear a Jewish star if any of his subjects were forced to wear one. When in 1943 Germans themselves at last took over the administration and secretly ordered the arrest of all "non-Aryans," their plans were thwarted. Courageous Danes had managed to spirit away almost the entire Jewish community to Sweden in boats. In the Netherlands a general strike was called in February, 1941, to stop the deportations. In France the detestation of the Nazi measures began to grow into the Resistance movement. In every country there were some courageous people who dared to risk everything to save the lives of the persecuted, who hid hunted Jews, fed them, or helped them to escape. All those who managed to survive in spite of the confusion of war and the terror of the Nazis owe their lives to such brave individuals. Even in Germany some Jews were saved in this way—although only a tiny percentage of them.

While the mass deportations were in progress, the Nazi rulers suddenly changed their plans overnight. The idea of a new settlement in the East for the deportees was dropped. In view of their enormous successes in the Russian campaign, they concluded they could go as far as they liked. In March, 1941, the decision was taken, at the highest echelons of the government and in strict secrecy, to accomplish the biological annihilation of Jewry. The task was to be carried out by the SS.

On January 20, 1942, SS Gruppenführer Reinhard Heydrich, Heinrich Himmler's deputy, made an announcement of the "Final Solution" at a secret conference in Berlin-Wannsee. The program projected the extermination of all the Jews living in Europe. Those incapable of work were to be killed immediately; forced labor for those fit for labor was to be imposed, under minimal living conditions, until they died of exhaustion. Establishment of death camps for immediate liquidation by gas and mass shootings was ordered.

The death camps were established in Auschwitz, Bergen-Belsen, Treblinka, Mauthausen, Majdanek, Sobibor, Dachau, Buchenwald.

In the initial period the victims were killed by diesel exhaust gases. The process was slow and painful. Later the technique of mass extermination was perfected. The firm of DEGESCH—Deutsche Gesellschaft für Schädlingsbekämpfung (a pesticide firm)—supplied the rapid killer, Zyklon B gas. It was used to murder the Jews in a "rationalized" procedure, in specially constructed railroad cars or rooms disguised as "shower baths." The victims were sent into the gas chambers naked. All their remaining possessions—clothes, shoes, rings, mementos—had been taken from them previously. As if that were not enough, gold teeth were removed from the bodies before cremation.

The gas chambers began to devour hecatombs of defenseless people whose only crime consisted in their having been born of Jewish parents, of belonging to the nation that had given humanity the Bible and the Ten Commandments, including that seditious Fifth: "Thou shalt not kill."

The horror and the magnitude of the hellish operation, instituted at the command of the Nazi rulers, carried out by seemingly civilized human beings, mock any description. In the death camps of Auschwitz and Birkenau alone, more than one million seven hundred and fifty thousand Jews were killed in two years; in Majdanek, more than one and a half million.

Independently of the death camps, "commando squads" of the SS raged through the East and Southeast, killing en masse. Assigned to each German army, they had orders to liquidate the Jewish population behind the fronts, in addition to partisans and communists. They drew on Lithuanian, Latvian, White Russian, and Ukrainian auxiliary police to assist them in their mass slaughters. Among the most horrifying scenes of those horrifying times were the shootings of sixty thousand Jews on an island in the Dvina near Riga, of twenty thousand in Lutsk, of thirty-two thousand in Sarny, and of sixty thousand in Kiev and Dnepropetrovsk. As an act of reprisal Rumanians in Odessa mowed down twenty-five thousand Jews with machine guns.

Only in a single case did potential victims of the Final Solution put up a bitter and heroic resistance—in the Warsaw ghetto.

On July 22, 1942, the order had been issued to deport all the Jews of Warsaw to the death camps without distinction of age and sex. At the time a half million Jews were vegetating hopelessly in the narrow confines of the ghetto, shut off from the outside world by high concrete walls, starving and decimated by typhus. Day after day some forty-five hundred persons were dragged out of the ghetto. By September the number of prisoners of the ghetto had shrunk by half. In April, 1943, when new shipments were being arranged, the Jews suddenly resisted the orders. The response was an attack by heavily armed German police and SS detachments, supported by artillery, upon the ghetto. With that attack on the night of April 18—the eve of Passover—there began the "most tragic and amazing event of the entire war": the death-defying defensive struggle by young and old, waged with weapons that had been secretly smuggled into the ghetto. Women and girls used machine guns; suicide detachments of Jewish men counterattacked the besiegers, destroying tanks with homemade hand grenades. Several times they succeeded in throwing back the superior forces of the Germans. But then the attackers set fire to the quarter. In the fierce heat and choking smoke of the fires the SS and police finally succeeded in overwhelming the center of the ghetto. Even then the defenders, hidden in cellars and underground passages, continued their resistance.

The final act of the frightful tragedy was played out in the last days of May. The survivors in the burned-out and shattered ghetto, some twenty thousand souls, were sent on their last journey to the death camps. The SS could report to Hitler and Himmler that Warsaw was *judenrein*.

Although the countries occupied by the Germans were almost hermetically sealed, reports of the horrors nevertheless trickled out. The rest of the world tended at first to regard them as "atrocity stories," products of war propaganda. Polish women who arrived in Palestine in August, 1942, in exchange for German prisoners of war reported the mass liquidations in Poland and the occupied areas of the USSR. But the accounts of escaped victims, who brought with them the first documents and could point to the scars on their own bodies in evidence of the tortures they had been subjected to, did not convince the world public. It was impossible to believe that outside of madhouses there might be human beings whose brains were capable of even planning the extermination of an entire people, let alone executing the plan. The facts of the mass exterminations became a ghastly certainty only after the American secret service, operating through Geneva, obtained corroborative information directly from Germany.

Even the corpses of hundreds of thousands of gassed and shot victims were being "exploited" to help finance the war—teeth, jewelry, and rings alone yielded seventeen tons of gold. No wonder, then, that the SS leadership had the thought of proposing a "deal" to the Allies, speculating on the still living Jews who were helpless pawns in their hands. The release of a million Jews was offered in exchange for delivery of ten thousand trucks. Adolf Eichmann, the "Jewish expert" in the State Security Office, was entrusted with these negotiations.

"I am prepared to sell you a million Jews," Eichmann on April 25, 1944, informed Joel Brand, the spokesman for the Hungarian Jews, who had been invited to Budapest for discussions. "Goods for blood—blood for goods. You can take this million from every country in which there are still Jews, from Poland, Austria, Theresienstadt, Auschwitz, wherever you like. What do you want saved? Men of begetting age? Women of bearing age? Children? Sit down and talk."

When the Russian advance drove the Germans from Poland, the gruesome operation was shifted to concentration camps on German soil, Dachau, Bergen-Belsen, and Buchenwald. In the autumn of 1944 Himmler ordered the exterminations stopped. The last months of the war brought no surcease for the prisoners, however. As the camps were evacuated in the face of Allied armies advancing from all sides, more tens of thousands of Jews died of hunger and of epidemics that broke out in the overcrowded camps.

Not until soldiers of the Allied countries had seen with their own eyes the death and concentration camps, with their gas chambers and cremation ovens, and with emaciated survivors reduced to tottering skeletons, did the world public become fully conscious that the most monstrous crime in the history of mankind had been committed by the Nazi government and its hangmen. Gradually, in the course of the war crimes trials, the horrifying details of torture, suffering, and medical experiments on prisoners came to light.

The final accounting of the deaths, the total number of those gassed, murdered, starved, or driven to suicide, will probably never be determined precisely. But independent studies have established a maximum and a minimum for the victims of Operation Final Solution alone. The estimates run from 4,581,200 to 4,192,200. These figures, however, omit from consideration all those who, in addition, succumbed to Nazi persecution between the years 1933 and 1945. *In toto,* the probability is that there were more than five million Jewish victims.

When the guns fell silent in 1945, a different Germany remained behind. Something had been done that nothing in the world could ever again undo—neither repentance nor shame, neither guilt feelings nor efforts at material compensation. The generation that experienced the Hitler period as adults will pass away before many more years. But even the future generations in the land will be burdened by the execrable memory, as are the growing youth of today, who were too young to bear any of the guilt. For the history of Germany will remain tainted for all time by the most atrocious crimes that human beings have ever inflicted upon helpless fellow human beings, by the extirpation of millions of innocent Jewish souls. No one will ever again be able to describe Germany as the land of Goethe and Bach, Kant and Lessing, and cathedrals. It was also and remains henceforth the land of Hitler, Himmler, and the death camps.

IN THE OLD HOMELAND

". . . Thus saith the Lord God: Behold, I will take the children of Israel from among the nations, whither they are gone, and will gather them on every side, and bring them into their own land; and I will make them one nation in the land, upon the mountains of Israel. . . ."

Ezekiel 37:21–22

ISRAEL—THE NEW STATE

It was a long road, full of disillusionments, setbacks, and hard sacrifices, that began in Palestine after Herzl's death. But the hope, once kindled, soon brought more and more Jewish families into the country, chiefly from Russia, whence the first settlers had started coming in 1882. They began to cultivate a stony, barren wasteland, to dry up the swampy, malaria-infested plain. Along the Lake of Galilee the first collective settlement, the "mother of the kibbutzim," was established. On a sand dune outside Jaffa, Tel Aviv was founded in 1909. Within a decade, forty-five thousand settlers came to the country; twenty-two pioneering farms were established. Then the First World War interrupted the arduous labors of construction. The Zionist movement came to a standstill; the land of hope itself became front-line territory.

Jewish volunteers, determined to fight for their right to Palestine, took England's side in the conflict. In Egypt Josef Trumpeldor, who had fought as a Russian officer at Port Arthur, gathered nine hundred volunteers. Along with him, Vladimir Jabotinsky founded the Jewish Legion. In London two Jewish battalions were organized; a third was set up in Palestine in 1917, after General Allenby entered Jerusalem. Chaim Weizmann, born in Motyli near Pinsk, who had become the tireless advocate of the Russian Zionists, had meanwhile contrived to win from England a commitment of historic importance.

Since 1903 Weizmann had been a teacher and subsequently professor of biochemistry at the University of Manchester; thanks to his scientific talents, he had performed a great service for his new country. England urgently needed acetone for war production. Without it, all naval guns would have had to be rebuilt. Weizmann, at the request of Winston Churchill, then First Lord of the Admiralty, succeeded in eliminating the dangerous bottleneck. He organized the production of acetone from horse chestnuts. The story goes that one day when he was asked what he would like as a measure of appreciation for his services, he replied: "A homeland for my people."

Whether or not the story is apocryphal, in 1917 the subsequently famous Balfour Declaration was issued—although it was not intended as a reward for Weizmann. London was acting out of a variety of complex political motives. On November 2, 1917, British Foreign Secretary Arthur Balfour addressed to Lord Lionel Walter Rothschild a letter stating:

> His Majesty's Government view with favour the establishment in Palestine of a national home for the Jewish people, and will use their best endeavours to facilitate the achievement of this object, it being clearly understood that nothing shall be done which may prejudice the civil and religious rights of the existing non-Jewish communities in Palestine, or the rights and political status enjoyed by Jews in any other country.

The Declaration had an enormous impact on the world public. For the Zionists, it represented a first decisive victory. On July 24, 1918, the cornerstone of the Hebrew University was laid on Mount Scopus, outside the gates of Jerusalem. In 1920 the Zionist Conference meeting in London elected Chaim Weizmann President of the World Zionist Organization. On July 1 of that year Sir Herbert Samuel, himself a Jew and a former Cabinet Minister, was appointed the first British High Commissioner for Palestine, which had been placed under civilian administration, and the British government applied to the League of Nations for a mandate for Palestine. Two years later the League of Nations conferred the mandate upon England.

The realization of the great dream seemed to have moved tangibly nearer. No one suspected that the hardest and bitterest part of the road still lay before the Zionists.

Arab resistance flared. The Arabs did not wish to live in a Jewish state and protested England's Palestine policy. Acts of terrorism began against the Jewish settlements in the country. The Arabs constituted an overwhelming majority. But the flow of immigration continued undiminished. From 1919 to 1923 another thirty-five thousand immigrants entered the country from Eastern Europe. England felt forced to adopt a policy of equilibrium between Jews and Arabs. Sir Herbert Samuel, endeavoring to dispel the distrust of the Palestine Arabs, took measures that bitterly disappointed the Jews. An Arab mayor was regularly appointed for Jerusalem and a passionate Arab nationalist, Emin el Husseini, confirmed as chief of all the Arabs in the country. The most valuable land was sold at knockdown prices to Arabs who did not work it, while only marginal land was available for Jews. Nevertheless, by 1928 more than one hundred thousand more immigrants had arrived. At the beginning of 1929 the Jews began building up the port at Haifa and establishing a potassium-and-bromine-salts industry by the Dead Sea. In the midst of the construction grave clashes occurred, with the Arabs attacking the Jewish population, devastating villages, and destroying houses and businesses. One hundred and thirty-three Jews were killed. In 1931 the census counted one hundred and seventy-five thousand Jews. Now the pace of immigration increased, as numerous German Jews entered the country in addition to those from Eastern Europe. By 1933 the number of two hundred and twenty thousand had been reached. In 1936 the Arabs proclaimed a general strike. Acts of violence by armed bands increased. Attacks on Jews in Jaffa marked the beginning of an organized rebellion. Syrian and Iraqui Arabs, supplied with money and weapons by Germany and Italy, participated. The proposal of a British government commission that Palestine be partitioned only stimulated Arab resistance. Armed Arab resistance continued up to 1939; acts of terrorism against the Jews did not cease, despite the presence of thousands of British soldiers.

Faced with this situation, England capitulated to Arab terrorism. The British government under Neville Chamberlain issued the White Paper of May 17, 1939. It set a quota of only fifteen thousand Jews to be permitted into Palestine each year. The White Paper furthermore contained the declaration that it was not England's aim to transform Palestine into a Jewish state. Thus, in the hour of European Jewry's worst peril, the gate of salvation was closed almost entirely, except for a tiny crack. In the House of Commons Winston Churchill denounced the White Paper as the "breach of a solemn obligation" and "a new Munich." Zionism had been caught up in the cogs of world politics.

The Zionist Congress that met in Geneva at the end of August, 1939, emphatically rejected the White Paper and demanded immediate admission of a hundred thousand Jews. "I must raise my voice in most vigorous protest," Weizmann declared. "We have not deserved such treatment." The shadow of a new world war was already plainly visible. On August 24, 1939, a week before the German invasion of Poland, Weizmann said, addressing the Western democracies on the last day of the Congress, "Your cause is our cause and your struggle is our struggle." Even after the outbreak of the war thousands of desperate refugees tried to make their way to Palestine by sea. Jewish organizations clandestinely chartered vessels, as they had done at the beginning of the thirties, but only a few ships succeeded in reaching their destination. Most of these "coffin ships"— old tubs scarcely seaworthy and overcrowded with fugitives—were stopped by the British navy and their passengers taken to Cyprus or Mauritius. England even vetoed a rescue operation involving some twenty thousand Polish children. Yet the desperate and dangerous voyages continued. In 1940 in the harbor of Haifa the *Patria* blew up, killing two hundred and fifty-two persons. In 1942 the *Struma,* on its way from Rumania with seven hundred and sixty-eight refugees on board, sank after an explosion off Istanbul.

One hundred and thirty thousand Jews volunteered for the British army operating in the North African theater of war. The British had their doubts about arming so many Jews. But they were driven by necessity and accepted twenty-five thousand. "We are fighting the war on the side of England as if there were no White Paper," declared David Ben-Gurion, "and we are fighting the White Paper as if there were no war." But Jewish Palestine itself did not have the opportunity to join the struggle against the Axis powers until 1944. Then, under a blue-and-white flag with a Star of David as its emblem, the Jewish Brigade was committed to front-line duty. It distinguished itself in the Italian campaign and participated in the occupation of Germany.

But the Jewish commitment in the war led to no change in British Palestine policy. Despite all protests, the British government continued to limit severely the number of Jews allowed into the country. These limits persisted after the war, when the Labour Party took control of the government. Foreign Secretary Ernest Bevin set the quota at only fifteen hundred refugees a month. In Austria and Germany the "displaced persons' camps" filled with European Jews who had survived the horror. When England rejected President Truman's proposal that a hundred thousand Jews be admitted to Palestine, a new and inexorable conflict began. While official Jewish agencies furthered illegal immigration, the Irgun Zwai'i Le'umi, the illegal "national military organization," organized a campaign of violence. It used partisan tactics both against the British Mandate authorities and against the Arabs who were bitter enemies of a Jewish national home. Thus, the King David Hotel, headquarters of the British civil administration in Jerusalem, was bombed, killing some ninety British officials and

Arab and Jewish servants and wounding seventy others. Illegal immigration continued; after 1945 some sixty ships containing seventy-five thousand refugees were dispatched. Some of these were secretly landed on the coasts of Palestine; others were forcibly removed to Cyprus by the British. Protection of settlements and cities against Arab attacks was entrusted to Haganah, an armed self-defense organization that abstained from terrorism. It, too, was regarded by the British as illegal, and whenever its members were caught "in the act," they were arrested and all their arms confiscated. At the same time, however, England undertook no action against the armed Arabs who were infiltrating Palestine by the thousands. The country was a seething cauldron. At last, in the spring of 1947, the British government decided to lay down its mandate. It handed the Palestine problem over to the United Nations.

In the summer of 1947 a special United Nations Commission, UNSCOP, visited the country. After it had presented its report, the United Nations decided, on November 29, 1947, to partition Palestine into Jewish and Arab states. On May 14, 1948, just before the last British high commissioner left Palestine at midnight, David Ben-Gurion in Tel Aviv proclaimed the new State of Israel. The following day the war began.

Five Arab armies invaded the country from all sides. All the Arabic countries had sent troops: Egypt, Transjordan, Syria, Lebanon, Iraq, and Saudi Arabia. Volunteer detachments from the Sudan and North Africa joined them. The situation of Israel was desperate; she was insufficiently armed; her territory was splintered; many settlements were scattered in the midst of Arab territory. Hardly anyone in the world gave her a chance to survive. Arab leaflets and radio stations called upon all Arabs in Palestine who were not engaged in fighting the Jews to leave the country at once and await the end of hostilities in the neighboring Arab lands. Within a week, the Arab propagandists proclaimed, the war would be over and the Jews driven into the sea. But the week became a month, and on June 11 the Arabs, glad for a breathing spell, agreed to the armistice proposed by Count Folke Bernadotte, the special envoy of the United Nations. As soon as the armistice expired, they attacked once more with still greater forces. But the Arabs lost the war they had provoked. In a life-and-death struggle the Israelis saved their country and their state, for themselves and for all those Jews throughout the world who might wish to come to it.

On February 14, 1949, in the new part of Jerusalem, the assembly met which on March 8 transformed itself into the Knesset, the parliament of Israel. Dr. Chaim Weizmann was elected first President of the new Jewish state, David Ben-Gurion Prime Minister. In 1950 the Law of Return was passed, which gave to every Jew the right to immigrate into Israel.

After two thousand years the circle had come round to its beginning again. From Mount Zion in Jerusalem the Star of David waved. The dispersed throughout the world had their ancient homeland again—Eretz Israel, the Promised Land that had been the cradle of the Jewish people.

A HISTORY OF THE JEWS IN AMERICA

BY RONALD SANDERS

Jewish history in America is founded upon three principal waves of immigration. The first of these—the smallest in size and the longest in duration—was made up mainly of members of that portion of Sephardic Jewry which, in the centuries following the expulsion from Spain and Portugal, had made its way to the more democratic and commercially enterprising countries of the north, especially the Netherlands and Great Britain, and their overseas colonies. This wave extended throughout the entire colonial period of American history. The second wave began in about the second decade of the nineteenth century, and was made up primarily of German-speaking Jews from Central Europe, many of whom had enjoyed a relative access of civil equality under Napoleonic domination, only to see it taken away under the revived old regimes. This "German" wave of immigration was larger than its predecessor, more conscious of its role as a cultural entity within American civilization, and more influential upon its environment. But by far the largest and most self-conscious of the waves of Jewish immigration to America, and the one that had the greatest impact upon American civilization at large, was the third one, made up almost entirely of Yiddish-speaking Jews from Eastern Europe, which began in force in the eighteen-seventies and eighties, just as the "German"-Jewish immigration was decisively tapering off, and lasted until the passage by Congress of the stringent immigration law of 1924. These three were followed by a small fourth wave, in the nineteen-

457

thirties and forties, of refugees from Hitlerite persecution, both Eastern and Western European Jews who, despite their relatively small numbers, have had a noticeable effect upon both Jewish life in America and American life in general.

American-Jewish history began, as did American history itself, with a flight from religious persecution. When, during the early part of the seventeenth century, a number of the Portuguese colonies in South America and the Caribbean had been captured by the insurgent Dutch Empire, the marranos living in these places had taken advantage of the relative reign of toleration that ensued to return openly to Judaism. But, in many cases, these colonies were eventually recaptured by the Portuguese, and the self-proclaimed Jews living in them were forced to flee. Such was the case with the colony of Pernambuco (Recife, Brazil), which became, during the twenty-four years of Dutch rule that began there in 1630, the seat of a flourishing Jewish community. With the return of the Portuguese in January, 1654, the Jews of Pernambuco scattered to various parts of both the New World and the Old. Some returned to the Netherlands, others went to the Dutch West Indian settlements at Surinam and Curaçao, and one group of twenty-three pushed on to the northernmost Dutch settlement in the New World, and arrived at New Amsterdam in September of the year they had fled their homes.

At first, Governor Peter Stuyvesant—no more a paragon of religious toleration than most American colonial governors at that time—refused to grant the new arrivals permanent asylum. Individual Jews had sojourned in New Amsterdam before, but this was the first Jewish community that wished to establish itself there; in the sequel, it proved to be the first in all North America. But when Stuyvesant wrote for advice to the West India Company headquarters in Amsterdam, the sponsors informed him by return mail that he was to allow the newcomers to settle. It would seem that one reason for this decision on the part of the company was the fact that a number of wealthy Amsterdam Jews were among its shareholders. But it can also be said of the Dutch in general, at this time, that they had learned, not only the democratic value of religious toleration, but also the commercial value of allowing Jewish entrepreneurial talent to flourish in their midst.

Nevertheless, the Jewish settlers in New Amsterdam did not enjoy complete religious freedom or civil equality. They were not permitted to practice crafts or engage in retail trade, nor were they allowed to practice their religion in public. Throughout the remaining period of Dutch rule, until the British captured the colony and renamed it New York, the only outward manifestation of Jewish community life on Manhattan Island was the Jewish burial plot there, obtained in 1656. After the coming of the British in 1664, however, the restrictions were eased though not rescinded. By 1700, the Jews of New York were freely entering into crafts and retail businesses, and in 1730 they built a synagogue, the first in North America. The original synagogue no longer stands, but that first Jewish congregation, Shearith Israel, is still a flourishing part of New York Jewish community life today, housed in the so-called Spanish and Portuguese Synagogue at Seventieth Street and Central Park West.

Through the course of the period preceding the Revolutionary War four more Jewish communities were established in the American colonies —in Newport, Philadelphia, Charleston, and Savannah. Among these, the prosperous Jewish community of Newport became the largest and most successfully integrated into its surrounding environment—a tribute to the tolerant spirit of Rhode Island's founder, Roger Williams—attaining a size of about twelve hundred persons by 1776. The Newport synagogue, a beautiful blend of traditional Jewish elements and the New England Congregationalist style, was completed in 1763 with the help of New York's Shearith Israel community, and still stands today, the oldest synagogue building in North America. But that original Newport congregation no longer exists, having dispersed in 1776 when the British captured the city and rewarded the Jewish merchants there for their loyalty to the revolutionary cause by confiscating their ships. After the Revolution, the Philadelphia Jewish community went on briefly to become the largest and most eminent in the United States, but the prosperity of New York City, and its situation as the chief port of entry into the country, inevitably made it in time the pre-eminent center of Jewish life in America.

At the beginning of the nineteenth century, Jewish life in America was not yet in any way the distinct cultural entity that it was eventually to become. The various congregations—which continued to bear the character of the predominant Sephardic group even though a few Central and even Eastern European Jews had begun to arrive in their midst— were strictly religious organs, both stringently orthodox in ritual and conception of personal conduct and narrowly unconcerned with the general impact of Judaism upon the lives of their members. Until the nineteenth century, there were no permanently established rabbis in America to interpret the problems of everyday life in terms of their religious implications. There was no organized Jewish education, with the result that the unvarying established ritual became increasingly devoid of meaning for the American-born generations. Finally, in 1824, a group of members of congregation Beth Elohim in Charleston, South Carolina, presented a petition requesting some modifications in the ritual—including the occasional recitation of prayers in English—but it was rejected. This group then broke away from the congregation—the first organized revolt in America against the normally severe discipline of the Sephardic community leaders, who had always opposed the founding of second congregations in any community—and established a Reformed Society of Israelites. This organization, which disintegrated after a few years for want of a leadership well educated in Jewish thought, is generally considered the forebear of Reform Judaism in America.

Outside the strict confines of home and synagogue, then, the only manifest characteristic of the early Sephardic Jews within the framework of American life in general was a certain tribalism which, at its best, gave rise to a palpable aristocratic pride and manner among them. Sephardic Jews, aware of the eminence of their ancestors in the courts of Moorish Spain, have usually considered themselves to be somehow more aristocratic than their Ashkenazic cousins, and the more romantic among them have sometimes been inspired by their origins to conduct their lives with a peculiar flamboyance. Benjamin Disraeli is the outstanding example of this, but early nineteenth-century America also saw a personality who, though a figure of much lesser stature, resembled the great Tory in many respects. Like Disraeli, Mordecai Manuel Noah was a Sephardic Jew who knew little about Judaism and thought of it primarily as a racial heritage of aristocratic import. Also like his more eminent British counterpart, Noah pursued careers in both literature and politics, and was led by an imagination nurtured in both these fields to conceive a project that was intended to bring about the eventual resettlement of the Jews in Palestine—the vision of Disraeli's novel *Tancred*.

Although Noah's later years differed from those of Disraeli in that the American came to devote himself to Jewish community affairs—Disraeli, after all, for all his Jewish racial pride, was a convert to Christianity— his early life was characterized by a complete lack of involvement in the arid world that American Judaism was at that time. At the age of twenty-one, upon completing an apprenticeship to a gilder and carver in his native Philadelphia, Noah began writing plays on various historical themes, none of them having to do with Jews, and was soon driven by his dauntless literary ambitions to produce a mediocre volume of Shakespearean criticism. From there he went into journalism, dabbled in politics, and eventually obtained—partly as a reward for his devoutly "war hawk" position in 1812, partly through the good offices of a wealthy and influential uncle —an appointment as American Consul in Tunis in 1813, at the age of twenty-eight. It was apparently while he held this office that the fact of his Jewishness first thrust itself upon his consciousness, although not necessarily, as he later maintained, by dint of an access of sympathy within him for the plight of the impoverished masses of Levantine Jews he saw in Tunis. An undoubtedly more shaking confrontation with the implications of his origins came when he was dismissed from his post in 1815. The main reason for the dismissal was that the American government considered him to have used funds excessively in one of his assignments—which he carried out successfully—that of obtaining the release of American sailors captured by Barbary pirates; but the principal reason offered in the letter of dismissal was that his religion was not appropriate to a representative of the American people abroad. The subsequent course of Noah's life was affected by this blow to his pride.

After settling in New York as the editor of the *National Advocate,* a prominent newspaper of the day, Noah turned his thoughts to possible solutions to the Jewish plight in the world, and eventually arrived at one commensurate with his pride and flair for the dramatic. In 1825 he conceived a plan to found a Jewish colony in North America, which would serve as the nucleus for an eventual Jewish mass return to Palestine. With the help of a wealthy Christian friend, he purchased Grand Island in the Niagara River as the site of the proposed Jewish colony, renaming it Ararat. On September 15, 1825, the site was dedicated in a grand processional through the streets of Buffalo, which included, among the various federal, state, military, and religious officials taking part in it, a contingent of American Indians, whom Noah considered to be descendants of the Ten Lost Tribes of Israel. Noah himself marched at the head of the procession clad in an ermine-trimmed crimson robe. The site was thus officially proclaimed to the world; but no Jews ever came to it. Noah then returned to his editor's chair and to a more modest role in Jewish community affairs. With that appropriately grandiose gesture, the period of Sephardic preponderance in American-Jewish history had come to an end.

In 1815 there were about three thousand Jews living in the United States of America, most of them members of the seven Jewish congregations—all predominantly Sephardic—that were then in existence. By 1840, the Jewish population of the country had leaped to about fifteen thousand, the greater part of this increase having been due to the sudden influx of large numbers of German-speaking Jews from Central Europe. There had long been a number of German-Jewish families scattered throughout the Jewish communities of America, but it was not until this mass arrival

in the nineteenth century that the German Jews made their presence felt
as a group; they then quickly went on to make decisive changes in the
character of Jewish life in their adopted country.

The first sign of the change was simply the displacement of Sephardic
preponderance by the growing German-Jewish community. In 1827 a
group of German-Jewish members of the venerable Shearith Israel congregation in New York City broke away and formed the first permanent
second congregation in any American city—B'nai Jeshurun, which is
still in existence. This was the starting point in a sudden vast proliferation
of German synagogues; after 1825, scarcely any new Sephardic congregations were founded, yet by 1855 there were one hundred and ten synagogues in America. At the same time, the richer conception of community
life harbored by the German Jews led to the founding of other types of
public institutions; the synagogue was soon no longer the sole focus of
Jewish communal activity. The first Jewish fraternal and charitable organizations in America were created; most notably, the B'nai B'rith,
now the largest Jewish order in the world, was founded in 1843. Jewish
education came into being in America in 1838, with the founding of the
first Hebrew Sunday school by Rebecca Gratz, the daughter of a celebrated
German-Jewish family of Philadelphia. A lively Jewish culture, relevant
to the character of everyday life, was now beginning to take shape in
America.

But this German phase in American-Jewish history achieved its most
characteristic expression in the rise and proliferation of Reform Judaism.
The large influx of German Jews into the United States in the nineteenth
century was part of a general German migration, Christian as well as
Jewish. The typical German-American in the nineteenth century was a
liberal who had been somewhat frustrated in his ideals on home soil and
was now seeking fulfillment of them in the New World. This state of mind
caused the United States, in which a large German-speaking community
came into being, to be a major outpost of German liberalism for a time,
a sort of alternative realization of German aspirations toward political
liberty. At the same time, American democracy was particularly appealing
to Germans because of the religious pietism that continued to prevail in
its midst. French liberalism, for example, tended to be anticlerical and
agnostic; in the nineteenth century, it was Germany and America that
seemed to be the two great repositories of the ideal of pious democracy,
and Germans and Americans spent a good part of that epoch diligently
recognizing their affinities with one another.

The Reform movement in Judaism was a natural outgrowth of German
Protestant liberalism. The Enlightenment had had considerable impact

upon the Jews of Germany when it began reaching them toward the end of the eighteenth century, and, drawn to the new universalism of outlook that it represented, many of them were inclined to reject a religion that, in addition to being a social burden, seemed determined to ignore all that was best in the general European culture of the day. Reform Judaism sought to stem the sudden tide of conversions to Christianity by formulating a religious outlook founded upon that general culture. Jewish thought was in need of such fertilization at that time; but, in the initial throes of its zeal to embrace the ideals of German Protestant universalism, the Reform movement relaxed its hold upon some fundamental principles traditional to Judaism—in particular, all those principles that tended to give the Jews a national identity. German liberalism was never as tolerant of ethnic as it was of religious diversity, and Reform Judaism concurred in this view, preferring to conceive of itself solely as "the Mosaic faith." As such, it could take up its place alongside any of the other liberal Protestant sects it came so closely to resemble.

This conception was transferred directly to American soil, just as German liberal Protestantism in general was brought to the United States in unadulterated form by the German immigrants. The chief architect of Reform Judaism in America, Rabbi Isaac Mayer Wise (1819–1900), had been exposed to the currents of modernization that were sweeping the Jewish communities of Central Europe even before his emigration to the United States in 1846. Born to an "enlightened" Jewish family—his father was a teacher, his grandfather a physician—in the town of Steingrub, Bohemia, he had received a training for the rabbinate that was already somewhat modern in character, even though orthodox. But during his student years he had also become exposed to the *Wissenschaft des Judentums*, and had grown fascinated early in life with the common historic origins of Judaism and Christianity. This was a theme to dominate many of his later writings, not only in his more formal scholarly and philosophical works, but also in the many novels and plays that he wrote. After completing his formal studies, he presided over a traditional synagogue in Radnitz, Bohemia, but when, after three years in this post, he departed for America, his spirit was already prepared for the major changes in his religious philosophy that were immediately to follow.

In July, 1846, when Wise and his family arrived at New York, there were three Reform congregations in existence in America: in Charleston (where the first stirrings of Reform in America had taken place in 1824), in Baltimore, and in New York—the latter being the congregation of Temple Emanu-El (then located at a different site from the present one), which was then and still is the largest Reform congregation in the country.

But beyond its clear desire to introduce an increasing amount of English (or German) into the service, along with other modernizations, Reform in America was not at all well defined at this time. Indeed, there were few enough leaders to help in the establishment of any such definition; there were only three rabbis in the entire United States. But this was a situation that favored Reform; two of the rabbis already professed their adherence to it, and the third, Max Lilienthal, who had arrived in America only a year before Wise and was then presiding over three orthodox congregations in New York, had already gained a reputation in Europe as a modernizer, and was soon to become one of Reform's most radical exponents. As for the remaining Jewish congregations in America, disorganized and leaderless as they were, their susceptibility to currents of religious change was bound to be considerable.

Within a few months of his arrival, Wise obtained a post with a congregation in Albany that had already shown inclinations toward Reform. It was in the course of his four years there that the shape of his future religious views became clearly defined. He soon was giving regular sermons in English, and then began gradually to introduce the various modifications of external ritual that brought the Reform Jewish service closer to that of some form of Protestantism in appearance: the use of family pews, an organ, a mixed choir; holding confirmation ceremonies. From the outset, Wise stressed decorum and group discipline in the service—a conscious repudiation of the noisy and somewhat anarchistic atmosphere that the tradition of self-expression in prayer had caused to arise in the orthodox synagogues of northern Europe over the centuries. These modifications even began—as Reform was soon to do with zealous consistency—to reach beyond the limitations of established religious law: Wise introduced the practice of counting women toward a minyan (the quorum of ten required before public prayer can be begun). Indeed, Wise's burgeoning religious radicalism became too much even for his Reform-minded Albany congregation when, one day on a public platform, he announced that he did not believe in the coming of the Messiah. He was dismissed from his post. For the next four years, he presided over a second Albany congregation formed as a result of the split that occurred over the controversy regarding his views, and in 1854 he was called to become rabbi of the Bene Yeshurun synagogue in Cincinnati. He spent the rest of his life in this post, and made Cincinnati the spiritual center of the American Reform movement, as symbolized by the founding there of the Hebrew Union College in 1875.

Under Wise's leadership, the Reform movement in America had two major aims, each intertwined with the other: revision and unification.

At the same time that he sought to create a thoroughly modern Jewish religion, attuned to the liberal, middle-class atmosphere of nineteenth-century America, Wise also hoped to organize all the Jewish congregations of America into a single body. As early as his first Albany ministry, he had composed a prayer book intended for common use in the synagogues of America, and much of his activity in later years was devoted to the formation of such national bodies as the Union of American Hebrew Congregations, established in 1873. But his zeal for religious revision alienated even many liberal Jewish leaders, and a group of rabbis broke away from the Union of American Hebrew Congregations only five years after its formation; today that body, far from being the ecumenical organization Wise wanted it to be, is simply the national organization of the Reform congregations of America. The radical revisions that the Reform movement sought—the switch from Saturday to Sunday services that was tried for a time, for example—were simply not compatible with its aspirations to become the spearhead toward a unified Judaism in America. Though most of the rabbis who came streaming into the United States in the middle decades of the nineteenth century were committed to religious liberalism by the same spiritual inclinations that had led them to emigrate, there were a substantial few among them who could not accept Wise's sweeping repudiation of the Talmud or of the elements of national pride in the Jewish tradition. They could not comfortably acquiesce in the spirit of Wise's dictum that "whatever makes us ridiculous before the world as it now is, may safely and should be abolished. . . ." They were drawn to Reform to the extent that it represented an organic, revitalized Judaism, adapted to the spiritual needs of the day; but they could not accept any aspect of it that seemed to mean mere conciliation to the tastes of the surrounding majority.

By 1878, dissidence within the American Reform movement, in favor of a somewhat more traditionalist approach than that represented by its leadership, had crystallized into a distinct school, which broke away in that year from the Union of American Hebrew Congregations. Calling themselves the Historical School, these dissident rabbis were concerned in varying degrees with the continuing authority of the Talmud (some of them were quite orthodox in personal practice, others inclined to a more liberal interpretation), and were unanimously devoted to the principle of Jewish *peoplehood*, to a continuing sense of community with Jews the world over—a conception that Reform was vigorously rejecting at that time. In 1886 this group founded a rabbinical school of its own in New York, the Jewish Theological Seminary of America, to counter the tendencies represented by the Hebrew Union College. At first, the new seminary had a difficult time of it, but in 1902 it was reorganized under the presidency of Solomon Schechter, a Rumanian-born scholar and theologian, the discoverer of the celebrated Cairo Genizah, and sometime lecturer in Judaism at Oxford University. Schechter was the first truly great Jewish thinker to make his home in America, and under his leadership the Jewish Theological Seminary became a major spiritual force, the headquarters of the movement that had come to be called Conservative Judaism.

In the end, among the two major modernizing movements in American Judaism, it is the Conservative trend (the direct descendant of the ideals of the Historical School) that has had the greatest success in winning adherents. The principal reason for this was the arrival of the Eastern European Jewish masses at the very moment Conservative Judaism was being created. As these new arrivals and their offspring gradually entered the mainstream of American life, the majority of them rejected the orthodoxy that had governed the lives of their ancestors, and, though many of them gave up religion altogether, those who sought a more modern form of religious life usually found Reform too remote, too seemingly un-Jewish for their tastes. Conservative Judaism was a more natural synthesis for most of them; indeed, some of the most prominent and wealthiest members of New York's eminent Reform congregation, Temple Emanu-El, had recognized that the immigrant masses would be more likely to be Americanized through Conservative than through Reform Judaism, and had provided the financial support that gave the Jewish Theological Seminary its new lease on life in 1902.

But this direct act of assistance to the competing movement on the part of some Temple Emanu-El leaders was not the only manifestation of a vital relationship between Reform and Conservative Judaism. It was, after all, a dialectic of tendencies begun by the Reform movement that had led to the establishment of the Conservative school in the first place. In time, the thrust of this same dialectic swung back; through the influence of Conservative Judaism, certain relatively traditionalist elements have re-entered Reform, such as the return to Saturday Sabbath services and a recent reawakening of a sense of Jewish peoplehood. The dialectic has worked in another direction, too, and the modernizing tendencies represented by the Conservative movement have affected a significant wing of American orthodox Judaism; furthermore, this neo-orthodoxy has, in turn, spurred the more traditionalist wing of the Conservative movement into greater vigor—and so on. All in all, there is a vitality in the religious life of American Judaism today that, ironically enough, owes its origins in no small way to the liberalizing zeal of Isaac Mayer Wise.

But religious reform was not the sole achievement of the German wave of Jewish immigration to America. For just as Sephardic-Jewish traders had formed a characteristic element in the colonizing period of American history, so also did German-Jewish peddlers play a vital role in the frontier period of the nineteenth century. These men were often the creators of the first major merchandising establishments in communities all over the western part of the United States. At the moment when America, toward the end of the nineteenth century, began passing from her initial phases of industrialization into the first phases of a mass-consumer economy, the German Jews entered the economic mainstream of the country and became foremost among the shapers of American patterns of consumption. Thus, the great department stores of America are the creations of German-Jewish families; German Jews were also pioneers of the mass-clothing industry, until their dominance in this field was replaced by that of their core-ligionists from Eastern Europe. Finance was another field in which a number of outstanding fortunes were made by German Jews in America, although Jews remained a small enough minority on the New York Stock Exchange to stultify any attempts on the part of anti-Semites to transfer to America the old European myths about "Jewish-controlled finance." Indeed, if Jews were showing in America the talent for commerce and finance that they had manifested in other places from time to time, they were here acting entirely in conformity with the ideals of the Christian establishment. There were few frictions between Jewish enterprise and the yeoman democracy of nineteenth-century America.

Furthermore, the German Jews—themselves originating in a culture that had long maintained an austere ideal of personal responsibility—tended to follow the American tradition of turning to public service once one's fortune had been established. Jews had already participated in relatively large numbers in the Civil War—mostly on the Union side (although the most outstanding Jewish figure of that period was Judah P. Benjamin, a Sephardic Jew born in the West Indies, who served the Confederate government as, successively, Attorney General, Secretary of War, and Secretary of State). By the end of the nineteenth century, German Jews and their American-born children, their wealth secured, began entering public service in large numbers. In 1896 Adolph S. Ochs acquired the nearly defunct New York *Times* and began transforming it into one of the most august institutions in American life. At about the same time, men like Bernard Baruch, Louis D. Brandeis, and Herbert Lehman were beginning their public careers. In an astonishingly short time, the German-Jewish community in America had raised itself from the status of humble immigrants to that of a kind of patriciate. This is the situation in which they were discovered by the masses of Eastern European Jews who began streaming into the United States at around the turn of the century.

There had been Eastern European Jews coming into America during the primarily "German" wave of Jewish immigration, just as there had been German Jews in the country during the period of Sephardic preponderance. Indeed, one eminent Polish-born Jew had made his appearance in American history as far back as the Revolutionary War period; this was Haym Salomon, who used his talents and international connections as a financier to obtain loans for the fledgling republic in its war against British domination. But, for the most part, the Jews who emigrated to America from Eastern Europe prior to 1870 were isolated adventurers rather than participants in a general exodus.

It was in the decade of the eighteen-seventies, when some forty thousand Eastern European Jews emigrated to the United States, as compared to about seventy-five hundred in the preceding seven decades, that the new wave began. This was precisely the moment in nineteenth-century history when currents from Western Europe were beginning to strike Eastern European Jewry with great force and modify their lives in many ways. For the most part, these currents came directly from German Jewry, the closest cousins to the Eastern Europeans both geographically and spiritually, and a major source of cultural influence upon them throughout the nineteenth century. It is significant that much of the initial burst of Eastern European Jewish immigration to America came from the Polish provinces that were adjacent to Germany. These provinces were, furthermore, in the Baltic Sea area, where German shipping companies had gone farther eastward to solicit transatlantic emigration at the moment when German unification was bringing about a virtual cessation of emigration from Central Europe.

Even this sudden influx of the seventies, however, was only a small-scale foreshadowing of the mass upheaval that was to follow, which came not just from places within the shadow of German influence, but from the farthest recesses of Russo-Polish Jewry. This upheaval was set in motion by a specific event: the Ukrainian pogroms of 1881, which had ensued from the reverberations following the assassination of Czar Alexander II. Many currents were set in motion amidst Eastern European Jewry by the events of that year, among them being the first stirrings of Zionism; but foremost among these currents in terms of numbers was the great westward migration that then began, primarily aimed at American shores. There were 5,692 Jewish immigrants to the United States in 1881, the very year of the pogroms, when there was not yet time enough for their impact to be reflected in the immigration figures; in 1882, the number leaped to 13,202. This was a record figure for Jewish immigration into the United States, but it was to be far exceeded in the course of the next few years. A momentary peak was reached in 1893, when the arrival of 76,373 Jewish immigrants was recorded. The vast majority of these were from Eastern Europe. There was then a slight lapse in this immigration for the next few years, until the pogroms of 1903 and 1905 in Russia and Poland spurred it on to new heights; in the year 1906, a peak was reached as 153,748 Jewish immigrants entered the United States. By 1910, the Jewish population of the United States was larger than that of any other country in the world, and New York had become the seat of the world's largest Jewish community.

The effect of this mass influx upon the American-Jewish community in general was not only to increase its size several times over—today the Jewish population of the United States is nearly six million—but to give it a predominantly Eastern European character. The initial reaction to this influx on the part of the established and largely prosperous German-Jewish community, who tended to view the less decorous newcomers as a threat to the image of respectability it had established for itself, was one of dismay. There had been scattered manifestations of anti-Semitism in America before, but none of these had been quite as virulent as the nativist resentment that was now being aroused against the exotic and seemingly unkempt masses of Jews from Eastern Europe. The German Jews had been part of the still primarily "Nordic" immigration into America, and they sedulously behaved in accordance with its standards of behavior and grooming. The Yiddish-speaking Jews from Eastern Europe, on the other hand, were very much part of the so-called new immigration, made up primarily of peasant masses from Southern and Eastern Europe— areas that had hitherto been sparsely represented by immigrants to America—who had come to provide the newly industrializing nation with its proletariat. A self-styled Nordic attitude of contempt on the part of the older American population was directed toward the manners and hygienic standards of all the new immigrant masses, but in the case of the Jews a traditional reflex of anti-Semitism added fuel to the fire of resentment. The impact of this resentment was felt with particular sensitivity by the old German-Jewish families, all the more so because many of them, in the innermost recesses of their hearts, shared in this attitude to some extent.

Whatever the private feelings of the German Jews about the mass arrival of their Yiddish-speaking cousins, however, their public response to the event was entirely in keeping with their traditions of civic responsibility. We have already seen how some of the wealthy leaders of the Reform Jewish community of New York gave financial support and a new lease on life to the Jewish Theological Seminary, primarily because they believed that Conservative Judaism, which was closer than Reform Judaism to the instincts of the tradition-bound Jews from Eastern Europe, would be a more effective force in adapting the latter to the mainstream of American life. In a similar fashion, the German Jews of America were the founders of some of the earliest charitable institutions to aid in the arrival and adjustment of the new Jewish immigrants, such as the old Hebrew Emigrant Aid Society (later superseded by the Hebrew Immigrant Aid Society) and the Educational Alliance. The latter organization functions to this day, on its original site at the corner of East Broadway and Jefferson Street on the Lower East Side of New York, as an adult education school for foreign-language-speaking immigrants.

But it was characteristic of the cultural reservations with which the old German-Jewish families approached the new arrivals that the Educational Alliance long refrained from giving any of its courses of instruction in Yiddish. The Yiddish language was no less important a cultural instrument for the Eastern European Jewish immigrants than German had been for the Central European Jews in America only a generation or two before—indeed, it was of vastly greater importance—but Yiddish has traditionally seemed to be something of a barbarism to anyone weaned on the German tongue. This linguistic difference between the older and the newer Jewish settlers in America can be perceived as the focus of the larger cultural and temperamental differences between them. On the whole more decorous and cultivated, the German Jews were, quite simply, more solidly middle-class. The largely proletarianized Eastern European Jews, on the other hand, were as vigorously informal as the language they spoke, and, if less equipped with a high culture in the Western bourgeois sense, they were far more immersed in a vivid folklore. The German Jews had been part of a general German emigration to America, and they conscientiously followed its course into the mainstream of American life, retaining only a formally separate religious identity. The Eastern European Jews were unique, and had come to America with a civilization entirely their own, which they sought to preserve to some extent.

In some ways, then, Jewish history in America in the early years of the twentieth century is the history of that more or less distinct Eastern European culture, symbiotically attached to American civilization in general and increasingly fading off into it, but also revolving around a spiritual axis of its own that was concentrated within a few square blocks of the Lower East Side of Manhattan, which is where the great majority of the new Jewish immigrants lived. It was here, for example, that there arose a theatrical tradition that inspired the envy of American writers like Lincoln Steffens and Hutchins Hapgood, who found an intensity of audience participation in the Yiddish theaters that could not be matched by the more polite and less passionate audiences for the English-language dramas uptown. Here, too, there was a flourishing literary culture, partly just the American branch of the renaissance of Yiddish letters that was then taking place in Eastern Europe, but also, in part, uniquely American, quite distinct in theme and style from the parent literature in Russia and Poland. But the main cultural force on the Lower East Side, to which the others were intimately related, was formed, on the one hand, by the socialist and labor politics that were the matrix of most of the intellectual ferment within this world, and, on the other hand, by the Yiddish periodical press—particularly the newspapers—which was the chief instrument of the Lower East Side's political as well as literary culture.

Far and away the most important thread in this tapestry of cultural and political activity is the history of the *Jewish Daily Forward,* which remains, even today, the most widely circulating Yiddish newspaper in the world, although its present circulation of about fifty thousand is far less than the nearly a quarter of a million that it could claim in the nineteen-twenties. And, more specifically, the history of the *Forward* in its period of pre-eminence in American Jewish life is the life story of Abraham Cahan, who was one of the founders of the newspaper, and who was its editor in chief for nearly half a century. Cahan ruled the *Forward* with an iron hand throughout the entire period of his editorship, and his powerful personality thus became a major force, not only in the political and literary culture of the Lower East Side, but also in the Americanization of the Eastern European Jewish immigrant—one of the principal aims of his life's work. Furthermore, his biography is something of a representative one in the history of the entry of the Eastern European Jews into the United States and then into American culture—a process he witnessed and participated in during his lifetime—and exemplifies the significant strand formed in this history by the Jewish intellectual in America: for unlike the earlier Sephardic and German-Jewish emigrants, the Eastern European Jews brought a whole intelligentsia to the New World with them.

Cahan was born in 1860 in a small Jewish village, or shtetl, in Lithuania, and grew up in nearby Vilna, then one of the cultural capitals of Eastern

European Jewry. Here he was exposed to the intellectual ferment that was then taking place among the Jews of Eastern Europe, and, becoming in rapid succession a lover of Russian language and literature(something that more conservative Russian Jews still resisted doing at that time, since Russian was the language of the oppressors), an atheist, and a socialist, he soon became involved in the revolutionary student activities that were flourishing in the Russian Empire in those years. At the very moment when the student terrorist organization Narodnaya Volya (People's Will) succeeded in assassinating Alexander II in March, 1881, Cahan was a member of a branch of that organization in the institution in which he was studying, a state-owned seminary in Vilna for the training of Jewish teachers. Cahan's own group had not even known that the assassination was being planned, but all its members were considered by the authorities to be accomplices in the plot, and so, sooner than spend his life escaping from the police, Cahan decided to sail to America. He had visions of helping to transform the United States into a socialist commonwealth.

Cahan arrived in the United States in June of 1882, the year that the great Jewish immigration was beginning. Thus, from the outset, his destiny was intertwined with that of those Eastern European masses in America to whom he was to become a kind of universal father and teacher; yet, at that time, he preferred to think of himself as having come to America not so much as a Jew, but as a socialist. Settling in New York, he participated in the life of the "Russian" émigré intelligentsia, with their endless succession of revolutionary discussion groups, and pleased his sensibilities by thinking of himself as both an anarchist and a Marxist. But by 1886 the tough-minded political realist that lurked within Cahan was beginning to supersede the youthful revolutionary dreamer. Having mastered English with astonishing rapidity, he was by then a teacher in an evening school for immigrants, and he had begun contributing articles to English-language newspapers. In this latter capacity he became emotionally involved in the Henry George campaign for Mayor of New York that year. Henry George's reasonably good showing in the election, on a platform that had a more or less socialist tinge, impressed upon Cahan the ways in which the workings of American democratic institutions could lead to social reform. He renounced all revolutionary and anarchist elements in his social philosophy.

The remarkable history of the Yiddish labor press begins effectively in 1889. In that year, a growing crisis between Yiddish-speaking anarchists —who were then quite strong in Jewish labor circles—and the politically more moderate Jewish socialist faction produced a split between them that resulted in the founding of two rival Yiddish newspapers. Cahan, who had stood on the fringe of the Yiddish-speaking world in the preceding years, half interested in pursuing a career as an English-language journalist, found himself drawn enthusiastically into the endeavors of the socialist group to start its own newspaper. The *Arbeiter-Zeitung* (*Workman's Journal*) began publication in March, 1890. Cahan had hoped to be its editor, but another Yiddish-language journalist, older and more experienced, had been brought in from London to fill that position; there was friction between the two men from the outset. This friction eventually took on political overtones, and led to a split in 1897. But in the meantime the *Arbeiter-Zeitung* enjoyed unexpected success. A Yiddish-speaking proletariat was growing in America, and there was a sudden demand for a newspaper of this sort. By 1894 the paper, which had started out as a weekly, could begin putting out a daily edition. Cahan was made editor of the weekly supplement; but a political division among members of the staff was now well under way.

In this period the Socialist Labor Party of America, which the *Arbeiter-Zeitung* supported, had fallen under the leadership of Daniel De Leon, a powerful orator of extreme radical propensities. De Leon had attempted to win control of the growing American Federation of Labor from Samuel Gompers, who was then leading it onto the politically moderate and generally nonpartisan course it was always thereafter to follow. Failing in this attempt, De Leon had organized an opposition body, the Socialist Trade and Labor Alliance, and tried to wreck the American Federation of Labor by organizing rival Alliance unions wherever possible. This policy caused a more moderate faction in the Socialist Labor Party to break away and form the Socialist Party of America, which was eventually to find its leader in Eugene V. Debs.

Meanwhile, two factions were forming in the *Arbeiter-Zeitung* along the same lines, one De Leonist, the other moderate. The editor and the editorial board supported De Leon; the moderate faction was led by Cahan. By this time, the broad outlines of all of Cahan's subsequent career were emerging; he was to move steadily, as he had already been doing, in the direction of political moderation, farther from the extremes of Russian radicalism in which he had begun, and into the mainstream of American political life. This was also the course that the Yiddish-speaking working classes of America were to follow, partly under his influence. The final crisis within the *Arbeiter-Zeitung* organization took place in December, 1896; at the end of a stormy meeting, the moderate faction walked out, determined to found a newspaper of its own. The first issue of the *Jewish Daily Forward* appeared, under the editorship of Abraham Cahan, on April 22, 1897.

But the new organization had not yet achieved complete harmony within its own midst. Cahan had by this time thoroughly absorbed the atmosphere of American journalism, and had grown impatient with the resolutely Eastern European approach of his colleagues. Even on the new paper many of his associates wanted to continue the political backbiting and ideological hairsplitting that had come to dominate their lives at the *Arbeiter-Zeitung,* and to use the pages of the *Forward* to pursue their quarrel with the parent newspaper. Cahan was no longer interested in an editorial policy founded upon narrow polemicizing of this sort—so characteristic of Yiddish journalism in those days—but wanted, rather, to follow some of the patterns of popular journalism that were then being developed with such success by his contemporaries Pulitzer and Hearst. Furthermore, he had become completely convinced of his abilities as a newspaperman, and could brook no opposition to his authority. But he found his ideas for journalistic reform being constantly blocked by his colleagues; and so, in August, 1897, only four months after the paper had started publication, he submitted his resignation.

The next five years were a remarkable interlude in Cahan's career. Cahan had never, for all his growing involvement in the Yiddish press and labor movement, completely renounced his English-language journalistic and literary ambitions. He had taken to writing short stories in English, and in 1896, while still with the *Arbeiter-Zeitung,* he had published a novel in that language—*Yekl, A Tale of the New York Ghetto*—an exercise in realism that had won the praise of William Dean Howells. After leaving the *Forward* he returned to his English-language fiction, producing a volume of short stories in 1898 and an inordinately idealized and romantic novel about Russian student revolutionaries, *The White Terror and the Red.* His greatest achievement in fiction, however, did not come until some years after his return in 1902 to the *Forward; The Rise of David Levinsky,* first published in book form in 1917, is still the definitive account of the triumphs and sorrows of the American immigrant become millionaire, and is now recognized as a minor literary classic. During the same period that Cahan made his first advances into this career as an American novelist, he also went to work as a full-time "American" newspaper reporter, forming part of the youthful brain trust that Lincoln Steffens organized around himself at the New York *Commercial Advertiser.* It was in these days that Cahan played the role of guide to Steffens and two younger colleagues, the brothers Hutchins and Norman Hapgood, leading them through the Lower East Side cafés and restaurants that were then the centers for the Yiddish-speaking bohemia of New York. Out of these expeditions eventually came Hutchins Hapgood's warmly admiring book of essays on Lower East Side Jewry, *The Spirit of the Ghetto*.

The *Forward* was in dire straits by 1902, and Cahan was recalled to his post as its editor in the latter part of that year. But Cahan this time demanded sovereign authority for his policies, and when he was not granted it right away he resigned again. By the spring of 1903, however, the Forward Publishing Association decided to accept his stipulations, and he returned once and for all to a position he was to hold, with virtually dictatorial powers, until his death in 1951 at the age of ninety-one. Cahan was now thoroughly schooled in American journalistic techniques, and his reforms quickly followed. Livelier headlines were introduced, along with a more sensational type of news coverage. Cahan's editorials gave all kinds of paternal advice to the immigrants, on everything from the proper attitudes to adopt toward the strange "American" ways of their children to the correct uses of the handkerchief. That forgotten person to Yiddish intellectual journalism, the ordinary Jewish housewife, was suddenly made the center of attention and the object of many of the paper's features; this development was capped with the introduction, in 1906, of a daily feature, which still appears, *"A Bintl Brif"* ("A Bundle of Letters"), the most unique and venerable "advice-to-the-forlorn" column in the world, tailored to the special personality traits and requirements of the Yiddish-speaking American lady through three generations—as maiden and bride, as mother, and as grandmother. At the same time, the religious susceptibilities, not only of these women, but also of many ordinary Jewish workingmen who were not socialists but who wanted a paper that spoke to them and for them all the same, were given greater regard than they had hitherto obtained from the Lower East Side radical intelligentsia. In those days, many of Cahan's socialist colleagues were given to organizing balls on the Jewish Day of Atonement, as a conscientious flouting of religious traditions, and to advertising these events in their newspapers; Cahan refused to carry such ads in the *Forward,* and demanded that the pages of his paper always show respect toward the feelings of the pious. These and many other changes in the character of the paper led not only to its immense success, but also to the eternal enmity toward Cahan of men who started out as his colleagues and ended as his rivals. For these modifications in style were also leading—as if inevitably—to modifications in political principles as well.

In this respect, the *Forward* simply followed the course that Cahan had embarked upon long before becoming its editor. In the years that followed his resumption of the *Forward* editorship, there was only one interval of delay in his steady progress toward a totally nonrevolutionary American liberalism. This occurred during the period of the First World War and the Russian Revolution. In 1914 Cahan was, first of all, opposed to the war in general, like socialists in neutral countries the world over (and like socialists in France and Germany until August of that year); but he was, in the second place, inclined, like a great many Eastern European Jews in America, to favor the side that was fighting *against* Czarist Russia. American entry into the war against the Central Powers tended to dispel this feeling among the Jewish masses, whose American patriotism superseded all other emotions, but Cahan continued for a while in his inclination to oppose the war, with the result that his paper, which reflected his views, was banned from use of the mail for a time. But the Russian February Revolution, which the *Forward* greeted as an event of virtually messianic import, had already begun to modify Cahan's previous opposition to the Allied cause, and by April, 1918, he had undergone a reluctant change of heart. From then on, the *Forward* carried articles supporting America's war effort, written and signed by members of the staff, but never by Cahan himself.

The *Forward*'s enthusiastic reception of the February Revolution in Russia led many of his friends and enemies to think that Cahan would also be an enthusiastic supporter of everything that ensued there. Indeed, for a time he insisted upon tolerance of Bolshevik excesses, though he was himself inclined to disapprove of them, arguing that the Russian Revolution needed a little while in which to find its equilibrium. But when, in 1921, the world-wide split in socialism that was being brought about by the Communist leadership in Russia led to a corresponding split in the Jewish Socialist Federation of America, Cahan became a virulent opponent of the Communist group and its Yiddish-language newspaper, the *Freiheit*. From then on, anti-Communism was a shaping factor in the development of Cahan's political outlook. He continued his support of the relatively moderate Socialist Party of America until 1936; but, in that year, the *Forward* made a sudden and dramatic switch, and supported Franklin Delano Roosevelt for re-election to the presidency. Since that time, the *Forward*'s main problem of political tactics has been how to go on supporting Democratic candidates—mainly for the presidency—without supporting the Democratic Party itself, since the *Forward*'s lifelong opposition to Tammany Hall has made identification with that party a violation of principle. The *Forward* has solved this problem by endorsing a succession of local, New York-based political organizations—first the American Labor Party, and now the Liberal Party—which have usually supported the national Democratic ticket. As for the masses of *Forward* readers and their offspring, their political history went on to become that of an alignment behind the liberal wing of the Democratic Party that was almost monolithic until the candidacy of General Eisenhower.

The political development of the *Forward* was representative of a historic symbiosis that was taking place between the labor politics of the Lower East Side and American liberalism, particularly in the era of the New Deal. During the first four decades of this century, as American unionism came of age following the course of moderation that had been charted for it by Samuel Gompers, a number of Jewish labor leaders arose from the intense political milieu of the Lower East Side to positions of national leadership, and were instrumental in imparting to the American labor movement its unique, statesmanlike character. The foremost among these leaders was Sidney Hillman. Starting out as a humble cutter in the garment industry—which was the principal industry of the Eastern European Jewish immigrant, forming the matrix within which some of them became laborers and others bosses, some union leaders and others millionaires—Hillman worked his way up to the presidency of the Amalgamated Clothing Workers of America, and eventually went to Washington, to work for the Roosevelt administration in various advisory posts. Although Hillman and Cahan were far from friendly toward one another, Hillman came to represent the very fulfillment of Cahan's lifelong thrust from the Lower East Side—which, for the Eastern European Jewish immigrant, was the catalyst for the ways of the Old World with those of the New— into the mainstream of American life and politics.

By the eve of the Second World War, the *Forward* had passed its peak of circulation and of glory. As if destined to witness this ironic tribute to its zealous endeavor to Americanize the Eastern European Jewish immigrant, the *Forward* watched its readers' utterly American sons and daughters turn away from it and become exclusive readers of the English-language press. A generation of American-born children of Eastern European Jewish immigrants—the so-called "second generation"—had now come of age, many of them, in time, to begin imparting a distinct quality to American urban life in the decade of the thirties, others only to put on the uniforms of the American armed services from 1941 to 1945 and participate in the war against the greatest scourge the Jewish people had ever known.

The Second World War and its aftermath brought about a great many changes in American Jewish life—as in American life in general—both through the internal effects upon the country of the dynamics of war and peace and through the external effects of the convulsions that had stricken Europe. In the course of a few years, the greater part of European Jewry had been wiped out, with the result that the largest concentration of Jewish population in the world—or, to put it another way, the pre-eminent Jewish community in the world—was now no longer in Europe, but in North America. This shift of balance was further accentuated by the emigration to the United States, both before and after the war, of tens of thousands of European Jewish survivors fleeing the holocaust. These refugees, coming from both Western and Eastern Europe, brought with them certain qualities unique among the waves of Jewish immigration to America. A substantial number of them were men and women of the highest European learning, in Jewish as well as in secular subjects; others were prominent artists, especially in certain fields that had virtually become Jewish specialties in Central and Eastern Europe, such as the performing of music. This influx of an elite from a continent that had stood at the pinnacle of civilization until it destroyed itself by an ex-plosion of barbarism from within brought a new refinement to American cultural life in general, and to American-Jewish cultural life in particular, at a moment when the latter was coming of age and beginning to achieve a fullness of identification with the former. The universities, the concert halls, the worlds of publishing and of communications in America are all still reverberating with the impact of this migration. And within the spirit-ual atmosphere that has thereby been created, many American Jews are finding the cultural means of recovering the historic roots of their identity.

The most significant moral effect of the European holocaust upon Amer-ican Jews was a widespread revival of concern with the problem of main-taining their Jewish identity. In particular, a great many Jewish intel-lectuals of the "second generation"—who, as children of the American ghettos, had at first been inclined, upon reaching maturity in the nineteen-twenties and thirties, to seek fulfillment of their youthful ideals entirely in radical political movements that were secular in content and purpose—have tried since the Second World War to incorporate a sense of their Jewish identity into their views. Many of them have come to perceive that there was even a uniquely Jewish quality to their youthful radicalism of prewar days. In the far more ambiguous atmosphere, ideologically and morally, of the nineteen-sixties, they look back nostalgically upon the clearer struggles of the thirties, recognizing that, among the other qualities of that epoch, there existed a perfect confluence of Jewish and socialist aspirations during that time. The Jew and the socialist faced a common enemy in fascism; and, like the struggling labor leader, the "second-generation" Jew in America could look back with both pride and anger upon a childhood of poverty. For a time, the masses of children of Eastern European Jewish immigrants who filled the halls of the College of the

City of New York and collected their degrees from it seemed to be the very fulfillment of the old socialist ideal of the working-class intellectual. These poor American-Jewish immigrant families, whose zeal to educate their children was unparalleled among most working classes, were better qualified than any other group anywhere in the world to demonstrate the possibilities of realizing their ideal in the course of a single generation. But in the process of realizing it, in sending the vast majority of their children to the high schools and colleges, the Jews of America have largely ceased to be working-class; and this fact is a source of difficulty for those who continue to seek the roots of their Jewish identity in an Eastern European Jewish tradition of poverty and a certain kind of radicalism, both of which came to an end in America in the nineteen-forties and fifties.

Nevertheless, it is precisely out of the tensions arising from this problematic situation—problematic, at any rate, to the Jewish radical intelligentsia—that a rich and distinctive American-Jewish literature has recently come into being. The hero (or antihero) of Saul Bellow's best-selling novel, *Herzog*—to take one of the most outstanding and representative specimens of this literature—is the very archetype of the "second-generation" Jewish intellectual in America, his richly learned, passionately inquisitive, and utterly neurotic spirit quite bewildered by its dizzying ascent, in the course of a single lifetime, from the depths of the ghetto up onto the summits of the meaninglessness often presented by American middle-class life in the nineteen-sixties. He is a man who (here we can generalize a little on the type) once read the literature of Marxism as avidly as he now reads that of psychoanalysis. To a certain extent, he is quite simply the disaffected urban American intellectual in middle life, regardless of religious or ethnic background. Yet there is something about the Jewishness of this type as presented in fiction that makes the delineation of him seem more exact, more true, and consequently more universal. To a certain extent, at the very moment when America has become overwhelmingly urban and middle-class, and has developed a quality of life among its educated classes that is, in some ways, more intellectual and more European than it had ever been throughout most of the nineteenth and early twentieth centuries, the American Jew has come forth as a significantly representative type. The particular set of tensions, longing, and nostalgia that beset Moses Herzog could only be those of the classic alienated Jew of modern Western culture. But now he is in America, a nation of peoples who have alienated themselves from their past and who continue to do so, not only through the primeval act of emigration, but also through the ruthless consistency with which the future is pursued at the expense of the past in every generation, and so he is all the more like his compatriots for being Jewish.

This quality of American life was perceived by the very founder of the tradition to which Saul Bellow belongs, the first truly *American-Jewish* novelist (as distinguished from an American novelist who happens to be Jewish, or from a Jewish novelist who happens to be an American), Abraham Cahan. From the very first of his novels, *Yekl, A Tale of the New York Ghetto,* Cahan was preoccupied with the spiritual disaster that overtakes Eastern European Jews when they pull up from their ancestral villages and transfer themselves into the fast-paced and alienating atmosphere of the American cities. Yekl is a simpleton who becomes inebriated with the sleazy attractions of New York life, and who finally divorces his virtuous and old-fashioned Jewish wife to go off in vain pursuit of a tart. In this and many other stories, Cahan stressed the spiritually compromising effects of America, at the same time that he pointed up the emigration to America as a necessity, an almost inevitable destiny for the Eastern European Jew. This is why there was no inconsistency between Cahan's stance as a novelist reflecting upon the pitfalls of Jewish destiny in America, and his stance as a Yiddish journalist ardently advocating the Americanization of his immigrant readers. For him, the entire Eastern European Jewish emigration to America was the unfolding of another epoch in the tragic destiny of the Jews, passionately searching through history for their Jerusalems and ever leaving them behind in the process. In his role as a Yiddish-language publicist, he met his responsibility by calling upon his flock to make the most of the situation and seize upon the unprecedented worldly opportunities offered to them by American life. But as a novelist, writing in another language for a different audience, he felt free to explore the tragedy to its depths.

The Rise of David Levinsky was Cahan's most mature realization of this tragic vision, as superior to his first novel in richness and subtlety as its hero is to Yekl in intellect. David Levinsky, the direct ancestor of Moses Herzog, is the first alienated American-Jewish intellectual, although his alienation is in a way far more severe than that of his counterpart of the nineteen-sixties, because, unlike the latter, he has cut himself off from the world of his own moral principles. For Levinsky's initial break with his heritage—his emigration to the United States, followed quickly by his repudiation of the religious beliefs of his boyhood—proves in the sequel to be less profound than his subsequent break with the underlying vision he had inherited from it. Levinsky, like many unskilled luftmenschen who came to New York from Eastern Europe, goes to work in the garment industry, and eventually rises from humble laborer to millionaire manufacturer. It is the classic American immigrant success story; except that Levinsky is at heart not a businessman, but a man of the spirit, who would probably have kept to his books—religious or secular, as the case may be—had he remained in the old country and not been lured into another way of life by the tempting American atmosphere of business opportunity. With every new increase in his fortune, Levinsky feels the emptiness grow in his spirit—a condition reflected in his external life by his complete inability to find a wife, for love becomes the sole preserve of his old idealistic visions. Looking back longingly upon the spiritual purity of his childhood as a Yeshiva student in Europe, Levinsky realizes that there had been available to him one possible way of maintaining some of the spiritual qualities of that time even here in America, the very way that he had implicitly renounced when he chose to rise above his lot as a garment worker by going into business for himself. For, instead of becoming a capitalist, he might have become a socialist, as so many immigrant Jewish intellectuals like himself had done. Throughout Cahan's writings, there is this clearly perceptible view that socialism is a kind of modern, secular counterpart to Judaism, a true fulfillment of the Jewish spirit; hence, socialism is depicted as the possible salvation that Levinsky had unthinkingly repudiated.

The tragic ironies that made up the vision of David Levinsky's creator take on greater force when we consider Cahan's subsequent career, and his own renunciation of socialism. To be sure, Cahan did not become a capitalist like David Levinsky, but in moving from socialism to New Deal liberalism in 1936, he was reaching the end of a path that he had embarked upon in 1897, when he chose to repudiate for good the attitudes of the radical Jewish intelligentsia and join hands with the average Jewish immigrant in a search for entry into the mainstream of American life. For that average Jewish workingman and his progeny simply went on to become the American-Jewish middle class, largely intelligent but not necessarily intellectual, overwhelmingly liberal but not necessarily radical or socialist, and generally more interested in the pursuit of career than of great moral or historic visions. Cast adrift on this spiritual sea of his own choosing, Cahan thus became even more of an archetype than David Levinsky was of the radical Jewish intellectual become middle-class, whose spiritual history is being relived today by another generation of American-Jewish intellectuals.

Among the notable differences between the Jewish moral commitment of this "second-generation" radical intelligentsia, which is pre-eminent in American literature today, and that of the great middle-class majority of the same generation—both pursuing the implications of the revival of interest in their own Jewishness that the Second World War provoked among them—are their respective attitudes toward Zionism in its past and present manifestations. Until the nineteen-thirties, Zionism had relatively little strength in the United States as compared with Europe, even though the Zionist Organization of America was adorned for a time, during and immediately after the First World War, with the name of Louis D. Brandeis. Not only were American-Jewish immigrants, by the very nature of their commitment to become Americans, little inclined for a long time to be concerned with the establishment of a Palestinian-Jewish nationality founded upon immigration, but they were also influenced by two of the most powerful and articulate institutions in American-Jewish life—the Reform movement and the Yiddish labor press—which were both resolutely opposed to Zionist aims. This period thus provided one of those rare and interesting instances of ideological agreement, concerning a certain set of issues, between a left-wing, socialist faction and a conservative upper class. Reform Judaism opposed Zionism at its inception in the same way that it had traditionally opposed any kind of stress upon the national elements in the Jewish legacy. The Yiddish labor press took that stance against Zionism, well established among Jewish socialists in Europe—particularly Eastern Europe—founded upon the view that the Zionists were "bourgeois chauvinists." In the eyes of the Yiddish-speaking socialist, Zionism represented an egoistic attempt on the part of a Jewish elite to evade the problems of the working classes in general and the Jewish working class in particular by leaving them all behind and departing for a far-away utopia. If the Zionists charged that the Jewish socialists were not sufficiently concerned with the uniqueness of Jewish problems, the socialists could reply, after 1897, by pointing to the Jewish Socialist Federation, or Bund, of Russia and Poland, which combined the vision of the class struggle with an ideal of Jewish cultural nationalism in the Diaspora, founded upon the Yiddish language. The *Jewish Daily Forward* subscribed ardently to the Bundist view.

But American Jewry began undergoing a change of heart toward Zionist endeavors in Palestine upon hearing the news of the Arab riots there in 1929. Even Abraham Cahan, who had visited Palestine in 1925 and again in the year of the riots, began arguing that Jewish solidarity demanded sympathy for the settlers there irrespective of one's ideological commitment. As for Reform Judaism, there was now a growing number of prominent rabbis in its midst who were ardent Zionists; indeed, in the last years before Jewish statehood in 1948, when the American-Jewish community was a major force in the world Zionist movement, the pre-eminent leader of American Zionism was a Reform rabbi, Dr. Abba Hillel Silver.

By 1935, when the threat of Nazism began making Jews the world over more amenable to the idea of a Jewish national home, the American Reform movement felt impelled to revise its official anti-Zionist stance of old in favor of a noncommittal position. Since 1948, Reform rabbis and their congregants have been as warmly disposed toward Israel as American Jews in general have been, with the exception of a very small but vociferous anti-Zionist group that broke with the Reform majority in 1942 and formed an organization called the American Council for Judaism.

But it was in the vast middle area of the Russian-Jewish immigration and its offspring—the same elements of the American-Jewish community that, with their entry into middle-class life, have been the chief well-springs of Conservative Judaism—that Zionism came to achieve its most enthusiastic support in the United States. In its early days in Eastern Europe, Zionism had been the ideal of a small elite capable of governing their lives by an abstraction; there was then not yet a real Jewish national community in Palestine, only the vision of one, remote indeed from the everyday concerns of the average, uneducated Jewish emigrant to America. But by the nineteen-thirties such a vision had clearly become a reality, a community capable of standing up against Arab rioters, arguing vigorously with the British Empire, and offering a real haven to the endangered Jews of Europe. Furthermore, this Palestinian Jewish community was made up of men and women who had come from the same towns and villages in Eastern Europe as the American-Jewish immigrants; in many cases, they were even relatives. The emergence of all these realities inevitably won the hearts of most American Jews in favor of their cousins in Palestine, even if it did not engender any widespread desire on their part to settle there themselves. It then needed only the moral impact of the Second World War and the holocaust, combined with the rapid post-war ascent of the American-Jewish majority well into the realms of middle-class security, to make American Jewry overwhelmingly Zionist. Whereas there had been only some eighteen thousand inscribed members of the Zionist Organization of America in 1929, there were about a quarter of a million by 1948. The political leverage exercised by this group as a democratic voting bloc within the most powerful country in the world, along with its considerable financial resources, enabled it to become a major force in the creation of the State of Israel and in the ushering of that fledgling nation through its perilous early years of growth.

Today, Zionism is an established part of American-Jewish middle-class life. Modern Hebrew education and fund-raising for Israel are two of the pillars upon which the organized Jewish community stands. The concern with Israel's destiny and character that these activities represent, combined with the firm refusal on the part of the vast majority of American Jewry to accept the view of some Israeli leaders—David Ben-Gurion the foremost among them—that the time has come for all the Jews in the world to seek to settle in Israel, has led to a broadly accepted revision of the ultimate purposes of Zionism. In keeping with the view that some Zionist intellectuals had always advocated, Zionism is now perceived by most of its American adherents to be primarily a *cultural* ideal, seeking the perpetuation of the Jews as a distinct people on the basis of the national elements in the Jewish tradition. It is essentially a secular ideal, although a religious interpretation is not excluded. It lays stress upon the Hebrew language and its literature, from the Bible to the works of the most freethinking modern Israeli poets and novelists, as the cultural sources of Jewish identity. Israel and its fortunes lie at the very center of Zionist attention, but the American Zionist is nonetheless committed to the ideal of a continuing Jewish people in the Diaspora as well.

Now, there has long been a small Zionist intelligentsia in America, but the fact is that it has never had, on the whole, the literary power of that "second-generation" radical intelligentsia represented by Moses Herzog, which has been largely indifferent to Zionism. If any commitment to a continuing Jewish identity in future generations prevails among its members, it is something closer to the old Bundist ideal of a Yiddish proletariat—or, in this case, of a kind of intellectual aristocracy drawn nostalgically to that old Yiddish-socialist culture when it was at its height, and determined somehow to perpetuate its essence—than to the Zionist one. Indeed, their diffidence toward Zionism tends to parallel the old Bundist feeling on the subject. In other words, a situation has materialized in American-Jewish life today in which cultural Zionism is more or less the creed of a vast middle-class establishment, its members economically powerful but beginning to lapse somewhat in spiritual vigor, as compared with their immigrant parents or grandparents, whereas a kind of quasi-Jewish radicalism—whether in politics or in personal morals—is the creed of the spiritually most vital and most interesting element in American Jewry. It goes without saying that this latter group exercises an attraction among the most vigorous-minded members of the younger generation of American Jews, those in the colleges and just beyond, for it offers them values that are far superior to anything in the often too self-satisfied middle-class environment in which they have been reared and against which many of them wish to rebel. The major flaw in this situation is that, from the standpoint of anyone wishing objectively to find a creed with a content capable of projecting a Jewish identity through future generations, Zionism seems to have qualifications superior to those of the creed offered by this radical intelligentsia.

But one other force has recently come back to the prominent position it once held in American-Jewish life before a long period of relative eclipse: religion. It is one of the ironies of history that, after some two hundred years of suffering the onslaughts of liberal rationalism, religion is making a noticeable return among those very peoples who had fought most ardently against it. France, for example, after spending most of the nineteenth century in internecine warfare between liberalism and Catholicism, is now becoming one of the principal heartlands of the vigorous liberal Catholicism that has transformed the character of the papacy in recent years. America, too, inveterately loyal to her religious traditions, has felt this liberal religiosity current in the world, with the result that there now prevails in this country a degree of institutional affiliation in all religious denominations that would not have seemed likely a generation ago, particularly in urban areas.

This trend has aided the re-formation of Jewish communal life in America primarily around the synagogue. Increasingly the sole repository of Jewish public activity in many communities, the synagogue has tended to supersede or to absorb the instruments of those two secularist forms of Jewish identification that were prominent a generation ago, Bundism and Zionism. Whereas these two secular nationalist inclinations tended to be based by their proponents upon a principle of ethnic or national pluralism in American society, the predominant Judaism of today has found its place mainly within a system of religious pluralism, and has taken up a position alongside Protestantism and Catholicism as one of the three major religious creeds of the United States. This situation represents, in a sense, a recovery of the ideal sought after by the German-dominated Reform movement of the nineteenth century. But despite its quasi-official status as simply a religion, American Judaism has been infused, as a result of the intervening arrival of the East European Jewish masses, with an ethnicity that prevails not only in the Orthodox and Conservative trends, but also in the Reform, which has absorbed a large influx of the new immigrants and their offspring through the years. All of American Judaism has been Eastern-Europeanized to some degree, and this has meant, along with the recovery of a certain religious intensity in however modernized a form, the revival of a sense of the national elements inextricably involved in that religious identification. Judaism in the United States today is thus a new, thoroughly American synthesis of liberal religiosity and the uniquely Jewish type of ethnicity, perpetuated by a group that aspires to demonstrate, with its passionate loyalty to American ideals, that such a synthesis is entirely in harmony with the system of democratic pluralism upon which American society has been founded.

This unique synthesis has provoked a certain stirring of religious or quasi-religious sentiments even among that Jewish intelligentsia whose grounds for attraction to Jewish traditions would once have been solely those of ethnicity. There is, in general, something of a religious revival taking place in America among a formerly secularist intelligentsia, Jewish and Christian alike, many of whom have been drawn to the broad philosophical trend often characterized by the term "religious existentialism." It is noteworthy that one of the foremost sources of inspiration of this theological revival has been, for American Protestants at least as much as for American Jews, the writings of the Jewish religious philosopher Martin Buber. Among Jewish intellectuals, Buber's popularizations of Hasidism have had great impact, and have opened the way to a mild Hasidic literary revival in America, led by the writings of Isaac Bashevis Singer. Now an American citizen living in New York, Singer is the last living representative of the great Eastern European Yiddish literary tradition. It is possible even to say that the mainstream of contemporary American literature was brought into a flirtation with Hasidism a few years ago, when the eminent novelist and essayist Norman Mailer published in the Jewish magazine *Commentary* a series of free-style explications of selections from Buber's *Tales of the Hasidim*—a latter-day, hip-Reichian-existentialist version of the kind of discourse epitomized by those Hasidic rebbes of old. Such a flirtation is also to be seen in Philip Roth's celebrated short story "Eli, the Fanatic," which describes the sudden attempt on the part of a guilt-ridden, middle-class, suburban Jew to make himself over into a Hasid—sidelocks, gaberdine, and all. The protagonist of the story has been inspired to behave in this way by his encounter with a Hasidic sect that arrived in the United States fleeing Hitlerite persecution, and it might be pointed out in this connection that the current interest in Hasidism on the part of American-Jewish intellectuals is partly another cultural by-product of the Jewish refugee influx of the nineteen-thirties and forties, which brought to American shores not only Isaac Bashevis Singer and other prominent Jews, but also a large number of Hasidic sects, most of which are clustered in the Williamsburg section of Brooklyn.

This is not to say that Jewish intellectuals are attracted to the external trappings of Hasidism, even if they might be inclined to appreciate the antibourgeois appearance presented by its adherents. Rather, what they are drawn to is a certain lyricism that seems to constitute the essence of the Hasidic tradition—or, at least, to have once constituted its essence.

There is a tradition among Eastern European Jewish intellectuals which maintains that the revolutionary spirit that dominated their lives in the early part of this century—manifesting itself both in Zionism and in the various forms of socialism—was the legacy of a kind of lyricism bequeathed by the Hasidic movement. It is significant, then, that among many of those for whom these secular creeds have lost their comprehensive spiritual power of old, there has been something of a return to the religious sources.

In recognition of the essential link between the lyricism of religion and the zeal for social and political justice, many rabbis in America today have felt impelled—like their counterparts among the Christian clergies —to seek an active involvement in the social and political causes of the day. These are responses, not only to individual feelings of conscience on their part, but also to their recognition of the fact that the young Jews who are noticeably present in large numbers within socially and politically idealistic movements are receiving guidance and inspiration less from religious than from secularist sources. These young people are not interested in the comfortable, middle-class Judaism of their parents, and to whatever extent they regard this to be the sole form that Judaism can take in America, to that extent they are willing to abandon it altogether. But many members of a new generation of rabbis are determined to prove their belief that involvement in the great moral issues of the day—and today, moral issues are primarily social and political ones—is the very core of the religion of the Hebrew prophets.

Judaism in America today thus stands strung in a tension between two prevailing impulses: on the one hand, to pursue to its fullest and most perilous possibilities an inclination toward moral and spiritual creativity, which has been of the essence of the Jewish tradition throughout most of its history, and, on the other hand, to shore up the underpinnings of the most socially secure and prosperous structure that a Jewish community has ever built in the Diaspora. The United States of America has been perhaps the least anti-Semitic of all the nations in which Jews have ever lived in large numbers. The situation is far from perfect, to be sure; and yet one of the most significant aspects of the record of anti-Semitism in America is that—unlike in most other countries containing large Jewish populations throughout history—the most notable outbursts against the Jews have usually met with vigorous opposition from the very pinnacles of the American establishment. General Ulysses S. Grant's notorious Order No. 11 of December, 1862, for example, which demanded that "the Jews, as a class violating every regulation of trade established by the Treasury Department," be expelled from the military district of Tennessee, was immediately revoked by President Lincoln when news of it reached him. This act on Lincoln's part was one belonging to a long tradition of opposition to anti-Semitism by the American presidency, reaching all the way back to George Washington himself, who lived well before the time when there was any significant "Jewish vote" in the country that might conceivably influence his views on the matter. Washington virtually established the standing contract between American Jewry and the American political establishment when he wrote, in the summer of 1790, to the Jewish congregation of Newport: "The Government of the United States, which gives to bigotry no sanction, to persecution no assistance, requires only that they who live under its protection should demean themselves as good citizens in giving it on all occasions their effectual support."

Observing the terms of this contract, the Jews of America have gone on to enjoy rights of citizenship unparalleled in the history of the Diaspora. Today there are Jewish governors, senators, and congressmen from many parts of the country, and tradition seems to have established that there must now always be a "Jewish seat" on the Supreme Court. Only the presidency itself has not yet been occupied by a Jew, but it was not until 1960 that a non-Protestant was elected President of the United States for the first time in history, and in recent years there has at least been talk of a Jewish vice-presidential candidacy. The colleges and universities, once restrictive about admitting Jews, now have yielded to the vast Jewish tide in the direction of higher education, and some of the leading academic institutions of the country have large Jewish pluralities and even majorities amidst their student bodies. Certain professions and academic fields in America are coming to be characterized by a substantial Jewish element within them. There are still a few places in America relatively closed off to Jews, but some of these, such as the large corporations, are beginning to open their doors, and others, such as private clubs and resort areas, have become less of a source for grievance because Jews have created parallel establishments of their own.

One area of American life that has become a major enclave of Jewish cultural activity, and that bears some of the stylistic marks of this Jewish presence, is the world of entertainment. The American stage reached a European level of sophistication in this century when a generation or two of great Jewish theatrical entrepreneurs from Central Europe—Shubert, Hammerstein, and Hurok are some of the most outstanding among them—began, in their own persons, to form an artistic bridge between America and the cultures in which they had been born. Similarly, a generation of producers, largely of Russian-Jewish origin, entered the Ameranalyst's couch, is epitomized by Jules Feiffer's wan, loveless girls, ts drowned in the sea of their own worldliness, and fast-talking ho zealously latch on to each new passing sophistry of their own in the momentary hope that it might turn out to be a genuine Highly attuned to the atmosphere of America in the nineteen- his world has naturally found a counterpart in the novel, especially writings of Bruce Jay Friedman, in Wallace Markfield's *To an rave,* and in *Portnoy's Complaint,* by Philip Roth; these "pop" however, may have literary antecedents going as far back as Malamud's first novel, *The Natural.*

f the distinguishing characteristics of Jewish comedy in America nt for pastiche, not only of established artistic styles—as in the ody of Dostoevsky, "A Farewell to Omsk," by S. J. Perelman, one of the Marx brothers' scriptwriters for a time—but of whole cultural traditions, as in the film version of *A Funny Thing on the Way to the Forum,* which derives much of its comic from the utterly incongruous appearance in Roman togas of giously Jewish music-hall stylists, Phil Silvers, Jack Gilford, and el. This talent for pastiche, particularly in musical comedy—or, that later manifestation of it known as the musical, which has ntly been the creation of Jewish artists—has also been used for amatic, rather than comic, purposes. The pastiche is most for an art form that is mainly concerned with rendering various lklore into a highly artificial medium. George Gershwin's pas- egro folklore, *Porgy and Bess,* for example, is artistically so -far more than a mere musical, but not precisely an opera, it considered to occupy an artistic category all its own, sometimes pera—that its cultural authenticity has often been exaggerated. ment in the contemporary urban American's vision of nine- ry rural life in this country has been formed by the works nd Hammerstein, Jerome Kern, Irving Berlin, and other Jew- f musicals. More recently, with his *West Side Story,* Leonard s tried to extend the domain of musical pastiche into the folk- mporary urban America.

recently have the techniques of musical pastiche been openly sly applied to Jewish traditions themselves, most notably in rnick's *Fiddler on the Roof.* This is the popular musical the Jewish literary revival mentioned earlier, represented erature by the writings of Harry Golden and others. In here are signs of a return to the kind of frank rendition of t is found in *The Jazz Singer*; Sidney Lumet's film version

ican film industry in its early days and brought with them a certain quality of cosmopolitanism and sophistication.

Although the contrast in speech and appearance between a type of Hollywood producer that was once fairly prevalent—the Jewish immigrant boy become movie tycoon—and the conscientiously Anglo-Saxon-looking actors who usually played the lead roles in his films was once itself a subject for humorous folklore in the entertainment world, there has rarely been an epoch in which Jewish cultural traits were entirely absent from American films. The era of the "talkies" was opened, for example, by a film, produced by a Jewish firm and starring a Jewish actor, which was quite candidly Jewish in its subject matter. This was Warner Brothers' *The Jazz Singer,* in which Al Jolson played the role of a cantor's son who refuses to follow the career intended for him, in his father's footsteps—the break with his parents is signalized by a scene that opens with a close-up of the plate of bacon and eggs he is eating—and employs his vocal talents to become a popular singer instead. The film's climax is a final act of filial piety, when the young man postpones the opening of his big show, scheduled for what happens to be Yom Kippur eve, and goes to the synagogue to replace his dying father in the singing of the Kol Nidre. By the nineteen-thirties, however, Jewish traits were less frankly presented, although they tended to break through in other ways, in some of the characteristics of what film makers may have intended as the distinctive traits of, say, Italian immigrants, or of proletarian families in general. One of the greatest film actors of the thirties, Paul Muni, had begun his career in the Second Avenue Yiddish theater of New York's Lower East Side, and could always be best perceived as a kind of Jewish sage, whether he was playing the role of an Italian gangster, a Slavic immigrant coal miner, or Louis Pasteur. The Warner Brothers film *The Life of Emile Zola,* in which Muni played the title role, and in which the roles of Cézanne and Anatole France were played in a thoroughly Jewish style by Vladimir Sokoloff and Morris Carnovsky, presented an image of the Dreyfusard intelligentsia, with its lofty vision of the moral purpose of art, that was a kind of fulfillment for the American-Jewish liberal of the nineteen-thirties.

But the most characteristic vein for a distinctly Jewish style, on stage, screen, and television, has been that of comedy; indeed, one can safely assert that the predominant comic style in America for some thirty years or so has been Jewish, to the extent that even comedians from other ethnic groups have often tended to employ patterns derived from their Jewish counterparts—Dick Gregory, for example, once treated his Negro traits with a comic style akin to Buddy Hackett's treatment of his Jewish ones. Jewish comedy, originating in the world of Second Avenue vaudeville and achieving national prominence through the simultaneously advancing media of talking pictures and radio, arose with the growing realization on the part of American society that it was becoming predominantly urban. In the early nineteen-thirties, Will Rogers, quietly radiating a quality of rural wisdom that was rapidly vanishing from the everyday lives of most Americans, was still a national culture hero, but he has since been relatively forgotten in favor of his younger contemporaries the Marx brothers, who epitomize the American-Jewish comic style in its first youthful burst of vitality. If Marcel Proust looked upon the vulgarities of the Jewish parvenu with some dismay, a whole generation of Jewish comedians (led by that consummate artist Groucho Marx, and including such cigar chewers as George Jessel, George Burns, and Sam Levene, and, recently, a younger heir to its crown, Walter Matthau, another son of New York's Lower East Side) has made parvenu vulgarity into a high comic form and a penetrating commentary upon American life. Their style is a direct outgrowth of the Second Avenue music hall. There, such a wry performer as the nearly forgotten Willie Howard would make a wreckage of all cultural pretentiousness—a favorite mission of the more wildly aggressive Groucho Marx, as well—by doing such things as delivering to the audience a French lesson whose Gallicisms were made up entirely of imaginative constructs from the Yiddish.

It is perhaps symptomatic of Jewish success in America, and of the enthusiastic embracing of American democracy by the Jewish immigrants and their children, that the most characteristic figure of traditional Jewish humor—the schlemiel—has scarcely been in evidence in American-Jewish popular comedy. In this respect, it seems significant that the outstanding interpreter of the schlemiel type in the American-Yiddish theater, Menasha Skulnik, has never quite achieved national prominence, even though he is one of the greatest comic artists in America. This traditional image of the poor Jewish blunderer, whose innocence sometimes borders on saintliness, but whose qualities are in the end often his author's cry of pain at Jewish submission to suffering, is much more germane to Europe, particularly Eastern Europe, than to the optimistic atmosphere of America. Among outstanding American-Jewish comedians, the nearest to the schlemiel type have been the greatly modified forms of it represented by Jack Benny and Danny Kaye; but their characterizations have generally been quite un-Jewish. This is especially so in the case of Jack Benny. Kaye, whose career originated in the "Borscht Belt," the celebrated Jewish vacation-resort area of the Catskill Mountain region of New York

State, is on occasion willing to rejoice in his dominated by a tone of acquiescence in the es is not true to the spirit of the schlemiel traditi

There had long been only one possible exce one—to this shunning of the schlemiel figur comedians of America. For many years th both his admirers and his detractors—that C partly of Jewish extraction. Chaplin's tramp is figures of all time, and so Jews were natura endeavor in which they were encouraged by ever mysterious about his origins, never did These speculations seem, however, to have since the publication of Chaplin's autobiog his parents' origins and says nothing about does go on in some circles, at least in the assertion that, if Chaplin isn't Jewish, he a then, one can only call this a marginal American culture, the schlemiel has large

It is, rather, the Groucho Marx tradit the social and cultural establishment th one among younger generations of Jewis iation in this approach has been in the and intellectuality. Sid Caesar, who belo and the era of "big" television variety new turn. Caesar reached his heights own, the comic monologue, particularly odies of popular movies. At the beginn niques of monologue and parody were intellectuality by a new school—her Sahl upon the scene—that came to "Sick" comedy reached its fullest dial late Lenny Bruce, who, gradually rer that comedy usually clings to, seen demon-prophet. At the same time, sively verbal emphasis of "sick" co although it seems to be most at literature and performance exempli Like the live comedians of this sch expression in the monologue, place who stands before the reader's e artistic commodity out of neurosi

psycho
innocer
men, w
creation
belief.
sixties,
in the
Early G
works,
Bernard
One
is its tale
great par
who was
folk and
Happened
absurdity
three egre
Zero Most
rather, in
predomina
straight dr
appropriate
kinds of fo
tiche of N
successful—
is generally
called folk
A large ele
teenth-centu
of Rodgers
ish authors
Bernstein ha
lore of cont
Only quite
and consciou
Bock and H
counterpart t
in popular li
movies, too,
Jewishness th

of Wallace Markfield's *To an Early Grave,* called *Bye Bye Braverman,* is a notable example of this. Among the mass media, television already has the oldest history of Jewish comedy openly proclaiming itself as such, going back to the earliest appearances of Sam Levenson, Myron Cohen, and the late Gertrude Berg. This may be because, of all the mass media, television most readily lends itself to the music-hall atmosphere that is the very seedbed of Jewish comedy in America.

It is in the realm of popular culture, then, that one can perceive the most complete realization of the joining of Jewish and American traditions. To the extent that mass culture extends its influence in American life, anti-Semitism—always much less pronounced in America than in Europe—is thereby rendered less and less virulent. In Europe, anti-Semitism has always derived its strength from the conception of the Jews as a culturally alien element within the larger society. On the other hand, in a country like Italy, where anti-Semitism was never very strong, the tendency always has been for Jewish communities to lose their distinct identity altogether and become absorbed into the tolerant and monolithic majority culture. But in the United States, where a culturally pluralistic atmosphere prevails, and where the Jews have made a significant contribution to its culture on both the popular and the serious artistic and intellectual levels, they have been able to be distinctly themselves and at the same time a well-integrated part of the community at large.

BIBLIOGRAPHY

ABRAHAMS, ISRAEL. *Jewish Life in the Middle Ages.* New York, 1958.

ADLER, H. G. *Die Juden in Deutschland.* Munich, 1960.

ALBRIGHT, W. F. *Von der Steinzeit zum Christentum.* Munich, 1949.

ALTMANN, ALEXANDER. *Saadiah Goan.* Oxford, 1946.

ANDICS, HELLMUT. *Der Ewige Jude.* Vienna, 1965.

ARENDT, HANNAH. *Rahel Varnhagen.* London, 1957.

ARNIM, BETTINA VON. *Goethes Briefwechsel mit einem Kinde.* Frankfurt am Main, 1960.

BAECK, LEO. *Aus drei Jahrtausenden.* Berlin, 1938.

———— *Dieses Volk: Jüdische Existenz.* Frankfurt am Main, vol. I, 1955; vol. II, 1957.

———— *Paulus, die Pharisäer und das Neue Testament.* Frankfurt am Main, 1961.

———— *Von Moses Mendelssohn zu Franz Rosenzweig.* Stuttgart, 1958.

———— *Wege im Judentum.* Berlin, 1933.

———— *Das Wesen des Judentums.* Cologne, 1959.

BAER, FRITZ. *Galuth.* Berlin, 1936.

BAER, YITZHAK. *A History of the Jews in Christian Spain.* Philadelphia, 1961.

BAHR, HERMANN. In *Zeitgenossen über Herzl.* Brünn, 1929.

BARON, SALO W. *A Social and Religious History of the Jews.* New York, 1937.

BEN-GURION, DAVID. *David und Goliath in unserer Zeit.* Munich, 1961.

BENTWICH, NORMAN. *The Jews in Our Time.* Baltimore, 1960.

BLUMENKRANZ, BERNHARD. *Juifs et chrétiens dans le monde occidental, 430–1096.* Paris, 1960.

BODENHEIMER, MAX. *So wurde Israel.* Frankfurt, 1958.

BORRIES, ACHIM VON (ed.). *Selbstzeugnisse des deutschen Judentums, 1870–1945.* Frankfurt am Main, 1962.

496 BIBLIOGRAPHY

BROD, MAX. *Heidentum, Christentum, Judentum*. 2 vols. Munich, 1922.

BROWE, P. *"Die Judenmission im Mittelalter und die Päpste."* In *Pontificia Universitas Gregoriana*, vol. 6. Rome, 1942.

BUBER, MARTIN. *An der Wende: Reden über das Judentum*. Cologne and Olten, 1952.

——— *Die chassidische Botschaft*. Heidelberg, 1952.

——— *Die chassidischen Bücher*. Berlin, n.d.

——— *Israel und Palästina*. Zurich, 1950.

——— *Kampf um Israel*. Berlin, 1933.

——— *Reden über das Judentum*. Berlin, 1932.

——— *Die Stunde und die Erkenntnis*. Berlin, 1938.

——— *Vom Geist des Judentums*. Leipzig, 1916.

——— *Zwei Glaubensweisen*. Zurich, 1950.

BÜRGER, CURT (ed.). *Antisemiten-Spiegel*. Berlin, 1911.

CARO, GEORG M. *Sozial- und Wirtschsftsgeschichte der Juden in Mittalter und der Neuzeit*. Frankfurt am Main, 1924.

CHONE, HEYMANN. *Nahmanides*. Nuremberg, 1930.

COHEN, HERMANN. *Ein Bekenntnis in der Judenfrage*. Berlin, 1880.

DIMONT, MAX A. *Jews, God and History*. New York, 1962.

Doch das Zeugnis lebt fort. Berlin, 1965.

DUBNOW, SIMON. *A History of the Jews in Russia and Poland*. Philadelphia, 1916–1918.

——— *Weltgeschichte des jüdischen Volkes*. 10 vols. Berlin, 1926–1929.

EHRLICH, ERNST L. *Geschichte der Juden in Deutschland*. Düsseldorf, 1960.

——— *Geschichte Israels*. Berlin, 1958.

ELBOGEN, ISMAR. *A Century of Jewish Life*. Philadelphia, 1944.

——— *Geschichte der Juden in Deutschland*. Berlin, 1935.

FINKELSTEIN, LOUIS. *Jewish Self-Government in the Middle Ages*. New York, 1924.

——— *The Jews: Their History, Culture and Religion*. New York, 1949.

——— *Rab Saadia Gaon*. New York, 1944.

FINN, JAMES. *The Jews in China*. London, 1843.

FISCHEL, WALTER J. *"The Jews of Central Asia in Medieval Hebrew and Islamic Literature."* In *Historia Judaica*, vol. 7. New York, 1945.

FOERSTER, F. W. *Die jüdische Frage*. Freiburg im Breisgau, 1959.

GAMM, HANS-JOCHEN. *Judentumskunde*. Munich and Recklinghausen, 1960.

GEIGER, LUDWIG. *Die Geschichte der Judan in Berlin*. Berlin, 1871.

GEIS, ROBERT RAPHAEL. *Vom unbekannten Judentum*. Freiburg im Breisgau, 1961.

GINZBERG, LOUIS. *Students, Scholars and Saints*. New York, 1958.

GLATZER, NAHUM NORBERT. *Gespräche der Weisen*. Berlin, 1935.

GLAZER, NATHAN. *American Judaism*. Chicago, 1953.

GLÜCKEL VON HAMELN. *Denkwürdigkeiten der Glückel von Hameln*. Edited by A. Feilchenfeld. Berlin, 1914.

GOETHE, J. W. VON. *Dichtung und Wahrheit*. Book Four.

——— *Zwei vertrauliche Reden*. Berlin, 1899.

GOLDSCHMIDT, H. L. *Das Vermächtnis des deutschen Judentums*. Frankfurt am Main, 1957.

GOODMAN, PAUL. *A History of the Jews.* New York, 1951.

GRAETZ, HEINRICH. *Geschichte der Juden.* 11 vols. Leipzig, 1897–1911.

GRAYZEL, SOLOMON. *A History of the Contemporary Jews.* New York, 1960.

——— *A History of the Jews.* Philadelphia, 1947.

GÜDEMANN, MORITZ. *Das jüdische Unterichtswesen.* Vienna, 1873.

HALPER, BEN-ZION. *Post-Biblical Hebrew Literature.* Philadelphia, 1921.

HANDLIN, OSCAR. *Adventure in Freedom.* New York, 1954.

HECHT, EMANUEL. *Handbuch der Israelischen Geschichte.* Leipzig, 1879.

HEINEMANN, I. *La loi dans la pensée juive.* Paris, 1962.

HENRIQUES, H. S. Q. *The Return of the Jews to England.* London, 1905.

HERBERG, WILL. *Judaism and Modern Man.* New York, 1951.

HERZL, THEODOR. *Gesammelte zionistische Schriften.* 5 vols. Berlin, 1934.

HESS, MOSES. *Jüdische Schriften.* Berlin, 1905.

——— *Rom und Jerusalem.* Vienna, 1935.

HEUSS, ALFRED. *Römische Geschichte.* Braunschweig, 1960.

HEYMANN, FRITZ. *Der Chevalier von Geldern.* Cologne, 1963.

HOLDE, ARTUR. *Jews in Music.* New York, 1959.

HUNKE, SIGRID. *Allahs Sonne über dem Abendland.* Stuttgart, 1960.

ISAAC, JULES. *L'Antisémitisme a-t-il des racines chrétiennes?* Vienna, 1960.

Das Israelbuch 1960/61. Düsseldorf, 1960.

JACOB, HEINRICH E. *Felix Mendelssohn and His Times.* Englewood Cliffs, N.J., 1963.

JACOBS, JOSEPH. *Jewish Contributions to Civilization.* Philadelphia, 1919.

JEREMIAS, ALFRED. *Jüdische Frömmigkeit.* Leipzig, 1929.

JOSEPHUS, FLAVIUS. *The Works of Flavius Josephus.* Translated by William Whiston. 2 vols. Philadelphia, 1846.

JOST, ISAK M. *Geschichte des Judenthums und seiner Secten.* 3 vols. Leipzig, 1857–1859.

Die Juden in Köln. Edited by Zvi Asria. Cologne, 1959.

Die jüdischen Gefallenen des deutschen Heeres, der deutschen Marine und der deutschen Schutztruppen, 1914–1918. Edited by the Reichsbund Jüdischer Frontsoldaten. Berlin, 1932.

JUSTER, JEAN. *Les Juifs dans l'empire romain.* 2 vols. Paris, 1914.

KAHLER, ERICH. *Israel unter den Völkern.* Zurich, 1936.

KARPELES, GUSTAV. *Geschichte der jüdischen Literatur.* 2 vols. Berlin, 1909.

KASTEIN, JOSEF. *Eine Geschichte der Juden.* Vienna, 1935.

KATSH, ABRAHAM. *Judaism in Islam.* New York, 1954.

KATZ, SOLOMON. *The Jews in the Visigothic and Frankish Kingdoms of Spain and Gaul.* Cambridge, Mass., 1937.

KAYSERLING, MEYER. *Christoph Columbus und der Anteil der Juden an den spanischen und portugiesischen Endeckungen.* Berlin, 1894.

——— *Geschichte der Juden in Spanien und Portugal.* 2 vols. Berlin, 1861 and 1867.

——— *Die jüdischen Frauen in der Geschichte, Literatur und Kunst.* Leipzig, 1879.

KAZNELSON, SIEGMUND (ed.). *Juden im deutschen Kulturbereich: Ein Sammelwerk.* Berlin, 1959.

KENYON, KATHLEEN MARY. *Archaeology in the Holy Land.* New York, 1960.

KISCH, GUIDO. *The Jews in Medieval Germany.* Chicago, 1949.

———— *Forschungen zur Rechts- und Sozialgeschichte der Juden in Deutschland während des Mittelalters.* Stuttgart, 1955.

KISCH, GUIDO, and ROEPKE, KURT. *Schriften zur Geschichte der Juden: Eine Bibliographie der in Deutschland und der Schweiz 1922–1955 erschienenen Dissertationen.* Tübingen, 1959.

KLAUSNER, JOSEPH. *Jesus von Nazareth.* Jerusalem, 1952.

———— *Von Jesus zu Paulus.* Jerusalem, 1950.

KOBLER, FRANZ. *Juden und Judentum in deutschen Briefen aus drei Jahrhunderten.* Vienna, 1935.

KOCH, THILO. *Porträts zur deutsch-jüdischen Geistesgeschichte.* Cologne, 1961.

KÖHLER, HANS. *Die Wirkung des Judentums auf das abendländische Geistesleben.* Berlin, 1952.

KOENEN, HENDRIK J. *Geschiedenes der Joden in Nederland.* Utrecht, 1843.

KOHN, J. H. *Bibel- und Talmudschatz.* Edited by Rabbi Dr. S. Bamberger. Hamburg, 1910.

KORN, BERTRAM W. *American Jewry in the Civil War.* Philadelphia, 1951.

KROJANKER, GUSTAV. *Juden in der deutschen Literatur.* Berlin, 1922.

KUPISCH, KARL. *Das Volk der Geschichte.* Berlin and Stuttgart, 1961.

LANDAU, RICHARD. *Geschichte der jüdischen Ärzte.* Berlin, 1895.

LANDMANN, SALCIA. *Jiddisch: Das Abenteuer einer Sprache.* Olten and Freiburg im Breisgau, 1962.

———— *Koschere Kostproben.* Zurich, 1964.

LAZARUS, MORITZ. *Gesammelte Reden und Vorträge.* Leipzig, 1887.

LEARSI, RUFUS. *Israel: A History of the Jewish People.* Cleveland, 1949.

LESCHNITZER, ADOLF F. *Saul und David.* Heidelberg, 1954.

LESTSCHINSKY, JAKOB. *Das wirtschaftliche Schicksal des deutschen Judentums.* Berlin, 1932.

LIBER, MAURICE. *Rashi.* Philadelphia, 1906.

LINDO, E. H. *The History of the Jews of Spain and Portugal.* London, 1848.

LOVSKY, FADLEY. *Antisémitisme et mystère d'Israël.* Paris, 1955.

LOWES, J. *Bildnisse in Berlin lebender Gelehrter in Selbstbiographien.* Berlin, 1806.

MARCUS, JACOB RADER. *The Jews in the Medieval World.* New York, 1960.

MARGOLIS, MAX L., and MARX, ALEXANDER. *A History of the Jewish People.* New York, 1959.

MARSCH, WOLF DIETER, and THIEME, KARL. *Christen und Juden.* Mainz, 1961.

MAURER, WILHELM. *Kirche und Synagoge.* Stuttgart, 1953.

MINKIN, JACOB S. *The World of Moses Maimonides.* New York, 1957.

MOMMSEN, THEODOR. *"Auch ein Wort über unser Judentum, 1880."* In *Reden und Aufsatze.* Berlin, 1905.

Monumenta Judaica, 2000 Jahre Geschichte und Kultur der Juden am Rhein. Edited by Konrad Schilling. Cologne, 1964.

MOORE, GEORGE F. *Judaism in the First Centuries of the Christian Era.* 3 vols. Cambridge, Mass., 1927–1930.

MURMELSTEIN, BENJAMIN. *Geschichte der Juden.* Vienna, 1938.

NADEL, B. *Juden in Osteuropa.* Warsaw, 1960.

NEUMANN, ABRAHAM. *The Jews in Spain.* 2 vols. Philadelphia, 1942.

NOTH, MARTIN. *Geschichte Israels.* Göttingen, 1954.

PARKES, JAMES W. *A History of Palestine from 135 A.D. to Modern Times.* New York, 1949.

——— *The Jew in the Medieval Community.* London, 1938.

——— *Judaism and Christianity.* Chicago, 1948.

PIRENNE, HENRI. *Mohammed and Charlemagne.* New York, 1940.

POLIAKOV, LÉON. *Histoire de l'antisémitisme.* 2 vols. Paris, 1955 and 1961.

PRINZ, JOACHIM. *Illustrierte Jüdische Geschichte.* Berlin, 1933.

——— *Jüdische Geschichte.* Berlin, 1930.

——— *Popes from the Ghetto.* New York, 1966.

RABINOWICZ, HARRY M. *A Guide to Hassidism.* New York, 1960.

RABINOWITZ, LOUIS I. *Jewish Merchant Adventurers.* London, 1948.

RAISIN, MAX. *History of the Jews in Modern Times.* New York, 1926.

REITLINGER, GERALD. *The Final Solution.* London, 1953.

REMEDIOS, J. MENDES DOS. *Os Judens em Portugal.* 1895.

RICCIOTTI, GIUSEPPE. *Storia d'Israele.* 2 vols. Turin, 1934 and 1935.

ROBACK, A. A. *Jewish Influences in Modern Thought.* Cambridge, Mass., 1929.

ROSIN, HEINRICH. *Die Juden in der Medizin.* Berlin, 1926.

ROTH, CECIL. *Geschichte der Juden.* Cologne and Berlin, 1964.

——— *A History of the Jews in Italy.* Philadelphia, 1946.

——— *A History of the Marranos.* Philadelphia, 1960.

——— *The Jewish Contribution to Civilization.* New York, 1940.

——— *The Jews in the Renaissance.* Philadelphia, 1959.

ROTHMÜLLER, ARON MARKO. *Die Musik der Juden.* Zurich, 1951.

RUDY, ZWI. *Soziologie des jüdischen Volkes.* Hamburg, 1965.

RUNES, DAGOBERT G. (ed.). *The Hebrew Impact on Western Civilization.* New York, 1951.

RUPPIN, ARTHUR. *Soziologie der Juden.* 2 vols. Berlin, 1930 and 1931.

SACHAR, HOWARD M. *The Course of Modern Jewish History.* New York, 1958.

SCHAPPES, MORRIS U. *A Documentary History of the Jews in the United States: 1654–1875.* New York, 1961.

SCHAY, RUDOLF. *Juden in der deutschen Politik.* Berlin, 1929.

SCHNEE, HEINRICH. *Die Hochfinanz und der moderne Staat: Geschichte und System der Hoffaktoren an deutschen Fürstenhöfen im Zeitalter des Absolutismus.* 5 vols. Berlin and Munich, 1953–1965.

——— *Das Hoffaktorentum in der deutschen Geschichte.* Göttingen, 1964.

SCHOEPS, HANS JOACHIM. *Barocke Juden, Christen, Judenchristen.* Bern and Munich, 1965.

——— *Jüdische Geisteswelt.* Darmstadt, 1953.

——— *Israel und Christenheit.* Munich, 1961.

——— *Israel und Christenheit: Jüdisch-christliches Religionsgespräch in 19 Jahrhunderten.* Frankfurt am Main, 1961.

SCHOLEM, GERSHOM. *Die jüdische Mystik in ihren Hauptströmungen.* Frankfurt am Main, 1957.

SCHOPEN, EDMUND. *Geschichte des Judentums im Abendland.* Bern and Munich, 1961.

——— *Geschichte des Judentums im Morgenland.* Bern and Munich, 1960.

SCHUDT, JOHANN JACOB. *Jüdische Merkwürdigkeiten*. Frankfurt am Main and Leipzig, 1714.

SCHÜRER, EMIL. *Geschichte des jüdischen Volkes im Zeitalter Jesu Christi*. 4 vols. Leipzig, 1901–1911.

SCHWARZ, KARL. *Die Juden in der Kunst*. Berlin, 1928.

SCHWARZ, LEO W. (ed.). *Great Ages and Ideas of the Jewish People*. New York, 1956.

SEIFERTH, WOLFGANG. *Synagoge und Kirche im Mittelalter*. Munich, 1964.

SIMON, MARCEL. *Verus Israel: Étude sur les relations entre chrétiens et juifs dans l'empire romain (135–425)*. Paris, 1948.

SINZHEIMER, HUGO. *Jüdische Klassiker der deutschen Rechtswissenschaft*. Amsterdam, 1938.

SOMBART, WERNER. *Die Juden und das Wirtschatftsleben*. Munich, 1928.

STEINBERG, MILTON. *The Making of the Modern Jew*. Indianapolis, 1934.

STERN, SELMA. *The Court Jew*. Philadelphia, 1950.

———— *Josel von Rosheim*. Stuttgart, 1959.

———— *Der preussiche Staat und die Juden*. 2 vols. Berlin, 1925.

STRACK, HERMANN L. *Einleitung in Talmud und Midrasch*. Munich, 1930.

SUSMAN, MARGARETE. *Das Buch Hiob und das Schicksal des jüdischen Volkes*. Zurich, 1948.

THEILHABER, FELIX A. *Juden in der deutschen Forschung und Technik*. Berlin, 1931.

———— *Der Untergang der deutschen Juden*. Berlin, 1927.

THIEME, KARL. *Dreitausend Jahre Judentum*. Paderborn, 1960.

———— (ed.). *Judenfeindschaft*. Frankfurt am Main, 1963.

ULLMANN, ARNO (ed.). *Israels Weg zum Staat*. Minden, 1964.

VOGT, HANNAH. *Joch und Krone*. Frankfurt am Main, 1963.

WAGNER, RICHARD. *Das Judenthum in der Musik*. Leipzig, 1869.

WAXMAN, MEYER. *A History of Jewish Literature*. 3 vols. New York, 1930–1936.

WEIZMANN, CHAIM. *Memoiren: Das Werden des Staates Israel*. Zurich, 1953.

WHITE, WILLIAM C. *Chinese Jews*. 3 vols. Toronto, 1942.

ZIELENZIGER, KURT. *Juden in der deutschen Wirtschaft*. Berlin, 1930.

ZWEIG, ARNOLD. *Bilanz der deutschen Judenheit*. Cologne, 1961.

GENERAL REFERENCE BOOKS AND ENCYCLOPEDIAS

ARONIUS, JULIUS. *Regesten zur Geschichte der Juden im fränkischen und deutschen Reich bis 1273*. Berlin, 1887.

———— *Quellen zur Geschichte der Juden in Deutschland*. Berlin, 1881.

AUSÜBEL, NATHAN. *The Book of Jewish Knowledge*. New York, 1964.

COHN, EMIL B. *Das jüdische ABC*. Berlin, 1935.

EHRLICH, ERNST L. *Geschichte der Juden in Deutschland*. Düsseldorf, 1961.

HAMBURGER, JACOB. *Real-Enzyklopädie des Judentums*. Leipzig, 1901.

HERLITZ, GEORG, and KIRSCHNER, BRUNO (eds.). *Judisches Lexicon*. 4 vols. Leipzig, 1901.

HÖXTER, JULIUS. *Quellenbuch zur jüdischen Geschichte und Literatur*. 5 vols. Frankfurt, 1927–1930.

STEINSCHNEIDER, MORITZ. *Die hebräischen Übersetzungen des Mittelalters.* 2 vols. Berlin, 1893.
Encyclopedia Judaica. 10 vols. Berlin, 1928–1934.
The Jewish Encyclopedia. 12 vols. New York, 1903–1906.
The New Jewish Encyclopedia. New York, 1962.
Philo-Lexikon: Handbuch des jüdischen Wissens, 4th ed. Berlin and Amsterdam, 1937.
Quellen zur Geschichte der Juden in Deutschland. 3 vols. Berlin, 1888–1898.
The Standard Jewish Encyclopedia. Jerusalem, 1962.
The Universal Jewish Encyclopedia. 10 vols. New York, 1948.

PERIODICALS

Freiburger Rundbrief. Freiburg im Breisgau, 1948 ff.
Germania Judaica. Cologne, 1961 ff.
Jewish Quarterly Review. Philadelphia, 1889 ff.
Monatsschrift für Geschichte und Wissenschaft des Judentums. Frankfurt am Main, 1851 ff.
Revue des Etudes Juives. Paris, 1880 ff.

BIBLIOGRAPHY FOR "A HISTORY OF THE JEWS IN AMERICA"

DAVIS, MOSHE. *The Emergence of Conservative Judaism.* Philadelphia, 1963.
GOLDBERG, ISAAC. *Major Noah.* Philadelphia, 1936.
GRINSTEIN, HYMAN B. *The Rise of the Jewish Community of New York, 1654–1860.* Philadelphia, 1945.
LEARSI, RUFUS. *The Jews in America: A History.* New York and Cleveland, 1954.
MARCUS, JACOB R. *Early American Jewry.* 2 vols. Philadelphia, 1951 and 1953.
PHILIPSON, DAVID. *The Reform Movement in Judaism.* New York, 1907.
RISCHIN, MOSES. *The Promised City.* Boston, 1962.
SANDERS, RONALD. *The Downtown Jews: Portraits of an Immigrant Generation.* New York, 1969.

INDEX

512